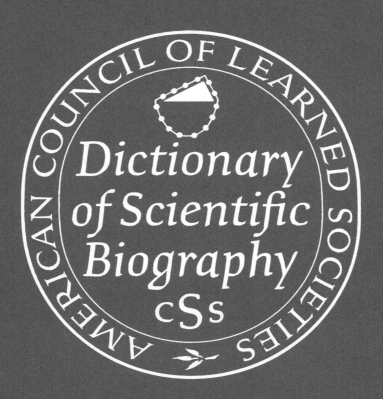

AMERICAN COUNCIL OF LEARNED SOCIETIES

Dictionary
of Scientific
Biography

cSs

DICTIONARY
OF
SCIENTIFIC BIOGRAPHY

PUBLISHED UNDER THE AUSPICES OF
THE AMERICAN COUNCIL OF LEARNED SOCIETIES

The American Council of Learned Societies, organized in 1919 for the purpose of advancing the study of the humanities and of the humanistic aspects of the social sciences, is a nonprofit federation comprising thirty-three national scholarly groups. The Council represents the humanities in the United States in the International Union of Academies, provides fellowships and grants-in-aid, supports research-and-planning conferences and symposia, and sponsors special projects and scholarly publications.

Member Organizations

AMERICAN PHILOSOPHICAL SOCIETY, 1743

AMERICAN ACADEMY OF ARTS AND SCIENCES, 1780

AMERICAN ANTIQUARIAN SOCIETY, 1812

AMERICAN ORIENTAL SOCIETY, 1842

AMERICAN NUMISMATIC SOCIETY, 1858

AMERICAN PHILOLOGICAL ASSOCIATION, 1869

ARCHAEOLOGICAL INSTITUTE OF AMERICA, 1879

SOCIETY OF BIBLICAL LITERATURE, 1880

MODERN LANGUAGE ASSOCIATION OF AMERICA, 1883

AMERICAN HISTORICAL ASSOCIATION, 1884

AMERICAN ECONOMIC ASSOCIATION, 1885

AMERICAN FOLKLORE SOCIETY, 1888

AMERICAN DIALECT SOCIETY, 1889

ASSOCIATION OF AMERICAN LAW SCHOOLS, 1900

AMERICAN PHILOSOPHICAL ASSOCIATION, 1901

AMERICAN ANTHROPOLOGICAL ASSOCIATION, 1902

AMERICAN POLITICAL SCIENCE ASSOCIATION, 1903

BIBLIOGRAPHICAL SOCIETY OF AMERICA, 1904

ASSOCIATION OF AMERICAN GEOGRAPHERS, 1904

AMERICAN SOCIOLOGICAL ASSOCIATION, 1905

COLLEGE ART ASSOCIATION OF AMERICA, 1912

HISTORY OF SCIENCE SOCIETY, 1924

LINGUISTIC SOCIETY OF AMERICA, 1924

MEDIAEVAL ACADEMY OF AMERICA, 1925

AMERICAN MUSICOLOGICAL SOCIETY, 1934

SOCIETY OF ARCHITECTURAL HISTORIANS, 1940

ECONOMIC HISTORY ASSOCIATION, 1940

ASSOCIATION FOR ASIAN STUDIES, 1941

AMERICAN SOCIETY FOR AESTHETICS, 1942

METAPHYSICAL SOCIETY OF AMERICA, 1950

AMERICAN STUDIES ASSOCIATION, 1950

RENAISSANCE SOCIETY OF AMERICA, 1954

SOCIETY FOR ETHNOMUSICOLOGY, 1955

DICTIONARY

OF

SCIENTIFIC BIOGRAPHY

CHARLES COULSTON GILLISPIE

EDITOR IN CHIEF

Volume II

HANS BERGER—CHRISTOPH BUYS BALLOT

CHARLES SCRIBNER'S SONS · NEW YORK

Editorial Staff

MARSHALL DE BRUHL, *MANAGING EDITOR*

SARAH FERRELL, *Assistant Managing Editor*

LELAND S. LOWTHER, *Associate Editor*

JOYCE D. PORTNOY, *Associate Editor*

ROSE MOSELLE, *Editorial Assistant*

ELIZABETH I. WILSON, *Copy Editor*

DORIS ANNE SULLIVAN, *Proofreader*

JOEL HONIG, *Copy Editor*

LINDA FISHER, *Secretary-Typist*

Panel of Consultants

Contributors to Volume II

Hans Aarsleff
L. R. C. Agnew
A. F. O'D. Alexander
G. C. Amstutz
R. Arnaldez
Richard P. Aulie
Cortland P. Auser
Lawrence Badash
D. L. Bailey
Walter Baron
Hans Baumgärtel
Silvio A. Bedini
Yvon Belaval
Luigi Belloni
James D. Berger
Francis Birch
Arthur Birembaut
R. P. Boas, Jr.
Uno Boklund
Carl B. Boyer
G. E. Briggs
L. Brillouin
T. A. A. Broadbent
Stephen G. Brush
Gerd Buchdahl
O. M. B. Bulman
John G. Burke
Harold L. Burstyn
H. L. L. Busard
G. V. Bykov
William F. Bynum
André Cailleux
Ronald S. Calinger
Walter F. Cannon
Albert V. Carozzi
Ettore Carruccio
J. G. van Cittert-Eymers
Thomas H. Clark
Edwin Clarke
William Coleman
George W. Corner
Ruth Schwartz Cowan
Paul F. Cranefield
M. P. Crosland

Michael J. Crowe
Charles A. Culotta
Glyn Daniel
Sally H. Dieke
Claude E. Dolman
Sigalia Dostrovsky
Stillman Drake
John Dubbey
Louis Dulieu
M. V. Edds, Jr.
Carolyn Eisele
H. Engel
Joseph Ewan
Eduard Farber
Lucienne Félix
E. A. Fellmann
Eugene S. Ferguson
J. O. Fleckenstein
Eric G. Forbes
Paul Forman
Vincenzo Francani
Pietro Franceschini
Eugene Frankel
H. C. Freiesleben
Walter Fricke
Henri Galliard
Gerald L. Geison
Wilma George
Ruth Anne Gienapp
Bertrand Gille
C. Stewart Gillmor
Owen Gingerich
Harry Godwin
Stanley Goldberg
G. J. Goodfield
D. C. Goodman
T. A. Goudge
J. B. Gough
Judith V. Grabiner
Edward Grant
Joseph T. Gregory
S. L. Greitzer
A. T. Grigorian
N. A. Grigorian

M. D. Grmek
J. Gruber
Henry Guerlac
Laura Guggenbuhl
Marie Boas Hall
Bert Hansen
Thomas Hawkins
John L. Heilbron
C. Doris Hellman
Mayo Dyer Hersey
Erwin N. Hiebert
J. E. Hofmann
Olaf Holtedahl
Gerald Holton
Dora Hood
David Hopkins
Michael A. Hoskin
Pierre Huard
Wlodzimierz Hubicki
G. L. Huxley
Jean Itard
Melvin E. Jahn
S. A. Jayawardene
Edouard Jeauneau
Børge Jessen
Sheldon Judson
Satish C. Kapoor
George B. Kauffman
Alan S. Kay
Suzanne Kelly
Edwin C. Kemble
Martha B. Kendall
E. S. Kennedy
Hubert C. Kennedy
Günther Kerstein
Geoffrey Keynes
Pearl Kibre
Lester S. King
Paul A. Kirchvogel
Marc Klein
B. Knaster
Zdeněk Kopal
Claudia Kren
P. G. Kulikovsky

CONTRIBUTORS TO VOLUME II

Louis I. Kuslan
Gisela Kutzbach
Henry M. Leicester
Jean-François Leroy
Erna Lesky
Jacques R. Levy
G. A. Lindeboom
Sten Lindroth
Jacob Lorch
Eric McDonald
Susan M. P. McKenna
Robert M. McKeon
H. Lewis McKinney
Nikolaus Mani
Željko Marković
Seymour H. Mauskopf
Kenneth O. May
Josef Mayerhöfer
Everett Mendelsohn
Philip Merlan
W. E. Knowles Middleton
G. H. Miller
S. R. Mikulinsky
Lorenzo Minio-Paluello
Ernest A. Moody
Edgar W. Morse
Marston Morse
Jean Motte
John E. Murdoch
Henry Nathan
A. Natucci
Axel V. Nielsen
W. Nieuwenkamp
Lowell E. Noland

Luboš Nový
C. D. O'Malley
Charles O'Neill
Jane Oppenheimer
Adolf Pabst
Jacques Payen
Olaf Pedersen
Giorgio Pedrocco
Georges Petit
Mogens Pihl
P. E. Pilet
David Pingree
J. B. Pogrebyssky
P. M. Rattansi
Nathan Reingold
Bernard Rochot
Jacques Roger
Colin A. Ronan
B. van Rootselaar
Leon Rosenfeld
K. E. Rothschuh
Alain Rousseau
M. J. S. Rudwick
Susan Schacher
H. Schadewaldt
Charles B. Schmitt
Rud. Schmitz
Herbert Schriefers
B. P. M. Schulte
E. L. Scott
J. F. Scott
Christoph J. Scriba
Jan Sebestik
Thomas B. Settle
Harold I. Sharlin

O. B. Sheynin
Diana Simpkins
W. A. Smeaton
C. S. Smith
Y. I. Soloviev
Jerry Stannard
William T. Stearn
Johannes Steudel
Bernhard Sticker
Hans Straub
Dirk J. Struik
A. H. Sturtevant
Edith Sylla
Charles Süsskind
C. H. Talbot
Juliette Taton
René Taton
George Taylor
Andrzej A. Teske
Arnold Thackray
Joachim Thiele
K. Bryn Thomas
Heinz Tobien
J. J. Verdonk
Stig Veibel
Jean Vieuchange
Fred W. Voget
William A. Wallace, O.P.
Deborah Jean Warner
Charles Webster
Adrienne R. Weill-Brunschvicg
Thomas Widorn
Frances A. Yates
A. P. Youschkevitch

DICTIONARY
OF
SCIENTIFIC BIOGRAPHY

DICTIONARY OF SCIENTIFIC BIOGRAPHY

BERGER—BUYS BALLOT

BERGER, HANS (*b.* Neuses bei Coburg, Germany, 21 May 1873; *d.* Jena, Germany, 1 June 1941), *psychiatry, electroencephalography.*

The son of Paul Friedrich Berger and of Anna Rückert, Berger graduated from the Gymnasium at Coburg and then entered the University of Jena in 1892. After one semester in astronomy he transferred to medicine. In 1897 he became assistant to Otto Binswanger at the university's psychiatric clinic. He was appointed chief doctor in 1912 and director and professor of psychiatry in 1919; he retired in 1938. His associates described Berger as punctual, strict, demanding, and reserved.

The central theme in Berger's work was the search for the correlation between objective activity of the brain and subjective psychic phenomena. In his work on blood circulation in the brain (1901) he described his efforts to gain insight into this correlation through plethysmographic registration of the brain pulsations. He investigated the influence of the heartbeat, respiration, vasomotor functions, and position of the head and body on brain pulsations, which were measured through an opening, made by trephination, in the skull. Berger also studied the effects of a number of medications—such as camphor, digitoxin, caffeine, cocaine, and morphine—on brain pulsations. The results of these investigations were disappointing, yet Berger continued his search for measurable expressions of psychic conditions through experiments on blood circulation (1904, 1907).

After 1907 Berger tried to discover a correlation between the temperature of the brain and psychic processes. He postulated that through dissimilation in the cortex, psychic energy (*P-Energie*) develops, along with heat, electrical energy, and neural energy. These experiments also came to a dead end, according to Berger's publication of 1910. Nevertheless, in his lectures on psychophysiology, given from 1905 on and published in 1921, the problem of *P-Energie* continued to hold his interest. His tenaciousness in this matter is apparent from a memo in his journal dated 14 December 1921, in which he says that the goal of his research continues to be the correlation between the expressions of the human mind and the processes of dissimilation in the brain.

After his disappointing experiments measuring the blood circulation and temperature of the brain, Berger (following his return from World War I) devoted himself mainly to the measurement of the brain's electrical activity. In 1902 he had taken measurements of electrical activity above skull defects with the Lippmann capillary electrometer, and later with the Edelmann galvanometer. In 1910, however, Berger mentioned in his journal that the results of these measurements were not satisfactory. Therefore, until 1925 he followed two methods of research: stimulation of the motor cortex through a defect in the skull, measuring the time between stimulus and contralateral motor reaction, and registration of the spontaneous potential differences of the brain surface. After 1925 Berger no longer used the stimulation method. He specialized, with ever increasing skill, in registering the spontaneous fluctuations in electrical potential that could be recorded through the skull from the cortex. In his first publication on electroencephalography (1929), he called 6 July 1924 the date of discovery of the human electroencephalogram. The EEG, the curves of the electrical potentials measured again and again between two points of the skull, did not give him a closer insight into the correlation between the electrical activity of the brain and psychic energy. However, electroencephalography has proved to be of ever increasing importance in diagnosing and treating neurological diseases (epilepsy, brain tumors, traumata).

Berger's work was strongly influenced by the exact psychology of the nineteenth century. In developing his psychophysiology, Berger used the ideas of J. F. Herbart, R. H. Lotze, G. T. Fechner, W. Wundt, and the Danish psychologist A. Lehmann as a base. In the experimental field, Berger was in all aspects a follower of A. Mosso. Berger's experiments on brain circulation and brain temperature were identical with Mosso's, and his publications on these subjects bore the same titles as Mosso's papers.

In developing electroencephalography, Berger was influenced by Caton and by Nemminski. Caton had measured electrical potentials on the exposed cortex of experimental animals in 1875, but he was not able to record these phenomena graphically. Nemminski recorded the first electrocerebrogram on dogs with the skull intact by means of the Einthoven string galvanometer in 1913.

Berger's historical significance lies in his discovery of the electroencephalogram of man. Although he began publishing his many papers on electro-encephalography in 1929, he did not receive international recognition until Adrian and Matthews drew attention to his work in 1934.

BIBLIOGRAPHY

I. ORIGINAL WORKS. Berger's writings include *Zur Lehre von der Blutzirkulation in der Schädelhöhle des Menschen namentlich unter dem Einfluss von Medikamenten* (Jena, 1901); *Ueber die körperlichen Äusserungen psychischer Zustände,* 2 vols. (Jena, 1904–1907); *Untersuchungen über die Temperatur des Gehirns* (Jena, 1910); *Hirn und Seele* (Jena, 1919); *Psychophysiologie in 12 Vorlesungen* (Jena, 1921); *Ueber die Lokalisation im Grosshirn* (Jena, 1927); "Ueber das Elektrenkephalogramm des Menschen," in *Archiv für Psychiatrie,* **87** (1929), 527–570; **94** (1931), 16–60; **97** (1932), 6–26; **98** (1933), 231–254; **99** (1933), 555–574; **100** (1933), 301–320; **101** (1934), 452–469; **102** (1934), 538–557; **103** (1935), 444–454; **104** (1936), 678–689; **106** (1937), 165–187, 577–584; **108** (1938), 407–431; and *Psyche* (Jena, 1940).

II. SECONDARY LITERATURE. Works on Berger are E. Adrian and B. Matthews, "The Berger Rhythm," in *Brain,* **57** (1934), 355–385; Mary A. B. Brazier, "The Historical Development of Neurophysiology," in *Handbook of Physiology,* I (Washington, D. C., 1959), 1–58; R. Caton, "The Electric Currents of the Brain," in *British Medical Journal* (1875), **ii,** 278; H. Fischgold, "Hans Berger et son temps," in *Actualités neurophysiologiques,* 4th ser. (1962), 197–221; R. Jung, "Hans Berger und die Entdeckung des EEG nach seinen Tagebüchern und Protokollen," in *Jenenser EEG-Symposion* (Jena, 1963), pp. 20–53; K. Kolle, "Hans Berger," in *Grosse Nervenärzte,* I (Stuttgart, 1956), 1–16; A. Mosso, *Ueber den Kreislauf des Blutes im menschlichen Gehirn* (Leipzig, 1881), pp. 104–197; and *Die Temperatur des Gehirns* (Leipzig, 1894), pp. 120–135; and W. Nemminski, "Ein Versuch der Registrierung der elektrischen Gehirnerscheinungen," in *Zentralblatt für Physiologie,* **27** (1913), 951–960.

B. P. M. SCHULTE

BERGER, JOHANN GOTTFRIED (*b.* Halle, Germany, 11 November 1659; *d.* Wittenberg, Germany, 2[?] October 1736), *physiology, medicine.*

Berger was the son of Valentin Berger, an important educator of the mid-seventeenth century. He studied mathematics and medicine at Jena from 1677 to 1680, chiefly under Georg Wolfgang Wedel, a physician who was especially interested in iatrochemistry. At Jena, Friedrich Hoffmann and Georg Ernst Stahl were among his fellow students. After a brief period at Erfurt, Berger returned to Jena and graduated in 1682 with a thesis entitled *De circulatione lymphae et catarrhis.* In connection with this work he traveled through France, Italy, and perhaps Holland. From 1684 to 1688 he worked at the University of Leipzig with Johannes Bohn, who influenced Berger to develop a critical attitude toward iatrochemistry. Berger wrote two dissertations at Leipzig: *De mania* (1685) and *De chylo* (1686). From 1688 until his death Berger worked at the University of Wittenberg; first as assistant professor and from 1689 as third-ranking professor of anatomy and botany. He celebrated his appointment to the latter with an inaugural address in the spirit of natural theology. In 1693 he assumed the chair of pathology, and in 1697 Friedrich August I, king of Poland and Saxony, appointed him physician in ordinary. From 1730 he was the *consiliarus aulae,* that is, the senior of the entire university.

Berger's chief scientific work is his *Physiologia medica* (1701). Written in perfect Latin, this work deals in a "modern" way with the physiological functions of the organs and organ systems. While the *Physiologia medica* of his teacher Wedel was, in spirit and structure, still modeled closely on Jean Fernel's neo-Aristotelian physiology, Berger's work is based on the recent discoveries in anatomy, physics, and chemistry; in this respect, it is similar to Bohn's *Circulus anatomico-physiologicus* of 1680. Berger tends heavily toward iatromechanics and the corpuscular theory of Descartes, whom he often quotes. The body is a natural machine connected with an immortal soul (*mens* is *substantia cogitans; corpus* is *substantia extensa*) and united harmoniously by divine design.

The first, larger part of the book deals with the physiology of the adult human being; the second with reproduction and development. He discusses extensively the circulation of the blood and argues that the flow of blood and the nerve fluid determine the rhythmical activity of the heart. He considers the arteries to be elastic, as Giovanni Borelli had suggested. Berger describes several experiments involving the injection of mercury and colored liquids into the blood vessels. He attributed body heat to the rapid movement of those fine particles mentioned by Descartes. It originates in a heavenly material, and not in the *calor innatus,* as the ancients had suggested. Berger confirmed the circulation of blood by exsanguinating a dog within a few minutes, and he determined the total amount of blood.

Berger deals very thoroughly with the function of nerves: they are porous and conduct a fluid that is distributed by arterial blood pressure from the brain by way of the nerves to the periphery. There is neither a *spiritus animalis* nor are there the *facultates* or *archei* of ancient physiology. Berger rejects the explosion theory of muscle contraction proposed by William Thomas and Borelli, stating that the intellect controls the nerve fluid during voluntary motions. The soul resides in the *corpus callosum,* not in the pineal gland. The soul does not, as Stahl maintained, influence the activity of the internal organs. Berger also states that complete section of the vagus nerve is not immediately followed by death, but only after some days; breathing does not serve to cool the blood, but to restore and refine it by means of contact with the air.

The *Physiologia* is a general, critical presentation of contemporary physiology. No particular discoveries are associated with Berger's name. The last of the four editions of the *Physiologia* was edited after Berger's death in 1737 by Cregut, who added a long introduction, "De Anthropologia," in which the then important literature of anatomy and physiology is discussed.

In addition to a short treatise concerning the large arterial branches, accompanied by a good chart (1698), Berger wrote about fifty treatises. One dealing with the springs at Karlsbad has been reprinted several times. An attack against Stahl's animism was published in 1702.

Berger was very well read, very critical, and an opponent of all obscurity; he fought against the weak points of the Galenists and Paracelsians, as well as against the students of Stahl.

BIBLIOGRAPHY

I. ORIGINAL WORKS. Berger's thesis is *De circulatione lymphae et catarrhis* (Jena, 1682); his main work, *Physiologia medica sive De natura humana liber bipartitus* (Wittenberg, 1701; Frankfurt, 1737). Albertus Haller, *Bibliotheca anatomica,* I (1774), 720–721, lists several physiological treatises: *De chylo* (1686); *De corde* (1688); *De ovo et pullo* (1689); *De polypo* (1689); *De homine* (1691); *De succi intrinseci per nervos transitu* (1695); *De respiratione* (1697); *De odoratu* (1698); *De somno* (1706); *De nutritione* (1708); *De vita longa* (1708); and *De secretione* (1712). Additional clinical treatises are listed in Haller's *Bibliography of Practical Medicine,* I (1779), 641–643. Additional works are *Dissertatio de natura morborum medico* (Wittenberg, 1702), a polemic against Stahl; and *De thermis carolinis commentatio qua omnium origo fontium calidorum itemque acidorum ex pyritide ostenditur* (Leipzig–Wittenberg, 1709), also published in German.

II. SECONDARY LITERATURE. Of especial value is E. A. Underwood, "Johann Gottfried von Berger (1659–1736) of Wittenberg and His Text-book of Physiology (1701)," in his *Science, Medicine and History,* II (Oxford, 1953), 141–172, which includes the locations of the *Physiologia medica* but no general bibliography. Biographical information can also be found in *Allgemeine deutsche Biographie,* II (1875), 375; Bayle and Thillaye, *Biographie médicale,* II (Paris, 1855), 94; *Biographie universelle ancienne et moderne,* IV (Paris, 1843), 15; *Biographisches Lexikon der hervorragenden Ärzte,* 2nd ed., I (Berlin–Vienna, 1929), 475; and J. C. Poggendorff, *Biographisch-literarisches Handwörterbuch,* I (1863), 148.

K. E. ROTHSCHUH

BERGIUS, FRIEDRICH (*b.* Goldschmieden, near Breslau, Germany, 11 October 1884; *d.* Buenos Aires, Argentina, 30 March 1949), *chemistry.*

Bergius became involved with chemistry in his very early years. His father was head of a chemical plant and his mother was the daughter of a classics professor; thus, he grew up in a home where learning was highly valued. Following high school and a practical course in the laboratory of a foundry, Bergius began his higher education in Leipzig. In 1907 he passed his doctorate examination and became, successively, assistant to Nernst, Haber, and Ernst Bodenstein. All three allowed him to participate in their research.

In 1909 Bergius qualified as a university lecturer in Hannover, and thereupon set up a private laboratory where he could conduct his own research. Systematically he began work on the influence of high pressure and high temperature, seeking to clarify the conditions in nature under which wood was transformed into coal. Within a short time, Bergius succeeded in developing a coal very similar to that produced in nature through his process of carbonization of peat and cellulose.

At the same time Bergius studied the origin of petroleum and conducted experiments in which he sought to make carboniferous materials react with hydrogen to yield liquid products. As early as 1913 he was granted (with John Billwiller) his first patent for the manufacture of liquid hydrocarbons from coal. Needless to say, research of this kind could not be conducted in a private laboratory. Bergius, who had acquired a fine reputation in scientific circles, became head of a new research laboratory at the Goldschmidt Company in Essen in 1914. The owner, Karl Goldschmidt, was an enthusiastic friend and promoter of Bergius. Soon afterward a private experimental plant was constructed for laboratory experiments, continuous processing of petroleum reserves (the daily output was twenty tons), and commercial experiments.

Bergius recognized that the hydrogenation-dehydrogenation balance was based on temperature, partial hydrogen pressure, and the size of the molecules in the hydrocarbon. For petroleum reserves, slight hydrogenation was found to be sufficient; hydrogen-poor coal, however, required greater hydrogenation before it could be thermally cracked. Hydrogenation of carbon was conducted in two stages, the first being to process the carbon into a paste with oil.

Conditions after World War I made it impossible for Bergius to continue his work, and in 1925 he sold his patent rights to the Badische Anilin- und Sodafabrik in Ludwigshafen, which had begun experimenting with hydrogenation of carbon. He then left the field and dedicated himself to a new problem: hydrolysis of wood by means of acid. With Hägglund, Bergius developed a process by which he obtained complete hydrolysis of wood cellulose by using concentrated hydrochloric acid. The product was either dextrose or, after transformation, ethanol or a nutrient yeast with a 50 percent albumin content.

In 1931 Bergius and Karl Bosch were awarded the Nobel Prize for chemistry. Bergius was one of the most individualistic of research scholars. He persistently attempted to go his own way and to remain completely independent, but the tasks to which he committed himself exceeded the ability of a single individual.

After World War II, no longer able to find work in Germany, Bergius founded a company in Madrid and in 1947 became a scientific adviser to the Argentine government.

BIBLIOGRAPHY

I. ORIGINAL WORKS. Bergius' works include *Die Anwendung hoher Drucke bei chemischen Vorgängen und eine Nachbildung des Entstehungsprozesses der Steinkohle* (Halle, 1913); "Die Verflüssigung der Kohle," in *Zeitschrift des Vereins deutscher Ingenieure,* **69** (1926); "Die Herstellung von Zucker aus Holz und ähnlichen Naturstoffen," in *Ergebnisse der angewandten physikalischen Chemie,* Vol. I (Leipzig, 1931); "Gewinnung von Alkohol und Glucose aus Holz," in *Chemical Age* (London), **29** (1933), 481–483; and "Chemische Reaktionen unter hohem Druck," in *Les prix Nobel en 1931* (Stockholm, 1933), which also includes an autobiographical notice.

II. SECONDARY LITERATURE. For a discussion of Bergius' work, see E. Farber, *Nobel Prize-winners in Chemistry, 1901–1950* (New York, 1953), pp. 123–131.

GÜNTHER KERSTEIN

BERGMAN, TORBERN OLOF (*b.* Katrineberg, Sweden, 9 March 1735; *d.* Medevi, Sweden, 8 July 1784), *chemistry, mineralogy, entomology, astronomy, physics, geography.*

The son of Barthold Bergman, sheriff on the royal estate at Katrineberg, and Sara Hägg, Bergman received a conventional early education in classical subjects at Skara, and was also given private instruction in natural history by Sven Hof, a teacher in the Gymnasium there. He entered Uppsala University in 1752 and graduated in 1756, after studying mathematics, philosophy, physics, and astronomy. In 1758 he gained his doctorate with a thesis entitled *De interpolatione astronomica,* published *De attractione universali,* and became a lecturer in physics at the university. Bergman was appointed associate professor of mathematics in 1761, and in 1767 succeeded J. G. Wallerius as professor of chemistry, a subject that was new to him but in which he became famous. He corresponded with scientists all over Europe and Frederick II offered him an appointment in the Berlin Academy, but he preferred to stay in Sweden. Often in poor health, he regularly visited the medicinal springs at Medevi, where he died. In 1771 he had married Catherine Trast, who survived him.

While a student, Bergman made important contributions to natural history, the most interesting being his discovery, praised by Linnaeus, that the "insect" *coccus aquaticus* was in fact a leech's egg from which ten to twelve young hatched. He studied and classified insect larvae, and in 1762 the Stockholm Academy of Science awarded him a prize for his research on the winter moths that damaged fruit trees. He observed that the female was wingless, and found that metamorphosis occurred in the ground and that after mating, the female climbed the tree and laid eggs around the buds. Damage could therefore be prevented by tying a wax-covered band around the trunk, and this became standard practice in orchards.

Bergman's early contributions to physical science included studies of the rainbow, twilight, and the aurora borealis, of which he estimated the height to be about 460 miles. More important was his discovery of an atmosphere on Venus during the transit of 6

June 1761. Others who took part in this early example of international scientific cooperation included Lomonosov, Dunn, and Chappe d'Auteroche. Like Bergman, they saw a luminous aureole around the planet when it entered and left the sun's disk, and interpreted it as being due to refraction in an atmosphere, but Bergman gave the clearest description of the phenomenon, which was overlooked by some other observers.

Bergman's inaugural address to the Stockholm Academy in 1764 was "The Possibility of Preventing the Harmful Effects of Lightning," and he was one of the first to support Franklin's belief in lightning conductors. However, he disagreed with Franklin's one-fluid theory of electricity, and developed a two-fluid theory similar to that of Wilcke in order to explain why a luminous discharge apparently flowed from both negative and positive conductors.

Following Aepinus, Bergman investigated the pyroelectricity of tourmaline. In 1766 he showed that when the temperature was raised, one end of the crystal became positive and the other negative, and that reducing the temperature reversed the polarity. This was discovered independently by B. Wilson and J. Canton, but none of the three offered an explanation. In 1785 R. J. Haüy was the first to relate crystal structure to electrical properties.

A comprehensive work on cosmography was published in Uppsala in three volumes. F. Mallet gave an account of astronomy; S. Insulin described the customs of the various races inhabiting the world; and in 1766 Bergman contributed *Physical Description of the Earth.* This was an important treatise on physical geography, but its influence was probably diminished by the lack of English and French translations at a time when British and French navigators were rapidly adding to knowledge of the globe. Bergman included a long account of minerals, and he soon became actively interested in mineralogy and chemistry.

Wallerius had lectured on chemistry without demonstrations, and Bergman reformed the teaching arrangements as soon as he succeeded to the chair. Since he believed in applying chemistry to mining and industry, he provided two displays of minerals, one arranged according to chemical composition and one according to geographical distribution, and an exhibition of models of industrial equipment. He taught his students, who came from many countries, not only theoretical chemistry but also new experimental methods, especially in mineral analysis.

The blowpipe had been used by Swedish analysts at least as early as the 1740's. A. Swab and S. Rinman were the pioneers, and A. F. Cronstedt introduced soda, borax, and microcosmic salt (sodium ammonium phosphate) as fluxes. In *De tubo feruminatoria* (1779) Bergman gave a full account of the instrument. He recorded the reactions of minerals with the three fluxes, fused in hollow charcoal supports or silver or gold spoons, and he distinguished between the oxidizing and reducing flames, as they are now called. The blowpipe was an excellent instrument for qualitative analysis, but he recognized that it was unsuitable for quantitative analysis, a branch of the art that he greatly improved by wet methods.

Bergman published analyses of many individual minerals and mineral waters, and dissertations on most of the metals. These frequently contained new qualitative and quantitative results, but three general treatises were more important. In *De analysi aquarum* (1778), he gave the first comprehensive account of the analysis of mineral waters. Dissolved gases, usually carbon dioxide or hydrogen sulfide, were driven out by heating and were collected over mercury. The water was then evaporated to dryness and the residue extracted by four solvents in succession: alcohol, water, acetic acid, and hydrochloric acid. The resulting solutions were each treated with about twenty-five reagents, but not in any particular order. Many were well known, but Bergman introduced important new reagents, notably oxalic acid as a test for lime, and barium chloride for sulfate. His method represented an advance in the analysis of mineral waters, but it was soon improved, notably by A. F. de Fourcroy, who in 1781 pointed out the desirability of using the reagents in a systematic order and found that several were redundant. However, Bergman determined the compositions of some important mineral waters, and from 1773 he successfully prepared artificial seltzer and Pyrmont waters by dissolving the necessary compounds in water saturated with carbon dioxide, which he called "aerial acid" after discovering its acidity.

In *De minerarum docimasia humida* (1780) Bergman described his procedures for qualitative and quantitative analysis of minerals by wet methods. The mineral was finely ground and dissolved in purified acids. Reagents were used for qualitative analysis, as in the case of mineral waters, but for quantitative analysis he introduced an entirely new procedure that soon was generally adopted. Previously it had been customary to attempt to isolate the substance being estimated (metal, earth, and so forth) in the pure state, but Bergman precipitated it as an insoluble compound of known composition, which was filtered through a previously weighed paper and then weighed after drying at the temperature of boiling water. It was necessary to ensure that the precipitate was not contaminated. Thus, iron was precipitated by potassium ferrocyanide; this reagent also formed an insoluble salt with manganese that could be removed by nitric acid.

The method depended on the purity and insolubility of precipitates of known composition. Bergman discussed these factors in a third treatise, *De praecipitatis metallicis* (1780), which contained a table listing the weights of precipitates obtained from 100 parts by weight of different metals by various reagents. Other chemists, notably R. Kirwan and C. F. Wenzel, obtained different results, but Bergman's prestige caused his figures to be generally accepted for many years. In 1789 L. B. Guyton de Morveau proved that Bergman's results were inconsistent, and most of them were abandoned (as were Kirwan's and Wenzel's), but his new analytical methods were of permanent value.

In *De praecipitatis metallicis* Bergman also considered the phenomena observed when metals dissolved in acids, and, as in other writings by him, he accepted the view that phlogiston was lost by the metal. He adopted the phlogistic explanation of combustion and calcination proposed by C. W. Scheele: phlogiston from the combustible or metal combined with "fire air" (oxygen) to form heat, a subtle material that escaped through the vessel. Bergman did, however, make an important original contribution to the phlogiston theory in 1782, when he attempted to measure the relative quantities of phlogiston in different metals by determining the weight of one metal that would precipitate another from solution. Thus, from solution in nitric acid, 100 parts of silver were precipitated by 135 of mercury, 234 of lead, 31 of copper, and so on; and these weights were considered to contain the same amount of phlogiston, for the reaction involved only its transfer. There were inconsistencies due to such effects as incomplete precipitation and the occasional evolution of hydrogen, and it would be reading too much into these results to say that Bergman had grasped the idea of equivalents. This work is, however, important as one of the few attempts ever made to put the phlogiston theory on a quantitative basis.

With his early mathematical training, Bergman was well equipped to seek a geometrical as well as a chemical explanation of the composition of matter, and he made a notable contribution to the early development of crystallography. He may have been influenced by C. F. Westfeld, who in 1767 expressed the opinion that all calcite crystals were composed of rhombohedra and that other shapes were built up from these. A similar suggestion was made by Gahn, but Bergman was the first to demonstrate this in the case of a definite form in which calcite occurred, the scalenohedron. In 1773 he showed how from a rhombohedral nucleus with angles of 101.5° and 78.5° the scalenohedron could be constructed by superimposing rhombic lamellae in sizes that decreased according to some law as the layers developed. This was not merely a geometrical construction on paper, but agreed with the results of cleavage experiments. Dodecahedral garnet crystals were similarly explained, but Bergman could not derive the hexagonal calcite prism with plane ends. This line of research was later developed by Haüy, whose earliest investigations were on garnet and the forms of calcite discussed by Bergman. Haüy's denial that he knew of Bergman's theories has been questioned, but of course there is no doubt about the originality of his subsequent work.

Crystallization was commonly believed to be caused by a "saline principle," but Bergman's analyses showed that many gems and crystalline minerals contained no saline material, and he rejected the concept. Like Guyton de Morveau, with whom he regularly corresponded, he accepted the Newtonian theory that crystals were formed by the mutual attraction of the molecules of matter, but he did not go so far as Guyton, who suggested that these molecules themselves had definite geometrical shapes that could be inferred from the shapes of the crystals.

His belief in attraction between molecules and the vast knowledge of chemical reactions acquired in the course of his analytical work put Bergman in a good position to study chemical affinity. Much had been written about this since E. F. Geoffroy published his table of affinities in 1718, after Newton expressed the view that chemical change was caused by a force acting between particles at very small distances.

Geoffroy's table contained sixteen columns, each with the symbol for one substance at the head and below it the symbols for the substances with which it combined, arranged so that each displaced only those below it. As chemical knowledge increased, affinity tables grew larger: Spielmann's table (1763) had twenty-eight columns, and Fourcy's (1773) had thirty-six. These tables were convenient for summarizing chemical knowledge, but their compilers generally did not speculate about the cause of reactions. Newton's followers were convinced that a modified gravitational attraction was the sole cause of affinity. While using the words "affinity" and "attraction" indiscriminately, Bergman made it clear that he was a Newtonian, although, unlike Guyton and some others, he made no attempt to calculate the strength of intermolecular forces.

Eighteenth-century chemists sometimes thought that the affinity between two substances was a variable quantity, for the course of many reactions could be altered, particularly by the action of heat. A. Baumé pointed this out in 1763, and suggested that two affinity tables should be drawn up, one for reactions "in the wet way" (in aqueous solution) and the other for reactions "in the dry way" (at high temperature, in the absence of water). Bergman was the first to do this, but he did not accept the view that affinities were variable. He stated emphatically that reactions in aqueous solution showed the true affinities of substances, and that changes in the order of affinities in the dry way were due to the action of heat. The first version of his *Disquisitio de attractionibus electivis* (1775) included a table with fifty columns representing reactions in the wet way and thirty-six in the dry way; in 1783 he enlarged these to fifty-nine and forty-three columns, respectively. These tables were widely praised and were reprinted as late as 1808 in William Nicholson's *Dictionary of Chemistry,* but it must be doubted whether they were of great utility, for, like all previous tables, they summarized experimental information without explaining it. Further, Lavoisier pointed out that while separate tables for wet and dry reactions were useful, the effect of heat was so great that there should really be an individual table for each degree of temperature.

In his theoretical discussion Bergman advanced a simplified version of P. J. Macquer's classification of the types of attraction. The union of two or more particles of the same substance was an example of "attraction of aggregation"; when two different substances united, it was "attraction of composition." "Single elective attraction" occurred when a simple substance combined with one of the constituents of a binary compound and set the other free; and "double elective attraction," when two binary compounds reacted and their constituents were exchanged to form two new binary compounds. Affinity tables showed single elective attractions, and Bergman considered that from these it should be possible to find the results of reactions involving several substances, for double elective attractions were to be calculated from the algebraic sums of single attractions. Bergman did not himself attempt to do this, for he did not give numerical values for elective attractions, although soon after the publication of his work this was done by Kirwan, Guyton, and others.

Although Bergman believed that single elective attractions were constant, he admitted that this was not immediately obvious. The apparent exceptions could, however, be explained. For example, it was sometimes difficult to ascertain the exact number of reactants, phlogiston in particular being often overlooked, so that what was apparently an example of single elective attraction might in fact be double. Bergman also noted that the proportions as well as the nature of reactants sometimes seemed to affect the course of a reaction—a line of investigation developed fruitfully by C. L. Berthollet between 1798 and 1803.

Descriptions of reactions in conventional prose were cumbersome, and Bergman introduced diagrams to represent reactions involving single and double elective attractions. These served the same purpose as the earlier diagrams of J. Black and W. Cullen, but were differently constructed. The reaction in the wet way between muriate (chloride) of soda and nitrate of silver is an example.

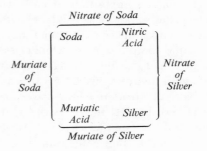

FIGURE 1

The vertical and horizontal brackets show the constituents of the reactants and the products, respectively.

In tables and diagrams Bergman represented substances by symbols, but his successors frequently preferred words. Their binary nomenclature for salts was partly due to Bergman, an early critic of the old unsystematic nomenclature in which the name of a substance was usually derived from its appearance, its discoverer, or some other chemically irrelevant factor. From 1775 he began to coin names related to chemical composition, and he attempted a general reform in *Sciagraphia regni mineralis* (1782). Guyton de Morveau's proposals for a systematic nomenclature were also published in 1782, and their influence can be seen in Bergman's final system, presented in *Meditationes de systemate fossilium naturali* (1784). Guyton wrote in French, but Bergman preferred Latin, which could be translated into all modern languages. Following Linnaeus, Bergman divided inorganic substances into classes, genera, and species; and, as Linnaeus had done for plants and animals, he defined each class and genus by one word and each species by two. There were four classes: salts (including acids and alkalies as well as neutral salts), earths, metals, and phlogistic materials. In the important and numerous class of salts, each acid or alkali constituted a genus, and a neutral salt was a species belonging to the genus of its acid. The acids were named *vitriolicum, nitrosum,* and so on; and the alkalies became *potassinum, natrum,* and *ammoniacum.* Neutral salts received such names as *vitriolicum potassinatum* and *nitrosum argentatum.* Provision was made for unusual salts containing excess acid or base, for example, or having more than two constituents. This was more comprehensive than Guyton's nomenclature of 1782; had he lived, Bergman would have collaborated with Guyton in perfecting the system.

Bergman's nomenclature was closely related to his classification of minerals by composition. Some mineralogists based their classification on external form, but he insisted that the best method demonstrated the inner composition of each mineral, for only thus would we know its utility. However, different external appearances were sometimes associated with the same composition; so while classes, genera, and species had to be defined by composition, varieties could be distinguished by appearance. This was the basis of *Meditationes de systemate fossilium naturali* (1784), his last major work. In the preface he announced his latest discoveries. He had found two sulfides of tin, one containing twice as much sulfur as the other; and resemblances between baryta (barium oxide) and calx (oxide) of lead made him suspect that baryta contained a metal. These final examples of experimental skill and chemical insight show that Bergman deserved the high esteem in which he was held by his contemporaries.

BIBLIOGRAPHY

I. ORIGINAL WORKS. More than 300 items are described in Birgitta Moström, *Torbern Bergman, A Bibliography of His Works* (Stockholm, 1957), which includes reprints and translations published up to 1956.

Bergman's manuscripts are preserved in the University Library, Uppsala. The letters that he received from foreigners are published in G. Carlid and J. Nordström, eds., *Torbern Bergman's Foreign Correspondence,* I (with an introductory biography by H. Olsson), *Letters From Foreigners to Torbern Bergman* (Stockholm, 1965). Vol. II will contain letters from Swedes living abroad, and Bergman's letters to his foreign correspondents.

II. SECONDARY LITERATURE. Several short biographies were written soon after Bergman's death, and later biographical accounts are based on these: P. F. Aurivillius, *Åminnelse-tal öfver . . . Bergman* (Uppsala, 1785); P. J. Hjelm, *Åminnelse-tal öfver . . . Bergman* (Stockholm, 1786); F. Vicq d'Azyr, in *Histoire de la Société royale de médecine de Paris* (1782/1783, pub. 1787), 141–187, repr. in his *Éloges historiques,* I (Paris, 1805), 209–248; A. N. de Condorcet, in *Histoire de l'Académie royale des sciences* (1784, pub. 1787), 31–47, repr. in his *Oeuvres* (Paris, 1847), III, 139–161.

Recent studies of several aspects of Bergman's scientific work can be listed in the order in which the topics are discussed above: D. Müller-Hillebrand, "Torbern Bergman as a Lightning Scientist," in *Daedalus, Tekniska museets årsbok, Stockholm* (1963), 35–76; A. J. Meadows, "The Discovery of an Atmosphere on Venus," in *Annals of Science,* **22** (1966), 117–127; F. Szabadvary, *History of Analytical Chemistry* (Oxford, 1966), pp. 71–81, 86–89; U. Boklund, "Torbern Bergman as a Pioneer in the Domain of Mineral Waters," in T. Bergman, *On Acid of Air . . .* (Stockholm, 1956), pp. 105–128; R. Hooykas, "Les débuts de la théorie cristallographique de R. J. Haüy, d'après les documents originaux," in *Revue d'histoire des sciences,* **8** (1955), 319–337; J. G. Burke, *Origins of the Science of Crystals* (Berkeley-Los Angeles, 1966), pp. 26–27, 79–84; A. M. Duncan, "Some Theoretical Aspects of Eighteenth-Century Tables of Affinity," in *Annals of Science,* **18** (1962), 177–194, 217–232; and "Introduction" to a facsimile repr. of Thomas Beddoes' trans. (London, 1785) of Bergman's *A Dissertation on Elective Attractions* (London, 1969); W. A. Smeaton, "The Contributions of P.-J. Macquer, T. O. Bergman and L. B. Guyton de Morveau to the Reform of Chemical Nomenclature," in *Annals of Science,* **10** (1954), 87–106; and M. P. Crosland, *Historical Studies in the Language of Chemistry* (London, 1962), pp. 144–167.

W. A. SMEATON

BERGSON, HENRI LOUIS (*b.* Paris, France, 18 October 1859; *d.* Paris, 4 January 1941), *philosophy.*

Henri Bergson was the son of a Polish musician and composer, Michael Bergson, and of an English mother (née Kate Lewison). The family settled in Paris, where Henri attended the Lycée Condorcet and the École Normale Supérieure. His main studies were mathematics, literature, and philosophy; and his academic record was brilliant. After becoming *agrégé* in 1881, Bergson began teaching philosophy at the Angers Lycée. He advanced steadily through a series of other posts, until in 1900 he was appointed professor at the Collège de France, where he eventually succeeded Gabriel Tarde in the chair of modern philosophy. By this time his books and lectures had given him an international reputation as the author of an original and impressive philosophical doctrine.

Bergson was elected to the Académie Française in 1914, was awarded the Nobel Prize for Literature in 1928, and received the Grand Cross of the Legion of Honor in 1930. After World War I, he devoted himself to the cause of the League of Nations and served as chairman of its Committee for Intellectual Cooperation. Ill health forced him to retire from academic life in 1921; he then lived in comparative seclusion with his wife (née Louise Neuburger) and daughter Jeanne. Bergson's parents were Jewish, but he himself had no formal religious affiliation, although toward the end of his life he expressed a sympathy for Roman Catholicism.

Bergson's philosophy offers a new interpretation of four main ideas: time, freedom, memory, and evolution. These ideas are construed so as to produce a doctrine that is opposed to materialism, as well as to mechanistic and deterministic theories of living things. The doctrine strongly emphasizes the phenomenon of change or process, which continually creates unpredictable novelties in cosmic history. The doctrine also emphasizes the importance of direct, conscious experience as the source of man's most reliable knowledge.

In his first book, *Essai sur les données immédiates de la conscience* (*Time and Free Will*), Bergson drew a distinction between two kinds of time. There is the time that occurs in the theories of the natural sciences, and there is the time that we experience directly. Scientific time is a mathematical conception, symbolized geometrically by a line or algebraically by the letter t, and measured by clocks and chronometers. Because these measuring instruments are spatial bodies, scientific time is represented as an extended, homogeneous medium composed of standard units (seconds, hours, years, and so forth). Most of man's practical life in society is guided by reference to such units. But time thus represented neither "flows" nor "acts"; it is wholly passive. When we turn to our direct experience, however, we find nothing like scientific time. What we find, Bergson contended, is a flowing, irreversible succession of phenomena which melt into one another to form an indivisible process. This process is not homogeneous, but heterogeneous. It is concrete, not abstract. In short, it is "lived time" (*temps vécu*) or "real duration" (*durée réelle*), something immediately experienced as active and ongoing. If we try to represent it by a spatial image such as a line, we will only generate abstract mathematical time, which is a fiction. The mistake of mechanistic modes of thought is to regard this fiction as a reality.

The recognition of real duration provides a basis, Bergson held, for vindicating human freedom and disposing of the bogey of determinism. A determinist contends that freedom of choice is illusory. A man may feel that he is free to choose, but theoretical considerations show that he never is. To support this contention, a determinist may depict the case in which a man confronts an ostensible choice as a situation similar to arriving at a point on a line where branching occurs, and then taking one of the branches. The determinist asserts that in fact the branch taken could not *not* have been taken and, indeed, that the choice

made was fully predictable beforehand, given complete knowledge of the antecedent states of mind of the agent.

This argument has a spurious plausibility, according to Bergson, because it represents the case of choice by a spatial image. The image may serve to symbolize a choice already made, but it is totally inadequate to symbolize a choice in the making: in acting, we do not move along a linear path through time. Deliberating about a course of action is not like being at a point in space where we oscillate between paths laid out before us. Deliberation and choice are temporal, not spatial, acts. Moreover, the determinist makes the mistake of supposing that the way in which the agent acts is determined by the totality of antecedent states of mind, each atomically independent of the rest. This conception of mental life as made up of basic units was the misconception promulgated by associationistic psychology. It invalidates all the traditional arguments for determinism.

Freedom of choice, Bergson held, is fully certified by direct experience. A man knows that he is free as he acts. However, one qualification must be added. Strictly speaking, a man is free only when his act springs spontaneously from his total personality as it has evolved up to the moment of action. If this spontaneity is absent, his action will be stereotyped and mechanical. Hence, free acts are far from being universal. Most people behave like automata most of the time. But the point is that they need not do so, for freedom is always attainable.

Bergson's second book, *Matière et mémoire,* advocates a dualism of body and mind, of the material and the spiritual. Each of us is alleged to know his own body in two ways: from without, as an object among other objects, and from within, as a center of action. Likewise, each of us knows his own conscious processes directly. How are the body and mind—i.e., brain activity and mental activity—related? The answer lies in a proper understanding of memory.

Living organisms, unlike nonliving things, retain their past in the present. This phenomenon is manifested, Bergson affirmed, in two kinds of memory. One kind consists of bodily habits fixed in the organism and designed to ensure its adaptation to the contemporary world. The other kind of memory, which man alone possesses, records in the form of images each event of his daily life as it takes place. This is "pure memory," which is wholly spiritual. It is quite independent of the brain, whose structure resembles that of a telephone exchange and which therefore has no facilities for storing memory traces.

How is pure memory related to the brain? Bergson's

answer depends on the assumption that each person's memory retains the whole of his past experience. If this is so, something must prevent all of one's memories from crowding into consciousness at every moment. The brain is the mechanism that performs this function. It is a device evolved to facilitate action by ensuring that only what is relevant to a particular occasion of action will be recalled. Hence, it acts as a filter which excludes the vast majority of memories at each instant. It is a device to promote forgetting, not remembering.

The relation between body and mind is, then, to be understood temporally. It is not to be envisaged as a spatial or quasi-spatial connection between two entities. On an occasion of action, body and mind (including memory) converge in time. A typical case is an act of perception. Traditional philosophers have thought of perception as being like a photographic process which provides a passive, cognitive reflection of the world. But this is a mistaken view. Perception is an adaptive response to the world in which the body contributes sense receptors to register the influences of environing objects, and the mind contributes relevant memory images to give a meaningful form to what is perceived. The aim is to put the organism in a condition in which it can act successfully. Body and mind are thus united in real duration, for perception is an event in the present, which is not a geometrical point or "knife edge" separating past from future, but a continuous flowing. Perceptual acts in which body and mind are fused are intrinsically temporal and practical.

In his next work, *Introduction à la métaphysique,* Bergson modified his position by affirming that sometimes "pure perception," detached from memory and action, can occur. This process is also called "intuition" and is contrasted with conceptual thought, the product of the intellect. Both processes arose in human evolution, intuition being derived from instinct and conceptual thought being derived from man's social existence, his tool-making capacity, and his power of speech. Because his inherently limited intellect is the human animal's distinctive instrument which he employs in his interactions with the world, conceptual thought has certain limitations. It has an inherent tendency to use spatial notions, to analyze things mechanically into ultimate units, and to interpret motion and change in static terms. Like a motion-picture camera, it translates everything into a series of discrete "frames." Intuition, on the other hand, is a type of consciousness which achieves a direct participation in, or an identification with, what is intuited. By means of it "one is transported into the interior of an object in order to coincide with what

is unique and consequently inexpressible about it."

In the case of ourselves, intuition is immersion in the flow of consciousness, a grasping of pure becoming and real duration. Unlike the intellect—which remains outside what it knows, requires symbols, and produces knowledge that is relative—intuition enters into what it knows, dispenses with symbols, and produces knowledge that is absolute.

The natural sciences were for Bergson a typical achievement of the intellect. Hence, they inevitably falsify time, motion, and change by interpreting these items in terms of static concepts. The sciences are equipped to deal with matter, but not with real becoming. Hence, there is need of a discipline to supplement them, if a full understanding of the universe is to be attained. Such a discipline, Bergson proposed, is metaphysics, not in the classical sense of rational speculation or system building, but redefined as a "true empiricism" that explores real becoming by participating directly in it. Thus, by adopting the method of intuition, metaphysics can provide a supplement to the sciences by giving a true account of duration, of becoming, and even of evolution.

This last topic was dealt with by Bergson in his most famous book, *L'évolution créatrice* (*Creative Evolution*). He accepted the historical fact of the evolution of living things on the earth, but rejected all mechanistic or materialistic explanations of the evolutionary process. In place of the theories of Darwin, Lamarck, and Spencer, he advanced a doctrine which owes much to the tradition of European vitalism and also draws inspiration from Plotinus. The result was a theory of cosmic evolution that goes far beyond the domain of biology.

Bergson did accept one aspect of Lamarck's doctrine, "the power of varying by use or disuse" certain bodily organs, and the transmission of such acquired variations to descendants. He may have derived this notion from his early study of Herbert Spencer, rather than from the study of Lamarck himself. However, he does not link the notion with a doctrine of "racial memory" (as did, for example, Samuel Butler). Bergson hints that the Lamarckian idea of "effort" has to be understood not in an individualistic sense, but in "a deeper sense" as a manifestation of the *élan vital.*

Bergson argued against the Darwinian doctrine that the cause of evolution was natural selection acting on random variations. This doctrine fails to give a satisfactory explanation of the evolution of complex organs and functions, such as the eye of vertebrates, for it obliges us to suppose that at each stage all the parts of an animal and of its organs vary contemporaneously, since integral functioning has to be preserved to ensure survival. But it is utterly implausible to suppose that such coadapted variations could have been random. Some agency must have been at work to maintain continuity of functioning through successive alterations of form.

Another fact that points in the same direction is the evolution of complex organisms from relatively simple ones. The earliest living things were minute, unicellular entities well adapted to their environment. Why did the evolutionary process not stop at this stage? Why did life continue to complicate itself "more and more dangerously"? Random variations and selection pressures cannot provide a satisfactory explanation. Something must have driven life on to higher and higher levels of organization, despite the risks involved. Neither Spencer, with his appeal to mechanistic notions, nor Lamarck, with his appeal to the "effort" exerted by individual organisms, can account for the great diversity and complexity which evolution has created.

The clue to this problem, Bergson affirmed, is to be found not in biology, but in metaphysics. Human beings, with their capacity for intuition, are typical constituents of the universe, and hence the forces that work in them may be supposed to work in all things. Intuition not only discloses pure duration and becoming in our experience, but also gives us a consciousness of a vital impulse (*élan vital*) within us. We are thus led to the idea of *"un élan original de la vie"* which pervades the whole evolutionary process and accounts for its dominant features. Accordingly, the history of life is to be understood as a process of creative evolution which has resulted from this primordial impulse.

Bergson spoke of the vital impulse as a "current of consciousness" that has penetrated matter, produced living organisms, and made possible an ever-increasing freedom of action. Yet the impulse is not striving to attain a final goal. Bergson was as opposed to radical finalism as he was to mechanism. Both doctrines disregard the creativity by which unpredictable novelties have periodically "leaped into existence." One of these novelties is man, for his appearance was in no sense designed or prefigured. Terrestrial evolution might have produced some other being "of the same essence." Such beings doubtless have arisen elsewhere, for the vital impulse must be supposed to animate countless planets in the universe. Creative evolution is thus cosmic in its scope.

Bergson's interest in science was shown not only by his discussion of biology but also by his discussion of physics. This subject is treated in *Durée et simultanéité,* which deals with the view of time set forth in Einstein's theory of relativity. Here, as in the case of evolution, Bergson sought to demonstrate how philosophy can supplement science by providing a more adequate account of phenomena. Einstein's theory has, of course, a precisely defined physical sense and stands in no need of support from metaphysics. But some persons have sought to derive from the theory certain "paradoxes" that have their source in the notion of multiple times which flow more rapidly or less rapidly, depending on the motion of the reference systems with which they are associated. Bergson contended that these paradoxes arise because of a philosophical misconception. They rest on an assumption that all of the times are real when the observers in the various systems disagree in their measurements. But from a philosophical standpoint only experienced or "lived" time (*temps vécu*) is real. Hence, the paradoxes can be avoided by considering just one observer and his time as real at each stage of the calculation. For that observer the times of all other reference systems are mathematical fictions, not realities. A similar treatment can be given to simultaneity. It is even possible in the light of this to reinstate the idea of universal time (*l'idée d'une durée de l'univers*) as a philosophical basis for physics.

The religious element in Bergson's thought became more pronounced in his later works. *Creative Evolution* contains a reference to the vital impulse as a "supraconsciousness" to which the name "God" might be applied. This was a use of the term quite alien to traditional Christian theology. For if God is the vital impulse, He is pure activity, limited by the material world through which He is struggling to manifest Himself and, hence, is evolving rather than complete and perfect. In Bergson's final book, *Les deux sources de la morale et de la religion,* this conception is qualified so that it moves closer to the Christian position. God is now affirmed to be love and the object of love. A divine purpose in evolution is also affirmed, for evolution is nothing less than God's "undertaking to create creators, that He may have, besides Himself, beings worthy of His love."

The discovery of this purpose and of the reality of God cannot be made by the intellect. It can be made only by the special sort of intuition that is the mystical experience. The vital impulse, Bergson declared, is "communicated in its entirety" to certain exceptional persons. These are the mystics who attain partial union with the creative effort that "is of God, if it is not God Himself." But the mystical experience does not lead to passive withdrawal from the world; it leads to intense activity. The true mystics are impelled to help the divine purpose to advance by helping mankind to advance beyond its present state.

An important step in this advance is the replacing

of a "closed" society with an "open" one. Bergson's analysis here is influenced by that of the French sociological school of Émile Durkheim. A closed society is one dominated by what is routine and mechanical. It is resistant to change, conservative and authoritarian. Its morality is static and absolutistic, and its religion is ritualistic and dogmatic. An open society is progressive, diversified, experimental, and continually growing. Its morality is flexible and spontaneous. Religion in this society will dispense with stereotyped dogmas formulated by the intellect. These dogmas will be replaced by the intuition and illumination now achieved by the mystics. Men in the open society will be free, integral, creative, and able to reflect in their lives the divine *élan* that is the basic reality in the universe.

Bergson's philosophy represents an impressive statement of the antimechanist position. His use of biological and psychological material to support his contentions, his capacity to invent striking metaphors, and above all his fluent, persuasive style gave his philosophy wide appeal. Philosophers such as William James, dramatists such as G. B. Shaw, and *littérateurs* such as Proust were all influenced by Bergsonian doctrines. Yet the absence of precise definition and of rigorous argument in his books leaves many doctrines obscure. It is far from clear, for example, how his theory of knowledge, which is a form of idealism, can be made compatible with his parabiological theory, which is a form of evolutionary realism. Intuition is said to disclose pure becoming, real duration, and the vital impulse. Yet the differences, if any, between these items are not clearly specified. Sometimes matter and spirit are treated as quite distinct from one another, and sometimes as the "inverse" of one another, matter being spirit that has become "devitalized" and uniform. These obscurities are perhaps to be expected in the work of a philosopher for whom intuition is superior to conceptual thought. Bergson displayed his greatest originality when he undertook to describe direct experience and the temporal dimension of life.

BIBLIOGRAPHY

I. Original Works. Bergson's works include *Écrits et paroles*, R. M. Mossé-Bastide, ed. (I, Paris, 1957; II and III, Paris, 1959); and *Oeuvres*, Édition du centenaire, annotated by André Robinet, intro. by Henri Gouhier (Paris, 1959). This edition contains the following works: *Essai sur les données immédiates de la conscience* (Paris, 1889); *Matière et mémoire* (Paris, 1896); *Le rire* (Paris, 1900); *Introduction à la métaphysique* (Paris, 1903); *L'évolution créatrice* (Paris, 1907); *L'énergie spirituelle* (Paris, 1919); *Les*

deux sources de la morale et de la religion (Paris, 1932); *La pensée et la mouvant* (Paris, 1934). The only major work omitted is *Durée et simultanéité* (Paris, 1922; 3rd ed., 1926), for the reasons given by E. Le Roy in "Lettre-préface" to *Écrits et paroles,* I, vii–viii.

English translations of Bergson's writings include *Laughter, An Essay on the Meaning of the Comic,* trans. C. Brereton and F. Rothwell (New York, 1910); *Time and Free Will: An Essay on the Immediate Data of Consciousness,* trans. F. L. Podgson (New York, 1910); *Creative Evolution,* trans. A. Mitchell (New York, 1911); *Matter and Memory,* trans. N. M. Paul and W. S. Palmer (New York, 1911); *Introduction to Metaphysics,* trans. T. E. Hulme (New York, 1914, 1949); *Mind-Energy,* trans. H. W. Carr (New York, 1920); *The Two Sources of Morality and Religion,* trans. R. A. Audra and C. Brereton (New York, 1935); and *The Creative Mind,* trans. M. L. Andison (New York, 1946).

II. Secondary Literature. Works on Bergson and his philosophy include H. W. Carr, *Henri Bergson, the Philosophy of Change* (London, 1912; new ed., rev., 1919); J. Chevalier, *Henri Bergson* (New York, 1928); J. Delhomme, *Vie et conscience de la vie: Essai sur Bergson* (Paris, 1954); M. V. Jankélévitch, *Henri Bergson* (Paris, 1959), a centenary completion of a work published in 1931 which undertakes to refute the view that Bergson's philosophy is dualistic and to relate it to the contemporary movement of European phenomenology; A. D. Lindsay, *The Philosophy of Bergson* (London, 1911); A. O. Lovejoy, *The Reason, the Understanding and Time* (Baltimore, 1961), contains a valuable discussion of Bergson's ideas in relation to post-Kantian thought in Germany; J. Maritain, *La philosophie bergsonienne* (Paris, 1930), trans. M. L. and G. Andison as *Bergsonian Philosophy and Thomism* (New York, 1955), a highly polemical work by an ex-Bergsonian turned Thomist; R. M. Mossé-Bastide, *Bergson éducateur* (Paris, 1955), a full and accurate account of Bergson's career, with a massive bibliography of primary and secondary sources; B. A. Sharfstein, *Roots of Bergson's Philosophy* (New York, 1943); and *Les études bergsoniennes* (Paris, 1948–1966), studies published at intervals under the editorship of various Bergsonian scholars, of which Vol. II (1949) contains the text of Bergson's doctoral thesis (1889), translated into French from Latin as *L'idée de lieu chez Aristote.*

T. A. Goudge

BÉRIGARD (in modern French, **Beauregard**), **CLAUDE GUILLERMET DE** (*b.* Moulins, France, 1578 [according to Niceron; possibly as late as 1591]; *d.* Padua, Italy, 1663/1664), *medicine, physics, philosophy.*

Bérigard studied both medicine and philosophy at Aix-en-Provence and lived quietly in Avignon, Lyons, and Paris. He could, therefore, have witnessed the condemnation by the parliament and the Sorbonne of Villon and de Claves for their support of atomism in 1624. Summoned to Tuscany in 1625, possibly by

Christine de Lorraine, mother of Ferdinand II, grand duke of Tuscany, he taught philosophy at Pisa in 1628. Hobbes met him there around 1635. In 1632 Bérigard published the *Dubitationes*, concerning Galileo's *Dialogue Concerning the Two Chief World Systems* (condemned in 1633). Galileo himself is quoted as saying to Elie Diodati (25 July 1634) that it was more out of obligation than conviction. Bérigard, who must have known Galileo personally, always praised him, but remained firmly convinced of the earth's immobility.

In 1640 Bérigard went to Padua, where he became well known as a teacher. He later published a synopsis of his courses as *Circulus pisanus* (1643). Since the preface to the chapter "De generatione et corruptione" named Galileo, Torricelli, Viviani, Cabeo, Bourdin, Boulliau, Mersenne, Descartes, Digby, Kircher, Kaspar Bartholin and his sons, and Borel as some of the contemporaries he admired, he was surely abreast of the intellectual movement of his time and was well disposed toward change. Yet the Scholasticism that he had to teach at times dominated his thought.[1]

The above list also includes Gassendi, although he is usually cited as following Bérigard in reviving atomism. In fact, the opposite was probably true. At first there was no reciprocal influence. Bérigard left Aix before Gassendi came to teach there, and as far as is known they did not meet in 1624–1625, when Gassendi came to Paris. But in his *Exercitationes paradoxicae* (1624) Gassendi criticized Aristotle after having taught his doctrines—as Bérigard did in the *Circulus*. Although Gassendi's great Epicurean works date from 1647 and 1649, he was already working on them in 1630, as Mersenne and Peiresc reveal in their correspondence. Between 1640 and 1643, in published works, Gassendi cited atomistic physics as evidence and corresponded with Liceti, whom Bérigard succeeded in 1653. Finally, the second edition of the *Circulus* shows the influence of Gassendi's *Syntagma philosophicum* (1658). It should be noted that as early as 1633 Mersenne and Peiresc called Gassendi's attention to the *Dubitationes*.[2]

On the other hand, the spirits of the two works are somewhat different. Both admit *corpuscula tenuia, a Deo creata,* while attributing essential qualities to them—but with far more caution on Gassendi's part than on Bérigard's. Moreover, Bérigard's corpuscles are not true atoms. As a humanist inclined to archaism, Bérigard went back to the pre-Socratics because Aristotle was against them; Gassendi, a historian above all, thought that Aristotle's successors had surpassed him. Bérigard was unable to tie the new scientific ideas to his own endeavor, while

Gassendi found new arguments in these ideas and tried to prepare the future for rational physics.

Actually, Bérigard found his inspiration less in Democritus, who was quite modern, than in the Ionians, who were still influenced by mythology: Anaximander, Empedocles, and Anaxagoras. In order to explain variations in being, these philosophers divided it into simple elements likely to combine. Because of this, the form of the elements must be that most suitable to movement: round and smooth. These elements achieved cohesion by all moving in the same direction or toward one center.

Around the masses thus formed there circulated an ether that consolidated them and, through the pores of these contiguous but not adherent elements, penetrated the masses and also escaped from them, sweeping particles in and out without leaving a vacuum.[3] However, the subject in question was a *qualitative atomism,* not a mechanical one, for the elements were not homogeneous; each had distinct properties, and the appearances resulting from their composition are infinitely different.[4] Only the local predominance of certain more or less similar qualities gave rise to the most common perceptible appearances and accounted for there being lead here, for instance, and gold there. But there was some of all things in each thing—gold in lead, lead in gold, with an infinite possibility of transmutations.

However, this vague relationship between a quantitative determination in the external cause and a qualitative appearance in the conscious effect is insufficient for making reality rational. The explanatory power of atomism is related to the supposition of perfect homogeneity in the components of bodies. Only the number, distance, and density of atoms in a given volume—that is, only the quantity measurable and expressible by mathematical means—enters into the action that the composites exert on each other and on those composites which are our sense organs. Atoms, then, are units capable of being combined, and these combinations can be calculated. Bérigard's qualified corpuscles end only in Heraclitus' perpetual flux, in which the same entities are never reproduced; thus no law can be formulated or imagined.

From the very beginning Bérigard and Gassendi held opposing views on the ontology of space and time. For Gassendi space (the Epicurean void) and time (which passes outside events) were "neither substance nor accidents."[5] Thus time and space escape in parallel ways from the Aristotelian categories and need not have been created in order to exist, because they make creation possible. Against this opinion, Bérigard absolutely refused to recognize that space and time are uncreated things, nor did he admit that they are neither substance nor mere accident (*Circulus,* 1661 ed., p. 51). But Bérigard here drew back, in spite of the fact that he renounced the Scholastic definition of space as "limite du corps environnant" (*ibid.,* p. 47).

Gassendi's view leads directly to the law of inertia, to the conservation of straight and uniform movement as long as nothing in inert space stops it. Newton found in Gassendi the ontological categories that made universal attraction conceivable. Yet Gassendi had not completely renounced qualitative atomism, and lacked the mathematical ability to found a mechanistic physics. Bérigard, even after having read Gassendi's works, remained deeply involved with qualitative physics. He was a great scholar; if, however, he did see the scientific promised land from afar, he did not move toward it. He was not aware of the implications of his own corpuscular philosophy or the importance of universal mechanism.

NOTES

1. For instance, although recognizing that sunspots prove that the sun is not incorruptible, he did not dare go so far as to say the same of the "heavens." (The list was taken from the 2nd ed., 1661.)
2. See *Correspondance de Mersenne,* III, 355 (5 January 1633, Mersenne to Gassendi) and 380 (2 March 1633, Gassendi to Peiresc).
3. Up to this point, the parallel with Descartes's physics could be easily noted, for Descartes would not be called an atomist and denied the void, although he admitted vortexes of subtle matter.
4. Here it is legitimate to speak of either *points-qualités* or *éléments-qualités,* as is done by Jean Zafiropoulo in his *Anaxagore de Clazomène* (Paris, 1948), pp. 313–315.
5. See *Animadversiones in X. librum D. Laertii* (Lyons, 1649), p. 614, and *Syntagma philosophicum* (Lyons, 1658), I 182*a*, 183*b*, 220*b*. In his controversy over the void with P. Noël in 1648, Pascal was led to use the same anti-Scholastic formulas as Gassendi; however, he may have found them only in Noël's writings (see *Oeuvres de Pascal,* Pléiade ed., pp. 383, 1450).

BIBLIOGRAPHY

I. ORIGINAL WORKS. Bérigard's major works are *Dubitationes in dialogum Galilaei Lyncei . . .* (Florence, 1632); and *Circulus Claudii Berigardi, de veteri et peripatetica philosophia . . .* (Udine, 1643); 2nd ed., *Circulus pisanus Claudii Berigardi, de veteri et peripatetica philosophia . . .* (Padua, 1661), in 1 vol., with considerable modification.

II. SECONDARY LITERATURE. Works on Bérigard are E. Brehier, *Histoire de la philosophie,* II (Paris, 1960), 13; J. Brücker, *Historia critica philosophiae* (Leipzig, 1742); David Clement, *Bibliothèque curieuse* (Göttingen, 1750), III, 182–185; Kurt Lasswitz, *Geschichte der Atomistik* (Leipzig, 1890; 1926), I, 488–498; D. G. Morhof, *Polyhistor* (1732); J. P. Niceron, *Mémoires pour servir à l'histoire des*

hommes illustres dans la république des lettres (Paris, 1727–1745), XXXI, 123–127; G. Sortais, *Philosophie moderne depuis Bacon jusqu'à Leibniz* (Paris, 1922), II, 71–75; and W. G. Tennemann, *Histoire de la philosophie* (Leipzig, 1798–1819). There is also a note on Bérigard in the Edizione Nazionale of Galileo (new ed., Florence, 1964), XX, 90. Franck's *Dictionnaire des sciences philosophiques* (1885) includes an article on Bérigard in which there is a serious error: Galileus Lynceus is not a pseudonym, but refers to Galileo Galilei in the full title of *Dubitationes.*

BERNARD ROCHOT

BERING, VITUS (*b.* Horsens, Denmark, summer 1681; *d.* Bering Island, Russia, 19 December 1741), *geography.*

Bering's parents were Jonas Svendsen and Anna Bering. There were many children in the family, and the need to earn a living sent Bering to sea at an early age. Returning from a voyage to the East Indies in 1703, he was recruited into the Russian navy, where he rose quickly in rank.

On 5 February 1725, Bering left St. Petersburg on his first expedition, which, under Peter the Great's orders, was to determine whether Asia and America were joined by land. He journeyed overland through Siberia and across to the Kamchatka Peninsula, which he was the first to map. On 9 July 1728 he sailed in a northerly direction along the east coast of Asia; on 15 August he reached latitude 67° 18′ N. There he turned back, having convinced himself that there was no more land to the north. Owing to poor visibility in the strait that was to be named after him, he could not sight the American mainland. He was much criticized for not having proved whether East Cape (now Cape Dezhnev) was the end of Asia.

In spite of that, Bering led a second and even more ambitious expedition to investigate the Kurile Islands and Japan, to make a landing in America, and to map the north coast of Siberia. The expedition achieved the first two objectives. Bering himself left St. Petersburg in 1733 and sailed from Kamchatka for the New World in June 1741. Setting his course in accordance with Delisle's map, he searched for the land mass of Gamaland on the 47th parallel. Failing to find it, he turned northeast and on 16 July 1741 sighted Alaska; four days later he landed on Kayak Island. Bering's return was delayed by the lateness of the season, by scurvy, and, again, by the inaccuracy of the maps. He returned along the hitherto unknown Aleutian Islands and was forced to winter on an uninhabited island only 300 miles short of home. There he died, and the crew named the island Bering Island.

BIBLIOGRAPHY

The translated report of the first expedition by Bering is reproduced in F. A. Golder, *Bering's Voyages, an Account of the Efforts of the Russians to Determine the Relations of Asia and America,* 2 vols. (New York, 1922–1925).

There is no complete biography of Bering. Of value are an account of the first expedition in W. H. Dale, "Notes on an Original Chart of Bering's Expedition of 1725–1730 and an Original Manuscript Chart of His Second Expedition, Together With a Summary of a Journal of the First Expedition, Kept by Peter Chaplin," Appendix 19 of *U.S. Coast and Geodetic Survey Report* for 1890 (Washington, D.C., 1891), pp. 759–774; accounts by members of the second expedition S. Khitrov, K. Yushin, and G. W. Steller, in F. A. Golder, *Bering's Voyages* (see above), I, 36–49; 50–230; II, 9–158, respectively; and Sven Waxell, *The American Expedition,* M. A. Michael, trans. (London, 1952), pp. 11–135.

WILMA GEORGE

BERINGER, JOHANN BARTHOLOMAEUS ADAM, also known as **Johann Barthel Adam Behringer** (*b.* Würzburg, Germany, *ca.* 1667; *d.* Würzburg, 11 April 1738),[1] *medicine, natural history.*

There is a signal lack of information regarding Beringer's life and career. His father was Johann Ludwig Beringer, professor at the University of Würzburg and senior physician and dean of the Faculty of Medicine there from 1669 to 1671. In 1693 Beringer passed the final examination (*periculum*) for the doctorate in medicine and on 14 December 1694 was named *professor quartus seu extraordinarius* at the University of Würzburg—where he remained, as far as is known, for his entire career. Appointed keeper in 1695, Beringer reordered and enlarged the botanical gardens of the university and the Julian Hospital.[2] In 1700 he was elevated to the rank of *professor ordinarius* and dean of the Faculty of Medicine; adviser and chief physician to the prince-bishop of Würzburg, Christoph Franz von Hutten; and chief physician to the Julian Hospital (1700/1701–1728). He frequently lectured at the university on reform in education, and succeeded in introducing a program for the education (at public expense) of poor but gifted students from various orphan asylums. In medicine Beringer was particularly concerned with the malpractices of wandering physicians.

Typical of the curious and learned men of the seventeenth and eighteenth centuries, Beringer was caught up in virtuoso endeavor. Occasionally his natural history lectures turned to the petrifactions found in the Würzburg Muschelkalk, from which he collected fossil shells for his cabinet. It was this interest that led to his involvement in the famous Würzburg *Lügensteine* hoax. Stones of shell lime carved in a great variety of forms were hidden about Mount Eibelstadt by two of Beringer's colleagues—J. Ignatz Roderick (an ex-Jesuit and professor of geography, algebra, and analysis at the university) and Johann Georg von Eckhart (privy councillor and librarian to the court and the university)—with the assistance of three young boys.[3] The stones were subsequently uncovered by Beringer and placed in his cabinet. The hoaxers soon realized the enormity of their actions, but in spite of their best efforts to dissuade him, Beringer published a preliminary report on the stones in 1726: *Lithographiae Wirceburgensis . . . Specimen primum. . . .* The fraud, however, was soon discovered. Roderick and Eckhart were taken to court by Beringer for the "saving of his honor," and were duly punished.[4]

Despite this partially successful attempt to discredit him, Beringer remained on the staff of the university, where he was occupied with teaching and research until his death in 1738. He was survived by two sons, Georg Philipp (who matriculated under the direction of his father in 1701, with the dissertation *Thesis de phthisi*) and Johannes Ludwig Anton (a student of metaphysics).

NOTES

1. Beringer's dates, especially that of his birth, are open to conjecture. His death is assigned both to 1738 and, without month, to 1740.
2. A catalog of the gardens, issued in 1722, contained a list of 423 species of plants arranged according to Tournefort's system.
3. The three youths, employed by Beringer for fieldwork, were Christian Zänger (age seventeen) and two brothers, Niklaus and Valentin Hehn (age eighteen and fourteen, respectively). Of the three only Zänger was involved in the hoax, being in the employ of Roderick and von Eckhart as well as of Beringer.
4. The judicial process was in three steps: first, the hearing at the Würzburg Cathedral Chapter on 13 April 1726; second and third, the municipal trials of 15 April and 11 June 1726. The transcripts are in the Staatsarchiv, Würzburg, and appear in a complete English translation in Jahn and Woolf, *Lying Stones,* pp. 125–141.

BIBLIOGRAPHY

I. ORIGINAL WORKS. Beringer's writings include the following: *Connubium Galenico-Hippocraticum, sive Idaea institutionum medicinae rationalium . . .* (Würzburg, 1708); *Tractatus de conservanda corporis humani sanitate . . .* (Würzburg, 1710); *Dissertatio prima de peste in genere et lue epidemica modo grassante in specie . . .* (Nuremberg, 1714); *Plantarum quarundam exoticarum perennium in horto medico Herbipolensi . . .* (Würzburg, 1722), written with Laurentius Anton Dercum—it is uncertain whether this catalog was actually published or was presented to the university in MS; *Lithographiae Wirceburgensis... Specimen primum* . . . (Würzburg, 1726; 2nd ed., Frankfurt–Leipzig, 1767), trans. by M. E. Jahn and Daniel J. Woolf in *The Lying Stones of Dr. Beringer* . . . (Berkeley–Los Angeles, 1963); and *Gründlich und richtigste Untersuchung deren kissinger Heyl- und Gesundheits-Brunnen* . . . (Würzburg, 1738).

The 2nd ed. of the *Lithographiae Wirceburgensis* consisted of original sheets with a new title page. The sheets undoubtedly came from copies of the original ed. recalled from booksellers and the press by Beringer but not destroyed. The reissue of the work as a literary curiosity is often attributed to one of Beringer's sons.

A partial list of dissertations directed by Beringer is in Sticker, p. 487.

II. SECONDARY LITERATURE. It would be impossible to cite more than a handful of the articles written about Beringer and the Würzburg *Lügensteine*. The following contain the correct story of the hoax and, in most cases, a bibliography of secondary sources: M. E. Jahn, "Dr. Beringer and the Würzburg 'Lügensteine,'" in *Journal of the Society for the Bibliography of Natural History*, **4**, no. 2 (Jan. 1963), 138–146, and "A Further Note on Dr. Johann Bartholomew Adam Beringer," *ibid.*, no. 3 (Nov. 1963), 160–161; Heinrich Kirchner, "Die würzburger Lügensteine im Lichte neuer archivalischer Funde," in *Zeitschrift der Deutschen geologischen Gesellschaft*, **87**, no. 9 (Nov. 1935), 607–615; P. X. Leschevin, "Notice sur l'ouvrage singulier intitulé: *Lithographia Wirceburgensis,* et sur la mystification qui y a donné lieu," in *Magasin encyclopédique,* **6** (Nov. 1808), 116–128; August Padtberg, "Die Geschichte einer vielberufenen paläontologischen Fälschung," in *Stimmen der Zeit,* **104** (1923), 32–48; and Georg Sticker, "Entwicklungsgeschichte der Medizinischen Fakultät an der Alma Mater Julia," in Max Bruchner, ed., *Festschrift zum 350 Jährigen bestehen der Universität* . . . (Würzburg, 1932), pp. 483–487.

The trial transcripts excerpted in Kirchner's article and included in full in Jahn and Woolf (pp. 125–141) exist in MS in the Staatsarchiv, Würzburg.

MELVIN E. JAHN

BERKELEY, GEORGE (*b.* County Kilkenny, Ireland, March 1685; *d.* Oxford, England, 14 January 1753), *philosophy of science.*

Berkeley was a critic of seventeenth- and eighteenth-century philosophical, scientific, mathematical, moral, political, and theological ideas and an important link in the development of general philosophy between the period of Descartes and Locke and that of Hume and Kant. From his earliest days at Trinity College, Dublin (1700–1713), he came under the influence of Bacon, Boyle, Newton, Locke, and Malebranche. In 1705 he helped to found a society with the aim of pursuing the inquiry into their "new philosophy"; the extent of this inquiry may be gauged from Berkeley's *Commonplace Book,* kept during the first few years

of that period. Subsequently, particularly in London, Berkeley formed intellectual associations with such prominent figures as Clarke, Swift, Addison, Steele, and Pope. After a brief interlude in America, connected with his abortive attempt to found a college in Bermuda (1729–1731), he retired to the bishopric of Cloyne in 1734. He moved to Oxford in 1752.

Berkeley's interests (excluding political economy, and his epistemological and theological inquiries except insofar as they bear on science) ranged from those with a primarily scientific focus to the scientifico-philosophical. In the former category belongs *A New Theory of Vision* (1709), reckoned by *Brett's History of Psychology* to have been "the most significant contribution to psychology produced in the eighteenth century," being "the first instance of clear isolation and purely relevant discussion of a psychological topic" (Peters ed., p. 409). The main problem examined in this work is the factors that determine our ability to see things at a distance, the assumption being that the sense of vision itself is incapable of doing so. Rather, seeing distant objects requires the *suggestions* supplied by other senses, especially that of touch, as well as such other experiences as visual distortion caused by failure of eye accommodation. We do not "judge" by means of quasi-optical calculation of the distance of objects (the traditional account of Berkeley's predecessors); rather, we let one group of sensations suggest another, in virtue of experience and custom. Moreover, from saying that all visual sensations "seem to be in the eye," Berkeley moves to his basic contention, later generalized in his *Principles of Human Knowledge* (1710), that visual ideas are in our minds. Given his general doctrine that the "being" of things amounts to their being perceived, i.e., being ideas in a mind (the ultimate reference is to the divine mind), he infers that external space is not basic, but is "only suggested" to us by visual ideas, via tactile and other ideas.

This close interweaving of science with epistemology, as well as of metaphysics with theology, is also very prominent in Berkeley's last major work, *Siris* (1744), which begins as an investigation of the medicinal virtues of tar water and ends with a disquisition on Platonic philosophy. The body of the book consists, on the one hand, of a discussion of contemporary chemical theory and, on the other, of a critique of Newtonian principles of explanation, of space and time, and of the true interpretation of the concept of causation. The sections on chemistry are of particular interest, for they display considerable acquaintance with most of the major chemical doctrines of Berkeley's period (e.g., Boerhaave, Homberg, Hales, the younger Lemery, etc.), including a discussion of acids, salts, alkalies, and air that leads to a discussion of fire and light, the latter providing a "bridge" to a spiritual interpretation of all phenomena. *Siris* thus involves an attempt to assimilate Newtonian concepts to the more complex phenomena of chemistry and animal physiology.

Apart from his more specifically scientific preoccupations, Berkeley's more general aim in these writings is to show that the goal of science can be no more than describing phenomena through the laws and theories ("hypotheses") of science that govern them, and thus to trace the "grammar" or "language of nature" without intervening concepts, at least insofar as these concepts might be construed existentially or as sources of "active power," which in Berkeley's terminology would amount to giving an "explanation." The opposition to a positive construction of such intervening concepts is paramount in Berkeley's writing on mathematics, as exemplified in his critique of the foundations of the differential calculus, whether our concern be with Newtonian "fluxions" or with Leibnizian "infinitesimals." Both, as Berkeley points out in *The Analyst* (1734), suffer from the fatal defect of demanding that certain "increments" vanish in a result whose demonstration requires these increments to have a finite value.

Berkeley's basic objection is to a sequence that is imagined to continue indefinitely, yet at the same time is conceived as suddenly ending. This difficulty formed the starting point of many discussions of the foundations of mathematics that continued in England until the nineteenth century, and he himself initially participated in them through replies to objections made to *The Analyst*. Berkeley does not impugn the employment of the differential calculus for "practical" purposes; his objection is to the quasi-existential positing of the "differential" entities involved. In the *Principles* this had been stated as an opposition to "abstract ideas." His fundamental thought (although he lacks the notion of the limit) is "operationalist," a concentration on the imaginative *process* of dividing a finite line into finite parts *indefinitely,* by always letting the new parts "grow" so that they remain finite lines; this conception is meant to replace "infinite divisibility" into the "infinitely small" (*Principles,* sec. 128). At a more technical level Berkeley developed an ingenious theory of compensating errors that was meant to explain the "correct" results of the calculus of fluxions, whose "faulty" foundations alone he deplored.

Berkeley's opposition to abstract ideas is closely connected with a theory of meaning the most relevant component of which is the contention that we should not suppose that to every noun there corresponds a particular idea. In *De motu* this is applied with special emphasis to the Newtonian concepts of gravitational attraction, action and reaction, and motion in general. Basically, Berkeley regards all such concepts as elements in "mathematical hypotheses" (i.e., what would now be called theoretical terms implicitly defined by certain theoretical axioms). Sometimes he holds that theoretical concepts are simply reducible to individual laws of phenomena (reductionism); at other times he emphasizes their place in the systematic constructions of these laws in overarching theories (a forerunner of the modern instrumentalist position).

The instrumentalist approach affected Berkeley's theory of explanation and causation, which also drew upon the basic doctrine that all phenomena must be construed as ideas. Since they stand in an accusative relation to a perceiver, the ideas are held to be inactive; this is the doctrine of *esse-percipi*. The logical counterpart of the doctrine that no idea can act on any other idea is that no necessary connections exist between any such ideas. As a result, causal explanation cannot be reducible to the "action" of any phenomenal agents, be they "attraction" or "insensible corpuscles." Causal action reduces to uniform "lawlike" association between ideas that function as signs for things signified; the logical center of gravity being again the theoretical system of scientific laws, laws whose ultimate inductive foundation Berkeley places in the uniform operation of the "Author of nature" (*Principles,* sec. 107).

It follows that the doctrine of the distinction between primary and secondary qualities, so central to the thinking of the "Newtonian century," in Berkeley loses its metaphysical relevance, reducing at most to no more than a difference of degree, since the opposition to abstract general ideas and the unavailability of the theoretical "corpuscles" for explanation rendered the conception unimportant. Berkeley does not so much deny unobservable entities; once again he is opposed only to treating them as genuine sources of transeunt causal action, since they are in reality no more than abstractions.

These approaches more or less naturally lead to Berkeley's critique of the Newtonian concepts of absolute space, time, and motion. For it follows at once that all motion must be relative and referred to a physical (phenomenal) system, a contention that Berkeley also urges against Newton's example of rotatory motion, thus anticipating part of what is now called Mach's principle. The impossibility of absolute motion is one of Berkeley's arguments against absolute space; another is its being an abstract idea. Moreover, it is otiose if taken to be an entity "existing without the mind" (*Principles,* sec. 116). This (somewhat weakly) seems to fit in with the conclusion drawn from the theory that distance and space cannot be determined visually. At best, empty space denotes a mere "possibility" for a body to be in motion, and certainly it is nothing "given in itself," separate from or prior to body.

Berkeley's general influence extended to such writers as Hume, Maclaurin, and Kant in the eighteenth century, and Mill, Helmholtz, and Mach in the nineteenth. He also anticipated many of the ideas of twentieth-century philosophers of science.

BIBLIOGRAPHY

I. ORIGINAL WORKS. The standard edition of Berkeley's writings is *The Works of George Berkeley, Bishop of Cloyne,* A. A. Luce and T. E. Jessop, eds., 9 vols. (Edinburgh, 1948–1957).

Berkeley's major writings on science and mathematics and their philosophy are *An Essay Towards a New Theory of Vision* (Dublin, 1709); *A Treatise Concerning the Principles of Human Knowledge*, pt. 1 (Dublin, 1710), the only part published; *Three Dialogues Between Hylas and Philonous* (London, 1713); *De motu* (London, 1721); *Alciphron, or the Minute Philosopher* (London, 1732); *Theory of Vision, or Visual Language, Vindicated and Explained* (London, 1733); *The Analyst* (London, 1734); *A Defence of Free-Thinking in Mathematics* (London, 1735); *Siris: A Chain of Philosophical Reflexions and Inquiries Concerning the Virtues of Tar-Water* (London, 1744); *Further Thoughts on Tar-Water* (London, 1752); and *Philosophical Commentaries* [*Commonplace Book*], A. A. Luce, ed. (London, 1944).

Collections that include scientific writings are *Selections From Berkeley Annotated,* A. C. Fraser, ed. (Oxford, 1874); *Berkeley: Philosophical Writings,* T. E. Jessop, ed. (Edinburgh, 1952); *Berkeley: Works on Vision,* C. M. Turbayne, ed., in Library of Liberal Arts (Indianapolis, 1963); and *Berkeley's Philosophical Writings,* D. M. Armstrong, ed., in Collier Classics in the History of Thought (New York, 1965).

II. SECONDARY LITERATURE. The standard biography is A. A. Luce, *The Life of George Berkeley* (Edinburgh, 1949).

Discussions of aspects of Berkeley's philosophy of science and mathematics since 1842 may be found in the following works: T. K. Abbott, *Sight and Touch: An Attempt to Disprove the Received (or Berkeleian) Theory of Vision* (London, 1864); G. W. Ardley, *Berkeley's Philosophy of Nature* (Auckland, 1962); D. M. Armstrong, *Berkeley's Theory of Vision* (Melbourne, 1960); S. Bailey, *A Review of Berkeley's Theory of Vision* (London, 1842); C. B. Boyer, *The History of the Calculus* (New York, 1959), ch. 6, pp. 224–229; *Brett's History of Psychology,* R. S. Peters, ed. (London, 1953), pp. 408–414; *British Journal for the Philosophy of Science,* **4** (May 1953), which honors the bicentenary of Berkeley's death; G. Buchdahl, *Metaphysics and the Philosophy of Science. The Classical Origins: Descartes to Kant* (Oxford, 1969), ch. 5; F. Cajori, *A History of the Conceptions of Limits and Fluxions in Great Britain From Newton to Woodhouse* (Chicago, 1919), pp. 57–95; D. W. Hamlyn, *Sensation and Perception. A History of the Philosophy of Perception* (London, 1961), pp. 104–116; T. H. Huxley, *Hume: With Helps to the Study of Berkeley* (London, 1894); G. A. Johnston, *The Development of Berkeley's Philosophy* (London, 1923); A. A. Luce, *Berkeley and Malebranche* (Oxford, 1934); J. S. Mill, *Dissertations and Discussions,* IV (London, 1875), 154–187; A. D. Ritchie, *George Berkeley. A Reappraisal* (Manchester, 1967); G. Stammler, *Berkeleys Philosophie der Mathematik* (Berlin, 1922); C. M. Turbayne, *The Myth of Metaphor* (New Haven, 1962); and G. J. Warnock, *Berkeley* (London, 1953).

GERD BUCHDAHL

BERKELEY, MILES JOSEPH (*b.* Biggin Hall, Oundle, Northamptonshire, England, 1 April 1803; *d.* Sibbertoft, Market Harborough, Northamptonshire, 30 July 1889), *mycology.*

Miles was the second son of Charles Berkeley and of the sister of Paul Sandby Munn, the well-known watercolor artist. Berkeley received his early education at the grammar school at Oundle and later at Rugby. He entered Christ's College, Cambridge, as a scholar in 1821 and obtained the B.A. in 1825. In the following year he entered the clergy, beginning his career as curate of St. John's, Margate. In 1833 he became perpetual curate of Apethorpe and Woodnewton, Northamptonshire; in 1868 he moved, on his appointment as vicar, to Sibbertoft. In 1830 he married Cecelia Emma Campbell; the couple had fifteen children. Berkeley was a man of splendid presence and great refinement, and had a sound classical background. He read the proofs of Bentham and Hooker's *Genera plantarum* to ensure the correctness of the Latin text. To support his family, he depended almost entirely on his meager clerical stipend, which for many years he supplemented by keeping a small boarding school for boys. His continued straitened circumstances were reflected in the grant of a Civil List pension of £100 per year in 1867. He was elected to the Linnean Society in 1836 and to the Royal Society in 1879, having already received its Royal Medal in 1863.

While at school at Rugby, Berkeley became intensely interested in natural history, particularly in animals, and built up an extensive shell collection. His first publications were on zoology and were illustrated with his own fine colored drawings. Later his bent toward biology was greatly fostered by his close acquaintance with J. S. Henslow, professor of botany at Cambridge and a friend of Charles Darwin. Probably encouraged by three well-known contemporary

cryptogamists—William Henry Harvey of Trinity College, Dublin; Robert Kaye Greville of Edinburgh; and Captain Dugald Carmichael of Appin—Berkeley gave up his zoological studies and began investigations on the lower plants. In 1833 he produced his *Gleanings of British Algae,* in which he described in detail and with color plates the structure of a number of marine and freshwater species. Soon he became engrossed in his studies of fungi. The work that established his preeminence as a mycologist was his account of fungi, which was prepared at the invitation of William Jackson Hooker for a volume of Sir James Edward Smith's *The English Flora.* The meticulously accurate descriptions, mostly drawn from living material, remain unsurpassed in their construction.

Between 1837 and 1883 he published, in the later years in collaboration with Christopher Edmund Broome, a series of papers entitled "Notices of British Fungi" in the *Annals and Magazine of Zoology and Botany* (later called the *Annals and Magazine of Natural History*). Over the years a vast amount of exotic material from the Royal Botanic Gardens, Kew, was referred to Berkeley, and he became the accepted authority for information on mycological matters. His herbarium, comprising some 10,000 specimens, including about 5,000 types that he had described, was presented to Kew.

Berkeley's significant contributions to cryptogamic botany were not by any means confined to the taxonomy of the fungi. Indeed, he can with some justification be regarded as the founder of plant pathology, for he was the first to appreciate the economic importance of the incidence of plant disease caused by fungi. His pioneer researches established that potato blight was the result of the ravages of *Phytophthora infestans,* but this was merely one of a series of investigations on pathogenic fungi that he undertook between 1854 and 1880; his important results are to be found in the articles that he published in the *Gardeners Chronicle.* Berkeley's most distinguished morphological investigations concerned the structure of the hymenium, and it was he who originally established the constant presence of basidia with apically borne spores in a large group of fungi, thus laying the basis of the primary classification into Basidiomycetes (with spores produced externally) and Ascomycetes (with spores formed within a sac, or ascus). In all he published over 400 papers on fungi, either alone or in collaboration.

BIBLIOGRAPHY

I. ORIGINAL WORKS. Berkeley's writings include "Fungi," in J. E. Smith, *The English Flora,* V, pt. 2 (1836); "On the Fructification of the Pileate and Clavate Tribes of the Hymenomycetous Fungi," in *Annals and Magazine of Natural History,* **1** (1838), 81; *Introduction to Cryptogamic Botany* (London, 1857); and *Outlines of British Fungology* (London, 1860).

II. SECONDARY LITERATURE. For further biographical information on Berkeley, see *Gardeners Chronicle,* 3rd ser., **6** (1889), 135 (portrait), 141; J. D. Hooker, in *Proceedings of the Royal Society,* **47** (1890), ix; and G. Massee, *Makers of British Botany,* F. W. Oliver, ed. (Cambridge, 1913).

GEORGE TAYLOR

BERNARD OF CHARTRES, also known as **Bernardus Carnotensis** (*d.* Chartres, France, *ca.* 1130), *philosophy.*

Bernard, who should not be mistaken for Bernardus Silvestris, was of Breton origin and an older brother of Thierry of Chartres. He taught the masters responsible for the glory of the school of Chartres during the first half of the twelfth century. William of Conches, Richard the Bishop, and Gilbert of Poitiers were his most famous disciples.

Bernard is known to have been studying at Chartres as early as 1114. From 1119 to 1126 he was chancellor of the episcopal schools of that city.

The information left concerning Bernard's doctrine is very fragmentary. According to John of Salisbury, he was the most perfect Platonist of his time; but this Platonism, influenced by the *Timaeus* (17A–53C), which Calcidius had made accessible to the Latins, is colored by many overtones. Bernard also attempted to reconcile Plato and Aristotle, an endeavor considered a vain one by John of Salisbury.

Bernard's pedagogical method is better known. Its aim was to obtain effective and continuous work from his students; as John of Salisbury expressed it: "Each passing day became the disciple of the previous day." Bernard is particularly well known for being the first to use the comparison of dwarfs and giants: "We are," he said, "like dwarfs sitting on the shoulders of giants. Our glance can thus take in more things and reach farther than theirs. It is not because our sight is sharper nor our height greater than theirs; it is that we are carried and elevated by the high stature of the giants" (*Metalogicon* III, 4, p. 136). This comparison, in which the giants stand for the ancients and the dwarfs for the moderns, should not be taken as an act of faith in the indefinite progress of the sciences and culture. Rather, Bernard modestly remained at the level of *grammatica*: the secrets of good writing are learned by reading and rereading the great works of the past, not in order to copy them slavishly but in order to be inspired by them, so that future generations may take us as models, as we ourselves took the ancients as our models.

BIBLIOGRAPHY

I. ORIGINAL WORKS. None of Bernard's works has survived in its entirety. The only fragments remaining are found in John of Salisbury's *Metalogicon,* C. Webb, ed. (Oxford, 1929). These are the famous comparison of dwarfs and giants, attributed to him by John of Salisbury and also transmitted by William of Conches—see E. Jeauneau, "Nani gigantum humeris insidentes. Essai d'interprétation de Bernard de Chartres," in *Vivarium,* **5** (1967), 79–99; a quotation from the *Expositio Porphyrii,* in the *Metalogicon* IV, 35, p. 206, 11. 19–25; and some fragments of philosophical poems: two elegiac distichs on form (*idea*) and matter (*ile*), cited in the *Metalogicon* IV, 35, p. 205, 11. 24–27, and recurring in some twelfth-century glosses on Plato's *Timaeus* (MS Vatican, Archivio di San Pietro, H 51, fol. 11v); six hexameters on the clear opposition of the eternally indestructible world of ideas to the realm of matter, destined to perish in time, also quoted in the *Metalogicon* IV, 35, p. 206, 11. 26–31; and three hexameters on the conditions favorable to the work of the mind, quoted in John of Salisbury's *Policraticus* VII, 13 (C. Webb, ed. [Oxford, 1909], II, p. 145, 11. 12–14), and commented on by Hugh of Saint Victor in his *Didascalicon* III, 13–20.

II. SECONDARY LITERATURE. Works containing further information on Bernard are A. Clerval, *Les écoles de Chartres au moyen âge, du Ve au XVe siècle* (Paris, 1895); E. Garin, *Studi sul platonismo medievale* (Florence, 1958), pp. 50–53; L. Merlet and R. Merlet, "Dignitaires de l'Église Notre-Dame de Chartres. Listes chronologiques," in *Archives du diocèse de Chartres,* V (Chartres, 1900), 103; A. Nelson, "Ett citat från Bernard av Chartres," in *Nordisk tidskrift för Bok-och Bibliotheksväsen,* **17** (1930), 41; and R. L. Poole, *Illustrations of the History of Medieval Thought and Learning,* 2nd ed. (London, 1920).

EDOUARD JEAUNEAU

BERNARD OF LE TREILLE (TRILIA) (*b.* near what is now Nîmes, France, *ca.* 1240; *d.* Avignon, France, 4 August 1292), *astronomy, philosophy.*

As a youth Bernard entered the Dominican Order in the province of Provence, possibly at Montpellier. Early catalogs of the order list him as a Spaniard; Quétif and Échard explain this by the supposition that Montpellier and Nîmes fell at the time under the king of Aragon, or had done so earlier under James I. Sometime between 1260 and 1265 Bernard was sent to Paris to study, and subsequently he taught at Montpellier (1266, 1268), Avignon (1267, 1274), Bordeaux (1271), Marseilles (1272), and Toulouse (1273, 1276). He returned to the priory of St.-Jacques in Paris to lecture on the *Sentences* in 1279, then continued teaching there as a bachelor (1282–1284) and as a master of theology (1284–1287). From 1288 until his death he held various administrative posts in his order in Provence.

Bernard is described by Duhem as a disciple of Albertus Magnus, and is thought by some to have attended the lectures of Thomas Aquinas. While he was undoubtedly well acquainted with the teachings of these fellow Dominicans, the chronology of his education rules out the possibility of his having studied under either. Bernard is the earliest known French Dominican to be identified as a Thomist, however, and his philosophical and theological writings—which constitute the bulk of his literary output—bear out this identification. He consistently explained and defended Aquinas' teachings on the real distinction between essence and existence, on the pure potentiality of primary matter, and on the unicity of substantial form. The last two points are of some importance in the history of medieval science, since they committed Bernard to a rejection of the *forma corporeitatis,* or "form of corporeity" (a teaching of Avicenna that led some later Scholastics to a mathematicist view of nature), and to an acceptance and elucidation of Thomas' distinctive thesis on the virtual presence of elements in compounds.

Bernard's principal interest in the history of science, however, derives from his having composed a series of questions (*Quaestiones*) on the *Sphere* of John of Sacrobosco, of which only two fourteenth-century manuscripts are known: one is in the municipal library at Laon, the other in St. Mark's in Venice. Early catalogs of the Dominican Order mention a treatise *Super totam astrologiam* ("On All of Astronomy"), which might be another variant of these same *Quaestiones;* more probably it is an erroneous listing of a work with the same title by the Franciscan Bernard of Verdun. Thorndike dates the work between 1263 and 1266, holding that it was composed at Nîmes for the instruction of young Dominicans there; the dating seems somewhat early in light of the chronology of Bernard's studies and teaching given above. The treatise, however, does bear the mark of classroom origin, being divided into *lectiones,* or lectures, and providing a rather philosophical commentary on Sacrobosco's work. Duhem furnishes some twenty pages of French translation of its text, dealing mainly with the concepts of epicycle and eccentric and with explanations of the movement of the fixed stars. They show Bernard favoring the Ptolemaic system of the universe over the stricter geocentric theories of more conservative Aristotelians, and attempting to reconcile the Hipparchian theory of continuous precession of the equinoxes with Thābit's erroneous theory of trepidation along lines suggested by Albertus Magnus, whom Bernard appears to have studied closely.

BIBLIOGRAPHY

I. ORIGINAL WORKS. Bernard's major work is *Bernardi Triliae Quaestiones de cognitione animae separatae a corpore,* Stuart Martin, ed., Vol. XI in the Pontifical Institute of Medieval Studies' series Studies and Texts (Toronto, 1965), a critical edition of the Latin text, with an introduction and notes. Frederick J. Roensch, *Early Thomistic School* (Dubuque, Iowa, 1964), pp. 84–88, 289–296, contains a complete listing of Bernard's other works, with a guide to sources and literature, and a summary of his philosophical teachings.

II. SECONDARY LITERATURE. Works on Bernard are Pierre Duhem, *Le système du monde,* III (Paris, 1915; repr. 1958), 363–383, 391, 417; Jacques Quétif and Jacques Échard, *Scriptores Ordinis Praedicatorum,* I (Paris, 1719; repr. New York, 1959), 432–434; Lynn Thorndike, *The Sphere of Sacrobosco and Its Commentators* (Chicago, 1949), pp. 23–26, 29, 49–51, 54; and George Sarton, *Introduction to the History of Science,* II, part 2 (Baltimore, 1931), 749, 758, 989.

WILLIAM A. WALLACE, O.P.

BERNARD SILVESTRE (BERNARDUS SILVESTRIS), also known as **Bernard de Tours (Bernardus Turonensis)** (*fl.* mid-twelfth century), *philosophy.*

The only certain date of Bernard's life is that of his *Cosmographia,* sometimes improperly called *De mundi universitate,* written between 1145 and 1148. He lived and taught in Tours, where he owned a house near the church of Saint Martin—evidence of which has been found by André Vernet among property titles. It is possible that Bernard also lived and taught in other cities, such as Orléans.

Bernard's most famous work is the *Cosmographia,* a poetical cosmogony alternately in prose and verse, dedicated to Thierry of Chartres; it describes the creation of the universe (*megacosmos*) and of man (*microcosmos*). The *Cosmographia* is less a treatise on cosmogony than a dramatic interpretation of philosophical thoughts drawn from many sources: from the *Timaeus,* translated and commented upon by Calcidius; from Asclepius, Apuleius, Boethius, Macrobius, Martianus Capella, Ovid, and Virgil.

The literary qualities of the *Cosmographia* are undeniable; its interest for the historian of science is perhaps less evident but not without importance. This work shows us, in fact, that the heritage of Greek science had not been entirely lost in the first half of the twelfth century and, further, that a man of letters could have mastered much of it simply by reading the Latin texts available to him. But Bernard's major concern was not to construct a rigorous doctrinal synthesis from such material. It is for this reason that it is pointless to ask, as modern historians often do, whether the *Cosmographia* is pagan or Christian in character.

Bernard was first of all a poet. His attitude toward nature was less "scientific" than that of his contemporary William of Conches. Thus while Bernard seems ready to admit that a state of chaos preceded the order found in the world, William believes that the chaotic state of matter is merely hypothetical. In his commentary on Martianus Capella, Bernard also admits the existence of the waters "above the firmament," while William rejects that idea as being contrary to the laws of physics and considers the biblical verse (Gen. 1:7) upon which it is based as purely allegorical.

BIBLIOGRAPHY

I. ORIGINAL WORKS. With the exception of works that are certainly apocryphal (*De cura rei familiaris, De forma honestae vitae*) and works that are probably apocryphal (*De gemellis, De paupere ingrato*), the literary output of Bernard can be divided into two groups: surely authentic and probably authentic.

Certainly authentic works are *Experimentarius* (a manual of geomancy of which Bernard was not the author but merely the editor), M. Brini Savorelli, ed., in *Rivista critica di storia della filosofia,* **14** (1959), 283–342; *Mathematicus* (or *De patricida,* or *De parricidali*), in J. P. Migne, ed., *Patrologia latina,* CLXXI (Paris, 1893), cols. 1365–1380, where it is erroneously attributed to Hildebert of Lavardin, and in B. Hauréau, *Le Mathematicus de Bernard Silvestris et la Passio sanctae agnetis de Pierre Riga* (Paris, 1895); and *Cosmographia* (or *De mundi universitate*), C. S. Barach and J. Wrobel, eds. (Innsbruck, 1876), a very defective edition; there is also an unpublished critical edition prepared by André Vernet and described in "Bernardus Silvestris et sa Cosmographia," in *École nationale des chartes. Positions des thèses . . . de 1937,* pp. 167–174.

Among works considered "probably authentic" must be classed Bernard's *Ars dictaminis;* although he almost certainly composed a treatise on this subject, so many have been attributed to him that we have no way of determining which represent later modifications. See Charles-V. Langlois, "Maître Bernard," in *Bibliothèque de l'École des chartes,* LIV (1893), 225–250; Ch. H. Haskins, "An Italian Master Bernard," in *Essays in History Presented to R. L. Poole* (Oxford, 1927), pp. 211–226; "The Early Artes dictandi in Italy," in *Studies in Mediaeval Culture* (Oxford, 1929), pp. 170–192; E. Faral, "Le manuscrit 511 du Hunterian Museum de Glasgow," in *Studi medievali,* **9** (1936), 18–121, esp. 80–88; H. Koller, "Zwei pariser Briefsammlungen," in *Mitteilungen des Instituts für österreichische Geschichtsforschung,* **59** (1951), 229–327; B. Berulfsen, "Et blad av en Summa dictaminum," in *Avhandlinger utgitt av det Norske Videnskaps-Akademi i Oslo,* II. *Historisk-Filosofisk Klasse* (1953), no. 3; F.-J.

Schmale, "Der Briefsteller Bernhards von Meung," in *Mitteilungen des Instituts für österreichische Geschichtsforschung,* **66** (1958), 1–28; and W. Zöllner, "Eine neue Bearbeitung der 'Flores dictaminum' des Bernhard von Meung," in *Wissenschaftliche Zeitschrift der Martin-Luther-Universität Halle-Wittemberg, Gesellschafts- und Sprachwissenschaftliche Reihe,* **13** (1964), 335–342.

Another "probably authentic" work is *Commentum super sex libros Eneidos Virgilii,* G. Riedel, ed. (Greifswald, 1924). For a better text, consult the manuscripts mentioned in the following studies: M. De Marco, "Un nuovo codice del commento di Bernardo Silvestre all' Eneide," in *Aevum,* **28** (1954), 178–183; and G. Padoan, "Tradizione e fortuna del commento all' Eneide di Bernardo Silvestre," in *Italia medioevale e umanistica,* **3** (1960), 227–240.

The third is *Commentum super Martianum Capellam.* Extracts are in E. Jeauneau, "Note sur l'École de Chartres," in *Studi medievali,* 3rd. ser., **5** (1964), 821–865, esp. 855–864.

II. SECONDARY LITERATURE. Works on Bernard are E. Gilson, "La cosmogonie de Bernardus Silvestris," in *Archives d'histoire doctrinale et littéraire du moyen âge,* **3** (1928), 5–24; L. Thorndike, *A History of Magic and Experimental Science During the First Thirteen Centuries of Our Era,* 3d ed., II (New York, 1947); T. Silverstein, "The Fabulous Cosmogony of Bernardus Silvestris," in *Modern Philology,* **46** (1948), 92–116; R. B. Woolsey, "Bernard Silvester and the Hermetic Asclepius," in *Traditio,* **6** (1948), 340–344; M. F. McCrimmon, "The Classical Philosophical Sources of the 'De mundi universitate' of Bernard Silvestris," dissertation (Yale University, 1952); F. Munari, "Zu den Verseinlagen in Bernardus Silvestris' De mundi universitate," in *Philologus,* **104** (1960), 279–285; J. R. O'Donnell, "The Sources and Meaning of Bernard Silvester's Commentary on the Aeneid," in *Mediaeval Studies,* **24** (1962), 233–249; and W. von den Steinen, "Bernard Silvestre et le problème du destin," ("Les sujets d'inspiration chez les poètes latin du XIIe siècle," III), in *Cahiers de civilisation médiévale,* **9** (1966), 363–383, esp. 373–383.

EDOUARD JEAUNEAU

BERNARD OF TREVISAN, also known as **Bernard of Treviso, Bernard of Treves** (*fl. ca.* 1378, although also thought to have flourished in the fifteenth or sixteenth century, in France, Italy, or Germany), *alchemy.*

Although it is uncertain whether two or even three persons are responsible for the tracts bearing the name of Bernard of Trevisan, his name first appears in manuscript texts of the fourteenth century; and the contents of all of these works fit well into fourteenth-century alchemical thought and practice, both in the nature of the alchemical doctrines expounded and in the authorities or authors cited. For example, in a reply to Thomas of Bologna, physician to King Charles V of France (*d.* 1380), Bernard maintained against Thomas the dominant fourteenth-century

theory that gold is made solely from quicksilver or mercury, although the process might be hastened by the addition of a small amount of gold. Bernard rejected the sulfur-mercury theory of the preceding century. He asserted that mercury contained within itself the four elements—that is, the air and fire of sulfur in addition to the earth and water usually associated with mercury. All these elements, he reported, remain when the mercury turns to gold. He also rejected Thomas of Bologna's association of the planets with the alchemical process.

The alchemical doctrine of the composition of the philosophers' stone by mercury alone was reiterated in the tracts that were printed under Bernard's name in the sixteenth and seventeenth centuries, particularly in *A Singular Treatise on the Philosophers' Stone* and in the *Traicté de la nature de l'oeuvf.* In the latter, Bernard asserted that the elixir is made of pure mercury and that this purified substance, which has lost all its terrestrial and consumable feces and which the philosophers call the water of volatility, contains within itself the entire *magisterium.*

Bernard, in common with other alchemists of the fourteenth century, likened the production of the philosophers' stone to human generation. In this process, he explained, the sun is the male and is hot and dry, the moon is the female and is cold and moist, and both are essential because nothing can be generated and brought to the light of existence without a male and a female. In the philosophers' stone, however, is to be found everything that is required for the production of the stone. This is demonstrated by the fact that it is composed of both body and spirit or of fixed and volatile elements, which, although they do not appear to be so, are indeed one in substance, i.e., quicksilver.

Furthermore, to demonstrate or explain the alchemical process, Bernard utilized another symbol commonly found in the alchemical literature of the time. He likened the mercury of the philosophers to the philosophers' egg, which contains in itself two natures in one substance, the white and the yellow, and from itself produces another—the chicken—which has life and the power of generation. Mercury, he held, similarly contains within itself two natures in the one body and from itself produces a whole that has body, soul, and spirit. Moreover, on the authority of Albertus Magnus, whom he had cited for the preceding exposition of the philosophers' egg as one and many, Bernard likened this oneness of spirit, soul, and body to the Holy Trinity, who are one in God without diversity of substance. In his view, mercury, the egg, contains in itself everything required for the perfection of its own *magisterium,* without the addition of

anything else and without any diminution of its own perfection. It has everything for the production of the chicken.

The works bearing Bernard's name also reveal the author's acquaintance with a number of alchemical writers, several of them from earlier centuries and others belonging to the thirteenth and fourteenth centuries. Among the earlier group are Geber, Rasis, Avicenna, Morienus, and Hermes. The later group comprised the Latin authors Albertus Magnus, Thomas Aquinas, Arnald of Villanova, and his brother Pierre of Villanova, as well as Hortulanus and Raymond Lull, John Dastin, and Christopherus Parisiensis. Furthermore, Bernard paraphrased Hippocrates' *Aphorisms* and cited Aristotle and Galen.

There are other interesting and engaging features in Bernard's works. For example, in the *Chemica miracula* there is a long autobiographical account of his quest for the philosophers' stone. In another tract he cites as his reason for departing from the usual admonitions to keep the alchemical art secret the fear that so noble an art or science might perish or be lost if it were not imparted to others. Possibly because the works attributed to Bernard reproduced in this attractive form alchemical doctrines and practices that were familiar to his contemporaries and were to become traditional in the centuries that followed, they were printed and reprinted not only in the sixteenth and seventeenth centuries but as late as the eighteenth century.

BIBLIOGRAPHY

I. ORIGINAL WORKS. For manuscript texts see Lynn Thorndike and Pearl Kibre, *A Catalogue of Incipits of Mediaeval Scientific Writings in Latin* (Cambridge, Mass., 1963). In addition to the MSS there noted are the following, written after 1500: British Museum, Sloane 299, 16c, ff. 10v–19r, in English; Sloane 3117, 17c, ff. 2r–84r; and Sloane 3737, 17c, ff. 93r–95r, extracts.

Printed editions of Bernard's "Responsio ad Thomam de Bononia" are found, in Latin, with Morienus, *De re metallica* (Paris, 1564), in *Artis auriferae* (Basel, 1610), II, 38, and in J. J. Manget, ed., *Bibliotheca chemica,* II (Geneva, 1702), 399; in English, as "Epistle to Thomas of Bononia," in *Aurifontina chemica* (London, 1680), pp. 187, 269; in German, as "Ein Antwort an Thomam de Bononia," with Philip Morgenstern, *Turba philosophorum,* II (Vienna, 1750); in German and Latin, as "Bernardi von Tervis, Vom Stein der Weisen . . . ," in J. Tanckius, *Opuscula chemica* (Leipzig, 1605), pp. 215–230; and in French, as "La response de Messire Bernard Conte de la Marche, Trevisane, à Thomas de Boulongne [*sic*] Medicin du roi Charles huictiesme," Gabriel Joly, trans., in *Trois anciens traictez de la philosophie naturelle* (Paris, 1626), pp. 27–89.

Chymica miracula quod lapidem philosophiae appellant (Strasbourg, 1567; Basel, 1583, 1600), also appeared in L. Zetzner, ed., *Theatrum chemicum,* I (Strasbourg, 1613), 148–776, and 2nd ed., I (Strasbourg, 1659), 683; and as "De secretissimo philosophorum opere chemico," in J. J. Manget, ed., *Bibliotheca chemica,* II (Geneva, 1702), 388.

De chemia. Opus historicum et dogmaticum ex Gallico in Latinum, Gulielmus Gratarolus, trans. (Strasbourg-Basel, 1567), pp. 139–223, also appeared with J. Franciscus Pico della Mirandola, *Libri III de auro* (Ursel, 1598), p. 149; and with D. Zacaire, *Opuscule* (Anvers, 1567).

Vom der hermetischen Philosophia (Strasbourg, 1574), a translation from the Latin, is also in *Hermetischer Rosenkrantz* (Hamburg, 1659, repr. 1682), pp. 98–110; and in *Hermetische Philosophia* (Frankfurt-Leipzig, 1709).

Tractatus singularis Bernhardi Comitis Treverensis. De lapide philosophorum is in *Tractatus aliquot chemici singulares* (Geismar, 1647), pp. 16–30, and *Ginaeceum chimicum,* I (Lyons, 1679), 503–509; an English translation is *A Singular Treatise of Bernard, Earl of Trevisan, Concerning the Philosophers' Stone* (London, 1683), and in *Collectanea chymica* (London, 1684), pp. 83–94.

Traicté de la nature de l'oeuf des philosophes, composé par Bernard, Comte de Treves, Allemand (Paris, 1659), pp. 1–64, also appeared as "Des Herrn Bernhards, Grafens von der Mark und Tervis," in *Abhandlungen von der Natur des philosophischen Eije* (Hildesheim, 1780).

"La parole delaissée traicté de Bernard, Comte de la Marche Trevisano," in *Trois traitez de la philosophie naturelle* (Paris, 1618), pp. 1–52, was also translated as "Verbum dimissum," in *Taeda trifida chimica* (Nuremberg, 1674), p. 97.

II. SECONDARY LITERATURE. Bernard of Trevisan is associated with the fourteenth century in Lynn Thorndike, *History of Magic and Experimental Science,* III (New York, 1934), 611–627, and V (New York, 1959), 601, 622–623, where he surveys both manuscript and printed texts; and in George Sarton, *Introduction to the History of Science,* III (Baltimore, 1948), 1480.

John Ferguson, *Bibliotheca chemica* (Glasgow, 1906), I, 103–104, and II, 466–467, differentiates between Bernardus Trevisanus of Padua (1406–1409), Bernardo Trevisano of Venice (1652–1720), and Bernardinus Trivisanus of Padua (1506–1583). He also has an extensive bibliography on the three Bernards.

PEARL KIBRE

BERNARD OF VERDUN, also known as **Bernardus de Virduno** (France, *fl.* latter part of the thirteenth century), *astronomy.*

Nothing is known with certainty about the life and career of Bernard of Verdun, except his place of origin (not necessarily the city on the Meuse), that he was a Franciscan, and that he was a professor in his order. It is possible that he is the Bernard who carried on a correspondence with the French scholar Nicolas of Lyra (*ca.* 1270–1349). Bernard's contribution to medieval astronomy is his *Tractatus super totam astrologiam,* most likely written in the late thirteenth century. It discusses a turquet similar to one described by Francon de Pologne in a manuscript dated 1284. If we assume that Bernard's sketchy account of this instrument is derived from Francon's more adequate description, we might consider 1284 as a possible *terminus post quem* for Bernard's *Tractatus.* However, it is quite possible that Bernard's work preceded that of Francon. The *Tractatus,* both a defense and a description of the Ptolemaic system, contains no astrological allusions. Bernard was familiar with the alternative system of al-Biṭrūjī, and he considered it unfavorably. He also rejected the theory of trepidation, which he associated with Thābit ibn Qurra.

In design, Bernard's treatise is similar to the *Almagest* of Ptolemy. The first two sections are devoted to preliminary matters both descriptive and mathematical, such as the characteristics of the four elements and the celestial region, the spherical nature of the heaven and its circular motion, the uniqueness of the world, the insensible size of the earth relative to the heaven, the construction of a table of arcs and chords, and the determination of declinations and ascensions. The remaining sections (excluding the tenth) treat the motion of the sun and the moon, eclipses, and lunar parallax, as well as the motion of the five planets visible to the naked eye. The solar, lunar, and planetary models are all derived from Ptolemy.

Bernard followed the popular rationalization that combined solid spheres with epicycles and eccentrics. Since in this adaptation of Ptolemy the greatest distance of any celestial body is equal to the least distance of the body immediately above, Bernard provides tables for the relative sizes and distances of the sun, moon, and planets. The values given correspond to those in the *Theorica planetarum* of Campanus of Novara, and were undoubtedly canonical in the Middle Ages. The tenth section describes the turquet (turketum, torquetum), a complex instrument designed for a variety of uses, e.g., to find the positions of the fixed stars and the planets, the altitude of the sun, the hour of the day or night. This section also contains a brief account of another astronomical instrument, a kind of noctilabium or "star-clock" that could be used to determine the hour of night by observation of the pole star and two other bright stars, the date being known.

Bernard's sources are few: Ptolemy, al-Battānī, and Aristotle are his most quoted authorities. His intent in his treatise is to present the Ptolemaic system in a clear and concise, although simplified, manner. It is possible that the work was originally intended to familiarize Bernard's students with the main outlines of Ptolemaic astronomy while avoiding the complexities of the *Almagest.* Insofar as it is a technical treatise on astronomy, the *Tractatus* falls in the same medieval astronomical tradition as the "theory of the planets" literature. The only distinctive difference between Bernard's treatise and others in this genre is his introductory defense of Ptolemy as having provided the only explanation that will account for astronomical phenomena.

BIBLIOGRAPHY

I. Original Works. A modern edition of Bernard's *Tractatus super totam astrologiam* is Polykarp Hartmann, ed., Vol. XV in the series Franziskanische Forschungen (Werl, 1961). This edition is based on two manuscripts in the Bibliothèque Nationale. Lynn Thorndike, however, mentions the following additional manuscripts: Erfurt, Wissenschaftliche Bibliothek, Amplonian Collection, F 393, f22-f43, and F 386, f1-f25 (where the work is entitled *Speculum celeste*); Vatican Palatine, 1380; Vatican (Bibliotheca Apostolica Vaticana) 3097, f51r-f71r. See also Thorndike, "Vatican Latin Manuscripts in the History of Science and Medicine," in *Isis,* 13 (1929–1930), 53–102; Thorndike and P. Kibre, *Incipits of Mediaeval Scientific Writings in Latin,* rev. and enl. ed. (Cambridge, Mass., 1963).

II. Secondary Literature. Works concerning Bernard are Pierre Duhem, *Le système du monde,* III (Paris, 1958), 442–460; E. Littré, *Histoire littéraire de la France,* XXI (Paris, 1847), 317–320; and Emmanuel Poulle, "Bernard de Verdun et le turquet," in *Isis,* 55 (1964), 200–208, esp. 202, n. 3.

Three works dealing with the turquet are R. T. Gunther, *Early Science in Oxford,* II (Oxford, 1923), 35–36, 370–375; L. Thorndike, "Franco de Polonia and the Turquet," in *Isis,* 36 (1945–1946), 6–7; and Ernst Zinner, *Astronomische Instrumente des 11.-18. Jahrhunderts* (Munich, 1956), pp. 177–183, plate 11, no. 2. See Zinner, p. 164, plate 57, for information on the noctilabium.

Claudia Kren

BERNARD, CLAUDE (*b.* St.-Julien, near Villefranche, Beaujolais, France, 12 July 1813; *d.* Paris, France, 10 February 1878), *physiology.*

Bernard's parents, Pierre François Bernard and Jeanne Saulnier, who were vineyard workers, lived in very modest circumstances. His father seems to have exerted so little influence that several biographers have erroneously asserted that he died when Bernard was an infant. On the other hand, Bernard always remained close to his mother, a gentle and pious woman. All his life he remained attached to the place of his birth, the hamlet of Chatenay at the outskirts of the village of St.-Julien. Every fall he returned home to relax and to help with the grape harvest. His entire life revolved about two poles of attraction: the laboratories of Paris and the vineyards of Beaujolais. As a child Bernard lived close to nature and maintained his deep love of it throughout his life. His education, first from the parish priest and then in religious schools in Villefranche and Thoissey, was humanistic rather than scientific. At the age of nineteen, he was apprenticed to an apothecary named Millet in Vaise, a suburb of Lyons. Thus he had occasion to observe the rude empiricism of the pharmacotherapy of that period. The apprentice pharmacist turned, however, not toward the sciences but toward the theater and belles-lettres. One of his comedies brought him some local success, which induced him to write a heroic drama entitled *Arthur de Bretagne.* (A first, posthumous edition of 1887 was suppressed by court decision upon the request of Bernard's widow; the work was republished in 1943.)

In 1834 Bernard went to Paris, where he planned to seek a career in literature. The illustrious critic Saint-Marc Girardin discouraged him, however, and urged him first to acquire a profession in order to earn a living. In the same year, with great difficulty, Bernard passed the baccalaureate and entered the Faculty of Medicine in Paris. Thus, as Renan remarked in his *Éloge,* by turning his back on literature, Bernard took the road that nevertheless led him to the Académie Française.

Bernard was an average student, conscientious but not really brilliant. In 1839 he passed the examinations for internship in the Paris municipal hospitals. A protégé of Pierre Rayer, he worked at the Charité and, as intern on the staff of François Magendie, at the Hôtel Dieu. What he admired in Magendie, however, was less the clinician than the physiologist, the bold experimenter, and the aggressive skeptic. It was in Magendie's laboratory at the Collège de France that Bernard, even before the end of his clinical studies, discovered his real vocation: physiological experimentation.

From 1841 to December 1844, Bernard worked as *préparateur* to Magendie at the Collège de France, assisting him in experiments concerning the physiology of nerves (especially the problem of "recurrent sensitivity" of the spinal nerve roots), the cerebrospinal fluid, the question of the seat of oxidation in the body of horses (by important experiments with cardiac catheterization), and the physiology of digestion. In order to carry out his own research, Bernard installed a very modest private laboratory in the Cour du Commerce de Saint-André-des-Arts. He also made use of the adjoining laboratory of Jules Pelouze,

where he enjoyed the intelligent help of his friend Charles-Louis Barreswil. It was Magendie who taught Bernard to use animal vivisection as the principal means of medical research and to be suspicious of generally accepted theories and doctrines. But Bernard knew how to go beyond the empiricism and skepticism of his master and to create an especially productive method of research on living creatures.

Although he had graduated M.D. at Paris on 7 December 1843, Bernard never practiced medicine and always entertained ambivalent feelings about physicians. Nevertheless, his work was such that it laid new foundations for the profession. His doctoral thesis, *Du suc gastrique et de son rôle dans la nutrition* (1843), was a work both useful to medicine and dedicated to pure science, since it furnished new facts on gastric digestion and the transformations of carbohydrates in the animal organism.

In 1844 Bernard failed to pass the examinations for a teaching post with the Faculty of Medicine. Nevertheless, he resigned his position with Magendie. After having tried vainly to organize a free course in experimental physiology (in collaboration with his friend Charles Lasègue), Bernard resigned himself to giving up scientific research and to setting up as a country doctor in his native village. Rather than resolve his economic embarrassments in this way, however, Bernard decided to take the advice of Pelouze, and in July 1845 he married Fanny Martin, daughter of a Paris physician (they were to have three children: a boy who died in infancy and two daughters, Jeanne-Henriette and Marie-Claude). This match was to become a source of unhappiness, but for the moment his wife's dowry enabled Bernard to continue his physiological research. He now entered the most fruitful and certainly the most hectic period of his scientific career.

In December 1847 Bernard was made *suppléant* to Magendie at the Collège de France. At first he gave the course in the winter term, while Magendie continued to teach experimental medicine during the summer semester. In 1852 Magendie retired completely and turned over his chair and his laboratory to Bernard. In 1848 the Société de Biologie was founded, and Bernard became its first vice-president. Named a *chevalier* of the Légion d'Honneur in 1849, he applied (unsuccessfully) for membership in the Académie des Sciences in 1850 and started to work on his thesis for the doctorate in science. On 17 March 1853 he received the doctorate in zoology at the Sorbonne after a brilliant presentation of his thesis, *Recherches sur une nouvelle fonction du foie.*

Bernard made his principal discoveries early in his scientific career, in the period between his first publication, "Recherches anatomiques et physiologiques sur la corde du tympan" (1843), and his thesis for the doctorate in science (1853). The discoveries on the chemistry and nerve control of gastric digestion (1843–1845) were followed by the first experiments with curare, the discovery of the role of bile in the digestion of proteins, and research on the innervation of the vocal cords and the functions of the cranial nerves (1844–1845). In 1846 he made his first observations on the mechanism of carbon monoxide intoxication, discovered the difference between the urine of herbivores and that of carnivores, began studies on absorption of fats and the functions of the pancreas, and observed the inhibitory action of the vagus nerve on the heart. He solved the problem of "recurrent sensitivity" in 1847. In August 1848 Bernard discovered the presence of sugar in the blood under fasting conditions (nonfood-connected glycemia) and the physiological presence of sugar in the liver— which led rapidly to the revolutionary theory attributing a glycogenic function to the liver (October 1848). In February 1849, he published an important paper on the role of the pancreas in digestion and, in the same month, observed for the first time the presence of sugar in the urine after artificial traumatization of some particular cerebral structures. The following year Bernard made other discoveries concerning the metabolism of carbohydrates and resumed fruitful experiments with curare. In 1852 came the discovery of the vasoconstrictor nerves and the description of the syndrome now called the Horner-Bernard syndrome. This period concluded with a critical examination of Lavoisier's theory on the seat of the production of heat in the animal and with the systematic presentation of discoveries concerning animal glycogenesis.

Bernard's reputation was further enhanced by these works, and soon extended beyond the borders of France. Honor followed honor in quick succession. The government created a chair of general physiology for him at the Faculty of Sciences in Paris, and on 1 May 1854 he delivered his inaugural lecture at the Sorbonne. On 26 June of the same year he was elected to the Académie des Sciences, and in 1855, following the death of Magendie, he became professor of medicine at the Collège de France. He became a member of the Académie de Médecine in March 1861.

Bernard consolidated and completed his physiological discoveries between 1854 and 1860: in 1855 he made the experiment of the perfused liver and discovered glycogen; in 1857 he isolated glycogen; in 1858 he discovered the vasodilating nerves; and in 1859 he made experiments on the glycogenic functions of the placenta and of fetal tissues. This period

of Bernard's work is further marked by the creation of new concepts that were to facilitate the generalization of the results of his experimentation: the concepts of "experimental determinism," and "internal secretion" (1855; it must be stated that for Bernard this term did not have its precise present meaning), the "milieu intérieur" (1857), "local circulation," "reciprocal innervation," "paralyzing reflex actions," and so on.

The transition from laboratory work to dogmatic synthesis was mirrored in Bernard's teaching and in his *Cahier de notes, 1850–1860* (also called the *Cahier rouge*). The *Cahier* clearly demonstrates a change of emphasis from the tenacious pursuit of concrete facts to a concentration on research methods and principles of biological science, and may be said to mark the junction between Bernard's analytical and philosophical work; his teaching led him to the formulation of a comprehensive and didactic theoretical elaboration of his laboratory experience. As early as 1858, Bernard conceived a "plan for a dogmatic work on experimental medicine" in consideration of the new direction indicated by his teaching.

From 1860 on, Bernard spent all his vacations at St.-Julien, where he had bought the manor house of the landlord on whose farm he had been born. In March 1860 he came here to recover from the first of a series of illnesses that were to mark his last years, and here, during the leisure enforced by a period of convalescence in 1862–1863, he drafted his principal theoretical work, *Introduction à l'étude de la médecine expérimentale*. This work was conceived of as the preface of a great treatise, *Principes de médecine expérimentale*, for which Bernard wrote the rough drafts of several chapters. The *Introduction* itself was rewritten in the course of the following two years, and was given its definitive form in the version published in August 1865. A grave illness in October 1865, from which he recovered after eighteen months, led Bernard to abandon the *Principes*. (In 1947 L. Delhoume published, under the same title, a reconstruction of the work based on the rough drafts and augmented by the unpublished text of Bernard's lecture course of 1865.)

During his convalescence of 1865–1867, Bernard turned his attention to philosophy, and read and annotated the philosophical works of Tenneman and of Comte; these notes revealed a subtle and critical attitude toward positivism. In 1866, at the request of the minister of public education, he prepared his *Rapport sur les progrès et la marche de la physiologie générale en France*. The *Rapport*, which was published on the occasion of the World Exposition of 1867, was to have been an objective, historico-encyclopedic treatment of physiology in France. Bernard used the opportunity, however, to issue a passionate statement of his personal opinions and presented a unified synthetic physiology, founded on the notion of the "milieu intérieur" and on the regulatory functions that, under the control of the nervous system, maintain the stability of the fluids and the living tissues.

On 12 December 1868 the chair of general physiology was transferred from the Sorbonne to the Muséum d'Histoire Naturelle; as the titular holder of the chair, Bernard succeeded Flourens (who had held the chair as professor of comparative physiology) on the council of professors of the museum. Flourens's chair was transferred to the Sorbonne, and was awarded to Paul Bert, one of Bernard's most faithful pupils.

In January 1869, after a hiatus of three years, Bernard resumed his courses in experimental medicine at the Collège de France. Although he was only a mediocre lecturer, he was able to hold the attention of his audience by the novelty and vividness of his arguments and by the experiments that he improvised in the amphitheater to support his statements. (At the beginning of his career, Bernard's audiences had been composed almost exclusively of physicians and physiologists, especially foreigners; gradually, however, they became larger, more varied, and more fashionable.)

Bernard's teaching at the College was analytical and dedicated to his own research—demonstrating, as he was wont to say, science in the making rather than science already made. His methods attracted such listeners and collaborators as d'Arsonval, Bert, Dastre, Gréhant, Jousset de Bellesme, Moreau, Pasteur (whose notes made from Bernard's lectures remain unpublished), Ranvier, and Tripier; the Germans Kühne and Rosenthal; the Russians E. de Cyon, Setchenov, and Tarkhanov; the Italians Mosso and Vella; the Dane Panum; the Englishmen Ball and Pavy; such Americans as J. C. Dalton, Austin Flint, W. E. Horner, and S. W. Mitchell; and Emperor Pedro II of Brazil. Even those physiologists and physicians who did not actually attend Bernard's lectures knew his ideas from the ten volumes of *Leçons* delivered at the Collège de France, publications that ranged from the *Leçons de physiologie expérimentale appliquée à la médecine* (1855) to the *Leçons de physiologie opératoire* (published posthumously, 1879).

The courses that Bernard taught at the Sorbonne were, from their inception, of a more general character. His *Leçons sur les propriétés des tissus vivants,* delivered in 1864 and published in 1866, illustrate these tendencies. In this course, it was Bernard's aim to "determine the elementary conditions of the phenomena of life," that is, "to return to the elementary condition of the vital phenomenon, a condition that is identical in all animals." In contrast to comparative physiology, general physiology "does not seek to grasp the differences that separate beings, but the common points that unite them and which constitute the essence of the vital phenomena." It is obvious why, when Bernard went to the Muséum d'Histoire Naturelle in 1868, the name of the chair that he was to occupy was changed.

In all the courses that he taught at the Muséum, Bernard sought to demonstrate the vital unity of all organisms. In contrast to the naturalists, Bernard was interested only in vital manifestations that did not differ from species to species. Encouraged by the general development of cellular theory and by his own research on the nonspecificity of the nutritive processes, he extended his work into plant physiology. In the first volume of his *Leçons sur les phénomènes de la vie communs aux animaux et aux végétaux* (1878; Bernard corrected the proofs on his deathbed), he went beyond the framework of traditional physiology to treat problems of general biology. His last experimental researches dealt with anesthesia of animals, influence of the ether application on plants, embryonic development, and fermentation.

Bernard was showered with honors in the final years of his life: he was commander of the Légion d'Honneur (1867), president of the Société de Biologie (1867), senator of the Empire (6 May 1869), member of the Académie Française (27 May 1869) and its president (1869). His legal separation from his wife and the Franco-Prussian War affected him profoundly, but he took pleasure in long stays at St.-Julien and in a tender friendship with Marie Raffalovich, to whom his letters reveal a glimpse of his poetic sensibility.

Bernard died of what was probably a kidney disease. He received a national funeral, an honor reserved until then for France's military and political leaders.

Scientific Works. As much through concrete discoveries as through the creation of new concepts, the work of Claude Bernard constitutes the founding of modern experimental physiology. His scientific career started with two series of precise and well delimited researches: on the one hand, the chemical and physiological study of gastric digestion, and on the other, experimental section of nerves. In both cases, the responsibility for the choice of method and subject rested less with Bernard than with his teacher Magendie. But once the initial impetus had been given, the disciple quickly gave his work a completely new orientation—one that had not been foreseen at the start.

Despite some errors (for example, Bernard believed that the acidity of the gastric juice was caused by the presence of lactic acid), his experiments on the digestive action of saliva, gastric juice, and bile resulted in discoveries of undeniable value: the presence of an organic enzymatic factor in the gastric juice (1843), the nervous control of gastric secretion, the decomposition of all carbohydrates into monosaccharides prior to their absorption, the special defense mechanism of the gastric wall against the digestive activity of the gastric juice, the proteolytic properties of bile (1844), the exact localization of gastric secretion, and so on.

Bernard's most impressive discoveries in the field of digestion proper concern the functions of the pancreas, especially the importance of pancreatic juice in the digestion and absorption of fats. Two observations showed him the road to follow. First, he had noted that the urine of herbivores is alkaline, while that of carnivores is acid. Bernard showed that fasting brought about acidity of the urine in herbivores (they lived off their body fat) and that man and carnivorous animals put on a vegetarian diet excreted alkaline urine (1846). Bernard then applied himself to the comparative study of the phenomena of digestion in both carnivores and herbivores. He initiated experiments by which to follow the changes in the chyle in the various parts of the intestinal tract of a dog and a rabbit. Thereby he noted that the absorption of fat by the chyliferous vessels occurred at a rather considerable distance from the pylorus in the rabbit and immediately at the beginning of the duodenum in the dog. Bernard discovered that this difference coincided with an anatomical difference at the point of discharge of the pancreatic juice into the intestine. Thus the role of the pancreas in the first phase of fat metabolism was demonstrated ("Du suc pancréatique et de son rôle dans les phénomènes de la digestion," 1849). In order to collect pancreatic juice in its pure state and to study the regulation of its secretion, Bernard conceived and made the temporary pancreatic fistula, later improved by Pavlov. Bernard found that pancreatic juice acted on fats by a saponification process.

In studying the digestive properties of the gastric and pancreatic juices, Bernard did not intend to restrict himself to a narrow view of the problem of local digestion alone, or of the decomposition of food in the gastrointestinal tract. Although he studied intensively the chemical changes in food exposed, both *in vivo* and *in vitro*, to saliva, gastric juice, or pancreatic juice, this was to him only one, fragmentary aspect of a vast research subject. What interested him above all was what happened to the food in the animal organism, from its entry until its total assimilation or excretion. Thus the horizon of Bernard's research kept widening and, by going beyond the limits of simple "digestion," it made its true object "nutrition" (or, in modern terminology, "metabolism").

Never wavering, Bernard was to advance beyond the then prevailing notions of "animal statics" and to set up the first milestones on the road to the understanding of intermediate metabolism. To begin with, Bernard accepted the theory of his teachers that animals are incapable of synthesizing sugar, fat, and albumin. These three substances would always originate in plants, and their percentage in the blood would vary and would depend essentially on the food consumed. Nutrition would consist of three stages: digestion, transport of digested substances, and chemical incorporation or combustion.

Then he discovered that the alleged transport of absorbed substances is an extremely complicated process, more chemical than physical, more a series of transformations than a series of displacements. He also understood that nutrition is a phenomenon of synthesis as much as it is an analytical process. If food intake is an intermittent process, "nutrition" (in the sense of metabolism) is continuous and is stopped only by death. "Nutrition" is also indirect: prior to being integrated into the tissues, the organic alimentary substances must be broken down to a certain degree and then recombined. In formulating and demonstrating these ideas, Bernard was able to talk with pride of his work on nutrition: "I am the first one to have studied the intermediary stage. The two extremes were known and the rest was accomplished by means of the physiology of probability."

In his thesis on gastric juice (1843), Bernard published, marginally to the principal subject, the first results of his experiments on the ingestion of food substances by other than natural means. His thesis relates two important discoveries: (1) if so-called "type 1" sugar (sucrose) is injected directly into the blood, it is eliminated by the kidneys, while the so-called "type 2" sugar (glucose) is retained in the organism; (2) gastric juice transforms sucrose into assimilable sugar, that is, sucrose exposed to the action of gastric juice and then injected into the blood no longer appears in the urine. "Type 2" sugars (in modern terminology, sugars of the monosaccharide group) represent the only "physiological" form of carbohydrates in the animal organism. Gastric juice changes all other forms of carbohydrates into assimilable physiological sugar.

Blinded by prevalent theories, Bernard searched in

vain for the site and the manner of breakdown of sugar in the animal organism. He wished especially to give experimental proof to Lavoisier's ideas, according to which sugar is burned in the lungs. After four years of experimentation an apparently contradictory observation, a new experimental fact, upset the entire theoretical structure. In August 1848, Bernard noted the presence of sugar in the blood of an animal from which all solid food had been withheld for several days. Greatly surprised, he turned his research in a new direction. Thus, he was soon able to discover (1) that glycemia is a normal and constant phenomenon, independent of food intake and (2) that the liver produces sugar and empties it into the blood. Published in October of the same year in "De l'origine du sucre dans l'économie animale," the discovery of the glycogenetic function of the liver compelled physiologists to revise certain fundamental notions and threw new light on the understanding of diabetes. Bernard was sometimes contradicted. If the criticisms by Louis Figuier, Pavy, and several other adversaries today appear justified with respect to certain details, Bernard was nevertheless on the right track.

In 1849 Bernard believed he had found a method of causing "artificial diabetes" by means of a local lesion of the nervous system. There followed the discoveries of the presence of sugar in the allantoic and the amniotic fluids (1850) and in the cerebrospinal fluid (1855), the proposition to utilize the quantitative determination of sugar in the liver of a fresh corpse in order to establish whether death had been sudden (January 1855), and the astonishing observation that the liver manufactures sugar even after the death of an animal (September 1855). By forcing a stream of water through the hepatic vessels into the still-warm liver, as soon as possible after the death of the animal, the hepatic tissue is completely freed of its sugar content. But if the liver is kept at moderate temperature, several hours afterward, or even the next day, the tissue will once more contain a quantity of sugar, produced since the irrigation. From this experiment Bernard derived proof of the existence of a special "glycogenetic substance." This was, strictly speaking, the first artificial perfusion of an organ separated from the body.

His handwritten notes reveal that Bernard had perfectly understood the general implication of this process and that he wanted to study the artificial survival of certain organs by means of continuous perfusion with blood. The discovery of glycogen, a kind of "animal starch" that could be converted into sugar and was barely soluble in water, was communicated to the Académie des Sciences on 24 September 1855, but this substance was not extracted in a rela-

tively pure state until February 1857. Almost simultaneously, V. Hensen, a young German physiologist, isolated glycogen by a process different from Bernard's.

In the glycogenetic function of the liver Bernard distinguished henceforth two types of phenomena: the creation (or synthesis) of glycogen in the liver and the transformation of this substance into sugar. According to Bernard, the first phenomenon was a "vital function whose true beginning is still unknown," while the second phenomenon is "purely chemical" and consequently can also be produced after the death of the individual. Thus, a fundamental distinction is established between the "plastic or organically created" phenomena and the "phenomena of attrition," or vital destruction.

The true culmination of Bernard's work in the field of carbohydrate metabolism was shown in the chapter on extrahepatic glycogenesis: the role of the placenta (1859), the ontogenetic and phylogenetic aspects of glycogenesis, production of sugar in animals without a liver, carbohydrate metabolism in muscle (for example, lactic fermentation of muscle glycogen), the breakdown of sugar in the tissues and its relation to the release of heat, the role of glycogenetic ferments, and, above all, the explanation of glycogenesis as a cellular process.

Since the discovery of the formation of sugar in the liver, Bernard had been convinced that the latter was subject to control by the nervous system. This hypothesis found strong support in the discovery of the so-called *piqûre sucrée*. In February 1849, Bernard experimented with severing the cerebellar peduncle in rabbits, in order to determine the accuracy of certain observations on the behavior of animals thus traumatized—observations that had been reported by Magendie and contradicted by François Longet. To his great surprise, Bernard found that this type of trauma caused glycosuria. He then showed that the lesion of a specific spot in the brain (the floor of the fourth ventricle) was regularly accompanied by increased glycemia. Experiments involving section of the vagus nerve also showed the influence of the nervous system on the intensity of glycogenesis.

In order to study the functions of nerves Bernard often resorted to severing them and to local galvanic stimulation. If the first research experiments on the chorda tympani (1843) today appear to have been a step in the wrong direction, his other work in this field represents a series of extraordinary successes: the "destruction" experiments on the spinal and vagus nerves and the innervation of the vocal cords (1844), the observation of the change in the sense of taste in paralysis of the facial nerves (1845), his research on the pneumonia that occurred in animals whose vagus nerves had been severed (1853), the fine experiments on the influence of the different nerves on saliva secretion (1857), and, above all, the discovery of the vasomotor nerves. Bernard had clarified the functions of the accessory nerve, particularly its connection with the vagus nerve in the innervation of the larynx.

Bernard put an end to a long dispute between Magendie and Longet on the significance of "recurrent sensitivity," that is, that stimulation of the anterior root of a spinal nerve (motor root) can, in certain cases, produce sensibility phenomena. In explaining the apparent contradictions between Magendie's experiments and those of Longet, Bernard drew a general conclusion: contradictions in experimental results always stem from a difference in the conditions under which such conflicting experiments are performed.

At the beginning of his important discovery of the vasomotor nerves, Bernard presented a brief communication ("Influence du grand sympathique sur la sensibilité et sur la calorification") in 1851 to the Société de Biologie relating the observations of phenomena that occurred after section of the cervical sympathetic nerve in rabbits. He had expected a cooling of the animal's face, since the experiment had been based on the hypothesis that the sympathetic system exerts a direct influence on the nutritive and calorific processes of the tissues. To his surprise, he found a very sharp increase in the temperature of the entire region innervated by the severed nerve. Although he noted and described the increased blood circulation in the parts affected, Bernard did not realize at the time—not even in his notes on this subject that were dated March and October 1852—the relation between these phenomena and vascular paralysis.

In November 1852 Bernard informed the Société de Biologie that the galvanization of the peripheral end of the sympathetic nerve produced effects that are the exact opposite of those obtained by severing this nerve. At that time Bernard did not know that he had been anticipated by Brown-Séquard. In fact, the latter had published in the United States—in August 1852—the results of experiments with the galvanization of the sympathetic nerve that preceded those performed by Bernard but were certainly inspired by Bernard's observations made in 1851, of which Brown-Séquard learned just before his departure for America.

Through the work of Brown-Séquard, Schiff, and Bernard, the knowledge of the vasoconstrictor nerves was incorporated into science. But we are indebted to Bernard alone for the second stage in the explanation of vasomotor function: the discovery of the vasodilator nerves and the establishment of the concept of the physiological equilibrium of the two antagonistic innervations. In analyzing the causes of changes in the color of venous blood in the salivary glands, Bernard discovered the active vasodilator reflex ("De l'influence de deux ordres de nerfs qui déterminent les variations de couleur du sang veineux dans les organes glandulaires," 1858). Research on vasomotor nerves was very closely connected with (1) the description of the so-called Horner-Bernard ocular syndrome (paralysis of the sympathetic nerve provokes miosis, narrowing of the palpebral fissure, and enophthalmos on the side of the lesion; see "Expériences sur les fonctions de la portion céphalique du grand sympathique," 1852); (2) the elaboration of the concept of "local circulation" subject to variations occurring in the various organs, depending on whether they are functioning or in a state of rest ("Sur la circulation générale et sur les circulations locales," 1859); and (3) the idea of double and reciprocal innervation that enables the organ to function not only as a result of stimulation but also as a result of an inhibitive mechanism (for example, according to Bernard, the chorda tympani determines salivary secretion by a "paralyzing action" on the tonus of the sympathetic nerve; see "Du rôle des actions paralysantes dans le phénomène des sécrétions," 1864).

Bernard was deeply involved in the problems of animal heat production and its regulation. While he accepted Lavoisier's theory, which attributed the origin of animal heat to a combustion process (i.e., oxidation), Bernard insisted on two fundamental modifications: (1) this vital combustion could not be direct oxidation, an immediate union of oxygen with tissue carbon; it had to be a particular organic process, an indirect combustion taking place with the aid of special ferments; (2) organic combustion could not occur in the lungs exclusively, as Lavoisier had taught, but in all tissues. In order to demonstrate the latter statement, Bernard used (particularly in June 1853) cardiac catheterization: comparison of blood temperature in the left and right ventricles furnished results that disproved Lavoisier's original theory of pulmonary combustion. Research concerning the site of sugar decomposition furnished additional proof for "respiration of the tissues." Bernard also conducted experiments on the lowering of body temperature either by severing the spinal cord and certain nerves or by prolonged exposure to cold. He connected these phenomena with those observed during the hibernation of certain animals, involving artificial transformation of a homoiothermic animal into a poikilothermic one.

Several other subjects of Bernard's research in this field deserve mention: the mechanism of death caused by exposure to high temperature, the slowing down of the vital processes in a cold environment, and the pathogenesis of fever. Bernard's experiments on rigor mortis and on the acidity and alkalinity of muscles after death represent an anticipation of twentieth-century discoveries.

Bernard was a true innovator in the study of the effects of toxic and medicinal substances. No one before him had understood so well the role of drug metabolization. He regarded poisoning as a local phenomenon, and advocated the use of certain poisons in physiological research. Curare and carbon monoxide had served him, he said, as "chemical bistoury," making it possible to destroy specific structures selectively.

As early as his first experiments with curare in 1844, Bernard had noted that this substance somehow isolated the contractile property of the muscle from the motor property of the nerve (observation published in 1850). But only ten years later he thought—practically at the same time as Albert von Kölliker—of an experiment that would prove that curare acted only upon the peripheral ends of the motor nerves. Contrary to what is generally believed, Bernard never wanted to accept the correct explanation of curare's action, that is, that it paralyzes the motor end plates described by his pupil Kühne.

In studying the mechanism of carbon monoxide intoxication, Bernard found that animals died of asphyxiation because this gas replaces oxygen in the red blood cells (1855–1856). At last Bernard's theory on organic combustion in the tissues was confirmed. In toxicology, we must not forget, moreover, Bernard's work on opium, on strychnine, and on anesthetics. According to him, anesthesia was a biological phenomenon common to all living things and caused by a reversible coagulation of protoplasm (1875). Etherization can eliminate the sensitivity reactions, temporarily arrest germination in grain, and suspend fermentation (1876).

Bernard's last works concentrated on the nature of alcoholic fermentation. In them he distinguished two types of fermentation, one produced by intervention of a "figurative" ferment, the other produced by soluble ferments. Nevertheless, he hoped to reduce the activities of the former (Pasteur's ferments) to the soluble chemical principles of the latter (Berthelot's ferments). After Bernard's death, a series of his notes on alcoholic fermentation were made public by Berthelot (see "La fermentation alcoolique. Dernières

expériences de Claude Bernard," 1878). Pasteur, surprised and embittered, published a rather angry reply. There was truth and error on both sides. Today we know that Berthelot and Bernard were wrong in accepting spontaneous generation of yeast in a fermentable medium and that they were right, in contrast with Pasteur, in claiming the existence of a soluble ferment, not living but nevertheless capable of causing alcoholic fermentation.

Philosophical Opinions. Although Bernard stated that he had "no philosophical pretensions," his works—particularly the *Introduction à l'étude de la médecine expérimentale* (1865)—are of such general scope that they enter the domain of philosophy. In the *lycées* of France, the *Introduction* is one of the official philosophy textbooks. Almost paradoxically, the "philosophical" aspects of Bernard's work resulted in a bibliography much larger than that of his strictly scientific work.

Bernard's views on philosophy and religion are imbued with the idea that the essence of things inevitably escapes us. Phenomena have two kinds of causes: immediate, or secondary, and primary causes. Only secondary causes are accessible to scientific investigation. The others remain beyond all possibility of proof and scientific control. It is the duty of the scholar to determine, by observation and experimentation, the immediate conditions of the phenomena. Investigation of primary causes lies beyond science, and the scholar—insofar as he is a scientist—must abandon it.

Such an attitude readily reflects the influence of positivism. Yet although he was indebted to this philosophical trend, Bernard deviated from it on several points and did not refrain from criticizing Comte with pronounced rudeness. Reaching beyond narrow positivism, Bernard rediscovered certain topics of Kantian thought and accorded extrascientific legitimacy to metaphysical deliberations.

What interested Bernard first of all, however, was not so much the general theory of knowledge as the psychology and logic of scientific research. Primarily a man of the laboratory, he was interested in philosophical questions principally as a theoretician of the experimental method.

Bernard's "experimental rationalism" is opposed both to Descartes's rationalism and to Magendie's empiricism while somehow embracing both and synthesizing them in a wider doctrine. For Bernard, the experimental method proceeds by three stages: observation, hypothesis, and experimentation. Observation and experiment, he wrote, are two extreme terms of "experimental reasoning." They furnish the knowledge of "facts," but between them there extends like a bridge the "experimental idea" (also called the "idea a priori" or simply "hypothesis"). The hypothesis is the *primum movens* of all scientific reasoning and the essential part of every discovery, but it is worthless if it is not followed and confirmed by experimental verification. Experiment is precisely an observation elicited under certain conditions for the verification of a hypothesis. Bernard's rationalism implies constant recourse to a test of the "experimental facts." If he can change the conditions of an event, man can become its master. This is the difference between the sciences of observation—essentially passive—and those of experimentation:

> With the aid of these active experimental sciences man becomes an inventor of phenomena, a real foreman of creation; and in this respect no limits could be set to the power man can acquire over nature through future progress of the experimental sciences [*Introduction,* I, ch. 1, § V].

The conscious aim of all of Bernard's work was to give medicine the decisive push along the road of its transformation into an "experimental" and "conquering" science.

Bernard confirmed the primordial role of "feeling" or "intuition" as the point of departure for "creative" experimental research. Convinced that "method by itself produces nothing," he did not insist on positive practical precepts. Nevertheless, he carefully set forth a series of precautions for the experimental biologist. His principal advice concerned the "experimental doubt" and the necessity to avoid fixed ideas and to keep one's mind free of doctrinal preconceptions. A good experimenter must—as he was himself—be simultaneously theoretician and practitioner: "A skilled hand without the head to direct it is a blind instrument; the head without the hand to carry out an idea remains impotent."

The success of the *Introduction* is due, at least in part, to the glimpse that it affords of the personal adventures of a great biologist and its claims to the revelation of the secrets of his scientific success. In fact, almost all the examples cited by Bernard in support of his general concepts stem from his own work. A careful analysis of his original laboratory notes shows, however, that at times there were some rearrangements in the chronology of Bernard's discoveries. The decisive turning point was almost always his extraordinary capacity for noting, in the course of an experiment, a fact that was somewhat marginal and did not accord with the prevailing theory.

Against a strong vitalist current—harking back to Bichat and the school of Montpellier—Bernard stressed the necessity of assuming that vital phenomena are subject to a determinism of the same kind as that which governs inert matter. This amounted to saying that "a vital phenomenon has—like any other phenomenon—a rigorous determinism, and [that] such determinism could only be a physicochemical determinism." Application of the experimental method in physiology would not be justified without acceptance of this principle. To proclaim this kind of determinism in biology signified rejection of vitalism in its classic form. Furthermore, Bernard was convinced that determinism renders the use of statistics in physiological research illusory. This criticism was nevertheless meant only for the method of the arithmetic mean.

Bernard's position between the vitalism and the materialism of his contemporaries was complex. He opposed the former by virtue of the principle of physicochemical determinism, but by the same token he did not rally to the cause of the latter, since he attributed a "directive and creative idea" to life. According to Bernard, life phenomena fall into two groups: the phenomena of organization, of creation, or of organic synthesis, on the one hand; and the phenomena of organic destruction, on the other. If the latter can be explained only by the laws of physics and chemistry, the phenomena of the first group (that is, embryonic development, the anabolic processes of nutrition, psychic life, and regeneration) defy physicochemical explanations, although they obey all the laws governing inert matter. "Life is creation"; it has a sense, a direction.

Bernard did not seek to reconcile opposing theories but, in going beyond them, to bring them into accord by means of an antisystematic attitude. In Bernard's mind, once research into determinism of the phenomenon is accepted as the only aim of the experimental method, there is no longer materialism, nor spiritualism, nor inanimate matter, nor living matter; there are only natural phenomena, the conditions of which should be determined.

The notion of "milieu intérieur" occupies a central place in Bernard's thought. It took form gradually: beginning in 1851 he formed a group of ideas on an intermediate animal milieu that nourished and protected. The term itself was coined in 1857 and, little by little, it was enriched with new meanings. The concept arose from the generalization of Schwann's theory of blastemas, and of the collision between Schwann's theory and the new forms of the cellular theory (Virchow, Brücke). It was strengthened by his research on how to overcome the conflict between Bichat's vitalism and the epistemological necessity of absolute determinism. Onto all this were grafted reflections on the "aquatic" character of life's elementary form and the idea of regulatory mechanisms that watch over the stability of the internal conditions of an organism. Life is a phenomenon of relationship—or, still better—a permanent conflict between the living particles and the outer world. The stability of the "milieu intérieur," Bernard declared, is the precondition of a free, independent life. The notion of homeostasis (Cannon) and even the beginnings of cybernetics relate to Bernard's ideas on the "milieu intérieur" and the way in which the equilibrium between this milieu, the tissues, and the outside world is maintained.

Although Bernard contributed to the spread of the cellular theory in France, he remained attached for a long time to the ideas of Schwann and never completely accepted Virchow's reform. For him, life was a protoplasmic, and not really a cellular, phenomenon. He thought life was tied more closely to chemical compounds than to histological structures. His astonishing criticism of Pasteur's experiments on spontaneous generation appears to us today as an extraordinary anticipation of molecular biology.

For Bernard, physiology had to be the basis of "experimental medicine." There is no qualitative difference between normal and pathological functions. Diseases have no ontological existence; in disease one always deals merely with exaggerated, weakened, or abolished physiological functions. If this is not the view of the majority of modern pathologists, it must be recognized that Bernard must be considered the pioneer of the "positive" concept of health (the state of health is not only the absence of illness) that characterizes modern hygiene.

BIBLIOGRAPHY

I. ORIGINAL WORKS. Bernard's books published during his lifetime are *Du suc gastrique et de son rôle dans la nutrition* (Paris, 1843), his thesis for the M.D.; *Des matières colorantes chez l'homme* (Paris, 1844), his thesis for the *agrégation*; *Recherches expérimentales sur les fonctions du nerf spinal ou accessoire de Willis* (Paris, 1851); *Recherches sur une nouvelle fonction du foie considéré comme organe producteur de matière sucrée chez l'homme et les animaux* (Paris, 1853), thesis presented to the Faculty of Sciences; *Notes of M. Bernard's Lectures on the Blood,* W. F. Atlee, ed. (Philadelphia, 1854); *Précis iconographique de médecine opératoire et d'anatomie chirurgicale* (Paris, 1854), written with C. Huette; *Recherches expérimentales sur le grand sympathique, et spécialement sur l'influence que la section de ce nerf exerce sur la chaleur animale* (Paris, 1854); *Illustrated Manual of Operative Surgery and Surgical Anatomy,* trans. with notes and addition by W. H. Van Buren and C. E. Isaacs (New York, 1855); *Leçons de physi-*

ologie expérimentale appliquée à la médecine, 2 vols. (Paris, 1855–1856); *Mémoires sur le pancréas et sur le rôle du suc pancréatique dans les phénomènes digestifs, particulièrement dans la digestion des matières grasses neutres* (Paris, 1856); *Leçons sur les effets des substances toxiques et médicamenteuses* (Paris, 1857); *Leçons sur la physiologie et la pathologie du système nerveux* (Paris, 1858); *Leçons sur les propriétés physiologiques et les altérations pathologiques des liquides de l'organisme* (Paris, 1859); *Introduction à l'étude de la médecine expérimentale* (Paris, 1865, and many later eds., including that of F. Dagognet, Paris, 1966), trans. into English by H. C. Greene (New York, 1927, 1957); *Leçons sur les propriétés des tissus vivants* (Paris, 1866); *Lectures on the Physiology of the Heart and Its Connections With the Brain,* J. S. Morel, trans. (Savannah, Ga., 1867); *Rapports sur les progrès et la marche de la physiologie générale en France* (Paris, 1867), repub. as *De la physiologie générale* (Paris, 1872); *Éloge de Flourens* (Paris, 1869), delivered before the Académie Française; *Leçons de pathologie expérimentale* (Paris, 1872); *Leçons sur les anesthésiques et sur l'asphyxie* (Paris, 1875); *Leçons sur la chaleur animale, sur les effets de la chaleur et sur la fièvre* (Paris, 1876); and *Leçons sur le diabète et la glycogénèse animale* (Paris, 1877).

Books published after Bernard's death are *Leçons sur les phénomènes de la vie communs aux animaux et aux végétaux,* A. Dastre, ed., 2 vols. (Paris, 1878–1879), Vol. I reed. by G. Canguilhem (Paris, 1966); *La science expérimentale* (Paris, 1878); *Leçons de physiologie opératoire,* M. Duval, ed. (Paris, 1879); *Pensées. Notes détachées,* L. Delhoume, ed. (Paris, 1937); *Philosophie,* J. Chevalier, ed. (Paris, 1937); *Le cahier rouge* (partial ed.), L. Delhoume, ed. (Paris, 1942); *Principes de médecine expérimentale,* L. Delhoume, ed. (Paris, 1947); *Lettres beaujolaises,* J. Godard, ed. (Villefranche, 1950); *Esquisses et notes de travail inédites,* L. Binet, ed. (Paris, 1952); *Cahier de notes 1850–1860* (complete ed.), M. D. Grmek, ed. (Paris, 1965); *Notes, mémoires et leçons sur la glycogénèse animale et le diabète,* selected by M. D. Grmek (Paris, 1965); and *Notes inédites de Claude Bernard sur les propriétés physiologiques des poisons de flèches (curare, upas, strychnine et autres),* M. D. Grmek, ed. (Paris, 1966).

Bernard's articles include "Recherches anatomiques et physiologiques sur la corde du tympan," in *Annales medicopsychologiques,* **1** (1843), 408–439; "De l'origine du sucre dans l'économie animale," in *Archives générales de médecine,* 4th ser., **18** (1848), 303–319; "Du suc pancréatique et de son rôle dans les phénomènes de la digestion," in *Mémoires de la Société de biologie,* **1** (1849), 99–115; "Recherches sur le curare," in *Comptes rendus hebdomadaires de l'Académie des sciences,* **31** (1850), 533–537, written with J. Pelouze; "Influence du grand sympathique sur la sensibilité et sur la calorification," in *Comptes rendus de la Société de biologie,* **3** (1851), 163–164; "Expériences sur les fonctions de la portion céphalique du grand sympathique," *ibid.,* **4** (1852), 155; "De l'influence de deux ordres de nerfs qui déterminent les variations de couleur du sang veineux dans les organes glandulaires," in *Comptes rendus hebdomadaires de l'Académie des sci-*

ences, **47** (1858), 245–253; "Études physiologiques sur quelques poisons américains. I. Curare," in *Revue des deux mondes,* **53** (1864), 164–190; "Du rôle des actions paralysantes dans le phénomène des sécrétions," in *Journal d'anatomie et de physiologie,* **1** (1864), 507–513; and "La fermentation alcoolique. Dernières expériences de Claude Bernard," M. Berthelot, ed., in *Revue scientifique,* **16** (1878), 49–56.

For a complete bibliography, see G. Malloizel, "Bibliographie des travaux scientifiques," in *L'oeuvre de Claude Bernard* (Paris, 1881); and M. D. Grmek, *Catalogue des manuscrits de Claude Bernard, avec la bibliographie de ses travaux imprimés et des études sur son oeuvre* (Paris, 1967).

II. SECONDARY LITERATURE. Works on Bernard are P. Bert, "Les travaux de Claude Bernard," in *Revue scientifique de la France,* 2nd ser., **16** (1879), 741–755; G. Canguilhem, *L'idée de médecine expérimentale selon Claude Bernard* (Paris, 1965); P. E. Chauffard, *Claude Bernard, sa vie et ses oeuvres* (Paris, 1878); L. Delhoume, *De Claude Bernard à d'Arsonval* (Paris, 1939); J. L. Faure, *Claude Bernard* (Paris, 1925); M. Foster, *Claude Bernard,* in the series Masters of Medicine (London, 1899); M. D. Grmek, "La conception de la maladie et de la santé chez Claude Bernard," in *Mélanges Koyré, I. L'aventure de la science* (Paris, 1964), pp. 208–227; "Les expériences de Claude Bernard sur l'anesthésie des plantes," in *Comptes rendus du 89° Congrès des sociétés savantes* (Lyons, 1964), pp. 65–80; "Examen critique de la genèse d'une grande découverte: La piqûre diabétique de Claude Bernard," in *Clio medica,* **1** (1966), 341–350; "First Steps in Claude Bernard's Discovery of the Glycogenic Function of the Liver," in *Journal of the History of Biology,* **1** (1968), 141–154; and *La glycogenèse et le diabète dans l'oeuvre de Claude Bernard* (Paris, 1968); B. Halpern, "Concepts philosophiques de Claude Bernard d'après l'*Introduction,*" in *Revue d'histoire des sciences,* **19** (1966), 97–114; H. Hermann, "À propos d'un centenaire. Comment se fit la découverte des nerfs vaso-moteurs," in *Biologie médicale,* **41** (1954), 201–230; G. L. Jousset de Bellesme, "Notes et souvenirs sur Claude Bernard," in *Revue internationale des sciences biologiques,* **10** (1882), 433–461; L. N. Karlik, *Klod Bernar* (Moscow, 1964), in Russian; P. Lamy, *Claude Bernard et le matérialisme* (Paris, 1939); N. Mani, *Die historischen Grundlagen der Leberforschung,* II (Basel, 1967), 339–369; P. Mauriac, *Claude Bernard,* 2nd ed., rev. (Paris, 1954); R. Millet, *Claude Bernard ou l'aventure scientifique* (Paris, 1945); G. Monod et Thyss-Monod, "Claude Bernard, l'homme, sa vie," in *Revue du mois,* **17** (1917), 222–242; J. M. D. Olmsted, *Claude Bernard, Physiologist* (New York–London, 1938); J. M. D. Olmsted and E. Harris Olmsted, *Claude Bernard and the Experimental Method in Medicine* (New York, 1952); E. Renan, *Éloge de Claude Bernard* (Paris, 1879); W. Riese, "Claude Bernard in the Light of Modern Science," in *Bulletin of the History of Medicine,* **14** (1943), 281–294; J. Rostand, *Hommes de vérité* (Paris, 1943), pp. 53–123; P. Van Tieghem, *Notice sur la vie et les travaux de Claude Bernard* (Paris, 1910); P. Vendryès, *Les "conditions déterminées" de Claude Bernard* (Paris, 1940); R. Virtanen, *Claude Bernard*

and His Place in the History of Ideas (Lincoln, Neb., 1960).

Collections are *L'oeuvre de Claude Bernard* (Paris, 1881); *Centenaire de Claude Bernard* (Paris, 1914); *Claude Bernard and Experimental Medicine,* F. Grande and M. B. Visscher, eds. (Cambridge, Mass., 1967); and *Philosophie et méthodologie scientifique de Claude Bernard,* B. Halpern, ed. (Paris, 1967).

M. D. GRMEK

BERNARD, NOËL (*b.* Paris, France, 13 March 1874; *d.* Mauroc [near Poitiers], France, 26 January 1911), *botany.*

During his short but productive career, Noël Bernard shed much light on the nature of the endophytic fungi found in orchids and their importance to the plant. His active research covered a period of only eleven years, cut short by his untimely death at the age of thirty-six. Moreover, the majority of Bernard's work was done before he received a university professorship. He began in 1899 as a demonstrator at the École Normale, and in 1902 moved to Caen as a lecturer. Six years later he was called to take charge of the course in botany at the Faculté des Sciences at Poitiers, and in 1909 he was named professor of botany there. He was to have been the director of the experimental botany research institute he was planning at Mauroc for the university, but he did not live to see it established.

When he began his work it had already been known for some time that orchids were mycorhizally infected plants. But it was Bernard, in a 1900 paper and his doctoral thesis of 1901, who determined that the relationship was obligatory; the presence of the fungus, he found, had become necessary for the germination of the seed. Since this infection was chronic and always present, the morphological features characteristic of many orchids, such as a tuberous root and atrophied vegetal organs, were actually fungus-induced symptoms. In analyzing the life cycles of several orchids, Bernard found differing degrees of fungal infection present. In some, such as the Ophrydeae, periods of noninfection and, therefore, morphological elaboration alternated with periods of infection and tuberization of the roots. In others, such as the Neottia, the plant is never free of the fungus, and its vegetal apparatus is reduced to no more than a rhizome.

Bernard's experimental work began with the isolation in pure culture for the first time of the endophyte. From more than twenty different orchid species three new species of fungus were isolated: *Rhizoctonia repens,* widespread among the Orchidaceae, and two more localized species, *Rhizoctonia mucorides* and *Rhizoctonia lanuginosa.* As a verification, he inoculated previously sterile orchid seeds with the fungus and, in 1904, brought about germination in this artificially produced symbiont, inducing tuber formation. On the basis of these results, he was able to advise horticulturists as to how to ensure the germination in hothouses of orchids, until that time a very uncertain, seemingly capricious event. By contaminating the soil with *Rhizoctonia repens,* he was able to improve greatly the growers' success.

Bernard announced this successful method for the germination of orchids at the international congress of horticulture held in Paris in 1905, only to find that his results were not unanimously confirmed by other workers. This disappointment led him to a reexamination of his fungal cultures, and therefore to the discovery of the phenomenon of attenuation of the fungi after having been cultured for lengths of time *in vitro.*

Further investigations revealed the physiological mechanism of the "disease" caused by fungal infection. From experiments, Bernard concluded that the fungus converted starch into sugar, and it was the increased osmotic pressure that stimulated growth and germination. In apparent verification of this, he found that tuberization could be produced in the orchid *Bletilla* without infection if the orchid were placed in a medium of high carbohydrate concentration. Similar results were obtained with the germination of orchids that normally required the presence of a virulent fungus. (It was later shown that the essential function of the fungus was to convert complex carbohydrates to simple sugars, and not necessarily to provide increased osmotic pressure.)

These results corresponded closely with observations made early in his career on potato tuberization, which is also dependent on the concentration of the medium. He was involved in further work on the potato tuber at the time of his death.

BIBLIOGRAPHY

I. Original Works. Works by Bernard include "Sur quelques germinations difficiles," in *Revue générale de botanique,* **12** (1900), 108–120; "Études sur la tubérisation," doctoral dissertation (Paris, 1901), also published *ibid.,* **14** (1902), 5–25, 58–71, 101–119, 170–183, 219–234 (mispaginated 139–154), 269–279; "La germination des Orchidées," in *Comptes rendus de l'Académie des sciences, Paris,* **137** (1903), 483–485; "Recherches expérimentales sur les Orchidées," in *Revue générale de botanique,* **16** (1904), 405–451, 458–476; "L'évolution dans la symbiose. Les Orchidées et leur champignons commensaux," *Annales des sciences naturelles (Botanique),* ser. 9, **9** (1909), 1–196 (a large work treating many aspects of the problem); *La Matière et la Vie* (Paris, 1909). Many of Bernard's later researches can be found in *Principes de biologie végétale,* edited after his death by Mme. M. L. Bernard (Paris, 1921).

II. Secondary Literature. The only substantial biographical reference to Bernard is a memoir written immediately after his death by a friend, C. Pérez, in *La Revue du Mois,* **11** (1911), 641–657. No bibliographical detail is provided, and none is available elsewhere in any complete form. A portrait of Bernard can be found in Boissonade *et al., Histoire de l'Université de Poitiers Passé et Présent (1432–1932)* (Poitiers, 1932), facing p. 424.

Alan S. Kay

BERNHEIM, HIPPOLYTE (*b.* Mulhouse, France, 27 April 1840; *d.* Paris, France, 1919), *psychology.*

Bernheim was an intern in Strasbourg hospitals, but left Alsace after the Franco-Prussian War and became a professor at the Faculté de Médecine in Nancy after his *agrégation.* He was particularly interested in pulmonary localizations of the Bouillaud syndrome (rheumatic fever); forms of prolonged typhus that affect the cerebrospinal nerves; the effect of arteriosclerosis in the circle of Willis on the Cheyne-Stokes respiratory phenomenon; and in a special form of the right asystole without retrograde intervention of the pulmonary stasis (sinking of the poorly developed right ventricle caused by the enlarged left ventricle), called the Bernheim syndrome by the South American school of cardiology.

After teaching in the medical clinics for thirteen years, Bernheim heard of a practitioner named Liebault (1823–1904) in one of Nancy's suburbs. Liebault was a philosopher and philanthropist who successfully treated his patients through induced sleep. Bernheim, although very skeptical, went to call; this was the beginning of his study of hypnotism, of suggestion, and of hysteria, which also interested Charcot and the Salpêtrière school, as well as Émile Coué (1857–1926), a pharmacist in Nancy.

As early as 1884 Bernheim stated his opposition to Charcot's concepts regarding hypnosis. He criticized the Parisian idea of hypnosis in three stages, and was the first to have the courage to say that it was a "cultural hypnosis," entirely explicable by suggestion.

Likewise, Bernheim demonstrated in 1904 that the great four-phase hysteria described by Charcot was not an illness, but an emotional, psychoneurotic reaction brought about through suggestion and curable by the same process. He thus anticipated Joseph Babinski, although there remained important differences between the latter's pithiatism, based on a very precise semeiology, and Bernheim's concepts. Bernheim's fame brought Paul Dubois, Economo, and Freud to visit him. The latter was much impressed, and wrote:

I went to Nancy in the summer of 1889 where I spent several weeks. I witnessed the astonishing experiments performed by Bernheim on his hospital patients, and it is there that I experienced the strongest impressions relating to the possible use of powerful psychical processes which remained hidden from human consciousness. I had many interesting discussions with him and I undertook to translate into German his two works on suggestion and its therapeutic effects.

It is not correct, however, to classify Bernheim as the father of psychoanalysis, for he remained a classical psychologist—he was a master of psychotherapy and a precursor of psychosomatic thought. At a time when the latter are both in full use, Bernheim's ideas have lost nothing of their interest and value.

BIBLIOGRAPHY

I. ORIGINAL WORKS. Bernheim's writings include "De la myocardite aiguë," thesis (Strasbourg, 1867); *Des fièvres typhiques en général* (Strasbourg, 1868); *De l'état cireux des muscles* (Strasbourg, 1870); *Leçons de clinique médicale* (Paris, 1877), Spanish trans. by E. Sánchez de Ocana (Madrid, 1879); *Contributions à l'étude des localisations cérébrales* (Paris, 1878); *Études sur les râles* (Paris, 1878); *De la suggestion dans l'état hypnotique et dans l'état de veille* (Paris, 1884), also in *Revue médicale de l'est*, **15** (1884), 513–520; 545–559; 577–592; 610–619; 641–658; 674–685; 712–721; **16** (1884), 7–20; *De la suggestion et de ses applications à la thérapeutique* (Paris, 1886), German trans. by Sigmund Freud (Leipzig–Vienna, 1888, 1889, 1896), English trans. by Christian A. Herter (New York–London, 1889); *Recueil des faits cliniques* (Paris, 1890), written with P. Simon; *Hypnotisme, suggestion, psychothérapie, études nouvelles* (Paris, 1891), Dutch trans. by A. W. Van Renterghem (Amsterdam, 1891), German trans. by Sigmund Freud (Leipzig–Vienna, 1892); *L'hypnotisme et la suggestion dans leurs rapports avec la médecine légale* (Nancy, 1897); *Hypnotisme, suggestion, psychothérapie avec considérations nouvelles sur l'hystérie* (Paris, 1903, 1910); *Doctrine de l'aphasie, conception nouvelle* (Paris, 1907); and *L'aphasie, conception psychologique et clinique* (Paris, 1914).

II. SECONDARY LITERATURE. Works on Bernheim are E. H. Ackerknecht, *A Short History of Psychiatry* (New York–London, 1959); G. Amselle, *Conception de l'hystérie* (Paris, 1907); P. Blum, *Des anesthésies psychiques* (Paris, 1906); K. Kolle, *Grosse Nervenärzte* (Munich, 1959), II, 220; III, 136–165; P. Kissel and P. Barrucand, "Le sommeil hypnotique d'après l'École de Nancy," in *L'encéphale*, **53** (1964), 5371–5388; P. E. Levy, *L'éducation rationnelle de la volonté. Son emploi thérapeutique* (Paris, 1898), Preface, 11, 21, 64–68; and H. H. Walsehr, "L'école hypnologique de Nancy," in *Médecine et hygiène*, no. 685 (1965), 443.

PIERRE HUARD

BERNOULLI,* **DANIEL** (*b.* Groningen, Netherlands, 8 February 1700; *d.* Basel, Switzerland, 17 March 1782), *medicine, mathematics, physics.*

Life. Daniel Bernoulli was the second son of Johann I Bernoulli and Dorothea Falkner, daughter of the patrician Daniel Falkner. At the time of Bernoulli's birth his father was professor in Groningen, but he returned to Basel in 1705 to occupy the chair of Greek. Instead, he took over the chair of mathematics, which had been made vacant by the death of his brother Jakob (Jacques) I. In 1713 Daniel began to study philosophy and logic, passed his baccalaureate in 1715, and obtained his master's degree in 1716. During this period he was taught mathematics by his father and, especially, by his older brother Nikolaus II. An attempt to place young Daniel as a commercial apprentice failed, and he was allowed to study medicine—first in Basel, then in Heidelberg (1718) and Strasbourg (1719). In 1720 he returned to Basel, where he obtained his doctorate in 1721 with a dissertation entitled *De respiratione* (1). That same year he applied for the then vacant professorship in anatomy and botany (2), but the drawing of the lot went against him. Bad luck also cost him the chair of logic (3). In 1723 he journeyed to Venice, whence his brother Nikolaus had just departed and continued his studies in practical medicine under Pietro Antonio Michelotti. A severe illness prevented him from realizing his plan to work with G. B. Morgagni in Padua.

In 1724 Bernoulli published his *Exercitationes mathematicae* (4) in Venice, which attracted so much attention that he was called to the St. Petersburg Academy. He returned to Basel in 1725 and declared his readiness to go to the Russian capital with Nikolaus. That same year, he won the prize awarded by the Paris Academy, the first of the ten he was to gain. Bernoulli's stay in St. Petersburg was marred by the sudden death of his beloved brother and by the rigorous climate, and he applied three times for a professorship in Basel, but in vain. Finally, in 1732, he was able to obtain the chair of anatomy and botany there.

His Petersburg years (1725–1733 [after 1727 he worked with Euler]) appear to have been Bernoulli's most creative period. During these years he outlined the *Hydrodynamica* and completed his first important work on oscillations (23) and an original treatise on the theory of probability (22). In 1733 he returned to Basel in the company of his younger brother Johann II, after a long detour via Danzig, Hamburg, and Holland, combined with a stay of several weeks in Paris. Everywhere he went, scholars received him most cordially.

*See p. 56 for genealogy chart.

Although largely occupied with his lectures in medicine, Bernoulli continued to publish in mathematics and mechanics, which interested him much more intensely. His principal work, the *Hydrodynamica* (31), had been completed as early as 1734 but was not published until 1738. About the same time his father published *Hydraulica,* predated to 1732.[1] This unjustifiable attempt to insure priority for himself was one among many instances that exhibited Johann I Bernoulli's antagonism toward his second son.

In 1743 Daniel Bernoulli was able to exchange his lectures in botany for those in physiology, which were more to his liking. Finally, in 1750, he obtained the chair of physics, which was his by rights. For almost thirty years (until 1776) he delivered his lectures in physics, which were enlivened by impressive experiments and attended by numerous listeners. He was buried in the Peterskirche, not far from his apartment in the Kleine Engelhof.

Works. Daniel Bernoulli's works include writings on medicine, mathematics, and the natural sciences, especially mechanics. His works in these different areas were usually conceived independently of each other, even when simultaneous. As a consequence it is legitimate to distinguish them by subject matter and to consider them in chronological order within each subject.

Medicine. Bernoulli saw himself, against his inclination, limited to the field of medicine. Thus the future physicist promptly turned his interest to the mechanical aspects of physiology.[2] In his inaugural dissertation of 1721 (1), as a typical iatrophysicist under the decisive influence of Borelli and Johann Bernoulli, he furnished a comprehensive review of the mechanics of breathing. During the same year he applied for the then vacant chair of anatomy and botany, presenting pertinent theses (2) in support of his candidacy. In St. Petersburg in 1728 he published a strictly mechanical theory of muscular contraction (10), which disregarded the hypothesis of fermentation in the blood corpuscles assumed by Borelli and Johann Bernoulli. That same year he furnished a beautifully clear contribution to the determination of the shape and the location of the entrance of the optic nerve into the bulbus, or blind spot (11). Also of great importance is a lecture on the computation of the mechanical work done by the heart (*vis cordis*). Bernoulli gave this address in 1737 at the graduation exercises of two candidates in medicine, and it was thus that he first developed a correct method for such calculations. Because of its lasting significance, this lecture was published with its German translation in 1941 (75). Contributions to the physiology of work, more particularly to the determination of the maximum work that a man can perform, are found in *Hydrodynamica* (sec. 9) and the prizewinning treatise of 1753 (47). (In this context, Bernoulli meant by "maximum work" the quantity that a man could do over a sustained period of time, e.g., a working day.)

Mathematics. Medical research, however, did not divert Bernoulli from his primary interest, the mathematical sciences. This is evidenced by the publication in 1724 of his *Exercitationes mathematicae,* which he wrote during his medical studies in Italy. This treatise combined four separate works dealing, respectively, with the game of faro, the outflow of water from the openings of containers, Riccati's differential equation, and the lunulae (figures bounded by two circular arcs). Ultimately, Bernoulli's talent proved to lie primarily in physics, mechanics, and technology, but his mathematical treatises originated partly from external circumstances (Riccati's differential equation) and partly from applied mathematics (recurrent series, mathematics of probability).

The discussions on Jacopo Riccati's differential equation were initiated in 1724 by the problem presented by Riccati in the *Supplementa* to the *Acta eruditorum.* Immediately thereafter Daniel Bernoulli offered a solution in the form of an anagram (5). In the two following papers, published in the *Acta eruditorum* (6, 7), as well as in the *Exercitationes mathematicae,* Bernoulli demonstrated that Riccati's special differential equation $ax^n\,dx + u^2\,dx = b\,du$ could be integrated through separation of the variables for the values $n = -4c/(2c \pm 1)$, where c takes on all integral values—positive, negative, and zero.

In the first part of the *Exercitationes* (4), dealing with faro, Bernoulli furnished data on recurrent series that later proved to have no practical application. According to De Moivre, these series result from the generative fraction

$$\frac{a + bz + cz^2 + \cdots + rz^m}{1 - \alpha z - \beta z^2 - \cdots - \sigma z^n}.$$

Bernoulli made use of these series in (16) for the approximate calculation of the roots of algebraic equations. For this purpose, the fraction is broken up into partial fractions, which are then developed into power series yielding, in the case of simple roots $1/p$, $1/q$, and so on, the general term

$$P = (Ap^n + Bq^n + \cdots)z^n$$

and the following member

$$Q = (Ap^{n+1} + Bq^{n+1} \cdots)z^{n+1}.$$

If p is considerably larger than $q \cdots$, etc., then, for sufficiently large n, P is approximated by Ap^n, Q by Ap^{n+1}, and thus the smallest root, $1/p$, is approximated by P/Q. In treatise (20) this method is applied to infinite power series.

Divergent sine and cosine series are treated by Bernoulli in three papers (62, 64, 66). The starting point is the thesis formulated by Leibniz and Euler that the equation $1 - 1 + 1 - 1 \cdots = 1/2$ is valid, which they base on the equation $1/(1 + x) = 1 - x + x^2 \pm \cdots$ for $x = 1$ and by observing that the arithmetic mean of the two possible partial sums of the series equals $1/2$. In reality, however, this divergent series can be summed to many values, depending on the expression from which it is derived. On the other hand, it can be demonstrated that the mean-value method for the equations found by Euler,

$$\sum_{n=1}^{\infty} \cos nx = -\frac{1}{2}$$

and

$$\sum_{n=1}^{\infty} \sin nx = \frac{1}{2}\frac{\sin x}{1 - \cos x} = \frac{1}{2} \cot \frac{1}{2}x,$$

leads to a correct result. For if x is commensurable with π, but not a multiple of π, then the terms of these series for a definite p and for each n satisfy the conditions $a_{n+p} = a_n$ and $a_1 + a_2 + a_3 + \cdots + a_p = 0$. For this case, according to the Leibniz-Bernoulli rule, the sum of the series $\Sigma_1^{\infty} a_n$ becomes equal to the arithmetic mean of the values a_1, $a_1 + a_2$, $a_1 + a_2 + a_3$, $\cdots a_1 + a_2 + a_3 + \cdots + a_p$.

Interestingly, in (64) the integration of the above cosine series, with application of Leibniz' series for $\pi/2$, yields the convergent series:

$$\sin x + \frac{1}{2} \sin 2x + \frac{1}{3} \sin 3x + \cdots = \frac{\pi - x}{2}.$$

In (66) Bernoulli let the formulas derived by Bossut[3] for the sums of the finite sine and/or cosine series n extend to the infinite. He assigned the value zero to the corresponding $\cos \infty x$ and $\sin \infty x$ and thereby obtained the correct sums.

In his later years Bernoulli contributed two additional papers (70, 71) to the theory of the infinite continued fractions.

Rational mechanics. In order to appreciate Daniel Bernoulli's contributions to mechanics, one must consider the state of this branch of science in the first half of the eighteenth century. Newton's great work was already available but could be rendered fruitful only by means of Leibniz' calculus. Collaterally there appeared Jakob Hermann's *Phoronomia* (1716), a sort of textbook on the mechanics of solids and liquids that used only the formal geometrical method. Euler's excellent *Mechanica* (1736) dealt only with the mechanics of particles. The first theory on the movement of rigid bodies was published by Euler in 1765. The fields of oscillations of rigid bodies and the mechanics of flexible and elastic bodies were new areas that Daniel Bernoulli and Euler dominated for many years.

In his earliest publication in mechanics (9), Bernoulli attempted to prove the principle of the parallelogram of forces on the basis of certain cases, assumed to be self-evident, by means of a series of purely logical extensions; this was in contrast with Newton and Varignon, who attempted to derive this principle from the composition of velocities and accelerations. Like all attempts at logical derivation, Bernoulli's was circular, and today the principle of the parallelogram of forces is considered an axiom. This was one of the rare instances when Bernoulli discussed the basic principles of mechanics. Generally he took for granted the principles established by Newton; only in cosmology or astronomy (gravity) and magnetism was he unable to break away completely from a modified vortex theory of subtle matter propounded by Descartes and Huygens. The deduction of gravity from the rotation of the subtle matter can be found in (79) and (31, ch. 11) and the explanation of magnetism in (41).

Treatise (13), inspired by Johann I Bernoulli's reports, is a contribution to the theory of rotating bodies, which at that time, considering the state of the dynamics of rigid bodies, was no trivial subject. The starting point was the simple case of a system consisting of two rigidly connected bodies rotating around a fixed axis. By means of geometric-mechanical considerations based on Huygens, Bernoulli solved a number of pertinent problems. Let us mention here only a special case of König's theorem (1751), derived by formal geometrical means. Written analytically, it states that

$$m_1 v_1{}^2 + m_2 v_2{}^2 = (m_1 + m_2)V^2 + m_1 v_1{}'^2 + m_2 v_2{}'^2,$$

where v_1 and v_2 represent velocities in a fixed system, V the velocity of the center of gravity, and $v_1{}'$ and $v_2{}'$ the velocities around the center of gravity.

The determination of a movement imparted to a body by an eccentric thrust and the calculation of the center of instantaneous rotation were accomplished by Bernoulli in 1737 (27). At his invitation Euler took up the problem simultaneously, with similar results. In this problem, Bernoulli limited himself to the simplest case, that involving rigid, infinitely thin rods. The motion caused by an impact on elastic rods was dealt with only much later (61).

The principle of areas and an extended version of the principle concerning the conservation of live force, both of which furnished integrals of Newton's basic equations, were published by Bernoulli, probably with Euler's assistance, in the *Berlin Mémoires* in 1745 and 1748 (40, 43). The principle of areas (40) was used and clearly formulated almost simultaneously by Bernoulli and Euler in their treatments of the problem involving the movement of a tube rotating around a fixed point and containing freely moving bodies.

The principle of conservation of live force (43) was developed by Bernoulli not only—as had been done before him—for the movements within a field of uniform gravity or within a field of one or several fixed centers of force, but also for a system of mobile, mutually attracting mass points. For example, given three centers with the masses m_1, m_2, m_3, whose mutual distances change from initial $a, b, c,$ to $x, y, z,$ Bernoulli finds that if the gravity constant equals ρ^2/μ for the difference of live forces,

$$\sum_{i=1}^{3} (m_i v_i^2 - m_i v_{io}^2) = 2\rho^2/\mu[m_1 m_2(1/x - 1/a) + m_1 m_3(1/y - 1/b) + m_2 m_3(1/z - 1/c)].$$

Most probably this is the first time that the double sum of $m_h m_k/r_{hk}$ appears. However, the force function for conservative systems was first discovered by Lagrange.

Bernoulli also investigated problems of friction of solid bodies (36, 57, 60). In his first such paper (36) he studied the movement of a uniformly heavy sphere rolling down an inclined plane and calculated the inclination at which the pure rotation changes into a motion composed of a rotatory and a sliding part.

The main problem of (60) consists in determining the progressive and rotatory motion of a uniformly heavy rod pressing upon a rough surface while a force oblique to the axis of the rod acts upon the rod.

A group of papers (14, 18, 21) dealing with the movement of solid bodies in a resisting medium is based on the presentation given by Newton in the *Principia.* The first two papers (14) deal with a rectilinear motion, the three subsequent ones (18, 21) with movement along a curve (pendulum swing). Here Bernoulli started with the usual premise that the resistance is largely proportional to the square of the velocity. At the same time he denied Newton's affirmation of a partial linear relation between resistance and velocity, but considered as probable the

assumption that part of the resistance, at least for viscous fluids, is proportional to time (i.e., independent of speed). The value of these five papers rests primarily on their consistent analytical presentation and on the treatment of certain special problems.

Hydrodynamics.[4] Traditionally, Bernoulli's fame rests on his *Hydrodynamica* (31)—a term he himself introduced. The first attempt at solving the problem of outflow as presented in the *Exercitationes mathematicae* was conceived in accordance with the concepts of the time, and did little to advance them. Essentially it contained a controversy with Jacopo Riccati over Newton's two different views on the force of a liquid issuing from an opening. But as early as 1727 Bernoulli succeeded in breaking through to an accurate calculation of the problem (12). Further progress was represented by the published experiments on the pressure exerted on the walls of a tube by a fluid flowing through it (19). In 1733 Bernoulli left behind in St. Petersburg a draft of the *Hydrodynamica* that agrees extensively in substance although not in form with the final version. Only the thirteenth chapter of the definitive work is missing (82).

The treatise opens with an interesting history of hydraulics, followed by a brief presentation of hydrostatics. The following three chapters contain formulas for velocity, duration, and quantity of fluid flowing out of the opening of a container. The author treats both the case of a falling level of the residual fluid and that of a constant level in the reservoir, and takes into consideration the starting process (non-stationary flow) and radial contraction of the stream. Bernoulli based these deductions on the principle of the conservation of live force or, as he says, the equality of the *descensus actualis* (actual descent) and *ascensus potentialis* (potential ascent), whereby these physical magnitudes, which pertain to the center of gravity, are obtained from the former through division by the mass of water in the container. If we equate the changes in *ascensus potentialis* and *descensus actualis* resulting from the water outflow, we obtain, in the case of a dropping water level, a linear differential equation. The kinematic principle used was the hypothesis of the parallel cross sections, which states that all particles of the liquid in a plane vertical to the flow have the same velocity, and that this velocity is inversely proportional to the cross section (principle of continuity).

Chapter 7 deals with the oscillations of the water in a tube immersed in a water tank and considers mainly the energy loss. Many years later Borda resumed these investigations, but arrived at another formula for the loss.

Chapter 9 contains a theory of machinery, lifting devices, pumps, and such, and their performance, as well as an extensive theory of the screw of Archimedes. A spiral pump related to the latter was discussed by Bernoulli much later (65). A theory of windmill sails concludes the chapter.

Chapter 10 is devoted to the properties and motions of "elastic fluids" (i.e., gases), and its main importance lies in its sketch of a "kinetic gas theory," which enabled Bernoulli to explain the basic gas laws and to anticipate—in incomplete form—Van der Waals' equation of state, which was developed some hundred years later. Further on, Bernoulli examined the pressure conditions in the atmosphere, established a formula for relating pressure to altitude, provided a formula for the total refraction of light rays from various stellar heights, and was the first to derive a formula for the flow velocity of air streaming from a small opening.

Chapter 12 contains the somewhat questionable derivation of a rather unusual form of the so-called Bernoulli equation for stationary currents. For the wall pressure p in a horizontal tube, connected to an infinitely wide container filled with water to the level a and having the cross section n and an outlet with the cross section 1, he determined the expression $p = [(n^2 - 1)/n^2]a$. Since $a/n^2 \sim u^2$ represents the height from which a body must fall to obtain the velocity u at the point observed, that expression becomes the equation $p + u^2 = a = $ const. More generally, for a current in a tube of any shape and inclination, u^2 must equal A/n^2, A or a being the distances between water surface and discharge opening or any cross section n. We then obtain the equation $p + A/n^2 = a$, and—with $A - z = a$ ($z = $ distance between n and opening)—the term $p + z + u^2 = A = $ const. for the stationary current. Because of the system of measures used by Bernoulli, the constant factors have values other than those customarily used.

Chapter 13 is concerned with the calculation of the force of reaction of a laterally discharged fluid jet as well as with the determination of its pressure upon a facing plate. With the aid of the impulse theorem, Bernoulli proved that both pressures p are equal to the weight of the cylinder of water whose base equals the area n of the opening for the discharge and whose length is double the height a of the water. It is thus $p = 2 \, gan = nu^2$. In contrast, Johann I Bernoulli advocated throughout his life the erroneous assumption of a cylinder length equal to the height of the water. A complicated calculation of the pressure of a water jet on an inclined plate is contained in (26). Toward the end of chapter 13 Daniel Bernoulli discusses the question of whether the traditional

propelling forces of sail and oar could be replaced by such a force of reaction. This principle was converted to practice only many years later.

The weaknesses in the deduction of the so-called Bernoulli equation and Daniel's incomplete concepts of internal pressure can only be mentioned here. In this respect, Johann Bernoulli's *Hydraulica* represents a certain progress, which in turn inspired Euler in his work on hydrodynamics.

Vibrating systems. From 1728, Bernoulli and Euler dominated the mechanics of flexible and elastic bodies,[5] in that year deriving the equilibrium curves for these bodies. In the first part of (15) Bernoulli determined the shape that a perfectly flexible thread assumes when acted upon by forces of which one component is vertical to the curve and the other is parallel to a given direction. Thus, in one stroke he derived the entire series of such curves as the velaria, lintearia, catenaria, etc.

More original was the determination of the curvature of a horizontal elastic band fixed at one end—a problem simultaneously undertaken by Euler. Bernoulli showed that the total moment of a uniform band around point s, by virtue of the weight P at its free end and of its own weight p acting on the center of gravity, relates to the curvature radius R by means of the equation

$$Px + \frac{p}{l} \int s \, dx = \frac{m}{R},$$

whereby the arc length s and the abscissa x are to be taken starting from the free end, with m being the modulus of bending and l the length of the string. A case involving a variable density and an optionally directed final load is quite possible.

When he departed from St. Petersburg in 1733, Bernoulli left behind one of his finest works (23), ready for the printer. Here, for the first time, he defined the "simple modes" and the frequencies of oscillation of a system with more than one degree of freedom, the points of which pass their positions of equilibrium at the same time. The inspiration for this work must have been the reports made by Johann I, toward the end of 1727, on treatment of a similar problem. In the first part of the treatise, Daniel Bernoulli discussed an arrangement consisting of a hanging rope loaded with several bodies, determined their amplitude rates and frequencies, and found that the number of simple oscillations equals the number of bodies (i.e., the degrees of freedom).

For a uniform, free-hanging rope of length l he found the displacement, y, of the oscillations at distance x from the lower end by means of the equation

$$y = AJ_o\left(2\sqrt{\frac{x}{\alpha}}\right),$$

where α has to be determined from the equation $J_o\left(2\sqrt{\frac{l}{\alpha}}\right) = 0$ and J_o is the first appearance of Bessel's function. It shows that α is the length of the simple pendulum of equal frequency. The above equation has an infinite number of real roots. Thus the rope can perform an infinite number of small oscillations with the frequencies $v = \frac{1}{2\pi}\sqrt{g/\alpha}$. These theorems were demonstrated in (25) on the basis of a principle that is equivalent to that subsequently named after d'Alembert.

Immediately following Bernoulli's departure from St. Petersburg, there began between him and Euler one of the most interesting scientific correspondences of that time. In its course, Bernoulli communicated much important information from which Euler, through his analytical gifts and tremendous capacity for work, was able to profit within a short time.

The above results were corroborated by Bernoulli and Euler through additional examples. Thus Bernoulli, in extending paper (30), investigated small vibrations of a plate immersed in water (32) and those of a rod suspended from a flexible thread (34). Both works stress the difference between simple and composite vibrations. He investigated only the former, however, for composite vibrations ultimately change into the slower ones.

The following two papers (37, 38), dating from 1741–1743, deal with the transversal vibrations of elastic strings, with (37) discussing the motion of a horizontal rod of length l, fastened at one end to a vertical wall. In order to derive the vibration equation, whose form he had known since 1735 (35), Bernoulli used the relation between curvature and moment, as detailed in (15): $m/R = M$. The resulting differential equation is $f^4 \, d^4y = y \, dx^4$, where y becomes the amplitude at distance x from the band end, and $f^4 = m^4L/g$, if L is the length of the simple pendulum isochronal with the band vibrations and g is the load per unit of length. Bernoulli used the solution $y = y(x/f)$ through infinite series as well as in closed expression by means of exponential and trigonometric functions. The series of the roots l/f is an example of nonharmonic oscillations. In (38) Bernoulli discusses the differential equation in the case of free ends.

Treatise (45), on vibrating strings, represented a reaction to the publications of d'Alembert and Euler, who calculated the form of the vibrating string from the partial differential equation

$$\partial^2 y/\partial t^2 = c^2 \partial^2 y/\partial x^2.$$

They thus moved the inference from the finite to the infinite up into the hypothesis, whereas Bernoulli always made this transition without thinking about it in the final, completed formula.

His deliberations in (45) started from the assumption that the single vibrations of a string of length a were furnished by $y = \alpha_n \sin n\pi x/a$ (n = any integral number). From this and from his previous deliberations he deduced that the most general motion could be represented by the superposition of these single vibrations, i.e., by a series of the form

$$y = \sum_{n=1}^{\infty} A_n \sin\frac{n\pi x}{a}\cos\frac{cn\pi t}{a}.$$

This equation appears nowhere explicitly, but it can be derived from a combination of various passages of this work and is valid only with the assumption of an initial velocity equaling zero.

In (46) Bernoulli determined the vibrations of a weightless cord loaded with n weights. He shows that in the case of $n = 2$, two simple vibrations, either commensurable or incommensurable, are possible, depending on the position and value of the two weights.

Treatise (53) is a beautiful treatment of the oscillations inside organ pipes, using only elementary mathematics. It is assumed that the movement of the particles parallel to the axis, the velocities, and the pressure are equal at all points of the same cross section and that the compression at the open end of the pipes equals zero. Among other things, this work contains the first theory of conical pipes and an arrangement consisting of two coaxial pipes of different cross sections as well as a series of new experiments.

In paper (54), on the vibrations of strings of uneven thickness, Bernoulli inquires about cases where oscillations assume the form $y = Aq \sin p \sin vt$, where p and q are functions of x only and v is a constant. Here, for the first time, are solutions for the inverse problem, the determination of vibration curves from the distribution of density. In (63) he treats a special case in which the string consists of two parts of different thickness and length.

In treatise (67) Bernoulli compared the two possible oscillations of a body suspended from a flexible thread with the movement of a body bound with a rigid wire, and showed that one of the two oscillations of the first arrangement closely approximated the oscillation of the second arrangement. The method followed by Bernoulli is applicable only to infinitely small vibrations, and thus represents only a special case of the problem treated simultaneously by Euler by means of the Newtonian fundamental equations of mechanics.

In (68, 69) Bernoulli once more furnished a comprehensive presentation of his views on the superposition principle, which he clarified by means of the example of the frequently studied double pendulum. These last papers show that he had nothing new to add to the problem of vibrations.

Probability and statistics. A number of valuable papers were published by Bernoulli on probability theory and on population statistics.[6] True, his youthful work on faro within the framework of the *Exercitationes mathematicae* contributed hardly anything new, but it was evidence of his early interest in the work on the theory of probability done by his predecessors Montmort and De Moivre, which had been nourished by discussions with his cousin Nikolaus I. The most important treatise, and undoubtedly the most influential, was the *De mensura sortis* (22), conceived while he was in St. Petersburg, which contains an unusual evaluation of capital gains, and thus also contains the mathematical formulation of a new kind of value theory in political economy.[7]

The basic idea is that the larger a person's fortune is, the smaller is the moral value of a given increment in that fortune. If we assume, with Bernoulli, the special case, that a small increase of assets dx implies a moral value, dy, that is directly proportional to dx and inversely proportional to the fortune a—i.e., $dy = b \, dx/a$—then it follows that the moral value y of the gains $x - a$ complies with the formula $y = \log x/a$.

If a person has the chances $p_1, p_2, p_3 \cdots$, to make the gains $g_1, g_2, g_3 \cdots$, where $p_1 + p_2 + \cdots = 1$, which reflects one and only one gain, then the mean value of the moral values of the gains is equal to

$$bp_1 \log a (a + g_1) + bp_2 \log a (a + g_2)$$
$$+ \cdots - b \log a$$

and the moral expectation (hope)

$$H = (a + g_1)^{p_1}(a + g_2)^{p_2} \cdots - a.$$

If gains are very small in comparison with the assets, then the moral hope converts to the mathematical expectation $H = p_1 g_1 + p_2 g_2 + \cdots$. There follow some applications of the preceding to risk insurance and a discussion of the Petersburg paradox.

Only in 1760 did Bernoulli again treat a problem of this sort: medical statistics concerning the rate of mortality resulting from smallpox in the various age groups (51). If ξ is the number of survivors and s the number of those who at age x have not yet had

smallpox, there results—given certain conditions—a differential equation containing three variables that defines the ratio s/ξ as a function of x. A table calculated on that basis contains the values of ξ, s, $\xi - s$, and so on valid for the first twenty-four years; ξ was taken from Halley's mortality table.[8] In (52) Bernoulli ardently advocated inoculation as a means of prolonging the average lifetime by three years.

In paper (55) Bernoulli treats, by means of urn models, problems of probability theory as applied to his treatise on population statistics (56). Their main purpose was to determine for every age the expected average duration of a marriage. Here and in his subsequent papers (58, 59) Bernoulli preferred to make use of infinitesimal calculus in probability theory by assuming continuously changing states. The problem treated in (58) is as follows: Given several urns, each of which contains n slips of the same color, but of a different color for each urn, one slip is taken from each urn and deposited in the next one, with the slip taken from the last urn deposited in the first. The question is, How many slips of each color do the various urns contain after a number r of such "permutations"? The problem treated in (59) belongs in the field of the theory of errors, and concerns the determination of the probability with which (expressed in modern terms) a random variable subject to binomial distribution would assume values between two boundaries on either side of the mean value.

In paper (72) Bernoulli seeks to deal with the theory of errors in observation as a branch of probability theory. He challenges the assumption of Simpson and Lagrange that all observations are of equal importance. Rather, he maintains that small errors are more probable than large ones. Thus Bernoulli approximates the modern concept, except that he selects the semicircle instead of Gauss's probability curve.

Treatise (73) deals with errors to be considered in pendulum clocks, which are calculated partially by means of the method presented in (59).

Prizes of the Paris Academy. Bernoulli was highly esteemed for clarifying problems for a general public interested in the sciences. Of his essays entered in the competitions of the Paris Academy, ten were awarded prizes. Most of them concerned marine technology, navigation, and oceanology; but astronomy and magnetism were also represented.

His prize-winning paper of 1725 (8) dealt with the most appropriate shape for and the installation of hourglasses filled with sand or water. The subject of the 1728 contest was the cause and nature of gravity, on which Bernoulli prepared a manuscript, but the prize went to the Cartesian G. B. Bilfinger (79). In his entry for the 1729 competition Bernoulli indicated several methods for determining the height of the pole, particularly at sea, when only one unknown star is visible, or when one or more known stars are visible. The essay did not win a prize (80), but the manuscript is extant.

The prize of 1734 (24) was shared with his father, who begrudged Daniel his share of success. Here Daniel postulated an atmosphere resembling air and rotating around the solar axis, resulting in an increasing inclination of the planetary orbits toward the equator of the sun.

Bernoulli shared the 1737 prize for the best form of an anchor with Poleni (28). The 1740 prize on the tides was shared with Euler and several others. This important paper (33) on the relationship, recognized by Newton, between the tides and solar and lunar attraction, respectively, is still of interest, inasmuch as it furnishes a complete equilibrium theory of these phenomena.

The prize-winning papers of 1743 (39) and 1746 (41) deal with problems of magnetism. In the first paper Bernoulli considered all possibilities for reducing the sources of error in the inclination compass by improving construction. According to his instructions, the Basel mechanic Dietrich constructed such needles (49). The 1746 paper, written with his brother Johann II, contains an attempt to establish a theory of magnetism. Both authors believed that there is a subtle matter which moves in the direction of the magnetic meridian and forms a vortex around the magnet.

The next prize, for the best method of determining the time at sea with the horizon not visible, was offered in 1745 for the first time. It was offered for a second time in 1747, and Bernoulli won (42). Included in the wealth of information contained in this paper are the proposals for improving pendulum and spring clocks and the description of a mechanism for holding a rod equipped with diopter in a vertical position, even in a turbulent sea. A detailed account of the determination of the time, with the position of a given star known, concludes this paper (see 17).

The 1748 prize, for the irregular movements of Saturn and Jupiter (81), went to Euler. Bernoulli's manuscript has been preserved. The prize essay for 1749–1751 (44) discussed the question of the origin and nature of ocean currents, and added suggestions for measuring current velocities.

The problem treated by the prize essay of 1753 (47), the effect on ships of forces supplementary to that of the wind (e.g., rudder forces), was answered by Bernoulli, mainly by means of detailed data on the maximum work that could be performed by a man in a given unit of time. Among other things, he calculated the number of oarsmen required for attaining a given ship velocity.

The subject of the prize essay for 1757 (48), proposals for reducing the roll and pitch of ships, gave Bernoulli the opportunity to air his views on the pertinent works of Bouguer and Euler, published several years earlier. Whereas Euler had limited himself to the free vibrations of a ship, Bernoulli extended his views to the behavior of ships in turbulent seas, i.e., to forced vibrations. His findings prevailed for almost a century.

Evaluation and Appreciation. In order to appreciate both Bernoulli's importance in science, as indicated by the above summaries of his published works, and his private life, it is necessary to consider his extensive correspondence.[9] This includes his exchange of letters with Christian Goldbach (1723–1730), Euler (1726–1767, especially 1734–1750), and his nephew Johann III (1763–1774). Also important are his contemporaries' evaluations of Bernoulli and of his work. Unfortunately, his extremely popular lectures on experimental physics, in which he often introduced unproved hypotheses that have since been confirmed, apparently are not extant. Among them was his assertion of the validity of the relation later known as Coulomb's law in electrostatics. All of these achievements brought Bernoulli considerable fame in intellectual circles during his lifetime. He was a member of the leading learned societies and academies, including Bologna (1724), St. Petersburg (1730), Berlin (1747), Paris (1748), London (1750), Bern (1762), Turin (1764), Zurich (1764), and Mannheim (1767).

We can now assert that Bernoulli was the first to link Newton's ideas with Leibniz' calculus, which he had learned from his father and his brother Nikolaus. He did not, however, attempt to solve the problems that confronted him by means of the fundamental Newtonian equations; rather, he preferred to use the first integrals of these equations, especially Leibniz' principle of the conservation of living force, which his father had emphasized. Like Newton, whose battles he fought on the Continent, Bernoulli was first and foremost a physicist, using mathematics primarily as a means of exploring reality as it was revealed through experimentation. Thus he was interested in physical apparatus as well as the practical application of the results of physics and other sciences.

Bernoulli's active and imaginative mind dealt with the most varied scientific areas. Such wide interests, however, often prevented him from carrying some of his projects to completion. It is especially unfortunate that he could not follow the rapid growth of mathematics that began with the introduction of partial differential equations into mathematical physics.

Nevertheless, he assured himself a permanent place in the history of science through his work and discoveries in hydrodynamics, his anticipation of the kinetic theory of gases, a novel method for calculating the value of an increase in assets, and the demonstration that the most common movement of a string in a musical instrument is composed of the superposition of an infinite number of harmonic vibrations (proper oscillations).

Otto Spiess instituted the publication of editions of the works and correspondence of the Bernoullis, a project that has continued since Spiess's death.

NOTES

1. *Johannis Bernoulli Hydraulica nunc primum detecta ac demonstrata directe ex fundamentis pure mechanicis*, in his *Opera omnia*, IV (Lausanne–Geneva, 1742), 387–488.
2. Friedrich Huber, *Daniel Bernoulli (1700–1782) als Physiologe und Statistiker*, Basler Veröffentlichungen zur Geschichte der Medizin und der Biologie, fasc. 8 (Basel, 1958).
3. Charles Bossut, "Manière de sommer les suites . . .," in *Mémoires de mathématiques et de physique de l'Académie royale des sciences, Paris*, 1769 (1772), 453–466.
4. For Daniel Bernoulli's hydrodynamic studies, see Clifford Truesdell, *Rational Fluid Mechanics*, intro. to Euler's *Opera omnia*, 2nd ser., XII, XIII (Zurich, 1954–1955).
5. Two excellent works are Clifford Truesdell, "The Rational Mechanics of Flexible or Elastic Bodies (1638–1788)"; his intro. to Euler's *Opera omnia*, 2nd ser., X, XI (Zurich, 1960); and H. Burkhardt, "Entwicklungen nach oscillierenden Funktionen und Integration der Differentialgleichungen der mathematischen Physik," in *Jahresbericht der Deutschen Mathematiker-Vereinigung*, **10**, no. 2 (1908), 1–24.
6. I. Todhunter, *A History of the Mathematical Theory of Probability From the Time of Pascal to That of Laplace* (Cambridge–London, 1865; repr. New York, 1949), pp. 213–238.
7. An English trans. by Louise Sommer appeared in *Econometrica*, **22** (Jan. 1954). There is also a German trans. with extensive commentary by Alfred Pringsheim (Leipzig, 1896).
8. Edmund Halley, "An Estimate of the Degrees of the Mortality of Mankind," in *Philosophical Transactions of the Royal Society of London*, no. 196 (1694), 596–610.
9. Correspondence with Euler and Christian Goldbach—as far as available—appeared in *Correspondance mathématique et physique de quelques célèbres géomètres du XVIIIème siècle*, II (St. Petersburg, 1843). Letters exchanged by Bernoulli and his nephew Johann III have not yet been published.

BIBLIOGRAPHY

The following abbreviations of journal titles are used in the listing of Bernoulli's published works: *AE*, *Acta eruditorum*; *AP*, *Acta Academiae Scientiarum Imperialis Petropolitanae*; *CP* (or *NCP*), *Commentarii* (or *Norvi commentarii*) *Academiae Scientiarum Imperialis Petropolitanae*; *Prix*, *Pièces qui ont remporté les prix de l'Académie royale des sciences* (Paris); *Hist. Berlin*, *Histoire de l'Académie royale des sciences et belles lettres, Berlin*; *Mem. Berlin*, *Mémoires de l'Académie royale des sciences et belles lettres, Berlin*; *Mem. Paris*, *Mémoires de mathématiques et de physique de l'Académie royale des sciences, Paris*.

The first year following a journal title is the serial year; the second is the year of publication.

1. *Dissertatio inauguralis physico-medica de respiratione* (Basel, 1721).
2. *Positiones miscellaneae medico-anatomico-botanicae* (Basel, 1721).
3. *Theses logicae sistentes methodum examinandi syllogismorum validitatem* (Basel, 1722).
4. *Exercitationes quaedam mathematicae* (Venice, 1724).
5. "Notata in praecedens schediasma Ill. Co. Jacobi Riccati," in *AE*, supp. **8** (1724).
6. "Danielis Bernoulli explanatio notationum suarum, quae exstant Supplem. Tomo VIII Sect II," *ibid.*, 1725 (1725), also published in (4).
7. "Solutio problematis Riccatiani propositi in Act. Lips. Suppl. Tom. VIII p. 73," *ibid.*, 1725 (1725), also published in (4).
8. "Discours sur la manière la plus parfaite de conserver sur mer l'égalité du mouvement des clepsidres ou sabliers," in *Prix*, 1725 (1725).
9. "Examen principiorum mechanicae, et demonstrationes geometricae de compositione et resolutione virium," in *CP*, **1**, 1726 (1728).
10. "Tentamen novae de motu musculorum theoriae," *ibid.*
11. "Experimentum circa nervum opticum," *ibid.*
12. "Theoria nova de motu aquarum per canales quoscunque fluentium," *ibid.*, **2**, 1727 (1729).
13. "De mutua relatione centri virium, centri oscillationis et centri gravitatis," *ibid.*
14. "Dissertatio de actione fluidorum in corpora solida et motu solidorum in fluidis," *ibid.*; "Continuatio," *ibid.*, **3**, 1728 (1732).
15. "Methodus universalis determinandae curvaturae fili," *ibid.*
16. "Observationes de seriebus quae formantur ex additione vel subtractione quacunque terminorum se mutuo consequentium," *ibid.*
17. "Problema astronomicum inveniendi altitudinem poli una cum declinatione stellae ejusdemque culminatione," *ibid.*, **4**, 1729 (1735).
18. "Theorema de motu curvilineo corporum, quae resistentiam patiuntur velocitatis suae quadrato proportionalem," *ibid.*; "Additamentum," *ibid.*, **5**, 1730/1731 (1738).
19. "Experimenta coram societate instituta in confirmationem theoriae pressionum quas latera canalis ab aqua transfluente sustinent," *ibid.*, **4**, 1729 (1735).
20. "Notationes de aequationibus, quae progrediuntur in infinitum, earumque resolutione per methodum serierum recurrentium," *ibid.*, **5**, 1730/1731 (1738).
21. "Dissertatio brevis de motibus corporum reciprocis seu oscillatoriis, quae ubique resistentiam patiuntur quadrato velocitatis suae proportionalem," *ibid.*
22. "Specimen theoriae novae de mensura sortis," *ibid.*
23. "Theoremata de oscillationibus corporum filo flexili connexorum et catenae verticaliter suspensae," *ibid.*, **6**, 1732/1733 (1738).

24. "Quelle est la cause physique de l'inclinaison des plans des orbites des planètes par rapport au plan de l'équateur de la révolution du soleil autour de son axe," in *Prix,* 1734 (1735).

25. "Demonstrationes theorematum suorum de oscillationibus corporum filo flexili connexorum et catenae verticaliter suspensae," in *CP,* **7,** 1734/1735 (1740).

26. "De legibus quibusdam mechanicis, quas natura constanter affectat, nondum descriptis, earumque usu hydrodynamico, pro determinanda vi venae aqueae contra planum incurrentis," *ibid.,* **8,** 1736 (1741).

27. "De variatione motuum a percussione excentrica," *ibid.,* **9,** 1737 (1744).

28. "Réflexions sur la meilleure figure à donner aux ancres," in *Prix,* 1737 (1737).

29. "Commentationes de immutatione et extensione principii conservationis virium vivarum, quae pro motu corporum coelestium requiritur," in *CP,* **10,** 1738 (1747).

30. "Commentationes de statu aequilibrii corporum humido insidentium," *ibid.*

31. *Hydrodynamica, sive de viribus et motibus fluidorum commentarii* (Strasbourg, 1738). The following trans. exist: German, with extensive commentary by Karl Flierl, in the series Veröffentlichungen des Forschungsinstituts des Deutschen Museums für die Geschichte der Naturwissenschaften und der Technik, Reihe C: Quellentexte und Uebersetzungen, nos. 1a, 1b (Munich, 1965); English, *Hydrodynamics by Daniel Bernoulli,* trans. Thomas Carmody and Helmut Kobus (New York, 1968), bound with Johann I Bernoulli's *Hydraulics* (pp. 343–451); and Russian, *Daniel Bernoulli. Gidrodinamika ili zapiski o silakh i dvizheniakh zhidkostei,* trans. A. I. Nekrasov, K. K. Baumgart, and V. I. Smirnov (Moscow, 1959).

32. "De motibus oscillatoriis corporum humido insidentium," in *CP,* **11,** 1739 (1750).

33. "Traité sur le flux et reflux de la mer," in *Prix,* 1740 (1741).

34. "De oscillationibus compositis praesertim iis quae fiunt in corporibus ex filo flexili suspensis," in *CP,* **12,** 1740 (1750).

35. "Excerpta ex litteris ad Leonhardum Euler," *ibid.,* **13,** 1741–1743 (1751).

36. "De motu mixto, quo corpora sphaeroidica super plano inclinato descendunt," *ibid.*

37. "De vibrationibus et sono laminarum elasticarum," *ibid.*

38. "De sonis multifariis quos laminae elasticae diversimode edunt disquisitiones mechanico-geometricae experimentis acusticis illustratae et confirmatae," *ibid.*

39. "Mémoire sur la manière de construire les boussoles d'inclinaison," in *Prix,* 1743 (1748).

40. "Nouveau problème de mécanique," in *Mem. Berlin,* 1745 (1746), trans. into German in Ostwald's Klassiker der Exacten Wissenschaften, no. 191 (Leipzig, 1914), pp. 29–43.

41. "Nouveaux principes de mécanique et de physique, tendans à expliquer la nature & les propriétés de l'aiman," written with Johann II, in *Prix,* 1746 (1748).

42. "La meilleure manière de trouver l'heure en mer," *ibid.,* 1745 and 1747 (1750).

43. "Remarques sur le principe de la conservation des forces vives pris dans un sens général," in *Mem. Berlin,* 1748 (1750), trans. into German in Ostwald's Klassiker der Exacten Wissenschaften, no. 191 (Leipzig, 1914), pp. 67–75.

44. "Sur la nature et la cause des courans," in *Prix,* 1749 and 1751 (1769).

45. "Réflexions et éclaircissemens sur les nouvelles vibrations des cordes," in *Mem. Berlin,* 1753 (1755).

46. "Sur le mélange de plusieurs espèces de vibrations simples isochrones, qui peuvent coexister dans un même système de corps," *ibid.*

47. "Recherches sur la manière la plus avantageuse de suppléer à l'action du vent sur les grands vaisseaux," in *Prix,* 1753 (1769).

48. "Quelle est la meilleure manière de diminuer le roulis & le tangage d'un navire," *ibid.,* 1757 (1771).

49. "Sur les nouvelles aiguilles d'inclinaison," in *Journal des sçavans,* 1757 (1757).

50. "Lettre de monsieur Daniel Bernoulli à M. Clairaut, au sujet des nouvelles découvertes faites sur les vibrations des cordes tendues," *ibid.,* 1758 (1758).

51. "Essai d'une nouvelle analyse de la mortalité causée par la petite vérole, & des avantages de l'inoculation pour la prevenir," in *Mem. Paris,* 1760 (1766).

52. "Réflexions sur les avantages de l'inoculation," in *Mercure de France* (June 1760).

53. "Sur le son & sur les tons des tuyaux d'orgues," in *Mem. Paris,* 1762 (1764).

54. "Mémoire sur les vibrations des cordes d'une épaisseur inégale," in *Mem. Berlin,* 1765 (1767).

55. "De usu algorithmi infinitesimalis in arte coniectandi specimen," in *NCP,* **12,** 1766/1767 (1768).

56. "De duratione media matrimoniorum, pro quacunque coniugum aetate," *ibid.*

57. "Commentatio de utilissima ac commodissima directione potentiarum frictionibus mechanicis adhibendarum," *ibid.,* **13,** 1768 (1769).

58. "Disquisitiones analyticae de novo problemate coniecturali," *ibid.,* **14,** 1769, pt. 1 (1770).

59. "Mensura sortis ad fortuitam successionem rerum naturaliter contingentium applicata," *ibid.;* "Continuatio," *ibid.,* **15,** 1770 (1771).

60. "Commentationes physico-mechanicae de frictionibus," *ibid.,* **14,** 1769, pt. 1 (1770).

61. "Examen physico-mechanicum de motu mixto qui laminis elasticis a percussione simul imprimitur," *ibid.,* **15,** 1770 (1771).

62. "De summationibus serierum quarundam incongrue veris," *ibid.,* **16,** 1771 (1772).

63. "De vibrationibus chordarum," *ibid.*

64. "De indole singulari serierum infinitarum quas sinus vel cosinus angulorum arithmetice progredientium formant, earumque summatione et usu," *ibid.,* **17,** 1772 (1773).

65. "Expositio theoretica singularis machinae hydraulicae," *ibid.*

66. "Theoria elementaria serierum, ex sinibus atque

cosinibus arcuum arithmetice progredientium diversimode compositarum, dilucidata," *ibid.*, **18**, 1773 (1774).

67. "Vera determinatio centri oscillationis in corporibus qualibuscunque filo flexili suspensis eiusque ab regula communi discrepantia," *ibid.*

68. "Commentatio physico-mechanica generalior principii de coexistentia vibrationum simplicium haud perturbatarum in systemate composito," *ibid.*, **19**, 1774 (1775).

69. "Commentatio physico-mechanica specialior de motibus reciprocis compositis," *ibid.*

70. "Adversaria analytica miscellanea de fractionibus continuis," *ibid.*, **20**, 1775 (1776).

71. "Disquisitiones ulteriores de indole fractionum continuarum," *ibid.*

72. "Diiudicatio maxime probabilis plurium observationum discrepantium atque verisimillima inductio inde formanda," in *AP*, 1777, pt. 1 (1778).

73. "Specimen philosophicum de compensationibus horologicis, et veriori mensura temporis," *ibid.*, pt. 2 (1780).

74. "Sur la cause des vents," in Berlin Academy's *Recueil des prix* without Bernoulli's name. Also at University of Basel, LIa753E5.

75. "Oratio physiologica de vita," with German trans. and historical essays, ed. O. Spiess and F. Verzár, in *Verhandlungen der Naturforschenden Gesellschaft Basel*, **52** (1940/1941), 189–266. Also at University of Basel, LIa-753E18.

The library of the University of Basel has most of Bernoulli's original MSS, and photocopies of the rest.

76. "Methodus isoperimetricorum ad novam problematum classem promota," LIa751C3. From all curves of equal length lying between two fixed points, to find the ones for which $\int R^m ds$ is a minimum, where R^m is the mth power of the radius of curvature R and ds is the arc element. This was first satisfactorily solved by Euler.

77. "Solutio problematis inveniendi curvam, quae cum aliis data sit tatuochrona" (1729), LIa751C4. Solution to the problem of finding the curves in which the oscillations of a center of mass moving in a vacuum are isochronous regardless of starting point. Also treated by Euler.

78. "De legibus motus mixti variati, quo corpus sphaericum super plano aspero progredietur," LIaC19.

79. "Discours sur la cause et la nature de la pesantur," LIa752D2, submitted in the 1728 prize competition of the Paris Academy. The prize was awarded to Bilfinger.

80. "Quelle est la meilleure méthode d'observer les hauteurs sur mer par le soleil et par les étoiles," LIa752D3, submitted in the 1729 prize competition of the Paris Academy. The prize was awarded to Bouguer.

81. "Recherches mécaniques et astronomiques sur la théorie de Saturne et de Jupiter," LIa33, submitted in the 1748 prize competition of the Paris Academy. The prize was awarded to Euler.

82. An outline of the *Hydrodynamica* (1733) is in Archives of the Academy of Sciences, Leningrad; a photocopy is in Basel.

Biographical works on Bernoulli include Daniel II Bernoulli, "Vita Danielis Bernoulli," in *Acta Helvetica*, **9**

(1787), 1–32, a memorial address with an almost complete bibliography of printed works; "Die Basler Mathematiker Bernoulli und Leonhard Euler. Vorträge von Fr. Burckhardt u.a.," in *Verhandlungen der Naturforschenden Gesellschaft Basel*, **7** (1884), appendix; Marquis de Condorcet, "Éloge de M. Bernoulli," in *Hist. Paris*, 1782 (1785), 82–107, and in *Oeuvres de Condorcet*, II (Paris, 1847), 545–585; *Gedenkbuch der Familie Bernoulli zum 300. Jahrestage ihrer Aufnahme in das Basler Bürgerrecht. 1622, 1922* (Basel, 1922); Peter Merian, *Die Mathematiker Bernoulli. Jubelschrift zur 4. Säcularfeier der Universität Basel, 6 September 1860* (Basel, 1860); Otto Spiess, *Basel anno 1760* (Basel, 1936); "Daniel Bernoulli," in Eduard Fueter, ed., *Grosse Schweizer Forscher* (Zurich, 1939), pp. 110–112; "Johann Bernoulli und seine Soehne," in *Atlantis* (1940), 663–669; "Die Mathematikerfamilie Bernoulli," in Martin Huerlimann, ed., *Grosse Schweizer*, 2nd ed. (Zurich, 1942), pp. 112–119; and "Bernoulli, Basler Gelehrtenfamilie," in *Neue deutsche Biographie* (1955), pp. 128–131; and Rudolf Wolf, "Daniel Bernoulli von Basel, 1700–1782," in *Biographien zur Kulturgeschichte der Schweiz*, 3rd ser. (Zurich, 1860), pp. 151–202.

HANS STRAUB

BERNOULLI, JAKOB (JACQUES) I (*b*. Basel, Switzerland, 27 December 1654; *d*. Basel, 16 August 1705), *mathematics, mechanics, astronomy.*

Bernoulli came from a line of merchants. His grandfather, Jakob Bernoulli, was a druggist from Amsterdam who became a citizen of Basel in 1622 through marriage. His father, Nikolaus Bernoulli, took over the thriving drug business and became a member of the town council and a magistrate; his mother, Margaretha Schönauer, was the daughter of a banker and town councillor. Jakob was married in 1684 to Judith Stupanus, the daughter of a wealthy pharmacist; their son Nikolaus became a town councillor and master of the artists' guild.

Bernoulli received his master of arts in philosophy in 1671, and a licentiate in theology in 1676; meanwhile, he studied mathematics and astronomy against the will of his father. In 1676 he went as a tutor to Geneva, where in 1677 he began his informative scientific diary, *Meditationes;* he then spent two years in France, familiarizing himself with the methodological and scientific opinions of Descartes and his followers, among whom was Nicolas Malebranche. Bernoulli's second educational journey, in 1681–1682, took him to the Netherlands, where he met mathematicians and scientists, especially Jan Hudde, and to England, where he met Robert Boyle and Robert Hooke. The scientific result of these journeys was his inadequate theory of comets (1682) and a theory of gravity that was highly regarded by his contemporaries (1683).

After returning to Basel, Bernoulli conducted experimental lectures, concerning the mechanics of solid and liquid bodies, from 1683 on. He sent reports on scientific problems of the day to the *Journal des sçavans* and the *Acta eruditorum,* and worked his way through the principal mathematical work of those days, *Geometria,* the Latin edition of Descartes's *Géométrie,* which had been edited and provided with notes and supplements by Frans van Schooten (2nd ed., Amsterdam, 1659–1661). As a result of this work, Bernoulli contributed articles on algebraic subjects to the *Acta eruditorum.* His outstanding achievement was the division of a triangle into four equal parts by means of two straight lines perpendicular to each other (1687). After these contributions had been extended and supplemented, they were published as an appendix to the *Geometria* (4th ed., 1695).

In four disputations published from 1684 to 1686, Bernoulli presented formal logical studies that tended toward the sophistical. His first publication on probability theory dates from 1685. By working with the pertinent writings of John Wallis (those of 1656, 1659, and 1670–1671) and Isaac Barrow (1669–1670), concerning mathematical, optical, and mechanical subjects, Bernoulli was led to problems in infinitesimal geometry.

In the meantime his younger brother Johann began attending the University of Basel after an unsuccessful apprenticeship as a salesman. As respondent to one of Jakob's scholarly logic debates, Johann earned his master of arts degree in 1685 and, by order of his father, studied medicine. Simultaneously, however, he secretly studied mathematics under his brother, becoming well versed in the fundamentals of the field. In 1687 Jakob became professor of mathematics at Basel, and with his brother he studied the publications of Leibniz and of Ehrenfried Walther von Tschirnhaus in *Acta eruditorum* (1682–1686), which had in essence been limited to examples and intimations of infinitesimal mathematics and its application to mechanics and dynamics. After much effort, Bernoulli was able to make himself master of these new methods, which he erroneously believed to be merely a computational formalism for Barrow's geometrical treatment of infinitesimals. His mathematical studies reached a first peak about 1689 with the beginnings of a theory of series, the law of large numbers in probability theory, and the special stress on complete induction.

Bernoulli showed his mastery of the Leibnizian calculus with his analysis (in May 1690) of the solutions given by Huygens in 1687 and by Leibniz in 1689 to the problem of the curve of constant descent in a gravitational field. (It was in that analysis that the term "integral" was first used in its present mathematical sense.) The determination of the curve of constant descent had been posed as a problem by Leibniz in 1687. As a counterproblem Bernoulli raised the determination of the shape of the catenary, to which he had, perhaps, been directed by Albert Girard's notes to the *Oeuvres* of Simon Stevin (1634); Girard claimed that the catenary is a parabola. Leibniz promptly referred to the significance of this counterproblem, which he had spontaneously solved (1690) and which was later treated by Johann Bernoulli, Huygens, and himself in the *Acta eruditorum* (1691). Jakob, who found himself at that time in difficulties at the university because of his open criticism of university affairs and saw himself being overshadowed by his brother, did not take part directly, but proposed generalizations of the problem, allowing the links of the chain to be elastic or of unequal weight. He also announced a treatise on the *elastica,* the form of a bent elastic beam, which, under certain conditions, satisfies the differential equation $dy/dx = x^2/\sqrt{a^4-x^4}$. Later he investigated this thoroughly, supposing arbitrary functions of elasticity (1694). In two notable contributions to differential calculus (1691), he examined the parabolic spiral (in polar coordinates: $r = a - b\sqrt{\phi}$, the elliptical integral for the curve length with its characteristic feature of symmetry) and the logarithmic spiral.

In Johann Bernoulli's study concerning the focal line of incident parallel rays of light on a semicircular mirror (1692), there is reference to Jakob's general procedure for determination of evolutes. This procedure is based on the generation of an algebraic curve as the envelope of its circles of curvature, and this procedure is worked out fully in the case of the parabola. Here Bernoulli corrected a mistake made by Leibniz (1686)—the statement that the circle of curvature meets the curve at four coinciding points—but he himself made a mistake in his assertion that the radius of curvature becomes infinite at every point of inflection. This error, corrected in 1693 by G. F. A. de L'Hospital, was the occasion for Bernoulli's removing of the singularity $a^2x^3 = y^5$ in the origin (1697). Almost simultaneously, and independently of each other, the brothers recognized that the form of a sail inflated by the wind is described by $(dx/ds)^3 = ad^2y/dx^2$. Jakob made a preliminary report in 1692 and a thorough one in 1695.

Further investigations concerned evolutes and caustics, first of the logarithmic spiral (*spira mirabilis*) and the parabola (1692), and later of epicycloids (1692) and diacaustic surfaces (1693), this in connection with Johann's similar studies. These last were included in his private instruction to L'Hospital

(1691–1692). Here, for the first time, public reference was made to the *theorema aureum,* which had been developed in the spring of 1692. The theorem, which gives the radius of curvature as $(ds/dx)^3 : (d^2y/dx^2)$, was published in 1694. Bernoulli's solution of the differential equation proposed by Johann Bernoulli (1693), $xdy - ydx/yds = a/b$, was completed by Huygens (1693). In treating the paracentric isochrone, a problem proposed by Leibniz (1689) that leads to the differential equation

$$(xdx + ydy)/\sqrt{y} = (xdy - ydx)/\sqrt{a},$$

Bernoulli separated the variables by substituting

$$x^2 + y^2 = r^2, \qquad ay = rt$$

and was able to relate the solution to the rectification of the *elastica;* later he found the reduction to the rectification of the lemniscate,

$$x^2 + y^2 = a\sqrt{x^2 - y^2}.$$

These and other studies—among which the kinetic-geometrical chord construction for the solution (1696) of $dy/dx = t(x)/a$ and the solution (1696) of the so-called Bernoullian differential equation $y' = p(x)y + q(x)y^n$ (1696) merit special attention—are proof of Bernoulli's careful and critical work on older as well as on contemporary contributions to infinitesimal mathematics and of his perseverance and analytical ability in dealing with special pertinent problems, even those of a mechanical-dynamic nature.

Sensitivity, irritability, a mutual passion for criticism, and an exaggerated need for recognition alienated the brothers, of whom Jakob had the slower but deeper intellect. Johann was more gifted in working with mathematical formulations and was blessed above all with a greater intuitive power and descriptive ability. Johann was appointed a professor at the University of Groningen in 1695, and in 1696 he proposed the problem to determine the curve of quickest descent between two given points, the brachistochrone. In connection with this he replied to the previous gibes of his brother with derisive insinuations. Jakob gave a solution (1697) that was closely related to that given by Leibniz (1697). It is based on the sufficient but not necessary condition that the extreme-value property of the curve in question (a common cycloid) is valid not only for the entire curve but also for all its parts. As a counterproblem Jakob set forth the so-called isoperimetric problem, the determination of that curve of given length between the points $A(-c; 0)$, $B(+c; 0)$ for which $\int_{-c}^{c} y^n dx$ takes a maximum value. Johann, in the *Histoire des ouvrages des savants* (1697), through a misunderstanding of the difficulty of the problem and of its

nature (calculus of variations), gave a solution based on a differential equation of the second degree. A differential equation of the third degree is necessary, however. After showing that a third-degree equation is required (1701), Jakob was able also to furnish the proof, which Johann and Leibniz had been seeking in vain, that the inexpansible and homogeneous catenary is the curve of deepest center of gravity between the points of suspension.

Johann Bernoulli may have comprehended the justification for his brother's argument soon after publication of the dissertation of 1701 (*Analysis magni problematis isoperimetrici*), but he remained silent. Only after Brook Taylor had adopted Jakob's procedure (1715) was he induced to accept Jakob's point of view. In the 1718 series of the *Mémoires* of the Paris Académie des Sciences, of which the brothers had been corresponding members since 1699, Johann gave a presentation, based on Jakob's basic ideas but improved in style and organization. It was not superseded until Leonhard Euler's treatment of the problems of variations (1744).

The antagonism between the brothers soon led to ugly critical remarks. In 1695 Jakob failed to appreciate the significance of Johann's extraordinarily effective series expansion (1694), which is based on iterated integration by parts and leads to a remainder in integral form. On the other hand, Johann, who in 1697 had challenged the criterion for geodetic lines on convex surfaces, complained in the following year that his brother knew how to solve the problem "only" on rotation surfaces. Other items of disagreement were the determination of elementary quadrable segments of the common cycloid and related questions. The brothers argued over this in print in 1699 and 1700. The formulas for the multisection of angles are connected with these problems. In his ingenious use of Wallis' incomplete induction (1656), Jakob presented $2 \cdot \cos n\alpha$ and $2 \cdot \sin n\alpha$ as functions of $2 \cdot \sin \alpha$. This is related to his notes from the winter of 1690–1691, in which, furthermore, the exponential series was derived from the binomial series in a bold but formally unsatisfactory manner.

Jakob Bernoulli's decisive scientific achievement lay not in the formulation of extensive theories, but in the clever and preeminently analytical treatment of individual problems. Behind his particular accomplishments there were, of course, notions of which Bernoulli was deeply convinced, primarily concerning continuity of all processes of nature (*natura non facit saltum*). Although Bernoulli assigned great significance to experimental research, he limited himself—for example, in investigations of mechanics—to a few basic facts to which he tried to cling and on which he sought to base full theories. For this reason his final results were intellectually interesting, and as points of departure they were significant for further investigation by his contemporaries and subsequent generations. Naturally enough, they usually do not conform to more modern conclusions, which rest on far wider foundations. It is to be regretted, however, that Bernoulli's contributions to mechanics are hardly ever mentioned in the standard works.

The theory that seeks to explain natural phenomena by assuming collisions between particles of the ether, developed in the *Dissertatio de gravitate aetheris* (1683), of course does not mean much to a later generation. There are extensive discussions about the center point of oscillation, which had been determined correctly for the first time by Huygens in his *Horologium oscillatorium* (1673), but this was strongly debated by some of the members of the Cartesian school. On this subject Bernoulli expressed his opinions first in 1684, and then in more detail in 1686 and 1691; finally he succeeded in developing a proof from the properties of the lever (1703–1704). Important also is his last work, on the resistance of elastic bodies (1705). Supplementary material from his scientific diary is contained in the appendix to his *Opera*. Additional, but unpublished, material deals with the center of gravity of two uniformly moved bodies, the shape of a cord under the influence of several stretching forces, centrally accelerated motion (in connection with the statements of Newton in his *Principia* [1687]), and the line of action and the collective impulse of infinitely many shocks exerted on a rigid arc in the plane.

In the field of engineering belongs the 1695 treatment of the drawbridge problem (the curve of a sliding weight hanging on a cable that always holds the drawbridge in balance), stemming from Joseph Sauveur and investigated in the same year by L'Hospital and Johann Bernoulli. Leibniz was also interested in the problem. In Bernoulli's published remains, the contour is determined upon which a watch spring is to be developed so that the tension always remains the same for the movements of the watch.

The five dissertations in the *Theory of Series* (1682–1704) contain sixty consecutively numbered propositions. These dissertations show how Bernoulli (at first in close cooperation with his brother) had thoroughly familiarized himself with the appropriate formulations of questions to which he had been led by the conclusions of Leibniz in 1682 (series for $\pi/4$ and log 2) and 1683 (questions dealing with compound interest). Out of this there also came the treatise in which Bernoulli took into account short-term compound interest and was thus led to the exponential

series. He thought that there had been nothing printed concerning the theory of series up until that time, but he was mistaken: most conclusions of the first two dissertations (1689, 1692) were already to be found in Pietro Mengoli (1650), as were the divergence of the harmonic series (Prop. 16) and the sum of the reciprocals of infinitely many figurate numbers (Props. 17–20).

The so-called Bernoullian inequality (Prop. 4), $(1 + x)^n > 1 + nx$, is intended for $x > 0$, n as a whole number > 1. It is taken from Barrow's seventh lecture in the *Lectiones geometricae* (1670). Bernoulli would have been able to find algebraic iteration processes for the solution of equations (Props. 27–35) in James Gregory's *Vera . . . quadratura* (1667). The procedure of proof is still partially incomplete because of inadmissible use of divergent series. At the end of the first dissertation Bernoulli acknowledged that he could not yet sum up $\Sigma_{k=1}^{\infty} k^{-2}$ in closed form (Euler succeeded in doing so first in 1737); but he did know about the majorant $\Sigma_{k=1}^{\infty} 2k^{-1}(k + 1)^{-1}$, which can be summed in elementary terms. In Proposition 24 it is written that $\Sigma_{k=1}^{\infty} (2k - 1)^{-m}/\Sigma_{k=1}^{\infty} (2k)^{-m}$ equals $(2^m - 1)/1$ (m integer > 1), and that $\Sigma_{k=1}^{\infty} k^{-1/2}$ diverges more rapidly than $\Sigma_{k=1}^{\infty} k^{-1}$. Informative theses, based on Bernoulli's earlier studies, were added to the dissertations; and theses 2 and 3 of the second dissertation are based on the still incomplete classification of curves of the third degree according to their shapes into thirty-three different types.

The third dissertation was defended by Jakob Hermann, who wrote Bernoulli's obituary notice in *Acta eruditorum* (1706). In the introduction L'Hospital's *Analyse* is praised. After some introductory propositions, there appear the logarithmic series for the hyperbola quadrature (Prop. 42), the exponential series as the inverse of the logarithmic series (Prop. 43), the geometrical interpretation of

$$\sum_{k=1}^{\infty} k^{-2}x^k$$

(Prop. 44), and the series for the arc of the circle and the sector of conic sections (Props. 45, 46). All of these are carefully and completely presented with reference to the pertinent results of Leibniz (1682; 1691). In 1698 previous work was supplemented by Bernoulli's reflections on the catenary (Prop. 49) and related problems, on the rectification of the parabola (Prop. 41), and on the rectification of the logarithmic curve (Prop. 52).

The last dissertation (1704) was defended by Bernoulli's nephew, Nikolaus I, who helped in the publication of the *Ars conjectandi* (1713) and the reprint of the dissertation on series (1713) and became a prominent authority in the theory of series. In the dissertation Bernoulli first (Prop. 53) praises Wallis' interpolation through incomplete induction. In Proposition 54 the binomial theorem is presented, with examples of fractional exponents, as an already generally known theorem. Probably for this reason there is no reference to Newton's presentation in his letters to Leibniz of 23 June and 3 November 1676, which were made accessible to Bernoulli when they were published in Wallis' *Opera* (Vol. III, 1699). In proposition 55 the method of indeterminate coefficients appears, without reference to Leibniz (1693). Propositions 56–58 and 60 deal with questions related to the *elastica*.

In Proposition 59 it is stated that the series

$$\sum_{k=1}^{\infty} (-1)^{k+1} k^{-1}$$

for log 2 should be replaced by

$$\sum_{k=1}^{\infty} 2^{-k} \, k^{-1},$$

which converges more rapidly. From the letter to Leibniz of 2 August 1704, we know that in Proposition 59 Bernoulli used an idea of Jean-Christophe Fatio-de-Duillier (1656–1720), an engineer from Geneva, for the improvement of convergence. The procedure was expanded by Euler in the *Institutiones calculi differentialis* (1755) to his so-called series transformation. In the dissertations on series Bernoulli apparently wished to reproduce everything he knew about the subject. In this he was primarily concerned with the careful rendering of the results and not so much with originality.

The *Ars conjectandi* is Bernoulli's most original work, but unfortunately it is incomplete. The first part is basically a first-rate commentary on Huygens' *De ratiociniis in aleae ludo,* which was published as an appendix to van Schooten's *Exercitationes mathematicae* (1657). In the second part Bernoulli deals with the theory of combinations, based on the pertinent contributions of van Schooten (1657), Leibniz (1666), Wallis (1685), and Jean Prestet's *Élémens de mathématiques* (1675; 2nd ed., 1689). The chief result here is the rigid derivation of the exponential series through complete induction by means of the so-called Bernoullian numbers. In the third part Bernoulli gives twenty-four examples, some simple, some very complicated, on the expectation of profit in various games.

The fourth part contains the philosophical thoughts on probability that are especially characteristic of Bernoulli: probability as a measurable degree of certainty; necessity and chance; moral versus mathematical expectation; a priori and a posteriori probability; expectation of winning when the players are divided according to dexterity; regard of all available arguments, their valuation, and their calculable evaluation; law of large numbers, and reference to the *Art de penser* (*Logique de Port Royal,* Antoine Arnauld and Pierre Nicole, eds., 1662). The last section contains a penetrating discussion of *jeu de paume,* a complicated predecessor of tennis that was very popular. This part is Bernoulli's answer to the anonymous gibes occasioned by his debate of 1686 on scholarly logic.

Bernoulli's ideas on the theory of probability have contributed decisively to the further development of the field. They were incorporated in the second edition of Rémond de Montmort's *Essai* (1713) and were considered by Abraham de Moivre in his *Doctrine of Chances* (1718).

Bernoulli greatly advanced algebra, the infinitesimal calculus, the calculus of variations, mechanics, the theory of series, and the theory of probability. He was self-willed, obstinate, aggressive, vindictive, beset by feelings of inferiority, and yet firmly convinced of his own abilities. With these characteristics, he necessarily had to collide with his similarly disposed brother. He nevertheless exerted the most lasting influence on the latter.

Bernoulli was one of the most significant promoters of the formal methods of higher analysis. Astuteness and elegance are seldom found in his method of presentation and expression, but there is a maximum of integrity. The following lines taken from the *Ars conjectandi* (published posthumously in 1713) are not without a certain grace, however, and represent an early statement, made with wit and clarity, of the boundaries of an infinite series.

Ut non-finitam Seriem finita cöercet,
    Summula, & in nullo limite limes adest:
Sic modico immensi vestigia Numinis haerent
    Corpore, & angusto limite limes abest.
Cernere in immenso parvum, dic, quanta voluptas!
    In parvo immensum cernere, quanta, Deum!

Even as the finite encloses an infinite series
    And in the unlimited limits appear,
So the soul of immensity dwells in minutia
    And in narrowest limits no limits inhere.
What joy to discern the minute in infinity!
    The vast to perceive in the small, what divinity!

BIBLIOGRAPHY

I. ORIGINAL WORKS. Bernoulli's most famous single writing is *Ars conjectandi* (Basel, 1713; Brussels, 1968). His *Opera,* G. Cramer, ed. (Geneva, 1744; Brussels, 1968), contains all his scientific writings except the *Neuerfundene*

Anleitung, wie man den Lauff der Comet- oder Schwantz-sternen in gewisse grundmässige Gesätze einrichten und ihre Erscheinung vorhersagen könne (Basel, 1681), as well as a *Prognosticon.* Its contents were incorporated in the *Conamen novi systematis cometarum . . .* (Amsterdam, 1682), which is reproduced in the *Opera* as part 1.

Two collections of letters are printed: those to Leibniz in Leibniz' *Mathematische Schriften,* Vol. III, C. I. Gerhardt, ed. (Halle, 1855; Hildesheim, 1962); those to his brother Johann, in *Der Briefwechsel von Johann Bernoulli,* Vol. I, O. Spiess, ed. (Basel, 1955).

His MSS at the library of the University of Basel are *Reisebüchlein* (1676–1683); *Meditationes, annotationes, animadversiones* (1677–1705); *Stammbuch* (1678–1684); *Tabulae gnomicae. Typus locorum hypersolidorum,* which concerns classification of the curves of the third degree into thirty-three types; *Memorial über die Missbräuche an der Universität* (1691); and *De arte combinatoria* (1692) (all unpublished manuscripts); and "De historia cycloidis" (1701), in *Archiv für Geschichte der Mathematik und Naturwissenschaften,* **10** (1927–1928), 345 ff.

Bernoulli's unpublished manuscripts at the library of the University of Geneva are lectures on the mechanics of solid and liquid bodies, *Acta collegii experimentalis* (1683–1690), parts of which have been transcribed.

The collected works are in preparation. Included are Bernoulli's correspondence with Nicolas Fatio-de-Duillier (1700–1701) and with Otto Mencke (1686, 1689). The most important correspondence with L'Hospital and Pierre Varignon seems to have been lost.

Translations from the *Opera* are in the series Ostwald's Klassiker der Exacten Wissenschaften: *Unendliche Reihen* (1689–1704), translated into German by G. Kowalewski, no. 171 (Leipzig, 1909); and *Abhandlungen über das Gleichgewicht und die Schwingungen der ebenen elastischen Kurven von Jakob Bernoulli (1691, 1694, 1695) und Leonh. Euler (1744),* translated into German by H. Linsenbarth, no. 175 (Leipzig, 1910). Other translations are *Abhandlungen über Variations-Rechnung. Erster Theil: Abhandlungen von Joh. Bernoulli (1696), Jac. Bernoulli (1697) und Leonhard Euler,* translated into German by P. Stäckel, no. 46 (Leipzig, 1894; 2nd ed., 1914); and *Jakob Bernoulli: Wahrscheinlichkeitsrechnung,* translated into German by R. Haussner, nos. 107 and 108 (Leipzig, 1899). The latter was translated into English by Fr. Masères in his *Doctrine of Permutations and Combinations* (London, 1795) and in *Scriptores logarithmici,* Vol. III (London, 1796).

II. SECONDARY LITERATURE. Works concerning Bernoulli and his contributions to mathematics are P. Dietz, "The Origins of the Calculus of Variations in the Works of Jakob Bernoulli," in *Verhandlungen der Naturforschenden Gesellschaft in Basel,* **70** (1959), 81–146, a dissertation presented at the University of Mainz in 1958; J. O. Fleckenstein, *Johann und Jakob Bernoulli* (Basel, 1949), which is supp. 6 to the journal *Elemente der Mathematik;* J. E. Hofmann, *Uber Jakob Bernoullis Beiträge zur Infinitesimalmathematik* (Geneva, 1956), no. 3 in the series *Monographies de l'Enseignement Mathématique;* and O. Spiess, "Bernoulli," in *Neue deutsche Biographie,* II (Berlin, 1955), 128–129,

and "Jakob Bernoulli," *ibid.,* pp. 130–131, which include supplementary bibliographical material.

The poem "On Infinite Series," Helen M. Walker, trans., appears in D. E. Smith, *A Source Book in Mathematics;* repr. by permission Harvard University Press.

J. E. HOFMANN

BERNOULLI, JAKOB (JACQUES) II (*b.* Basel, Switzerland, 17 October 1759; *d.* St. Petersburg, Russia, 15 August 1789), *mathematics.*

Jakob II was Johann II's most gifted son. He graduated in jurisprudence in 1778 but successfully engaged in mathematics and physics. In 1782 he presented a paper (6) to support his candidacy for the chair of his uncle Daniel. The decision (made by drawing lots) was against him, however, and he traveled as secretary of the imperial envoy to Turin and Venice, where he received a call to St. Petersburg. There he married a granddaughter of Euler and published several treatises (2–4) at the Academy. When only thirty years old, he drowned while swimming in the Neva.

BIBLIOGRAPHY

Jakob's writings include (1) "Lettre sur l'élasticité," in *Journal de physique de Rozier,* **21** (1782), 463–467; (2) "Considérations hydrostatiques," in *Nova acta Helvetica,* **1,** 229–237; (3) "Dilucidationes in Comment. L. Euleri de ictu glandium contra tabulam explosarum," in *Nova acta Petropolitana,* **4** (1786), 148–157; (4) "De motu et reactione aquae per tubos mobiles transfluentis," *ibid.,* **6** (1788), 185–196; (5) "Sur l'usage et la théorie d'une machine, qu'on peut nommer instrument ballistique," in *Mém. Acad. Berl.* (1781), pp. 347–376; and (6) *Theses physicae et physico-mathematicae quas vacante cathedra physica die 28 Maii 1782 defendere conabitur Jacobus Bernoulli* (Basel, 1782).

J. O. FLECKENSTEIN

BERNOULLI, JOHANN (JEAN) I (*b.* Basel, Switzerland, 6 August 1667; *d.* Basel, 1 January 1748), *mathematics.*

The tenth child in the family, Johann proved unsuited for a business career, much to his father's sorrow. He therefore received permission in 1683 to enroll at his native city's university, where his brother Jakob (or Jacques), who was twelve years older and who had recently returned from the Netherlands, lectured as *magister artium* on experimental physics. In 1685 Johann, respondent to his brother in a logical disputation, was promoted to *magister artium* and began the study of medicine. He temporarily halted his studies at the licentiate level in 1690, when his first publication appeared, a paper on fermentation processes.[1] (His doctoral dissertation of 1694[2] is a mathematical work despite its medical subject, and reflects the influence of the iatromathematician Borelli.)

Bernoulli privately studied mathematics with the gifted Jakob, who in 1687 had succeeded to the vacant chair of mathematics at the University of Basel. From about this time, both brothers were engrossed in infinitesimal mathematics and were the first to achieve a full understanding of Leibniz' abbreviated presentation of differential calculus.[3] The extraordinary solution[4] of the problem of *catenaria* posed by Jakob Bernoulli (*Acta eruditorum,* June 1691) was Johann's first independently published work, and placed him in the front rank with Huygens, Leibniz, and Newton. Johann spent the greater part of 1691 in Geneva. There he taught differential calculus to J. C. Fatio-de-Duillier (whose brother Nicolas later played a not very praiseworthy role in the Leibniz-Newton priority dispute) and worked on the deepening of his own mathematical knowledge.

In the autumn of 1691 Bernoulli was in Paris, where he won a good place in Malebranche's mathematical circle as a representative of the new Leibnizian calculus, and did so by virtue of a "golden theorem" (stemming actually from Jakob)—the spectacular determination of the radius of curvature of a curve by means of the equation $\rho = dx/ds : d^2y/ds^2$. During this period he also met L'Hospital, then probably France's most gifted mathematician. "Grandseigneur of the science of mathematics"—he corresponded also with Huygens—L'Hospital engaged Bernoulli to initiate him into the secrets of the new infinitesimal calculus. The lessons were given in Paris and sometimes in L'Hospital's country seat at Oucques, and Bernoulli was generously compensated. L'Hospital even induced Bernoulli to continue, for a considerable fee, these lessons by correspondence after the latter's return to Basel. This correspondence[5] subsequently became the basis for the first textbook in differential calculus,[6] which assured L'Hospital's place in the history of mathematics. (Bernoulli's authorship of this work, which was still doubted by Cantor,[7] has been substantiated by the Basel manuscript of the *Differential Calculus* discovered in 1921 by Schafheitlin,[8] as well as by Bernoulli's correspondence with L'Hospital.[9])

In 1692 Bernoulli met Pierre de Varignon, who later became his disciple and close friend. This tie also resulted in a voluminous correspondence.[10] In 1693 Bernoulli began his exchange of letters with Leibniz, which was to grow into the most extensive correspondence ever conducted by the latter.

Bernoulli's most significant results during these years were published in the form of numerous memoirs in *Acta eruditorum* (*AE*) and shorter papers in the *Journal des Sçavans* (*JS*). Bernoulli's two most important achievements were the investigations concerning the function $y = x^x$ and the discovery, in 1694, of a general development in series by means of repeated integration by parts, the series subsequently named after him:

$$\int_0^x y\, dx = xy - \frac{x^2}{2!}y' + \frac{x^3}{3!}y'' - + \cdots$$

(cf. *Addidamentum AE,* 1694, letter to Leibniz of 2 September 1694). This series—whose utility, incidentally, Jakob Bernoulli failed to recognize—is based on the general Leibnizian principle for the differentiation of a product:

$$d^m[f(x)g(x)] = (df + dg)^{(m)} = \sum_{\nu=0}^{m} \binom{m}{\nu} d^{m-\nu}f d^\nu g.$$

This formalism is characteristic of a large part of the Bernoulli-Leibniz correspondence between 1694 and 1696.

Integration being viewed as the inverse operation of differentiation, Bernoulli worked a great deal on the integration of differential equations. This view was generally accepted in the Leibniz circle. In Paris he had already demonstrated the efficacy of Leibniz' calculus by an anonymous solution of "Debeaune's problem" (*JS,* 1692), which had been put to Descartes as the first inverse tangent problem. Five years later he demonstrated that with the aid of the calculus much more complex differential equations could be solved. In connection with Debeaune's problem, Jakob Bernoulli had proposed the general differential equation since called by his name,

$$y' + P(x)y + Q(x)y^n = 0,$$

and had solved it in a rather cumbersome way. Johann, more flexible with regard to formalism, solved this equation by considering the desired final function as the product of two functions, $M(x)$ and $N(x)$. In the resulting equation,

$$\frac{dM}{M} + \frac{dN}{N} + P(x)\,dx + (MN)^{n-1}Q(x)\,dx = 0,$$

the arbitrariness of the functions M and N makes it possible to subject one of them (e.g., M) to the secondary condition

$$\frac{dM}{M} + P(x)\,dx = 0,$$

resulting in $M = \exp[-\int P(x)\,dx]$. This substitution promptly leads to a linear differential equation in N.

Bernoulli's "exponential calculus" is nothing other than the infinitesimal calculus of exponential functions. Nieuwentijt, in a paper criticizing the lack of logical foundations in Leibniz' calculus,[11] pointed out the inapplicability of Leibniz' published differentiation methods to the exponential function x^y. Thereupon Bernoulli developed, in "Principia calculi exponentialium seu percurrentium" (AE, 1697), the "exponential calculus," which is based on the equation

$$d(x^y) = x^y \log x \, dy + yx^{y-1} \, dx.$$

Also in 1695 came Bernoulli's summation of the infinite harmonic series

$$\sum_{K=1}^{n} (-1)^{K-1} K^{-1} \binom{n}{K}$$

from the difference scheme, the development of the addition theorems of trigonometric and hyperbolic functions from their differential equations, and the geometric generation of pairs of curves, wherein the sum or difference of the arc lengths can be represented by circular arcs. Neither Johann nor Jacob Bernoulli succeeded in mastering the problem, originated by Mengoli, of the summation of reciprocal squares ($\Sigma_{k=1}^{\infty} 1:k^2$). This problem was solved only by Johann's greatest pupil, Leonhard Euler.[12]

In 1695 Bernoulli was offered both a professorship at Halle, and, through the intervention of Huygens, the chair of mathematics at Groningen. He eagerly accepted the latter offer, particularly since his hopes of obtaining a chair in Basel were nil as long as his brother Jakob was alive. On 1 September 1695 he departed for Holland with his wife (the former Dorothea Falkner) and seven-month-old Nikolaus, his first son, not without resentment against Jakob, who had begun to retaliate for Johann's earlier boastfulness when he solved the differential equation of the velaria (JS, 1692): Jakob termed Johann his pupil, who after all could only repeat what he had learned from his teacher. This cutting injustice was promptly paid back by Johann, now his equal in rank.

In June 1696, Johann posed (in AE) the problem of the brachistochrone, i.e., the problem of determining the "curve of quickest descent." Since no solution could be expected before the end of the year, Bernoulli, at Leibniz' request, republished the problem in the form of a leaflet dedicated to *acutissimis qui in toto orbe florent mathematicis* ("the shrewdest mathematicians of all the world") and fixed a six-month limit for its solution. Leibniz solved the problem on the day he received Bernoulli's letter, and correctly predicted a total of only five solutions:

from the two Bernoullis, Newton, Leibniz, and L'Hospital. (It should be noted that it was only through Johann's assistance—by correspondence—that L'Hospital had arrived at his solution.)

This problem publicly demonstrated the difference in the talents of the two brothers. Johann solved the problem by ingenious intuition, which enabled him to reduce the mechanical problem to the optical problem already resolved by means of Fermat's principle of least time. He deduced the differential equation of the cycloid from the law of refraction. Jakob, on the other hand, furnished a detailed but cumbersome analysis, and came upon the roots of a new mathematical discipline, the calculus of variations. Unlike Jakob, Johann failed to perceive that such extreme-value problems differed from the customary ones in that it was no longer the unknown extreme values of a function that were to be determined, but functions that made a certain integral an extreme.[13]

In connection with his solution of the brachistochrone problem, Jakob (AE, May 1697) posed a new variational problem, the isoperimetric problem.[14] Johann underestimated the complexity of this problem by failing to perceive its variational character; and he furnished an incomplete solution (wherein the resulting differential equation is one order too low) in *Histoire des ouvrages des savants* (VI, 1697), and thereby brought on himself the merciless criticism of his brother.[15] This was the beginning of alienation and open discord between the brothers—and also the birth of the calculus of variations. A comparison of Jakob's solution (Basel, 1701; AE, May 1701) with Johann's analysis of the problem (which he presented through Varignon to the Paris Academy on 1 February 1701) clearly shows Johann's to be inferior. Nevertheless, Jakob was not able to enjoy his triumph, since—for reasons that remain mysterious—the sealed envelope containing Johann's solution was not opened by the Academy until 17 April 1706, the year following Jakob's death.

Soon after publication of Jakob's *Analysis magni problematis isoperimetrici* (1701), Johann must have felt that his brother's judgment was valid, although he never said so. Only after having been stimulated by Taylor's *Methodus incrementorum* (1715) did he produce a precise and formally elegant solution of the isoperimetric problem along the lines of Jakob's ideas (*Mémoires de l'Académie des sciences*, 1718). The concepts set forth in this paper contain the nucleus of modern methods of the calculus of variations. Also in this connection Bernoulli made a discovery pertaining to the variational problem of geodetic lines on convex surfaces: in a letter addressed to Leibniz, dated 26 August 1698, he perceived the characteristic property of geodetic lines, i.e., three consecutive points determine a normal plane of the surface.

Bernoulli's studies on the determination of all rationally quadrable segments of the common cycloid —the "fateful curve of the seventeenth century" (*AE*, July 1699)—in connection with the cyclotomic equation (*AE*, April 1701; more detailed in his correspondence with Moivre[16])—resulted in a systematic treatment of the integrals of rational functions by means of resolution into partial fractions. The general advance in algebraic analysis under Bernoulli's influence is evident in the typical case of the relation

$$2i \text{ arc tan } x = \log \frac{x - i}{x + i}.$$

Nevertheless, Bernoulli had not yet perceived that such logarithmic expressions may take on infinitely many values.

Immediately after Jakob's death, Johann succeeded him in Basel, although he would undoubtedly have preferred to accept the repeated invitations extended to him by the universities of Utrecht and Leiden (see correspondence of the rector of Utrecht University, Pieter Burman, with Bernoulli's father-in-law, Falkner[17]). Family circumstances, however, caused him to settle in Basel.

Bernoulli's criticism of Taylor's *Methodus incrementorum* was simultaneously an attack upon the method of fluxions, for in 1713 Bernoulli had become involved in the priority dispute between Leibniz and Newton. Following publication of the Royal Society's *Commercium epistolicum* in 1712, Leibniz had no choice but to present his case in public. He released —without naming names—a letter by Bernoulli (dated 7 June 1713) in which Newton was charged with errors stemming from a misinterpretation of the higher differential. Thereupon Newton's followers raised complicated analytical problems, such as the determination of trajectories and the problem of finding the ballistic curve, which Newton had solved only for the law of resistance $R = av$ ($R =$ resistance, $a =$ constant, $v =$ velocity). Bernoulli solved this problem (*AE*, 1719) for the general case ($R = av^n$), thus demonstrating the superiority of Leibniz' differential calculus.

After Newton's death in 1727, Bernoulli was unchallenged as the leading mathematical preceptor to all Europe. Since his return to Basel in 1705, he had devoted himself—in the field of applied mathematics—to theoretical and applied mechanics. In 1714 he published his only book, *Théorie de la manoeuvre des vaisseaux*. Here Bernoulli (as Huygens had done before him) criticizes the navigational theories advanced in 1679 by the French naval officer Bernard Renau d'Eliçagaray (1652–1719), a friend of Varignon's. In this book Bernoulli exposed the confusion in Cartesian mechanics between force and *vis viva* (now kinetic energy). On 26 February 1715—and not 1717, as stated in the literature because of a printing error in Varignon's *Nouvelle mécanique* (1725)—Bernoulli communicated to Varignon the principle of virtual velocities for the first time in analytical form. In modern notation it is

$$\partial A = \sum_{i=1}^{n} \vec{K}_i \, \vec{\partial s}_i = 0.$$

Since this principle can be derived from the energy principle $A + mv^2/2 =$ const., which Bernoulli applied several times to conservative mechanical systems of central forces, he considered it a second general principle of mechanics—which, however, he had demonstrated only for the statical case. For central forces, Bernoulli applied the *vis viva* equation to the inverse two-body problem, which he for the first time expressed in the form used today for the equation of the orbit (*Mémoires de l'Académie des sciences,* 1710):

$$\varphi(r) = \varphi\left(\frac{1}{u}\right) = \vartheta(u) = \int \frac{c \, du}{\sqrt{2(u + h) - u^2 c^2}}.$$

For the corresponding problem of centrally accelerated motion in a resisting medium (*ibid.,* 1711), he solved the differential equation

$$\frac{a}{\rho} \frac{dv}{v} \frac{ds}{d\theta} \pm av^{n-2} \, ds + \frac{dv}{v} = 0$$

($\rho =$ radius of curvature of the orbit) on the premise that $v = M(r)N(r)$, and determined the central force, in accordance with Huygens' formula, from

$$\rho(r) = \frac{v^2}{\rho} \frac{ds}{rd\theta}.$$

Newton severely criticized the Cartesian vortex theory in Book II of the *Principia*. Bernoulli's advocacy of the theory delayed the acceptance of Newtonian physics on the Continent. In three prize-winning papers, Bernoulli treated the transmission of momentum (1727), the motions of the planets in aphelion (1730), and the cause of the inclination of the planetary orbits relative to the solar equator (1735). Bernoulli's 1732 work on hydraulics (*Opera,* IV) was generally considered a piece of plagiarism from the hydrodynamics of his son Daniel. Nevertheless, Bernoulli did try to manage without Daniel's formulation of the principle of *vis viva*.

Bernoulli also worked in experimental physics. In several papers (*Mémoires de l'Académie des sciences,* 1701; Basel, 1719), he investigated the phenomenon of the luminous barometer within the framework of contemporary Cartesian physics, although he was unable to furnish a sufficient explanation for the electrical phenomenon of triboluminescence discovered by Picard.

Bernoulli was a member of the royal academies of Paris and Berlin, of the Royal Society, of the St. Petersburg Academy, and the Institute of Bologna. As son-in-law of Alderman Falkner, he not only enjoyed social status in Basel, but also held honorary civic offices there. He became especially well known as a member of the school board through his efforts to reform the humanistic Gymnasium. His temperament might well have led him to a career in politics, but instead it only involved him in scientific polemics with his brother Jakob and in the Leibniz-Newton priority dispute. Even abroad he was unable to curb his "Flemish pugnacity." In 1702, as professor in Groningen, he became involved in quarrels with the theologians, who in turn, because of his views in natural philosophy, accused him of what was then the worst of heresies, Spinozism.

Bernoulli's quarrelsomeness was matched by his passion for communicating. His scientific correspondence comprised about 2,500 letters, exchanged with some 110 scholars.

NOTES

1. *De effervescentia et fermentatione.*
2. *De motu musculorum.*
3. Leibniz, *Nova methodus de maximis et minimis.*
4. J. E. Hofmann, "Vom öffentlichen Bekanntwerden der Leibniz'schen Infinitesimalmathematik."
5. O. Spiess, ed., *Der Briefwechsel von Johann Bernoulli.*
6. L'Hospital, *Analyse des infiniten petits.*
7. Cantor, *Vorlesungen über Geschichte der Mathematik.*
8. *Lectiones de calculo differentialium,* MS Universitätsbibliothek, Basel.
9. O. J. Rebel, *Der Briefwechsel zwischen Johann Bernoulli und dem Marquis de l'Hôpital.*
10. E. J. Fedel, *Johann Bernoullis Briefwechsel mit Varignon aus den Jahren 1692–1702.*
11. *Considerationes secundae circa calculi differentialis principia.*
12. O. Spiess, *Die Summe der reziproken Quadratzahlen.*
13. P. Dietz, *Die Ursprünge der Variationsrechnung bei Jakob Bernoulli;* J. E. Hofmann, *Ueber Jakob Bernoullis Beiträge zur Infinitesimalmathematik.*
14. J. O. Fleckenstein, *Johann und Jakob Bernoulli.*
15. Hofmann, *Ueber Jakob Bernoullis Beiträge zur Infinitesimalmathematik.*
16. K. Wollenschlaeger, *Der mathematische Briefwechsel zwischen Johann I Bernoulli und Abraham de Moivre.*
17. O. Spiess, ed., *Der Briefwechsel von Johann Bernoulli.*

BIBLIOGRAPHY

I. ORIGINAL WORKS. Among Bernoulli's writings are *De effervescentia et fermentatione* (Basel, 1690); *De motu musculorum* (Basel, 1694), his doctoral dissertation; and *Lectiones de calculo differentialium,* MS in library of Univ. of Basel, also trans. and ed. by P. Schafheitlin as no. 211 in Ostwald's Klassiker der Exakten Wissenschaften (Leipzig, 1924). His works were collected as *Opera Johannis Bernoullii,* G. Cramer, ed., 4 vols. (Geneva, 1742). For his correspondence, see Bousquet, ed., *Commercium philosophicum et mathematicum G. Leibnitii et Joh. Bernoullii* (Geneva, 1745); his correspondence with Euler in *Bibliotheca mathematica,* 3rd ser., **4** (1903)–**6** (1905); E. J. Fedel, *Johann Bernoullis Briefwechsel mit Varignon aus den Jahren 1692–1702* (Heidelberg, 1934), dissertation; O. J. Rebel, *Der Briefwechsel zwischen Johann Bernoulli und dem Marquis de l'Hôpital* (Heidelberg, 1934), dissertation; O. Spiess, ed., *Der Briefwechsel von Johann Bernoulli,* I (Basel, 1955); and K. Wollenschlaeger, *Der mathematische Briefwechsel zwischen Johann I Bernoulli und Abraham de Moivre* (Basel, 1932), dissertation, publ. separately in *Verhandlungen der Naturforschenden Gesellschaft in Basel.* Handwritten material is in the library of the University of Basel.

II. SECONDARY LITERATURE. Writings on Bernoulli, on his work, or on background material are Jakob Bernoulli, *Analysis magni problematis isoperimetrici* (Basel, 1701); M. Cantor, *Vorlesungen über Geschichte der Mathematik,* 2nd ed., III (Leipzig, 1901), 207–233; C. Carathéodory, "Basel und der Beginn der Variationsrechnung," in *Festschrift zum 60. Geburtstag von Andreas Speiser* (Zurich, 1945), pp. 1–18; P. Dietz, *Die Ursprünge der Variationsrechnung bei Jakob Bernoulli* (Basel, 1959), dissertation, Univ. of Mainz; J. O. Fleckenstein, "Varignon und die mathematischen Wissenschaften im Zeitalter des Cartesianismus," in *Archives d'histoire des sciences* (1948); and *Johann und Jakob Bernoulli* (Basel, 1949), supp. no. 6 of *Elemente der Mathematik;* J. E. Hofmann, *Ueber Jakob Bernoullis Beiträge zur Infinitesimalmathematik,* no. 3 in the series Monographies de l'Enseignement Mathématique (Geneva, 1956); "Vom öffentlichen Bekanntwerden der Leibniz'schen Infinitesimalmathematik," in *Sitzungsberichte der Oesterreichischen Akademie der Wissenschaften,* no. 8/9 (1966), 237–241; and "Johann Bernoulli, Propagator der Infinitesimalmethoden," in *Praxis der Mathematik,* **9** (1967/1968), 209–212; Guillaume de L'Hospital, *Analyse des infiniment petits* (Paris, 1696); G. Leibniz, "Nova methodus de maximis et minimis," in *Acta eruditorum* (Oct. 1684); B. Nieuwentijt, *Considerationes secundae circa calculi differentialis principia* (Amsterdam, 1696); A. Speiser, "Die Basler Mathematiker," *Neujahrsblatt der G.G.G.,* no. 117 (Basel, 1939); O. Spiess, "Johann B. und seine Söhne," in *Atlantis* (1940), pp. 663 ff.; "Die Summe der reziproken Quadratzahlen," in *Festschrift zum 60. Geburtstag von Andreas Speiser* (Zurich, 1945), pp. 66 ff.; *Die Mathematiker Bernoulli* (Basel, 1948).

E. A. FELLMANN
J. O. FLECKENSTEIN

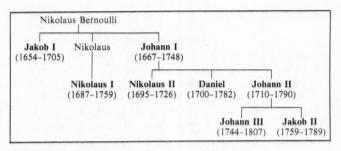

The Bernoullis. Names in boldface are discussed in articles.

BERNOULLI, JOHANN (JEAN) II (*b.* Basel, Switzerland, 28 May 1710; *d.* Basel, 17 July 1790), *mathematics.*

Johann II was perhaps the most successful of Johann I's sons, inasmuch as he succeeded his father in the chair of mathematics after having previously taught rhetoric. In 1727 he obtained the degree of doctor of jurisprudence (1). Subsequently he won the prize of the Paris Academy four times, either by himself or with his father (2–5)—undoubtedly sufficient qualification to make him Johann I's successor. But thereafter his mathematical production dwindled to occasional academic papers and a treatise (6), although he lived to be almost as old as his father. His shyness and frail constitution did not, however, prevent him from engaging in extensive scientific correspondence (about 900 items) and from furthering the publication, in four volumes, of his father's *Opera omnia.* He personified the mathematical genius of his native city in the second half of the eighteenth century. In 1756, after resigning as president of the Berlin Academy, Maupertuis found refuge with him in Basel, where he died in 1759.

BIBLIOGRAPHY

Bernoulli's writings include (1) *De compensationibus* (Basel, 1729), dissertation for the doctor of jurisprudence; (2) "Recherches physiques et géométriques sur la question: Comment se fait la propagation de la lumière," in *Recueil des pièces qui ont remporté les prix de l'Académie royale des sciences,* III (1736); (3) "Discours sur les ancres," *ibid.* (1737); (4) "Discours sur le cabestan," *ibid.,* V (1741); (5) "Nouveaux principes de mécanique et de physique tendans à expliquer la nature et les propriétés de l'Aiman," *ibid.,* V (1743); and (6) "Réponse à une lettre anonyme sur la figure de la terre," in *Journal Helvét.* (1740), pp. 219 *et seq.*

J. O. FLECKENSTEIN

BERNOULLI, JOHANN (JEAN) III (*b.* Basel, Switzerland, 4 November 1744; *d.* Berlin, Germany, 13 July 1807), *mathematics, astronomy.*

The most successful of the sons of Johann II—al-though his mathematical achievements were insignificant—Johann was a universally knowledgeable child prodigy. At fourteen he obtained the degree of master of jurisprudence, and at twenty he was invited by Frederick II to reorganize the astronomical observatory at the Berlin Academy. His frail health and his encyclopedic inclinations hampered him in his practical scientific activities, however. His treatises are of no particular interest. On the other hand, his travel accounts (1772–1776; 1777–1779; 1781) had a great cultural and historical impact. With Hindenburg he published the *Leipziger Magazin für reine & angewandte Mathematik* from 1776–1789.

Johann was entrusted with the administration of the mathematical estate of the Bernoulli family. The major part of the correspondence was sold to the Stockholm Academy; and its existence there was overlooked until his letters were rediscovered by Gylden at the Stockholm Observatory in 1877. His correspondence, comprising about 2,800 items, exceeded that of Johann I.

BIBLIOGRAPHY

Johann's writings include various essays in *Mém. Acad. Berlin* (1766–1775), as well as astronomical observations and computations, 1767–1807, in *Neue Berliner Ephemeriden* and *Bodes astronomisches Jahrbuch.* Other works are *Recueil pour les astronomes,* 3 vols. (Berlin, 1772–1776); *Liste des astronomes connus actuellement* (Berlin, 1776); *Lettres écrites pendant la cours d'un voyage par l'Allemagne 1774/75,* 3 vols. (Berlin, 1777–1779); "Essai d'une nouvelle méthode de déterminer la diminution séculaire de l'obliquité de l'écliptique," in *Mém. Acad. Berlin* (1779), pp. 211–242; and *Lettres astronomiques* (Berlin, 1781).

J. O. FLECKENSTEIN

BERNOULLI, NIKOLAUS I (*b.* Basel, Switzerland, 21 October 1687; *d.* Basel, 29 November 1759), *mathematics.*

The son of Nikolaus Bernoulli, a Basel alderman and painter, Nikolaus I studied with his two uncles, Jakob I and Johann I, and made rapid progress in mathematics. As early as 1704, studying under Jakob I, he obtained his master's degree by defending Jakob's last thesis on infinite series (1), in which quadratures and rectifications are determined by means of series expansions, arrived at by the method of undetermined coefficients or by interpolation, after Wallis, for binomial expansions. In 1709 he obtained the degree of doctor of jurisprudence (2) with a dissertation on the application of the calculus of probability to questions of law. In 1712 Nikolaus undertook a journey to Holland, England, and

France, where he met Montmort, later his friend and collaborator. He became a member of the Berlin Academy in 1713, of the Royal Society in 1714, and of the Academy of Bologna in 1724. In 1716 he succeeded Hermann as professor of mathematics in Padua, but in 1722 he returned to Basel in order to accept the chair of logic, which he exchanged in 1731 for a professorship in law. He served four times as rector of the University of Basel.

Nikolaus was a gifted but not very productive mathematician. As a result, his most important achievements are hidden throughout his correspondence, which comprises about 560 items. The most important part of his correspondence with Montmort (1710–1712) was published in the latter's *Essai d'analyse sur les jeux de hazard* (2nd ed., Paris, 1713). Here Nikolaus formulated for the first time the problem of probability theory, later known as the St. Petersburg problem.

In his correspondence with Leibniz (1712–1716), Nikolaus discussed questions of convergence and found that the binomial expansion $(1 + x)^n$ diverges for $x > 1$. In his letters to Euler (1742–1743) he criticized Euler's indiscriminate use of divergent series. In this correspondence he also solved the problem of the sum of reciprocal squares $\sum_{\nu=1}^{\infty} 1/\nu^2 = \pi^2/6$, which had confounded Leibniz and Jakob I. His personal copy of the *Opera omnia* of his uncle Jakob, which he had published, contains the proof, which does not require the help of analytical methods.

To his edition of his uncle's *Opera*, he added as an appendix thirty-two articles from Jakob I's diary ("Annotationes et meditationes"). His concern with editing his uncle's works went back to at least 1713, when he published the *Ars conjectandi.*

In the priority quarrel with Newton, Nikolaus sided with his uncle Johann in defending the interests of Leibniz. It was he who pointed out Newton's misunderstanding of the higher-order derivatives (3), which had caused Newton's errors with the inverse problem of central force in a resisting medium (5). He also considered the problem of orthogonal trajectories (6) and Riccati's differential equation (6, 8, 10–12).

BIBLIOGRAPHY

Jakob I's last thesis on infinite series is (1) *De seriebus infinitis earumque usu in quadraturis spatiorum et rectificationibus curvarum* (Basel, 1704). Nikolaus' writings include (2) *De usu artis conjectandi in jure* (Basel, 1709); (3) "Addition au Mém. de Mr. Jean Bernoulli touchant la manière de trouver les forces centrales dans les milieux résistans . . . ," in *Mémoires de l'Académie des Sciences*

(1711), pp. 53–56; (4) "Solutio generalis problematis 15 propositi a D. de Moivre in Transactiones de mensura sortis," in *Philosophical Transactions of the Royal Society,* **29** (1714), 133–144; (5) "Calculus pro invenienda linea curva, quam describit projectile in medio resistente," in *Acta eruditorum* (1719), 224–226; (6) "Modus inveniendi aequationem differentialem completam ex data aequatione differentiali incompleta . . . ," *ibid.*, supp. **7** (1719), pp. 310–859; (7) "Tentamen solutionis generalis problematis de construenda curva, quae alias ordinatim positione datas ad angulos rectos secat," *ibid.* (1719), pp. 295–304; (8) "Novum theorema pro integratione aequationum differentialium secundi gradus, quae nullam constantem differentialem supponunt," *ibid.*, supp. **9** (1720); (9) *Theses logicae de methodo analytica et synthetica* (Basel, 1722); (10) "Annotazioni sopra lo schediasma del Conte Jacopo Riccati etc. coll'annessa soluzione propria del problema inverso delle forze centrali . . . ," in *Giornale de letterati d'Italia,* **20,** 316–351; (11) "Dimostrazione analitica di un teorema, il qual serve per la soluzione del problema proposto nel T.XX. del Giorn. Lett. Ital. . . . ," *ibid.,* **29,** 163–171; and (12) "Osservazione intorno al teorema proposto dal Conte Jacopo de Fagnano," *ibid.,* pp. 150–163. See also *Athenae Rauricae* (Basel, 1778), pp. 148–151.

J. O. FLECKENSTEIN

BERNOULLI, NIKOLAUS II (*b.* Basel, Switzerland, 6 February 1695; *d.* St. Petersburg, Russia, 31 July 1726), *mathematics.*

Nikolaus was the favorite son of Johann I, whose mediation made it possible for him to enter the University of Basel at the age of thirteen. There he passed the master's examinations at sixteen, and in 1715 he became a licentiate in jurisprudence (1). Nikolaus assisted his father with his correspondence, particularly in the priority quarrel between Leibniz and Newton, during which he drafted the reply to Taylor (6) and supplied valuable contributions to the problem of trajectories (2–4). With his brother Daniel he traveled in France and Italy, where both received and accepted appointments to the St. Petersburg Academy. Within the year, however, he contracted and died of a hectic fever.

BIBLIOGRAPHY

Nikolaus' writings are (1) *Dissertatio de jure detractionis* (Basel, 1715); (2) "Solutio problematis invenire lineam, quae ad angulos rectos secet omnes hyperbolas ejusdem verticis et ejusdem centri," in *Acta eruditorum* (1716), pp. 226–230; (3) "Exercitatio geometrica de trajectoriis orthogonalibus . . . ," *ibid.* (1720), pp. 223–237; (4) "De trajectoriis curvas ordinatim positione datas ad angulos rectos vel alia lege secantibus," *ibid.* (1718), pp. 248–262; (5) "Animadversiones in Jac. Hermanni solutionem propriam duorum problematum geometricorum . . . ," *ibid.,* supp. **8** (1720), pp. 372–389; (6) "Responsio ad Taylori Angli querelas . . . ," *ibid.* (1720), pp. 279–285; (7) "Analysis aequationum quarundam differentialium," in *Comment. Acad. Petrop.,* **1** (1728), 198–207; and (8) "De motu corporum ex percussione," *ibid.,* pp. 121–126.

J. O. FLECKENSTEIN

BERNSTEIN, FELIX (*b.* Halle, Germany, 24 February 1878; *d.* Zurich, Switzerland, 3 December 1956), *mathematics.*

Bernstein's grandfather, Aron, was an author and journalist; his father, Julius, studied under Du Bois-Reymond and was an early writer on electrobiology. Felix began his studies with Cantor in Halle, then went to Göttingen to study with Hilbert and Klein. In 1901 he returned to Halle for his *Abitur,* then taught mathematics and studied physiology there with his father until 1911. Bernstein received his doctorate at Göttingen in 1907 and returned there in 1911 as associate professor of mathematical statistics. During World War I, having received a medical exemption from military service, he headed the statistical branch of the Office of Rationing in Berlin and in 1921 became the commissioner of finance. Also in 1921 he became full professor and founded the Institute of Mathematical Statistics, of which he remained director until 1934; in that year, having been deprived of his chair, he emigrated to the United States. Bernstein, who became a U.S. citizen in 1940, taught at Columbia, New York, and Syracuse universities. In 1948 he returned to Göttingen as professor emeritus. His interests in the sciences and arts, especially sculpture and architecture, were intense and wide. His health seems never to have been robust.

It was in 1897, while a student in Cantor's seminar, that Bernstein gave the first proof of the equivalence theorem of sets: If each of two sets, A and B, is equivalent to a subset of the other, then A is equivalent to B. This theorem establishes the notion of cardinality and is thus the central theorem in set theory. It bears some similarity to the Eudoxean definition of equal irrationals.

Bernstein's subsequent work in pure and applied mathematics shows great versatility, and includes some of the earliest applications of set theory outside pure mathematics, contributions to isoperimetric problems, convex functions, the Laplace transform, and number theory, as well as set theory itself.

Toward the 1920's Bernstein became increasingly interested in the mathematical treatment of questions in genetics; he was to contribute decisively to the development of population genetics in the analysis of modes of inheritance. The discovery of human blood groups had made possible an entirely new approach to human genetics. In 1924 Bernstein was able to show that the A, B, and O blood groups are inherited on the basis of a set of triple alleles, and not on the basis of two pairs of genes, as had been thought. He compared a population genetic analysis of the frequencies of the four blood groups—numerous records of racially variant blood-group frequencies had been available since the discovery of this phenomenon by L. and H. Hirschfeld—with the expectations for the blood-group frequencies according to the expanded Hardy-Weinberg formula $p^2:2pq:q^2$, and found significant and consistent differences. When he applied the same technique to an expectation based on a triple-allelic system of a single locus, the agreement with observation was excellent.

Bernstein also applied the techniques of population genetics to such problems as linkage, to the measures of the degree of inbreeding for individuals and populations, to determination of the presence of recessive inheritance, to a method for deriving genetic ratios based on an a priori expectation, and to use of the development of presbyopia as an indicator of age. He also interpreted the direction of hair whorl and variations in singing voice, as found in different populations, in terms of allelic differences of single pairs of genes, but this interpretation has not withstood the test of time.

BIBLIOGRAPHY

Bernstein's writings are *Untersuchungen aus der Mengenlehre,* dissertation (Halle, 1901); "Ueber die Reihe der transfiniten Ordnungszahlen," in *Mathematische Annalen,* **60,** no. 2 (1905), 187–193; "Die Theorie der reellen Zahlen," in *Jahresbericht der Deutschen Mathematikervereinigung,* **14,** no. 8/9 (1905); "Zur Theorie der trigonometrischen Reihe," in *Bericht. Königliche Sächsische Gesellschaft der Wissenschaften zu Leipzig,* Math.-phys. Klasse, **60** (meeting of 7 Dec. 1908); "Ueber eine Anwendung der Mengenlehre auf ein aus der Theorie der säkularen Störungen herrührendes Problem," in *Mathematische Annalen,* **71** (1909), 417–439 (see also *ibid.,* **72** [1912], 295–296, written with P. Bohl and E. Borel); "Ueber den letzten Fermatschen Lehrsatz," in *Nachrichten von der Gesellschaft der Wissenschaften zu Göttingen,* Math.-phys. Klasse (1910); "Zur Theorie der konvexen Funktionen," in *Mathematische Annalen,* **76,** no. 4 (1915); "Die Mengenlehre Georg Cantors und der Finitismus," in *Jahresbericht der Deutschen Mathematikervereinigung,* **28,** no. 1/6 (1919), 63–78; "Die Theorie der gleichsinnigen Faktoren in der Mendelschen Erblichkeitslehre vom Standpunkt der mathematischen Statistik," in *Zeitschrift für induktive Abstammungs- und Vererbungslehre* (1922); "Probleme aus der Theorie der Wärmeleitung. I. Mitteilung. Eine neue Methode zur Integration partieller

Differentialgleichungen. Der lineare Wärmeleiter mit verschwindender Anfangstemperatur," in *Mathematische Zeitschrift*, **22**, no. 3/4 (1925), written with Gustav Doetsch; "Zusammenfassende Betrachtungen über die erblichen Blutstrukturen des Menschen," in *Zeitschrift für induktive Abstammungs- und Vererbungslehre* (1925); "Ueber die numerische Ermittlung verborgener Periodizitäten," in *Zeitschrift für angewandte Mathematik und Mechanik*, **7** (1927), 441–444; "Fortgesetzte Untersuchungen aus der Theorie der Blutgruppen," in *Zeitschrift für induktive Abstammungs- und Vererbungslehre* (1928); "Ueber Mendelistische Anthropologie," in *Verhandlungen des V. internationalen Kongresses für Vererbungswissenschaft* (Berlin, 1927), repr. in *Zeitschrift für induktive Abstammungs- und Vererbungslehre* (1928); "Ueber die Anwendung der Steinerschen Fläche in der Erblichkeitslehre, insbesondere in der Theorie der Blutgruppen," in *Zeitschrift für angewandte Mathematik und Mechanik*, **9** (1929); "Ueber die Erblichkeit der Blutgruppen," in *Zeitschrift für induktive Abstammungs- und Vererbungslehre* (1930); "Berichtigung zur Arbeit: Zur Grundlegung der Chromosomentheorie der Vererbung beim Menschen mit bes. Berücksichtigung der Blutgruppen," *ibid.* (1931, 1932); "Principles of Probability in Natural Science," in *Journal of Mathematics and Physics*, **14** (Mar. 1935); "The Continuum Problem," in *Proceedings of the National Academy of Sciences*, **24**, no. 2 (Feb. 1938), 101–104; and "Law of Physiologic Aging as Derived from Long Range Data on Refraction of the Human Eye," in *Archives of Ophthalmology*, **34** (Nov.–Dec. 1945), written with Marianne Bernstein.

HENRY NATHAN

BERNSTEIN, S. N. See **Supplement.**

BERNTHSEN, HEINRICH AUGUST (*b.* Krefeld, Prussia, 29 August 1855; *d.* Heidelberg, Germany, 26 November 1931), *chemistry.*

Bernthsen was the son of Heinrich Friedrich Bernthsen, a construction contractor, and Anna Sybilla Terheggen. He first studied mathematics and natural sciences but later turned to chemistry, which he studied in Bonn and then in Heidelberg under Bunsen and Kopp. Uninterested in the work on gases being pursued there, Bernthsen thought of leaving Heidelberg, but remained to study with Kekulé and Victor Meyer. In 1877 he became lecturer-assistant to Kekulé, and two years later he gave his inaugural academic lecture. In 1883 he was appointed extraordinary professor. Bernthsen left the University of Heidelberg in 1887 to join the Badische Anilin- und Sodafabrik as head of the main laboratory; he later headed the patent division. In 1884 he married the daughter of a judge, Maria Magdelene Haubenschmied. Bernthsen was a member of the Deutsche Chemische Gesellschaft, an editor of the *Jahresbericht*

über die Fortschritt der Chemie, and received honorary degrees from the Technische Hochschule in Berlin and the University of Heidelberg.

Bernthsen's chemical work was mainly industrial and dealt with dyes of the acridine and azine groups. He explained the composition of such substances as methylene blue and safranine. He also gave the correct composition of sodium hyposulfite. Although he was generally more interested in analysis than in synthesis, he developed technically feasible processes for producing indigo, rhodamine, and tolyl red. As a patent director, he secured patents for his indigo process, contact sulfuric acid, and lac dye. In the course of obtaining patents for his firm, Bernthsen became active in the movement for a patent law to protect industrial chemical processes and to strengthen the chemical industry.

BIBLIOGRAPHY

I. ORIGINAL WORKS. Among Bernthsen's writings are "Zur Kenntniss der Derivate der Alpha-toluylsäure," in *Berichte der Deutsche chemische Gesellschaft*, **8** (1875), 691–693; "Zur Kenntniss der Amidine und der Thiamide ein basischer organischer hydrosäuren," in *Annalen der Chemie*, **184** (1877), 290–320; **192** (1878), 1–60, 197; **197** (1879), 341–351; "Ueber die Zusammensetzung des unterschwefligsäuren Natrons," in *Berichte der Deutsche chemische Gesellschaft*, **14** (1881), 438–440; "Ueber das Methylenblau," *ibid.*, **16** (1883), 1025–1028, 2896–2904; *Kurzes Lehrbuch der organischen Chemie* (Brunswick, 1887); "Zur Kenntniss der Konstitution der blawen Schwefelfarbstoffe," in *Chemiker-Zeitung*, **32** (1908), 956–957; and *Fünfzig Jahre Tätigkeit in chemischer Wissenschaft und Industrie* (Heidelberg, 1925).

II. SECONDARY LITERATURE. Works on Bernthsen are M. Bodenstein, "H. A. Bernthsen," in *Berichte der Deutsche chemische Gesellschaft*, **65** (1932), 21a; K. Elbs, "August Bernthsen zum 70. Geburtstag," in *Zeitschrift für angewandte Chemie*, **38** (1925), 737–739; K. Holdermann, "August Bernthsen," in *Zeitschrift für Elektrochemie*, **38** (1932), 49, and "August Bernthsen zum Gedächtnis," in *Zeitschrift für angewandte Chemie*, **45** (1932), 141–143; and J. R. Partington, *A History of Chemistry*, IV (1964), 839.

RUTH ANNE GIENAPP

BERT, PAUL (*b.* Auxerre, France, 19 October 1833; *d.* Hanoi, Indochina [now People's Republic of Vietnam], 11 November 1886), *physiology, comparative anatomy, natural history, education.*

Bert was the son of Joseph Bert, lawyer and *conseiller de préfecture* of the Department of Yonne, and of Jeanne Henriette Massy, who was of Scottish extraction on her father's side. He attended the elementary school and the Collège Amyot at Auxerre from 1843 to 1852. In 1853 he went to Paris, where he studied jurisprudence and obtained the licentiate in law. He studied medicine and science from 1857 to 1866, receiving the licentiate in natural sciences in 1860 and the M.D., with a thesis on animal transplantation, in 1863. From 1863 to 1866 Bert was the student and *préparateur* of Claude Bernard at the Collège de France. In 1866 he was awarded the doctorate in natural sciences with the thesis *De la vitalité propre des tissus animaux.* In 1865 he married Josephina Clayton, a Scotswoman.

Bert was professor of zoology and physiology at the Faculté des Sciences of the University of Bordeaux in 1866–1867. In 1868 he replaced Flourens (as *suppléant*) in the chair of comparative physiology at the Muséum d'Histoire Naturelle, and the following year he succeeded Claude Bernard in the chair of physiology at the Sorbonne.

Bert was a member of the Société des Sciences Historiques et Naturelles de l'Yonne, the Société Philomathique de Paris, the Société de Biologie de Paris, and the Académie des Sciences de Paris.

The Franco-Prussian War caused Bert to enter politics. After the capitulation of the French Imperial Army at Sedan in September 1870 and the resignation of Napoleon III, Bert joined the forces led by the Government of National Defense, whose driving force was Léon Gambetta, who was also his personal friend. The following January he became Préfet du Nord and organized a hopeless resistance. After the war, Bert joined the Liberal Republican party and was elected in 1872 to the Chamber of Deputies. His political aims were regeneration and *revanche,* the recovery of the lost eastern provinces, Alsace and Lorraine.

The means of political, economic, industrial, intellectual, and moral regeneration was, for him, a radical reform of education at all levels, and particularly of the elementary schools. As a deputy, as chairman of important parliamentary committees, and as minister of public instruction (from 14 November 1881 to 26 January 1882) he fought for enactment of the laws proposed by Jules Ferry, a well-known liberal politician and influential minister of public instruction. In a masterful report on elementary education presented to the Chamber of Deputies, Bert explained Ferry's principles. He demanded free, compulsory elementary schooling, with a secular program and lay personnel. The schoolteacher must not belong to the clergy. He is the soldier of the secular republic.

The program of the elementary school must include the elements of science, for the sciences sharpen the intellect: the natural sciences develop the power of observation, and the physical sciences sow the seeds of causal thinking. History and paleontology will reveal the gradual development of man from a cave dweller to a culture-bearing, free, republican citizen; thus evolution, and not revolution, will be man's guiding principle. The "Ferry laws" were enacted between 1880 and 1886.

Bert supported secondary education for girls. For many years he lectured at the Sorbonne on biology and zoology to girls aged sixteen to eighteen. Bert also published elementary and secondary textbooks on natural history, zoology, and the physical sciences. These books, which show his remarkable didactic ability, were reprinted many times and translated into English, Italian, and Spanish. It was Bert's firm belief that the principles of science should pervade the whole of society in order to make it better. The *Revues scientifiques,* a periodical that he edited from 1879 to 1885, bears witness to Bert's endeavor to popularize science.

In 1885 the French people were alternately enraged and perplexed by the revolts in Indochina against the new French colonial regime. In the stormy debates in the National Assembly, Bert sternly defended the French colonial expansion in Indochina. Appointed as the first civil governor of Annam and Tonkin in 1886, Bert sought a true partnership between France and Indochina. He eliminated the military interference in administration and "pacified" the areas he governed. In Annam he strengthened the power of the emperor, and in Tonkin he relied on popular forces, which he strengthened by political and social reforms. In addition, he established the Tonkin Academy and founded numerous schools.

In 1855, when still a law student, Bert became a member of the Société des Sciences Historiques et Naturelles de l'Yonne. This marked the beginning of his research. Bert's scientific thought and method were later shaped by three eminent scientists who taught him: Pierre Gratiolet, Henri Milne-Edwards, and Claude Bernard. He studied with Gratiolet in the laboratory of comparative anatomy at the Muséum d'Histoire Naturelle in Paris. There he learned that within the great variety of structures "the problem of life was but one." Bert was also deeply influenced by Milne-Edwards' *Introduction to General Zoology* (1851). This book revealed to him how nature worked through "the law of economy," the "division of labor," and the perfection of functions by means of specialization. It was to Claude Bernard, however, that Bert owed his greatest debt. As a student and collaborator of Bernard, he became acquainted with the methods of experimental physiology, the critical evaluation of experimental findings, and the attempt to describe the basic laws of physiology. Bert was deeply impressed by Bernard's concept of an internal environment.

Bert's scientific activity can be divided into three periods: (1) In the 1860's—as a student of medicine and science, as *préparateur* for Bernard, and as professor of zoology and comparative physiology at Bordeaux and Paris—he dealt with questions of general physiology, plant physiology, and comparative anatomy and physiology. During that period he published important monographs on animal transplantation and the vitality of tissues, and a comprehensive study on the comparative physiology of respiration. (2) After the Franco-Prussian War, he published his magnum opus, *La pression barométrique* (1878). (3) A last period of scientific activity, which was a direct offshoot of his barometric work, dealt with the experimental and clinical study of anesthesia and with the properties of blood at high altitude.

Through all his scientific work we can perceive the constant endeavor to study the phenomena of life in the context of the exterior and interior environment.

Bert's first important work dealt with animal transplantation. This study was not intended to be a contribution to experimental surgery, for transplantation was conceived of as a physiological problem: How can transplanted organs and tissues live in a new environment? Bert succeeded in creating "double monsters," uniting two rats by suturing their skins together. He also implanted the tip of the tail of a young albino rat under the skin of its back; the proximal end of the tail was then cut, so that it formed the tip of the grafted tail. The transplanted tail grew, formed new bone, and reestablished circulation and sensibility—but the direction of the sensory impulse was reversed.

Bert's investigation of the specific vitality of animal tissues was a pure environmental study. He used the transplantation technique as a means of examining the vital resistance of organs and tissues. Isolated tails of rats were exposed to different temperatures and humidities, and to various gases and chemical agents. After these exposures the tails were transplanted under the skins of rats. The transplantation reestablished a physiological internal milieu and made it possible to test the survival of the tail tissues after they had been subjected to various changes of environment. Bert emphasized that the cells and tissues lived their own lives, growing and differentiating independently of any superior vital force as long as they were in a suitable milieu.

During his professorship at Bordeaux, Bert dealt with problems of marine biology and plant physiology. He studied the mechanism of death in marine fishes exposed to fresh water, and he observed the occurrence of *Amphioxus lanceolatus* on the southwestern coast of France. He also published his classic study on the movements of the "sensitive plant" (*Mimosa pudica*). Using ether, he succeeded in differentiating spontaneous movements from induced ones. The spontaneous movements depended on differences of osmotic pressure, which was regulated by light and darkness.

In 1870 Bert published an important work dealing with problems of the comparative physiology of respiration. This monograph was based on his lectures delivered at the Muséum d'Histoire Naturelle, Paris, in the spring semester of 1868. Bert analyzed the anatomical structures and the physiological functions of the respiratory organs of vertebrates and invertebrates. He also dealt with the problem of tissue respiration and showed that the oxygen content of the blood depended on the exterior air pressure. The respiratory movements of aquatic and air-breathing animals were investigated with novel methods and techniques. He studied the nervous regulation of the respiratory rhythm and investigated the respiration of diving animals. He analyzed the death mechanism of asphyxia and succeeded in clearly differentiating true asphyxia caused by lack of oxygen from carbon dioxide poisoning. This work, rich in facts and new views, also provided a critical evaluation of a vast number of problems.

Bert's definitive work, *La pression barométrique,* published in 1878, represented an environmental study on the largest scale. The great questions were How does the changing exterior milieu—the atmospheric pressure—act on an organism? What are the effects of low pressure at high altitudes? How does the high pressure to which the caisson worker is exposed affect the body? How does the blood, the interior milieu, behave under high and low pressures? What is the mechanism of mountain sickness? Bert's interest in these problems arose early in his scientific work. In 1864, while a student of Bernard, he had discussed the question of whether the amount of gases dissolved in the blood depended on atmospheric pressure. The French physician Denis Jourdanet, who had practiced in Mexico and was interested in the biological and medical aspects of high-altitude climates, provided Bert with the necessary means to build the costly apparatus needed for the experimental study of the physiological effects of air pressure. Jourdanet had constructed pressure chambers for therapeutic use and had formulated the hypothesis that the blood contained less oxygen under the low atmospheric pressure of high altitudes, a condition he called barometric anoxemia.

In his first series of experiments Bert studied the following problem: What extremes of air pressure can a living being endure? He first examined the effects of low pressure and found that animals died after the partial pressure of oxygen sank below a critical level that was constant for each species. Bert therefore announced the following principle: Oxygen tension is everything; barometric pressure in itself does nothing or almost nothing.

Bert then studied the physiological effects of pure oxygen or air inhaled under high pressure: the dogs used died with tonoclonic cramps. Thus he discovered the phenomenon of acute oxygen poisoning and was able to state that if the organism receives too little oxygen, it suffocates; and if it is exposed to oxygen at high pressure, it is poisoned. In a second series of experiments he studied the behavior of blood gases under various pressures. These investigations relied on the fundamental studies of blood gases made by Carl Ludwig and his students. Bert found: "The combination of oxygen with hemoglobin is likely to be partially destroyed, to be dissociated at low pressures. . . . Everything seems to indicate that there exists in the neighborhood of normal pressure a point of chemical saturation of the oxyhemoglobin, and that beyond this point there is added to the blood only oxygen dissolved in the serum according to Dalton's law."

Bert also experimented on himself in the pressure chamber in order to study the effects of low atmospheric pressure on the human body. When the pressure was decreased to 400 millimeters of mercury, he noted increased pulse rate, headache, dizziness, darkening of the vision, mental lassitude, and nausea. These complaints disappeared as soon as he inhaled oxygen. Bert also trained balloonists in his pressure chamber and provided them with oxygen bags for their flights to high altitudes. He recognized that when the partial pressure of oxygen is reduced, the altitude sickness of the aviator, the mountain sickness of the alpinist, and the complaints encountered in low-pressure experiments appear. Bert also clarified experimentally the mechanism of decompression sickness (caisson disease). Sudden decompression from high atmospheric pressures (five–ten atmospheres) produced gas bubbles in the blood and tissues. These gas bubbles consisted primarily of nitrogen that had previously been dissolved under high pressure and was liberated by the decompression. Bert emphasized that the duration of compression was of great importance. As prophylaxis for caisson disease he devised a slow, gradual decompression; treatment was recompression and low decompression.

The results of Bert's monumental work were manifold: He fully realized the physiological importance of the partial pressures of the respiratory gases. He described the relationship between the external

partial pressure and the behavior of the blood gases. He recognized that mountain sickness and altitude sickness are a consequence of the low partial pressure of oxygen. He introduced oxygen apparatus to avert the dangerous consequences of ascent to high altitudes. He was the first to study in a pressure chamber the conditions of high-altitude ascents. He discovered and described oxygen poisoning, and explained the cause and mechanism of caisson disease.

Bert applied his knowledge of the physiological effects of atmospheric pressure to the field of anesthesia. He reasoned that the pressure at which nitrous oxide induces anesthesia is about one atmosphere. Therefore pure nitrous oxide has to be used, but it induces asphyxia. To avoid this, Bert prepared a mixture of one-sixth oxygen and five-sixths nitrous oxide. He administered this mixture to dogs under the slightly increased pressure of $1\frac{1}{5}$ atmospheres. Thus the blood was supplied with enough oxygen to sustain life and enough nitrous oxide to produce anesthesia. Bert went on to the application of this method to clinical anesthesia, constructing a horse-drawn anesthetic chamber in which the surgeon, his assistants, and the patient could be placed under slightly increased pressure.

In *La pression barométrique* Bert discussed the problem of acclimatization to high altitudes. Is the blood of individuals at high altitudes capable of absorbing more oxygen than the blood of individuals living at sea level? Three possibilities might be conceived: a qualitative change in the hemoglobin, an increase in the hemoglobin content of the red corpuscles, or an increase in the number of erythrocytes. Starting from Bert's hypothesis that people living at high altitudes might possess more red corpuscles, François Viault examined human and animal blood in the Peruvian Andes from 1890 to 1892. He observed on himself and on his companions that the number of erythrocytes increased from 5,000,000 to 7,000,000 within three to five weeks. This important fact, which showed a substantial change of what is normally a biological constant, initiated the systematic high-altitude research in the Alps (conducted by Hugo Kronecker, A. Mosso, and others).

As a true disciple of Bernard, Bert hailed the emergence of physiology as an exact scientific discipline. He refused to adhere to any dogmatic materialism. He emphasized that the cerebral function was indispensable for the production of psychic phenomena. But organized matter could not be the only cause, the sufficient condition, for intellectual manifestations, for this would mean transcending the realm of scientific physiology. Outside of physiology, he believed, remained the immense field of subjective phenomena that cannot be investigated with the methods of physiology.

BIBLIOGRAPHY

I. ORIGINAL WORKS. Bert's scientific works include "De la greffe animale," M.D. thesis (Paris, 1863); *Recherches expérimentales pour servir à l'histoire de la vitalité propre des tissus animaux*, Ph.D. thesis (1866), pub. in *Annales des sciences naturelles* (Zoologie), **5** (Paris, 1866), 123–218; "Recherches sur les mouvements de la sensitive (*Mimosa pudica*, Linn.)," in *Mémoires de la Société des Sciences Physiques et Naturelles de Bordeaux*, **4** (1866), 11–46, also published separately (Paris, 1867); *Leçons sur la physiologie comparée de la respiration* . . . (Paris, 1870); *Recherches expérimentales sur l'influence que les modifications dans la pression barométrique exercent sur les phénomènes de la vie* (Paris, 1873); "Sur la possibilité d'obtenir, à l'aide du protoxyde d'azote, une insensibilité de longue durée, et sur l'innocuité de cet anesthésique," in *Comptes rendus hebdomadaires de l'Académie des Sciences* (Paris), **87** (1878), 728–730; *La pression barométrique, recherches de physiologie expérimentale* (Paris, 1878), his masterpiece, trans. into English by M. A. Hitchcock and F. A. Hitchcock as *Barometric Pressure. Researches in Experimental Physiology* (Columbus, Ohio, 1943); "Anesthésie par le protoxyde d'azote mélangé d'oxygène et employé sous pression," in *Comptes rendus hebdomadaires de l'Académie des Sciences* (Paris), **89** (1879), 132–135; *Leçons de zoologie* . . . (Paris, 1881); *Leçons, discours et conférences* (Paris, 1881), which includes political and educational papers as well as scientific ones; *La première année d'enseignement scientifique, sciences naturelles et physiques: animaux, végétaux, pierres et terrains, physique, chimie, physiologie végétale* (Paris, 1882), trans. by Josephina Clayton (his wife) as *First Year of Scientific Knowledge* (Paris, 1885).

II. SECONDARY LITERATURE. Works on Bert are E. H. Ackerknecht, "Paul Bert's Triumph," in *Bulletin of the History of Medicine,* supp. **3** (1944), 16–31, which treats Bert's place in French intellectual history and includes an important bibliography; E. Bérillon, *L'oeuvre scientifique de Paul Bert* (Paris, 1887); C. A. Culotta, "A History of Respiratory Theory: Lavoisier to Paul Bert, 1777–1880," thesis (Univ. of Wisconsin, 1968), which includes a detailed discussion of Bert's work on blood gases; L. Dubreuil, *Paul Bert* (Paris, 1935), comprehensive biography with special emphasis on Bert's political importance; J. Ducloz, "L'enfance et la jeunesse de Paul Bert," in *Bulletin de la Société des Sciences Historiques et Naturelles de l'Yonne,* **78** (1924), 5–102; and N. Mani, "Paul Bert als Politiker, Pädagog und Begründer der Höhenphysiologie," in *Gesnerus,* **23** (1966), 109–116.

NIKOLAUS MANI

BERTHELOT, PIERRE EUGÈNE MARCELLIN[1] (*b*. Paris, France, 25 October 1827; *d*. Paris, 18 March 1907), *chemistry*.

His father, Jacques Martin Berthelot, had married Ernestine Sophie Claudine Biard in 1824. Marcellin was the second of three children; the first died in infancy. The father, who was from a family of ironsmiths in the region of Orléans, had come to Paris in 1822 to study medicine. After qualifying he spent most of his life tending the sick in the poorer districts of Paris. Only in his heroic work during the cholera epidemic of 1832, about which he wrote a book, did he rise above obscurity. His income was just sufficient to support his family, and his wife, who came from the bourgeoisie, brought only a small dowry.

At the age of eleven Marcellin Berthelot entered the Collège Henri IV in Paris. He showed himself reserved in the extreme but brilliant at his lessons, distinguishing himself particularly in Latin verse. In 1846 he won first prize for philosophy among pupils from *lycées* throughout France. At fourteen Berthelot became a boarder; four years later he met Ernest Renan, whose room was adjacent to his in the *pension.* Renan was twenty-two and was employed as an assistant master. In 1847 Berthelot became *bachelier ès lettres* and then attended courses in the Paris Faculty of Medicine and the Faculty of Science, graduating from the latter in July 1849. He undertook a rigorous program of reading, including languages and the main branches of science. Berthelot asserted his independence by deliberately avoiding the two great educational institutions, the École Polytechnique and the École Normale, the training ground of so many French men of science. He obtained entry to the private laboratory of the chemist Pelouze, where he learned some practical chemistry. In February 1851 there was a vacancy for the post of demonstrator to Balard at the Collège de France. Berthelot accepted the post although it carried only a nominal salary; in his spare time he prepared for his doctorate. On 24 June 1854 he defended his thesis, "Mémoire sur les combinaisons de la glycérine avec les acides et sur la synthèse des principes immédiats des graisses des animaux." Berthelot carried out further studies at the École de Pharmacie in Paris, graduating as a pharmacist on 29 November 1858. He also visited Italy and Germany during this time. Thus, until he was over thirty, Berthelot lived the life of a student, relying on his father for financial support.

Berthelot became a leading advocate in France of science as an ideal with direct moral implications. Although his parents were Roman Catholic and brought him up in the same faith, he reacted to his philosophy course at school by soon questioning the validity of religion and becoming a skeptic. In this he was influenced by Renan but also by his republican feelings, since the Roman Catholic Church in mid-nineteenth-century France was unsympathetic to radical thought. In his later writings Berthelot attacked clerical influence, particularly in education.

On 30 May 1861 Berthelot married Sophie Caroline Niaudet, a girl from a Protestant family and ten years younger than he. His wife was a descendant of the famous clockmaker Breguet. The couple had six children. They were devoted to each other for forty-five years, and within an hour of the death of Sophie Berthelot, Marcellin, who had tended her night and day, also died. A special law was passed to permit Berthelot and his wife to be buried together in the Panthéon.

Berthelot was appointed to a chair of organic chemistry created at the École de Pharmacie on 2 December 1859. The success of his book *La chimie organique fondée sur la synthèse* resulted in his giving a course of lectures at the Collège de France (1863–1864), and on 8 August 1865 this course was attached to a chair of organic chemistry entrusted to Berthelot. From that time until his death, if Berthelot was in Paris he went daily to his laboratory at the Collège de France. Although he gave more attention to research than to teaching, he had a number of distinguished students, including Jungfleisch, Sabatier, and A. Werner. Berthelot was elected to the Académie de Médecine in 1863, and the Académie des Sciences (after three unsuccessful attempts) in 1873. He was made permanent secretary of the latter in 1889. He became a member of the Académie Française in 1901. First nominated as *chevalier* of the Legion of Honor in 1861, he received the highest grade, *Grand-Croix,* in 1900. He was also a member of a large number of foreign academies.

When Paris came under siege in the Franco-Prussian War (1870–1871), Berthelot was made president of the Comité Scientifique pour la Défense de Paris. His activities during the siege of Paris called much attention to himself, and in the election of 1871 he was given a large vote, although he had not put himself forward as a candidate. He first took his seat in the Senate in 1871. In 1874 he was appointed to a War Ministry commission on explosives, and in 1878, when a new commission on explosives was formed, Berthelot was named president. In July 1881 the Senate elected him to a permanent senatorship. Berthelot sat with the parties on the Left and spoke frequently on educational matters. In 1886 he presided over a commission on the laicization of primary education. Berthelot was minister of education from 11 December 1886 to 30 May 1887 in the cabinet of René Goblet. In 1895 he was appointed foreign minister in the cabinet of Léon Bourgeois but resigned after five months because of disagreements over policy on Egypt and the Sudan.

In 1869, on the occasion of the opening of the Suez Canal, Berthelot visited Egypt, the country traditionally associated with the birth of chemistry; but it was not until 1884 that he committed to paper a few ideas on alchemy. Attracted both by the mysticism of the alchemists and by the connection of other parts of their art with the rational science he professed, he began to use his knowledge of Greek to interpret unpublished alchemical manuscripts. Like Hermann Kopp, Berthelot took the view that alchemy had developed as a misunderstanding of the earlier empirical knowledge of Egyptian metalworkers. He and Kopp were the two nineteenth-century figures who were able not only to make outstanding contributions to chemistry but also to undertake an extensive study of its history. Berthelot studied the transmission of ancient alchemy to the Middle Ages. He distinguished a practical tradition, exemplified by the *Liber ignium* of Marcus Graecus, from a theoretical approach transmitted through Syriac and Arabic sources. He argued that the Latin author Geber was distinct from Jābir ibn Ḥayyān. In much of his alchemical studies Berthelot was dependent on his collaborators, who translated the original Syriac and Arabic manuscripts. His interpretation was, therefore, not faultless.

On a more practical plane, Berthelot's analysis of metallic objects from ancient Egypt and Mesopotamia laid the foundations of chemical archaeology. In 1889, to celebrate the centenary of the French Revolution, Berthelot, as secretary of the Académie des Sciences, was called upon to commemorate men of science. He prepared material for a lecture on Lavoisier, and on the basis of this and Grimaux's study of 1888 he produced a book, *La révolution chimique, Lavoisier.* One detects special sympathy by the patriotic nineteenth-century French chemist for the eighteenth-century liberal who had also used his scientific knowledge to help his country. Berthelot's publication of extracts from the laboratory notebooks of Lavoisier, which were in the possession of the Academy, performed a valuable service to the history of science. Whatever criticisms may be leveled at Berthelot's earlier publications on the history of chemistry, this study was an astonishing achievement for a man who was simultaneously carrying out important research on thermochemistry and agricultural chemistry.

In the last years of his life Berthelot published books that suggest his concept of science as an all-embracing philosophy: *Science et philosophie* (1886), *Science et morale* (1897), *Science et education* (1901), *Science et libre pensée* (1905). He regarded it as unreasonable to assign limits to the possible progress of science. He foresaw a Utopia through science that could be realized by the year 2000. In this new world he considered chemistry to have a central place not only because of its almost unlimited powers of synthesis but also through the exploitation of agriculture and natural resources. Berthelot continually fought against clerical influence in education. He wanted a greater place for science in the school curriculum, but not at the expense of classical studies. The moral value of science for Berthelot lay not only in its respect for truth but also in its justification for work. Berthelot, like Claude Bernard, favored a positivistic philosophy. It was in this spirit of accepting only the observable that he regarded atomic and molecular theories with great suspicion.

Berthelot's publications were particularly numerous. Jungfleisch lists 1,600 titles of papers on inorganic, organic, physical, analytical, technical, agricultural, and physiological chemistry, as well as on the history of chemistry. His work in organic chemistry may, however, be singled out as being of special importance; and if his contributions to physical chemistry hold second place, even they may be considered as originating in the context of his interest in the reactions and formation of organic compounds. In order to systematize Berthelot's vast work, covering a period of sixty years, Graebe divided his productive life into four periods:

(1) The first organic period, 1850–1860. This covers his work on alcohols and includes his early work on synthesis. In the fall of 1860 he published his definitive work on organic synthesis.

(2) The second organic period, 1861–1869. This period is characterized by research and synthesis of acetylene, benzene, and aromatic compounds occurring in coal tar. It was in the early 1860's that Berthelot collaborated with Péan de Saint-Gilles on the formation and decomposition of esters, research that constituted a bridge between his interest in organic and physical chemistry. At the end of this period Berthelot was using hydrogen iodide to reduce organic compounds.

(3) The period 1869–1885, which covers Berthelot's most important contributions to thermochemistry.

(4) The period 1885–1907, in which Berthelot's most original work was his contribution to agricultural chemistry and to the history of chemistry.

Berthelot's first publication, read to the Académie des Sciences on 27 May 1850, was concerned with a simple method of liquefying a gas by applying pressure. The choice of this physical topic may have been inspired by his admiration for Regnault, but in the next year his deep interest in organic chemistry

revealed itself. He studied the action of red heat on alcohol and acetic acid. It was already known that at high temperatures alcohol could be transformed into a crystalline solid, naphthalene. Berthelot was able to show that in addition benzene and phenol were formed. Acetic acid at red heat produced naphthalene and benzene. He concluded very significantly that the synthesis (*synthèse*) of naphthalene, benzene, and possibly phenol, could now be considered as an established fact, since they could all be obtained from acetic acid, which in turn could be prepared via the respective stages: carbon disulfide, carbon tetrachloride, trichloracetic acid. This was one of the first examples of the use of the word *synthesis* to denote the production of organic compounds from their elements.[2]

Two compounds to which Berthelot gave considerable attention were oil of turpentine and camphor. It was known that on reaction with hydrochloric acid, turpentine formed a hydrochloride, $C_{10}H_{16} \cdot HCl$. In 1852 Berthelot showed that the reaction could be taken further to produce a product identical with oil of lemon. It was Berthelot who first discovered isomeric changes in oil of turpentine, from which he obtained the solid hydrocarbon camphene. He distinguished what we would now call *d*-pinene and *l*-pinene and *d*-, *l*-, and *dl*-camphene. He found that camphene may be oxidized by chromic acid (or by air in the presence of platinum black) into a camphor-like substance; in 1870 he proved that the product was true camphor.

The classical work on fats had been carried out by Chevreul. In 1853 and 1854, Berthelot established his reputation in this field by his research on the derivatives of glycerin. By heating glycerin with hydrochloric acid and a selection of fatty acids, he obtained compounds of glycerin with acetic, valeric, benzoic, and sebacic acids. He went on to obtain compounds of glycerin with one, two, or three molecules of acid, the other product being contained in natural fats, e.g., tristearin. Thus, with stearic acid and glycerin he obtained successively monostearin, distearin, and tristearin. He also investigated the products of glycerin with other acids, including acetic acid, the reactions for which he formulated as follows (C = 6, O = 8):

$$\text{monoacetin} = \underset{\text{acetic acid}}{C^4H^4O^4} + \underset{\text{glycerin}}{C^6H^8O^6} - \underset{\text{water}}{2HO}$$

$$\text{diacetin} = \underset{\text{acetic acid}}{2C^4H^4O^4} + \underset{\text{glycerin}}{C^6H^8O^6} - \underset{\text{water}}{4HO}$$

$$\text{triacetin} = \underset{\text{acetic acid}}{3C^4H^4O^4} + \underset{\text{glycerin}}{C^6H^8O^6} - \underset{\text{water}}{6HO}$$

Whichever of the above esters was hydrolyzed, the product was glycerin. From these reactions Berthelot concluded that glycerin in organic chemistry corresponded to phosphoric acid in inorganic chemistry as alcohol corresponded to nitric acid. In other words, this was the beginning of the idea that, corresponding to polybasic acids in inorganic chemistry, there were polyatomic alcohols in organic chemistry. Berthelot's younger contemporary and rival, Adolphe Wurtz, is sometimes given credit for this work, although Wurtz's contribution in 1855 was to make the correct analogy between different salts of the same (orthophosphoric) acid rather than the three different acids of phosphorus to which Berthelot had referred. Berthelot's most important contribution in his work on glycerin was to introduce the concept (and name) of polyatomic alcohols, but hardly less important was his synthesis of stearin and palmitin, the chief constituents of ordinary hard fats. He also carried out further work on the esterification of glycerin, some of it in collaboration with his pupil S. de Luca.

From glycerin Berthelot turned his attention to sugars and succeeded in isolating several new sugars. He showed that sugars behave partly as polyatomic alcohols (i.e., with the —OH group) and partly as aldehydes (i.e., with the —COH group). With the object of systematizing the confused knowledge of sugars, he divided carbohydrates into three classes: (1) ordinary sugars, which are like either (*a*) glucose (i.e., monosaccharides) or (*b*) cane sugar (i.e., polysaccharides); (2) carbohydrates, such as starch, cellulose, etc.; and (3) polysaccharides, which on hydrolysis combine with water to form glucoses:

$$(C^6H^{10}O^5)^n + nH^2O = nC^6H^{12}O^6.$$

Berthelot gave cane sugar the systematic name *saccharose*. From his researches on sugar and alcohol he naturally had an interest in fermentation. He showed that the conversion of cane sugar into invert sugar in fermentation is caused by an enzyme (*ferment glucosique*) present in yeast. He succeeded in obtaining it from an extract of yeast through precipitation by alcohol. Having obtained new sugars and thrown some light on the relation of sugars to other compounds, Berthelot turned to the alcohols. He prepared new alcohols from cholesterol, ethal, Borneo camphor, etc. He gave a definition of alcohols as neutral compounds consisting of carbon, hydrogen, and oxygen, and which with acids had water eliminated to form another neutral compound. The latter was capable of taking up water to form the original alcohol and acid. He was the first to consider the phenols as a group, which he characterized in a similar way.

One of the earliest of Berthelot's triumphs in his program of synthesis was in the preparation of alcohol. This was, of course, traditionally the product of fermentation of sugars with yeast; but in 1854 Berthelot showed that it could be prepared from ethylene. When ethylene was subjected to prolonged and vigorous shaking with sulfuric acid, it dissolved; and when the product was heated with water and distilled, the alcohol passed over. An obvious objection to this preparation was that the ethylene had itself been obtained from alcohol. Berthelot therefore obtained ethylene from coal gas as ethylene iodide by passing the crude gas into a solution containing iodine. Hennel had already suggested in 1828 that ethylene could be converted to alcohol by treatment with sulfuric acid but had been criticized by Liebig, so that most chemists in the mid-nineteenth century regarded the possibility of this conversion as doubtful. The fact that previous work had been done on the subject was emphasized by Chevreul in an attack on Berthelot, who had neglected to mention this. By a similar method Berthelot synthesized isopropyl alcohol from propylene.

Berthelot had now begun his program of general synthesis of organic compounds, and in 1856 he set out to prepare formic acid. He reasoned that formic acid was related to carbon monoxide in the same way as alcohol was to ethylene. As he wrote it:

$$C^2H^2O^4 = C^2O^2 + 2HO$$
formic acid

$$C^4H^6O^2 = C^4H^4 + 2HO$$
alcohol

As he had produced alcohol by adding water to ethylene in the presence of an acid capable of fixing the alcohol, so he should be able to react water with carbon monoxide in the presence of an alkali to fix the acid product. He accordingly heated moist caustic potash in an atmosphere of carbon monoxide for seventy hours. This produced potassium formate, which, when distilled with sulfuric acid, yielded formic acid in no way different from that occurring naturally in the ant.

Berthelot then synthesized methane (contaminated with a little ethylene) by passing a mixture of carbon disulfide vapor and hydrogen sulfide over red-hot copper. Then in 1857, by reacting methane with chlorine, he obtained methyl chloride, which, on hydrolysis, formed methyl alcohol. There is an obvious parallel between the success of Cannizzaro two years earlier in obtaining benzyl alcohol from toluene via benzyl chloride. Berthelot, nevertheless, achieved the first true synthesis of an aliphatic alcohol, and in 1858 he summarized his achievements in a long table, "Sur la synthèse des carbures d'hydrogène," in which he described his preparation of the hydrocarbons methane, ethylene, propylene, butylene, amylene, ethane, and propane, as well as benzene and naphthalene. The first stage in synthesis, the preparation of these hydrocarbons and their conversion to the corresponding alcohol, was the most difficult stage; but once the alcohol had been prepared, it was possible "to achieve the synthesis of an almost infinite number of organic compounds." Berthelot attacked the idea of a vital force distinguishing organic from inorganic compounds. Chemistry had proceeded up to then by the method of analysis, but by the complementary method of synthesis he claimed to have shown that the forces acting in organic chemistry were no different from those operating in inorganic compounds.

In Berthelot's memoir of 1858 he wrote that "carbon does not combine directly with hydrogen." Before he achieved this he wrote his monumental *Chimie organique fondée sur la synthèse,* in which he presented a review of his work in organic chemistry during the previous ten years. The work begins with an extensive historical introduction, which contains no more than a passing reference to Wöhler's preparation of urea in 1828. One obtains the impression from the book that the author was the first to recognize the importance of synthesis in organic chemistry and that it was he who had undertaken the basic research. The first volume is devoted to a discussion of the synthesis of hydrocarbons and the synthesis of alcohols. In the second volume glycerin and sugars are discussed, and toward the end there is a chapter dealing with the evidence for genuine synthesis and the implications for physiological chemistry. Berthelot emphasized throughout the work that the success of synthesis in organic chemistry meant that the claim of vitalists that vegetable and animal substances were essentially different from those made in the laboratory was no longer tenable. There were not two chemistries but one, and chemical reactions in both the inorganic and organic realms depended ultimately on purely mechanical factors. In his conclusion Berthelot argued that chemistry differed from a descriptive science such as natural history by being creative and that in this it resembled the mathematical sciences.

Acetylene was first prepared in 1836 by Edmund Davy, for whom it was "a new carburet of hydrogen." The gas was then forgotten until it was rediscovered by Berthelot in 1860. Berthelot prepared it by passing either ethylene, or methyl or ethyl alcohol in the vapor state, or ether through a red-hot tube. Alternatively it could be prepared by passing an electric discharge through a mixture of cyanogen and hydrogen. To isolate it he made use of its reaction with ammoniacal cuprous chloride solution to form cuprous acetylide, a substance discovered by Quet in 1858. Berthelot gave the gas the name "acetylene," saying that it was derived from acetyl (C_2H_3—H) in the same way that ethylene was related to ethyl (C_2H_5—H). Having already found that acetylene is the product formed when ethylene or methane is strongly heated or sparked, Berthelot concluded that it is the most stable of hydrocarbons and might therefore be produced by direct combination of carbon and hydrogen. Taking special precautions to ensure the purity of his materials, he therefore passed hydrogen through an electric arc formed between carbon poles. By reduction of acetylene Berthelot obtained ethylene and ethane and, by oxidation, acetic acid and oxalic acid, all reactions of great use to their author in extending his program of synthesis. As the direct reaction of acetylene with chlorine usually produced an explosion, Berthelot and Jungfleisch used antimony chloride (as a negative catalyst) and succeeded in obtaining two addition products.

Berthelot opened a new field when he carried out a systematic investigation of hydrocarbons obtained by heating suitable substances in the temperature range from red to white heat. His most famous experiment was that in which he heated acetylene in a glass tube; polymerization took place, forming benzene with some toluene. This was the first demonstration that it was possible to effect a simple conversion of an aliphatic to an aromatic compound. By passing benzene vapor through a red-hot iron tube filled with broken glass, Berthelot obtained diphenyl. Similarly, he obtained styrolene and naphthalene from benzene and acetylene, and acenaphthene from naphthalene and ethylene. These reactions had the additional value of throwing light on the formation of by-products in the manufacture of coal gas. For example, Berthelot first discovered acenaphthene ($C_{10}H_6 \cdot C_2H_4$) as described above and then as a constituent of coal tar. He also discovered fluorene ($C_{13}H_{10}$) in crude anthracene and heavy coal-tar oil.

After Berthelot's success in obtaining acetylene directly from carbon and hydrogen, he considered acetylene to be the most important starting point in his whole system of synthesis, since from it could be obtained ethylene, methane, and benzene:

$$C_2H_2 \longrightarrow C_2H_4 \longrightarrow C_2H_6$$
$$C_2H_2 \longrightarrow CH_3 \cdot COOH \longrightarrow CH_4$$
$$3C_2H_6 \longrightarrow C_6H_6$$

Previously Berthelot had deliberately used molecular formulas only, but from 1864, when he gave a lecture on isomerism to the Société Chimique in Paris, he began to develop the molecular implications of his researches. Nevertheless, he remained outside the development of the theory of chemical structure developed by Butlerov and Kekulé and the notational reforms arising from the Karlsruhe Congress of 1860, so that he continued to use the old equivalent notation. He distinguished hydrocarbons according to their degree of saturation, as follows (using modern atomic weights):

carbure complet   e.g., ethane C_2H_6

carbure incomplet   e.g., ethylene $C_2H_4(-)$

carbure incomplet du 2me ordre
                           e.g., acetylene $C_2H_2(-)(-)$

According to this system, and wishing to call attention to its method of synthesis, Berthelot considered benzene an incomplete hydrocarbon of the fourth order. This formulation was acceptable for its reduction to hexane but was unsatisfactory in accounting for the majority of benzene's reactions, where it behaves as a saturated hydrocarbon. Berthelot rejected Kekulé's formula for benzene (1865–1866), and it was not until 1897 that he accepted modern structural formulas.

Berthelot's last major research in organic chemistry was the application of hydrogen iodide as a reducing agent—he called it "une méthode universelle d'hydrogenation." His publications on this research covered the period 1867–1870. Although he claimed that they were a continuation of work published in 1855, it must be mentioned that meanwhile Lautemann had already used hydrogen iodide as a reducing agent in organic chemistry. Berthelot, anxious to carry out even the most difficult reductions, was prepared to use concentrated hydriodic acid saturated at 0°C. and heated with the substance to be reduced in an oil bath up to 280°C. He succeeded in reducing a large number of unsaturated aliphatic hydrocarbons. His results with aromatic hydrocarbons were less definite. His study of the mechanism of decomposition of hydrogen iodide provides a further link with his work in physical chemistry.

One of the earliest papers in which Berthelot revealed his interest in physical chemistry was published in 1856. In this he paid special attention to the boiling point, specific gravity, specific heat, heat of combustion, and refractive index of organic compounds, particularly esters. His great contributions to physical chemistry began in the 1860's. Berthelot later explained how he had become interested in physical chemistry:

In a succession of publications for several years I endeavored to compare experimentally the origins of organic compounds with those of inorganic compounds and to formulate general methods of synthesis. To extend my research I considered it appropriate to make a special study of the mechanism of these changes. The experiments which I have published on the laws governing the production of esters were published with this intention. Now I propose to examine what thermal phenomena accompany the formation and the decomposition of organic compounds—in other words the extent of the energy change [*le travail des forces vives*] necessary to bring about their synthesis.[3]

Thus Berthelot's contributions to physical chemistry arose directly from his consuming interest in the synthesis of organic compounds. His studies on chemical equilibrium published in 1862 and 1863 were followed by equally fundamental work on thermochemistry.

Berthelot and L. Péan de Saint-Gilles studied the reaction of alcohols with acids to form the corresponding ester and water. They found that the reaction never went to completion but arrived at an equilibrium state that was independent of the quantities (measured in equivalents) of alcohol, acid, ester, or water present at the beginning. On the other hand, the rate of reaction did depend on the quantities of alcohol and acid present: "The amount of ester produced at each moment is proportional to the product of the active masses [*masses actives*] present."[4] Such a statement appears to be an anticipation of the law of mass action later formulated by Guldberg and Waage. Berthelot attempted a mathematical treatment and drew graphs illustrating the formation and decomposition of esters. Berthelot and Saint-Gilles, however, while appreciating that the equilibrium was affected by the reverse reaction (ester + water), failed to take this into consideration in deriving a general mathematical expression. In their comprehensive experiments they varied temperature, pressure, concentration, and types of alcohols and acids used. They recorded the increase in reaction velocity with rise of temperature, although the final position of equilibrium was found to be almost independent of temperature. As one of their experiments on the effect of mass, one equivalent of ethyl alcohol was reacted with increasing amounts of acetic acid and the various yields of ester formed were recorded. With one equivalent of acid reacting with x equivalents of alcohol the amount of ester formed was also recorded:

X	1	1.5	2	3	4	5.4	12	19
% ester	66.5	77.9	82.8	88.0	90.9	92.0	93.2	95.0

During their investigation of a large number of alcohols Berthelot and Saint-Gilles found that the rate of reaction of borneol with acids was excessively slow, but it was left to Menschutkin to clear up the relation between the constitution of an alcohol and its rate of esterification. When Guldberg and Waage announced their law of mass action, they fully acknowledged their debt to the studies of esterification by Berthelot and Saint-Gilles.

In 1856, in the course of his investigations of esters, Berthelot established that the heat of combustion of an ester is almost exactly equal to the sum of the heats of combustion of the alcohol and acid from which it is formed. In this, as in some later work, he was able to make use of the experimental results of Favre and Silbermann. It was not until 1865, however, that Berthelot seriously turned his attention to problems of thermochemistry. He chose this subject for his lectures at the Collège de France, but he made it clear from the beginning that his interest was really in the heat changes involved in the formation and decomposition of organic compounds so that these could be compared with the comparatively well-known basic thermochemistry of inorganic chemistry as a further basis of comparison between the two branches of the science. It was in these lectures that Berthelot introduced the terms *exothermic* and *endothermic*.

Berthelot enunciated the principle that the heat evolved or absorbed in a chemical change depends only on the initial and final states of the reactants and products, provided no external work is done. This is Berthelot's "second principle," analogous to Hess's law of constant heat summation. He based this principle on the assumption of an equivalence between internal work (*le travail moléculaire*) and heat changes in a chemical reaction (Berthelot's "first principle"). Best known is Berthelot's "third principle," or "law of maximum work," which was first published in its complete form in 1873: "Every chemical change accomplished without the intervention of energy from outside tends toward the production of a body or system of bodies which produce the most heat." In the same publication Berthelot introduced the expression "principle of maximum work." The honor of beginning a new epoch in thermochemistry must be shared between Berthelot and Julius Thomsen, who had arrived in 1853 at essentially the same principle as that established by Berthelot in 1873. The principle was soon recognized as no more than a useful approximation, strictly true only at a temperature of absolute zero; it was superseded by the researches of Helmholtz, Gibbs, and van't Hoff. The accuracy of

Berthelot's thermochemical data has often been criticized, but sometimes it was his arithmetic rather than his experimental work that was at fault. In interpreting nineteenth-century thermochemical data it is also necessary to know that Berthelot's calories refer to water at O°C., whereas Thomsen, for example, used the range 18°C.–20°C.

Berthelot tried to improve the experimental technique of thermochemistry. Recognizing the unreliability of the mercury calorimeter used by Favre and Silbermann, for example, he used a water calorimeter and either a platinum reaction chamber or one made of glass to facilitate direct observation. By the use of a water jacket, a mechanical stirrer, and a thermometer reading to .005°C., he was able to carry out experiments accurately over small temperature ranges. After more than ten years' research on thermochemistry, Berthelot published a major two-volume work for which he significantly chose the title *Essai de mécanique chimique fondée sur la thermochimie.* In the first volume, entitled *Calorimétrie,* Berthelot gave a general survey of thermochemistry, with particular reference to his own apparatus and results. The second volume, entitled *Mécanique,* was a general account of chemical reactions and decompositions. Berthelot continued his thermochemical research by determining the heats of combustion of gases. He introduced the use of the bomb calorimeter, in which the gas under test was mixed with excess oxygen compressed to 20–25 atmospheres and then sparked. This method enabled him to determine heats of combustion with an accuracy hitherto unattainable. With his bomb calorimeter, Berthelot made a fundamental contribution to both pure and applied chemistry. This was immediately recognized, and a stream of foreign scientists came to Paris to acquire firsthand knowledge from Berthelot of the new thermochemical methods. Through Berthelot, his pupils, and such collaborators as Vieille and Recoura, there was established a substantial body of reliable data of heats of combustion, solution, neutralization, and so on. Berthelot's continuing interest in thermochemistry is suggested by the publication in 1897, when he was seventy years old, of another two-volume work, *Thermochimie. Données et lois numériques.* He had already devoted to practical methods the smaller work *Traité pratique de calorimétrie chimique* (1893).

Almost as important was the fundamental work carried out by Berthelot, largely in collaboration with Jungfleisch, and published in the years 1869 and 1872. Studying the distribution of a solute between two immiscible solvents (e.g., water and benzene) or partially miscible solvents (e.g., water and ether), they were able to enunciate the partition law: "At a given temperature the quantities of solute dissolved by equal volumes of two solvents is a constant." They called this constant the partition coefficient (*coefficient de partage*). Some twenty years later Nernst investigated some apparent exceptions to this law.

While serving as president of the scientific commission appointed to bring any possible aid from science to help in the defense of Paris during the Franco-Prussian War, Berthelot investigated the possibility within the city of extracting saltpeter for gunpowder. Also in November 1870 he presented to the Académie des Sciences three memoirs on explosives, which were published in full in the *Comptes rendus* under the heading "Art militaire." Combining his patriotic duty as a Frenchman and his interest in thermochemistry, Berthelot showed how the power of explosive materials could be quantitatively expressed. He expanded this research in his book *Sur la force des matières explosives d'après la thermochimie,* first published in 1871 but greatly expanded in the two-volume definitive work published as a third edition in 1883. In the intervening period Berthelot had made a particular study of the thermochemistry of nitrogen compounds used as the basis of explosives. But it was his work carried out in collaboration with Vieille that laid the foundations of a new scientific study of the mechanism of explosions. They found that explosions were propagated in a manner in many ways analogous to that of a sound wave. They accordingly introduced the concept of an explosive wave (*onde explosive*), found to have a velocity much greater than that of sound; for example, with an explosive mixture of hydrogen and oxygen the velocity was 2,841 meters per second. The explosive wave was propagated uniformly. Its velocity depended on the nature of the explosive rather than on the material or dimensions of the vessel. Apart from its direct utility, Berthelot found his research on explosives interesting because in it he witnessed natural forces acting under extreme conditions. He insisted that his studies of explosives could have peaceful uses; and in 1896, after accidents with liquid acetylene used for illumination, he and Vieille collaborated in a study to establish how acetylene could be used with safety.

The possibility of finding new reactions by using a silent electric discharge also appealed to Berthelot. He constructed an ozonizer, essentially the same as that devised earlier by Brodie. By passing a silent electric discharge for up to ten hours through a mixture of sulfur dioxide and oxygen, Berthelot discovered persulfuric anhydride, S_2O_7. This is the anhydride of an acid of both theoretical and practical importance for the use of its salts as oxidizing agents.

It was Berthelot's lifelong interest in energy states that prompted his studies of allotropic forms of sulfur, phosphorus, and arsenic, and his discovery in 1891 (simultaneously with Mond and Quincke) of iron carbonyl.

Berthelot's first study of animal heat was in 1865, and in this he followed the thermal tradition of Lavoisier and Laplace. In 1890 he took up the subject again, carefully distinguishing the heat produced in the lungs by the action of oxygen in the blood from the later reaction in which carbon dioxide is produced, and he was able to show that the former reaction produced only one-seventh of the total heat.

In other experiments Berthelot was able to show that the combustion of foodstuffs in the laboratory produced no less heat than in the body. There was therefore no energy to relate to any vital force, a conclusion in which Berthelot took particular satisfaction. He opposed Pasteur's vitalistic interpretation of fermentation, preferring a theory of fermentation fully analogous to that of inorganic catalysts, thus once more championing the view of the strict parallel between the organic and the inorganic.

In 1883 Berthelot founded a research establishment for vegetable chemistry, and during the last twenty-five years of his life he undertook research into aspects of chemistry useful to agriculture. He found that certain carbohydrates, such as cellulose, could be made to absorb nitrogen under the action of a silent electric discharge. By treating them with lime, the absorbed nitrogen was liberated as ammonia. He was able to demonstrate that the fixation of atmospheric nitrogen by sparking is parallel to the natural process in plants. In 1885 he made his first reference to microorganisms capable of fixing nitrogen and in 1893, in collaboration with Guignard, he succeeded in isolating and forming a culture of such bacteria. In accordance with his usual practice, he brought together work done by himself and his collaborators (particularly G. André) and published it in book form. The result was his *Chimie végétale et agricole* (1899). Berthelot's last chemical book, *Traité pratique de l'analyse des gaz* (1906), concerned a subject he had studied practically from the time of his early syntheses of hydrocarbons.

NOTES

1. The spelling "Marcelin" was used on his birth certificate, and Berthelot himself sometimes wrote it that way, particularly toward the end of his life in the signing of official documents.
2. In 1850 Williamson had described the production of ethyl methyl ether from sodium ethoxide and methyl iodide as a "synthesis," *Philosophical Magazine,* 3rd ser., **37** (1850), 350.
3. *Annales de chimie et de physique,* 4th ser., **6** (1865), 290–291.
4. *Ibid.,* 3rd ser., **66** (1862), 112.

BIBLIOGRAPHY

I. ORIGINAL WORKS. Berthelot wrote the following books (all published in Paris): *Chimie organique fondée sur la synthèse,* 2 vols. (1860); *De la synthèse en chimie organique. Leçon professée le 16 Mars 1860 à la Société chimique de Paris* (1861); *Sur les principes sucrés. Leçons professées à la Société chimique de Paris* (1863); *Leçons sur les méthodes générales de synthèse en chimie organique, professées au Collège de France* (1864; 1876; 1879; 1880; 1883; 1887; 1891; 1897; 1903; 1910); *Sur l'isomérie. Leçons de chimie professées devant la Société chimique de Paris* (1866); *Sur la force de la poudre et des matières explosives* (1871; 2nd ed., 1872; see also *Sur la force . . .,* 1883); *Traité élémentaire de chimie organique* (1872; later eds. with Jungfleisch, 2 vols., 1881, 1886, 1898 [Vol. I]; 1904 [Vol. II]; new ed. of Vol. I, 1908); *Essai de mécanique chimique fondée sur la thermochimie,* 2 vols. (1879; supp., 1881); *Sur la force des matières explosives d'après la thermochimie,* 3rd ed., 2 vols. (1883); *Les origines de l'alchimie* (1885); *Science et philosophie* (1886; 1905); *Collection des anciens alchimistes Grecs,* 3 vols. (1887–1888); *Introduction à l'étude de la chimie des anciens et du moyen age* (1889); *La révolution chimique. Lavoisier* (1890; 2nd ed., 1902); *Histoire des sciences. La chimie au moyen age,* 3 vols. (1893); *Traité pratique de calorimétrie chimique* (1893; 2nd ed., 1905); *Science et morale* (1897); *Thermochimie. Données et lois numériques,* 2 vols. (1897); *Chaleur animale. Principes chimiques de la production de la chaleur chez les êtres vivants,* 2 vols. (1899); *Chimie végétale et agricole. Station de chimie végétale de Meudon,* 4 vols. (1899); *Les carbures d'hydrogène, 1851–1901. Recherches expérimentales,* 3 vols. (1901); *Science et éducation* (1901); *Science et libre pensée* (1905); *Archéologie et histoire des sciences* (1906); *Traité pratique de l'analyse des gaz* (1906).

A selection from Berthelot's principal research papers is listed below. The order follows that of the text. "Sur un procédé simple et sans danger pour démontrer la liquéfaction des gaz et celle de l'acide carbonique en particulier," in *Comptes rendus,* **30** (1850), 666–667; "Action de la chaleur rouge sur l'alcool et sur l'acide acétique," in *Annales de chimie et de physique,* **33** (1851), 295–302; "Sur le bichlorhydrate d'essence de térébenthine," in *Comptes rendus,* **35** (1852), 736–738; "Sur les diverses sortes d'essence de térébenthine," *ibid.,* **36** (1853), 425–429 (see also *Annales,* **38** [1853], 38; **39** [1853], 5; **40** [1854], 5); "Sur la série camphénique," in *Comptes rendus,* **47** (1858), 266–268; "Sur l'oxidation des carbures d'hydrogène," in *Annales,* **19** (1870), 427–429; "Sur les combinaisons de la glycérine avec les acides," in *Comptes rendus,* **36** (1853), 27–29; "Mémoire sur les combinaisons de la glycérine avec les acides et sur la synthèse des principes immédiats des graisses des animaux," in *Annales,* **41** (1854), 216–319, esp. 296; "Sur quelques matières sucrées," *ibid.,* **46** (1856), 66–89; "Sur divers carbures contenus dans le goudron de houille," *ibid.,* **12** (1867), 195–243; "Sur plusieurs alcools nouveaux. Combinaisons des acides avec la cholesterine, l'éthal, le camphre de Bornéo et la méconine," *ibid.,* **56** (1859), 51–98; "Sur la reproduction de l'alcool par le bicarbure d'hydrogène," in *Comptes rendus,* **40** (1855),

102–106; "Transformation de l'oxyde de carbone en acide formique," *ibid.,* **41** (1855), 955; "Synthèse des carbures d'hydrogène," *ibid.,* **43** (1856), 236–238; "Synthèse de l'esprit-de-bois," *ibid.,* **45** (1857), 916–920; "Sur la synthèse des carbures d'hydrogène," in *Annales,* **53** (1858), 69–208; "Note sur une nouvelle série de composés organiques, le quadricarbure d'hydrogène et ses dérivés," in *Comptes rendus,* **50** (1860), 805–808; "Recherches sur l'acétylène," in *Annales,* **67** (1863), 52–77, esp. 65–68; "Nouvelle méthode pour la synthèse de l'acide oxalique et des acides homologues," in *Comptes rendus,* **64** (1867), 35–38; "Les polymères de l'acétylène. Première partie: Synthèse de la benzine," *ibid.,* **63** (1866), 479–484; "Action de la chaleur sur quelques carbures d'hydrogène," in *Annales,* **9** (1866), 445–469, esp. 454; "Action reciproque des carbures d'hydrogène. Synthèse du styrolene, de la naphtaline, de l'anthracène," *ibid.,* **12** (1867), 5–52; "Sur divers carbures contenus dans le goudron de houille," *ibid.,* 195–243; "Méthode universelle pour réduire et saturer d'hydrogène les composés organiques," in *Comptes rendus,* **64** (1867), 710–715, 760–764, 786–791, 829–832; "Remarques sur quelques propriétés physiques des corps conjugués," in *Annales,* **48** (1856), 332–347; "Recherches sur les affinités:—De la formation et de la décomposition des éthers," *ibid.,* **65** (1862), 385–422; **66,** 5–110; **68** (1863), 225–359, esp. 290–291, written with Péan de St. Gilles; "Recherches de thermochimie. Premier mémoire. Sur la chaleur dégagée dans les réactions chimiques," *ibid.,* **6** (1865), 290–328; "Sur la statique des dissolutions salines," in *Comptes rendus,* **76** (1873), 94–98; "Méthode pour mesurer la chaleur de combustion des gaz par detonation," in *Annales,* **23** (1881), 160–187; "Nouvelle méthode pour la mesure de la chaleur de combustion du charbon et des composés organiques," in *Comptes rendus,* **99** (1884), 1097–1103, written with Vieille; "Sur les lois qui président au partage d'un corps entre deux dissolvants (expériences)," *ibid.,* **69** (1869), 338–342, written with Jungfleisch; "L'onde explosive," in *Annales,* **28** (1883), 289–332, written with Vieille; "Sur l'acide persulfurique, nouvel acide oxygéné du soufre," in *Comptes rendus,* **86** (1878), 20–26; "Sur la chaleur animale, chaleur dégagée par l'action de l'oxygène sur le sang," in *Annales,* **20** (1890), 177–202, esp. 199; "Fixation directe de l'azote atmosphérique libre par certains terrains argileux," in *Comptes rendus,* **101** (1885), 775–784; "Nouvelles recherches sur les microorganismes fixateurs de l'azote," in *Annales,* **30** (1893), 419–431.

II. SECONDARY LITERATURE. The following studies describe Berthelot's life and work. The articles by Graebe and Jungfleisch are particularly thorough. H. E. Armstrong, "Marcelin Berthelot and Synthetic Chemistry," in *Journal of the Royal Society of Arts,* **76** (1927–1928), 145–171; A. A. Ashdown, "Marcellin Berthelot," in *Journal of Chemical Education,* **4** (1927), 1217–1232; G. Bredig, "Marcelin Berthelot," in *Zeitschrift für angewandete Chemie,* **20,** pt. 1 (1907), 689–694; A. Boutaric, *Marcellin Berthelot* (Paris, 1927); E. Farber, "Berthelot," in *Das Buch der grossen Chemiker,* G. Bugge, ed., II (Berlin, 1930), 190–199, trans. in E. Farber, ed., *Great Chemists* (1961), pp. 677–685; C. Graebe, "Marcelin Berthelot," in *Berichte der Deutschen*

Chemischen Gesellschaft, **41** (1908), IIIB, 4805–4872; E. Jungfleisch, "Notice sur la vie et les travaux de Marcellin Berthelot," in *Bulletin de la Société chimique de France,* **13** (1913), i–cclx; L. Velluz, *Vie de Berthelot* (Paris, 1964); and R. Virtanen, *Marcelin Berthelot. A Study of a Scientist's Public Role,* University of Nebraska Studies, no. 31 (Lincoln, 1965).

M. P. CROSLAND

BERTHIER, PIERRE (*b.* Nemours, France, 3 July 1782; *d.* Paris, France, 24 August 1861), *mineralogy, mining engineering, agricultural chemistry.*

Berthier entered the École Polytechnique in Paris in 1798, where he studied under Monge and Berthollet. On completing his course, he entered the École des Mines in 1801, and was one of the few students who moved with the school to Montier. Schreiber, the head of the school, was an experienced mining engineer who stressed fieldwork, including actual mining experience in the lead and silver mine at Pesey.

Berthier was called in 1806 to the newly completed central laboratory of the Board of Mines. In 1816, after additional field experience, he was appointed professor of assaying and chief of the laboratory at the École des Mines. Even after he retired in 1848, Berthier maintained his laboratory there. He was paralyzed in 1851 as a result of a street accident.

With Arago's warm support, Berthier was elected a member of the Académie des Sciences in 1825, and became a *chevalier* of the Legion of Honor in 1828. In 1859 he was awarded the Grand Gold Medal of the Society of Agriculture of France.

Berthier published more than 150 papers on a wide variety of scientific subjects. Most appeared in *Annales de chimie* and *Annales des mines,* with later papers in Erdmann's *Journal,* Liebig's *Annalen,* and the *Quarterly Journal of Science.* He analyzed kaolin, pioneered in locating deposits of native phosphates for use in agriculture, analyzed dozens of minerals and metalliferous ores, and discovered several new mineral species, including bauxite and Berthierite. Berthier is credited with knowing, before Mitscherlich's work on isomorphism, that substances that are chemically different may have the same crystalline form and may even cocrystallize.

Berthier put forth no new concepts, preferring instead to add to man's stock of chemical and mineralogical facts. His well-known *Traité des essais par la voie sèche* was widely used by mineralogists and mining engineers because his analytical procedures were simple, relatively accurate, and practical. Berthier maintained a lifelong interest in plant chemistry, and his analyses of plant constituents received

some notice, but his importance lies in what he added to French geology, mineralogy, and metallurgy.

BIBLIOGRAPHY

I. ORIGINAL WORKS. Berthier's papers are too numerous to cite individually. A nearly complete list is in the *Catalogue of Scientific Papers,* Royal Society of London, 1st ser., pp. 315–319. The list in Poggendorff, I (1863), 166, is incomplete. Berthier's major work is *Traité des essais par la voie sèche ou des propriétés, de la composition et de l'essai des substances, métalliques et des combustibles,* 2 vols. (Paris, 1834).

II. SECONDARY LITERATURE. The best recent, although somewhat uncritical, account is R. Samuel LaJeunesse, *Grands mineurs français* (Paris, 1948), ch. 7. See also *Dictionnaire de biographie française,* VI (1954), 218; Jerome Nicklès, "Correspondence of Jerome Nicklès . . .," in *American Journal of Science,* 2nd ser., **32** (1861), 108; École Polytechnique, *Livre du centenaire,* III (Paris, 1897), *passim;* and J. R. Partington, *A History of Chemistry,* IV (London, 1964), 97–98.

LOUIS I. KUSLAN

BERTHOLD, ARNOLD ADOLPHE (*b.* Soest, Germany, 26 February 1803; *d.* Göttingen [?], Germany, 3 February 1861), *physiology.*

Berthold, who came from a simple family of artisans, began his medical studies at Göttingen in 1819 and presented his doctoral thesis in 1823. Following custom, he visited various German and foreign universities—including Berlin in 1824 and Paris in 1825—in order to increase his knowledge of practical medicine and comparative anatomy. Having qualified as *Privatdozent* at Göttingen in 1825, he began his lifetime career there. He was named extraordinary professor of medicine in 1835 and ordinary professor the following year. He was also curator of the zoological collections.

Since he was absorbed in both the practice and the teaching of medicine, Berthold left many and varied published works. As early as 1829 he wrote *Lehrbuch der Physiologie des Menschen und der Thiere,* which was reissued many times. His monographs, articles, and notes were published in medical, scientific, and even literary periodicals. A piece of research done with Bunsen (1834) led to the discovery of hydrated iron oxide as an antidote for arsenic poisoning. Some of his other works dealt with myopia, the length of pregnancy, male hermaphroditism, and the formation of fingernails and hair. His short work commemorating Goethe's centennial in 1849 was one of the first German publications to do justice to Goethe as a naturalist. According to Gurlt, Berthold's life was typical of a nineteenth-century German university professor with a high reputation. Gurlt's article has been reprinted without modification and without special mention of the experiment that made Berthold a forerunner of modern endocrinology.

In 1849 Berthold published "Transplantation der Hoden," a four-page article that in its conciseness was a model for experimental investigation. It is the report of the experiments he performed on six cockerels, using each pair for the removal and transplantation of the testicles. The most remarkable result was the successful grafting of testicles from one cockerel into the abdominal cavity of another, with the cockerel receiving the transplant retaining the secondary sexual characteristics of crowing and combativeness. This article completely escaped notice at the time and remained in oblivion until 1910, when Biedl, in his *Innere Sekretion* (p. 5), demonstrated that Berthold should be considered the first scientist to have shown by experimental means the correlation of a gland with the *milieu intérieur* of an organism. (In reality, as early as 1905 Nussbaum had analyzed and evaluated Berthold's experiments before reproducing them on batrachians.) Since then, all historical accounts have considered Berthold as one of the founders of endocrinology. In reality, he was a forerunner without immediate successor.

Berthold's article was translated into English and commented upon by Rush (1929), Quiring (1944), and Forbes (1949), who speculated upon the origin of this particular experiment. From a study of the text it is apparent that Berthold was preoccupied with the trophic nerves:

> Since, however, transplanted testes are no longer connected with their original innervation, and since, as indicated [above], no specific secretory nerves are present, it follows that the results in question are determined by the productive function of the testes (*productive Verhältniss der Hoden*), i.e., by their action on the bloodstream, and then by corresponding reaction of the blood upon the entire organism, of which, it is true, the nervous system represents a considerable part [Quiring, p. 401].

It was not the first time that Berthold showed interest in the physiology of reproduction. He was the author of an important, comprehensive study of sexual characteristics in Wagner's *Handwörterbuch*, a reference book highly regarded at the time and still of great interest in the history of biology.

BIBLIOGRAPHY

I. ORIGINAL WORKS. Among Berthold's writings are *Erster Abriss der (menschlichen und thierischen) Physiologie*

(Göttingen, 1826); *Lehrbuch der Physiologie des Menschen und der Thiere* (Göttingen, 1829); *Das Eisenoxydhydrat, ein Gegengift der arsenigen Säure* (Göttingen, 1834), written with R. G. E. Bunsen; "Geschlechtseigentümlichkeiten," in R. Wagner, *Handwörterbuch der Physiologie,* I (Brunswick, 1842), 597–616; *Lehrbuch der Physiologie für Studierende und Aerzte,* 3rd ed., 2 vols. (Göttingen, 1848); *Am 28 August des J. 100, nach der Geburt Göthes in einem Kreise Göttingischer Verehrer . . .* (Göttingen, 1849); and "Transplantation der Hoden," in *Archiv für Anatomie, Physiologie und wissenschaftliche Medicin . . .* (1849), 42–46, trans. by D. P. Quiring as "Transplantation of Testis," in *Bulletin of the History of Medicine,* **16** (1944), 399–401.

II. SECONDARY LITERATURE. Works on Berthold are A. Biedl, *Innere Sekretion. Ihre physiologische Grundlagen und ihre Bedeutung für die Pathologie* (Berlin–Vienna, 1910); T. R. Forbes, "A. A. Berthold and the First Endocrine Experiment: Some Speculations as to Its Origin," in *Bulletin of the History of Medicine,* **23** (1949), 263–267; E. Gurlt, "A. A. Berthold," in *Biographisches Lexikon der hervorragenden Ärzte aller Zeiten und Völker* (Leipzig–Vienna, 1884; 3rd ed., 1962), I, 501–502; M. Klein, "Goethe et les naturalistes français," in *Publications de la Faculté des lettres, Université de Strasbourg,* **137** (1958), 169–191, see 177; N. Nussbaum, "Innere Sekretion und Nerveneinfluss," in *Ergebnisse der Anatomie und Entwickelungsgeschichte,* **15** (1905), 39–89, esp. 67–68; and H. ·P. Rush, "A Biographical Sketch of Arnold Adolf Berthold," in *Annals of Medical History,* n.s. **1** (1929), 208–214.

MARC KLEIN

BERTHOLLET, CLAUDE LOUIS (*b.* Talloire, near Annecy, Savoy, 9 December 1748; *d.* Arcueil, France, 6 November 1822), *chemistry.*

Berthollet came from a French family that had emigrated to Savoy during the previous century and had become members of the *noblesse de robe.* The family was, however, in straitened circumstances when Claude Louis was born. He first studied at the *collèges* in Annecy and Chambéry, and later qualified as a physician at the University of Turin in 1768. After this he settled in the Piedmont for four years before moving to Paris in 1772, where he studied chemistry under Macquer and Bucquet while continuing to study medicine. As a Savoyard he could introduce himself to his near-compatriot Tronchin, from Geneva, an associate of the Académie des Sciences, propagator of vaccination in France, and the chief personal physician to the regent, the duke of Orléans. Upon Tronchin's recommendation, the duke had Berthollet appointed private physician to Mme. de Montesson, and allowed him to carry out research in the private laboratory installed by the regent and his son in the Palais Royal. Here Berthollet repeated the experiments on elastic fluids of Lavoisier, Priestley, and Scheele, and met Lavoisier. He qualified as a doctor of medicine at the University of Paris in 1778 and married Marguerite Baur in the same year.

Between 1778 and 1780 Berthollet presented seventeen memoirs to the Academy; these led to his election as a member on 15 April 1780, on the death of Bucquet (Fourcroy opposed him). In 1784, on Macquer's death, he was appointed inspector of dye works and director of Manufacture Nationale des Gobelins. He subsequently collaborated with Lavoisier, Fourcroy, and Guyton de Morveau in the publication of *Méthode de nomenclature chimique* (1787), incorporating the principles of the new chemistry of Lavoisier.

Berthollet flourished under four different political regimes. In 1792 he was appointed a member of the commission for the reform of the monetary system, and in 1793 the Committee of Public Safety made him an important member of the scientific commission concerned with war production, particularly that of munitions. He was appointed to the commission on agriculture and arts on 22 September 1794 and was made a professor at the École Normale. Berthollet was also charged, with his lifelong friends Monge and Guyton de Morveau, with the organization of the École Polytechnique, where for a time he taught animal chemistry. In 1795 he was one of the first members elected to the Institut de France, which replaced the suppressed Academy in 1793.

With the fall of Robespierre and the revolutionaries, Berthollet's star shone even more brightly under Napoleon, who showed a deep admiration and affection for the chemist. In 1796 Napoleon appointed Berthollet and Monge to accompany the commission that was to bring back the great works of Italian art to France. In the execution of this assignment Berthollet developed some of the earliest chemical methods for the restoration of paintings. Two years later, Berthollet and Monge accompanied Napoleon as scientific members of his expedition to Egypt, where they stayed for two years and established an Institute modeled on that of Paris. In 1804 Napoleon made Berthollet a count, senator for Montpellier, administrator of the mint, and *grand officier* of the Légion d'Honneur. After this, Berthollet led a semi-retired existence in the Paris suburb of Arcueil. In 1807 he and Laplace founded the Société d'Arcueil, which met regularly to discuss scientific problems, and published three volumes of its proceedings. In 1811 Berthollet's son, Amédée, committed suicide when his business (manufacturing sodium carbonate according to a new method developed by his father) failed.

In tracing the development of Berthollet's scientific work, it must be emphasized that, for all his original contributions, he was essentially part of the continuous historical tradition of chemistry. Unlike his senior contemporary Lavoisier, Berthollet wanted to improve rather than to revolutionize the basis of the science. Whereas Lavoisier had tried to found a new chemistry deriving from the analysis of its most fundamental principles, Berthollet wanted to reinvigorate the traditional science by synthesizing ideas derived from various sources. He was trained as a physician, as was common for chemists from Paracelsus to Boerhaave and Black; in addition, like them, he not only sought an adequate theoretical explanation of chemical phenomena but also strove to find an immediate application for his ideas. His enthusiastic espousal of the ideals of the French Encyclopedists reinforced this longing to put science at the service of man's practical needs.

From 1778 to 1783 Berthollet sent a large number of memoirs to the Academy, all of them admitting the essential correctness of the phlogiston theory. The main characteristic of his mature work is foreshadowed in these early contributions: the quest for a synthesis that would lead to a more adequate understanding of chemical phenomena, by fusing the divergent principles of Stahl's and Lavoisier's systems while incorporating the eighteenth-century tradition of the chemistry of affinities. His preoccupation with practical applications was revealed in such investigations as the attempt to revive asphyxiated animals with the help of "dephlogisticated air." He also studied the properties of soap, which he explained by assuming different distributions of the respective affinities of its components during their interaction with a solvent, and developed original procedures for making new types of "metallic" soap that would have been useful for medicinal purposes.

Berthollet's earlier investigations were largely concerned with Lavoisier's major preoccupation, the study of gases. In the beginning he opposed Lavoisier's ideas while defending the phlogiston theory. It might help to dispel the popular caricature of the opponents of Lavoisier if we recall some of Berthollet's arguments in this debate.

Tradition. Stahl's doctrine, according to Berthollet, had been so successful in accounting for chemical phenomena that there appeared to be no adequate reason for rejecting it. Berthollet argued that the study of air and other elastic fluids (or gases) had shown the need for modifying this doctrine in some details, with which many of the other chemists agreed, but he did not think that it followed from this that the traditional basis of chemistry was to be swept aside. Lavoisier alone appeared radical, setting out systematically to disprove the existence of phlogiston by a series of experiments, the precision of which Berthollet admired. Berthollet held that Lavoisier's positive contributions could be synthesized with a revised phlogiston theory, while the negative conclusions as to the existence of phlogiston could only be harmful to chemistry, the unity of which would be destroyed by such iconoclasm.

Weight. While later historians have made the whole debate on phlogiston revolve about Lavoisier's so-called crucial experiments showing the increase in weight of substances during combustion, it can be seen by studying Berthollet's earlier work that it was possible to have accepted this part of Lavoisier's work without rejecting Stahl. In a series of experiments on the conversion of sulfur, phosphorus, and arsenic to the corresponding "acids" (oxides), Berthollet confirmed Lavoisier's conclusion that there was an increase in weight in all three cases because "vital air" was added. He also agreed that, notwithstanding earlier investigations in which a diminution in the quantity of the surrounding air had been observed, Lavoisier was the first to have indicated that there was an increase in weight when metals, sulfur, and phosphorus were calcinated. So far from seeing any inconsistency between these ponderable considerations and the phlogiston theory, Berthollet, although a supporter of Stahl, felt justified in criticizing Lavoisier for not having been sufficiently vigorous in insisting on his conclusions (a deficiency attributed, paradoxically enough, to Lavoisier's rejection of the phlogiston theory). While it would be tedious to go into the explanations offered by Berthollet in accordance with Stahl's doctrines, it is historically interesting to list some alleged inconsistencies on Lavoisier's part when dealing with quantitative relations.

(*a*) Lavoisier had maintained that the causticity of metals was due to their combination with "vital air." To Berthollet this was doubly suspect. First, oxygen combined with all the metals in almost the same proportion to form calces, yet the latter varied greatly in their causticity, contrary to what should have happened according to Lavoisier's doctrine. Second, the red precipitate of mercury was a highly caustic calx. This implied that it contained a large amount of oxygen, if causticity were due to the presence of this substance—but in fact the red oxide of mercury contained only a tiny proportion of oxygen, not more than one part to every ten or twelve parts of the metal.

(*b*) When hydrogen and carbon were separately burned, Lavoisier's theory led to inconsistencies with regard to the quantity of oxygen required in each case. For hydrogen, he had to say that the heat generated was due only fractionally to the consumption of the oxygen present—about 1/21 of the total—while the rest was due to hydrogen itself. For the burning of carbon, he attributed all the heat to the oxygen consumed. Berthollet rightly questioned the discrepancy in the quantitative factors involved in the explanation of the same type of chemical phenomenon, combustion.

Accompanying effects. The rejection of phlogiston had led Lavoisier to postulate an alternative set of explanations for the physical phenomena accompanying combustion: production of a flame (heat and light), and the change of physical state from solid or liquid to vapor. This he achieved by postulating a generic principle called caloric, which was also brought in to explain the existence of substances that were permanently in the gaseous state. Berthollet pointed out that not only was it impossible to clarify, even in principle, the exact relationship of heat to light in Lavoisier's system (unlike Stahl's, in which all such phenomena were explained uniformly by the presence of phlogiston), but also that empirical evidence refuted Lavoisier's ideas about such physical effects. Thus carbon, sulfur, and the metals detonated strongly, producing a flame, when distilled with niter. For Lavoisier substances in the solid state, such as all the reactants in these cases, were deprived of caloric and therefore should not have been able to produce a flame giving out heat and light. He had explicitly stated that only substances in the gaseous or liquid state contained sufficient caloric to produce these effects.

Lavoisier had asserted that the physical effects accompanying combustion required a diminution in the volume of the elastic fluids or air present, since caloric was required for the production of the effects. On the other hand, Berthollet pointed out that in cases such as the detonation of a mixture of carbon and gunpowder, an elastic fluid possessing a greater volume than the reactants was actually given out. Consequently this experiment should have been accompanied by the production of cold, since caloric was being absorbed and not given out, contrary to the experimental evidence, which showed that heat and light were produced.

Berthollet had here seized upon the real weakness of Lavoisier's explanation of combustion: that this was not only a chemical phenomenon in which something (oxygen) was absorbed, but also a physical phenomenon in which something (energy or, rather, enthalpy, heat minus entropy) was released. This inquiry was not undertaken, however, until the notion of energy was clarified in the third and fourth decades of the nineteenth century.

The foregoing controversy ushered in Berthollet's preoccupation in his later scientific career, the desire to reformulate the basic principles of chemistry by synthesizing the traditional views with the important new discoveries of Lavoisier, a task that was to take him the better part of twenty years. In the intervening period he rejected the phlogiston theory and embraced Lavoisier's doctrine.

In 1785, after he had set out to test its correctness by performing a large number of experiments on "dephlogisticated marine acid" (chlorine), Berthollet explicitly stated for the first time that "this principle, which Stahl had ingeniously imagined in order to explain a large number of phenomena, and by means of which a genuine relationship could be established between them, namely phlogiston, having sufficed for the needs of chemistry during a long period," had at last become a useless hypothesis. Ironically, the test case chosen was more correctly explained by the followers of Stahl than by Lavoisier. As the name suggested, Stahl correctly thought of chlorine as marine (hydrochloric) acid that had lost phlogiston (often identified with hydrogen), while Lavoisier assumed that he was dealing with oxygenated marine acid (oxygen plus hydrochloric acid).

Berthollet's reasons for agreeing with Lavoisier were summarized in the statement that in the preparation of chlorine, using a mixture of manganese dioxide and hydrochloric acid, the "vital air" of the former could be shown to have combined with the latter, thereby proving that oxygenated marine acid had been formed during the reaction. The actual details of Berthollet's reasoning were rather obscure. He cited the formation of fixed air and common salt (by boiling oxygenated marine acid with soda) as an important detail in this context, without making it clear why and how it was relevant. Three other experiments were also given in support of the Lavoisienne view. All of them, however, appeared to be curiously vitiated by circular reasoning, in that Berthollet assumed that the phenomena observed were best explained by supposing that oxygen was combined with marine acid in chlorine. These experiments were (a) the dissolution of metals in a solution of oxygenated marine acid when no gas was given off, because Berthollet thought that the metals combined directly with the oxygen of the acid and therefore did not decompose the water, which otherwise would have given off hydrogen; (b) the conversion of hydrogen sulfide gas into vitriolic acid when it was passed through the solution of chlorine, which he explained by assuming that the oxygen of the latter combined with the gas; and (c) the transformation of mercury into a corrosive sublimate which contained a large proportion of "vital air" and marine acid, the two supposed ingredients of the solution of chlorine in which the metal was dissolved.

Two points are worth observing here. First, Berthollet was already preoccupied with finding an explanation of phenomena, interpreted on Lavoisienne principles, that would finally be understood through a complete theory of affinity. Thus, he mentioned that it was not a simple elective affinity between the two that caused marine acid to combine with the oxygen of manganese dioxide, but that a more complex distribution of affinities was required to account for the production of oxygenated marine acid. He suggested that marine acid had only a feeble affinity for oxygen and believed that its combination with the "vital air" of the calx was to be explained by a change in the state of manganese, which was easily dissolved by the marine acid, this dissolution being accompanied by an expulsion of oxygen with which the metal was originally combined. In this process a more concentrated form of oxygen, which lost a large part of its caloric when separated from the manganese, was obtained. The more concentrated form of the oxygen helped it to combine with marine acid despite their weak mutual affinities. Berthollet later expanded this explanation into a complete system of chemistry.

Second, Berthollet's change of allegiance from Stahl to Lavoisier was directed more by practical expediency than by any apparent superiority in either the logic or the adequacy of the new system. Lavoisier's ideas enabled Berthollet to give a much simpler explanation of the phenomena, although one that was obviously quite inadequate on many counts. Not only were Berthollet's original objections to Stahl's system not answered, but many new ones also arose in the application of Lavoisier's principles.

A glaring instance was Lavoisier's explanation of the properties of acids as deriving from the presence of oxygen. Berthollet had already shown, in 1778, that hydrogen sulfide, while possessing the characteristics of a feeble acid, did not contain oxygen. He was to reconfirm this discovery nearly twenty years later. But Berthollet's most important contribution in this domain was his analysis of prussic acid (1787), which he correctly showed to be composed of hydrogen, carbon, and nitrogen. Although he did not succeed in determining the relative proportions of its components, he was convinced that it contained no oxygen. Lavoisier himself accepted these results but avoided their theoretical implications by suggesting that prussic acid was perhaps not an acid after all. Several years later Berthollet followed up this investigation with those of some other acids—hydrochloric, uric, boric, and fluoric—all of which contained no oxygen, according to him.

Although Berthollet never rejected Lavoisier's ideas after 1785, he gave indications of how he was eventually going to suggest an alternative explanation that would avoid such difficulties as that of the composition of acids. Lavoisier had explained the properties of substances by referring to the elements of which they were composed; Berthollet proposed to derive them from the relations between their constituents. He did not define acidity in isolation, depending upon the presence of oxygen, but by the interaction between the components of one substance in the presence of another; the former was an acid if it was neutralized by a base, and if together the two gave rise to a series of salts.

A valuable consequence of Berthollet's adherence to Lavoisier's system was the determination of the composition of ammonia, for which he gave the earliest accurate analysis (1785). He had tried in 1778 to explain the origin of this alkali, which had been formed in various experiments concerned with distilling alcohol over ammonium carbonate and other "fixed" alkalies. Lavoisier, who had given an account of this work to the Academy, had enjoined Berthollet not to publish it because it contained serious errors. This advice was accepted, although Berthollet intended to repeat the analysis of ammonia, which he carried out soon after his conversion to Lavoisier's ideas.

Berthollet also acknowledged his debt to Priestley (who had decomposed ammonia in 1775–1777) in the method of the analysis: the passage of an electric current through ammonia. The resulting mixture of gases was exploded with oxygen and its composition was analyzed. From the results obtained it was shown that ammonia was composed of 2.9 volumes of inflammable gas (hydrogen) to 1.1 volumes of moffette (nitrogen).

These investigations into pneumatic chemistry were prompted not only by Berthollet's interest in the theoretical issues raised by the differences between the systems of Lavoisier and Stahl, but also by his interest in the practical implications of these new discoveries. An illustration of this was his study of chlorine, which immediately led to two separate applications. The first of these stemmed from his preparation of potassium chlorate by saturating a concentrated solution of caustic potash with chlorine. A mixture of the chlorate and carbon exploded energetically, leading Berthollet to try to replace niter with potassium chlorate to obtain a more powerful kind of gunpowder. A public experiment was carried out with this new type of gunpowder in 1788, with unex-

pected results—the director of the plant and four other people were killed on the spot. It appears that this innovation was later effectively used in military operations.

Berthollet was more successful in his other attempt to put the properties of chlorine to practical use. Having observed that chlorine had bleaching properties, he wanted to find a simple technique for introducing it as a bleaching agent for textiles. This was partly prompted by his affiliations with Gobelins, but chiefly (as he often insisted) by the humanitarian ideals inculcated in him by the Encyclopedists. The traditional methods of bleaching, which involved soaking cloth in whey and spreading it in a sunny field, was, he said, wasteful, since it prevented large tracts of land from being tilled. It was a measure of his humanitarian impulse that, unlike such contemporaries as Watt, who amassed large fortunes from their industrial inventions, Berthollet published his technique for the bleaching of textiles by chlorine without bothering to patent it. It is some reflection on the morality of pioneers in the same field that they invited Berthollet to demonstrate the application of his method—which he did gratis—and then tried to patent his discovery of the bleaching liquid, calling it *lye de Javelle*.

Berthollet's method of chlorine bleaching consisted of pouring sulfuric acid on a mixture of six ounces of manganese monoxide and sixteen ounces of salt. This mixture was heated by immersion in boiling water and a bleaching solution was obtained by collecting the chlorine in water (100 quarts for every pound of salt). The cloth to be bleached was first soaked in diluted caustic potash, then washed and eventually immersed in the bleaching solution for three to four hours; the operation was repeated several times. Finally the bleached cloth was washed with soft soap and rinsed in diluted sulfuric acid.

Another of Berthollet's important contributions to the textile industry was the treatise in which he endeavored to place the ancient craft of dyeing on a scientific basis by a systematic discussion of its procedures, coupled with an attempt to find an adequate set of theoretical principles to explain the chemical actions involved. His explanation was that, depending on the variable physical conditions of temperature, quantity of solvent employed, and so forth, when a cloth was dyed the reciprocal affinities of the particles of the dye, the mordants, and the cloth itself were responsible for the kind and quality of dyeing. The colors produced were due to the oxidation of the mordant by the atmosphere.

During his stay in Egypt, Berthollet noticed the apparently inexhaustible source of sodium carbonate constituted by Lake Natron, at the threshold of the desert. He sought an explanation for this natural phenomenon in terms of a chemical theory of affinity that had been maturing in his mind over the years. The ground surface of Egypt, he reflected, was covered with a layer of ordinary salt, while the neighboring mountains of Libya were formed of limestone. If these substances reacted with each other, a double decomposition would have occurred, forming sodium carbonate and calcium chloride. But limestone did not ordinarily react with salt—an explanation in terms of double decomposition for the formation of sodium carbonate in Egypt would therefore have been acceptable only if some special circumstances obtained in this case. Berthollet pointed out that the physical conditions in the area were sufficiently unusual to warrant this assumption. Two factors probably intervened: the high temperatures prevailing in the region and the relatively large quantities of limestone present. When a salt solution filtered slowly through the pores of the limestone, the relatively weak affinities between these two substances were enhanced by the combined effects of the temperature and the enormous mass of limestone. This led to decomposition of the salt, assuring a constant production of sodium carbonate and calcium chloride through double decomposition, as a result of the redistribution of the affinities between the original reactants.

These observations lent a renewed interest to Berthollet's earlier suggestion that such physical conditions as temperature, relative concentration, and quantities of reactants affected the nature and direction of affinities in a chemical reaction. Berthollet read a memoir on the general theory of affinities while he was still in Egypt. This was the starting point of his complete new system of chemistry, first briefly sketched in *Recherches sur les lois de l'affinité* (1801) and later developed into the comprehensive, two-volume *Essai de statique chimique.* Here he attempted to provide a proper basis for chemistry, so that its experimental results could be viewed in the light of theoretical first principles. Berthollet developed a theory and a model adequate for the understanding and the interpretation of the rapidly growing body of chemical knowledge in his time. He was aware that the positive work of constructing a new theory had yet to be performed after the shock of Lavoisier's criticism of the old chemistry.

In his attempt to provide chemistry with an adequate theoretical foundation, Berthollet recognized the importance of the theory of affinity. He pointed out that for lack of a proper critical appraisal of the principles involved, his predecessors' ideas on affinity, as expressed in the construction of "tables of affinity"

through the eighteenth century, were perhaps somewhat crude and immature. The main objection to these tables was that they assumed affinity to be a general force, unaffected by the experimental conditions and always constant. For example, it had been supposed that if two acids, A and B, were considered, the table of affinities could show at a glance which of the two had a stronger affinity for a base, Z. This led to the view that the acid with the stronger affinity could always replace the other acid in a compound with the base, no matter what the experimental conditions might be. Thus if, according to a table of affinities, A had a stronger affinity for Z than B did, then it would always be the case that on adding acid A to a compound of B and Z, all the B would be replaced in the compound by A, giving the substitution product AZ. With the introduction of rudimentary quantitative methods in the latter half of the eighteenth century, this view had been extended to justify the doctrine that all substances combined in constant proportions: two substances always combined in the same proportion because of their fixed affinity for each other.

Before the time of Berthollet, it had already been maintained by various chemists that this view oversimplified the nature of chemical combinations. Lavoisier had shown, for example, that the nature of chemical combination varied with the temperature. Consequently, he pointed out, a separate table of affinity should be constructed for each degree of temperature. Bergman actually constructed tables showing how affinity varied with temperature. In spite of a few efforts along these lines, affinity remained in some sense an "absolute" that could be determined once and for all from a given table, irrespective of any variation of the conditions under which a reaction took place.

Berthollet undertook a thorough examination of the notion of affinity as his predecessors had employed it. His main contribution to its development was the proof that affinity was a relative concept which varied with the physical conditions accompanying an experiment: quantity, temperature, solubility, pressure, and physical state (solid, liquid, or gas) determined the relative force with which one substance attracted another. Berthollet then tried to prove that the proportions in which two substances combined also varied according to the conditions. This led to his famous controversy with J. L. Proust.

According to the *Essai,* there were two main types of forces in nature: gravitation, which accounted for astronomical phenomena, and chemical affinity. It was quite possible that they had a common origin, but they were best treated separately, so as not to lose sight of the very important differences between chemical affinity and astronomical attraction. For, unlike affinity, astronomical attraction operated at such enormous distances that its action could always be considered to be uniform. The shapes, sizes, and specific properties of the molecules composing a particular substance determined the way in which chemical affinity was defined in any given case, so that the exercise of this force was not uniform in all cases. Besides, the results produced were quite different in the two cases. The end product of chemical affinity was always a combination of the substances concerned, whereas no such phenomenon could be associated with astronomical attraction.

To elucidate the nature of chemical combination and affinity, Berthollet employed an explanatory model. This was a mixture of the two main types of methods later utilized by chemists, the atomic and the planetary, although he was not very consistent in the use of either model. Thus, he envisaged substances as composed of minute particles or molecules, which roughly corresponded to atoms. But he also asserted that the proportions in which two substances combined varied continuously, thereby making it impossible to think of these molecules as possessing the most characteristic property of atoms, that of indivisibility. Berthollet's molecules were supposed to be endowed with mutual attraction. The interplay between the total number of forces in a given substance was supposed to lead to the production of a stable system. This was analogous to a planetary system, where the sum of the forces between the heavenly bodies results in a state of equilibrium. The analogy did not extend further than this: there was no central nucleus or sun around which the molecules of the substances revolved as in a planetary system. It is not clear whether the model was a dynamic one.

Berthollet pointed out that a chemical substance represented a state of equilibrium between the forces of its component molecules. Likewise, all chemical combinations were caused by an interplay of the forces of molecules composing the reactants. The manner in which the different forces influenced a chemical reaction required that they be distinguished from each other. The former theories of affinity had failed to take these differences into account because of the belief in a uniform force of affinity. The factors that had to be considered in evaluating these forces, according to Berthollet, were the following:

Chemical affinity. The attraction that different substances had for each other, or that the molecules of the same substance exercised upon one another, ultimately depended on their chemical natures, which determined their chemical affinities for each other. The affinity of one substance for another had an upper, but generally no lower, limit. The proportions in which two substances combined could vary from the smallest part to the maximum. The variation normally was continuous and differed very slightly from one compound to another. When the maximum reciprocal affinities between two substances had been satisfied, they were said to be "saturated" with respect to each other.

Quantity. Given a certain force of attraction between two substances, it was natural to suppose that the larger the quantities used, the greater the force deployed. Since a substance was thought of as an aggregate of minute particles or molecules, it was only natural to suppose that each of these would bear a determinate portion of the total force. In any reaction, therefore, affinity was not a constant force that could be determined once and for all: it would vary according to the quantities of the substances. The nature of the combination resulting from the interaction of two or more substances was not a simple function of their respective affinities, considered independently of their masses: in fact, it was not possible to give any precise meaning to the idea of chemical affinity unless it was associated with that of the masses of the reactants. If a salt was formed by the combination of an acid, A, and a base, Z, then it could not be determined in advance whether another acid, B, would displace A in the given salt. For example, A might have a greater affinity for Z than B had for Z in a given reaction. Nevertheless, if a sufficient quantity of B was added to AZ, a point would be reached at which the joint action of the quantity of B and its (relatively weaker) affinity for Z would start to counteract the affinity of A for the base: part of AZ would be converted into BZ.

The forces responsible for chemical combinations depended on the relative attraction or affinity of one substance for another, according to its chemical nature, as well as on the number of its reacting molecules, measured by its quantity. Instead of considering affinity in isolation, as in the tables of affinity, Berthollet proposed to use a more complex concept combining the idea of affinity with that of the mass of a reacting substance.

The relative affinities of different substances could be measured by comparing the quantities of each that would saturate a given amount of the same substance, provided the physical conditions were constant. The idea of saturation was extended by Berthollet to the maximum quantity of any given substance that would combine with another under given conditions, rather than limiting it to the neutralization of acids by bases and of bases by acids.

Berthollet combined the concept of relative affinity with that of the mass of reactants in a chemical combination. This gave the total force with which a given quantity of a substance reacted with another. Instead of taking the quantity of the affinity by itself, Berthollet suggested the use of a concept such as "effective mass" or "chemical mass" of a substance in given reaction. He added that the use of such terms as "mass" and "affinity," which implies that they have clear meanings, should be abandoned if chemistry did not want to be stunted for lack of properly analyzed theoretical foundations. Instead of saying, for instance, that sulfuric acid had a greater affinity for caustic soda than acetic acid did, it was necessary to take into account how much of either would combine with the alkali under given conditions. This would indicate the total attraction exerted by either acid, under similar conditions, upon the alkali: this idea is properly expressed by the complex concept of chemical mass, representing the product of the power of saturation and its mass. Although this was one of the most important ideas introduced into chemistry by Berthollet, its importance was generally overlooked until the second half of the nineteenth century, when there was a revival of interest in the nature of chemical equilibrium and the physical conditions that affect that equilibrium.

Distance (*cohesion and elasticity*). Besides affinity and quantity, Berthollet pointed out that a chemical reaction was strongly influenced by the physical conditions under which substances were made to react. This was one of his most original contributions: he was probably the first chemist to undertake an exhaustive examination of these conditions. In order to grasp his position, we have to understand the details of the model he constructed to represent the course of a reaction. Although his model was not stated very explicitly, the following appears to be the most coherent interpretation of his ideas on the subject.

It was generally observed that substances increased in volume when they were heated, and contracted when cooled. From this Berthollet inferred a particulate structure of matter: substances were composed of small, discrete particles, invisible to the naked eye, and located at definite distances from each other. The application of heat increased the distances between these particles. If substances had been compact masses or undivided wholes, rather than aggregates of discrete particles, it would have been difficult to account for the expansion of bodies when they were heated and their contraction when cooled. This was particularly true when one attempted to explain how an apparently compact mass, such as a solid, could

contract when cooled. The different states of matter were thus explicable by relative increases or decreases in the distances between particles as a substance passed from one state to another.

Berthollet used this model to elucidate the relationship between the physical states of matter and the phenomena of chemical combination. This made him the first chemist to attempt a detailed explanation of chemical reactions in quasi-mechanical terms. He asserted that the affinity between two particles attracted to each other was influenced by their distances. The closer together they were, the more strongly they were attracted. It followed that the following minimum conditions had to be fulfilled before any two substances combined: The chemical nature of each substance had to be such that its molecules attracted, and were attracted by, those of the other. Also, the attraction of the molecules of substance A for substance B had to be greater than the reciprocal attraction of the molecules of A for each other. Conversely, the attraction that the molecules of A exercised upon those of B, combined with the attraction of B for A, had to be powerful enough to overcome the reciprocal affinity between the molecules of B. The closer together the molecules of a given substance, the stronger their reciprocal affinity and, consequently, the more difficult would it be for them to combine with any other substance. In more concrete terms, it was often difficult to make two substances combine in the solid state, although they might combine readily in the liquid state. As solids, their molecules were so closely packed together that the reciprocal affinity was too great to be overcome by the attraction exerted on them by the molecules of another substance. In the liquid state, however, the distances between the molecules of a substance were much greater. There was a corresponding decrease in their reciprocal attractions, which rendered them more susceptible to the affinity exerted by the molecules of another substance. For the same reason, chemical combinations took place more easily between substances in the gaseous state than in either the solid or the liquid state: in a gas the distances between the molecules were, relatively speaking, the greatest, so that their reciprocal attractions were reduced to a minimum. For instance, when steam was passed over iron filings, an oxide of iron was formed more readily than when the metal was immersed in water. The reaction took place with far greater facility when the iron had been powdered into small filings than when a block of the metal was used.

Apart from this effect on the physical states, the relative distances between the molecules of reacting substances explained the role of such factors as temperature and pressure. The most important factor influencing chemical combination was heat. The reason for this was to be sought in the expansive power of caloric, the active principle underlying the effects of heat. Caloric caused substances to expand, thereby increasing the distances between their molecules. The reciprocal attraction between the molecules of any given substance consequently decreased. If a substance in the solid state was heated, it passed, as a general rule, through the liquid to the gaseous state. When the reciprocal affinities between the molecules of the same substance decreased, the molecules were more easily attracted to those of another substance, with which they could then combine. For the same reason, the variation of pressure was important in studying the reactions between gases: distances were inversely proportional to the pressure.

A problem that arose in Berthollet's model, with the important role he assigned to the variation of distance between molecules when they reacted with a given substance, was the explanation of the nature of the force responsible for the increase and the decrease of distances between molecules. So far as the more compact states of matter were concerned, the closeness of the molecules could be attributed to the force of reciprocal attraction. Thus, crystallization was explained as a consequence of the tendency to attain a maximum effect by the symmetrical arrangement of molecules: distances were thus reduced to a minimum, with a corresponding increase in reciprocal affinities. The tendency to cohere as closely as possible was the result of mutual attraction between the molecules, and crystallization was a secondary effect derived from this primary attraction. In fact, the *Essai* distinguished between the different kinds of effects due to affinity. One of them accounted for chemical combination of two or more different substances. The other expressed itself as the reciprocal affinity between the molecules of a given substance: its intensity was measured by the state of cohesion. Obviously the two effects could work in opposite directions during a chemical reaction. Berthollet may therefore be considered to be the originator of crystal chemistry; unlike his contemporary Haüy, he did not have to assume that the internal symmetry of the crystal (i.e., the symmetry around a particular atom or molecule) had to be the same as its external (or macroscopic) symmetry.

Thanks to this model and the accompanying analysis of chemical reactions, especially combination, the analyzed idea of affinity had been replaced by a group of concepts. This had an important influence upon early nineteenth-century chemistry. On the negative side, chemists dispensed with the use of

tables of affinity as guiding hypotheses after the publication of the *Essai.* Nobody could accept such a simplified account of chemical phenomena after Berthollet's criticisms. On the positive side, there were the continued efforts of chemists to provide theories accompanied by adequate models showing the internal workings and structure of chemical substances. This was nowhere more evident than in the development of chemical kinetics and thermochemistry in the late 1850's, with the accompanying clarifications of the notion of mass action and the mechanism of chemical equilibria.

Berthollet's compatriot J. L. Proust had asserted in 1799 that all combinations occurred in definite proportions; in the formation of any chemical compound the same elements were always combined in the same proportions by weight. Berthollet interpreted this to be yet another version of the doctrine of elective affinities and challenged Proust's notions.

From Berthollet's concept of chemical mass it followed that the proportions in which one substance combined with another increased directly with its chemical mass, the "active" quantity in any given reaction. There were a maximum and a minimum proportion in which one substance would combine with another. Between these two limits, which one might call the "threshold" and "saturation" points, the substances would combine in any proportions, depending on their respective quantities, the difference in the proportions being continuous between one extreme and the other. From this it obviously followed that the proportions in which substances combined were not fixed, at least within limits. This was not borne out, however, by the facts in all cases—a point that Berthollet had to concede to Proust. There was at least an appearance that substances combined, in some cases, in definite proportions that could not be made to vary indefinitely. For instance, oxygen and hydrogen did not combine in varying degrees, but in the same proportions, to form water; likewise, ammonia was always formed by the same proportions of nitrogen and hydrogen, as Berthollet himself had been the first to demonstrate. Berthollet did not contest such evidence, although he continued to affirm that in the majority of cases, combinations occurred in conformity with his theory of variability of proportions. For him the problem was to reconcile these two apparently conflicting views of chemical combination. He attempted to do this in two different ways.

On the one hand, Berthollet admitted the existence of fixed proportions. Some substances did combine in only one fixed proportion, but this could be explained quite satisfactorily in accordance with his principles. The reason was to be found in the special conditions under which some combinations took place, so that it was not possible for the substances involved to follow the general law of variability of proportions within limits. On the other hand, he maintained that it was only the poverty or superficiality of experimental observations that had led chemists to attribute a fixity of proportions in combinations where, in fact, there was none to be discovered. A case such as the fixed proportions in which hydrogen and oxygen combined to form water vapor was explicable in terms of the physical state of the resulting combination. The reaction was accompanied by a strong condensation: in fact, with the application of slight pressure the resulting product was converted into the liquid state instead of being gaseous; such a conversion was accompanied by a thousandfold (or more) condensation in the volume of the product. As a result of the condensation, the molecules of water vapor were packed together more closely than the molecules of hydrogen and oxygen surrounding them. The reciprocal affinity between the compound molecules of water vapor was considerably greater, due to their closeness, than that between the individual hydrogen and oxygen molecules surrounding them. Berthollet assumed that it was a special characteristic of such molecules that their combination would be accompanied by condensation only when they came together in a particular proportion, such as 2:1 for hydrogen and oxygen. When they were mixed in proportions other than this, they did not form stable compounds for two reasons. First, their distances might be too great for the mutual affinity to be effective. Second, even if they did combine in small quantities, the surrounding molecules, by their physical impact or their opposing affinities (e.g., of cohesion), succeeded in dissociating whatever compound molecules might be produced. This explained why oxygen and hydrogen combined in a fixed proportion to produce water. When they were present in the ratio of 1:2, their molecules were so combined that the particles of the product were closer together, and hence relatively isolated, due to condensation.

The arguments advanced by Berthollet and Proust in their controversy (1801–1807) were both empirical and theoretical. The empirical objections revolved about the ability to distinguish between a genuine chemical compound and a mere mixture. Here Proust's intuition was more often correct than Berthollet's. The theoretical difficulties showed Berthollet at an advantage because, unlike Proust, he had worked out a complete set of principles in terms of which he tried to account for all the known chemical phenomena. While Berthollet agreed that there was clearly a difference between such substances as

glass and the metallic oxides, he could discover no criterion by which any definite distinction could be established between them. On Berthollet's model it was quite possible to account for the existence of the substances in which the constituents were always combined in the same proportions, but no difference of principle was involved in distinguishing substances held together by weaker affinities (their combination being unaccompanied by condensation). Proust's reply was a circular one. He was supposed to state a principle by which substances that he considered to be of fixed composition could be distinguished from those that he acknowledged to be of variable composition. His reply took the form that compounds were substances whose constituents always combined in fixed proportions, whereas solutions or mixtures were substances having variable constitutions.

BIBLIOGRAPHY

I. ORIGINAL WORKS. Most of Berthollet's papers were published in *Mémoires de l'Académie/Institut* or, after 1789, in *Annales de chimie*. He also wrote three books: *Éléments de l'art de la teinture,* 2 vols. (I, 1791; 2nd ed., 1804); *Recherches sur les lois de l'affinité* (1801); and *Essai de statique chimique,* 2 vols. (1803). Also see *Mémoires de physique et de chimie de la Société d'Arcueil,* 3 vols. (1807–1817).

II. SECONDARY LITERATURE. No comprehensive study of Berthollet's life and works has been published, but see E. F. Jomard, *Notice sur la vie et les ouvrages de C. L. Berthollet* (Annecy, 1844); and S. C. Kapoor, "Berthollet, Proust, and Proportions," in *Chymia,* **10** (1965), 53–110. Also of value is M. P. Crosland, *The Society of Arcueil. A View of French Science at the Time of Napoleon I* (Cambridge, Mass., 1967).

SATISH C. KAPOOR

BERTHOLON, PIERRE (*b.* Lyons, France, 28 October 1741; *d.* Lyons, 21 April 1800), *physics.*

Bertholon, a priest of the Lazarist order, spent time in Lyons, Paris, and Béziers before settling in Montpellier, where he was invited by the États de Languedoc to teach all aspects of contemporary science. He held the chair of physics specially created for him in 1784 by the Société Royale des Sciences de Montpellier. His courses were greatly appreciated and were given regularly until the Revolution—and privately even later. Bertholon taught physics at the École Centrale de l'Hérault in 1791 and in Lyons in 1797. His renunciation of the priesthood was probably the cause of his leaving the school in Lyons. He died three years later.

Bertholon's scientific contribution is important both

qualitatively and quantitatively, for it included areas of great diversity—including urban public health, agriculture, aerostatics, and fires. He is particularly well known for his work in physics, especially in electricity. He played the same role in the south of France that the Abbé Nollet played in Paris; that is, he contributed greatly to the development of research in electricity—as much by work and personal experience as by his lectures. Three principal works brought him fame. *De l'électricité des météores* is a study of all atmospheric manifestations, as well as of volcanoes and earthquakes; Bertholon proposed to overcome the latter by sinking metal shafts into the ground. Influenced by his friend Benjamin Franklin, he supplied southern France with lightning rods. *De l'électricité des végétaux* deals with the application of electricity to the growth of plants; for this Bertholon used an electrovegetometer of his own invention. *De l'électricité du corps humain dans l'état de santé et de maladie* classifies all ailments according to their positive or negative electrical reactions. Appropriate therapy is advised for each: positive or negative electricity, electric baths, aigrettes, electric sparks, electric shock, or *impressions de souffle*—"When the face, the back of the hand, or another part of the body the sensitivity of which is not too weakened by touch is brought near an electrified conductor, there is felt the impression of a fresh breeze, of a light breath, or of a cobweb."

BIBLIOGRAPHY

Louis Dulieu, "L'Abbé Bertholon," in *Cahier lyonnais d'histoire de la médecine*, **6**, no. 2 (1961), includes a complete bibliography of Bertholon's works (publications, letters, and manuscripts, as well as writings that have not been found) and a bibliography of secondary literature.

LOUIS DULIEU

BERTI, GASPARO (*b.* Mantua [?], Italy, *ca.* 1600; *d.* Rome, Italy, 1643), *physics, astronomy.*

Berti seems to have been a native of Mantua who spent most of his life in Rome. He was first mentioned (under the name of Alberti) as a distinguished mathematician who about 1629 collaborated with Francesco Contini in the mapping of the Roman catacombs. Berti's friendship with Luc Holste, Athanasius Kircher, and Rafaello Magiotti suggests that he was born about 1600. In 1636, Holste described him to Nicholas Peiresc as an expert in mathematics and in the construction of mathematical instruments. About the same time, Berti's observations of an eclipse came to the attention of Pierre

Gassendi, who spoke of him as young, industrious, and erudite. Berti also refined the earlier observations of Christopher Clavius in order to determine the precise latitude of Rome; this he communicated to the English geographer John Greaves, who called him a celebrated astronomer. In July 1638, Magiotti informed Galileo that Berti had been recommended for a chair of mathematics by Benedetto Castelli, who considered him particularly well versed in the Galilean doctrines. Upon Castelli's death in 1643, Berti was named his successor as professor of mathematics at the Sapienza, but died shortly afterward.

Berti's historical importance, however, is in physics rather than in mathematics or astronomy. It was his experimental apparatus, constructed in Rome sometime between 1640 and 1643, that ultimately led to Evangelista Torricelli's work on atmospheric pressure. Berti's experiment seems to have been inspired by Galileo's *Discorsi* (1638), in which it was asserted that water could not be raised more than eighteen cubits by a lift pump. Berti's apparatus was described and illustrated in Magiotti's letter to Marin Mersenne dated 12 March 1648. It consisted of a lead tube no higher than twenty-two cubits, bent downward at the top and terminating at either end in a valve submerged in a container filled with water. Magiotti stated that Berti, who thought he had refuted Galileo's statement, had improperly measured the distance from the water surface in the upper container to the floor rather than to the water surface in the lower container. Properly measured, Magiotti said, the height was indeed eighteen cubits. He went on to say that in writing of the experiment to Torricelli, he had suggested that if seawater were used, a lower level would result; and it was this suggestion that led to Torricelli's experiments using mercury.

A more elaborate apparatus, which was attached to the façade of Berti's house, is illustrated in Athanasius Kircher's *Musurgia* (1650) and in Gaspar Schott's *Technica curiosa* (1664). It consisted of a lead tube about eleven meters long that terminated at its lower end in a valve and at its upper end in a globe, said to have been originally of copper and later of glass. From the juncture of globe and tube, a second lead tube that terminated in a valve was brought to a window about ten meters above the pavement. At Kircher's suggestion, a bell that could be struck by a hammer activated by an external magnet was enclosed in the globe. The fact that a sound was heard convinced Berti that no vacuum existed; but, as Emanuel Maignan later remarked to him, the attachment of the bell to the tube could communicate the sound to the air outside.

Cornelis De Waard assigned to Berti's experiment

a probable date after the spring of 1639 (when Kircher returned to Rome after a long absence) and before 1642, taking a phrase in Magiotti's letter to imply that Galileo was still living when the experiment was first performed. That implication is questionable, however, for the passage reads: "Il Sig^r Berti credeva con questa esperienza convincere il Sig^r Galileo . . . ," and *convincere* usually meant "refute" rather than "convince." Probably the first experiment was performed not earlier than June 1641, when Torricelli left Rome, for it appears that he was informed of it by letter. The magnetic device escaped mention in both the 1641 and 1643 editions of Kircher's *Magnes,* in which all manner of devices employing magnets were described and illustrated, which suggests that the elaborate apparatus was not earlier than 1643. Thomas Cornelius, recounting various Italian experiments of this kind in his *Progymnasmata physica* (1663), spoke of Berti as professor of mathematics at the Roman Academy when the experiment using the glass globe took place, which also suggests the year 1643. Torricelli's mercury experiments of 1644 probably occurred soon after he received Magiotti's first communication; if so, the various forms of Berti's apparatus may all belong to the period 1642–1643.

BIBLIOGRAPHY

All present knowledge of Berti is from secondary literature, which has been collected by Cornelis De Waard in *L'expérience barométrique. Ses antécédents et ses explications* (Thouars, 1936), pp. 104 ff., 169 ff. Works cited herein and letters mentioning Berti may most readily be found in that work.

STILLMAN DRAKE

BERTIN, LOUIS-ÉMILE (*b.* Nancy, France, 23 March 1840; *d.* La Glacerie, France, 22 October 1924), *naval architecture, hydraulics.*

Bertin was the son of Pierre-Julien Bertin, a hosiery dealer, and Anne-Frédéric Merdier. He entered the École Polytechnique in 1858 and, after graduating in 1860, joined the Naval Engineering Corps. In 1862 Bertin finished his studies at the School of Naval Engineering in Paris. Assigned to the Cherbourg naval district, he proved to be an inventive engineer who had a good sense of the practical but at times lacked critical insight into the mathematical development of his thought.

In 1864 the French navy sought to improve the ventilation of its horse transport ships. In 1865 Bertin presented the winning design, which brought its inventor the Plumey Prize (2,500 francs) of the Academy of Sciences in 1873.

In 1866 Bertin produced artificial waves in calm water and measured the decrease of successive amplitudes. The following year he observed sea swells while aboard a ship, measured the roll by means of a simple recording apparatus he had made, and began to give his observations a mathematical form. In accordance with the course given at the School of Naval Engineering, he at first believed that the swell was a cylindrical surface with a sinusoidal section. At that time French engineers still did not know of Franz von Gerstner's "Theorie der Wellen" (1804), even though it had been republished in 1809 by L. W. Gilbert in the *Annalen der Physik.* English engineers had long known of Gerstner's trochoidal swell, and Bertin obtained his knowledge from references in their publications. Accordingly, he published a series of articles in the *Mémoires de la Société des sciences naturelles de Cherbourg.* In order to complete his observations on shipboard, he ordered an oscillograph with two pendulums of different periods and used it, from 1872, to record swell and roll on the same band.

The Franco-Prussian War led to Bertin's work on compartmentalization, the enduring part of his work as an engineer. In order to limit damage, he suggested protecting the horizontal compartment adjoining the waterline by combining armor plate with a cellular compartment. The first French-built compartmentalized cruiser was based on his plans.

In 1881 Bertin was sent to Brest, where he drew up the plans for a cruiser that attained a speed of eighteen knots, a world record at that time. He was placed at the disposal of the Japanese government from 1886 to 1890, and the ships he helped build enabled the Japanese navy to defeat the Chinese navy in 1894. Upon his return to France, Bertin served in Toulon and then in Rochefort, where he was appointed director of naval construction in 1892. From 1893 to 1895 he directed the School of Naval Engineering, and in November 1895 he became head of the Technical Department of Naval Construction of the Naval Ministry, a post he held until his retirement in 1905.

BIBLIOGRAPHY

I. ORIGINAL WORKS. Among Bertin's books are *Notice sur la marine à vapeur de guerre et de commerce depuis son origine jusqu'en 1874* (Paris, 1875); *État actuel de la marine de guerre* (Paris, 1893), section de l'ingénieur, no. 42A of *Encyclopédie scientifique des aide-mémoire,* M. Léauté, ed.; *La marine des États-Unis* (Paris, 1896); *Chaudières marines, cours de machine à vapeur professé à l'École d'application du génie maritime* (Paris, 1896, 1902), trans. and ed. by Leslie S. Robertson as *Marine Boilers, Their Construction and Working, Dealing More Specially With Tubulous Boilers* (London, 1898, 1906); *Machines marines, cours de machines à vapeur professé à l'École d'application du génie maritime* (Paris, 1899); *Les marines de guerre à l'Exposition Universelle de 1900* (Paris, 1902); *Évolution de la puissance défensive des navires de guerre, avec un complément concernant la stabilité des navires* (Paris, 1907); and *La marine moderne, ancienne histoire et questions neuves* (Paris, 1910, 1914).

His articles appeared in *Mémoires de la Société imperiale* [*nationale* after 1871] *des sciences naturelles* [*et mathématiques* after 1879] *de Cherbourg* between **15** (1869–1870) and **31** (1898–1900); the *Mémoires présentés par divers savants à l'Académie des sciences . . .* between **22**, no. 7 (1876) and **26**, no. 5 (1879); in *Comptes rendus hebdomadaires des séances de l'Académie des sciences* between **69** (26 July 1869) and **158** (2 June 1914).

Also of value are *Notes sur mes travaux scientifiques et maritimes* (Cherbourg, 1879); three vols. with the title *Notice sur les travaux de M. L.-E. Bertin* (Paris, 1884, 1885, 1896); and the autographed album "Projets de navires à flottaison cellulaire (1870–1873)," presented by Bertin to the library of the Institute in 1884.

II. SECONDARY LITERATURE. Works containing information on Bertin are Barrillon, "Émile Bertin," in *Neptunia*, no. 10 (2nd trimester 1948), 22–24; Henri Bouasse, *Houle, rides, seiches et marées* (Paris, 1924); Edgar de Geoffroy, "Bertin (Louis-Émile)," in *Larousse mensuel illustré,* no. 216 (Feb. 1925), 691–692; E. Sauvage, "Louis Émile Bertin," in *Bulletin de la Société d'encouragement pour l'industrie nationale* (June 1925), 438–459; and Togari, *Louis-Émile Bertin. Son rôle dans la création de la Marine japonaise* (n.p., 1935). Also used in preparing this article were the birth records for 1840 and the death records for 1843 of Nancy; the register of students of the École Polytechnique, IX, covering 1855–1862; *Annuaire de la marine et des colonies* for 1863–1870 and 1872–1889; *État du personnel de la marine, décembre 1871* (Versailles, 1871); and *Annuaire de la marine* for 1890–1906.

ARTHUR BIREMBAUT

BERTINI, EUGENIO (*b.* Forlì, Italy, 8 November 1846; *d.* Pisa, Italy, 24 February 1933), *mathematics.*

In 1863 Bertini registered at the University of Bologna, intending to study engineering, but after taking the course taught by Luigi Cremona, he turned to pure mathematics. In 1866 he fought with Garibaldi in the third war for Italian independence. On the advice of Cremona, he resumed his studies and transferred to the University of Pisa, from which he received his degree in mathematics in 1867. During the academic year 1868–1869 he attended the course in Milan taught by L. Cremona, F. Brioschi, and F. Casorati. This course, dealing with Abel's integrals, exerted considerable influence on Bertini's own research.

In 1870 Bertini began his teaching career in the secondary schools of Milan, and in 1872 taught in Rome. There, on the recommendation of Cremona, he was appointed a special lecturer to teach descriptive and projective geometry. In 1875 he accepted the professorship of advanced geometry at the University of Pisa. From 1880 to 1892 he taught at the University of Pavia, and then returned to his former professorship at Pisa, a post he held until his retirement at the age of seventy-five. For the next ten years he taught an elective course in geometrical complements, which he had started as an introductory course to higher geometry.

Bertini's research deals particularly with algebraic geometry and constitutes definite progress in relation to the studies pursued by the school of Cremona. In this connection it is necessary to note that Cremona, having formulated the theory on plane and space transformations that bears his name, availed himself of the same transformations to change higher geometric figures into simpler figures and then apply to the higher figures the properties of the simpler ones. Bertini studied the geometric properties that remain constant during such transformations. He conceived the idea of exploring this field after studying the problem of the classification of plane involutions. In 1877 he succeeded in determining the various types, irreducible from each other, in which the planar involutions may be reduced through Cremona's transformations. His treatises are noteworthy for their order and clarity.

BIBLIOGRAPHY

I. ORIGINAL WORKS. Bertini's works include "La geometria delle serie lineari sopra una curva piana, secondo il metodo algebrico," in *Annali di matematica pura ed applicata,* 2nd ser., **22** (1894), 1–40; *Introduzione alla geometria proiettiva degli iperspazi* (Pisa, 1906; Messina, 1923); and *Complementi di geometria proiettiva* (Bologna, 1927).

II. SECONDARY LITERATURE. More information on Bertini may be found in G. Castelnuovo, "Commemorazione del socio Eugenio Bertini," in *Atti della Reale Accademia nazionale dei Lincei. Rendiconti,* Classe di scienze fisiche, matematiche e naturali, 6th ser., **17** (1933), 745–748; and F. Enriques, *Le matematiche nella storia e nella cultura* (Bologna, 1938), pp. 284, 286, 287, 292.

ETTORE CARRUCCIO

BERTRAND, CHARLES-EUGÈNE, or **Charles-Egmont** (*b.* Paris, France, 2 January 1851; *d.* Lille, France, 10 August 1917), *plant anatomy.*

After studying natural science at the Sorbonne and working for a short time in the laboratory of the

Faculty of Sciences at Paris, Bertrand spent the rest of his scientific career at the University of Lille. He considered himself primarily a botanist, although much of his work furthered geologists' understanding of coals and the evolution of the extinct plants found in them. He concentrated on aberrant or anomalous forms, and by this method discovered the phylogenetic relations not recognizable solely from normal types. Bertrand's monographs on aberrant forms developed primarily the affinities and filiations of thallophytes, higher vascular cryptogams (the ferns and club mosses), and lower phanerogams (the ancient gymnosperms).

Because plant fragments in coal are generally mutilated, Bertrand endeavored to learn the comparative anatomy of the vegetative structures (primarily stems), which are preserved. This anatomical knowledge permitted him to identify numerous forms for which the usual keys—leaf and flower morphology—failed. He was one of the earliest to examine thin sections of the carbonaceous rocks by means of the ordinary light microscope. This new technique contributed further to his success in differentiating the natures and compositions of the various types of coal. He showed bogheads to be primarily accumulations of algae, sometimes with other debris mixed in, all cemented by a primitive, humic paste (*gelée fondamentale*). In cannel coals, spores predominate. The *gelée fondamentale* is also a primary constituent in common coals and in two kinds of bituminous shales (*charbons humiques* and *charbons de purins*).

Part of Bertrand's fame rests on his establishment at the University of Lille of a laboratory famous for both education and research. Many of his studies were produced with collaborators, most notably with his son Paul, a paleobotanist.

BIBLIOGRAPHY

E. Morvillez, *Charles-Eugène Bertrand* (Caen, 1918), is the most complete biography and includes a bibliography of Bertrand's writings. Another bibliography is in Giuseppe de Toni, ed., *Bibliographia algologica universalis* (Forlì, 1932), pp. 247–252. For his geological work in particular, see the following unsigned articles: "L'oeuvre géologique de C. Eg. Bertrand," in *Annales de la Société géologique du nord,* **44** (1919), 47–64 (see also 6–7); and "Célébration du centenaire de Ch. Barrois et Ch.-E. Bertrand et du souvenir de P. Bertrand," *ibid.,* **71** (1951), 135–143.

BERT HANSEN

BERTRAND, GABRIEL (*b.* Paris, France, 17 May 1867; *d.* Paris, 20 June 1962), *biochemistry.*

Gabriel Bertrand introduced into biochemistry both the term "oxidase" and the concept of trace elements. The son of a Paris merchant, Bertrand early showed an interest in the natural sciences, especially in the botanical specimens in the collections of the Muséum d'Histoire Naturelle. After obtaining his baccalaureate degree in 1886, he entered the École de Pharmacie in Paris, at the same time enrolling in Edmond Frémy's courses at the chemical laboratory of the museum.

In 1890 Bertrand was appointed *préparateur* to Albert Arnauld, who had just taken over the course in organic chemistry after the death of his teacher Michel Chevreul; Bertrand held this post for ten years. He had also been noticed by Émile Duclaux, Pasteur's successor at the Institut Pasteur, and in 1900 was appointed to the staff of the recently created institute of biochemistry at the Institute.

Duclaux was professor of biochemistry in the Faculté des Sciences, Paris, although his teaching was done at the Institut Pasteur. After Duclaux's death in 1904, Bertrand was placed in charge of his courses; in 1908, he was named to the vacant chair, a position he held until his retirement in 1937. But retirement for Bertrand did not mean the end of work, and for many years thereafter he remained a familiar sight at the Institute.

Bertrand obtained his doctorate in 1904 with a dissertation that was a study of the conversion of sorbitol (D-sorbitol) into sorbose (L-sorbose), a sugar first identified in the sorb berry. He found ultimately that the conversion depended on the presence of a microbe, *Bacterium xylinum* (i.e., *Aerobacter xylinum*), and that it was an oxidation occurring only in the presence of oxygen.

In the years 1894–1897 Bertrand investigated the process of the darkening and hardening of the latex of lacquer trees. He recognized that the color change was caused by the oxidation of a phenol—laccol—in the presence of another substance, laccase. Other phenolic compounds, he found, underwent similar organic oxidation reactions, also in the presence of substances similar to laccase. In 1896 Bertrand first used the term "oxidase" for these oxidizing enzymes (including tyrosinase, which he had described). During the following year he published several studies of oxidases.

Bertrand made another important advance in the analysis of enzymes when he observed that laccase ash contained a large proportion of manganese. Throughout the last half of the nineteenth century it had been known that plants contained minerals, and in 1860 it was demonstrated that in artificial situations plants could be grown in a water culture containing only metallic salts. Researchers still accepted the presence of minerals in the plant as incidental, however, and thought them the result of the presence of minerals in the soil. Bertrand's work in 1897, and especially his later claim that a lack of manganese caused an interruption of growth, forced a change in thinking on this matter. He concluded that the metal formed an essential part of the enzyme, and, more generally, that a metal might be a necessary functioning part of the oxidative enzyme. From this and similar researches he developed his concept of the trace element, essential for proper metabolism.

During his career Bertrand published hundreds of papers on the organic effects of various metals. In 1911 he showed that the development of the mold *Aspergillis niger* was greatly influenced by the presence of minute amounts of manganese. For such researches Bertrand was forced to develop more precise methods of organic analysis, many of which later came into widespread use.

Bertrand's researches were immediately applied to the elimination of previously undiagnosable pathological conditions, thereafter recognized as the result of deficiencies of trace elements. His work also provided the basis for further elaboration of the enzymatic systems involved in respiration and metabolic processes.

BIBLIOGRAPHY

I. ORIGINAL WORKS. Among Bertrand's articles are "Sur le latex de l'arbre à laque," in *Comptes rendus de l'Académie des sciences* (Paris), **118** (1894), 1215–1218, which also appeared in *Bulletin de la Société chimique de France,* **11** (1894), 717–721; "Sur le latex de l'arbre à laque et sur une nouvelle diastase contenue dans ce latex," in *Comptes rendus de la Société biologique* (Paris), **46** (1894), 478–480; "Sur la présence simultanée de la laccase et de la tyrosinase dans le suc de quelques champignons," in *Comptes rendus de l'Académie des sciences* (Paris), **123** (1896), 463–465; "Sur une nouvelle oxydase, ou ferment soluble oxidant, d'origine végétale," in *Comptes rendus de l'Académie des sciences* (Paris), **122** (1896), 1215–1217, which also appeared in *Bulletin du Muséum d'histoire naturelle* (Paris), **2** (1896), 206–208, and in *Bulletin de la Société chimique* (Paris), **15** (1896), 793–797; "Nouvelles recherches sur les ferments oxidants ou oxidases," in *Annales agronomique,* **23** (1897), 385–399; "Les oxidases ou ferments solubles oxidants," in *Revue scientifique,* 4th ser., **8** (1897), 65–73; "Recherches sur la laccase, nouveau ferment soluble, à propriétés oxydantes," in *Annales de chimie,* **12** (1897), 115–140; "Sur l'emploi favorable du manganèse comme engrais," in *Comptes rendus de l'Académie des sciences* (Paris), **141** (1905), 1255–1257.

With M. Javiller, Bertrand wrote "Influence du manganèse sur le développement de l'*Aspergillis niger,*" "Influence combinée du zinc et du manganèse sur le développement de l'*Aspergillis niger,*" and "Influence du zinc et du manganèse sur la composition minérale de l'*Aspergillis niger,*" all of which appeared in *Comptes rendus de l'Académie des sciences* (Paris), **152** (1911), 225–228, 900–902, and 1337–1340, respectively.

II. SECONDARY LITERATURE. Two biographical memoirs appeared soon after Bertrand's death, one by Y. Raoul in *Bulletin de la Société de chimie biologique,* **44** (1962), 1051–1055, and the other by Marcel Delépine in *Comptes rendus de l'Académie des sciences* (Paris), **255** (1962), 217–222. The former was to be reprinted separately as a pamphlet containing a complete bibliography of Bertrand's works, but has not yet appeared. No other complete bibliographical listings are available, although partial listings may be found in the *Royal Society Catalogue of Scientific Papers*, XIII, and in Poggendorff, V and VI. Bertrand's relationship with the Institut Pasteur is discussed in Albert Delaunay, *L'Institut Pasteur. Des origines à aujourd'hui* (Paris, 1962).

The presence of metallic salts in plants was demonstrated in the nineteenth century, as was their ability to maintain plant life. See W. Knop, "Ueber die Ernährung der Pflanzen durch wässerige Lösungen bei Ausschluss des Bodens," in *Landwirtschaftliche Versuchsstationen,* **2** (1860), 65–99, 270–293; and J. Sachs, "Ueber die Erziehung von Landpflanzen in Wasser," in *Botanisches Zentralblatt,* **18** (1860), 113–117.

ALAN S. KAY

BERTRAND, JOSEPH LOUIS FRANÇOIS (*b.* Paris, France, 11 March 1822; *d.* Paris, 5 April 1900), *mathematics.*

Bertrand's father was Alexandre Bertrand, a writer of popular scientific articles and books. Alexandre had attended the École Polytechnique in Paris with Auguste Comte and Jean Marie Constant Duhamel, and the latter married his sister. When his father died, young Bertrand went to live with the Duhamels. A well-known professor of mathematics at the École Polytechnique, Duhamel was the right man to guide his precocious nephew. At the age of eleven the boy was allowed to attend classes at the École Polytechnique. In 1838, at sixteen, Bertrand took the degrees of bachelor of arts and bachelor of science, and at seventeen he received the doctor of science degree with a thesis in thermomechanics. The same year (1839) he officially entered the École Polytechnique, and in 1841 he entered the École des Mines. Bertrand's first publications date from this period, the first being "Note sur quelques points de la théorie de l'électricité" (1839), which deals with Poisson's equation, $\Delta V = -4\pi\rho$, and the law of Coulomb.

In 1841 Bertrand became a professor of elementary mathematics at the Collège Saint-Louis, a position that he filled until 1848. In May 1842 he and his brother, returning to Paris from a visit to their friends the Aclocques at Versailles, were nearly killed in a railroad accident which left a scar on Bertrand's face. Bertrand married Mlle. Aclocque in 1844, in which year he also became *répétiteur d'analyse* at the École Polytechnique. Three years later he became *examinateur d'admission* at this school and *suppléant* of the physicist Jean-Baptiste Biot at the Collège de France. In 1848, during the revolution, Bertrand served as a captain in the national guard. He published much during these years—in mathematical physics, in mathematical analysis, and in differential geometry. The first of Bertrand's many textbooks, the *Traité d'arithmétique,* appeared in Paris in 1849 and was followed by the *Traité élémentaire d'algèbre* (1850); both were written for secondary schools. They were followed by textbooks for college instruction. Bertrand always knew how to fascinate his readers and his lecture audiences, and his books had a wide appeal because of content and style. In 1853 he edited and annotated the third edition of J. L. Lagrange's *Mécanique analytique.* From the many publications in this period, one, "Mémoire sur le nombre de valeurs . . .," introduces the so-called problem of Bertrand: to find the subgroups of the symmetric groups of lowest possible index. Another publication, "Mémoire sur la théorie des courbes à double courbure" (1850), discusses curves with the property that a linear relation exists between first and second curvature; these are known as curves of Bertrand.

In 1852 Bertrand became professor of special mathematics at the Lycée Henry IV (then Lycée Napoléon). He also taught at the École Normale Supérieure. In 1856 he replaced Jacques Charles François Sturm as professor of analysis at the École Polytechnique, where he became the colleague of Duhamel. He then left secondary education to pursue his academic career. In 1862 he succeeded Biot at the Collège de France. Bertrand held his position at the École Polytechnique until 1895, that at the Collège de France until his death.

In 1856 Bertrand was elected to the Académie des Sciences, where in 1874 he succeeded the geologist Élie de Beaumont as *secrétaire perpétuel.* In 1884 he replaced the chemist Jean-Baptiste Dumas in the Académie Française. These high academic positions, combined with his erudition, his eloquence, and his natural charm, gave him a position of national prominence in the cultural field.

During the Commune of 1871 Bertrand's Paris house was burned, and many of his manuscripts were lost, among them those of the third volume of his textbook on calculus and his book on thermodynamics. He was able to rewrite and publish the latter as *Thermodynamique.* Afterward he lived at Sèvres and then at Viroflay. At his home Bertrand enjoyed being the center of a lively intellectual circle. Many of his pupils became well-known scientists—for instance, Gaston Darboux, who succeeded him as *secrétaire perpétuel.* In his *Leçons sur la théorie générale des surfaces,* Darboux elaborated many results of Bertrand and his mathematical circle.

Bertrand's publications, apart from his textbooks, cover many fields of mathematics. Although his work lacks the fundamental character of that of the great mathematicians of his period, his often elegant studies on the theory of curves and surfaces, of differential equations and their application to analytical mechanics, of probability, and of the theory of errors were widely read. Many of his articles are devoted to subjects in theoretical physics, including capillarity, theory of sound, electricity, hydrodynamics, and even the flight of birds. In his *Calcul des probabilités,* written, like all his books, in an easy and pleasant style, there is a problem in continuous probabilities known as Bertrand's paradox. It deals with the probability that a stick of length $a > 2l$, placed blindly on a circle of radius l, will be cut by the circle in a chord of less than a given length $b < 2l$. It turns out that this probability is undetermined unless specific assumptions are made about what constitute equally likely cases (i.e., what is meant by "placed blindly").

From 1865 until his death Bertrand edited the *Journal des savants.* For this periodical, as for the *Revue des deux mondes,* he wrote articles of a popular nature, many dealing with the history of science. This interest in history of science appears also in the many *éloges* he wrote as *secrétaire perpétuel* of the Academy, among which are biographies of Poncelet, Élie de Beaumont, Lamé, Leverrier, Charles Dupin, Foucault, Poinsot, Chasles, Cauchy, and F. F. Tisserand. He also wrote papers on Viète, Fresnel, Lavoisier, and Comte, and books on d'Alembert and Pascal.

Bertrand spent the later part of his life in the midst of his large family, surrounded by his friends, who were many and distinguished. His son Marcel and his nephews Émile Picard and Paul Appell were his fellow members in the Académie des Sciences. In 1895 his pupils gave him a medal in commemoration of his fifty years of teaching at the École Polytechnique. The influence of Bertrand's work, however, is hardly comparable to that of several of his contemporaries and pupils. Lest it be judged ephemeral, it must be viewed in the context of nineteenth-century Paris and of Bertrand's brilliant academic career, his exalted social position, and the love and respect given him by his many pupils.

BIBLIOGRAPHY

I. ORIGINAL WORKS. Bertrand's works include "Note sur quelques points de la théorie de l'électricité," in *Journal de mathématiques pures et appliquées,* **4** (1839), 495–500; "Mémoire sur le nombre de valeurs que peut prendre une fonction quand on y permute les lettres qu'elle renferme," in *Journal de l'École polytechnique,* **30** (1845), 123–140; *Traité d'arithmétique* (Paris, 1849); "Mémoire sur la théorie des courbes à double courbure," in *Journal de mathématiques pures et appliquées,* **15** (1850), 332–350; *Traité élémentaire d'algèbre* (Paris, 1850); *Traité de calcul différentiel et de calcul intégral,* 2 vols. (Paris, 1864–1870); *Les fondateurs de l'astronomie moderne* (Paris, 1867); *Rapport sur les progrès les plus récents de l'analyse mathématique* (Paris, 1867); *L'Académie des sciences et les académiciens de 1666 à 1793* (Paris, 1869); "Considérations relatives à la théorie du vol des oiseaux," in *Comptes rendus de l'Académie des sciences,* **72** (1871), 588–591; *Thermodynamique* (Paris, 1887); *Calcul des probabilités* (Paris, 1889; 2nd ed., 1897); *D'Alembert* (Paris, 1889); *Éloges académiques* (Paris, 1889); *Leçons sur la théorie mathématique de l'électricité* (Paris, 1890); *Pascal* (Paris, 1891); *Éloges académiques, nouvelle série* (Paris, 1902), which has a complete bibliography of Bertrand's works on pp. 387–399.

II. SECONDARY LITERATURE. Gaston Darboux, "Éloge historique de J. L. F. Bertrand," in Bertrand's *Éloges académiques, nouvelle série,* pp. 8–51, and in Darboux's *Éloges académiques et discours* (Paris, 1912), pp. 1–60. Another source of information is *Comptes rendus de l'Académie,* **130** (1900), 961–978, addresses delivered in the Academy to honor Bertrand and used by G. H. Bryan for his article "Joseph Bertrand," in *Nature,* **61** (1899–1900), 614–616. The library of the Institut de France nos. 2029–2047 comprises correspondence and some papers of Bertrand; 2719 (5) contains "Notes autobiographiques" (information from Henry Nathan)—these are probably the notes used by Darboux in his *Éloge.* Discussion of Bertrand's problem may be found in H. Weber, *Lehrbuch der Algebra,* II (Brunswick, 1899), 154–160. The curves of Bertrand are dealt with in books on differential geometry, e.g., G. Darboux, *Leçons sur la théorie générale des surfaces,* I (Paris, 1887), 13–17, 44–46, and III (Paris, 1894), 313–314.

D. J. STRUIK

BERTRAND, MARCEL-ALEXANDRE (*b.* Paris, France, 2 July 1847; *d.* Paris, 13 February 1907), *geotectonics, stratigraphy, general geology.*

Bertrand's father was the mathematician Joseph Bertrand. Marcel studied at the École Polytechnique and the École des Mines in Paris. After graduation he worked in the Geological Survey of France, and in 1886 he succeeded his teacher Béguyer de Chancourtois at the École des Mines. In 1896 the Académie des Sciences elected him to the chair Pasteur had held.

Inspired by the writings of Eduard Suess, Bertrand always maintained a concern for what he called the grand problems of general geology. Early in his career he devoted his attention to the general problems of mountain structure while producing a dozen sheets of the geologic map of France. He solved the anomaly of le Beausset (and was awarded the Prix Fontannes by the Geological Society of France for it in 1889) by discovering that the islands of Triassic sediments resting on Cretaceous formations are the eroded remains of an enormous overturned fold. His conception of very large-scale overturned folds and overthrusts related the geological structure of Provence to that of the Alps. Bertrand was the first to conceive of the overthrust structure of the Alps, and by this theory of *grandes nappes* he attempted to connect the structures of the Pyrenees, Provence, and the Alps. His analysis of horizontal crustal compression and the displacements resulting from it won the Prix Vaillant of the Académie des Sciences of the Institut de France in 1890, but the essay was not published until 1908.

Bertrand developed an orogenic wave concept that he used to separate earth history into natural divisions on the basis of successive periods of intense folding and orogeny, each division identified with a chain of mountains. Working from Suess's brilliant synthesis, Bertrand demonstrated in 1887 that the Caledonian, Hercynian, and Alpine deformation produced consecutively those three mountain chains, thus building up the European continent gradually from north to south.

In 1894, at Zurich, Bertrand offered his very original conception of the complete sedimentary cycle with its recurring facies; each cycle represented one of the fundamental deformations. He showed that four kinds of facies are repeated in the different mountain chains, typically gneiss, followed by schistous flysch, then coarse flysch and coarse sandstone. At this time he also added the Huronian orogeny of Precambrian time to the other three deformations. In essaying a mechanism for these orogenies, Bertrand revived, then abandoned, the tetrahedral plan of the earth of Lowthian Green and Michel-Lévy.

BIBLIOGRAPHY

I. ORIGINAL WORKS. *Oeuvres géologiques de Marcel Bertrand,* Emmanuel de Margerie, ed., 3 vols. (Paris, 1927–1931), contains all Bertrand's published works except the sheets of the *Carte géologique détaillée de la France* (scale 1:80,000); "Études sur les terrains secondaires et tertiaires dans les provinces de Grenade et de Malaga," in *Mémoires de l'Académie des sciences,* **30** (1899), 377–579;

and the posthumously published "Mémoire sur les refoulements qui ont plissé l'écorce terrestre et sur le rôle des déplacements horizontaux," *ibid.,* **50** (1908), 1–267. It includes Bertrand's own notice of his scientific works to 1894.

II. SECONDARY LITERATURE. The most complete biographical notice is the *éloge* by Pierre Termier, in *Bulletin de la Société géologique de France,* 4th ser., **8** (1908), 163–204, including a bibliography. Other notices are Archibald Geikie, in *The Quarterly Journal of the Geological Society of London,* **61** (1908), 1–liv; W. Kilian and J. Révil, in *Annales de l'Université de Grenoble,* **20** (1908), 15–35; and Otto Wilckens, in *Centralblatt für Mineralogie, Geologie, und Paläontologie* (1909), 499–501. V. V. Beloussov, in his *Basic Problems in Geotectonics* (New York, 1962), pp. 39–43, sets some of Bertrand's contributions in historical perspective.

BERT HANSEN

BERWICK, WILLIAM EDWARD HODGSON (*b.* Dudley Hill, England, 11 March 1888; *d.* Bangor, Wales, 13 May 1944), *mathematics.*

Berwick's total output of original work is relatively small (thirteen papers and a monograph), due in part to ill health, and is concerned primarily with the theory of numbers and related topics, including the theory of equations. A penchant for problems involving numerical computation is reflected throughout his publications.

Much of Berwick's work is concerned with the following problem: Given a simple algebraic extension of the rational field, establish methods for computing its algebraic integers and the ideals they form. In the monograph *Integral Bases* (1927) Berwick made his most significant contribution to the resolution of this problem by developing methods for constructing an integral basis for the algebraic integers in such a field. The theoretical existence of integral bases is easily established but does not afford a practicable computational procedure. Methods for special cases—such as quadratic, cubic, and cyclotomic fields—had already been devised, but Berwick was the first to attack the much more formidable problem of developing methods that would apply to simple algebraic extensions in general. Although his method is not workable in certain exceptional cases, it possesses a wide range of applicability. Its strong numerical orientation, however, kept his work outside the mainstream of developments in algebraic number theory.

Berwick also obtained a necessary and sufficient condition that the general quintic equation be solvable by radicals in the field of its coefficients (1915), and was instrumental in bringing about the publication of tables of reduced ideals in quadratic fields by the British Association for the Advancement of Science (1934).

BIBLIOGRAPHY

Further information on Berwick is in H. Davenport, "W. E. H. Berwick," in *The Journal of the London Mathematical Society,* **21** (1946), 74–80, which contains references to all of Berwick's scientific work. See also the notes by Davenport and E. H. Neville in *Nature,* **154** (1944), 265, 465.

THOMAS HAWKINS

BERZELIUS, JÖNS JACOB (*b.* Väversunda, Östergötland, Sweden, 20 August 1779; *d.* Stockholm, Sweden, 7 August 1848), *chemistry.*

Berzelius came from an old Swedish family. A number of his ancestors had been clergymen. His father, Samuel, a teacher in the Linköping Gymnasium, died when his son was four years old. The mother, Elizabeth Dorothea, two years later married Anders Ekmarck, the pastor at Norrköping and himself the father of five children. Young Berzelius and his sister were raised with the Ekmarck children and educated by Ekmarck and private tutors. In 1788 Berzelius' mother died and within two years Ekmarck remarried. The two Berzelius children were sent to the home of their maternal uncle, Magnus Sjösteen. Young Jöns and his cousins quarreled frequently. Even after he entered the Linköping Gymnasium in 1793 conflicts continued, and to escape them Berzelius took a position in 1794 as tutor on a nearby farm, where he developed a strong interest in collecting and classifying flowers and insects. He had originally intended to become a clergyman, but he instead chose to develop his interest in natural science and decided on a career in medicine. Two years later he began his medical studies at Uppsala, but had to interrupt his work to earn money as a tutor. Fortunately, in 1798 he received a three-year scholarship which permitted him to continue his medical studies.

At this time his oldest stepbrother introduced him to chemistry, of which Jöns knew nothing. Together they studied Girtanner's *Anfangsgründe der antiphlogistischen Chemie.* Thus in his first studies Berzelius learned of the new chemistry which had not yet had much influence on the older Swedish chemists. The professor of chemistry at Uppsala, Johan Afzelius, did not offer much encouragement to Berzelius who therefore began to carry out experiments in his own quarters. During the next summer, lacking any financial support, he intended to stay at the home of an aunt, but her husband did not approve of the young man and sent him to work in a pharmacy at Vadstena. Here he was able to learn glassblowing. Later in the summer his uncle, to get rid of him, introduced him to Sven Hedin, chief physician at the

Medevi mineral springs. He took Berzelius as his assistant for the summer of 1800. There he began his scientific career by analyzing the mineral content of the spring water. At the same time he read of the newly described voltaic pile, the first reliable source of a continuous electric current. He soon built one for himself from sixty pairs of alternating zinc disks and copper coins. In 1802 he used the knowledge thus gained in his doctoral thesis, a study of the effect of the galvanic current on patients with a number of different diseases. He found that the current had no effect on the patients, but his interest in electrical phenomena remained strong.

Sven Hedin was aware of Berzelius' interest in chemistry and soon after the latter's medical degree was granted, Hedin arranged for his appointment as an unpaid assistant to the professor of medicine and pharmacy at the College of Medicine in Stockholm. His duties involved the preparation of artificial mineral waters. He lived in a house owned by Wilhelm Hisinger, a wealthy mine owner with a great interest in mineralogy and chemistry. Berzelius soon began to undertake serious chemical investigations with Hisinger. The electrochemical and mineralogical investigations that the two enthusiasts carried out laid the foundations for Berzelius' future work.

Meanwhile, Berzelius became involved in serious financial difficulties. His only income came from his position as physician to the poor in several Stockholm districts, and the salary was very low. Business ventures that he attempted turned out disastrously, and he was deep in debt. His position improved in 1807 when the professor of medicine and pharmacy died and he was appointed to the post. He now had an increased salary and access to a laboratory. In this period he began to work on the textbooks whose composition strongly influenced the direction of his later career. In 1810 the Medical College became the Karolinska Institutet, an independent medical school, and Berzelius was able to devote most of his time to chemistry. He became a member of the Swedish Academy of Science in 1808 and its president in 1810.

During this time Berzelius began the series of travels abroad through which he became personally acquainted with almost all of the leading chemists of his day. In 1807 he met Hans Christian Oersted, the noted discoverer of electromagnetism. In 1812 he visited England and met all the important British chemists. He was especially anxious to meet Humphry Davy, whose electrochemical researches had been closely related to those of Berzelius and Hisinger. At first Davy and Berzelius got on well, but later some of Berzelius' criticisms of one of Davy's books were reported indirectly to Davy and a coolness developed between the two which was never entirely eliminated. In 1818 Berzelius visited Paris, where he remained for a year, meeting his French colleagues. He spent a part of his time working with Dulong at the home of Berthollet in Arcueil. On his way back to Stockholm he traveled through Germany, where he met the most prominent German chemists. He created such a strong impression there that he was later followed to Sweden by a number of younger chemists who wished to work in his laboratory. These included Eilhard Mitscherlich and Gustav and Heinrich Rose. Friedrich Wöhler, who spent a year (1823–1824) with Berzelius, maintained a close personal friendship with him for the rest of his life, translating many of his important works into German.

While he was in France, Berzelius was elected secretary of the Swedish Academy of Science. This doubled his income and furnished him with an excellent laboratory. He was able to devote himself almost entirely to his laboratory research and to his voluminous writings, including correspondence with scientists all over Europe. He became the recognized authority on chemical questions, although he became involved in a number of polemics, especially with Dumas and Liebig.

Berzelius suffered from poor health through much of his life. He was subject to severe periodic headaches which occurred regularly each month at the time of the new and full moon. In later life these disappeared, but were replaced by attacks of gout and periods of prolonged depression and apathy which interfered with his scientific work. Feeling the need for a more domestic life, he finally decided he should marry, and so in 1835, at the age of fifty-six, he married Elizabeth Poppius, the twenty-four-year-old daughter of one of his old friends. On this occasion the king of Sweden gave him the title of baron. The marriage, which was childless, eased the remaining years of his life.

As he grew older, he became more and more set in his ideas, refusing to accept the newer developments in chemistry which contradicted some of his own theories. He withdrew more and more from the laboratory and spent much time trying to discredit the ideas which the growth of the new field of organic chemistry was forcing upon younger chemists. The last years of his life were not happy ones. At the time of his death he had become a respected figure, but one whose opinions were generally disregarded by his younger colleagues.

Berzelius' most active and productive years were those in which chemistry was beginning to show the full effects of Lavoisier's revolution. The fundamental tools which he created were extremely influential in determining the direction in which the science developed. His achievements were many and varied, and at first glance they seem rather unrelated to each other. Upon closer examination we find an underlying unity of thought and a logical interconnection and development of this thought in most of his work.

He was almost self-taught in chemistry. His first textbook adhered to the antiphlogistic viewpoint. The theories of Lavoisier came late to Sweden, but Berzelius never learned the theory of phlogiston. From the time of one of the earliest experiments that he carried out in his rooms, the preparation of oxygen, he was a firm believer in the essential participation of this element in the constitution of chemical compounds. His first scientific papers were rejected for publication by the Academy because he used the antiphlogistic nomenclature. Berzelius was also heir to the chemical work of his own countrymen. The systematization of chemistry and the interest in the nature of chemical affinity which were characteristic of the work of Torbern Bergman as well as the discovery of new minerals and elements carried out by Scheele and other Scandinavian chemists were certainly influential in determining the direction of Berzelius' theoretical and laboratory studies. These men had developed mineral analysis to a high degree and it is not strange that one of the first pieces of chemical work by Berzelius was the analysis of the composition of Medevi mineral waters.

Aside from these influences of older workers, Berzelius was always keenly aware of the importance of the current literature. He studied it carefully, making critical surveys at first for his own use and later for the benefit of all chemists. His earliest book, published in 1802, was a treatise on galvanism, a review of all the work done up to that time on the action of electricity on salts and minerals. This reflected his early appreciation of the importance of the voltaic pile. It showed his ability to synthesize the literature, and it formed the basis for his pioneering studies with Hisinger.

His association with Hisinger during the first decade of the nineteenth century was particularly fruitful. Through this association Berzelius gained access to the largest voltaic pile in Sweden, owned by the Galvanic Society, of which Hisinger was a leading member. In 1803 Hisinger and Berzelius published the results of their studies on the action of the electric current on a number of sodium, potassium, ammonium, and calcium salts. They found that all the salts were decomposed by electricity. Oxygen, acids, and oxidized bodies accumulated at the positive pole, while combustible bodies, alkalies, and alkaline earths

passed to the negative pole. Some acids were converted to a lower oxidation state and passed to the negative pole. Thus the lower oxidation state represented a "combustible body." Similar results were obtained and extended by Humphry Davy in England in the years from 1806 to 1807 and led him to the isolation of the alkali and alkaline earth metals. Berzelius with his friend Pontin also continued this type of work, and in 1808 introduced the use of mercury as the negative electrode. This permitted obtaining amalgams of the metals and even ammonium amalgam.

These studies aroused the interest of Berzelius and Davy in each other and was one of the reasons Berzelius visited England in 1812. More important, they convinced him of the significance of electricity in binding chemical elements together and also strengthened his conviction, gained from reading Lavoisier, that oxygen was an essential constituent not only of all acids, but also of bases as well. From these ideas he was later to develop his dualistic theory of the nature of salts.

Hisinger was not solely interested in electrochemical studies. He had also been interested since boyhood in the minerals found in and around his mines. He had had analyses made of a number of minerals that he had collected, and he himself had analyzed a number of them. Among his minerals was a very heavy stone found near the iron mine of Bastnäs, in which Scheele had vainly tried to find tungsten. Since Berzelius had been carrying out mineral analyses, Hisinger proposed that they should study this mineral together. In 1803 they found that it contained a new element which they named cerium. This was discovered at the same time by Klaproth in Berlin.

While these studies were in progress, Berzelius was acting as assistant in medicine at the School of Medicine in Stockholm. In the course of his work he realized that there were no adequate Swedish textbooks on chemical subjects, and so he decided to prepare such texts himself. The first of these was a book on animal chemistry, published in 1806, which included the results of numerous analyses he had made on animal tissues and fluids. In the course of this work he noted that muscle tissues contain lactic acid, previously found by Scheele in milk. He developed an interest at this time in organic acids, which he later studied in greater detail. After completion of this text, Berzelius turned to the composition of a general textbook of chemistry, and in 1808 he published the first volume of his *Lärbok i kemien*, which was destined to become the most authoritative chemical text of its day. While he was writing it, problems occurred to Berzelius and the search for solutions to these led him to carry out much of the research which occupied his most productive period.

At this time chemists were still debating the questions of whether chemical compounds had a fixed composition. The Berthollet-Proust controversy had nearly been decided in favor of the Proustian view that the composition of salts was invariant, but the actual evidence in support of this view was far from conclusive, largely because of the inadequate number of analyses of salts that existed, and the inaccuracies of many of the analyses which did exist. Furthermore, there was no theoretical reason for assuming a fixed composition. The Berthollet-Proust controversy had Berzelius studied the work of Jeremias Benjamin Richter, who in 1792 had published a work on stoichiometry in which he reported measurements of the amounts of various acids required to neutralize certain bases and of bases to neutralize acids. The work actually demonstrated the law of constant proportions. Berzelius saw that his own analyses, so far as they had been carried, also agreed with this law. He decided to devote himself to the analysis of a large number of salts to confirm or disprove this law. At just this time he learned of the atomic theory of Dalton, which supplied a theoretical basis for the law. Berzelius now realized that he did not yet possess the information needed to complete the second volume of his textbook. For the next four years he carried on his analytical studies and finally summarized them in the second volume, which appeared in 1812. In every subsequent edition he presented further results of his continuing analytical studies. In the meantime, he published many of them in the *Afhandlingar i fysik, kemi och mineralogi,* a journal which Hisinger had founded in 1806 because neither he nor Berzelius were satisfied with the brief form required by the Academy for publication of papers in its *Proceedings.* Berzelius took over publication of later volumes of this journal, and it continued to appear until 1818 when he became secretary of the Academy and could himself have an influence on its policies. Most of Berzelius' important papers were also published in foreign journals, and the various editions of his textbook appeared in German, French, Dutch, Italian, and Spanish. Wöhler's German translations were especially helpful in making his ideas known abroad.

The scientific apparatus and reagents available in Sweden when Berzelius began his work were very inadequate. In consequence, he had to design and build almost everything he needed and to synthesize most of his own reagents. The new forms of apparatus that he built were described in the various editions of his textbook and became standard pieces of equipment in laboratories all over the world. He was especially skillful in the use of the blowpipe, which had been developed in the Scandinavian countries. He utilized it in many of his analytical procedures, and the book that he wrote concerning it popularized its use abroad. It was not until his visit to Paris in 1818 that he was able to secure better materials for his laboratory; he sent home twelve large packing cases of apparatus.

Not only did Berzelius have to design his apparatus, but he also had to work out new analytical methods, and in the planning of such methods he showed his chemical genius. He spent much time in the preliminary work for each analysis, so that when he performed the analysis itself he was sure of his results and seldom felt the need to repeat the work.

He set himself the task "to find the definite and simple proportions in which the constituents of inorganic nature are bound together." In general he based his work on oxygen compounds. His conviction of the importance of oxides had begun with his studies of Lavoisier's work and had been strengthened by his electrochemical experiments. He determined the ratio of metal to oxygen in a number of metallic oxides by reducing the oxide to the metal with hydrogen, or sometimes by converting the metal to its oxide. Similarly he determined the oxygen to sulfur ratio in sulfur dioxide and trioxide. From these results he went on to analyses of sulfates and other salts. He reported his analyses in terms of the positive and negative components; for example, for calcium sulfate as CaO and SO_3. This method of reporting analytical results was long continued by analytical chemists. To his great delight all his analyses fitted into his original assumption of the validity of the law of constant proportions. His results permitted him to determine the atomic weights of the elements he studied, although at first he had no way of determining whether a given value or some multiple of it represented the true atomic weight. When Dulong and Petit in 1819 announced the law that the product of atomic weight and specific heat is a constant, Berzelius recognized that he had a new tool for his purpose, and when Mitscherlich, who later studied with him, published the law of isomorphism in 1820, he saw another. By applying these laws to his own results, he was able to correct his values, and only in the case of the alkali metals did he finally accept values that were double the correct ones. He published revised tables of atomic weights in 1814, 1818, and 1828, and a separate pamphlet was issued in French in 1819 to give wider circulation to his values. In the 1818 table he reported the atomic weights of forty-five of the forty-nine elements then known. Thirty-nine of the determinations were his; the other six were by his students.

The table included the chemical composition of nearly 2,000 compounds.

This work with so many salts of so many elements brought home to him the need for a simple and logical system of symbols to represent the compounds he discussed. His first publication in this field was a pamphlet in French issued in 1811, and he explained his ideas in German and English papers published over the next three years. His basic suggestion was that as the symbol for each element the first letter of the Latin name be chosen, or, if more than one element began with the same letter, the next letter of the name be added to the initial for one of them. The use of letters to represent the names of elements and compounds was not entirely new, but Berzelius introduced a new quantitative concept with his symbols. The letter stood for the atomic weight of the element as well, and so the chemical formulas of the compounds of these elements represented the chemical proportions of the elements in that compound. To indicate these proportions he wrote the appropriate small numbers in the formulas. He placed the numbers as superscripts resembling algebraic exponents in these formulas (e.g., SO^3), a practice that continued to be used in France, although elsewhere the numbers came to be written as subscripts. At first there was some opposition to the use of these formulas, but their advantages eventually came to be recognized and their use became universal. Berzelius later introduced certain modifications which he believed made the formulas simpler. Instead of writing O for oxygen he placed a dot for each oxygen atom above the symbol of the element combined with it, and for a double atom he placed a bar through the letter involved. Thus the symbol for water became Ḧ. Such formulas were not easily set in type, and these innovations did not survive for very long. The basic principles of the Berzelius system have served chemistry well, however.

In accord with the interest that Swedish chemists had long shown in mineralogical studies, Berzelius had from time to time analyzed minerals that came into his hands. As was noted above, the discovery of cerium was the result of such an analysis. However, when he began his systematic studies to establish the law of constant proportions, he worked largely with simple salts. In 1812 he received a gift of a large number of minerals which he later decided to classify. The methods of mineral classification existing at that time were based on appearance and physical properties. These seemed highly unsystematic to Berzelius. He concluded from his analytical experience that a logical classification could be based only on chemical composition. In his original system, first published in

1814, he arranged the minerals in terms of their basic constituents, although he later revised this and placed chief emphasis on the acid component. Like many of Berzelius' innovations, his system of mineral classification was at first received with some hostility, but this was gradually overcome. During his visit to Paris in 1818 he won the approval of Haüy, the leading mineralogist of the day, whose own system was based on physical properties.

Interest in the composition of inorganic substances and even of industrial wastes led to the discovery of a number of new elements in the Berzelius laboratory. He himself discovered selenium and thorium, while, as students working with him, Arfwedsen isolated lithium, Sefström found vanadium, and Mosander discovered a number of rare earth elements.

Berzelius was not only a brilliant laboratory experimenter. He constantly tried to bring together the isolated facts discovered by experiment and to produce a synthesis that could explain the basic problems of his science. The major synthesis of his career was his dualistic theory, by which he believed he had explained the long-discussed problem of the nature of the affinity that held chemical substances together. His analytical work furnished him with numerous examples of salts composed of acid and basic radicals, and his early electrochemical studies suggested to him the mechanism that he sought.

He had found that an electric current splits salts into positive and negative components. Berzelius believed in the two-fluid theory of electricity and he held that electricity was itself a substance. Therefore when a salt was split by a current, the negative electricity combined with the positive component of the salt, while the positive electricity combined with the negative component. This maintained electrical neutrality. When the electricities were not present, the negative and positive components of the salt would combine and neutralize each other. Berzelius built his theory by elaboration of these facts and ideas. He believed that one pole of a magnet could be stronger than the other, and similarly the electricity in a substance might be concentrated at one point in it, leading to a predominance at that point of either negative or positive electricity. This condition of unipolarity determined the electrical behavior of the substance. The intensity of the polarity was another important factor, since the more intense the polarity, the stronger would be the affinity for another substance which would neutralize it. Thus, as he said,

. . . every chemical combination is wholly and solely dependent on two opposing forces, positive and negative electricity, and every chemical compound must be composed of two parts combined by the agency of their electrochemical reaction, since there is no third force. Hence it follows that every compound body, whatever the number of its constituents, can be divided into two parts, one of which is positively and the other negatively electrical [*Essai sur la théorie des proportions chimiques* (1819), p. 98].

Berzelius arranged all the elements in a series of decreasing electronegativity. Since oxygen combined with everything and was liberated at the positive pole, it was obviously the most electronegative element, while potassium was the most electropositive. In compounds, the electrochemical nature of the element combined with oxygen determined the total polarity of the compound. This followed because the amounts of electricity in the two parts of an oxide seldom exactly neutralized each other. Therefore, when oxygen combined with an element, a compound of the "first order" resulted, such as potassium oxide, in which a positive charge remained, due to the strong electropositive character of the potassium. In the case of sulfuric acid (SO_3, the anhydride) a negative charge predominated, for sulfur stood next to oxygen in the table of decreasing electronegativities. If now potassium oxide and sulfuric acid were brought together, potassium sulfate was formed, $KO \cdot SO_3$ as Berzelius would write it, since he doubled the atomic weight of potassium. This would be a compound of the second order. A charge could still remain, since the two parts would not exactly neutralize each other, and another charged salt such as aluminum sulfate could combine with the potassium sulfate to form alum, a third-order compound. Finally, to neutralize completely the various charges, water could be taken up to give the fourth-order compound, hydrated alum.

This theory involves several physical difficulties. Unipolarity, either in magnets or atoms, is not possible, and Berzelius confused quantity and intensity of electricity, a distinction which had been made by Faraday. Berzelius was not well trained in physics, and physicists in general did not pay much attention to his theory. Among chemists, however, it attracted many followers, since it explained so easily the behavior of inorganic substances and since the great authority of Berzelius gave it added weight. It can be seen that it contains many features that were later incorporated into the more modern theories of the structure of polar compounds. Until the discovery of organic compounds, which did not fit readily into the scheme, the dualistic theory dominated the thinking of almost all chemists.

Although the dualistic concept was the most influential of the theoretical syntheses of Berzelius, he drew together other scattered facts and gave generalized definitions of other chemical phenomena upon which much later chemistry developed. These generalizations were made in the course of his compilation of the annual reviews of the progress of chemistry which he published from 1821 until his death.

In the days following the Lavoisier revolution, chemical analyses and syntheses revealed a great variety of new compounds. It was generally assumed that each of these compounds must have an individual composition. Eventually, however, analytical results indicated that quite distinct compounds might have the same chemical composition. The most famous case was the identity in analytical results for the fulminates and cyanates as revealed by Liebig and Wöhler. Berzelius became interested in these strange results and collected a number of other cases in which the same phenomenon was observed. In 1831 he proposed the name isomerism for this phenomenon. The name was chosen by analogy with the term isomorphism used by Mitscherlich for different compounds with the same crystal structures. In 1840 Berzelius suggested the name allotropy for the existence of different forms of the same element.

An even more important generalization was made when Berzelius gathered together a rather large number of cases in which a reaction occurred only when some third substance was present, although this substance seemed to remain unchanged throughout the reaction. In 1835 he suggested that here a new force must exist whose nature was not clear to him. He suggested the name catalytic force and called decomposition of bodies by this force catalysis "as one designates the decomposition of bodies by chemical affinity analysis."

Another term suggested by Berzelius was the word *protein,* which he proposed in a letter to Gerardus Mulder when the latter was investigating these compounds. He derived it from the Greek word *proteios* ("primitive"), since he recognized the prime importance of these compounds.

Berzelius was primarily interested in inorganic chemistry and most of his theoretical ideas were derived from the behavior of inorganic compounds. Nevertheless much of his early work involved analysis of animal products, and he continued to investigate organic compounds throughout most of his life. He developed a form of combustion apparatus which permitted him to analyze a number of carbon compounds, but which required a great amount of time. It took him eighteen months to carry out twenty-one analyses of seven organic acids. Liebig later developed this method to permit much more rapid determinations. However Berzelius was never as happy dealing with organic compounds as he was with inorganic salts. He considered organic chemistry not as the chemistry of carbon compounds, but as the chemistry of the living organism. To the day of his death he remained a vitalist. In the last edition of his textbook he said, "In living nature the elements seem to obey entirely different laws than they do in the dead." His attitude toward the rapidly developing field of organic chemistry became more and more antagonistic in the later years of his life. This fact emphasizes certain characteristics which were always important in his scientific outlook and which significantly determined the course of his work.

Berzelius was essentially a scientific conservative. His great experimental ability and his power to draw together diverse facts to produce important generalizations should not obscure the point that his work was based almost entirely upon the principles that he had learned in the first decade of his scientific activity. At that period chemical investigations were based very largely on the reactions of inorganic compounds, and this explains why Berzelius never really felt at home with organic chemistry. It involved new principles which were not his own. He resisted change when he felt his ideas were being violated. In the first part of his life he could gradually come to accept unpalatable conclusions. Thus, at first he refused to believe in the elementary nature of chlorine and nitrogen, believing them to be oxides of as yet undiscovered radicals. By 1818, however, he admitted that chlorine was an element, and by 1824 he came to the same conclusion for nitrogen.

As he grew older, it became more and more difficult to convince him that any change in his theories was possible. The mass of facts accumulated by the organic chemists alarmed him. Although at first he welcomed the radical theory expounded by Liebig and Wöhler from their investigation of the benzoyl radical, he soon realized that in this radical oxygen was present as a relatively unimportant constituent. This violated the dualistic theory. He tried to write formulas for radicals which could combine with oxygen as did metals or acids, and these formulas became more and more complicated as new facts contradicted them. Eventually all these formulas were rejected by his colleagues. The final blow came with the discovery by Dumas that chlorine could substitute for hydrogen in organic radicals without altering the essential properties of the compounds. Dumas and Laurent expanded the substitution principle into a major feature of organic chemistry. It was impossible for Berzelius to accept this, since for him negative chlorine could not replace positive hydrogen. His whole dualistic theory would collapse if he agreed to such a substitution.

Actually even the organic chemists recognized that they could not account for affinity in the compounds they studied. In developing their theory of types and later structural chemistry they simply represented chemical bonds by brackets or lines and made no attempt to explain what these represented. The relation of the forces holding salts together and those binding carbon to carbon or hydrogen could not be established until the electron theories of chemical bonding began to develop in the twentieth century. Then it was seen that there had been much truth in the Berzelius dualism, at least so far as polar compounds were concerned. This was of no help to Berzelius when he saw his precious theory discarded and his attempts to salvage it patronizingly disregarded by the new organic chemists. His attacks on Liebig, Dumas, and Laurent became more violent and much of the bitterness of his last years resulted from his inability to admit to any modification of the ideas he had developed in his most active years.

The tremendous influence which Berzelius exerted on the chemists of his time came not only from his experimental discoveries and his theoretical interpretations. His voluminous writings were translated into all important European languages and circulated everywhere in the chemical world. He reported his own discoveries in the various editions of his textbook, and he surveyed the whole progress of chemistry in his annual reports, the *Arsberättelser över vetenskapernas framsteg,* which were translated into German, mostly by Wöhler, and were read everywhere. Aside from these formal writings, Berzelius was personally acquainted with almost all the active chemists of Europe and after his visits to them he kept up an extensive correspondence, learning of new developments as they occurred and informing his friends about them even before he described them in his books. Much of his correspondence has been published.

In his own laboratory he worked directly with a succession of young Swedish and foreign students who thus learned his methods and thoughts firsthand and spread them abroad when they left him. Most of them maintained close friendship with him. In his autobiographical notes Berzelius lists twenty-four Swedes and twenty-one foreigners who worked in his laboratory. By the force of his personality, by the skill of his laboratory techniques, and by his power to collect, synthesize, and publicize the chemistry of his day, he exerted an influence on his own time which is still reflected in chemistry more than a century after his death.

BIBLIOGRAPHY

I. ORIGINAL WORKS. The publications of Berzelius were so numerous and appeared in so many editions, translations, and excerpts that a listing of even the major ones would consume a large amount of space. Fortunately a complete bibliography of all works by, and most works about, Berzelius has been compiled by Arne Holmberg, *Bibliografi över Berzelius* (Uppsala–Stockholm), Vol. I (1933), supp. 1 (1936), supp. 2 (1953); Vol. II (1936), supp. 1 (1953). A bibliography of the most important works is also given by J. R. Partington, *A History of Chemistry,* IV (London, 1964), 144–147. Berzelius' own account of some of his work is found in *Jöns Jacob Berzelius Autobiographical Notes,* Olof Larsell, trans. (Baltimore, 1934).

II. SECONDARY LITERATURE. The standard biography is H. G. Söderbaum, *Jac. Berzelius, Levnadsteckning,* 3 vols. (Uppsala, 1929–1931). A detailed account of the most important work is given in H. G. Söderbaum, *Berzelius Werden und Wachsen 1779–1821* (Leipzig, 1899). Useful shorter biographies are Wilhelm Prandtl, *Humphry Davy, Jöns Jacob Berzelius* (Stuttgart, 1948) and J. Erik Jorpes, *Jac. Berzelius, His Life and Work* (Stockholm, 1966).

HENRY M. LEICESTER

BESSEL, FRIEDRICH WILHELM (*b.* Minden, Germany, 22 July 1784; *d.* Königsberg, Germany [now Kaliningrad, U.S.S.R.], 17 March 1846), *astronomy, geodesy, mathematics.*

Bessel's father was a civil servant in Minden; his mother was the daughter of a minister named Schrader from Rheme, Westphalia. Bessel had six sisters and two brothers, both of whom became judges of provincial courts. He attended the Gymnasium in Minden but left after four years, with the intention of becoming a merchant's apprentice. At school he had had difficulty with Latin, and apart from an inclination toward mathematics and physics, he showed no signs of extraordinary talent until he was fifteen. (Later, after studying on his own, Bessel wrote extensively in Latin, apparently without difficulty.)

On 1 January 1799 Bessel became an apprentice to the famous mercantile firm of Kulenkamp in Bremen, where he was to serve for seven years without pay. He rapidly became so proficient in calculation and commercial accounting that after his first year he received a small salary; this was gradually increased, so that he became financially independent of his parents.

Bessel was especially interested in foreign trade, so he devoted his nights to studying geography, Spanish, and English, learning to speak and write the latter language within three months. In order to qualify as cargo officer on a merchant ship, he studied books on ships and practical navigation. The problem of determining the position of a ship at sea with the aid of the sextant stimulated his interest in astronomy, but knowing how to navigate by the stars without deeper insight into the foundations of astronomy did not satisfy him. He therefore began to study as-

tronomy and mathematics, and soon he felt qualified to determine time and longitude by himself.

Bessel made his first time determination with a clock and a sextant that had been built to his specifications. The determination of the longitude of Bremen and the observation of the eclipse of a star by the moon are among his first accurate astronomical exercises. He learned of observations and discoveries through the professional astronomical journals *Monatliche Correspondenz* and *Berliner astronomisches Jahrbuch,* and thus was able to judge the accuracy of his own observations.

In a supplementary volume of the *Berliner astronomisches Jahrbuch* Bessel found Harriot's 1607 observations of Halley's Comet, which he wanted to use to determine its orbit. He had equipped himself for this task by reading Lalande and then Olbers on the easiest and most convenient method of calculating a comet's orbit from several observations. The reduction of Harriot's observations and his own determination of the orbit were presented to Olbers in 1804. With surprise Olbers noted the close agreement of Bessel's results with Halley's calculation of the comet's elliptical elements. He immediately recognized the great achievement of the twenty-year-old apprentice and encouraged him to improve his determination of the comet's orbit by making additional observations. After Bessel had done so, this work was printed, upon Olbers' recommendation, in *Monatliche Correspondenz.* The article, which was on the level of a doctoral dissertation, attracted much attention because of the circumstances under which it had been written. It marks the turning point in Bessel's life; from then on he concentrated on astronomical investigations and celestial mechanics. Later, Olbers claimed that his greatest service to astronomy was having encouraged Bessel to become a professional astronomer.

At the beginning of 1806, before the expiration of his apprenticeship with Kulenkamp, Bessel accepted the position of assistant at Schröter's private observatory in Lilienthal, near Bremen, again on Olbers' recommendation. Schröter, a doctor of law and a wealthy civil servant, was renowned for his observations of the moon and the planets; and as a member of various learned societies, he was in close contact with many scientists. In Lilienthal, Bessel acquired practical experience in observations of comets and planets, with special attention to Saturn and its rings and satellites. At the same time, he studied celestial mechanics more intensively and made further contributions to the determination of cometary orbits. In 1807 Olbers encouraged him to do a reduction of Bradley's observations of the positions of 3,222 stars, which had been made from 1750 to 1762 at the Royal Greenwich Observatory. This task led to one of his greatest achievements.

When Friedrich Wilhelm III of Prussia ordered the construction of an observatory in Königsberg, Bessel was appointed its director and professor of astronomy (1809), on the recommendation of Humboldt. He had previously declined appointments in Leipzig and Greifswald. He took up his new post on 10 May 1810. The title of doctor, a prerequisite for a professorship, had been awarded to him without further formalities by the University of Göttingen after Gauss had proposed it. Gauss had met Bessel in 1807 at Bremen and had recognized his unusual ability.

While the observatory in Königsberg was being built (1810–1813), Bessel made considerable progress in the reduction of Bradley's observations. In 1811 he was awarded the Lalande Prize of the Institut de France for his tables of refraction derived from these observations, and the following year he became a member of the Berlin Academy of Sciences. In 1813 Bessel began observations in Königsberg, primarily of the positions of stars, with the Dollond transit instrument and the Cary circle. The observatory's modest equipment was markedly improved by the acquisition of a Reichenbach-Ertel meridian circle in 1819, a large Fraunhofer-Utzschneider heliometer in 1829, and a Repsold meridian circle in 1841. Bessel remained in Königsberg for the rest of his life, pursuing his research and teaching without interruption, although he often complained about the limited possibilities of observation because of the unfavorable climate. He declined the directorship of the Berlin observatory, fearing greater administrative and social responsibilities, and nominated Encke, who was appointed in his stead. Of Bessel's students, several became important astronomers; Argelander is perhaps the most famous.

Bessel married Johanna Hagen in 1812, and they had two sons and three daughters. The marriage was a happy one, but it was clouded by sickness and by the early death of both sons. Bessel found relaxation from his intensive work in daily walks and in hunting. He corresponded with Olbers, Schumacher (the founder of the *Astronomische Nachrichten*), and Gauss, and left Königsberg only occasionally.

From 1840 on, Bessel's health deteriorated. His last long trip, in 1842, was to England, where he participated in the Congress of the British Association in Manchester. His meeting with important English scientists, including Herschel, impressed him deeply and stimulated him to finish and publish, despite his weakened health, a series of works.

After two years of great suffering, Bessel died of cancer. He was buried near the observatory. Bessel

was small and delicate, and in his later years he appeared prematurely aged because of his markedly pale and wrinkled face. This appearance altered, however, as soon as he began to talk; then the force of a strong mind was evidenced in brilliant, rapid speech, and his otherwise rigid expression revealed mildness and friendliness.

Newcomb, in his *Compendium of Spherical Astronomy* (1906), has called Bessel the founder of the German school of practical astronomy. This German school started with astrometry and, after Bessel's death, was expanded to astrophysics by Bunsen and Kirchhoff's discovery of spectral analysis. Foremost among the interests of this school were the construction of precision instruments, the study of all possible instrument errors, and the careful reduction of observations. Bessel's contributions to the theory of astronomical instruments are for the most part restricted to those instruments used for the most accurate measurement of the positions of the stars and planets. The principles he laid down for the determination of errors were later followed so painstakingly by less gifted astronomers that the goal to be achieved—the making of a great number of good observations—was relegated to the background in favor of important investigations relative to the instruments themselves. Such was never Bessel's intention; he was undoubtedly one of the most skillful and diligent observers of his century. His industry is well illustrated by the twenty-one volumes of *Beobachtungen der Königsberger Sternwarte*.

Bessel recognized that Bradley's observations gave a system of very accurate star positions for the epoch 1755 and that this could be utilized in two ways. First, a reference system for the measurement of positions of stars and planets was required. Second, the study of star motions necessitated the determination of accurate positions for the earliest possible epoch. Tobias Mayer had determined fundamental star positions from his own observations around the middle of the eighteenth century, but Bradley was never able to reduce his own numerous observations.

The observations of star positions had to be freed of instrumental errors, insofar as these could be determined from the measurements themselves, and of errors caused by the earth's atmosphere (refraction). The apparent star positions at the time of a particular observation (observation epoch) had to be reduced to a common point in time (mean epoch) so that they would be freed of the effects of the motion of the earth and of the site of observation. For this a knowledge of the precession, the nutation, and the aberration was necessary. Bessel determined the latitude of Greenwich for the mean epoch 1755 and the obliquity of the ecliptic, as well as the constants of precession, nutation, and aberration. To determine precession from proper motions, Bessel used both Bradley's and Piazzi's observations. Bessel's first published work on the constant of precession (1815) was awarded a prize by the Berlin Academy of Sciences.

The positions of Bradley's stars valid for 1755 were published by Bessel as *Fundamenta astronomiae pro anno 1755* (1818). This work also gives the proper motions of the stars, as derived from the observations of Bradley, of Piazzi, and of Bessel himself. It constitutes a milestone in the history of astronomical observations, for until then positions of stars could not be given with comparable accuracy: through Bessel's work, Bradley's observations were made to mark the beginning of modern astrometry. During this investigation Bessel became an admirer of the art of observation as practiced by Bradley; and because Bradley could not evaluate his own observations, Bessel followed and also taught the principle that immediately after an observation, the reduction had to be done by the observer himself. Further, he realized that the accurate determination of the motions of the planets and the stars required continuous observations of their positions until such motions could be used to predict "the positions of the stars . . . for all times with sufficient accuracy."

Later, when many unpublished observations of Bradley's were found and when, about 1860, Airy had made accurate observations of the same stars at the Royal Greenwich Observatory, Auwers improved Bessel's reductions and derived proper motions of better quality. Auwers' star catalog was published in three volumes (1882–1903).

Bessel's first and very important contribution to the improvement of the positions and proper motions of stars consisted of the observations of Maskelyne's thirty-six fundamental stars. As Bradley's successor, Maskelyne had chosen these stars to define the system of right ascensions. Bradley had been able to make differential measurements of positions with such accuracy that the star positions for 1755 and those determined by Airy for 1860 resulted in proper motions with the excellent internal accuracy of about one second of arc per century. Greater difficulties were experienced, however, with the measurement of positions with respect to the vernal equinox as zero point of the right ascensions. The continuously changing position of the vernal equinox had to be determined at the time of the equinoxes from the differences in time of the transits of bright stars and the sun through the meridian. In 1820 Bessel succeeded in determining the position of the vernal equinox with an accuracy

of .01 second by observing both Maskelyne's stars and the sun. This can be verified by measurements made in the twentieth century.

In *Tabulae Regiomontanae* (1830), Bessel published the mean and the apparent positions of thirty-eight stars for the period 1750–1850. He added the two polar stars α and δ Ursae Minoris to Maskelyne's thirty-six fundamental stars. The foundations for the ephemerides were the mean positions for 1755 and the positions derived for 1820 from observations at Königsberg. The position of the vernal equinox for 1822, as determined by Bessel, served as the zero point for counting the right ascensions. Bessel derived the ephemerides of the *Tabulae Regiomontanae* without using a specific value of the constant of precession, for in order to find a third position from two given positions of a star, it is necessary to know only the annual variation of precession, not the value of precession itself. Therefore Bessel's ephemerides are correct (aside from errors in observation) up to and including the first magnitude for the proper motions and up to the second magnitude for precession. Only for the two polar stars did Bessel determine the proper motions and also give the values, since for these stars the terms of higher order in proper motion and precession could not be neglected. In calculating the data of the *Tabulae Regiomontanae* Bessel improved his 1815 determination of the precession by utilizing his Königsberg observations of Bradley's stars.

The star positions given for one century in the *Tabulae Regiomontanae* constitute the first modern reference system for the measurement of the positions of the sun, the moon, the planets, and the stars, and for many decades the Königsberg tables were used as ephemerides. With their aid, all observations of the sun, moon, and planets made since 1750 at the Royal Greenwich Observatory could be reduced; and thus these observations could be used for the theories of planetary orbits.

During observations of the stars α Canis Major (Sirius) and α Canis Minor (Procyon), which are among Maskelyne's fundamental stars, Bessel discovered the variation of their proper motions. He concluded that these stars must have dimmer companions whose masses, however, were large enough to make visible the motions of the brighter double-star components around the center of gravity. Arguing from the variation of the proper motion, more than a hundred years later astronomers discovered stars with extremely low luminosity, called dark companions.

Observing the positions of numerous stars with the Reichenbach meridian circle, Bessel pursued two aims: the determination of the motions of the stars in such a way that their positions could be predicted for all time, and the definition of a reference system for the positions of the stars. Between 1821 and 1833 he determined the positions of approximately 75,000 stars (brighter than ninth magnitude) in zones of declination between $-15°$ and $+45°$. With these observations he also developed the methods for determining instrumental errors, including those of the division of the circle, and eliminated such errors from his observations. He published all measurements in detail, and thus they can be verified. These observations were continued by Argelander, who measured the positions of stars in zones of declination from $+45°$ to $+80°$ and from $-16°$ to $-32°$. The work of Bessel and Argelander encouraged the establishment of two large-scale programs: Argelander's *Bonner Durchmusterung* and the first catalog of the Astronomische Gesellschaft (*AGK 1*) with the positions of the stars of the entire northern sky. The *Bonner Durchmusterung* is a map of the northern sky that contains all stars up to magnitude 9.5, and the catalog is the result of meridian circle observations made at many observatories.

One of Bessel's greatest achievements was the first accurate determination of the distance of a fixed star. At the beginning of the nineteenth century, the approximate radius of the earth's orbit (150,000,000 km.) was known, and there was some idea of the dimensions of the planetary system, although Neptune and Pluto were still unknown. The stars, however, were considered to be so far away that it would be hopeless to try to measure their distances. The triangulation procedure was already known, and for this the diameter of the earth's orbit could serve as the base line, since its length was known. It was also known that the motion of the earth around the sun must be mirrored in a periodic motion of the stars within the period of a year, in such a way that a star at the pole of the ecliptic would describe a circular orbit around the pole, stars at ecliptical latitudes between $0°$ and $90°$ would describe ellipses, and stars at the ecliptic would undergo periodic variations of their ecliptical longitudes. This change of position of the stars, as evidenced by the motion of the earth, was considered to be immeasurably small, however. The radius of the circle, of the ellipse, or of the ecliptical segment of arc—the so-called parallax figure—is the parallax of the star; the parallax π is the angle subtended by the radius of the earth's orbit at the position of the star. If this angle π can be measured, then the distance r of a star can be obtained from $\sin \pi = a/r$, where a represents the radius of the earth's orbit. An angle of $\pi = 1''$ corresponds to 206,265 radii of the earth's orbit (or $3.08 \cdot 10^{13}$ km., or 3.26 light-years).

In the first half of the eighteenth century Bradley had attempted to determine the parallaxes of the stars γ Draco and η Ursa Major by measurements of the angular distances of these stars from the zenith (zenith distances). Both stars culminate in the vicinity of the zenith of Greenwich and thus are particularly suitable for the accurate measurement of zenith distances. The "absolute" parallax of the stars—that is, the parallactic change of position with respect to a fixed direction on earth (direction of the plumb line at Greenwich)—should be determinable from the variation of the zenith distances. Bradley found an annual variation with an amplitude of twenty seconds of arc, but the phase was shifted by three months from the expected parallactic change of position. He correctly interpreted the phenomenon as a change in direction —arising from the motion of the earth in its orbit—of the stellar light that reaches the earth, and thus discovered the aberration of light. However, he could not detect parallaxes of the stars, but could only conclude that the parallaxes must be smaller than .50 second of arc for the stars he observed.

As a result of this knowledge of the small size of the parallaxes to be expected, the measuring procedures were changed in later experiments, for the accuracy of the measurements of zenith distances was obviously inadequate for the purpose. The angular distance between two stars very close together on the sphere could be determined much more accurately. If one star of a star pair is very far from the sun and the other is near the sun, then the parallax figure of the nearer star must become visible as a result of frequent measurements of the angular distances between the two stars. It was therefore suggested that astronomers measure "relative" parallaxes, that is, the parallactic changes in the position with reference to other stars that can be assumed to be very far away. Herschel's attempts to measure stellar parallaxes in this way led to the discovery of the physical double stars; he found that the components of most star pairs are near to each other in space, as is shown by their motion around the common center of gravity. Herschel's attempt to determine parallaxes failed, however.

This lack of success led to a search for signs that one of the stars would be especially near, with great brightness of an individual star regarded as an indication of its great nearness. (This assumption would be correct if all stars had the same luminosity and if there were no inhomogeneous interstellar absorption. Since both of these conditions are not fulfilled, the relation between apparent magnitude and distance holds only in the statistical mean.) In determining proper motions, Bessel found that individual stars are marked by especially great motions and that these stars are not among the brightest. He concluded that great proper motions are, in most cases, the result of small star distances. Therefore, in order to determine the parallax, he selected the star with the greatest proper motion known to him (5.2″ per year), a star of magnitude 5.6, which had been designated as 61 Cygni in Flamsteed's star catalog.

To determine the parallax Bessel used the Fraunhofer heliometer, an instrument intended primarily for the measurement of the angular diameter of the sun and the planets. The heliometer is a telescope with an objective that can be rotated around the optical axis. The objective is cut along a diameter; both halves can be shifted along the cutting line and the displacement can be measured very accurately. Each half of the objective acts optically as a complete objective would, so that upon moving the halves, two noncoincident images of one object arise. The distance of two stars, A and B, that are in the field of view is measured by sliding the halves so that the image of A coincides with the image of B produced in the second half; thus the two stars appear as one. In Bessel's day this procedure of coincidence determination permitted more accurate measurements than did the customary micrometer determinations with an ordinary telescope; the latter were used to determine the angular distances of the components of double stars. Further, with the heliometer one could measure greater angular distances than with the micrometer (up to nearly two degrees with Bessel's heliometer). For determining the parallax of 61 Cygni, Bessel selected two comparison stars of magnitude 9–10 at distances of roughly eight and twelve minutes of arc. 61 Cygni is a physical double star whose components differ in brightness by less than one magnitude. The distance of sixteen seconds of arc between the components favored the accuracy of the determination of the parallax because pointing could be carried out with two star images. After observing for eighteen months, by the fall of 1838 Bessel had enough measurements for the determination of a reliable parallax. He found that $\pi = 0.314''$ with a mean error of $\pm 0.020''$. This work was published in the *Astronomische Nachrichten* (1838), the first time the distance of a star became known. Bessel's value for the parallax shows excellent agreement with the results obtained by extensive modern photographical parallax determinations, which have yielded the value $\pi = 0.292''$, with a mean error of $\pm 0.0045''$. The distance of 61 Cygni thus amounts to $6.9 \cdot 10^5$ radii of the earth's orbit, or 10.9 light-years.

Bessel's conjecture that the stars with the greatest proper motions are among the nearest was later proved correct, and the amount of proper motion has remained a criterion for the choice of stars for parallax programs. Only one year after the completion of Bessel's work, two other successful determinations of parallaxes were made known. F. G. W. Struve in Dorpat determined the parallax of the bright star α Lyra (Vega) by means of micrometric measurements. The value he found, $\pi = 0.262'' \pm 0.037''$ (m.e.) nevertheless deviates considerably from the now reliably known value $\pi = 0.121'' \pm 0.006''$ (m.e.). In addition, Thomas Henderson had observed the bright star α Centaurus at the Cape Observatory and had found a parallax of approximately one second of arc. The reliable value for this today amounts to $\pi = 0.75''$. The pioneering work of Bessel, Henderson, and Struve not only opened up a new area of astronomical research but also laid the foundation for the investigation of the structure of our star system.

Bessel was also an outstanding mathematician whose name became generally known through a special class of functions that have become an indispensable tool in applied mathematics, physics, and engineering. The interest in the functions, which represent a special form of the confluent hypergeometric function, arose in the treatment of the problem of perturbation in the planetary system. The perturbation of the elliptic motion of a planet caused by another planet consists of two components, the direct effect of the perturbing planet and its indirect effect, which arises from the motion of the sun caused by the perturbing planet. Bessel demonstrated that it is appropriate to treat the direct and the indirect perturbations separately, so that in the series development of the indirect perturbation, Bessel functions appear as coefficients. In studying indirect perturbation, Bessel made a systematic investigation of its functions and described its main characteristics. This work appeared in his Berlin treatise of 1824. Special cases of Bessel coefficients had been known for a long time; in a letter to Leibniz in 1703, Jakob Bernoulli mentioned a series that represented a Bessel function of the order 1/3. In addition, in a work on the oscillations of heavy chains (1732) Daniel Bernoulli used Bessel coefficients of the order zero, and in Euler's work on vibrations of a stretched circular membrane (1744) there was a series by means of which $J_n(z)$ was defined. Probably a work by Lagrange on elliptical motion (1769), in which such series appear, had led Bessel to make these investigations. The impulse, however, did not come from pure mathematical interests, but from the necessity of applying such series in the presentation of indirect perturbations. Bessel left few mathematical works that do not have some practical astronomical application.

Like nearly all great astronomers of his era, Bessel was obliged to spend part of his time surveying wherever the government wished. In 1824 he supervised the measurement of a 3,000-meter base line in the Frischen Haff because he liked to spend a day in the fresh air once in a while. In 1830 he was commissioned to carry out triangulation in East Prussia, after Struve had completed the triangulation of the Russian Baltic provinces. Bessel designed a new measuring apparatus for the determination of base lines that was constructed by Repsold; he also developed methods of triangulation by utilizing Gauss's method of least squares. Bessel's measuring apparatus and method of triangulation have been widely used. The triangulation in East Prussia and its junction with the Prussian-Russian chain of triangulation was described in a book written with J. J. Baeyer (1838). From his own triangulations and from those of others, Bessel made an outstanding determination of the shape and dimensions of the earth that won him international acclaim.

Among Bessel's works that contributed to geophysics were his investigations on the length of the simple seconds' pendulum (1826), the length of the seconds' pendulum for Berlin (1835), and the determination of the acceleration of gravity derived from observing the pendulum. Bessel achieved the standardization of the units of length then in use by introducing a standard measure in Prussia, the so-called Toise (1 Toise = 1.949063 meters). The necessity of a standard of length had become apparent to him during his work on triangulation in East Prussia, as did the necessity of an international organization to define the units of measures. This need led to the founding of the International Bureau of Weights and Measures.

BIBLIOGRAPHY

I. ORIGINAL WORKS. A collection of Bessel's numerous papers is *Abhandlungen von Friedrich Wilhelm Bessel,* Rudolf Engelmann, ed., 3 vols. (Leipzig, 1875). Vol. I contains Bessel's account of his youth, "Kurze Erinnerungen an Momente meines Lebens," with a supp. by the ed., 23 papers on the motions of planets, and 28 papers on spherical astronomy. Vol. II contains 25 papers on the theory of astronomical instruments, 29 papers on stellar astronomy, and 19 papers on mathematics. Vol. III contains 11 papers on geodesy, 17 papers on physics (mostly geophysics), and 33 on other subjects. Engelmann's collection is not complete, however. *Beobachtungen der Königsberger Sternwarte,* 21 vols., presents Bessel's observations. Major separate publications are *Fundamenta astronomiae pro anno 1755 deducta ex observationibus viri incomparabilis James Bradley in specola astronomica*

Grenovicensi per anno 1750–1762 institutis (Königsberg, 1818) and *Tabulae Regiomontanae reductionum observationum astronomicarum ab anno 1750 usque ad annum 1850 computatae* (Königsberg, 1830). A complete list of Bessel's publications, presented at the end of *Abhandlungen,* III, has 399 entries, including books and book reviews by Bessel.

II. SECONDARY LITERATURE. A bibliography of sketches of Bessel's life and astronomical works is given in *Abhandlungen,* III, 504. Noteworthy are C. Bruhns, in *Allgemeine deutsche Biographie,* pt. 9 (Leipzig, 1875), 558–567; and Sir William Herschel's addresses delivered to Bessel on presenting honorary medals of the Royal Astronomical Society, in *Monthly Notices of the Royal Astronomical Society,* **1** (1829), 110–113, and **5** (1841), 89. A biography of Bessel in anecdotal style is J. A. Repsold, in *Astronomische Nachrichten,* **210** (1919), 161–214. An excellent review of the first determination of a stellar parallax is H. Strassl, "Die erste Bestimmung einer Fixsternentfernung," in *Naturwissenschaften,* 33rd year (1946), 65–71.

WALTER FRICKE

BESSEY, CHARLES EDWIN (*b.* Milton Township, Ohio, 21 May 1845; *d.* Lincoln, Nebraska, 25 February 1915), *botany, education.*

Protagonist of a leading hypothesis of angiosperm phylogeny that, when revised to admit recent research, will probably stand as the accepted system of classification for flowering plants; advocate of the values of scientific meetings for the communication of ideas; author of the most successful textbook of botany published in the United States between 1880 and 1910; exceptional teacher who carried modern botany and its symbol, the microscope, across the Mississippi and planted them firmly in Iowa and then Nebraska and who had among his 4,000 students an impressive number of prominent biologists of the early twentieth century: Charles Bessey was all of these.

Bessey's father, Adnah Bessey, a schoolteacher of Huguenot ancestry, married Margaret Ellenberger, who had been his pupil, in 1841. Educated in rural schools and at home, Charles Bessey was certified to teach at seventeen. In July 1866 he entered Michigan Agricultural College, where he came under the influence of Albert Nelson Prentiss and William James Beal, two botanists noted for their teaching skills. He graduated from the scientific course in 1869 and remained as an assistant in horticulture, but soon left to inaugurate botany and horticulture at Iowa Agricultural College, Ames. His single room, which held two chairs, a table, bureau, washstand, and bedstead, was to serve as office, library, study, and bedroom for three years. Nevertheless, Bessey opened his first botany class for forty-three sophomores the month after his arrival, using Gray's *Lessons in Botany*. In 1871 he added laboratory work to his undergraduate botany course, using his one Tolles compound microscope.

Bessey took part in the Iowa Farmers' Institute, the first of its kind in the country, and encouraged the launching of the Iowa Academy of Sciences. Asa Gray, attracted by Bessey at the American Association for the Advancement of Science meeting at Dubuque, Iowa, in 1872, persuaded him to go to Harvard that year. In Gray's laboratory he was impressed by the importance of morphology and cell structure in plant systematics, whereas previously he had approached the subject from gross macroscopical characteristics alone. Bessey lectured in botany at the University of California in 1875 at the invitation of President Gilman, and returned to Harvard that same year to study under the mycologist William Farlow. From this inoculation Bessey produced four papers on plant diseases that were among the first published in the United States.

Gray's recommendation that Bessey prepare an American adaptation of Julius von Sachs's *Lehrbuch der Botanik,* under the title *Botany for High Schools and Colleges* (1880), reoriented botanical instruction in this country. Bessey's text introduced cryptogamic botany and physiological plant anatomy into American colleges.

Bessey gave direction to botanical literature through his associate editorship of the *American Naturalist* (1880–1897) and *Science* (1897–1915), two of the most influential journals of the time. He offered the first laboratory course in botany at the University of Minnesota in the summer of 1881, using compound microscopes borrowed from Iowa Agricultural College. After teaching at Ames for fifteen years and after repeated solicitations, he moved to the University of Nebraska as professor of botany in September 1884. Bessey's teaching philosophy was later identified with John Dewey's "science with practice." He wrote of the "relatedness of knowledge" and that "the teacher represents the *life* of the subject." He believed introductory classes should be taught by the best-informed, usually senior, professors. His comradeship with students was demonstrated by "Sem. Bot.," where ten advanced botany students conducted investigations, reported in technical detail—and interspersed their seminars with limericks and refreshment. Bessey's second highly successful text, *Essentials of Botany* (1884), had seven editions by 1896. He wrote more than 150 papers and reviews, but his writings on plant phylogeny, "Evolution and Classification" (1893) and "Phylogenetic Taxonomy of Flowering Plants" (1915), established his permanent place in botany.

Bessey took the two well-known systems of angiosperm classification, those of Engler and Prantl, and of Bentham and Hooker, and rearranged the families on the basis of twenty-eight "dicta," producing a scheme that by its logic and attractive phyletic patterns has proved effective in teaching systematic botany—a success fostered by the textbook of his student Raymond J. Pool. Thousands of students have come to know "Bessey's cactus," a cartoon-like table suggestive of a many-jointed *Opuntia*. Bessey's dicta were a refinement of Candolle's concept that three principal factors have been effective in the differentiation of the angiosperms: loss, or fusion, or specialization of floral parts from a multimerous, free-membered prototype. The fused and few-membered condition was construed as advanced. Whereas apetalous catkin-bearing genera had been considered primitive by the Engler and Prantl school, Bessey viewed them as derived from petaliferous flowers often borne in conelike clusters. Another concept was that monocotyledonous families have been derived from dicotyledonous forms.

Bessey's deep, modulated voice and his genial, persuasive, generous, perennially enthusiastic manner made him popular as a lecturer and officer in many of the some twenty organizations to which he belonged. His memberships ranged from the State Teachers' Association of Nebraska (president in 1888) and the American Microscopical Society (president in 1903 and 1908) to the American Association for the Advancement of Science, of which he was national president in 1910.

Bessey married Lucy Athearn of West Tisbury, Massachusetts, on Christmas Day 1873. All three sons, Edward, Carl, and Ernst, graduated from the University of Nebraska; Ernst Athearn Bessey became internationally known as a mycologist.

BIBLIOGRAPHY

I. ORIGINAL WORKS. Note references in text. "Evolution and Classification" appeared in *Proceedings of the American Association for the Advancement of Science,* **42** (1894), 237–251; "Phylogenetic Taxonomy of Flowering Plants," in *Annals of the Missouri Botanical Garden,* **2** (1915), 109–164. Bessey's MSS in the University of Nebraska botany department and the Nebraska Historical Society Archives include "Discussion of a Plan of a Scientific Course," read before the Nebraska State Teachers' Association 28 December 1876.

II. SECONDARY LITERATURE. There is no biography of Bessey. Works on him are Ernst Athearn Bessey, "The Teaching of Botany Sixty-five Years Ago," in *Iowa State College Journal of Science,* **9** (1935), 227–233; L. H. Pammel, "Prominent Men I Have Met. Dr. Charles Edwin

Bessey," in *Ames* [Iowa] *Daily Tribune and Evening Times,* 26 Nov. 1927, p. 19, and 17 Dec. 1927, p. 20, a eulogy; Raymond J. Pool, "A Brief Sketch of the Life and Work of Charles Edwin Bessey," in *American Journal of Botany,* **2** (1915), 505–518, with portrait and bibliography; Andrew Denny Rodgers, III, *John Merle Coulter* (Princeton, N.J., 1944), *passim,* with short quotations from Bessey's correspondence; and the anonymous "Some Men Under Dr. Bessey," in [Nebraska] *State Journal* (newspaper).

JOSEPH EWAN

BETANCOURT Y MOLINA, AUGUSTIN DE (*b.* Tenerife, Canary Islands, 1758; *d.* St. Petersburg, Russia, 14 July 1824), *physics, engineering.*

Betancourt was a descendant of the Norman navigator Jean de Béthencourt, who discovered the Canary Islands in 1402. After completing his studies in Paris, he was sent by the Spanish government to France, England, Germany, and Holland to study methods of shipbuilding, navigation, mechanics, and using steam engines. He brought back a number of drawings and models which formed the nucleus of the scientific cabinet of the king of Spain. While in France he submitted two important reports to the Académie des Sciences of Paris. In the first he revealed to the Continent the double-action steam engine, which he had observed in action in England. This memoir led Jacques-Constantin Périer to construct the first double-action steam engine in France.

In the second report (1790), Betancourt gave the results of a series of measurements establishing the relation of temperature and steam pressure. This was the first work of its kind, but Betancourt underestimated the importance of the disturbances caused by the presence of even a minimum quantity of residual air.

After another trip to England to study its mining industry Betancourt returned to France. There he became interested in the optical telegraph invented by Claude Chappe, and constructed a line from Madrid to Cadiz. He was then entrusted with the organization of a school of civil engineering in Spain, and became its inspector general. Disturbances in Spain led him to settle temporarily in Paris, where he became well known, especially for a system of water-saving locks.

In 1808 Betancourt accepted an offer from the Russian government, and on 30 November was made chief of staff of the czar's retinue. In Russia he improved the arms industry and constructed bridges using a new system of arches. In collaboration with Carbonnier, Betancourt built the riding school of Moscow, which was then the largest hall without inner supports; the span of its roof was said to be forty

meters. He also constructed the aqueduct of Taïtzy and set up a state paper industry. In 1810 a school of civil engineering was founded in St. Petersburg, and Betancourt became its inspector as well as a professor; in 1819 he was made director of the Central Administration of Civil Engineering.

On 22 August 1822 Betancourt was summarily retired when an official investigation revealed numerous irregularities in the running of the Central Administration of Civil Engineering. Undoubtedly he was simply caught up in a general wave of reform, for he did not lose the czar's favor. He was in the midst of rebuilding St. Isaac's Cathedral when he died.

BIBLIOGRAPHY

I. ORIGINAL WORKS. Among Betancourt's works are *Mémoire sur la force expansive de la vapeur de l'eau* (Paris, 1790); *Mémoire sur un nouveau système de navigation intérieure* (n.p., n.d. [Paris, *ca.* 1808]); and *Essai sur la composition des machines* (Paris, 1808, 1819), written with Lanz. See also the *Procès-verbaux des séances de l'Académie des Sciences tenues depuis la fondation de l'Institut jusqu'au mois d'août 1835,* 10 vols. (Hendaye, 1910–1921): I, 306 (11 Frimaire an VI); 308, 309, 313 (16 Frimaire an VI); 353 (11 Ventose an VI); 373–375 (21 Germinal an VI); III, 504 (2 March 1807); 563 (17 August 1807); 581–585 (14 September 1807); IV, 77 (13 June 1808); 78 (20 June 1808); 88 (8 August 1808), the presentation of the memoir "Nouveau système de navigation . . ."; 279 (27 November 1809); 286 (5 December 1809), Betancourt's election as corresponding member of the Première Classe of the Institut; 331 (12 March 1810); VI, 233 (3 November 1817); 395 (21 December 1818); 448 (10 May 1819); VII, 9 (31 January 1820); VIII, 131 (30 August 1824, 6 September 1824, the latter a replacement).

II. SECONDARY LITERATURE. Works on Betancourt are Jean-Baptiste-Joseph Delambre, "Rapport sur un nouveau télégraphe de l'invention des citoyens Breguet et Bétancourt" (read 21 Germinal an VI), in *Mémoires de l'Institut,* 1st ser., **3,** pt. 1 (an IX), *Histoire,* 22–32; Sebastián Padrón Acosta, *El ingeniero Augustín de Bethencourt y Molina* (Tenerife, 1958); Jacques Payen, "Bétancourt et l introduction en France de la machine à vapeur à double effet (1789)," in *Revue d'histoire des sciences,* **20** (1967), 187–198, an edition of "Mémoire sur une machine à vapeur à double effet" (read before the Académie Royale des Sciences on 16 December 1789); and Antonio Ruiz Álvarez, "En torno al ingeniero canario don Augustín de Bethencourt y Molina," in *El museo canario,* nos. 77–84 (1961–1962), 139–147.

JACQUES PAYEN

BETTI, ENRICO (*b.* near Pistoia, Italy, 21 October 1823; *d.* Pisa, Italy, 11 August 1892), *mathematics.*

Since his father died when Betti was very young,

the boy was educated by his mother. At the University of Pisa, from which he received a degree in physical and mathematical sciences, he was a disciple of O. F. Mossotti, under whose leadership he fought in the battle of Curtatone and Montanara during the first war for Italian independence.

After having taught mathematics at a Pistoia high school, in 1865 Betti was offered a professorship at the University of Pisa; he held this post for the rest of his life. He also was rector of the university and director of the teachers college in Pisa. In addition, he was a member of Parliament in 1862 and a senator from 1884. His principal aim, however, was always pure scientific research with a noble philosophical purpose.

In 1874 Betti served for a few months as undersecretary of state for public education. He longed, however, for the academic life, solitary meditation, and discussions with close friends. Among the latter was Riemann, whom Betti had met in Göttingen in 1858, and who subsequently visited him in Pisa.

In algebra, Betti penetrated the ideas of Galois by relating them to the previous research of Ruffini and Abel. He obtained fundamental results on the solubility of algebraic equations by means of radicorational operations. It should be noted that the most important results of Galois's theory are included—without demonstration and in a very concise form—in a letter written in 1832 by Galois to his friend Chevalier on the eve of the duel in which Galois was killed. The letter was published by Liouville in 1846. When Betti was able to demonstrate—on the basis of the theory of substitutions, which he stated anew—the necessary and sufficient conditions for the solution of any algebraic equation through radicorational operations, it was still believed in high mathematical circles that the questions related to Galois's results were obscure and sterile. Among the papers in which Betti sought to demonstrate Galois's statements are "Sulla risoluzione delle equazioni algebriche" (1852) and "Sopra la teorica delle sostituzioni" (1855). They constitute an essential contribution to the development from classical to abstract algebra.

Another area of mathematical thought developed by Betti is that of the theory of functions, particularly of elliptic functions. Betti illustrated—in an original way—the theory of elliptic functions, which is based on the principle of the construction of transcendental entire functions in relation to their zeros by means of infinite products.

Betti published these results in a paper entitled "La teorica delle funzioni ellitiche" (1860–1861). These ideas were further developed by Weierstrass some fifteen years later. However, Betti, who in the mean-time had turned to another theory of elliptic functions—this one inspired by Riemann—did not wish to claim priority. These two methods are linked with the two basic aspects of Betti's mathematical thought: the algebraic mode of thought, which went deep into Galois's research, and the physicomathematical mode of thought, developed under Riemann's influence. Betti, an enthusiastic supporter of theoretical physics, had turned toward the procedures already started in electricity and subsequently applied to analysis.

Among Betti's physicomathematical researches inspired by Riemann are *Teorica della forze newtoniane* (1879) and "Sopra le equazioni di equilibrio dei corpi solidi elastici." A law of reciprocity in elasticity theory, known as Betti's theorem, was demonstrated in 1878. Having mastered the methods by which Green had opened the way to the integration of Laplace's equations, which constitute the basis for the theory of potentials, Betti applied these methods to the study of elasticity and then to the study of heat.

Of particular interest is Betti's research on "analysis situs" in hyperspace, which is discussed in "Sopra gli spazi di un numero qualunque di dimensioni" (1871). This research inspired Poincaré in his studies in this field and originated the term "Betti numbers," which subsequently became common usage for numbers characterizing the connection of a variety.

Betti played an important role in the rebirth of mathematics after the Risorgimento. He loved classical culture, and with Brioschi he championed the return to the teaching of Euclid in secondary schools, for he regarded Euclid's work as a model of discipline and beauty. This led to *Gli elementi d'Euclide* (1889).

His enthusiasm and brilliance made Betti an excellent teacher. At the University of Pisa and at the teachers college, he guided several generations of students toward scientific research, among them the mathematicians U. Dini, L. Bianchi, and V. Volterra.

BIBLIOGRAPHY

I. ORIGINAL WORKS. Betti's collected writings are *Opere matematiche,* R. Accademia dei Lincei, ed., 2 vols. (Milan, 1903–1915). Among his works are "Sulla risoluzione delle equazioni algebriche," in *Annali di scienze matematiche e fisiche,* **3** (1852), 49–115; "Sopra la teorica delle sostituzioni," *ibid.,* **6** (1855), 5–34; "La teorica delle funzioni ellitiche," in *Annali di matematica pura e applicata,* **3** (1860), 65–159, 298–310; **4** (1861), 26–45, 57–70, 297–336; "Sopra gli spazi di un numero qualunque di dimensioni," *ibid.,* 2nd ser., **4** (1871), 140–158; "Sopra le equazioni di equilibrio dei corpi solidi elastici," *ibid.,* **6** (1874), 101–111; *Teorica della forze newtoniane* (Pisa, 1879);

and *Gli elementi d'Euclide con note aggiunte ed esercizi ad uso dei ginnasi e dei licei* (Florence, 1889), written with Brioschi.

II. Secondary Literature. Works on Betti are F. Brioschi, "Enrico Betti," in *Annali di matematica pura e applicata,* 2nd ser., **20** (1892), 256, or his *Opere matematiche,* III (Milan, 1904), 41–42; F. Enriques, *Le matematiche nella storia e nella cultura* (Bologna, 1938), pp. 187, 203–204, 222, 224–226; and his article on Betti in *Enciclopedia italiana Treccani,* VI (1930), 834; G. Loria, *Storia delle matematiche,* III (Turin, 1933), 497, 541, 556–557; and V. Volterra, *Saggi scientifici* (Bologna, 1920), pp. 37, 40–41, 46–50, 52–54.

Ettore Carruccio

BEUDANT, FRANÇOIS-SULPICE (*b.* Paris, France, 5 September 1787; *d.* Paris, 9 December 1850), *mineralogy, geology.*

Educated at the École Polytechnique and the École Normale Supérieure in Paris, Beudant began his career as *répétiteur* at the latter institution, leaving this post to become professor of mathematics at Avignon (1811) and then professor of physics at Marseilles (1813). During these years his primary interests were zoology and paleontology, tastes he acquired while studying with Gilet de Laumont. He studied species of coelenterates and mollusks, trying to determine whether freshwater varieties could adapt to saltwater and whether marine forms could have originated from freshwater fauna. Some of his observations were included in "Mémoire sur la possibilité de faire vivre des mollusques fluviatiles dans les eaux salées et des mollusques marins dans les eaux douces . . . "

Louis XVIII appointed Beudant as assistant director of his cabinet of mineralogy in 1814, charging him with the task of cataloguing the enormous mineralogical collection of the Comte de Bournon, which was to be moved to Paris from England the following year. This work directed Beudant's attention from natural history to mineralogy and geology, with which he was thereafter concerned. In 1818 he was sent by the state on a scientific expedition to Hungary, where he gathered masses of important data that were published in his three-volume *Voyage minéralogique et géologique en Hongrie* (1822).

In 1820 Beudant became professor of mineralogy and physics on the Faculty of Sciences at the Sorbonne but resigned the chair of physics so that Ampère might have it. In 1839 he left the university and became *inspecteur général des études,* which was equivalent to being supervisor for the entire French educational system. He held this position until his death. In 1841 he wrote a grammar of the French language that was favorably received by his contemporaries.

Mineralogical investigations, particularly experiments with carbonates and other salts, revealed to Beudant a principle of the combination of mineral substances that he expressed in Beudant's law. Essentially, he found that some compounds dissolved in the same solution would precipitate together, forming a crystal whose properties they determined in common. The interfacial angles of this new crystal would have a value intermediate between the angles of the original compounds, proportional to the quantity of each. The same idea had been put forth by Robert Boyle in "The Origine of Form and Qualities" (1666). Beudant was rather conservative about the generality of his proposition, although Delafosse enthusiastically maintained that it should apply to all crystals.

The generalization of this idea, the law of isomorphism, was proposed by Mitscherlich in 1819.

BIBLIOGRAPHY

I. Original Works. Beudant published a great number of papers in geology, mineralogy, zoology, and paleontology. The most important are "Mémoire sur la possibilité de faire vivre des mollusques fluviatiles dans les eaux salées et des mollusques marins dans les eaux douces, considérée sous le rapport de la géologie," in *Journal de physique,* **83** (1816), 268–284, and "Recherches sur les causes qui déterminent les variations des formes cristallines d'une même substance minérale," in *Annales de chimie,* **8** (1818), 5–52. Among his texts are *Voyage minéralogique et géologique en Hongrie pendant l'année 1818,* 3 vols. (Paris, 1822); *Traité élémentaire de minéralogie* (Paris, 1824); *Traité élémentaire de physique* (Paris, 1824); *Nouveaux éléments de grammaire française* (Paris, 1841); and *Cours élémentaire de minéralogie et de géologie* (Paris, 1842).

II. Secondary Literature. Articles on Beudant are in *Dictionnaire de biographie française,* V (1951), 358–359, and *Larousse grande dictionnaire du XIX siècle,* III (Paris, 1867), 656.

Martha B. Kendall

BEXON, GABRIEL-LÉOPOLD-CHARLES-AMÉ (*b.* Remiremont, France, 10 March 1747; *d.* Paris, France, 15 February 1784), *biology.*

Bexon, whose short scientific career was closely linked with that of the great French naturalist Buffon, received his early education from his parents, Amé Bexon, a lawyer, and Marthe Pillement. Having shown considerable intelligence, he was sent north to the seminary at Toul to continue his education and prepare for the clergy. He completed the course of study and received his doctorate in theology at the

Faculty of Theology at the University of Besançon in 1766 or 1767, and then returned to Toul to accept a post as a subdeacon. There Bexon spent some time studying canon law; he was ordained in 1772.

Bexon's first published works appeared in 1773. *Catéchisme d'agriculture,* written about 1768, was published anonymously in Paris. It was a very simply written book that dealt as much with morals as with agriculture, and was meant to aid and educate the French peasants. In the same year he also published, under his brother Scipion's name, *Le système de la fertilisation.*

Although Bexon had announced plans for a two-volume history of Lorraine, and had later expanded the project to a four-volume work that would include one volume on the natural history of the province, he ceased work on the project in 1774. Only one volume appeared (*Histoire de Lorraine,* Paris, 1777), and was dedicated to Marie Antoinette. Probably as a result of this dedication, Bexon was appointed canon of Sainte-Chapelle in Paris in 1778 and three years later was elevated to the post of precentor.

From childhood, Bexon had been interested in natural history. He was a keen observer, and knew the mineralogy of the Vosges region especially well. While at Paris for a six-month visit in 1768–1769 he may have tried to meet Buffon, hoping to help with the *Histoire naturelle.* At that time Buffon's collaborator, Guéneau de Montbéliard, overworked and in poor health, was seeking an assistant; and there is an ambiguous reference to "the abbé" in a letter from Buffon to Montbéliard dated 17 May 1769.

Bexon did meet Buffon in 1772. The young man spoke of the influence of Buffon's works on him and of his desire to be of some assistance, which timely offer the naturalist accepted. Soon thereafter Bexon began to supply information and descriptions for various articles in the *Histoire naturelle.*

Although he supplied Buffon with descriptions, Bexon did not actually begin to collaborate in the writing of the articles until 1777. From then on, though, his contributions were numerous, appearing ultimately in six of the nine volumes of the *Histoire des oiseaux* and in the *Histoire des minéraux.*

When he began to assist Buffon, at the age of twenty-five, Bexon's writing style was extremely erudite and flowery, but under Buffon's tutelage it became more concise and exact. He worked hard, inspired by a love of natural history and by the need to support a sick mother and a young sister. Buffon publicly acknowledged his work on the *Histoire des oiseaux* in the preface to the seventh volume (1780), where he noted not only Bexon's scholarly researches but also the "solid reflections and ingenious ideas"

he had supplied. From this collaboration there developed an increasingly close friendship that ended only with Bexon's untimely death.

Despite their friendship, Bexon did not agree with the philosophical aspects of Buffon's system; he regarded it as "an ingenious and learned hypothesis" but not a true system of nature. In an unpublished manuscript on religion in relation to the universe, written about 1773, Bexon said he believed he could use the phenomena that supported the theory to show that nature contradicted Buffon's views.

The complete *Histoire naturelle* consisted of forty-four volumes published over a span of fifty-five years, and it proved to be a very popular and influential work. But although it is known as the product of Buffon's genius and industry, the work could not have appeared had it not been for the aid of Buffon's collaborators—Daubenton, Guéneau de Montbéliard, and the Abbé Bexon.

BIBLIOGRAPHY

I. ORIGINAL WORKS. Bexon's earlier works are quite scarce today. The articles in the *Histoire naturelle* that P. Flourens attributed to Bexon are listed in Flourens's *Des manuscrits de Buffon* (see below), pp. 221–222. Flourens also mentions (p. 58 f.) Bexon's unpublished manuscript on religion and natural history, which he entitles "De la religion par rapport à l'univers." Although no letters from Bexon to Buffon have ever been published, several from master to collaborator have been. One group of letters was originally published in the year VIII (1799–1800) by François de Neufchateau in his journal *Le conservateur,* **1,** 101–146. These were later reprinted by Flourens in *Histoire des travaux et des idées de Buffon* (Paris, 1850), pp. 307–344, and by Henri Nadault de Buffon in *Correspondance inédite de Buffon,* II (Paris, 1860). Several letters were added by Lanessan in his edition of the *Oeuvres complètes de Buffon* (Paris, 1855), XIII and XIV. These letters were reprinted, with Lanessan's notes, in H. M. J. A. P. de Bremond d'Ars, *Un collaborateur de Buffon: l'abbé Bexon* (see below).

II. SECONDARY LITERATURE. Of the several short accounts of Bexon's life that have appeared in the periodical literature, the most useful are E. Buisson, "Un collaborateur de Buffon. L'abbé Bexon—sa vie & ses oeuvres," in *Bulletin de la Société philomatique vosgienne,* **14** (1888–1889), 275–317, and Paillart, "L'abbé Bexon. Étude biographique et littéraire," in *Mémoires de l'Académie de Stanislas* (1867), 195–230. Flourens discusses Bexon in his *Des manuscrits de Buffon* (Paris, 1860), pt. III, ch. 3. Bexon's mother wrote a sympathetic, motherly sketch of her son after his death, and Humbert-Bazile, Buffon's secretary, published it in conjunction with his discussion of Bexon in his *Buffon. Sa famille, ses collaborateurs et ses familiers,* Nadault de Buffon, ed. (Paris, 1863). Relying on all these sources, Bremond d'Ars published the only extensive treatment of Bexon, *Un collaborateur de Buffon: L'abbé Bexon* (Paris, 1936).

ALAN S. KAY

BEYRICH, HEINRICH ERNST (*b.* Berlin, Germany, 31 August 1815; *d.* Berlin, 9 July 1896), *geology, paleontology.*

Beyrich was born into a substantial old Berlin merchant family. After completing his secondary education he entered Berlin University at the age of sixteen in order to study the natural sciences, especially mineralogy under Christian Samuel Weiss. In 1834 he transferred to the University of Bonn, where Goldfuss inspired him to specialize in paleontology. Geology and paleontology were his major interests throughout most of his life.

Before and after completing his studies Beyrich wandered through much of Germany, Switzerland, and Italy in order to add to his knowledge of geology and paleontology. In the course of his travels he met a number of eminent geologists and paleontologists, including Peter Merian, Agassiz, and Studer in Switzerland and Élie de Beaumont, Deshayes, and Brongniart in Paris. He had been recommended to these men by Leopold von Buch and Alexander von Humboldt.

Beyrich received the Ph.D. from Berlin University in 1837 with a Latin dissertation dealing with the goniatites of the Rhenish Schiefergebirge. His choice of topic was greatly influenced by Buch. In 1841 Beyrich was appointed *Privatdozent* at Berlin University, where he spent the rest of his life, holding a wide range of academic and civil service posts. In 1846 he was appointed associate professor, and in 1865 he became full professor. He was made custodian of the geological collections of the Prussian Mining Administration in 1855, and from 1857 he taught mining students.

Beyrich was one of the founders of the German Geological Society in 1848, and for the rest of his life he was one of its most active promoters; from 1872 to 1895 he was its president. In 1853 Beyrich was elected a full member of the Prussian Academy of Sciences, and when the Königliche Geologische Landesanstalt und Bergakademie was founded in Berlin in 1873, he was appointed its scientific director. In the same year he became director of the Museum of Natural History.

In 1842 Beyrich was commissioned by the Prussian Mining Administration to make a geological survey of Silesia. His findings were published in 1844 as "Über die Entwickelung des Flötzgebirges in Schlesien," a masterpiece that combines clear presentation, acute perception, and thoroughness. The work established Beyrich's reputation as a geologist and stratigrapher; its most important chapters deal with Paleozoic, Jurassic, Cretaceous, and Tertiary strata, as well as the tectonic structures of the area. The investigation comparing the malm strata in Poland (Wieluń, Krakow) and in Moravia (Štramberk, Mikulov, Brno), with the Upper Jurassic in southern France and northern Italy, and the clarification of certain stratigraphic problems of the Mesozoic and Tertiary formations in the Carpathians are a continuation of his Silesian studies.

Beyrich's explorations of the north German Tertiary formations were of particular importance. They started around 1847 and occupied him for most of his life, although during his last years he published little on the subject. The most important work on these explorations is "Die Conchylien des norddeutschen Tertiärgebirges" (1852–1855), which remained unfinished. The result of this paleontological study was a classification of the north German Tertiary ("Über den Zusammenhang der norddeutschen Tertiärbildungen . . ., 1855); its best-known result is the conception of an independent Oligocene interpolated between Lyell's Eocene and Miocene. The Oligocene, the north German counterpart of the Belgian Tongrian and the Rupelian, was first mentioned in 1854 and briefly defined in "Über die Stellung der hessischen Tertiärbildungen." Ever since, the Oligocene has occupied its established place in the stratigraphy of the Tertiary.

In his treatise of 1855, Beyrich describes the classification and extension of the north German Tertiary strata. He points out that in Belgium the Tongrian stage immediately follows the Upper Eocene, whereas in the large adjoining sections to the northeast and east there is no Eocene and the north German Tertiary strata cover the older pre-Tertiary strata in transgressive deposits. In 1855 Beyrich wrote:

> Their connected and independent geognostic distribution, independent of the presence of older Eocene Tertiary formations, is the prime reason which prevents me from classifying them—in accordance with Lyell— merely as an upper part of the Eocene Tertiary series. Their diverse formations and their abundance in specific organic remains—the extent of which was first revealed in Germany—have motivated me to consider them, rather, as a separate part of the Tertiary period (i.e., Oligocene) instead of assigning them to the Miocene Tertiary stage, as I had done earlier in accordance with d'Orbigny and other authors ["Über den Zusammenhang . . .," p. 11].

Beyrich's studies resulted in a subdivision of the Oligocene into Lower, Middle, and Upper Oligocene. He defined the marine sands of Egeln, near Magdeburg, as Lower Oligocene (i.e., Lower Tongrian); the septarian clay of the Brandenburg region and the sands of the Stettin area connected to the latter's facies by lateral transition as Middle Oligocene (Rupelian); and the so-called Sternberg rocks and the sedimentary rocks of the same period in central Germany as Upper Oligocene.

Some minor details of Beyrich's concepts have been changed, but his initial theory has been retained in principle. Even today his definition of the Oligocene inspires a flood of discussions and treatises. Beyrich also investigated stratigraphic problems of the Paleozoic in Germany. In 1865 he published a classification of the Permian (Continental Rothliegende [i.e., Lower Permian] and marine Zechstein [i.e., Upper Permian]) on the southern edge of the Harz Mountains. Beyrich then applied his paleontological knowledge to the clarification of the difficult and tectonically complicated conditions of the Devonian in the Harz Mountains.

Beyrich further defended the division of the Carboniferous in Germany into an older marine system (Carboniferous limestone and culm, respectively) and a younger system (with coal-bearing strata) on several occasions. He was especially interested, too, in comparing the development of the Triassic system in Germany with the Alpine Triassic system. He obtained data primarily by the paleontological findings from the Middle Triassic system (i.e., Muschelkalk) of Upper Silesia.

Geological cartography constitutes a large part of Beyrich's scientific work, beginning with his fieldwork in Silesia in 1842. In the 1860's he mapped the Harz Mountains, their northern and southern foothills, and the vicinity of Magdeburg. After that Beyrich emerged as the organizer and coordinator of the geological mapping operations in Prussia and Thuringia, for which he was officially commissioned in 1867 by the Prussian government.

One of Beyrich's most effective organizational accomplishments was the introduction of the 1:25,000 topographic map as the basis for geological mapping in Prussia. The other German geological surveys, and those of some foreign countries, adopted this scale.

The main part of Beyrich's work, reflected in his published papers, concerned studies in paleontology and biostratigraphy. More than half of his total of 205 publications are devoted to this subject. His doctoral thesis dealt with paleontological stratigraphy, in that it treated the Devonian goniatites of the Rhenish Schiefergebirge and their stratigraphic distribution. This part of his scientific work is significant not only in scope but also in diversity. There are many

groups of individual or multiple fossil representatives of the animal kingdom that were treated by Beyrich. Among them are Mammalia, Stegocephalia, Pisces, Cystoidea, Crinoidea, Echinoidea, Graptolitoidea, Trilobita, Phyllopoda, Cephalopoda, Gastropoda, Pelecypoda, and Brachiopoda; he also investigated corals, sponges, and trace fossils. He dealt with paleobotanical subjects in a number of short papers on Tertiary and Carboniferous plants.

Nevertheless, Beyrich left few purely paleozoological works. Of these, mention should be made of his papers on the Muschelkalk Crinoidea (1857, 1871), which had been suggested by Johannes Müller's classic studies on the living *Pentacrinus*. In addition to a precise and thorough description of the Crinoidea of the German Muschelkalk, which were then little known, Beyrich furnished important information on the organization of the crinoidean skeleton. Thus he was the first to demonstrate the canals in the plates of the crinoid cup and to discuss the symmetrical principles in the cup structure and their taxonomic value.

In his treatise "Über einige Cephalopoden aus dem Muschelkalk der Alpen" (1866) Beyrich made the first attempt to establish connections between Triassic and Jurassic ammonites. This work also contains the first approaches to the taxonomic classification of the later ammonites and their evolutionary relations.

In "Conchylien des norddeutschen Tertiärgebirges" Beyrich split the rather largely classified genera of the older conchologists into subdivisions, so that their relationships could be better understood. Furthermore, such smaller groups were apt to offer more reliable material in discussions of stratigraphic and paleobiogeographic problems. On the other hand, Beyrich was an enemy of unfounded and wanton classification of species. In the introduction to his doctoral thesis (1837) we find the following passage:

> I was least inclined to imitate the methods of some excellent scholars of great merit who are wont to label everything in the collections available to them and to publicize such names without scruples simply to add to and to decorate synonymics. In classifying new species I shall always proceed with the greatest care. I am absolutely disinclined to consider the authorship of the newest species possible as an accomplishment or as something enviable. It would appear much more deserving to me to do away with useless divisions and to solidify already known facts by more precise observations [pp. 1–2].

If we take into account that Beyrich was only twenty-two when he wrote this paper, we must admire the great maturity of his systematic and taxonomic insights and principles. Yet in questions of zoological nomenclature, he took more liberties. He did not think much of the system of nomenclatural priorities, of the system of generic and specific classification, or of the use of synonymy lists.

Beyrich also investigated vertebrates. His main work in this field is on the catarrhine monkey *Mesopithecus pentelici* of the Lower Pliocene at Pikermi, near Athens. He established its difference from the hominoid *Hylobates* and its close relationship to the cynomorph *Semnopithecus*. He also produced memoranda on the Oligocene *Anthracotherium,* the Pliocene mastodons and rhinoceroses, the Pleistocene elephants and rhinoceroses, the Triassic labyrinthodonts, the Devonian *Pterichthyodes* and Coccosteidae, the Permian *Acanthodes,* the Triassic ganoid *Tholodus,* and the Tertiary selachian *Carcharodon.*

The range of Beyrich's paleontological works was due, first, to the era in which he lived, an era in which the differentiation of the geological sciences did not extend so far as today. At that time important fields, such as paleontology, were still comprehensible for the single scientist. Second, under Beyrich's direction the Berlin Museum started to receive a great volume of paleontological materials from all parts of Germany and many other European countries, the processing of which was entrusted to Beyrich by virtue of his office.

Most of Beyrich's work dealt with the geology and paleontology of Germany and adjoining European countries. During the last third of the nineteenth century, however, Berlin also received paleontological collections from overseas that were of great interest to Beyrich. These included Devonian, Carboniferous, and Cretaceous samples from Tripoli, ammonites of the Upper Malm, and Pelecypoda of the Lower Cretaceous from the Zanzibar coast.

Another collection from the island of Timor contained Permian marine fossils: an early work by Beyrich concerned the Timor fauna made famous by Wanner and others. Beyrich also occupied himself for years with the Cretaceous fauna between Cairo and Suez; he received the materials from the explorer Georg Schweinfurth. He also treated the Himalayan ammonite fauna of the Triassic era, and demonstrated that the Triassic contained not only elements of the European Upper Triassic fauna but also of the Middle Triassic.

BIBLIOGRAPHY

I. ORIGINAL WORKS. Beyrich's major writings are "Beiträge zur Kenntniss der Versteinerungen des rheinischen Übergangsgebirges," in *Abhandlungen der Preussischen Akademie der Wissenschaften* (1837); *De goniatitis in montibus rhenanis occurrentibus* (Berlin, 1837), his doctoral dissertation; "Über die Entwickelung des Flötzgebirges in Schlesien," in *Karsten's Archiv,* **18** (1844), 3–68; "Untersuchungen über Trilobiten. Als Fortsetzung zu der Abhandlung: Ueber einige böhmische Trilobiten," in *Abhandlungen der Preussischen Akademie der Wissenschaften* (1845), 1–38; "Die Conchylien des norddeutschen Tertiärgebirges," in *Zeitschrift der Deutschen geologischen Gesellschaft,* **5** (1853), 273–358; **6** (1854), 408–500, 726–781; **8** (1856), 21–88; "Über die Stellung der hessischen Tertiärbildungen," in *Verhandlungen der Preussischen Akademie der Wissenschaften* (1854), 640–666; "Über den Zusammenhang der norddeutschen Tertiärbildungen, zur Erläuterung einer geologischen Übersichtskarte," in *Abhandlungen der Preussischen Akademie der Wissenschaften* (*für 1855*), 1–20; "Über die Crinoiden des Muschelkalkes," *ibid.* (*für 1857*), 1–50; "Über eine Kohlenkalk-Fauna von Timor," *ibid.* (*für 1864*), 61–98; "Über einige Cephalopoden aus dem Muschelkalk der Alpen und über verwandte Arten," *ibid.* (*für 1866*), 105–150; and "Über die Basis der Crinoidea brachiata," in *Monatsberichte der Preussischen Akademie der Wissenschaften* (*für 1871*), 33–55.

II. SECONDARY LITERATURE. Works on Beyrich are H. W. Dames, "Gedächtnisrede auf Ernst Beyrich," in *Abhandlungen der Königlichen Akademie der Wissenschaften, Berlin* (1898), 3–11; W. Hauchecorne, "Nekrolog auf E. Beyrich," in *Jahrbuch der Königlichen Preussischen Geologische Landesanstalt und Bergakademie,* **17** (Berlin, 1897), pp. 102–148, with complete bibliography; and E. Koken, *Die Deutsche geologische Gesellschaft in den Jahren 1848–1898 mit einem Lebensabriss von Ernst Beyrich* (Berlin, 1901).

HEINZ TOBIEN

BEZOLD, ALBERT VON (*b.* Ansbach, Bavaria, 7 January 1836; *d.* Würzburg, Bavaria, 2 March 1868), *physiology.*

Bezold's father, Johann Daniel Christoph, was a physician in Rothenburg and Ansbach. After attending secondary school at Ansbach, Albert began to study medicine at the University of Munich in 1853, with the aim of devoting himself to experimental research; he transferred to Würzburg the following year. At the beginning of 1854 he contracted rheumatic endocarditis, which recurred several times. The ailment led to a mitral stenosis, which resulted in his death at the age of thirty-two.

For the completion of his studies Bezold went in the fall of 1857 to Berlin, where he worked under the physiologist Emil Du Bois-Reymond, famous for his electrophysiological investigations; from him Bezold learned to apply physical methods to the study of biological phenomena. In 1858 Du Bois-Reymond made him an assistant in his institute and in 1859, at the age of twenty-three, he received a surprise appointment to the newly created chair of physiology at the University of Jena. Before he assumed his post in Jena, he went for several days to Würzburg to complete the requirements for the M.D. by presenting the dissertation "Über die gekreuzten Wirkungen des Rückenmarks." He had tried by experimental means to elucidate the cross effects of the motor and sensory paths while studying there. In 1865 Bezold was called to the new chair of physiology in Würzburg. Although he was active there for only three years, he made it a renowned center for physiological research.

Bezold's investigations were primarily on the physiology of the nerves and muscles, as well as of the heart. At Würzburg he also made pharmacological investigations, especially on the effects of veratrine, atropine, and curare on the muscles, nerves, and the heart and circulatory system. He confirmed Pflüger's law in *Untersuchungen über die elektrische Erregung der Nerven und Muskeln* (1861) and demonstrated that it is also valid for the direct stimulation of the muscle fiber.

In the physiology of the heart, Bezold occupied himself primarily with the problem of which nerve impulses influence the work of the heart. Galen had assumed that the contractions of the heart were independent of the brain. When Bezold turned to these problems, intracardial sources of heart stimulation had already been described; he localized them in the collection of ganglia in the *septum interatriale* (Bezold's ganglia). Through cleverly planned experiments Bezold settled the controversy over the relationship between the vagus nerve and the heartbeat. He proved that stimulation of the vagus decreases the rate of heartbeat and that it depresses the total energy output of the heart. In the *Untersuchungen über die Innervation des Herzens* (1863), Bezold also presented his experiments on the function of the sympathetic nerve, from which he concluded that stimulation of the cervical sympathetic would increase the frequency and the force of the heartbeat.

Bezold's experiments with veratrine led to the discovery of an effect on the circulation that originated from the heart and was characterized by bradycardia and lowering of the blood pressure. In the heart, veratrine stimulates the sensory ("depressing") vagus fibers and thus stimulates the vagus center. The efferent component of the reflex, via the vagus tract, decreases the heartbeat; through the vasomotor center, it lessens the tone of the vessels and thus decreases the blood pressure. In 1937 the pharmacologist Adolf Jarisch reexamined this regulatory heart-circulation reflex and recognized its general significance; today it has become important, as the "Schonreflex" (protective reflex) of the heart, for the

understanding of pathological processes and is known as the Bezold-Jarisch reflex.

BIBLIOGRAPHY

I. ORIGINAL WORKS. Among Bezold's writings are *Untersuchungen über die elektrische Erregung der Nerven und Muskeln* (Leipzig, 1861); *Untersuchungen über die Innervation des Herzens,* 2 vols. (Leipzig, 1863); and "Über die physiologischen Wirkungen des essigsäuren Veratrins," written with L. Hirt, in *Untersuchungen aus dem physiologischen Laboratorium in Würzburg* (Leipzig, 1867), pp. 73–123.

A complete bibliography of his writings is in Robert Herrlinger and Irmgard Krupp, *Albert von Bezold,* pp. 123–124; see also pp. 113–114.

II. SECONDARY LITERATURE. Works on Bezold are Paul Diepgen, *Unvollendete* (Stuttgart, 1960), pp. 34–37; Robert Herrlinger, "Albert von Bezold und die Entdeckung der Innervation des Herzens," in *Von Boerhaave bis Berger,* ed. K. E. Rothschuh (Stuttgart, 1964), pp. 106–120; Robert Herrlinger and Irmgard Krupp, *Albert von Bezold* (Stuttgart, 1964); and Friedrich von Recklinghausen, "Gedächtnisrede auf Albert von Bezold," in *Verhandlungen der physikalisch-medizinischen Gesellschaft in Würzburg,* n.s. **1** (1869), xli–xlviii.

JOHANNES STEUDEL

BEZOUT, ÉTIENNE (*b.* Nemours, France, 31 March 1739; *d.* Basses-Loges, near Fontainebleau, France, 27 September 1783), *mathematics.*

Étienne Bezout, the second son of Pierre Bezout and Hélène-Jeanne Filz, belonged to an old family in the town of Nemours. Both his father and grandfather had held the office of magistrate (*procureur aux baillage et juridiction*) there. Although his father hoped Étienne would succeed him, the young man was strongly drawn to mathematics, particularly through reading the works of Leonhard Euler. His accomplishments were quickly recognized by the Académie des Sciences, which elected him *adjoint* in 1758, and both *associé* and *pensionnaire* in 1768. He married early and happily; although he was reserved and somewhat somber in society, those who knew him well spoke of his great kindness and warm heart.

In 1763, the duc de Choiseul offered Bezout a position as teacher and examiner in mathematical science for young would-be naval officers, the Gardes du Pavillon et de la Marine. By this time, Bezout had become a father and needed the money. In 1768 he added similar duties for the Corps d'Artillerie. Among his published works are the courses of lectures he gave to these students. The orientation of these books is practical, since they were intended to instruct people in the elementary mathematics and mechanics needed for navigation or ballistics. The experience of teaching nonmathematicians shaped the style of the works: Bezout treated geometry before algebra, observing that beginners were not yet familiar enough with mathematical reasoning to understand the force of algebraic demonstrations, although they did appreciate proofs in geometry. He eschewed the frightening terms "axiom," "theorem," "scholium," and tried to avoid arguments that were too close and detailed. Although criticized occasionally for their lack of rigor, his texts were widely used in France. In the early nineteenth century, they were translated into English for use in American schools; one translator, John Farrar, used them to teach the calculus at Harvard University. The obvious practical orientation, as well as the clarity of exposition, made the books especially attractive in America. These translations considerably influenced the form and content of American mathematical education in the nineteenth century.

A conscientious teacher and examiner, Bezout had little time for research and had to limit himself to what was, for his time, a very narrow subject—the theory of equations. His first two papers (1758–1760) were investigations of integration, but by 1762 he was devoting all his research time to algebra. In his mathematical papers, Bezout often followed a "method of simplifying assumptions," concentrating on those specific cases of general problems which could be solved. This approach is central to the conception of Bezout's first paper on algebra, "Sur plusieurs classes d'équations" (1762).

This paper provides a method of solution for certain nth-degree equations. Bezout related the problem of solving nth-degree equations in one unknown to the problem of solving simultaneous equations by elimination: "It is known that a determinate equation can always be viewed as the result of two equations in two unknowns, when one of the unknowns is eliminated."[1] Since an equation can be so formed, Bezout investigated what information could be gained by assuming that it actually was so formed. Such a procedure resembles the eighteenth-century study of the root-coefficient relations in an nth-degree equation by treating it as formed by the multiplication of n linear factors. Now, if one of the two composing equations had some very simple form—for instance, had only the nth-degree term and a constant—Bezout saw that he could determine the form of its solution. Conversely, if the coefficients of a given nth-degree equation in one unknown had the form built up from such a special solution, that nth-degree equation could be solved. Bezout's principal example considers

$$x^n + mx^{n-1} + px^{n-2} + \cdots + M = 0$$

as resulting from the equations

$$y^n + h = 0 \quad \text{and} \quad y = \frac{x + a}{x + b}.$$

The importance of this paper lay in drawing Bezout's attention from the problem of explicitly solving the nth-degree equation—an important concern of eighteenth-century algebraists—to the theory of elimination, the area of his most significant contributions. The central problem of elimination theory for Bezout was this: given n equations in n unknowns, to find and study what Bezout called the resultant equation in one of the unknowns. This equation contains all values of that unknown that occur in solutions of the n given equations. Bezout wanted to find a resultant equation of as small degree as possible, that is, with as few extraneous roots as possible. He wanted also to find its degree, or at least an upper bound on its degree.

In his 1764 paper, "Sur le degré des équations résultantes de l'évanouissement des inconnues," he discussed Euler's method for finding the equation resulting from two equations in two unknowns, and computed an upper bound on its degree.[2] He extended this method to N equations in N unknowns. But, although Euler's method yielded an upper bound on the degree of the resultant equation, Bezout observed that it was too clumsy to use for equations of high degree.

Another procedure, which gives a resultant equation of lower degree (now called the Bezoutiant) is given at the end of the 1764 paper. The equations to be solved are

(1) $\qquad Ax^m + Bx^{m-1} + \cdots + V = 0$
(2) $\qquad A'x^{m'} + B'x^{m'-1} + \cdots + V' = 0$

where $A, A', B, B', \cdots$ are functions of y, and where $m \geqslant m'$. From these, he obtained m polynomials in x, of degree less than or equal to m-1, which have among their common solutions the solutions of (1) and (2). For the case $m = m'$, these polynominals are

$$A'(Ax^m + Bx^{m-1} + \cdots + V)$$
$$- A(A'x^{m'} + \cdots + V') = 0,$$
$$(A'x + B')(Ax^m + \cdots + V)$$
$$- (Ax + B)(A'x^{m'} + \cdots + V) = 0, \text{ etc.}$$

He considered these polynomial equations as m linear equations in the unknowns $x, x^2, \cdots, x^{m-1}$. And he observed that (1) and (2) have a common solution if these linear equations do. But when can the linear equations be solved?

At the beginning of this 1764 paper, Bezout had

expressed what we would call a determinant by means of permutations of the coefficients, in what is sometimes called the Table of Bezout. He described the use of this table in solving simultaneous linear equations and, in particular, as a criterion for their solvability. This gave him a criterion for finding the resultant of (1) and (2). J. J. Sylvester, in 1853, explicitly gave the determinant of the coefficients of these m linear equations, and called it the Bezoutiant. The Bezoutiant, considered as a function of y, has as its zeros all the y's that are common solutions of equations (1) and (2).

It was not until 1779 that Bezout published his *Théorie des équations algébriques,* his major work on elimination theory. Its best-known achievement is the statement and proof of Bezout's theorem: "The degree of the final equation resulting from any number of complete equations in the same number of unknowns, and of any degrees, is equal to the product of the degrees of the equations."[3] Bezout, following Euler, defined a complete polynomial as one that contains each possible combination of the unknowns whose degree is no more than the degree of the polynomial. Bezout also computed that the degree of the resultant equation is less than the product of the degrees for various systems of incomplete equations. Here we shall consider only the complete case.

The proof makes one marvel at the ingenuity of Bezout, who, like Euler, not only could manipulate formulas but also had the ability to choose those manipulations that would be fruitful. He was compelled to justify his nth-order results by a naive "induction" from the observed truth of the statements for 1, 2, 3, $\cdots$. Also, numbered subscripts had not yet come into use, and the notations available were clumsy.

Here is Bezout's argument. Given n equations in n unknowns, of degrees t, t', t'', $\cdots$. Let us call the equations $P_1(u,x,y,\cdots)$, $P_2(u,x,y,\cdots)$, $\cdots$. (Bezout wrote them $(u\cdots n)^t$, $(u\cdots n)^{t'}$, $\cdots$). Suppose now that P_1 is multiplied by an indeterminate polynomial, which we shall designate as Q for definiteness, of degree T. If a Q can be found such that P_1Q involves only the unknown u, P_1Q will be the resultant; Bezout's problem then becomes to compute the smallest possible degree of such a P_1Q.

Bezout stated, and later[4] gave an argument to show, that he could solve the equations

$$P_2(u, x, y, \cdots) = 0, \cdots P_n(u, x, y, \cdots) = 0$$

to determine, respectively, $x^{t'}$, $y^{t''}$, $z^{t'''}$, $\cdots$ in terms of lower powers of the unknowns. Substituting the values for $x^{t'}$, $y^{t''}$, $\cdots$ in the product P_1Q would eliminate all the terms divisible by those powers of the unknowns.

The key to Bezout's proof was in counting the number of terms in the final polynomial, P_1Q. Bezout began his book with a derivation, by means of finite differences, of a complicated formula for the number of terms in a complete polynomial in several unknowns which are not divisible by the unknowns to particular powers; that is, for a complete polynomial in u, x, y, z, $\cdots$ of degree T, he gave an expression for the number of terms not divisible by u^p, x^q, y^r, $\cdots$, where $p + q + r + \cdots < T$. Bezout used this formula to compute the number of terms in the polynomials P_1Q and Q which remained after the elimination of $x^{t'}$, $y^{t''}$, $\cdots$.

Let us write N (instead of Bezout's complicated expression) for the number of terms remaining in P_1Q, M for those remaining in Q. If the degree of the resultant is to be D, then it will have $D + 1$ terms, since it is an equation in the single unknown u. Then the coefficients of Q must be such that $N - (D + 1)$ terms in the product P_1Q will be annihilated by them. But, since Q or any multiple of Q would have the same effect, one of the coefficients of Q may be taken arbitrarily. Thus, Bezout argued, there were $M - 1$ coefficients at his disposal to annihilate the number of terms beyond $D + 1$ remaining in the product P_1Q. In other words, Bezout had to solve $N - (D + 1)$ linear equations in $M - 1$ unknowns—these unknowns being the coefficients of Q. This can be done if the number of equations equals the number of unknowns, although Bezout did not explicitly state this. Equating $N - (D + 1)$ with $M - 1$, and using his formulas for N and M, Bezout was able to compute that $D = t, t', t'', t''', \cdots$.[5] Bezout briefly noted that his theorem has a geometric interpretation: "The surfaces of three bodies whose nature is expressible by algebraic equations cannot meet each other in more points than there are units in the product of the degrees of the equations."[6] We should note that Bezout did not show that the equations for the coefficients of Q form a consistent, independent set of linear equations, or that extraneous roots can never occur in the resultant equation. Further, the geometric statement must be modified to deal with special cases, since, for instance, three planes can have a straight line in common.

Later on in the work,[7] Bezout discussed another method of finding the resultant equation; this was by finding polynomials, which we may write $Q_1, \cdots, Q_n$, such that

$$P_1Q_1 + P_2Q_2 + \cdots + P_nQ_n = 0$$

is the resultant equation. Each Q_k has indeterminate coefficients, which Bezout explicitly determined for many systems of equations by comparing powers of the unknowns $x, y, z, \cdots$.

Bezout's work on resultants stimulated many investigations in the modern theory of elimination, including Cauchy's refinements of elimination procedure and Sylvester's work on resultants and inertia forms. Bezout's theorem is crucial to the study of the intersection of manifolds in algebraic geometry. In the preface to the *Théorie des équations,* Bezout had complained that algebra was becoming a neglected science. But his accomplishment showed that the fact that his contemporaries could not solve the general equation of *n*th degree did not mean that there were no fruitful areas of investigation remaining in algebra.

NOTES

1. "Sur plusieurs classes d'équations," 20.
2. For Euler's method, see *Introductio in analysin infinitorum* (Lausanne, 1748), **2**, secs. 483 ff.
3. *Théorie des équations algébriques,* 32.
4. *Ibid.,* 206.
5. *Ibid.,* 32.
6. *Ibid.,* 33.
7. *Ibid.,* 187 ff.

BIBLIOGRAPHY

I. ORIGINAL WORKS. Bezout's major works are the following: "Sur plusieurs classes d'équations de tous les degrés qui admettent une solution algébrique," in *Mémoires de l'Académie royale des sciences* (1762), 17–52; *Cours de mathématiques à l'usage des Gardes du Pavillon et de la Marine,* 6 vols. (Paris, 1764–1769), reprinted many times with slight variations in the title, often translated or revised in parts; "Sur le degré des équations résultantes de l'évanouissement des inconnues," in *Mémoires de l'Académie royale des sciences* (1764), 288–338; "Sur la resolution des équations de tous les degrés," *ibid.* (1765), 533–552; and *Théorie générale des équations algébriques* (Paris, 1779).

II. SECONDARY WORKS. Secondary works are Georges Bouligand, "À une étape décisive de l'algèbre. L'oeuvre scientifique d'Étienne Bezout," in *Revue générale des sciences,* **55** (1948), 121–123; Marquis de Condorcet, "Éloge de M. Bezout," in *Éloges des académiciens de l'Académie Royale des Sciences,* **3** (1799), 322–337; E. Netto and R. Le Vavasseur, "Les fonctions rationnelles," in *Encyclopédie des sciences mathématiques pures et appliquées,* I, pt. 2 (Paris–Leipzig, 1907), 1–232; and Henry S. White, "Bezout's Theory of Resultants and Its Influence on Geometry," in *Bulletin of the American Mathematical Society,* **15** (1909), 325–338.

JUDITH V. GRABINER

BHĀSKARA I (*fl.* 629), *astronomy.*

Bhāskara I, who was one of the leading exponents of Āryabhaṭa I's two systems of astronomy (see Essays V and VI), composed his commentary on the *Āryabhaṭīya* in 629. In this work he mentions Valabhī (Vala, in Saurāṣṭra), Bharukaccha (Broach, in Gujarat), Śivabhāgapura (Śivarājapura, in Saurāṣṭra), and Sthāneśvara (Thanesar, in the Panjab). But in this same work, and in the *Mahābhāskarīya,* Bhāskara constantly speaks of the *Āryabhaṭīya* as the *Āsmakatantra* and its followers as the *Āsmakīyāḥ.* This seems to indicate that he belonged to a school of followers of the *Āryabhaṭīya* which flourished in Aśmaka (probably the Nizamabad District of Andhra Pradesh). It is supposed by Shukla that Bhāskara was born in either Saurāṣṭra or Aśmaka, and later migrated to the other.

Bhāskara is the author of three works: the *Mahābhāskarīya,* the *Laghubhāskarīya,* and the *Āryabhaṭīyabhāṣya.* The first contains eight chapters:

1. On the mean longitudes of the planets.

2. On the correction due to local longitude.

3. On the three problems relating to diurnal motion, and on the conjunctions of the planets with the stars.

4. On the true longitudes of the planets.

5. On solar and lunar eclipses.

6. On heliacal risings and settings, on the lunar crescent, and on the conjunctions of the planets.

7. The parameters according to the *audayaka* (*Āryapakṣa*) and the *ārdharātrika* systems.

8. Examples.

There are two published commentaries on the *Mahābhāskarīya: Bhāṣya,* by Govindasvāmin (*fl. ca.* 800–850), on which there is a supercommentary (*Siddhāntadīpikā*) by Parameśvara (*fl.* 1400–1450), and *Karmadīpikā,* by Parameśvara. The anonymous *Prayogaracanā* is unpublished, and no manuscripts are known of the *Govindasvāmya* of Sūryadeva and the *Ṭīkā* of Śrīkaṇṭha. The text was published with the *Karmadīpikā* by Balavanta Rāya Āpte, as Ānandāśrama Sanskrit Series, no. 126 (Poona, 1945); with Govindasvāmin's *Bhāṣya* and Parameśvara's *Siddhāntadīpikā* by T. S. Kuppanna Sastri, as Madras Government Oriental Series, no. 130 (Madras, 1957); and with an English translation and commentary by Kripa Shankar Shukla (Lucknow, 1960).

The *Laghubhāskarīya* also contains eight chapters:

1. On the mean longitudes of the planets.

2. On the true longitudes of the planets.

3. On the three problems relating to diurnal motion.

4. On lunar eclipses.

5. On solar eclipses.

6. On the visibility of the moon and on its crescent.

7. On the heliacal risings and settings of the planets and on their conjunctions.

8. On the conjunctions of the planets with the stars.

There exist three commentaries on the *Laghubhāskarīya:* Śaṅkaranārāyaṇa's *Vivaraṇa* (869), Udayadivākara's *Sundarī* (1073), and Parameśvara's *Parameśvara.* No manuscripts are known to me of the *Bālaśaṅkara* of Śaṅkara (*b.* 1494) nor of the *Ṭīkā* of Śrīkaṇṭha. The text was edited with the *Parameśvara* by Balavanta Rāya Āpṭe, as Ānandāśrama Sanskrit Series, no. 128 (Poona, 1946); with the *Vivaraṇa* of Śaṅkaranārāyaṇa, as Trivandrum Sanskrit Series, no. 162 (Trivandrum, 1949); and with an English translation and commentary by Kripa Shankar Shukla (Lucknow, 1963).

BIBLIOGRAPHY

In addition to works listed in the text, readers may consult B. Datta, "The Two Bhāskaras," in *Indian Historical Quarterly,* **6** (1930), 727–736.

DAVID PINGREE

BHĀSKARA II (*b.* 1115), *astronomy, mathematics.*

Bhāskara II has been one of the most impressive Indian astronomers and mathematicians, not only to modern students of the history of science but also to his contemporaries and immediate successors. An important inscription discovered at Pāṭnā, near Chalisgaon in East Khandesh, Mahārāṣṭra, by Bhāu Dājī, and reedited by F. Kielhorn (*Epigraphia Indica,* **1** [1892], 338–346), records the endowment, by Soïdeva the Nikumbha, on 9 August 1207, of an educational institution (*maṭha*) for the study of Bhāskara's works, beginning with the *Siddhāntaśiromaṇi.* There is further reference in this inscription to Soïdeva's brother and successor, Hemāḍideva, who was a feudatory of the Yādava king of Devagiri, Siṅghaṇa, whose rule began in 1209/1210. The following genealogy is given in the inscription.

Trivikrama belonged to the Śāṇḍilya *gotra*—which indicates that he and his descendants were Brāhmaṇas. His son was Bhāskarabhaṭṭa, who was given the title of Vidyāpati by Bhojarāja (the Paramāra king of Dhārā from *ca.* 995 to *ca.* 1056). The next four generations were respectively Govinda, Prabhākara, Manoratha, and Maheśvara; the last was the father of Bhāskara II. Bhāskara's son, Lakṣmīdhara, was made chief of the Paṇḍitas by Siṅghaṇa's predecessor, Jaitrapāla (1191–1209); and Lakṣmīdhara's son, Caṅgadeva, was the chief

astrologer to Siṅghaṇa himself. It is confirmed in Bhāskara's works—e.g., in the concluding verses of the *Siddhāntaśiromaṇi*—that his father was Maheśvara of the Śāṇḍilya *gotra;* it is further added that he came from the city Vijjaḍaviḍa (Bījāpur in Mysore), which was probably named after the Kalacūri king Vijjala II (1156–1175). If this identification is correct—since the *Siddhāntaśiromaṇi* was written in 1150—Bhāskara II must have been in Vijjala's capital while the latter was still *daṇḍanāyaka* of the Cālukya kings, Jagadekamalla II (1138–1150) and Taila III (1150–1156). We further know from Trivikrama's *Damayantīkathā* that he was the son of Nemāditya (Devāditya?) and the grandson of Śrīdhara; and there exists a popular astrological work by Maheśvara, Bhāskara II's father, entitled *Vṛttaśataka.*

Bhāskara II is the author of at least six works, and possibly of a seventh as well:

1. *Līlāvatī* (see Essay XII).
2. *Bījagaṇita* (see Essay XII).
3. *Siddhāntaśiromaṇi* (see Essay IV).
4. *Vāsanābhāṣya* on the *Siddhāntaśiromaṇi* (see Essay IV).
5. *Karaṇakutūhala* (see Essay IV).
6. *Vivaraṇa* on the *Śiṣyadhīvṛddhidatantra* of Lalla (see Essay V).
7. *Bījopanaya* (see Essay IV).

The *Līlāvatī* and the *Bījagaṇita* are sometimes taken to be parts of the *Siddhāntaśiromaṇi;* the ascription of the *Bījopanaya* to Bhāskara II is questionable.

1. The *Līlāvatī* is a work on mathematics addressed by Bhāskara II to a lady (his daughter or wife?) named Līlāvatī. It contains thirteen chapters:

1. Definitions of terms.
2. Arithmetical operations.
3. Miscellaneous rules.
4. Interest and the like.
5. Arithmetical and geometrical progressions.
6. Plane geometry.
7–10. Solid geometry.
11. On the shadow of a gnomon.
12. Algebra: the pulverizer (*kuṭṭaka*). This is the same as chapter 5 of the *Bījagaṇita.*
13. Combinations of digits.

The *Līlāvatī* has been commented on many times:

1. *Karmapradīpikā* of Nārāyaṇa (*fl.* 1356).
2. *Vyākhyā* of Paraśurāma Miśra (1356).
3. *Vyākhyā* of Parameśvara (*fl.* 1400–1450).
4. *Gaṇitāmṛtasāgarī* of Gaṅgādhara (*ca.* 1420).
5. *Vyākhyā* of Lakṣmīdāsa (*fl.* 1501).
6. *Gaṇitāmṛtakūpikā* of Sūryadāsa (1541). See K. Madhava Krishna Sarma, *Siddha-Bhāratī,* part 2 (Hoshiarpur, 1950), 222–225.

7. *Buddhivilāsinī* of Gaṇeśa (1545). Published. See below, Sanskrit text of the *Līlāvatī* no. 14.

8. *Kriyākramakarī* of Śaṅkara (*fl.* 1556).

9. *Vivaraṇa* of Mahīdhara, alias Mahīdāsa (1587). Published. See below, Sanskrit text of the *Līlāvatī* no. 14.

10. *Mitabhāṣiṇī* of Raṅganātha (1630).

11. *Nisṛṣṭārthadūtī* of Munīśvara, alias Viśvarūpa (1635).

12. *Gaṇitāmṛtalaharī* of Rāmakṛṣṇa (1687). See P. K. Gode, "Date of Gaṇitāmṛtalaharī of Rāmakṛṣṇa," in *Annals of the Bhandarkar Oriental Research Institute,* **11** (1930), 94–95.

13. *Sarvabodhinī* of Śrīdhara (1717).

14. *Udāharaṇa* of Nīlāmbara Jhā (*fl.* 1823).

15. *Ṭīkā* in Kannada of Alasiṅgārya, alias Aliśiṅgarāja.

16. *Vyākhyā* of Bhaveśa.

17. *Udāharaṇa* of Candraśekhara Paṭanāyaka.

18. *Ṭīkā* of Dāmodara(?).

19. *Vilāsa* of Devīsahāya.

20. *Bhūṣaṇa* of Dhaneśvara. Refers to Sūryadāsa (1541).

21. *Ṭīkā* (in vernacular) of Giridhara.

22. *Vyākhyā* of Keśava.

23. *Ṭippaṇa* of Mukunda.

24. *Vṛtti* of Moṣadeva.

25. *Subodhinī* of Rāghava.

26. *Gaṇakabhūṣaṇa* of Rāmacandra, son of Soṣaṇabhaṭṭa.

27. *Kautukalīlāvatī* of Rāmacandra, son of Vidyādhara.

28. *Ṭippaṇa* of Rāmadatta (?).

29. *Manorañjana* of Rāmakṛṣṇadeva.

30. *Ṭīkā* of Rāmeśvara.

31. *Ṭīkā* of Śrīkaṇṭha.

32. *Gaṇitāmṛtavarṣiṇī* of Sūryamaṇi.

33. *Udāharaṇa* of Vīreśvara. Refers to Lakṣmīdāsa (1501).

34. *Udāharaṇa* of Viśveśvara.

35. *Ṭīkā* of Vṛndāvana (?).

In addition to these and a number of anonymous commentaries, there are others in Marāṭhī and Gujarātī. A modern Sanskrit commentary (aside from those which accompany some of the editions listed below) was published by Candra Śekhara Jhā under the title *Vyaktavilāsa* (Benares, 1924).

There are also numerous editions of the Sanskrit text of the *Līlāvatī:*

1. Calcutta, 1832.

2. Tārānātha Śarman, ed. (Calcutta, 1846).

3. Baptist Mission Press (Calcutta, 1846; 2nd ed., Calcutta, 1876).

4. With the *Vivaraṇa* of Mahīdhara and a Telugu commentary by Taḍakamalla Veṅkaṭa Krṣṇarāva, Vāvilla Rāmasvāmin Śāstrin, ed. (Madras, 1863).

5. Jīvānanda Vidyāsāgara, ed. (Calcutta, 1876).

6. Sudhākara Dvivedin, ed. (Benares, 1878).

7. Edited, with his own Sanskrit commentary, by Bāpūdeva Śāstrin (Benares, 1883).

8. Bhuvanacandra Basak, ed. (Calcutta, 1885).

9. Edited as an appendix to Banerji's edition of Colebrooke's translation (Calcutta, 1892; 2nd ed., Calcutta, 1927).

10. Edited, with a Marāṭhī commentary, by Vināyaka Pāṇḍuraṅga Khānāpūrkar (Poona, 1897).

11. Sudhākara Dvivedin, ed., Benares Sanskrit Series, no. 153 (Benares, 1912).

12. Rādhāvallabha, ed. (Calcutta, 1914).

13. Edited, with his own Sanskrit commentary, by Muralīdhara Thākura, as Śrī Harikṛṣṇa Nibandha Maṇimālā Series, no. 3 (Benares, 1928; 2nd ed., Benares, 1938).

14. With *Buddhivilāsinī* of Gaṇeśa and *Vivaraṇa* of Mahīdhara, Dattātreya Āpṭe, ed., Ānandāśrama Sanskrit Series, no. 107, 2 vols. (Poona, 1937).

15. With Sanskrit commentary, edited by Dāmodara Miśra and Payanātha Jhā, as Prācīnācārya Granthāvalī Series, no. 8 (Durbhanga, 1959).

16. With Sanskrit and Hindī commentaries of Laṣaṇa Lāla Jhā, edited by Sureśa Śarman, as Vidyābhavana Saṃskṛta Granthamālā Series, no. 62 (Benares, 1961).

There are also many translations of the *Līlāvatī.* A Kannada version is supposed to have been made by Bhāskara II's contemporary Rājāditya, who flourished, apparently, under the Hoysala king Viṣṇuvardhana (1111–1141). There also exists a Hindī translation, and the various commentaries in Gujarātī, Marāṭhī, and Telugu have already been referred to. Three Persian translations are known. That made by Abū al-Fayḍ Fayḍī at the request of Akbar in 1587 was published at Calcutta in 1827; another was done by Dharma Nārāyan ibn Kalyānmal Kāyath *ca.* 1663 (H. J. J. Winter and A. Mirza, in *Journal of the Asiatic Society of Science,* **18** [1952], 1–10); and the third was made in 1678 by Muḥammad Amīn ibn Shaykh Muḥammad Saʿīd. There are also two English translations. That by J. Taylor was published at Bombay in 1816, and that by H. T. Colebrooke in his *Algebra, With Arithmetic and Mensuration: From the Sanscrit of Brahmegupta and Bháscara* (London, 1817). The latter was republished by Haran Chandra Banerji as *Colebrooke's Translation of the Lilávati* (Calcutta, 1892; 2nd ed., Calcutta, 1927).

2. The *Bījagaṇita,* on algebra, contains twelve chapters:

1. On positive and negative numbers.

2. On zero.

3. On the unknown.

4. On surds.

5. On the pulverizer (*kuṭṭaka*).

6. On indeterminate quadratic equations.

7. On simple equations.

8. On quadratic equations.

9. On equations having more than one unknown.

10. On quadratic equations having more than one unknown.

11. On operations with products of several unknowns.

12. On the author and his work.

The commentaries on the *Bījagaṇita* are all relatively late, and they are far fewer in number than those on the *Līlāvatī*.

1. *Sūryaprakāśa* of Sūryadāsa (1538). See K. Madhava Krishna Sarma, in *Poona Orientalist*, **11** (1946), 54–66, and his article in *Siddha-Bhāratī*, part 2 (Hoshiarpur, 1950), 222–225.

2. *Navāṅkura* (or *Bījapallava*, or *Bījāvataṃsa*, or *Kalpalatāvatāra*) of Kṛṣṇa (1602). See M. M. Patkar, in *Poona Orientalist*, **3** (1938), 169. Published. See below, Sanskrit texts nos. 13 and 16.

3. *Bījaprabodha* of Rāmakṛṣṇa (1687). See P. K. Gode in *Annals of the Bhandarkar Oriental Research Institute*, **10** (1929), 160–161, and **11** (1930), 94–95.

4. *Bālabodhinī* of Kṛpārāma (1792).

5. *Vāsanābhāṣya* of Haridāsa.

6. *Bījālavāla* of Nijānanda.

7. *Kalpalatā* of Paramaśukla (most likely Kṛṣṇa's work?).

8. *Bījavivaraṇa* of Vīreśvara (?).

The Sanskrit text has been frequently published:

1. Calcutta, 1834; rev. ed., Calcutta, 1834.

2. Calcutta, 1846.

3. Partial edition with a German translation by H. Brockhaus, "Über die Algebra des Bhāskara," in *Berichte über die Verhandlungen der Königlich Sächsischen Gesellschaft der Wissenschaften zu Leipzig, Philosophisch-historische Klasse*, **4** (Leipzig, 1852), 1–46.

4. Calcutta, 1853.

5. Gopinātha Pāṭhaka, ed. (Benares, 1864).

6. Bāpūdeva Śāstrin, ed., 2 parts (Calcutta [?], 1875).

7. Jīvānanda Vidyāsāgara, ed. (Calcutta, 1878).

8. Edited, with his own Sanskrit commentary, by Jīvanātha Śarman (Benares, 1885).

9. Edited, with his own Sanskrit commentary, by Sudhākara Dvivedin (Benares, 1888).

10. Edited, with a Marāṭhī translation and commentary, by Vināyaka Pāṇḍuraṅga Khānāpūrkar (Poona, 1913).

11. Edited, with his own Sanskrit commentary, by Rādhāvallabha (Calcutta, 1917).

12. Edited, with Sudhākara Dvivedin's Sanskrit commentary and one of his own, by Muralīdhara Jhā, as Benares Sanskrit Series, no. 154 (Benares, 1927).

13. Edited, with the *Navāṅkura* of Kṛṣṇa, by Dattātreya Āpṭe, as Ānandāśrama Sanskrit Series, no. 99 (Poona, 1930).

14. Edited, with his own Sanskrit and Hindī commentaries, by Durgāprasāda Dvivedin (3rd. ed., Lakṣmaṇapura, 1941; the preface is dated Jayapura, 1916).

15. Edited, with Jīvanātha Śarman's Sanskrit commentary and with his own in Sanskrit and Hindī, by Acyutānanda Jhā, as Kāśī Sanskrit Series, no. 148 (Benares, 1949).

16. Edited, with the *Bījapallava* of Kṛṣṇa, by T. V. Rādhākṛṣṇa Śāstrin, as Tanjore Sarasvati Mahal Series, no. 78 (Tanjore, 1958).

There are two Persian translations of the *Bījagaṇita*, one anonymous and the other by ʿAtā allāh Rashīdī ibn Aḥmad Nādir for Shah Jahan in 1634/1635. An English translation of the latter by E. Strachey, with notes by S. Davis, was published at London in 1813. It was also translated into English directly from the Sanskrit by H. T. Colebrooke in *Algebra, With Arithmetic and Mensuration . . .* (London, 1817).

3. The *Siddhāntaśiromaṇi*, which was written in 1150, consists of two parts—the *Grahagaṇitādhyāya* (or *Gaṇitādhyāya*) and the *Golādhyāya*—which are sometimes preserved singly in the manuscripts. The first part, on mathematical astronomy, contains twelve chapters:

1. On the mean longitudes of the planets.

2. On the true longitudes of the planets.

3. On the three problems involving diurnal motion.

4. On the syzygies.

5. On lunar eclipses.

6. On solar eclipses.

7. On planetary latitudes.

8. On the heliacal risings and settings of the planets.

9. On the lunar crescent.

10. On planetary conjunctions.

11. On conjunctions of the planets with the stars.

12. On the *pātas* of the sun and moon.

The second part, on the sphere, contains thirteen chapters:

1. Praise of (the study of) the sphere.

2. On the nature of the sphere.

3. On cosmography and geography.

4. Principles of planetary mean motion.

5. On the eccentric-epicyclic model of the planets.

6. On the construction of an armillary sphere.

7. Principles of spherical trigonometry.

8. Principles of eclipse calculations.

9. Principles of the calculation of the first and last visibilities of the planets.

10. Principles of the calculation of the lunar crescent.

11. On astronomical instruments.

12. Descriptions of the seasons.

13. On problems of astronomical computations. The chapter on the sine function is placed differently in different editions. The *Golādhyāya*, then, is to a large extent an expansion and explanation of the *Gaṇitādhyāya*.

The following commentaries on the *Siddhāntaśiromaṇi* are known (besides various anonymous ones):

1. *Mitākṣarā* (or *Vāsanābhāṣya*) of Bhāskara II himself (see **4,** below). Published. See below, under Sanskrit texts.

2. *Gaṇitatattvacintāmaṇi* of Lakṣmīdāsa (1501).

3. *Śiromaṇiprakāśa* of Gaṇeśa (*b.* 1507). Published in part. See below, Sanskrit text of *Grahagaṇitādhyāya,* no. 4.

4. *Marīci* of Munīśvara, alias Viśvarūpa (*b.* 1603). Published. See below, under Sanskrit texts.

5. *Ṭīkā* of Rāmakṛṣṇa (*fl.* 1687).

6. *Ṭīkā* of Cakracūḍāmaṇi (?).

7. *Vyākhyā* of Dhaneśvara.

8. *Vyākhyā* of Harihara (?).

9. *Ṭīkā* of Jayalakṣmaṇa (?).

10. *Lakṣmīnāthī* of Lakṣmīnātha Miśra (?).

11. *Bhāṣya* of Maheśvara (?).

12. *Vāsanā* of Mohanadāsa (?).

13. *Vyākhyā* of Raṅganātha.

14. *Ṭīkā* of Vācaspati Miśra (?).

The *Ṭippaṇīvivaraṇa* of Buddhinātha Jhā was published at Benares in 1912.

The list of editions of the text is arranged under three headings: *Siddhāntaśiromaṇi, Grahagaṇitādhyāya,* and *Golādhyāya.*

Siddhāntaśiromaṇi.

1. *Siddhāntaśiromaṇiprakāśa* (of Gaṇeśa?), with a Marāṭhī translation (Bombay, 1837).

2. *Siddhāntaśiromaṇi,* with the *Prakāśa* (of Gaṇeśa?), Rāmacandra, ed. (Madras, 1837).

3. Edited, with the *Vāsanābhāṣya,* by Bāpūdeva Śāstrin (Benares, 1866); revised by Candradeva (Benares, 1891); revised by Gaṇapatideva Śāstrin, as Kāśī Sanskrit Series, no. 72 (Benares, 1929).

4. Edited, with the *Vāsanābhāṣya,* the

Vāsanāvārttika of Nṛsiṃha, and the *Marīci* of Munīśvara, by Muralīdhara Jhā, in *The Pandit,* n.s. **30-38** (1908-1916)—incomplete; the first chapter of the *Grahagaṇitādhyāya* was reprinted at Benares in 1917.

5. Edited, with a Sanskrit commentary, by Girijāprasāda Dvivedin (Ahmadabad, 1936).

Grahagaṇitādhyāya.

1. Edited, with the *Mitākṣarā,* by L. Wilkinson (Calcutta, 1842).

2. Edited, with the *Mitākṣarā,* by Jīvānanda Vidyāsāgara (Calcutta, 1881).

3. Edited, with a Marāṭhī translation and commentary, by Vināyaka Pāṇḍuraṅga Khānāpūrkar (Poona, 1913).

4. Edited, with the *Vāsanābhāṣya* and the *Śiromaṇiprakāśa* of Gaṇeśa, by Dattātreya Āpṭe, as Ānandāśrama Sanskrit Series, no. 110, 2 vols. (Poona, 1939-1941).

5. Edited, with the *Vāsanābhāṣya* and his own Sanskrit commentary, by Muralīdhara Ṭhakkura, as Kāśī Sanskrit Series, no. 149 (Benares, 1950)—the first two chapters only.

6. Edited, with the *Vāsanābhāṣya,* the *Marīci* of Munīśvara, and his own Sanskrit and Hindī commentaries, by Kedāradatta Jośī, 3 vols. (Benares, 1961-1964); this edition does not include the *Marīci* on chapter 1.

Golādhyāya.

1. Edited, with the *Mitākṣarā,* by L. Wilkinson (Calcutta, 1842).

2. Calcutta, 1856.

3. Edited, with the *Vāsanābhāṣya,* by Jīvānanda Vidyāsāgara (Calcutta, 1880).

4. Edited, with the *Vāsanābhāṣya* and a Bengali translation, by Rasikamohana Chattopādhyāya (Calcutta, 1887).

5. Edited, with the *Vāsanābhāṣya* and a Bengali translation, in *Aruṇodaya,* **1** (1890), part 6.

6. Edited, with a Marāṭhī translation and commentary, by Vināyaka Pāṇḍuraṅga Khānāpūrkar (Bombay, 1911)—chapters 1-8 only.

7. Edited, with the *Vāsanābhāṣya* and a Hindī commentary, by Girijāprasāda Dvivedin (Lucknow, 1911).

8. Edited, with the *Vāsanābhāṣya* and a Bengali translation, by Rādhāvallabha (Calcutta, 1921).

9. Edited, with the *Vāsanābhāṣya* and the *Marīci* of Munīśvara, by Dattātreya Āpṭe, as Ānandāśrama Sanskrit Series, no. 122, 2 vols. (Poona, 1943-1952).

Aside from the translations into the vernacular mentioned above, I know only of the following two: a Latin translation of the *Grahagaṇitādhyāya* published by E. Roer in *Journal of the Royal Asiatic*

Society of Bengal, **13** (1844), 53–66, and an English translation of the *Golādhyāya* by L. Wilkinson, revised by Bāpūdeva Śāstrin, as Bibliotheca Indica, no. 32 (Calcutta, 1861), with the Paṇḍit's translation of the *Sūryasiddhānta.* See also L. Wilkinson, "On the Use of the Siddhāntas in the Work of Native Education," in *Journal of the Royal Asiatic Society of Bengal,* **3** (1834), 504–519.

4. The *Vāsanābhāṣya* or *Mitākṣarā* is Bhāskara II's own commentary on the *Siddhāntaśiromaṇi.* A commentary on it, the *Vāsanāvārttika,* was written by Nṛsiṃha of Golagrāma in 1621. Editions of both these works have been listed in the preceding material on the *Siddhāntaśiromaṇi.*

5. The *Karaṇakutūhala,* which is also known as the *Brahmatulya,* the *Grahāgamakutūhala,* and the *Vidagdhabuddhivallabha,* was written in 1183; it gives simpler rules for solving astronomical problems than does the *Siddhāntaśiromaṇi.* There are ten sections:

1. On the mean longitudes of the planets.
2. On the true longitudes of the planets.
3. On the three problems involving diurnal motion.
4. On lunar eclipses.
5. On solar eclipses.
6. On heliacal risings and settings.
7. On the lunar crescent.
8. On planetary conjunctions.
9. On the *pātas* of the sun and moon.
10. On the syzygies.

There are, aside from the usual quantity of anonymous commentaries on the *Karaṇakutūhala,* eight whose authors' names are known:

1. *Bhāṣya* of Ekanātha (*ca.* 1370).
2. *Nārmadī* of Padmanābha (*ca.* 1575).
3. *Udāharaṇa* of Viśvanātha (1612).
4. *Gaṇakakumudakaumudī* of Sumatiharṣa Gaṇi (1622). Published. See below.
5. *Ṭīkā* of Caṇḍīdāsa.
6. *Brahmatulyasāra* of Keśavārka (?).
7. *Ṭīkā* of Śaṅkara.
8. *Ṭīkā* of Soḍhala.

For a set of tables based on the *Karaṇakutūhala,* see David Pingree, "Sanskrit Astronomical Tables in the United States," in *Transactions of the American Philosophical Society,* n.s. **58,** no. 3 (1968), 36–37.

The *Karaṇakutūhala* has twice been edited: by Sudhākara Dvivedin, with his own Sanskrit commentary (Benares, 1881); and, with the *Gaṇakakumadakaumudī* of Sumatiharṣa Gaṇi, by Mādhava Śāstrī Purohita (Bombay, 1902).

6. Bhāskara II's *Vivaraṇa* on the *Śiṣyadhīvṛddhidatantra* of Lalla has not been studied or pub-lished. There are three manuscripts: in Benares, in Bikaner, and in Ujjain.

7. A short text of fifty-nine verses entitled *Bījopanaya* is attributed to Bhāskara II. The author claims to be that scholar and to have written this work in 1151. A *Tithinirṇayakārikā* published with it is the only other Sanskrit work to mention it; the author of this text claims to be Śrīnivāsa Yajvan, who flourished in Mysore in the second half of the thir-teenth century and wrote a *Śuddhidīpikā* and a com-mentary on the *Karaṇaprakāśa* of Brahmadeva. Both works, despite their acceptance by Mukhopadhyaya and Sengupta, are evidently late forgeries.

Kuppanna Sastri has shown that the *Bījopanaya,* which gives rules for computing a correction to the moon's equation of the center and variation, was most probably forged in south India in the early 1870's to buttress the position of the partisans of the *dṛk* system against those of the *vākya* system. His argu-ment is based on three main points:

(1) The first correction is astronomically invalid and would have appeared so to the author of the *Siddhāntaśiromaṇi.*

(2) The style is completely at variance with Bhāskara's normal method of exposition.

(3) There are oblique references in the *Vāsanābhāṣya,* a commentary accompanying the *Bījopanaya,* which is also alleged to be by Bhāskara II, to Raṅganātha's commentary on the *Sūr-yasiddhānta,* which was written in 1602 and was pub-lished in 1859.

These arguments seem to this writer quite convinc-ing.

The *Bījopanaya* has been published twice: by Cintāmaṇi Raghunāthācārya and Taḍhakamalla Veṅkaṭakṛṣṇa Rāya at Madras in 1876; and by Ekendranāth Ghosh at Lahore in 1926.

BIBLIOGRAPHY

The following bibliography generally excludes articles that deal only in part with Bhāskara II. It is divided into five sections: General, *Līlāvatī, Bījagaṇita, Sid-dhāntaśiromaṇi,* and *Bījopanaya.* All entries are listed in chronological order.

I. GENERAL. The following deal with Bhāskara II and his works in general: Bhāu Dājī, "Brief Notes on the Age and Authenticity of the Works of Aryabhaṭa, Varāhamihira, Brahmagupta, Bhaṭṭotpala, and Bhāskarāchārya," in *Journal of the Royal Asiatic Society* (1865), 392–418, esp. 410–418; Janārdana Bāḷajī Moḍaka, *Bhāskara Āchārya and His Astronomical System* (n.p., 1887); Sudhākara Dvivedin, *Gaṇakataraṅgiṇī* (Benares, 1933; repr. from *The Pandit,* n.s. **14** [1892]), pp. 34–42; Bāpūdeva Śāstrin, "A

Brief Account of Bhāskara, and of the Works Written, and Discoveries Made, by Him," in *Journal of the Asiatic Society of Bengal,* **62** (1893), 223–229; S. B. Dīkṣita, *Bhāratīya Jyotiḥśāstra* (Poona, 1931; repr. of Poona, 1896), pp. 246–254; G. Thibaut, *Astronomie, Astrologie und Mathematik, Grundriss der indo-arischen Philologie und Altertumskunde,* III, pt. 9 (Strasbourg, 1899), 60; S. K. Ganguly, "Bhāskarāchārya's References to Previous Teachers," in *Bulletin of the Calcutta Mathematical Society,* **18** (1927), 65–76; B. Datta, "The Two Bhāskaras," in *Indian Historical Quarterly,* **6** (1930), 727–736; and Brij Mohan, "The Terminology of Bhāskara," in *Journal of the Oriental Institute, Baroda,* **9** (1959/1960), 17–22.

II. LĪLĀVATĪ. The *Līlāvatī* is discussed in E. Strachey, *Observations on the Mathematical Science of the Hindoos, With Extracts From Persian Translations of the Leelawuttee and Beej Gunnit* (Calcutta, 1805); H. Suter, "Über die Vielecksformel in Bhāskara," in *Verhandlungen des 3. Mathematikerkongresses in Heidelberg* (Leipzig, 1905), pp. 556–561; Sarada Kanta Ganguly, "Bhāskarācārya and Simultaneous Indeterminate Equations of the First Degree," in *Bulletin of the Calcutta Mathematical Society,* **17** (1926), 89–98; M. G. Inamdar, "A Long Forgotten Method," in *Annals of the Bhandarkar Oriental Research Institute,* **9** (1927/1928), 304–308; A. A. Krishnaswami Ayyangar, "Bhaskara and Samclishta Kuttaka," in *Journal of the Indian Mathematical Society,* **18** (1929), 1–7; Saradakanta Ganguli, "Bhāskara and Simultaneous Indeterminate Equations of the First Degree," *ibid.,* **19** (1931/1932), 6–9; A. S. Bhandarkar, " 'Method of False Assumption' of Pacioli, an Italian Mathematician," in *Indian Culture,* **8** (1941/1942), 256–257; K. S. Nagarajan, "Bhaskara's Leelavathi," in *The Aryan Path* (1949), 310–314; D. A. Somayaji, "Bhaskara's Calculations of the Gnomon's Shadow," in *The Mathematics Student,* **18** (1950), 1–8; and Brij Mohan, "The Terminology of Līlāvatī," in *Journal of the Oriental Institute, Baroda,* **8** (1958/1959), 159–168.

III. BĪJAGAṆITA. The *Bījagaṇita* is dealt with in Reuben Burrow, "A Proof That the *Hindoos* Had the *Binomial Theorem,*" in *Asiatick Researches,* **2** (1790), 487–497; A. A. Krishnaswami Ayyangar, "New Light on Bhaskara's Chakravala or Cyclic Method of Solving Indeterminate Equations of the Second Degree in Two Variables," in *Journal of the Indian Mathematical Society,* **18** (1929), 225–248; K. J. Sanjana, "A Brief Analysis of Bhaskara's *Bījagaṇita* With Historical and Critical Notes," *ibid.,* 176–188; and D. H. Potts, "Solution of a Diophantine System Proposed by Bhaskara," in *Bulletin of the Calcutta Mathematical Society,* **38** (1946), 21–24.

IV. SIDDHĀNTAŚIROMAṆI. Works discussing the *Siddhāntaśiromaṇi* are Bapudeva Sastri, "Bhāskara's Knowledge of the Differential Calculus," in *Journal of the Asiatic Society of Bengal,* **27** (1858), 213–216; W. Spottiswoode, "Note on the Supposed Discovery of the Principle of the Differential Calculus by an Indian Astronomer," in *Journal of the Royal Asiatic Society* (1860), 221–222; H. Suter, "Eine indische Methode der Berechnung der Kugeloberfläche," in *Bibliotheca mathematica,*

3rd ser., **9** (1908/1909), 196–199; R. Sewell, "The Siddhanta-siromani," in *Epigraphia Indica,* **15** (1919/1920), 159–245; M. G. Inamdar, "A Formula of Bhaskara for the Chord of a Circle Leading to a Formula for Evaluating Sin α°," in *The Mathematics Student,* **18** (1950), 9–11; and A. A. Krishnaswami Ayyangar, "Remarks on Bhaskara's Approximation to the Sine of an Angle," *ibid.,* 12.

V. BĪJOPANAYA. Further discussion of the *Bījopanaya* can be found in Dhirendranath Mukhopadhyaya, "The Evection and the Variation of the Moon in Hindu Astronomy," in *Bulletin of the Calcutta Mathematical Society,* **22** (1930), 121–132; P. C. Sengupta, "Hindu Luni-solar Astronomy," *ibid.,* **24** (1932), 1–18; and T. S. Kuppanna Sastri, "The Bījopanaya: Is It a Work of Bhāskarācārya?," in *Journal of the Oriental Institute, Baroda,* **8** (1958/1959), 399–409.

DAVID PINGREE

BIAGGIO PELICANI. See **Blasius of Parma.**

BIAŁOBRZESKI, CZESŁAW (*b.* Pošechonje, near Jaroslavl, Russia, 31 August 1878; *d.* Warsaw, Poland, 12 October 1953), *physics, natural philosophy.*

Białobrzeski studied physics at the University of Kiev from 1896 to 1901 and received the *veniam legendi* there in 1907. From 1908 to 1910 he worked in Langevin's laboratory at the Collège de France. After his return to Russia he held the chair of physics and geophysics at the University of Kiev from 1914 to 1919. Białobrzeski assumed the chair of theoretical physics at Warsaw University in 1921 and occupied it for the rest of his life. In 1935 he was appointed to the International Institute of Intellectual Cooperation of the League of Nations, filling the vacancy created by the death of Marie Curie-Skłodowska. Białobrzeski served several terms as president of the Polish Society of Physics, was a vice-president of the International Union of Pure and Applied Physics (1947–1951), and belonged to the Polish Academy of Science, among many others.

Białobrzeski's work may be divided into three periods. From 1900 to 1912 he carried out experimental and theoretical research on the electrical and optical phenomena in fluid and solid dielectrics.

In 1912 Białobrzeski turned his attention to the role of radiation pressure in the equilibrium of the star interior. His paper on this (1913) drew the attention of the Polish physicists Smoluchowski and Natanson but attracted little notice abroad because the journal had only a limited circulation. Other works dealing with radiation pressure were his papers on the mechanism of light absorption (1923–1926). The second period closed with the publication of *La thermodynamique des étoiles* (1931).

In the third period Białobrzeski concentrated on the philosophical problems of physics, mainly on the interpretation of quantum-theory foundations. He initiated and was elected chairman of the international scientific conference in Warsaw (1938) where this problem was discussed by many famous theorists. During World War II, Białobrzeski prepared a three-volume work to be entitled *Podstawy poznawcze fizyki świata atomowego* ("Epistemological Foundations of the Physics of the Atomic World"), in which he developed his philosophical interpretation of the quantum theory. Unfortunately, the manuscripts of the first two volumes were burned during the Warsaw Insurrection (1944). After the war Białobrzeski returned to Warsaw University and started to reconstruct the book. The work, limited to one volume, was finished in 1951 and published in 1956.

BIBLIOGRAPHY

Among Białobrzeski's works are "Sur les théories des diélectriques," in *Le radium,* **9** (1912), 250; "Sur l'équilibre thermodynamique d'une sphère gazeuse libre," in *Bulletin international de l'Académie des sciences de Cracovie,* ser. A (1913), 264–290; "Sur l'absorption vraie de la lumière," in *Annales de physique,* **5** (1926), 215; "Szkic autobiograficzny i uwagi o twórczości naukowej" ("Autobiographical Essay and Remarks on Scientific Work"), in *Nauka Polska* ("Polish Science"), **6** (1927), 49–76, also in *Wybór pism* (see below), pp. 13–48; *La thermodynamique des étoiles* (Paris, 1931); "Sur l'interprétation concrète de la mécanique quantique," in *Revue de métaphysique et de morale,* **41** (1934), 83–103; the introductory discourse in *New Theories in Physics* (Paris, 1939), also published in French (Paris, 1939); *Podstawy poznawcze fizyki świata atomowego* ("Epistemological Foundations of the Physics of the Atomic World"; Warsaw, 1956); and *Wybór pism* ("Selected Papers"; Warsaw, 1964), a selection of philosophical papers, with a bibliography.

W. Scisłowski, "Czesław Białobrzeski (1878–1953)," in *Acta physica Polonica,* **13** (1954), 301–308, an obituary with a bibliography, also appeared in Polish in *Postepy fizyki,* **5,** no. 4 (1954), 413–422.

ANDRZEJ A. TESKE

BIANCHI, LUIGI (*b.* Parma, Italy, 18 January 1856; *d.* Pisa, Italy, 6 June 1928), *mathematics.*

The son of Francesco Saverio Bianchi, a jurist and senator of the kingdom of Italy, Bianchi entered the Scuola Normale Superiore of Pisa after passing a competitive examination in November 1873. He studied under Betti and Dini at the University of Pisa, from which he received his degree in mathematics on 30 November 1877. He remained in Pisa for two additional years, pursuing postgraduate studies. Later he attended the universities of Munich and Göttingen, where he studied chiefly under Klein.

Upon his return to Italy in 1881, Bianchi was appointed professor at the Scuola Normale Superiore of Pisa, and after having taught differential geometry at the University of Pisa, in 1886 he was appointed extraordinary professor of projective geometry on the basis of a competitive examination. During the same year he was also made professor of analytic geometry, a post he held for the rest of his life. By special appointment Bianchi also taught higher mathematics and analysis. After 1918 he was director of the Scuola Normale Superiore. He was a member of many Italian and foreign academies, and a senator of the kingdom of Italy.

Bianchi concentrated on studies and research in metric differential geometry. Among his major results was his discovery of all the geometries of Riemann that allow for a continuous group of movements, that is, those in which a figure may move continuously without undergoing any deformation. These results also found application in Einstein's studies on relativity. In addition, Bianchi devoted himself to the study of non-Euclidean geometries and demonstrated how the study of these geometries may lead to results in Euclidean geometry that, through other means, might have been obtained by more complex methods.

A writer of clear and genial treatises, Bianchi wrote many works on mathematics, among which are some dealing with functions of a variable complex, elliptic functions, and continuous groups of transformations.

BIBLIOGRAPHY

I. ORIGINAL WORKS. *Lezioni di geometria differenziale* (Pisa, 1886; 3rd ed., 1922–1923); *Lezioni sulla teoria dei gruppi di sostituzioni e delle equazioni algebriche secondo Galois* (Pisa, 1900); *Lezioni sulla teoria aritmetica delle forme quadratiche binarie e ternarie* (Pisa, 1912); *Lezioni di geometria analitica* (Pisa, 1915); *Lezioni sulla teoria delle funzioni di variabile complessa e delle funzioni ellittiche* (Pisa, 1916); *Lezioni sulla teoria dei gruppi continui finiti di trasformazioni* (Pisa, 1918); *Lezioni sulla teoria dei numeri algebrici e principii di geometria analitica* (Bologna, 1923). Bianchi's works were collected in *Opere,* Edizioni Cremonese, 11 vols. (Rome, 1952–1959); Vol. I, pt. 1 contains a bibliography and analyses of Bianchi's scientific work by G. Scorza, G. Fubini, A. M. Bedarida, and G. Ricci.

II. SECONDARY LITERATURE. Works on Bianchi are G. Fubini, "Luigi Bianchi e la sua opera scientifica," in *Annali di matematica,* 4th ser., **6** (1928–1929), 45–83, and "Commemorazione di Luigi Bianchi," in *Rendiconti della Accademia nazionale dei Lincei,* Classe di scienze fisiche matematiche e naturali, ser. 6a, **10** (1929), xxxiv–xliv (appendix).

ETTORE CARRUCCIO

BICHAT, MARIE-FRANÇOIS-XAVIER (*b*. Thoirette, Jura, France, 14 November 1771; *d*. Paris, France, 22 July 1802), *surgery, anatomy, physiology*.

The son of Jean-Baptiste Bichat, a physician and graduate of the Faculté de Médecine of Montpellier, who was then practicing in Poncin-en-Bugey, and of Jeanne-Rose Bichat, a cousin of her husband, Bichat studied humanities at the Collège de Nantua, completed the course in rhetoric, and was then sent to the Séminaire Saint-Irénée at Lyons to study philosophy. In 1791 he became the pupil of Marc-Antoine Petit at the Hôtel-Dieu in Lyons, in order to study surgery and anatomy. Three years later he went to Paris, where he was the favorite student and collaborator of Pierre Desault (1738–1795), who had created the surgical clinic at the Hôtel-Dieu, then called Grand Hospice d'Humanité by the Revolutionary powers. Desault was very skillful in the treatment of fractures and was particularly interested in vascular surgery. His death temporarily interrupted the publication of his *Journal de chirurgie,* but Bichat, encouraged by Corvisart, published as its fourth volume observations of Desault that he himself had written up. On 23 June 1796 Bichat founded, with Henri Husson and Guillaume Dupuytren, the Société Médicale d'Émulation, which Cabanis, Corvisart, and Pinel then joined.

At this time Bichat also started a private course in anatomy in a house on the Petite Rue de Grès (today the Rue Cujas). This course was transferred, in 1798, to the Rue des Carmes. It was then that Bichat added demonstrations in physiology using animal vivisections to his teaching of anatomy and of medical operations. Simultaneously he worked on the *Oeuvres chirurgicales de Desault* (1798–1799); wrote up, for the Société Médicale d'Émulation, several reports on surgery; and composed the memoirs *Sur les membranes et leurs rapports généraux d'organisation* (1798), which led to the *Traité des membranes* and *Anatomie générale,* and *Sur les rapports qui existent entre les organes à forme symétrique et ceux à forme irrégulière* (1798), which ushered in *Recherches physiologiques sur la vie et la mort.* In 1801 he was made *médecin expectant* (supernumerary) at the Grand Hospice d'Humanité.

Sensing that his life would not be long, Bichat published, between 1799 and 1801, the three works that made him famous: the *Traité des membranes,* the *Recherches physiologiques sur la vie et la mort,* and the *Anatomie générale.* The *Anatomie descriptive* was left unfinished at his death. Bichat's funeral services were held at Notre-Dame de Paris.

Bichat's most important contribution to modern anatomy consists in the generalization of a theory set forth by Pinel in his *Nosographie philosophique* (1798). Pathology must be based not upon the topographical situations of organs, but upon the structure of the membranes (i.e., of the tissues making up the organs), regardless of the location of the latter in the organism. Bichat recognized his debt to Pinel in the *Traité des membranes* (art. 1, sec. iv), but Magendie, in the preface to its new edition (1827), says that Bichat, by his extension of Pinel's idea, showed "that he was of such a stature as to owe the idea only to himself."

Bichat's best statement on his own method as an anatomist is in the sixth and seventh paragraphs of "Considérations générales," a preface to the *Anatomie générale.* Just as chemistry is the science of elementary bodies, says Bichat, anatomy is the science of elementary tissues, which differ from each other in the composition and the arrangement of their fibers, the combination of which forms organs. General anatomy is the study of the simple organic elements and of the similarly elementary structures. Bichat distinguished twenty-one organized elements, characterized by their textures and their properties. Since it differs from others in its vital properties, each tissue also differs in its diseases because diseases are nothing more than alterations of its vital properties. As a background to the diversity of symptoms and the uneven duration of illnesses, the physician must consider the diversity of the tissues. Therefore, general anatomy should set up a new pathological anatomy, substituting for the descriptive order, generally accepted since Morgagni, a systematic order of the diseases common to each elementary structure, to each tissue.

Bichat distinguished the properties of tissues according to their texture, properties that are retained after death: extensibility, contractility, and the vital properties—organic contractility and sensibility ("insensible" or subliminal) on the one hand, and animal contractility and sensibility ("sensible" or conscious) on the other. Vital properties were, in his eyes, irreducible to physical laws. *Recherches physiologiques sur la vie et la mort* begins with the famous sentence "Life is the ensemble of functions that resist death." Without completely admitting Barthez's vital principle, Bichat was hostile to the traditional medicine of Boerhaave and praised the doctors of the Montpellier school for having "more or less followed the impetus given by Stahl" (animism).

Bichat's ideas had a profound influence not only in medicine but also in philosophy. General anatomy and the pathology of tissues were both transformed and confirmed in the nineteenth century by the development of histology, cytology, and cellular pathology. Claude Bernard, while recognizing that in his time the morphological analysis of organized bodies had decentralized the seat of life "beyond the term fixed by Bichat,"—beyond tissue and down to the cell—wrote, "Modern opinions concerning vital phenomena are based on histology and really have their origin in Bichat's ideas" (*Leçons sur les phénomènes de la vie*, II, 452). No less hostile than Claude Bernard toward all metaphysical vitalism, Auguste Comte expressed his admiration for Bichat insofar as the latter had helped to establish the specificity of a general science of life, at the very time when Lamarck and Treviranus simultaneously invented the term "biology" (1802) in order to denote it. The German philosopher Schopenhauer insisted upon calling himself a disciple of Bichat, as did Cabanis.

BIBLIOGRAPHY

I. ORIGINAL WORKS. Bichat's writings include *Oeuvres chirurgicales de Desault,* 3 vols. (Paris, 1798–1799; new ed., rev. and enl., 1801–1803); *Recherches physiologiques sur la vie et la mort* (Paris, 1800; new ed., with notes by M. Magendie, 1822), translated by F. Gold as *Physiological Researches on Life and Death* (London, 1815); *Traité des membranes en général et de diverses membranes en particulier* (Paris, 1800; new ed., rev. and enl., with notes by M. Magendie, 1827), new ed. with a notice on Bichat's life and works by M. Husson; *Anatomie générale, appliquée à la physiologie et à la médecine,* 4 vols. (Paris, 1801), supplemented by P.-A. Beclard, *Additions à l'Anatomie générale de X. Bichat* (1821), prefaced by a historical note on Bichat by Scipion Pinel; and *Traité d'anatomie descriptive,* 5 vols. (Paris, 1801–1803)—Bichat wrote the first three volumes, Mathieu-François Buisson wrote the fourth, and Philibert-Joseph Roux wrote the fifth.

II. SECONDARY LITERATURE. Works on Bichat are *Bulletin de la Société française d'histoire de la médecine,* **1** (1902; repr. 1967), which contains a series of articles and documents relating to Bichat and was published on the centenary of his death—see especially the articles by R. Blanchard and Émile Gley; J. Coquerelle, *Xavier Bichat* (Paris, 1902); "Bichat," in Dezeimeris, Ollivier, and Raige-Delorme, *Dictionnaire historique de la médecine ancienne et moderne,* I (Paris, 1928), 385–396; Michel Foucault, *Naissance de la clinique* (Paris, 1963), ch. 8; Geneviève Genty, "Bichat, médecin du Grand Hospice d'Humanité," thesis (Paris, 1943); Maurice Genty, "Bichat," in *Biographies médicales,* II (Paris, 1929–1931), 35–36, and "Bichat et son temps," in *Médecine internationale* (1934), nos. 7–12 and (1935), nos. 1–10; M. Laignel-Lavastine, "Sources, principes, sillage et critique de l'oeuvre de Bichat," in *Bulletin de la Société française de philosophie,* **46** (1952), 1; and Entralgo P. Lain, "Sensualism and Vitalism in Bichat's *Anatomie générale,*" in *Journal of the History of Medicine and Allied Sciences,* **3** (1948), 47–64.

GEORGES CANGUILHEM

BICKERTON, ALEXANDER WILLIAM (*b.* Alton, England, 1842; *d.* London, England, 22 January 1929), *cosmology, natural philosophy.*

An orphan at an early age, Bickerton was given an engineering education by his uncle in Bridgwater; however, he found the time an engineer had to spend outdoors was too much for his health, and turned his attention to science. In 1864 he established a small factory in the Cotswolds to develop his woodworking inventions; three years later he organized technical classes at Birmingham while studying at the Royal School of Mines in London. In 1870 Bickerton accepted a post on the staff of the Hartley Institution in Southampton, and was later appointed lecturer in science at Winchester College. In the meantime his publications on the relation between electricity and heat attracted some attention, and as a result he was invited to accept the professorship of physics and chemistry at Canterbury College in Christchurch, New Zealand, a post he held until 1903.

Most of the scientific work for which Bickerton is remembered was carried out during his New Zealand years, and is characterized by originality and boldness of approach. His theory of the build-up of celestial bodies by collisions, published in a number of papers from 1880 on, attracted considerable attention and some hostility in astronomical quarters. Among his scientific papers are "On a New Relation of Heat and Electricity"; "On Temporary and Variable Stars," containing an outline of a view that novae originate by collisions of two stars in space; "On the Problem of Stellar Collisions"; "On the Origin of Double Stars, of Nebulae and of the Solar System"; and "On Agencies Tending to Alter the Eccentricities of Planetary Orbits."

BIBLIOGRAPHY

Bickerton's books include *Materials for Lessons in Elementary Science* (1883), *A New Story of the Stars* (1894), *Some Recent Evidence in Favour of Impacts* (1894), *The Romance of the Earth* (1900), *The Romance of the Heavens* (1901), and *The Birth of Worlds and Systems* (1911).

ZDENĚK KOPAL

BIDDER, FRIEDRICH HEINRICH (*b.* Kurland, Russia, 28 October 1810; *d.* Dorpat, Russia [now Tartu, Estonian S.S.R.], 27 August 1894), *anatomy, physiology.*

His father, Ernst Christian, was an agriculturalist. In 1834 Friedrich received a medical degree from the University of Dorpat and was appointed professor extraordinary and prosector in anatomy. Before assuming his duties, Bidder spent a year in Berlin studying anatomy with J. Müller, C. Ehrenberg, J. Henle, and F. Schlemm. His itinerary included a tour of the research facilities at Dresden, Halle, and Leipzig. He became a full professor of anatomy in 1842, and accepted the new chair of physiology and pathology in 1843. He served as dean of the medical faculty from 1843 to 1845 and as rector of the university in 1858. Bidder found an outlet for his humanitarian interests in the social problems of the city. He helped to found a public baby nursery and was president of Dorpat's Hülfsverein, a charitable institution. Bidder received the Karl E. von Baer medal in 1879 for his contributions to biology.

Bidder was not a gifted teacher in the conventional sense, but he was highly successful at providing fruitful research topics for his students. Over seventy-five dissertations were completed under his direction. Bidder's superior grasp of scientific literature and his command of anatomy, physiology, histology, and embryology enabled him to single out important questions for study. With few exceptions, Bidder selected his research topics from published differences of opinion. This habit reveals Bidder's confidence and broad knowledge of biology; it also explains why Bidder's name is not associated with any major innovations. His best-known works were published in cooperation with other scientists. Bidder's partnerships brought to light his most innovative and creative abilities. When Bidder did reach out to creative projects, his efforts frequently were not appreciated. His contributions to intermediary metabolism and nerve physiology were too advanced for the majority of his contemporaries.

In 1852, Bidder and Carl Schmidt, a student of Justus von Liebig, published their classic *Verdauungssäfte und der Stoffwechsel*. The treatise was a brilliant extension of the concepts suggested by Liebig's *Animal Chemistry* (1842). *Verdauungssäfte* was the first major publication on intermediary metabolism (*intermediären Kreislauf*). Bidder examined the effects of digestive juices (salivary, pancreatic, biliary, intestinal, and gastric) on foodstuffs. He elucidated the chemical changes induced by enzymes and the effects of nervous control on the secretion of digestive juices. He was able to show that bile was not an excretion but a secretion serving a physiological function.

Bidder opened the bile duct and inserted a cannula to draw off the biliary liquids. By controlling the diet of cats fitted with this fistula, he found that digestive disturbances occurred when the nutrients contained large amounts of fat. The chemical composition of bile was not similar to fat but to carbohydrate or protein. Yet, further fistula experiments indicated that bile did have some unknown complex function in fat metabolism. When bile flowed into the gut, animals could digest more fat than when bile was removed through the fistula. Oil mixed with bile rose higher in capillary tubes than did untreated samples of oil. *In vitro* mixtures of fat, water, and bile rendered the fat water-soluble and neutral to litmus paper. Fat globules in the lymphatics, however, were acidic. Bidder hypothesized that bile aids in the absorption of fats in the stomach and is then reabsorbed in the gut. By comparing the concentrations of bile salts in the feces and urine with the concentration of bile in the gut, Bidder concluded that such a hypothesis was correct.

Although Bidder worked on a wide spectrum of problems, he maintained a persistent interest in the physiology and anatomy of the nervous system. He provided an improved description of the rods and cones of the retina (1839), repeated many of Flourens's experiments on the regeneration of sectioned nerves, investigated olfaction, and was successful in joining the severed ends of the lingual and hypoglossal nerves (although the crossed fibers were not functional). He cataloged all of the inhibitory nerves known to him and traced their fibers to the autonomic ganglia (1871). He discovered the auriculoventricular and interauricular ganglion cells in the hearts of frogs ("Bidder's ganglia") and demonstrated that the ganglia contained fibers of the vagus nerve.

His best-known work on the nervous system was the outcome of collaboration. Bidder and Alfred W. Volkmann made an extensive histological study of the autonomic nervous system and the spinal cord. They demonstrated that although certain fibers of the intercostal nerve were unmyelinated, they were genuine nerve fibers. They established the general rule that postganglionic fibers are not covered by a myelin sheath. Detailed numerical analysis revealed that the peripheral nerves contained more fibers than could be accounted for by the spinal cord and the sympathetic chain alone. This discovery provided anatomical evidence for the theory of double innervation of the organs from (1) the sympathetic chain and (2) the ganglionic system.

In 1857 Bidder and Carl Kupffer made a histological study of the embryonic and adult spinal cord in order to settle the dispute whether or not the spinal nerve fibers are continuous with the gray matter of the brain. Employing a new chromic-acid stain developed by Schroeder van der Kolk, the authors were able to show the continuity of cord fibers with cell bodies located in the gray matter of the brain. Bidder was an advocate of the neuron theory.

Bidder's name is also associated with an organ found only in certain frogs (*Bufonides*). It is a circular mass of tissue located slightly ventral to, and between, the kidneys and testes. Bidder suspected it was testicular tissue; following an interesting array of speculative theories, it was shown in the twentieth century to be endocrine tissue.

A great deal of Bidder's work was excellent but his virtuosity and diverse interests prevented its recognition. His tendency to resolve minor conflicts rather than carry out sustained research on any one topic reduced his impact. His interest in controversies, however, increases the historical value of his work. Bidder's discussions of opposing views provide insights into the research problems of the nineteenth century.

BIBLIOGRAPHY

I. ORIGINAL WORKS. Bidder's most important monographs are *De graviditatis vi medicatrice* (Dorpat, 1834); *Neurologische Beobachtungen* (Dorpat, 1836); *Neue Beobachtungen über die Bewegungen des weichen Gaumens und über den Geruchssinn* (Dorpat, 1838); "Reichen," in Rudolph Wagner's *Handwörterbuch der Physiologie*, II (Brunswick, 1844), 916–926; *Vergleichend-anatomische Untersuchungen über den Harn und die Geschlechtswerkzeuge der nachten Amphibien* (Dorpat, 1846); and *Zur Lehre von dem Verhältniss der Ganglienkörper zu den Nervenfasern. Neue Beiträge* (Leipzig, 1847). His most famous joint efforts are *Untersuchungen über die Textur des Rückenmarks und die Entwicklung seiner Formelelemente* (Leipzig, 1857), with C. Kupffer; *Verdauungssäfte und der Stoffwechsel. Eine physiologisch-chemische Untersuchung* (Leipzig, 1852), with C. Schmidt; and *Die Selbständigkeit des sympathischen Nervensystems, durch anatomische Untersuchung nachgewiesen* (Leipzig, 1842), with A. W. Volkmann. The bulk of Bidder's papers appeared in the *Archiv für Anatomie, Physiologie und wissenschaftliche Medicin*, Johannes Müller, ed. Those relevant to the subjects discussed are the following: "Zur Anatomie der Retina" (1839), pp. 371–388, (1841), pp. 248–262; "Versuche über die Möglichkeit des Zusammenheilens funktionell verschiedener Nervenfasern" (1842), pp. 102–120; "Versuche zur Bestimmung der Chylusmenge die durch den Ductus thoracicus dem Blute zugeführt wird" (1845), pp. 45–60; "Ueber functionell verschiedene und räumlich getrennte Nervencentra im Froschherzen" (1852), pp. 163–177; "Erfolge von Nervendurchschneidung an einem Frosch" (1865), pp. 67–79; "Beobachtung doppelsinniger Leitung im Nervus lingualis nach Vereinigung desselben mit dem N. hypoglossus" (1865), pp. 246–260; "Ueber die Unterschiede in den Beziehungen des Pfeilgifts zu verschiedenen Abtheilungen des Nervensystems" (1865), pp. 337–359; "Zur näheren Kenntniss des Froschherzens und seiner Nerven" (1866), pp. 1–25; "Die Endigungsweise der Herzzweige des Nervus vagus beim Frosch" (1868), pp. 1–50; "Einige Bemerkungen über Hemmungsnerven und Hemmungscentren" (1871), pp. 447–472; and "Erfahrungen über die functionelle Selbständigkeit des sympathetischen Nervensystems" (1841), pp. 359–380, with A. Volkmann.

II. SECONDARY LITERATURE. Further biographical details can be found in the *Allgemeine deutsche Biographie*, XLVI (Leipzig, 1902), 538–540; *Leopoldina*, **3**, nos. 17–18 (1894), 145, 162; and the *Saint Petersburger medicinische Wochenschrift*, **19** (1894), 314–315. Bidder's nutritional research is discussed in Graham Lusk, "A History of Metabolism," in *Endocrinology and Metabolism*, III (New York, 1922), 3–78; Nikolaus Mani, *Die historischen Grundlagen der Leberforschung II Teil. Die Geschichte der Leberforschung von Galen bis Claude Bernard* (Basel, 1967); Elmer V. McCollum, *A History of Nutrition* (Boston, 1957); and Fritz Lieben, *Geschichte der physiologischen Chemie* (Leipzig, 1935). An enumeration of Bidder's minor contributions can be found in Karl Rothschuh, *Entwicklungsgeschichte physiologischen Probleme in Tabellenform* (Munich, 1952). References to Bidder's research on the nervous system are inadequate. Brief discussions appear in John Langley, *The Autonomic Nervous System* (Cambridge, 1921); R. Herrlinger, "Albert von Bezold und die Entedeckung der Innervation des Herzens," in K. Rothschuh, ed., *Von Boerhaave bis Berger* (Stuttgart, 1964), pp. 106–120; and V. Kruta, "G. Prochaska and J. E. Purkyně's Contributions to Neurophysiology," *ibid.*, pp. 134–156. A history of the interpretations given to Bidder's organ can be traced through H. King, "The Structure and Development of Bidder's Organ in Bufo Levtiginosus," in *Journal of Morphology*, **19** (1908), 439–465; W. Harms, "Untersuchungen über das Biddersche Organ der männlichen und weiblichen Kröten," in *Zeitschrift für Anatomie und Entwicklungsgeschichte*, **62** (1921), 1–38; and N. Takahashi, "Biological and Anatomical Studies of the Nuptial Excrescence and Bidder's Organ of the Toad," in *Endocrinology*, **7** (1923), 302–304.

CHARLES A. CULOTTA

BIELA, WILHELM VON (*b.* Rossla, Stolberg am Harz, Germany, 19 March 1782; *d.* Venice, Italy, 18 February 1856), *astronomy.*

Descended from a Bohemian noble family, Biela was educated at the school for pages of the Elector of Saxony. In 1802 he became a cadet in an Austrian infantry regiment and fought in the Napoleonic Wars. He became a lieutenant in 1809 and later was promoted to captain. During the battle of Leipzig (1813) he was wounded, and while recuperating in Prague, attended the astronomical lectures of Alois David. Subsequently he became a very successful amateur astronomer. In 1825 the army transferred him to Naples, and in 1832 he became local governor of Rovigo, Italy. Biela suffered a stroke in 1844 and retired two years later with the rank of major. His health led him to move to Venice, and since he could no longer devote himself to astronomy, he turned to art and became a well-known connoisseur.

Biela made many valuable astronomical observations, mainly of comets and meteors; the most remarkable was that of a comet in 1826. On 27 February of that year, in Josefstadt, Bohemia, he saw a comet and recognized it as one already seen in 1772 and 1805. On 14 March he found its period to be six years and nine months, a discovery that made him famous throughout Europe. Other astronomers confirmed that his comet was indeed identical with those of 1772 and 1805—a determination difficult to establish because of the disturbances caused by Jupiter. The most remarkable phenomenon appeared when the comet returned in 1846: it separated into two parts of the same shape but of changing intensity. It was last seen in 1852. E. Weiss of Vienna has pointed out that fragments of Biela's comet constitute the periodic shower of certain meteors, the Andromedides.

Biela was respected by all astronomers of his time, and he corresponded with many of them. A crater on the moon was named for him, and the Andromedides are now called Bielides or Belides. His only published work shows the influence of the romantic philosophy of nature prevalent at the time.

BIBLIOGRAPHY

Biela's only published work is *Die zweite grosse Weltenkraft nebst Ideen über einige Geheimnisse der physischen Astronomie oder Andeutungen zu einer Theorie der Tangentialkraft* (Prague, 1836).

Works on Biela or his contributions are Alois David, *Geschichte des Kometen, den Hauptmann von Biela entdeckte* (Prague, 1827); Josef von Hepperger, "Bahnbestimmung des Bielaschen Kometen," in *Sitzungsberichte der mathematisch-naturwissenschaftlichen Classe der Kaiserlichen Akademie der Wissenschaften, Wien,* **107**, pt. 2a (1898), 377–489 and **109**, pt. 2a (1900), 299–382, 623–655; J. Hirtenfeld and H. Meynert, eds., *Österreichisches Militär-Konversations-Lexikon,* I (Vienna, 1851), p. 410; and Constant von Wurzbach, *Biographisches Lexikon des Kaiserthums Oesterreich,* I (Vienna, 1856), 388–390.

JOSEF MAYERHÖFER

THOMAS WIDORN

BIENEWITZ, PETER. See **Apian, Peter.**

BIESTERFELD, J. H. See **Bisterfeld, Johann Heinrich.**

BIGOURDAN, CAMILLE GUILLAUME (*b.* Sistels, Tarn-et-Garonne, France, 6 April 1851; *d.* Paris,

France, 28 February 1932), *astronomy, history of science.*

Bigourdan was born to a peasant family from the Bigorre (whence his surname) and from them inherited his passion for work, his strong character, and his deep religious convictions. His teacher, Félix Tisserand, introduced him to the study of astronomy in Toulouse, and in 1879 summoned him to the Paris Observatory, where Bigourdan was astronomer-in-chief from 1897 to 1925. He was a member of the Bureau des Longitudes (1903), of the Académie des Sciences (1904), and, for his work in meteorology, of the Académie d'Agriculture (1924).

Bigourdan was a remarkable observer, and most of his contributions to astronomy were visual surveys of position: meridian observations and equatorial observations of double stars, asteroids, comets, and especially nebulae. He also perfected instruments and methods. His catalog of the positions of 6,380 nebulae brought him the gold medal of the Royal Astronomical Society in 1919.

His work has been made partially obsolete by technical progress, but his studies on time and the history of astronomy are still of value. After serving as a promoter, with Gustave Ferrié, of the International Congress on Time (1912), Bigourdan became the director of the Bureau International de l'Heure when it was created in 1919. He deliberately oriented this originally technical agency toward science. His emphasis on science, although it led to his dismissal in 1929, greatly benefited astronomy.

Moreover, Bigourdan left numerous authoritative historical studies. He also discovered various lost manuscripts, particularly those of the French astronomer J. A. G. Pingré, which allowed him to publish his *Annales célestes du XVIIe siècle* in 1901.

BIBLIOGRAPHY

I. ORIGINAL WORKS. Bigourdan's astronomical works include "Sur l'équation personnelle dans les mesures d'étoiles doubles" (doctoral thesis, 1886), in *Annales de l'Observatoire de Paris* (*Mémoires*), **19** (1889), C1–C74; *Observations de nébuleuses et d'amas stellaires, 1884–1909,* 6 vols. (Paris, 1899–1917); "Détermination de la différence de longitude entre les méridiens de Greenwich et de Paris, exécutée en 1902," written with F. Lancelin, in *Annales de l'Observatoire de Paris* (*Mémoires*), **26** (1910), B1–B214; and *Gnomonique ou Traité théorique et pratique de la construction des cadrans solaires* (Paris, 1921).

In the history of science Bigourdan published *Le système métrique des poids et mesures* (Paris, 1901); *De l'origine à la formation de l'Observatoire de Paris,* Vol. I of *Histoire de l'astronomie d'observation et des observatoires en France*

(Paris, 1918); "Un institut d'optique à Paris au XVIIIᵉ siècle," in *Comptes rendus du Congrès des Sociétés Savantes en 1921, Sciences* (Paris, 1922), pp. 19–74; and *De la fondation de l'Académie à la fin du XVIIIᵉ siècle,* Vol. II of *Histoire de l'astronomie de l'observation et des observatoires en France* (Paris, 1930).

His articles in the *Bulletin astronomique* include "Honoré Flaugergues, sa vie et ses travaux," in **1** (1884), 569–576, and **2** (1885), 151–156, 491–500; "Histoire des observatoires de l'École Militaire," in **4** (1887), 497–504, and **5** (1888), 30–40; and "La prolongation de la méridienne de Paris, de Barcelone aux Baléares, d'après des correspondances inédites de Méchain, de Biot et d'Arago," in **17** (1900), 348–368, 390–400, 467–480.

Articles in the *Annuaire du Bureau des Longitudes* are "Le jour et ses divisions" (1914), B1–B107; "Le calendrier babylonien" (1917), A1–A20; "Le calendrier égyptien" (1918), A1–A42; "Les comètes, liste chronologique de celles qui ont paru depuis l'origine à 1900" (1927), A1–A76; and "Le Bureau des Longitudes. Son histoire et ses travaux depuis l'origine (1795)" (1928), A1–A72; (1929), C1–C92; (1930), A1–A110; (1931), A1–A151; (1932), A1–A117; and (1933), A1–A91.

II. SECONDARY LITERATURE. Works on Bigourdan are A. Collard, "L'astronome G. Bigourdan," in *Ciel et terre,* **48** (1932), 165–167; F. W. Dyson, "G. Bigourdan," in *Monthly Notices of the Astronomical Society,* **93** (1933), 233–234; and P. A. MacMahon, "Address . . . on the Award of the Gold Medal . . . to G. Bigourdan," *ibid.,* **79** (1919), 306–314.

JACQUES R. LEVY

BILHARZ, THEODOR (*b.* Sigmaringen, Germany, 23 March 1825; *d.* Cairo, Egypt, 9 May 1862), *anatomy, zoology.*

Bilharz' name is perpetuated in the name of the disease bilharziasis, which he described in 1851; the following year he discovered its cause. The son of Anton Bilharz, a counsellor of the exchequer, and Elisa Fehr, Bilharz grew up in the small, *biedermeierlich* south German city of Sigmaringen. He attended the secondary school there, and having developed a particular interest in natural history during his school years, he entered the University of Freiburg im Breisgau in 1843. There he studied under Friedrich Arnold, who gave him insight into anatomical research. In 1845 Bilharz accompanied Arnold to the University of Tübingen, where in 1849 he passed the state examination and received the M.D.

At Tübingen he became acquainted with Wilhelm Griesinger, who in 1850 asked Bilharz to accompany him to Egypt when he was named director of the Egyptian Department of Hygiene. Bilharz began as Griesinger's assistant; and after Griesinger's return to Germany in 1852, he was promoted to chief physician of a medical department. In 1856 he became professor of descriptive anatomy at the Cairo medical school, Kasr-el Aïn. There he had the opportunity to perform numerous dissections and thus discovered peculiar pathological changes—white extuberances of cancerous aspect—in the mucous membranes of the bladder, intestines, ureters, and seminal glands. He found that the cause of the changes was a hitherto unknown trematode, which he described to his zoology teacher Carl Theodor von Siebold in nine letters from 1 May 1851 to 1 January 1853; Siebold published these letters in 1853. In them Bilharz gave not only a detailed anatomical description of the parasite and the anatomical changes produced by it, but he also supplied excellent diagrams of a pair of the copulating flatworms, which he called *Distomum haematobium,* and diagrams of the eggs. In these diagrams he also depicted the *Schistosomum mansoni,* which was not mentioned again until 1907, when Sambon named it for his teacher Patrick Manson. The terms "bilharzia" and "bilharziasis" were coined by Heinrich Meckel von Hemsbach, who introduced them into scientific nomenclature in 1856, two years before David F. Weinand introduced the term "schistosoma."

Bilharz never considered this consequential discovery to be as important as the work he did on the electrical organ of the thunderfish; in 1857 he wrote a monograph on the latter subject. He took his only European vacation in 1858, at which time he had the chance to report on his zoological research. In the following years Bilharz occupied himself with investigating native fauna—he gave the first description of a Nile fish, the *Alestes macrolepidotus*—and with anthropological and etymological activities.

In 1862 Bilharz accompanied the German explorer Ernst von Coburg-Gotha to Ethiopia; there, while treating a patient, he contracted typhoid fever and, just after his return to Cairo, he died. His discovery of the agent of tropical hematuria, which was by no means recognized by Bilharz' contemporaries as epoch-making, was nevertheless to introduce a new era of tropical parasitology; and it initiated a successful fight against an illness that still infects millions of the earth's inhabitants.

BIBLIOGRAPHY

I. ORIGINAL WORKS. Among Bilharz' writings are "Ein Beitrag zur *Helminthographia humana,* aus brieflichen Mittheilungen des Dr. Bilharz in Cairo," in *Zeitschrift für wissenschaftliche Zoologie,* **4** (1853), 53–76, table 5; 454–456, table 17; "*Distomum haematobium* und sein Verhältnis zu gewissen pathologischen Veränderungen der menschlichen Harnorgane," in *Wiener medizinische Wochenschrift,* **6**

(1856), 49–52, 65–68; "Über *Pentastomum constrictum*," in *Zeitschrift für wissenschaftliche Zoologie,* **7** (1856), 329–330, table 17; *Das electrische Organ des Zitterwelses. Anatomisch beschrieben* (Leipzig, 1857); and "Über die Eingeweidewürmer Ägyptens," in *Zeitschrift der kaiserlich-königlichen Gesellschaft der Ärzte Wien,* **14** (1858), 447–448.

II. SECONDARY LITERATURE. The most comprehensive biography is E. Senn, *Theodor Bilharz: Ein deutsches Forscherleben in Ägypten, 1825–1862,* Schriften des Deutschen Auslandsinstituts Stuttgart, series D, V (Stuttgart, 1931); see also H. Ben-Amram, "L'histoire de la draconculose et de la bilharziose et leur incidence économique et sociale," thesis (Rennes, 1959); A. Bilharz, "Theodor Bilharz," in *Archiv für die Geschichte der Naturwissenschaften und der Technik,* **8** (1918), 232–236; J. Roos, "Theodor Bilharz," M.D. dissertation (Würzburg, 1929); and H. Schadewaldt, "Theodor Bilharz," in *Deutsche medizinische Wochenschrift,* **80** (1955), 1053–1055; "Die Erstbeschreibung und -abbildung von *Bilharzia haematobia* und *mansoni* durch Theodor Bilharz," in *Zeitschrift für Tropenmedizin und Parasitologie,* **4** (1953), 410–414; "Theodor Bilharz, einer der Begründer deutscher tropen-medizinischer Forschung," in *Münchener medizinische Wochenschrift,* **104** (1962), 1730–1734; "Theodor Bilharz und die Bilharziose," in *Berliner medizinische Zeitschrift,* **14** (1963), 244–250; and "Unveröffentlichte Zeichnungen aus dem Nachlass von Theodor Bilharz," in *Münchener medizinische Wochenschrift,* Bildbeilage 7 (1963).

HANS SCHADEWALDT

BILLINGS, ELKANAH (*b.* Billings Bridge, near Bytown [now Ottawa], Ontario, 5 May 1820; *d.* Montreal, Quebec, 14 June 1876), *paleontology.*

Billings' father, Bradish, was a farmer in comfortable circumstances. After attending several private schools, Elkanah entered St. Lawrence Academy at Potsdam, New York, in 1837. Returning to Bytown in 1839, he enrolled in the Law Society of Upper Canada and was admitted to the bar in 1844. For eight years he practiced law in Toronto, Renfrew, and Bytown, but in 1852 he virtually gave up his law practice to become editor of the Bytown *Citizen;* in it he began to publish popular articles on natural history, including local fossils, of which he had a large collection. His proficiency in paleontology earned him membership in the Canadian Institute of Toronto in 1854, and his first scientific papers were read before that institute the same year and were published in its *Journal.*

In 1856 Billings wrote: "I have abandoned my [legal] profession, and intend to devote the rest of my life to the study of Natural History." He thereupon began publication of the *Canadian Naturalist & Geologist,* and for the first year (1856) was its owner, editor, and sole contributor. Although he relinquished

official connection with that journal in 1857, he subsequently contributed at least forty articles to it.

Billings' love for natural history may have been fostered by his eldest brother, who became an accomplished botanist and entomologist; as a paleontologist he was entirely self-taught. While living in Toronto he doubtless had access to scientific libraries and collections. Indeed, he could not have written his first two papers (1854) without detailed knowledge of the morphology of echinoderms, both living and fossil, of the available literature on that subject, and of the rules of taxonomic nomenclature. From 1852 on, he corresponded with William E. Logan, director of the Geological Survey of Canada, who considered his scientific attainments of such high caliber that in 1856 he obtained for Billings the post of paleontologist with the Survey. This necessitated his moving to the Survey headquarters in Montreal, where a large collection of fossils, some identified and some not, had accumulated in its museum. Billings plunged at once into the task of identifying and classifying these fossils so that they could form a meaningful public display and could provide a standard against which new collections could be compared. Within two years this task was accomplished.

Except for two scientific papers (1854) concerned with technical descriptions of cystids from the Trenton limestone, Billings' writings prior to the Survey appointment were essays on natural history. After becoming an officer of the Survey, he turned his attention strictly to the exacting scientific descriptions of fossils, mostly from Paleozoic formations of eastern Canada. His first official "Report . . . as Palaeontologist" (1857) contains detailed descriptions of 106 new species belonging to thirty-five genera (of which thirteen were new), a remarkable achievement. His second report (1858) was similarly constituted, and was immediately followed by Decades 3 (1858) and 4 (1859) of the Canadian Organic Remains series, which were concerned almost wholly with fossil echinoderms. Billings began a second series of paleontological works, *Palaeozoic Fossils,* of which he wrote the first volume (1865) and the first part of the second (1874). Among other publications are his 1866 report on fossils from Anticosti Island and his continuing work on Devonian fossils from western Canada and on Silurian (i.e., Ordovician and Silurian) crinoids and cystids. The last category embraced what might be called his specialty. In all he published descriptions of sixty-one new genera and 1,065 new species of fossils. His bibliography contains nearly 200 titles, of which ninety are concerned directly or indirectly with paleontological subjects.

Although he accomplished much in purely descriptive taxonomic paleontology, Billings is also re-membered for the stratigraphic interpretation of his identifications. Because of his determination of the age of the rocks of the "Quebec Group" as Beekmantown and Chazy, Logan was able to demonstrate his "great overlap," which is now referred to as Logan's line.

BIBLIOGRAPHY

I. Original Works. Billings' writings include "Report for the Year 1856 as Palaeontologist," in Geological Survey of Canada, *Report of Progress for 1853–56* (Montreal, 1857), pp. 247–345; "Report for the Year 1857 as Palaeontologist," in Geological Survey of Canada, *Report of Progress for 1857* (Montreal, 1858), pp. 147–192; *Figures and Descriptions,* Canadian Organic Remains, Decade 3 (Montreal, 1858) and Decade 4 (Montreal, 1859); *Palaeozoic Fossils,* Vol. I (Montreal, 1865) and Vol. II, pt. 1 (Montreal, 1874); and "Catalogue of the Fossils of the Island of Anticosti," in *Special Report of the Geological Survey of Canada* (Montreal, 1866), pp. 1–82.

II. Secondary Literature. Articles on Billings are H. M. Ami, "Brief Biographical Sketch of Elkanah Billings," in *American Geologist* (May 1901), 265–281; B. E. Walker, "List of the Published Writings of Elkanah Billings, F. G. S.," in *Canadian Record of Science,* **8** (1902), 366–388; and J. F. Whiteaves, "Obituary Notice of Elkanah Billings, F. G. S.," in *Canadian Naturalist,* **8** (1876), 251–261.

T. H. Clark

BILLROTH, CHRISTIAN ALBERT THEODOR (*b.* Bergen, on the island of Rügen, Germany, 26 April 1829; *d.* Abbazia, Istria, Italy [now Opatija, Yugoslavia], 6 February 1894), *pathological anatomy.*

Billroth's father, Theodor, was a clergyman; his mother, Christine Nagel, was the daughter of a Berlin *Kammerrat* (counsellor of the exchequer). His father died when Theodor was five, and his mother then moved to Greifswald, where Billroth attended the Gymnasium. He was musically inclined (a family characteristic) and probably for that reason was not an exceptional pupil, even needing tutoring at home; he seemed unable to master languages and mathematics, was not quick-witted, and spoke slowly.

His mother and two professors of medicine in Greifswald, Baum and Seiffert, induced Billroth to become a doctor for financial reasons. He was nevertheless an artist: intuitive, humane, inventive. His home in Vienna later became a musical center where he played second violin or viola and became friends with Johannes Brahms and with the musical theorist and writer Eduard Hanslick. Two of Brahms's string quartets are dedicated to Billroth, and during his last

illness Billroth was working on the physio-psychological book *Wer ist musikalisch?*, published by Hanslick in 1896.

During his first semester as a medical student in Greifswald, Billroth studied natural sciences and began the multifaceted activity and careful use of his time that characterized his later years. He followed Baum to the University of Göttingen, where he established a lasting friendship with Georg Meissner. Like Billroth, Meissner was interested in music and a pupil of the physiologist Rudolf Wagner, who taught Billroth microscopy. With Wagner and Meissner, Billroth went to Trieste to study the origin and insertion of the nerves of the torpedo fish. In 1851 he continued his studies at Berlin with Bernard von Langenbeck, Johann Lukas Schönlein, Moritz Romberg, and Ludwig Traube. Traube taught him experimental pathology and encouraged him to write the thesis "De natura et causa pulmonum affectionis quae nervo utroque vago dissecto exoritur." On 30 September 1852 Billroth received his doctorate, and that winter he passed the state medical examination, after which he worked in the ophthalmological clinic of Albrecht von Graefe.

In order to take courses in dermatology with Ferdinand von Hebra, in pathology with Henschel, and in internal medicine with Johann von Oppolzer, Billroth went to Vienna in the spring of 1853. That fall he tried in vain to establish himself as a general practitioner in Berlin, but after a few months he was appointed assistant to Langenbeck at the surgical clinic of Berlin University. He published on pathological histology and in 1856 became *Privatdozent* in surgery and pathological anatomy. Later he lectured on surgery and gave practical demonstrations.

It was in Berlin that Billroth met his wife Christine, daughter of the court physician Edgar M. Michaelis and of Karoline Eunike. They were married in 1858, and of their four daughters and one son, three daughters survived.

In 1860 Billroth was nominated ordinary professor and director of the well-known surgical hospital and clinic at Zurich. He added greatly to its fame and its growth during the seven years he was its director. Modern surgery was in its infancy, and Billroth was especially interested in the causes of wound fever. He insisted on regular temperature-taking and believed that wound fever was caused by a chemical poison produced by some living organism. His *Die allgemeine chirurgische Pathologie und Chirurgie in fünfzig Vorlesungen* (1863) is a classic surgical textbook. Billroth collaborated with Pitha on *Handbuch der Chirurgie* (1865–1868) and with Lücke on *Deutsche Chirurgie* (1879). After having declined calls to

Rostock and Heidelberg, he was appointed professor of surgery and director of the surgical clinic at the University of Vienna, where he remained until his death, much beloved by his students, assistants, and patients.

Billroth excelled as a surgeon, as a teacher, and as a scientist. He performed many hazardous operations successfully because of his great ability and caution. *Chirurgische Klinik* (1869–1876), his collection of clinical experiences and the surgical results of his Zurich and Vienna years, is notable because it reports failures and successes alike. Billroth was one of the first to introduce antisepsis on the Continent and was the first to resect the esophagus (1872), to perform total laryngectomy (1873), and to resect a cancerous pylorus (1881), which caused a great sensation in medical circles. His methods of resection, although modified, remained in use for many years. Plastic surgery, especially of the face, was another of his specialties.

Billroth founded the House of the Society of Physicians in Vienna and the Rudolfinerhaus, a nursing school for which he wrote the handbook *Ueber die Krankenpflege im Hause und im Hospitale* (1881). He was a member of the Academy of Sciences in Vienna and honorary member of thirty-two scientific societies, and a member of the Austrian Herrenhaus (from 1886); he was also honored with sixteen high decorations. His bibliography contains some 150 items.

Billroth kept his robust health until February 1887, when he contracted pneumonia and suffered from cardiac weakness that increased during his last years. His pupils, who spread his teaching all over the Continent, included Czerny, Gussenbauer, Mikulicz, Eiselsberg, Wölfer, Nikoladoni, Hacker, Winiwarter, Gersuny, Salzer, Fraenckel, and Narath.

BIBLIOGRAPHY

I. ORIGINAL WORKS. A full list of Billroth's publications is K. Gussenbauer, in *Wiener klinische Wochenschrift,* **7** (1894), 118–120; and Mikulicz, in *Berliner klinische Wochenschrift,* **31** (1894), 203–205. His thesis was "De natura et causa pulmonum affectionis quae nervo utroque vago dissecto exoritur" (Berlin, 1852). His major publications include "Beobachtungsstudien über Wundfieber und accidentelle Wundkrankheiten," in *Archiv für klinische Chirurgie,* **2** (1861); **6** (1864); **8** (1866); **13** (1872); *Die allgemeine chirurgische Pathologie und Chirurgie in fünfzig Vorlesungen* (Berlin, 1863; 16th ed., 1906), translated as *General Surgical Pathology and Therapy* (1871; 3rd ed., 1880); and *Chirurgische Klinik,* 4 vols. (Berlin, 1869–1879). Billroth collaborated with Pitha on *Handbuch der Chirurgie* (1865–1868) and with Lücke in editing *Deutsche Chirurgie*

(1879). On the study of medicine he wrote *Ueber das Lehren und Lernen der medizinischen Wissenschaften* (Vienna, 1876) and *Aphorismen* to it (Vienna, 1886). His handbook for nurses is *Ueber die Krankenpflege im Hause und im Hospitale* (Vienna, 1881; 7th ed., 1905). Among his special studies are *Chirurgische Briefe aus den Kriegslazarethen in Weissenburg und Mannheim 1870* (Berlin, 1872); *Untersuchungen über die Vegetationsformen von Coccobacteria septica* (Berlin, 1874); and "Offenes Schreiben und Herrn Dr. D. Wittelshöfer" (on the stomach resection performed 29 January 1881), in *Wiener medizinische Wochenschrift,* **31** (1881), cols. 161–165. Billroth's autobiography is in *Wiener klinische Wochenschrift,* **7** (1894), 120–122, and *Wiener medizinische Blätter,* **17** (1894), 91–95. His last work, *Wer ist musikalisch?*, was published by his friend Hanslick (Berlin, 1896).

II. SECONDARY LITERATURE. Articles on Billroth's operations are K. Gussenbauer (on the first laryngectomy, 27 November 1873), in *Archiv für klinische chirurgie,* **17** (1874), 343–356; Mikulicz, "Ueber die Totalexstirpation des Uterus," in *Wiener medizinische Wochenschrift,* **31** (1881), cols. 241–245; and "Zur Resektion des carcinomatösen Magens," *ibid.,* cols. 634–635. J. Mundy, "Ein neues Buch von Th. Billroth," in *Wiener medizinische Wochenschrift,* **31** (1881), cols. 225–229 and 251–254, consists of notes on Billroth's work and a bibliography. On his Zurich period see A. Huber, "Prof. Dr. Theodor Billroth in Zürich 1860–1867," in *Züricher medizinische Geschichte,* I (1924). On Billroth's relation to Brahms see O. G. Billroth, *Billroth und Brahms im Briefwechsel* (Berlin-Vienna, 1935). His genealogoy is P. von Gebhardt, "Ahnentafel berühmter Deutscher, 1," in *Familiengesch. Blätter,* **27** (1929), 88–89. Additional correspondence is in G. Fischer, ed., *Briefe von Theodor Billroth* (Hannover-Leipzig, 1895; 9th ed., 1922); W. von Brunn, *Jugendbriefe Theodor Billroths an Georg Meiszner* (Leipzig, 1941); and *Wiener klinische Wochenschrift,* **7** (1894), 122–124, 425–427.

Obituaries are K. Gussenbauer, in *Wiener klinische Wochenschrift,* **7** (1894), 115–117, with complete bibliography and list of honors; *Jahrbuch der Universität Wien* (Vienna, 1893–1894), pp. 37–46, with Gussenbauer's bibliography and list of honors; and J. Mikulicz, in *Berliner klinische Wochenschrift,* **31** (1894), 199–205, based on R. Gersuny's biography in *Nord und Süd,* **141** (1888), with complete bibliography; see also Oehlschläger, "Jugenderinnerungen an Theodor Billroth," *ibid.,* 229–230; and E. von Bergmann, memorial speech, *ibid.,* 205–207. Additional obituaries are A. von Bardeleben, in *Deutsche medizinische Wochenschrift,* **20** (1894), 145; E. von Bergmann and E. Gurlt, in *Archiv für klinische Chirurgie* (1894); M. Benedikt, in *International klinische Rundschau,* **8** (1894), 184–189; E. Hanslick, in *Deutsche Rundschau,* **20** (1893–1894), 274–277; E. Kappeler, in *Archiv für klinische chirurgie* (1894), 161; Sozin, in *Korr. bl. für Schweizer Ärtze* (1894), 129; and A. Wölfer, in *Archiv für klinische Chirurgie* (1894), *Wiener medizinische Wochenschrift* (1894), 339, and *Zentralblatt für Chirurgie* (1894).

There is a biography by R. Gersuny (Berlin-Leipzig-Munich, 1922). See also I. Fischer, *Billroth und* seine Zeitgenossen (Berlin-Vienna, 1929); H. Fischer, in Medical Life, **37** (1930), 432–440; J. C. Hemmeter, in Johns Hopkins Hospital Bulletin, **11** (1900), 297–317; R. E. Weise, in Annals of Medical History, **10** (1928), 278–286; Mitteilungen für die Geschichte der Medizin und Naturwissenschaften, **28**, 238–314; and Winiwarter, in Wiener klinische Wochenschrift, **20** (1909), 309–312.

H. ENGEL

BILLY, JACQUES DE (b. Compiègne, France, 18 March 1602; d. Dijon, France, 14 January 1679), mathematics, astronomy.

A Jesuit, Billy spent his teaching career in the collèges of the society's administrative province of Champagne—Pont à Mousson, Rheims, and Dijon. He taught either theology or mathematics, depending on which was needed. In 1629–1630 he taught mathematics at Pont à Mousson while he was still a theology student and not yet ordained a priest. Billy taught mathematics at Rheims from 1631 to 1633. Around this time he became a close friend of Claude Gaspar Bachet de Méziriac, the commentator on Diophantus who introduced him to indeterminate analysis.

Billy became master of studies and professor of theology at the Collège de Dijon, where one of his students was Jacques Ozanam, whom he taught privately because there was no chair of mathematics at the collège, and in whom he instilled a profound love for calculus. Finally, a professorship having been created in mathematics, he taught his favorite subject from 1665 to 1668.

An active correspondence between Billy and Fermat began before 1659, of which one letter remains. Some of Billy's writings originated in this exchange, including parts of the Doctrinae analyticae inventum novum, through which his name is still known to number theorists. It is an elaborate study of the techniques of indeterminate analysis used by Fermat and, on the whole, it explains them correctly. From it one can guess at Fermat's general line of activity in a field in which there are few pertinent documents.

In astronomy Billy published numerical tables applicable to the three important theories (Ptolemy, Brahe, Copernicus) of the time. There are also a study on comets and several critiques against forensic astrology.

BIBLIOGRAPHY

I. ORIGINAL WORKS. Billy's works are Abrégé des préceptes d'algèbre (Rheims, 1637); Le siège de Landrecy (Paris, 1637); Nova geometriae clavis algebra (Paris, 1643); Tabulae Lodoicae, seu eclipseon doctrina (Dijon, 1656);

Tractatus de proportione harmonica (Paris, 1658); Diophantus geometria, sive opus contextum ex arithmetica et geometria simul. . . . (Paris, 1660); Opus astronomicum (Dijon, 1661); Discours de la comète qui a paru l'an 1665 au mois d'avril (Paris, 1665); Crisis astronomica de motu cometarum (Dijon, 1666); Diophanti redivivi pars prior . . . pars posterior (Lyons, 1670); and "Doctrinae analyticae inventum novum, collectum a R. P. Jacobo de Billy . . . ex variis epistolis quas ad eum diversis temporibus misit D. P. de Fermat. . . .," a study in Samuel Fermat, Diophanti Alexandrini arithmeticorum libri sex (Toulouse, 1670), Latin text and German trans. by P. von Schaewen (Berlin, 1910), French trans. by Paul Tannery, in Oeuvres de Fermat, III (Paris, 1896).

The Dijon municipal library owns several of Billy's autograph manuscripts. Paul Tannery wished to publish the part of the correspondence concerned with indeterminate analysis, but he died before he could carry out the project.

II. SECONDARY LITERATURE. There is a notice on Billy in R. P. Niceron, Mémoires pour servir à l'histoire des hommes illustres dans la république des lettres, XL (Paris, 1739), 232–244.

JEAN ITARD

BINET, ALFRED (b. Nice, France, 8 July 1857; d. Paris, France, 18 October 1911), psychology.

The career of Binet, the founder of French experimental psychology, developed on the periphery of the traditional institutions and established frameworks. His training was unusual: he was a licentiate in jurisprudence and a doctor of natural sciences, but he did no teaching, with the exception of a course in psychology at the University of Bucharest, where he had been invited in 1895. In 1892 he was named assistant director of the Laboratory of Physiological Psychology created at the Sorbonne in 1889 and directed by Henri Beaunis. In 1895 Binet and Beaunis founded the first French journal of psychology, Année psychologique. In the same year he succeeded Beaunis at the Laboratory, now connected with the École Pratique des Hautes Études, where he worked until his death.

About 1900 Binet's experiments began to go beyond the somewhat narrow framework of the Laboratory. He interviewed children in nurseries, schools, and school camps. In 1898 he and Ferdinand Buisson founded the Société Libre pour l'Étude Psychologique de l'Enfant, which after his death became the Société Alfred Binet. In 1904 the minister for public education appointed Binet to a commission for the study of problems connected with the education of retarded children. This appointment resulted in a series of studies leading to the creation of the metric intelligence scale.

Young Binet was interested in psychiatry; frequented the Salpêtrière, where Charcot taught; and studied Hippolyte Taine, Théodule Ribot, and John Stuart Mill. His first book, *Psychologie du raisonnement* (1886), based on experiments with hypnosis, related the reasoning process to an organization of images and taught associationism. It also touched off a long series of researches into intelligence and the thought process. To this series belong his studies on mathematical prodigies and chess players, retarded children, and especially the *Étude expérimentale de l'intelligence* (1903), which completed his break with Ribot's associationism. The work described experiments with and observations of Binet's two daughters, to whom he presented simple problems, insisting on justification of the replies as well as on the solution itself. These experiments demonstrated the impossibility of translating reasoning in sensory terms and proved the unity and activity of thought and its independence with respect to images. R. S. Woodworth and K. Bühler were to arrive at analogous results in 1907. Binet's study was also a fine in-depth investigation of the individual differences of the two subjects; the experiment was made complete by introspection and was oriented toward a qualitative typology.

Binet expanded the idea of experimentation in psychology. Although he worked on esthesiometric thresholds, tactile sensibility, and optic illusions, he preferred to proceed by means of questionnaires, investigations, and personal interviews rather than the complicated apparatus and artificial techniques of the laboratory. His research covered much ground: he wrote on personality changes, suggestibility, intellectual fatigue, and graphology.

His major contribution to psychology consists in the introduction of new methods of measuring intelligence. When expansion of the educational system created the need to find criteria for detecting the mentally defective, Binet, at the government's request, pursued his former work on the evaluation of intelligence in children. He proposed the metric intelligence scale, based on the idea of classifying the subjects according to the observed differences between individual performances. In 1905 Binet drew up a whole series of tests: a large number of short, varied problems related to daily situations, bringing into play "superior processes" such as memory and ratiocination. The series was arranged according to mental levels, and the measure of intelligence was established by comparison of the results and their classification. A revision of the scale in 1908 resulted in an important innovation: assuming that intelligence increases with age, Binet ranked the tests in accordance with age levels corresponding to performances by the average child. The mental age (the age the child attains on the scale) was distinguished from chronological age. This latter work of Binet, in collaboration with Théodore Simon, enjoyed wide popularity. It was translated, adapted, imitated, and administered on a large scale. It was the beginning of a new era in testing.

BIBLIOGRAPHY

I. ORIGINAL WORKS. Binet's writings include *La psychologie du raisonnement, recherches expérimentales par l'hypnotisme* (Paris, 1886); *Le magnétisme animal* (Paris, 1887), written with C. Féré; *On Double Consciousness* (Chicago, 1889); *Les altérations de la personnalité* (Paris, 1892); *Contribution à l'étude du système nerveux sous-intestinal des insectes* (Paris, 1894), his thesis at the Sorbonne; *Introduction à la psychologie expérimentale* (Paris, 1894), written with P. Courtier and V. Henri; *Psychologie des grands calculateurs et joueurs d'échecs* (Paris, 1894); *La fatigue intellectuelle* (Paris, 1898), written with V. Henri; *La suggestibilité* (Paris, 1900); *L'étude expérimentale de l'intelligence* (Paris, 1903); *L'âme et le corps* (Paris, 1906); and *Les idées modernes sur les enfants* (Paris, 1911). Binet and Simon's tests were published in *Année psychologique*, **11** (1905–1906), 163–336, and **14** (1908–1909), 1–94, and in the final form, in their *La mesure du développement de l'intelligence chez les enfants* (Paris, 1911), which has gone through numerous editions.

II. SECONDARY LITERATURE. Works on Binet are F.-L. Bertrand, *Alfred Binet et son oeuvre* (Paris, 1930), which contains a bibliography of Binet's writings; R. Martin, *Alfred Binet* (Paris, 1924); E. Varon, *The Development of Alfred Binet's Psychology,* Psychological Monographs, Vol. XLVI (Lancaster, N. Y., 1935); and F. Zuza, *Alfred Binet et la pédagogie expérimentale* (Paris, 1948), with a bibliography of Binet's works and secondary literature.

JAN SEBESTIK

BION, NICOLAS (*b. ca.* 1652; *d.* 1733), *instrumentation.*

There are almost no biographical data available on Bion. His workshop was located on the Quai de l'Horloge in Paris, at the sign of the Quart de Cercle or of the Soleil d'Or. This last sign may have been simply that of his printer–bookseller, Boudot. Bion had the title of king's engineer for mathematical instruments, and his name was often mentioned in his time; however, very few of his instruments are extant and no important technical innovations can be attributed to him. Undoubtedly he was extremely clever and had excellent manufacturing facilities at his disposal. Less specialized than most of his colleagues, he seems to have made globes, sundials, mathematical instruments, and mechanical machines with equal accuracy.

Also unlike his colleagues, Bion published several

works, and they as well as his instruments were probably responsible for his fame. Two pamphlets concern a sphere and globes executed for the dauphin and a celestial planisphere constructed to reflect the most recent observations made by the members of the Académie des Sciences. He also published three important treatises on globes and cosmography, on astrolabes, and on precision instruments in general. These writings had great success and went into many editions, the most recent of which were printed under the supervision of Bion's son after his father's death.

The *Traité de la construction . . . des instruments mathématiques* gives a fairly complete list of instruments normally constructed during the first quarter of the eighteenth century. It should, however, be noted that some of the instruments described by Bion—such as astrolabes, marine astrolabes, the jacob staff, and the Davis quadrant—were no longer used. There are deficiencies also in the descriptions of eyeglasses, microscopes, and micrometers. Bion apparently did not wish to have his instruments copied by others. All of his treatises were more for the user and the amateur than for the manufacturer.

The extant instruments are sundials of the Butterfield type, a pair of calipers, a proportional compass, an artillery calibrating compass, a theodolite, a graphometer, and a water level with pinnules of a special type.

BIBLIOGRAPHY

Bion's writings are *L'usage des globes célestes et terrestres et des sphères suivant les différents systèmes du monde, précédé d'un traité de cosmographie* (Paris, 1699; 6th ed., 1751); *L'usage des astrolabes tant universels que particuliers accompagné d'un traité qui en explique la construction* (Paris, 1702); *Description de la sphère et des globes dédiés et présentés à Mgr. le Dauphin* (Paris, 1704); *Description et usage du planisphère céleste nouvellement construit suivant les dernières observations de Messieurs de l'Académie des Sciences* (Paris, 1708); and *Traité de la construction et des principaux usages des instruments de mathématiques* (Paris, 1709; 5th ed., 1752).

Another work on Bion is Maurice Daumas, *Les instruments scientifiques aux XVIIe et XVIIIe siècles* (Paris, 1953), pp. 109–110.

JACQUES PAYEN

BIOT, JEAN-BAPTISTE (*b.* Paris, France, 21 April 1774; *d.* Paris, 3 February 1862), *physics*.

Biot's father, Joseph, was of Lorraine peasant stock; he had risen on the social scale and held a post in the treasury. Jean-Baptiste attended the Collège Louis-le-Grand in Paris and distinguished himself in the classical curriculum. About 1791, he left the school and took private lessons in mathematics. His father intended him to have a career in commerce, but Biot rebelled and, taking an opportunity provided by the Revolutionary Wars, volunteered for the army, enlisting as a gunner in September 1792. Biot, who had not abandoned mathematics, took the entrance examination for the École des Ponts et Chaussées and was accepted in January 1794. Shortly afterward, the École Polytechnique was founded; Biot transferred to it, and was appointed section leader of a group of students in November 1794. At the École Polytechnique, Biot's outstanding ability drew the attention of the director, Monge.

Under the influence of the ideas of the Revolution, and later of Laplace, Biot became skeptical of all belief in a personal God. Yet in 1825, in Rome, he sought and obtained a personal audience with Pope Leo XII and he became increasingly attracted to the religion of his childhood. In 1846 he made a formal return to the Roman Catholic Church. In 1797 Biot married the daughter (then aged sixteen) of Antoine François Brisson of Beauvais, *inspecteur général du commerce et des manufactures,* whose son was Biot's friend at the École Polytechnique. Biot instructed his wife in science and mathematics, and since she was a competent linguist, she was able to collaborate with him in a translation into French of E. G. Fischer's physics textbook.

Biot was closely associated with many of the institutions for education and research that were a prominent feature of France after the Revolution. On graduation from the École Polytechnique in 1797, he was appointed professor of mathematics at the École Centrale of the Oise department at Beauvais. From 1799 he was entrance examiner for the École Polytechnique, a post he retained when, in 1800, he was appointed professor of mathematical physics at the Collège de France. Under the patronage of Laplace, Biot was given the post of assistant astronomer at the Bureau des Longitudes in 1806. When the University of France was established by Napoleon in 1808, Biot was appointed professor of astronomy at the Paris Faculté des Sciences. From 1816 to 1826, however, while retaining the official title of professor of astronomy, he agreed to teach physics related to his own research and gave courses on light, sound, and magnetism. From 1840 until his retirement in 1849, Biot was dean of the Faculty.

Biot joined the Société Philomathique in Paris in 1801. His association with Laplace and Berthollet at about this time qualifies him for consideration as one of the original members of the Société d'Arcueil. In 1800 he was elected a nonresident member of the

First Class of the Institute, and when, in 1803, a vacancy for full membership in the mathematics section occurred, he was elected. Biot was unsuccessful in his candidature for the post of permanent secretary of the Académie des Sciences on the death of Delambre in 1822, but was elected vice-president of the Academy in 1835. By virtue of his research on Egyptian, Babylonian, and Chinese astronomy, Biot was elected a member of the Académie des Inscriptions et Belles Lettres in 1841. In 1856 he received the honor, unusual for a man of science, of election to the Académie Française. Biot, who in his youth had detested the Jacobins, also had little sympathy for Napoleon. Upon the restoration of the Bourbons in 1814, Biot was awarded the Legion of Honor (*chevalier*) for his services to science and education, and was successively promoted to officer (1823) and commander (1849) of the order. Unlike many of his contemporaries in France, Biot took no part in politics, living a long and active life devoted almost entirely to scientific research.

Throughout his life Biot made contributions to literature beyond those expected of a man of science. His *Essai sur l'histoire générale des sciences pendant la révolution française* was published in 1803. When in 1812 the Académie Française proposed the subject of Montaigne for a prize, Biot's essay received an honorable mention. He was commissioned to write a hundred-page biography of Newton for the *Biographie universelle.* Biot was well known as an ardent follower of Newton. In 1813, in the *Journal de physique,* he described Newton as a person "whose conceptions seem to have surpassed the limits of thought of mortal man" (p. 131). Biot continued: "Words fail to convey the profound impression of astonishment and respect which one experiences in studying the work of this admirable observer of nature." In the biography, Biot's solution to the problem of the interrelation of Newton's natural philosophy and his theology was to suggest that all the original scientific work had been completed early in Newton's life and that he had become seriously interested in theology only after mental illness. Biot later took issue with Brewster's interpretation of Newton. In the last years of his life, Biot wrote appreciations of Gay-Lussac and Cauchy.

Biot was the author of several important textbooks. His *Traité élémentaire d'astronomie physique* was the source from which Sir George Airy, later British astronomer royal, learned his basic astronomy; and he claimed that he had acquired his interest in the subject through Biot's work. Biot's *Traité de physique* (1816) constitutes a comprehensive account of contemporary physics, including not only recent original

research by himself (e.g., on polarization) but also the recent and often unpublished work of his associates, particularly Laplace, Gay-Lussac, and Dulong.

Although Biot's first publications were in mathematics, he soon came strongly under the influence of Laplace, whose advice he followed in the application of analysis to physical problems. In 1802 Biot demonstrated that the attraction of an ellipsoid at an external point might be deduced by simple differentiations from a particular expression, which is theoretically known when the attraction is known for all points situated in the plane of one of the principal sections. Biot's memoir, however, constituted little more than a commentary on the earlier writings of Legendre and Laplace. His introduction to Laplace had come about through his offer to read the proofs of Laplace's *Mécanique céleste.* Laplace encouraged Biot to undertake experimental investigation of a wide range of problems, many of which constituted a deliberate extension of the Newtonian framework of science. This can be seen particularly in Biot's research on refraction, polarization of light, and sound. If we were to select any one branch of physics to which Biot made the most important contribution, the choice would be the polarization of light, but, since none of his contributions in this field occurred before 1812, it will be convenient to deal first with his varied contributions to other branches of physical science.

An unusual piece of research at the beginning of Biot's career was concerned with a meteorite said to have fallen from the sky at l'Aigle in the Orne department on 26 April 1803. Biot was ordered by Chaptal, minister of the interior, to confirm the report. Shortly before, M. A. Pictet had called attention to reports of meteorites—reports that many rationalists had dismissed as superstitious. Biot questioned people in the locality where the meteoric stones had fallen. Various specimens were examined and compared with the composition of the ground from which they had been taken, and some were subjected to chemical analysis. Biot's report, read to the First Class of the Institute on 18 July 1803, marks the beginning of a general recognition in France of the reality of meteorites.

In the years 1804–1809 Biot undertook several scientific projects in collaboration with other men, notably fellow members of the Arcueil group or the Bureau des Longitudes. On 24 August 1804, Biot made a balloon ascent with Gay-Lussac. The ascent was notable in that it was undertaken entirely for purposes of scientific research and had the approval of the French government. The primary purpose was to find whether the magnetic intensity of the earth decreased at great altitudes, as had been suggested by Horace de Saussure's experiments in the Alps. From their experiments, in which they timed the oscillations of a magnetized needle at various altitudes, Biot and Gay-Lussac concluded that up to 4,000 meters there was no change.

Biot undertook further work on magnetism in collaboration with Humboldt, who furnished much of the data used in their joint memoir (1804). Biot attempted to derive general laws governing inclination, using as a basis the hypothesis of an infinitely small magnet situated at the center of the earth and placed perpendicular to the magnetic equator. The theoretical values for the inclination agreed well with Humboldt's readings, particularly in the northern hemisphere. Anomalies were attributed to purely local factors.

Biot collaborated with Arago in 1805–1806 in research which, in a typically Newtonian spirit, they presented with the title "Mémoire sur les affinités des corps pour la lumière, et, particulièrement sur les forces réfringentes des différents gaz" (1806). The accurate determination of the refractive indices of various gases and vapors at different pressures was a legitimate subject of study for two members of the Bureau des Longitudes who were concerned with astronomical observations. In another memoir, Biot reported on the refraction of light rays near the horizon. He made a full study of mirages, taking the subject beyond Wollaston's work of 1803. In later years, in a succession of memoirs, Biot made further contributions to the subject of atmospheric refraction. As regards the joint work with Arago, however, not the least important part of Biot's research was the accurate determination of the densities of gases weighed in glass globes. The values obtained were part of the data used by Gay-Lussac to establish his law of combining volumes of gases. When Gay-Lussac and the chemist Thenard carried out combustion analyses of organic compounds, they calculated their results with atomic weights for carbon and hydrogen deduced from the density measurements of Biot and Arago. Prout also used the data of Biot and Arago to support his hypothesis.

In 1807 Biot collaborated with Thenard in a thorough comparative study of rhombic aragonite and hexagonal calcite. Apart from obvious chemical tests, they compared the refractivity not only of the crystals but also of their solutions in hydrochloric acid and of the carbon dioxide evolved from each. They concluded that aragonite and calcite were composed of the same chemical elements in the same proportions, but with a different arrangement of the molecules, which resulted in physically different substances. This was one of the earliest examples of what was later called dimorphism.

Biot made a number of contributions to the determination of the velocity of sound. His first memoir in 1802 mentions that he had undertaken this research at the instigation of Laplace. Biot was not then able to measure directly the tiny temperature changes produced by sound waves, although Laplace believed that this was the key to solving the discrepancy between Newton's formula for the velocity of sound and the value obtained in practice. In 1807 Biot carried out more experiments at Arcueil on the transmission of sound through vapors. In 1808 the extensive laying of water mains in Paris gave Biot the opportunity of carrying out further experiments on sound. With cast iron pipes forming a continuous length of 951 meters Biot determined, by repeated experiments, the time interval between transmission and reception of sound through the pipe and through the air. Knowing the velocity of sound in air under the temperature and pressure conditions of the experiment, Biot was able to compare the two velocities. One factor limiting the accuracy of the experiments was the presence of lead, used to join the iron pipes. Biot therefore did not give an explicit value for the velocity of sound in cast iron, but concluded that it was 10.5 times that in air—a value that was long considered authoritative because of the difficulty of direct determination.

In 1806 Biot and Arago were sent by the Bureau des Longitudes to determine the arc of the meridian in Spain and the Balearic Islands, a task begun by Méchain but left incomplete at his death in 1804. The post-Revolution metric system was based on the idea of a "natural" unit, the meter, which was supposed to be exactly one ten-millionth of a meridian quadrant of the earth. Méchain and Delambre had made measurements over a meridian arc of 10° stretching from Dunkirk to Barcelona, and from their readings the length of the standard meter was obtained. It was proposed that this should be redetermined with greater accuracy by extending measurements farther south to the Balearic Islands. Special difficulties in triangulation were encountered because of the distance of the islands from the mainland, but these difficulties were eventually overcome. Biot presented a report on this expedition to the Institute in 1810. Meanwhile, in the company of Mathieu, Biot measured the length of the seconds pendulum at Bordeaux and at Dunkirk. In 1817, Biot took part in another expedition, this time to Scotland and the Shetland Islands in order to confirm the geodesic work that had recently been undertaken by the British under Colonel Mudge. In 1818, Biot was again in Dunkirk; in 1824 and 1825 he went to Italy and Sicily with his son, and then revisited Formentera and Barcelona to correct his earlier geodesic measurements. From a comparison of his determinations, Biot concluded that the weight of a given body is not the same on all points with the same latitude, nor is its variation uniform along a particular meridian. This work established the necessity of revising the generally accepted simple ellipsoid theory of the earth.

During Biot's visit to Spain in 1806 and 1807 for geodesic work, he carried out other experimental work which is not generally known. He made a special study of the composition of the air contained in the swim bladders of fish found off the islands of Ibiza and Formentera. He can claim credit for recording the extremely high proportion of oxygen in the swim bladders of certain fish which live at great depths. He found a maximum of 87 percent oxygen, a figure that agrees well with the modern value. Another series of experiments that he carried out in the Mediterranean on the compression of gases (published in 1809) is of some theoretical interest. He lowered mixtures of gases, in appropriate proportions, to great depths to see whether they would combine to form the corresponding compounds. Combination did not take place up to pressures of about thirty atmospheres, and he was able to conclude that even when the pressure was increased thirty times and the distance between the molecules was correspondingly reduced, the molecules were still too far apart to exercise their chemical affinity.

In 1804 Biot carried out an experimental investigation of the conductivity of metal bars by maintaining one end at a known high temperature and taking readings of thermometers placed in holes along the bar. He was able to report the significant result that the steady-state temperature decreased exponentially along the length of the bar. He saw that this could be explained in terms of a balance of loss of heat at the surface and transfer of heat along the bar, which he analyzed in terms of adjacent pairs of cross-sectional areas. Unfortunately he was unable to present the differential equation corresponding to his physical model because of his inability to find plausible physical reasons for dividing a second difference of temperatures by the square of the infinitesimal element of length. Hence he could not convert his second difference into a second derivative. This was later achieved by Fourier. (I owe the above analysis of Biot's work on conductivity to Dr. J. R. Ravetz.)

In 1813 Biot attempted to derive a general formula for the expansion of liquids, and in 1815 he made a critical examination of Newton's law of cooling. Biot's friend Delaroche had already shown that at high temperatures heat losses were greater than the simple proportionality suggested by Newton. Biot proposed the equation

$$t = aT + bT^3,$$

where t represents the heat loss, T is the difference in temperature between the hot body and its surroundings, and a and b are constants. While considering Biot's early work on heat, it will be convenient to mention two later contributions. Biot proposed a general formula for the pressure, p, of a saturated vapor:

$$\log p = a + b\alpha^\theta + c\beta^\theta,$$

where a, b, c, α, and β are determined by means of five experiments and θ is the temperature measured from a convenient zero, such as the lowest temperature in the five experiments used to determine the constants. Biot's formula was a considerable improvement in generality and precision over the earlier formula of Delaroche. Biot also derived a formula (occasionally referred to as Biot's law) relating the intensity of solar radiation to the thickness of the atmosphere. If I is intensity of radiation of incident beam and I' is intensity of radiation transmitted through a thickness, t, of a medium whose coefficient of absorption is k, then

$$I' = Ie^{-kt}.$$

In 1800, the announcement of the voltaic pile aroused general interest; and when Volta came to Paris in 1801, the official report of the committee appointed by the First Class to examine Volta's work was edited and presented by Biot. On 14 August 1801, Biot read a memoir to the First Class describing his study of the "movement of the galvanic fluid," based on the hypothesis of Laplace that it consisted of mutually repellent particles. In collaboration with Cuvier, Biot investigated the chemistry of the voltaic pile. Expanding the work of W. H. Pepys, they confirmed that the voltaic pile in action absorbed oxygen, which they measured. They found that as long as any oxygen remained to be absorbed, the voltaic pile was still active, but with decreasing intensity. Nevertheless, the pile continued to function in the exhausted receiver of an air pump.

In the first edition of his physics textbook, Biot adopted a theory of electrolytic decomposition that was substantially that of Grotthus, but he later suggested that the liquid undergoing decomposition is most positive at the positive pole and most negative at the negative pole. When a particle of a salt is decomposed at the negative pole, the latter communicates a strong negative charge to the acid part. By repulsion from the surrounding negatively charged particles and by attraction toward the positive pole, it moves toward the latter. Only at the poles does decomposition take place. Biot made a brief study of the distribution of electricity on the surface of irregular spheroids, an extension of earlier work by Laplace. By analysis, he also established that when a Leyden jar is discharged by successive contacts, the losses of electricity form a geometrical progression.

News of Oersted's discovery of the connection between magnetism and electricity was brought to Paris by Arago in September 1820. Immediately the Paris scientists, including Ampère, began to explore the subject. Biot was away at the time, but on his return he was said to be working day and night to make up for lost time. He presented the result of his research with Savart to the Academy on 30 October 1820. They had measured the rate of oscillation of a suspended magnet placed at various distances from a conductor carrying a current. They were thus able to show that the magnetic force acts at right angles to the perpendicular joining the point considered to the conductor, and that its intensity is inversely proportional to the distance (Biot and Savart's law).

After this review of Biot's miscellaneous contributions to science, we must turn to the field in which he did his most important work—the study of polarization of light, the research for which Biot was awarded the Rumford Medal in 1840 by the Royal Society of London. The polarization of light by reflection had been discovered by Malus in Paris in the fall of 1808. This was of fundamental importance in the history of optics, since it showed that a phenomenon that had previously been observed in a few crystalline substances, such as Iceland spar, was a general property of light. Malus's discovery opened up an entirely new field of research, and no one was stimulated more than his two associates in the Arcueil group, Arago and Biot. In August 1811, Arago announced that he had found that white light polarized by reflection could, on passing through certain crystals, be split into two differently colored beams.

Biot repeated Arago's experiments and established the relationship between the thicknesses of the crystal plates and the colors produced. He observed that for perpendicular incidence, the colors seen correspond to those seen by reflection and transmission in thin films of air; and he concluded that the thicknesses at which the colors appeared were proportional to the thickness of the air gap that gave the same color on Newton's scale. These thicknesses depended on the nature of the crystal, but were always much greater than the thicknesses of thin films of air that gave the same tint. Biot found that the colors disappeared if the plate was extremely thin, and there was also an upper limit—for example, no colors would be seen

if the thickness of a plate of gypsum was greater than 0.45 mm. In this research the exact measurement of the plate was of the utmost importance, and Biot was fortunate in being able to use the spherometer, newly invented by Cauchoix. He began his research by taking eleven plates of gypsum, varying in thickness from 0.087 mm. to 0.345 mm. He determined the color produced by each and compared it with the color on Newton's scale. For oblique incidence, Biot found that the color depended on the thickness of the crystal traversed by the refracted ray and varied as the square of the sine of the angle that the direction of the ray formed with the optical axis.

Biot's interpretation of his results was in terms of a repulsive force that caused polarization by acting on the particles of light. This conception was first worked out in detail in a memoir presented to the First Class on 30 November 1812. The discovery of polarization had greatly encouraged Laplace, Biot, and others who supported a corpuscular theory of light. Malus had been successful in deriving the fundamental cosine law of polarization on such a model. To explain the complementary polarization in crystalline plates, Biot developed a theory of "mobile polarization." The particles of a polarized ray were supposed to preserve their original polarization until they reached a certain depth in the crystal, when they began to oscillate around their center of gravity so that the axes of polarization were carried alternately to each side of the axes of the crystal. The period was considered to vary with the color (as in Newton's theory of fits). When the ray emerged from the crystal, oscillation stopped, and the ray assumed "fixed polarization," in which the axes of the particles were arranged in two perpendicular directions. The theory was plausible up to a point, but Biot had considerable difficulty in accounting for the difference in the effect of thin and thick plates on polarized light. In 1841 Biot considered that he had found a new phenomenon of polarization, which was dependent on the existence of different layers in the crystal and which he called lamellar polarization.

In 1812 Biot observed that the rotation of polarized light produced by a plate of quartz decreased progressively with change of color from violet to red. In a paper read to the Academy on 22 September 1818, Biot was able to announce what has become known as Biot's law of rotatory dispersion and would now be expressed by the equation

$$\alpha = \frac{k}{\lambda^2},$$

where α is the rotation and λ is the wavelength. For Biot, however, it was "la loi de rotation réciproque aux quarrés des longueurs des accès" (the law of rotation in inverse proportion to the squares of the lengths of the fits)—a reminder that Biot did not accept a wave theory, but followed Newton's theory of "fits." Biot also found that the amount of rotation is proportional to the thickness of the crystalline plate traversed by the ray and that the rotation effected by two plates is the algebraic sum of the rotations produced by each separately.

Biot deduced his law without the use of monochromatic light, and his wavelength values given in the graph (Fig. 1) are Newton's values for the boundaries of different colors.

The horizontal axis in Biot's graph represents the square of the wavelength of light, and the vertical axis denotes the thickness of the plates of quartz required to produce rotations of 180°, 360°, 540°, etc., in light of a given color. Biot found that the same

law apparently applied equally to liquids. Later, when trying to compensate levorotatory turpentine against dextrorotatory oil of lemon, Biot observed that exact compensation of all rays was not possible. The amendment to the expression of Biot's law that this implied was not achieved until much later (Drude, 1898; Lowry and Dickson, 1913).

In 1814, Biot found that in certain crystalline substances the refractive index was less for the ordinary ray than for the extraordinary ray, unlike the standard doubly refracting substance calcite. Huygens had explained the formation of the extraordinary ray in calcite by the construction of an oblate spheroid. Biot modified this construction, drawing a prolate spheroid to describe the new phenomenon.

Tourmaline was known to be a doubly refracting substance. In 1815 Biot found that a plate of a certain thickness of tourmaline crystal cut parallel to the axis

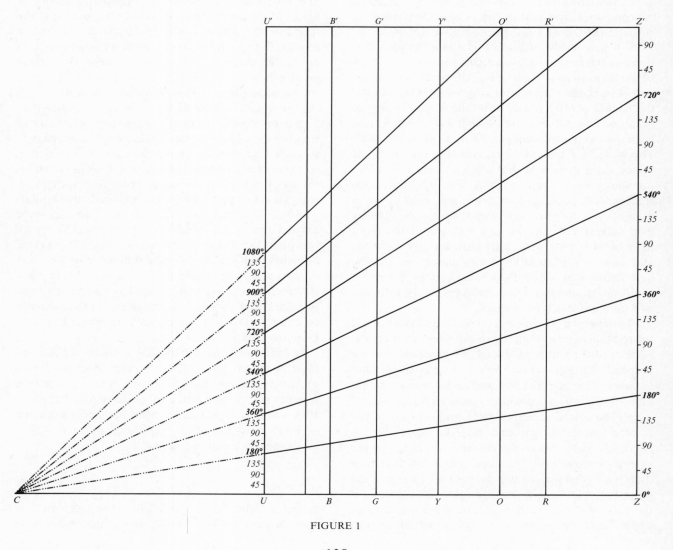

FIGURE 1

138

had the property of transmitting only light polarized in one plane. If light was allowed to pass through two plates and the second was rotated until it was perpendicular to the first, the light would gradually be extinguished. Biot's difficulty in explaining the action of polarized light on certain crystals such as calcium sulfate was overcome only when Brewster distinguished biaxial crystals from uniaxial ones. Nevertheless, in 1818 Biot did clearly distinguish a uniaxial form of magnesia mica from the more common biaxial types, and his work is commemorated in the name biotite given to a type of mica by J. F. L. Hausmann in 1847.

Until 1815 it had been assumed that only in the solid state did substances have the effect of rotating the plane of polarized light. It was Biot who discovered that certain crystalline solids, which had no effect on polarized light, did have an effect when in solution. On 23 October 1815, Biot announced to the First Class that the property of rotating the plane of polarized light was shared by liquids. Turpentine placed in a long tube with plane glass at each end exhibited a similar property, although to a less marked degree. Within a week he found a similar effect with oil of laurel and oil of lemon. Biot appreciated the immense importance of his discovery—that since this was a property of liquids, it must be a property of the molecules. To confirm this, he demonstrated that the effect on polarized light applied equally to turpentine in the liquid and vapor states.

In 1811 Arago found that in plates of quartz, the colors polarized along the axis were different from those he had studied in other crystals. When they were analyzed through a prism of Iceland spar, he found that the two images had complementary colors and changed through the spectrum as the prism was rotated. Biot repeated these experiments and found that while in some quartz crystals the tints descended in the scale of colors by turning the analyzing prism from left to right, in others the same effect was obtained by turning the prism from right to left. He thus distinguished what he called right-handed and left-handed quartz. Biot found that liquids also had opposite effects on polarized light. If liquids that rotated the plane of polarization in opposite directions were mixed in suitable proportions, the effect was canceled out. For this effect, Biot introduced the term compensé ("compensated"). He found that the rotation of the plane of polarization for a given liquid was proportional to its concentration or, with a given concentration, to the length of the tube containing the solution. It was Biot who introduced the practice of denoting the effect of polarized light on a liquid or solution by the value of the rotation produced by a column of standard length. Biot's major contribution to instrumentation in polarimetry was to design one of the first polariscopes.

In 1816 Biot suggested that the equal effect of polarized light on respective solutions of cane sugar and beet sugar constituted an additional proof of their identity. After 1820 he put his optical research aside, and for the next twelve years his work was mainly in astronomy and electricity. From 1832 he resumed his optical research with renewed vigor, going back to his earlier work and carrying out comparative tests on sugars. In 1833, working with Persoz, Biot found that when cane sugar was heated with dilute sulfuric acid, a chemical change took place; this was revealed by the solution's rotating the plane of polarized light to the left instead of to the right. He described the effect as "inversion," a term which is still used. In further collaboration with Persoz, Biot studied the conversion of starch by dilute acids into sugar and a gum which, from its effect on polarized light, they named dextrine. Biot introduced the polarimetric method of quantitative estimation of sugar remaining in molasses.

In 1832 Biot recorded the property of a solution of tartaric acid of rotating polarized light, and he remarked on the anomalous dispersion it gave, the rotation being greater for "less refrangible rays." In 1836 he presented to the Academy a memoir devoted entirely to the study of the rotatory power of tartaric acid under different conditions. He stressed that tartaric acid constituted an outstanding exception to his law of inverse squares (of wavelength). Biot accordingly divided optically active substances into two classes, those that obeyed his law and those that did not. He observed the crystalline forms of some salts of tartaric acid, but it was left to Pasteur to show the relationship between the crystalline form and the effect on polarized light. Biot was, significantly, an ardent champion of Pasteur at the beginning of his career. Pasteur, for his part, felt that Biot's work on the rotation of polarized light by liquids constituted a valuable scientific tool that had been hitherto unjustly neglected by chemists.

BIBLIOGRAPHY

I. ORIGINAL WORKS. *The Royal Society Catalogue of Scientific Periodicals* lists some three hundred memoirs by Biot published in scientific periodicals. It also lists fifteen memoirs written with collaborators.

A few of Biot's most significant memoirs are "Mémoire sur la propagation de la chaleur, et sur un moyen simple et exact de mesurer les hautes températures," in *Journal des mines,* **17** (1804), 203–224; "Mémoire sur les affinités des corps pour la lumière, et, particulièrement sur les forces réfringentes des différents gaz" (written with Arago), in *Mémoires de l'Institut,* **7** (1806), 301–385; "Mémoire sur l'analyse comparée de l'arragonite et du carbonate de chaux rhomboïdal" (written with Thenard), in *Mémoires de la Société d'Arcueil,* **2** (1809), 176–206; "Mémoire sur des nouveaux rapports qui existent entre la réflexion et la polarisation de la lumière par les corps cristallisés," in *Mémoires de l'Institut* (1811), 135–280; "Sur une loi remarquable qui s'observe dans les oscillations des particules lumineuses, lorsquelles traversent obliquement des lames minces de chaux sulfatée ou de cristal de roche, taillées parallèlement à l'axe de cristallisation," in *Société philomatique, Bulletin* (1815), 149–156; "Phénomènes de polarisation successive, observés dans des fluides homogènes," in *Société philomatique, Bulletin* (1815), 190–192; "Mémoire sur les rotations que certaines substances impriment aux axes de polarisation des rayons lumineux," in *Mémoires de l'Académie des sciences de l'Institut,* **2** (1817), 41–136; "Note sur le magnétisme de la pile de Volta" (written with Savart), in *Annales de chimie et de physique,* **15** (1820), 222–223; "Mémoire sur les modifications que la fécule et la gomme subissent sous l'influence des acides" (written with Persoz), in *Annales de chimie et de physique,* **52** (1833), 72–90; "Mémoire sur la polarisation circulaire et sur ses applications à la chimie organique," in *Mémoires de l'Académie des sciences de l'Institut,* **13** (1835), 39–175; "Méthodes mathématiques et expérimentales, pour discerner les mélanges et les combinaisons définies ou non définies qui agissent sur la lumière polarisée; suivies d'applications aux combinaisons de l'acide tartrique avec l'eau, l'alcool, et l'esprit de bois," in *Mémoires de l'Académie des sciences de l'Institut,* **15** (1838), 93–279.

The following are the principal books by Biot: *Analyse du Traité de mécanique céleste de P. S. Laplace* (Paris, 1801); *Traité analytique des courbes et des surfaces du second degré* (Paris, 1802; 8th ed., 1834), translated by Frances H. Smith as *An Elementary Treatise on Analytical Geometry; Translated From the French and Adapted to the Present State of Mathematical Instruction in the Colleges of the United States* (New York–London, 1840); *Traité élémentaire d'astronomie physique,* 2 vols. (Paris, 1802; 3rd ed., 10 vols., 1841–1857); *Essai sur l'histoire générale des sciences pendant la Révolution française* (Paris, 1803); *Recherches sur les réfractions extraordinaires qui ont lieu près de l'horizon* (Paris, 1810); *Recherches expérimentales et mathématiques sur les mouvements des molécules de la lumière autour de leur centre de gravité* (Paris, 1814); *Traité de physique,* 4 vols. (Paris, 1816); *Précis élémentaire de physique expérimentale,* 2 vols. (Paris, 1817; 3rd ed., 1824), translated as *J. B. Biot's . . . Anfangsgrunde der Erfahrungs—Naturlehre, aus dem französisch übersetzt von F. Wolff,* 2 vols. (Berlin, 1819); *Recueil d'observations géodésiques, astronomiques et physiques, executées par ordre du Bureau des Longitudes de France en Espagne, en France, en Angleterre et en Écosse pour déterminer la variation de la pesanteur et des degrés terrestres sur le prolongement du méridien de Paris . . . rédigé par MM Biot et Arago* (Paris, 1821); *Recherches sur plusieurs points de l'astronomie égyptienne, appliquées*

aux monuments astronomiques trouvés en Égypte (Paris, 1823); *Notions élémentaires de statique* (Paris, 1828); *Instructions pratiques sur l'observation et la mesure des propriétés optiques appelées rotatoires, avec l'exposé succinct de leur application à la chimie médicale, scientifique et industrielle* (Paris, 1845); *Mélanges scientifiques et littéraires,* 3 vols. (Paris, 1859); *Études sur l'astronomie indienne* (Paris, 1859); *Études sur l'astronomie indienne et sur l'astronomie chinoise* (Paris, 1862).

II. SECONDARY LITERATURE. There is an anonymous biography of Biot in American Academy of Arts and Sciences, *Proceedings,* **6** (1862–1865), 16–23. Other works on Biot are D. Brewster, "Optics," in *Encyclopaedia Britannica,* 8th ed. (Edinburgh, 1858), XVI; M. P. Crosland, *The Society of Arcueil. A View of French Science at the Time of Napoleon I* (Cambridge, Mass. 1967); F. Lefort, "Un savant chrétien. J. B. Biot," in *Le correspondant,* n.s. **36** (1867), 955–995; T. M. Lowry, "Optical Rotatory Dispersion. A Tribute to the Memory of Jean Baptiste Biot (1774–1862)," in *Nature,* **117** (1926), 271–275; E. Mach, *The Principles of Physical Optics* (New York, 1926), ch. X; P. F. de Mottelay, *Bibliographical History of Electricity and Magnetism* (London, 1922); C. E. Picard, "La vie et l'oeuvre de Jean Baptiste Biot," in *Éloges et discours académiques* (Paris, 1931), pp. 221–287; D. Sidersky, "Le centenaire du premier polarimètre," in Association des Chimistes, *Bulletin de l'Association des chimistes* (Jan.–Feb. 1940).

M. P. CROSLAND

BIRD, JOHN (*b.* Bishop Auckland, England, 1709; *d.* London, England, 31 March 1776), *mathematics, optics.*

Bird was an eminent maker of mathematical instruments; the precision of his products made possible considerable advancement of practical astronomy. Almost nothing is known of his early life, which was spent in northeast England. He worked as a weaver and developed an interest and a proficiency in metal engraving. He also divided and engraved clock dial plates, demonstrating considerable skill in this work. About 1740 Bird moved to London, where he was employed by the well-known maker of astronomical and navigational instruments, Jonathan Sisson. Shortly after his arrival in London, Bird devised an instrument for finding the latitude at sea. He soon came to the attention of George Graham, another maker of astronomical instruments and clocks. Graham, impressed with the accuracy and quality of his work, assisted Bird in establishing his own shop for the making of mathematical instruments in 1745.

The nature of the instruments first produced by Bird at his own shop is not precisely known, but among them were portable quadrants with radii ranging from ten to twenty-four inches, as well as transit instruments ranging in length from one foot to five feet.

Bird received his first major order in 1749. The astronomer royal, James Bradley, had applied to and received from George II a grant of £1,000 for the construction of new instruments for the Royal Observatory at Greenwich. Bradley thereupon commissioned Bird to produce a movable forty-inch-radius quadrant cast in brass. He labored three years over the production of this instrument, which required 2,000 screws and weighed nearly 800 kilograms. Bird provided against error due to temperature change, and when the instrument was completed in June 1750 it was found to be a mere .05 greater than 90°.

This achievement brought Bird considerable fame, and by means of the instrument Bradley was able to achieve numerous important astronomical observations. When the Imperial Academy of Science at St. Petersburg remodeled its observatory within the next several years, Bird was employed to provide the instruments, including an eight-foot quadrant. He produced similar instruments for the Royal Observatory at Paris and for the Naval Observatory at Cádiz. In 1754 Bird constructed a six-foot mural quadrant that was presented by the king to Tobias Mayer at the University of Göttingen. Other important instruments made by Bird were two eight-foot quadrants for Radcliffe Observatory at Oxford. In 1758 and 1759 he was commissioned to produce a standard yard measure for the committees of the House of Commons and an apparatus for determining capacity measures.

During this same period Bird was engaged in commercial production of reflecting telescopes, barometers, thermometers, octants, and drafting instruments. He produced the reflecting circles, designed by Tobias Mayer, that were tested by Captain John Campbell for the Admiralty in 1757–1759, and in 1773 he was called upon by the Board of Longitude to examine the sextant scale divided by Jesse Ramsden's new dividing engine.

Bird's methods for the accurate division of scientific instruments were made available to others in two published works in which he described his methods and tools.

Not only were Bird's instruments the most accurately graduated prior to the invention of the dividing engine, but by his example and his publications others were enabled to achieve greater precision in scientific instrumentation.

BIBLIOGRAPHY

I. ORIGINAL WORKS. Bird's published writings are *The Method of Dividing Astronomical Instruments* (London, 1767) and *The Method of Constructing Mural Quadrants* (London, 1768).

II. SECONDARY LITERATURE. Writings on Bird or his work are Jean Bernoulli, *Lettres astronomiques* (Berlin, 1771), pp. 107–108, 126–129; C. Doris Hellman, "John Bird (1709–1776) Mathematical Instrument-Maker in the Strand," in *Isis,* **17** (1932), 127–153; Thomas Hornsby, ed., *Astronomical Observations Made at the Royal Observatory at Greenwich, From the Year MDCCL, to the Year MDCCLXII, by the Rev. James Bradley,* I (Oxford, 1798), Preface, ii–iii, vii, xiv, xv; Henry C. King, *The History of the Telescope* (London, 1955), pp. 115–118; Pierre-Charles Le Monnier, "Description et usage des principaux instruments d'astronomie où l'on traite de leur stabilité, de leur fabrique, et de l'art de les diviser," in *Description des arts et métiers,* **42** (1774), 1–60, plates I–XIV; and W. Ludlam, *An Introduction and Notes, on Mr. Bird's Method of Dividing Astronomical Instruments, to Which Is Added a Vocabulary of English and French Astronomical Terms* (London, 1786).

SILVIO A. BEDINI

BIRGE, EDWARD ASAHEL (*b.* Troy, New York, 7 September 1851; *d.* Madison, Wisconsin, 9 June 1950), *limnology.*

Birge's father, Edward White Birge, was an English-born carpenter of limited means; his mother was Ann Stevens, of Troy, New York. After completing grammar school and high school in Troy, Birge attended Williams College from 1869 to 1873. There Mark Hopkins (philosophy), John Bascom (English literature), and Sanford Tenney (natural history) were his most influential teachers. Following Tenney's advice, Birge next studied zoology under Louis Agassiz at the Museum of Comparative Zoology in Cambridge, Massachusetts, during the fall of 1873.

After Agassiz's death in December 1873, Birge transferred to the Harvard Graduate School. In January 1876 he assumed the position of instructor in natural history and curator of cabinet at the University of Wisconsin, at the behest of John Bascom, then president of that institution. In 1878 Birge returned briefly to Harvard for his doctoral examination and to receive his doctorate. He became professor of biology at Wisconsin in 1879, and soon thereafter he married Anna Grant, a friend since childhood. Accompanied by her, he spent the year 1880–1881 at the University of Leipzig in postdoctoral study under the physiologist Ludwig and under Gaule, from whom he learned the newly devised paraffin sectioning technique, which he introduced to Wisconsin upon his return.

Birge spent the rest of his life at the University of Wisconsin, where he was professor and chairman of zoology (1879–1911), dean of the College of Letters and Science (1891–1918), acting president (1900–1903), president (1918–1925), and president emeritus (1925–1950). In addition he served the state of Wisconsin as commissioner of fisheries (1895–1915), director of the Geological and Natural History Survey (1879–1919), and member of the Conservation Commission (1908–1915). He received honorary degrees from Williams College; the universities of Pittsburgh, Wisconsin, and Missouri; and Rensselaer Polytechnic Institute.

At Wisconsin, Birge continued his undergraduate interest in water fleas by studying plankton crustaceans in Lake Mendota in relation to depth, light, temperature, and currents. This led him to the independent discovery of the thermocline (observed only shortly before in European lakes) and to a study of dissolved oxygen at different depths and times, its depletion by respiration of organisms, and its interchange with carbon dioxide at the water surface. Birge came to regard the lake as a kind of superorganism with a physiology of its own—respiring, metabolizing, and exchanging matter and energy with its environment.

In 1900 Birge brought Chancey Juday to Wisconsin and, greatly assisted by him, in 1911 published a major monograph on the dissolved gases in lakes and their biological significance. From this time on, Birge turned his attention more toward the physical factors in lakes, especially heat distribution and light penetration, while Juday specialized in lake chemistry and biological productivity. Their collaboration continued, and most of their work was published jointly.

From a study of the Finger Lakes of New York in 1910 and comparable investigations in Wisconsin, Birge worked out the principle of the "heat budget" of lakes; he also studied the thermal exchange between lake water and air in considerable detail, including the very significant role of wind in the process. Impressed by the importance of sunlight in the heat budget and in productivity, Birge next began a detailed study of light penetration into inland lake waters. With the help of physicists, he devised an instrument, which he named the pyrlimnometer, that was in principle a delicate thermocouple capable of recording (as heat) light delivered by the sun to different lake depths. Later, equipped with filters, it was used to study separately the penetration of light of different wavelengths into the water.

Upon Birge's retirement from the presidency of the University of Wisconsin, he and Juday established the Trout Lake Limnological Laboratory near Minocqua, in Vilas County, Wisconsin, a region of numerous lakes. Thus Birge was able to extend his studies of light penetration to many lakes with different intensities of water coloration. The results were published in a series of reports written with Juday and H. J. James between 1929 and 1933. Birge showed that the upper meter of water absorbs nearly all the infrared and a large part of the ultraviolet light. The depth of penetration of the remaining rays was shown to depend on the amount of suspended matter (e.g., algae and sediment) and dissolved stains (e.g., humic acids from bogs). The amount and kind of organic matter was presented in a comprehensive report in 1922.

Birge was the first great American limnologist. Ably assisted by Juday, he gave the initial and major impetus to the development of limnology in the United States, just as Forel, the founder of limnology, had done a generation before in Europe.

BIBLIOGRAPHY

I. Original Works. Birge's writings include "The Inland Lakes of Wisconsin. The Dissolved Gases," in *Bulletin of the Wisconsin Geological and Natural History Survey,* science ser. 7, no. 22 (1911), written with Juday; "The Water Fleas (*Cladocera*)," in Ward and Whipple, *Fresh-Water Biology* (New York, 1918), pp. 676–740; and "The Inland Lakes of Wisconsin. The Plankton," in *Bulletin of the Wisconsin Geological and Natural History Survey,* science ser. 13, no. 64 (1922), written with Juday.

II. Secondary Literature. John L. Brooks et al., "Edward Asahel Birge (1851–1950)," in *Archiv für Hydrobiologie,* **45** (1951), 235–243, includes a nearly complete bibliography of Birge's works; G. C. Sellery, *E. A. Birge* (Madison, Wis., 1956), contains an appraisal of Birge as a limnologist by C. H. Mortimer.

Lowell E. Noland

BIRINGUCCIO, VANNOCCIO (*b.* Siena, Italy, 20 October 1480; *d.* Rome [?], Italy, *ca.* 1539), *metallurgy.*

The son of Lucrezia and Paolo Biringuccio, the latter an architect and public servant, Biringuccio traveled as a young man throughout Italy and Germany, inspecting metallurgical operations. After running an iron mine and forge at Boccheggiano for Pandolfo Petrucci, he was appointed to a post with the arsenal at Siena and in 1513 directed the mint. In 1516, after the fall of the Petrucci family, he was exiled by the Republic of Siena on a charge of having debased the coinage. Biringuccio returned with the Petruccis in 1523, and was again exiled in 1526. Thereafter he served the Venetian and Florentine republics, and cast cannon and built fortifications for the Este and Farnese families. In 1531, with political peace, he returned once more to Siena, this time in honor, as senator and, succeeding Baldassare Peruzzi, as architect and director of building construction at the Duomo. He later moved to Rome. In 1538 Biringuccio was appointed head of the papal foundry and director of papal munitions, but he died soon after, probably in Rome and certainly before 30 April 1540.

Biringuccio's reputation derives from a single work, his *Pirotechnia,* published posthumously in 1540. The work is divided into ten books, which deal with (1) metallic ores; (2) the "semiminerals" (including mercury, sulfur, alum, arsenic, vitriol, several pigments, gems, and glass); (3) assaying and preparing ores for smelting; (4) the parting of gold and silver, both with nitric acid and with antimony sulfide or sulfur; (5) alloys of gold, silver, copper, lead, and tin; (6) the art of casting large statues and guns; (7) furnaces and methods of melting metals; (8) the making of small castings; (9) miscellaneous pyrotechnical operations (including alchemy; the distillation of acids, alcohol, and other substances; the working of a mint "both honestly and with profit"; the goldsmith, silversmith, and ironsmith; the pewterer; wire-drawing; mirror-making; pottery; and bricks); and (10) the making of saltpeter, gunpowder, and fireworks for warfare and celebration. Virtually all of Biringuccio's descriptions are original. He is important in art history for his description of the peculiarly Renaissance arts of casting medallions, statues, statuettes, and bells. His account of typecasting, given in considerable detail, is the earliest known. The *Pirotechnia* contains eighty-three woodcuts, the most useful being those depicting furnaces for distillation, bellows mechanisms, and devices for boring cannon and drawing wire.

As the first comprehensive account of the fire-using arts to be printed, the *Pirotechnia* is a prime source on many practical aspects of inorganic chemistry. Biringuccio emphasizes the adaptation of minerals and metals to use—their alloying, working, and especially the art of casting, of which he writes in great detail. In this area he is far better than the two other sixteenth-century authors with whom he is inevitably compared, Georgius Agricola and Lazarus Ercker. Although Agricola excels on mining and smelting, his famed sections on glass, steel, and the purification of salts by crystallization are in fact taken nearly verbatim from the *Pirotechnia.*

Biringuccio's approach is in strong conflict with that of the alchemists, whose work he evaluates in eleven pages of almost modern criticism, distinguishing their practical achievements from their theoretical motivations. His interest in theoretical questions is limited to the repetition of an essentially Aristotelian view of the origins of metallic ores and the nature of metals, with a rather forced extension to account for the observed increase in weight of lead when it is turned to litharge.

Biringuccio has been called one of the principal exponents of the experimental method, for he states that "It is necessary to find the true method by doing it again and again, continually varying the procedure and then stopping at the best" and "I have no knowledge other than what I have seen with my own eyes." He gives quantitative information wherever appropriate. He was certain that the failure of an operation was due to ignorance or carelessness, not to either ill luck or occult influences: Fortune could be made to favor the foundryman by paying careful attention to details. Biringuccio's method, however, is not that of the scientist, for none of his operations is planned to test theory or even reflects the conscious application of it. He represents the strain of practical chemistry that had to develop and to be merged with philosophy before it could become science. Yet the enjoyment of the diverse properties of matter and the careful recording of a large number of substances and types of reactions that had been established by various craftsmen were just as necessary as the works of the philosophers, and in some sense were nearer the truth.

BIBLIOGRAPHY

I. ORIGINAL WORKS. Biringuccio's only work was *De la pirotechnia. Libri .X. dove ampiamente si tratta non solo di ogni sorte & diuersita di miniere, ma anchora quanto si ricerca intorno à la prattica di quelle cose di quel che si appartiene à l'arte de la fusione ouer gitto de metalli come d'ogni altra cosa simile à questa* (Venice, 1540; repr. 1550, 1558, 1559; Bologna, 1678). Books I and II only were reprinted with an important introduction by A. Mieli (Bari, 1914). There is a French translation by Jacques Vincent (Paris, 1556; repr. 1572, 1627); a German translation by Otto Johannsen (Brunswick, 1925); and an English translation by C. S. Smith and M. T. Gnudi (New York, 1942; repr. 1943, 1959; Cambridge, Mass., 1966).

II. SECONDARY LITERATURE. Icilio Guareschi, *Enciclopedia di chimica,* XX (Turin, 1903–1904), supplemento annuale, 419 ff.; Aldo Mieli, "Vannoccio Biringuccio e il metodo sperimentale," in *Isis,* **2** (1914), 90–99; and "Vannoccio Biringuccio," in *Gli scienziati italiani dall'inizio del medio evo ai nostri giorni,* I (Rome, 1921), pt. 1; Otto Johannsen, "Vannoccio Biringuccio," in Günther Bugge, ed., *Das Buch der grossen Chemiker,* I (Berlin, 1929), 70–84; M. T. Gnudi and C. S. Smith, *Of Typecasting in the Sixteenth Century* (New Haven, 1941). See also the introductions to the 1914 Italian edition and to the German and English translations listed above.

C. S. SMITH

BIRKHOFF, GEORGE DAVID (*b.* Overisel, Michigan, 21 March 1884; *d.* Cambridge, Massachusetts, 12 November 1944), *mathematics.*

The son of a physician, Birkhoff studied at the Lewis Institute (now Illinois Institute of Technology) in Chicago from 1896 to 1902. After a year at the University of Chicago he went to Harvard, where he received the A.B. in 1905. Returning to the University of Chicago, he was awarded the Ph.D., *summa cum laude,* in 1907. His graduate study at the University of Chicago was followed by two years as an instructor in the University of Wisconsin. In 1908 he was married to Margaret Elizabeth Grafius.

In 1909 Birkhoff went to Princeton as a preceptor and in 1911 was promoted to a full professorship in response to a call from Harvard. The following year he accepted an assistant professorship at Harvard, where he became professor in 1919, Perkins professor in 1932, and dean of the Faculty of Arts and Sciences from 1935 to 1939. As Perkins professor, the major part of his academic life was devoted to mathematical research and direction of graduate students.

Birkhoff was very generally regarded, both in the United States and abroad, as the leading American mathematician of his day. Honors came early in life and from all over the world. He was president of the American Mathematical Society in 1925 and of the American Association for the Advancement of Science in 1937.

Of Birkhoff's teachers, Maxime Bôcher of Harvard and E. H. Moore of the University of Chicago undoubtedly influenced him most. He was introduced by Bôcher to classical analysis and algebra. From Moore he learned of "general analysis." There are indications that Birkhoff preferred the approach of Bôcher to that of Moore. Through his reading, Birkhoff made Henri Poincaré his teacher and took over Poincaré's problems in differential equations and celestial mechanics. Like Moore, Birkhoff was a pioneer among those who felt that American mathematics had come of age.

He had many close friends among his colleagues in Europe. With Hadamard he shared a deep interest and understanding of Poincaré. Neils Nörlund and Birkhoff had common ground in their study of difference equations. Between Levi-Città and Birkhoff there were deep ties of friendship cemented by their common interest in the problem of three bodies. The correspondence of Sir Edmund Whittaker and Birkhoff on the existence of periodic orbits in dynamics was intense, illuminating, and friendly.

Birkhoff's thesis was concerned with asymptotic expansions, boundary-value problems, and the Sturm-Liouville theory. Nonself-adjoint operators

$$L(z) = \frac{d^n z}{dx^n} + * + p_2(x)\frac{d^{n-2}z}{dx^{n-2}} + \cdots + p_n(x)z$$

$$(a \leq x \leq b)$$

were introduced with continuous coefficients and n boundary conditions, $U_i(u) = 0$, $i = 1, \cdots, n$, linear and homogeneous in u and its first n-1 derivatives at $x = a$ and $x = b$. Birkhoff defined an operator $M(z)$ adjoint to $L(z)$, and boundary conditions $V_i(v) = 0$, $i = 1, \cdots, n$ adjoint to the conditions $U_i(u) = 0$. For $n > 2$ he introduced a parameter λ, as in the classical Sturm-Liouville equations, and, with suitable conditions on the matrix of coefficients in the boundary conditions, obtained an expansion of a prescribed real function $x \rightarrow f(x)$, "piecewise" of class C^1. This expansion was shown to converge essentially as does the classical Fourier expansion. This work of depth admitted extension both by Birkhoff and by such pupils as Rudolph Langer and Marshall Stone; he collaborated with Langer on "The Boundary Problems and Developments . . ." (1923).

Birkhoff next devoted his attention to linear differential equations, difference equations, and the generalized Riemann problem. With Gauss, Riemann, and Poincaré showing the way, second-order differential equations of the Fuchsian type with regular singular points have become central in conformal mapping, in the theory of automorphic functions, and in mathematical physics, including quantum mechanics. Linear differential systems with irregular singular points appeared as a challenging new field, and Birkhoff turned to it.

Thomé had used formal solutions; Poincaré and Jakob Horn, asymptotic expansions; Hilbert and Josef Plemelj, unknown to Birkhoff, had solved one of the relevant matrix problems; and Ebenezer Cunningham had generalized Poincaré's use of Laplace's transformation. It remained for Birkhoff to formulate a program of so vast a scope that it is still an object of study today.

Among analytic systems with a finite number of irregular singular points with prescribed ranks, Birkhoff defined a "canonical system" and a notion of the "equivalence" of singular points. Under the title "generalized Riemann problem," Birkhoff sought to construct a system of linear differential equations of the first order with prescribed singular points and a given monodromy group. That he carried his program as far as he did is remarkable. The total resources of modern function space analysis are now involved.

Carmichael's thesis, done under Birkhoff's supervision at Princeton in 1911, was perhaps the first significant contribution on difference equations in America. Birkhoff extended his notion of a "generalized Riemann problem" to systems of difference equations. In "Analytic Theory of Singular Difference Equations," he collaborated with Trjitzinsky in an extension and modification of earlier work.

Birkhoff's major interest in analysis was in dynamical systems. He wished to extend the work of Poincaré, particularly in celestial mechanics. One can divide his dynamics into formal and nonformal dynamics. The nonformal portion includes the metrical and topological aspects.

Birkhoff was concerned with a real, analytic Hamiltonian or Pfaffian system. A periodic orbit gives rise, after a simple transformation, to a "generalized equilibrium point" at which the "equations of variation" are independent of t. First-order formal stability at such a point requires that the characteristic multipliers at the point be purely imaginary. Formal trigonometric stability is then defined. It is a major result of Birkhoff's work that under the limitations on generality presupposed by Poincaré, first-order formal stability at a generalized equilibrium point implies formal trigonometric stability.

Possibly the most dramatic event in Birkhoff's mathematical life came when he proved Poincaré's "last geometric theorem." In "Sur un théorème de géométrie" (1912), Poincaré had enunciated a theorem of great importance for the restricted problem of three bodies, acknowledging his inability to prove this theorem except in special cases. The young Birkhoff formulated this theorem in "Proof of Poincaré's Geometric Theorem" (1913, p. 14):

> Let us suppose that a continuous one-to-one transformation T takes the ring R, formed by concentric circles C_a and C_b of radii a and b ($a > b > 0$), into itself in such a way as to advance the points of C_a in a positive sense, and the points of C_b in a negative sense, and at the same time preserve areas. *Then there are at least two invariant points.*

Birkhoff's proof of this theorem was one of the most exciting mathematical events of the era.

In 1912, in "Quelques théorèmes sur le mouvement des systèmes dynamiques," Birkhoff introduced his novel conceptions of minimal or recurrent sets of motions and established their existence under general conditions. This was the beginning of a new era in the theory of dynamical systems. Birkhoff continued by introducing the concepts of wandering, central, and transitive motions.

Metric transitivity, as defined by Birkhoff and Paul Smith in "Structure Analysis of Surface Transformations" (1928), requires that the only sets that are invariant under the "flow" in phase space be sets of measure zero or measure of the space. Metric transitivity implies topological transitivity (i.e., the existence of a transitive motion). Great problems abound and are today the object of research. On a compact regular analytic manifold it is not known, even today, whether topological transitivity implies metric transitivity.

From these concepts of Birkhoff's the main body of modern dynamics has emerged, together with such branches as symbolic dynamics and topological dynamics. Other concepts of Birkhoff's, his minimax principle and his theorem on the fixed points of surface transformations, have motivated some of the greatest advances in global analysis and topology.

One of Birkhoff's theorems of major current interest in his "ergodic theorem." Following an idea of Bernard Koopman, Von Neumann established his "mean ergodic theorem" in 1931. Stimulated by these ideas, Birkhoff presented his famous "pointwise ergodic theorem." As formulated by Khintchine, Birkhoff's theorem takes the form "The space M is assumed to have a finite measure m invariant under the flow. Let f be integrable over M and let P be a point of M. Then

$$\lim_{T \to \infty} \frac{\int_0^T f(P_t)\, dt}{T}$$

exists for almost all P on M."

Birkhoff thought critically for many years about the foundations of relativity and quantum mechanics. His philosophical and scientific ideas found vivid expression in "Electricity as a Fluid" (1938), where he described a "perfect fluid" that he proposed as a model from which to deduce the observed spectrum of hydrogen without postulating "energy levels." In "El concepto matemático . . ." (1944) he formulated a theory of gravitation in flat space-time, and deduced from it the three "crucial effects." Both of these models were consistent with special relativity; both avoided the general curvilinear coordinates basic to Einstein's general relativity but always considered by Birkhoff to be unnecessary and difficult to interpret experimentally.

Although Birkhoff's physical models may be controversial, his original critiques and interpretations are stimulating and illuminating.

Birkhoff wrote on many subjects besides those of his major works; for example, he devised a significant formula for the ways of coloring a map. At sixteen, he began a correspondence with H. S. Vandiver, who was eighteen, on number theory. A significant paper resulted in 1904.

Another paper, written in collaboration with his colleague Oliver Kellogg (1922), was one of the openers of the age of function spaces. Schauder and Leray acknowledged this paper as an inspiration for their later, more powerful theorem.

In 1929 Birkhoff and Ralph Beatley joined in writing a textbook on elementary geometry, which they called "basic geometry." After a period of revision and development, the pedagogical conceptions of this book have been widely adopted in current teaching of high school geometry.

Birkhoff's lifelong interest in music and the arts culminated in his book *Aesthetic Measure* (1933), in preparation for which he had spent a year traveling around the world, observing objects of art, ornaments, tiles, and vases, and recording impressions of music and poetry.

BIBLIOGRAPHY

I. ORIGINAL WORKS. Among Birkhoff's works are "On the Integral Divisors of $a^n - b^n$," in *Annals of Mathematics,* **5** (1904), 173–180, written with H. S. Vandiver; "On the Asymptotic Character of the Solutions of Certain Differential Equations Containing a Parameter," in *Transactions of the American Mathematical Society,* **9** (1908), 219–231; "Boundary Values and Expansion Problems of Ordinary Linear Differential Equations," *ibid.,* 373–395; "Quelques théorèmes sur le mouvement des systèmes dynamiques," in *Bulletin de la Société mathématique de France,* **40** (1912), 305–323; "Proof of Poincaré's Geometric Theorem," in *Transactions of the American Mathematical Society,* **14** (1913), 14–22; "Invariant Points in Function Space," *ibid.,* **23** (1922), 96–115, written with O. D. Kellogg; "The Boundary Problems and Developments Associated With a System of Ordinary Linear Differential Equations of First Order," in *Proceedings of the American Academy of Arts and Sciences,* **58** (1923), 49–128, written with R. E. Langer; "Structure Analysis of Surface Transformations," in *Journal de mathématiques pures et appliquées,* 9th ser., **7** (1928), 345–379, written with P. A. Smith; "On the Number of Ways of Coloring a Map," in *Proceedings of the Edinburgh Mathematical Society,* 2nd ser., **2** (1930), 83–91; *Aesthetic Measure* (Cambridge, Mass., 1933); "Analytic Theory of Singular Difference Equations," in *Acta mathematica,* **60** (1933), 1–89, written with W. J. Trjitzinsky; "Electricity as a Fluid," in *Journal of the Franklin Institute,* **226** (1938), 315–325; *Basic Geometry* (1940), written with Ralph Beatley; "El concepto matemático de tiempo y la gravitación," in *Boletín de la Sociedad matemática mexicana,* **1** (1944), 1–24; and *Dynamical Systems,* rev. ed. (Providence, R.I., 1966), with introduction, bibliography, and footnotes by Jürgen Moser.

His works have been brought together by the American Mathematical Society as *Collected Mathematical Works of George David Birkhoff,* 3 vols. (Providence, R.I., 1950).

II. SECONDARY LITERATURE. Works on Birkhoff are American Mathematical Society Semicentennial Publications, I, *History* (Providence, R.I., 1938), p. 212, a list of his honors up to 1938; P. Masani, "On a Result of G. D. Birkhoff on Linear Differential Systems," in *Proceedings of the American Mathematical Society,* **10** (1959), 696–698; and H. L. Turrittin, "Reduction of Ordinary Differential Equations to the Birkhoff Canonical Form," in *Transactions of the American Mathematical Society,* **107** (1963), 485–507.

MARSTON MORSE

BIRMINGHAM, JOHN (*b.* probably at Millbrook, near Tuam, Ireland, *ca.* 1816; *d.* Millbrook, 7 September 1884), *astronomy.*

Birmingham was a country gentleman and amateur astronomer who first became prominent when, on 12 May 1866, while walking home from a friend's house, he noticed in Corona Borealis a new star of the second magnitude, later termed T Coronae. This nova was the brightest since that of 1604 and the first to be identified with an existing star: it had been listed in the *Bonn Durchmusterung* as of magnitude 9.5, and by the beginning of June 1866 it had returned to the ninth magnitude. It was also the first nova to be subjected to spectroscopic examination, and William Huggins' visual and spectroscopic observations showed that it consisted of a star surrounded by a shell of hydrogen. T Coronae is remarkable for the fluctuations in the decline of its brightness and for its recurrence in 1946.

In 1872, at the suggestion of T. W. Webb, Birmingham undertook the revision of the catalog of red stars assembled in 1866 by H. C. F. C. Schjellerup. This task occupied him for four years. His catalog of 658 red stars, supplemented by numerous spectroscopic observations, was presented to the Royal Irish Academy on 26 June 1876, and was recognized by the award of the Academy's Cunningham Medal in 1884. On his deathbed Birmingham requested that Webb produce a revision of the catalog, but the task was undertaken by T. E. Espin and completed by him in 1888.

In the 1870's Birmingham published a number of papers on the members of the solar system, especially on features of the moon and of Jupiter. He was also a man of many parts: musician, linguist, antiquarian, poet, and the author of several geological papers. At the time of his death he was an inspector of applications for loans under the Land Law (Ireland) Act. He never married.

BIBLIOGRAPHY

I. ORIGINAL WORKS. Birmingham's most substantial publication is "Catalogue of Red Stars," in *Transactions of the Royal Irish Academy,* **26** (1879), 249–354; rev. by T. E. Espin, in Royal Irish Academy's *Cunningham Memoirs,* no. 5 (Dublin, 1890). Minor astronomical papers published by Birmingham between 1869 and his death are scattered among a number of English-language astronomical and scientific journals. For details see the Royal Society's *Catalogue of Scientific Papers,* I (1867), 388; VII (1877), 178; IX (1891), 246–247; XIII (1914), 567; J. C. Houzeau and A. Lancaster, *Bibliographie générale de l'astronomie jusqu'en 1880,* new ed., II (London, 1964); and Poggendorff, III (1898), 133. Details of his discovery of T Coronae are given in *Monthly Notices of the Royal Astronomical Society,* **26,** no. 8 (1866), 310.

II. SECONDARY LITERATURE. Birmingham has attracted almost no attention. The main sources are two unsatisfactory items in the (now extinct) *Tuam News* (12 Sept. 1884). More accessible are the biographical sketch by Agnes Clerke in *Dictionary of National Biography,* V, 85–86; and the obituary notice in *Astronomische Nachrichten,* **110,** no. 2632 (1885), 255.

M. A. HOSKIN

BIRT, WILLIAM RADCLIFF (*b.* Southwark [London], England, 15 July 1804; *d.* Leytonstone, England, 14 December 1881), *astronomy.*

Birt's capacity for the measurement and analysis of observational data, exhibited in his early studies of the brightness fluctuations of the stars β-Lyra and α-Cassiopeia, which he submitted for publication in the *Memoirs of the Royal Astronomical Society,* so impressed the society's president, Sir John Herschel, that from 1839 to 1843 he employed Birt as his assistant in the arrangement and reduction of numerous series of barometric measurements. In the course of this work, Birt discovered large fluctuations in the readings that lent strong support to Herschel's view that well-defined atmospheric waves were produced by contrary winds blowing across Britain and western Europe.

The results of Birt's subsequent research on this and other meteorological phenomena, including electrical measurements made at the Kew Observatory, are in the annual reports of the British Association (1844–1849) and in a series of articles in the *Philosophical Magazine* (1846–1850). By this time Birt had become convinced that the height of the column of mercury in the barometer was a reliable index for forecasting the occurrence of storms and for obtaining one's position relative to the center of a "revolving storm" (cyclone). The manner in which such data can be used by ships' captains to provide working rules for steering away from the storm center is described in his *Handbook on the Laws of Storms* (1853).

Shortly after being elected a fellow of the Royal Astronomical Society on 14 January 1859, Birt began making systematic observations of sunspots, solar rotation, and lunar markings. It is for his work in selenography—he was the Selenographical Society's first president—which he pursued between 1861 and 1866 at Dr. John Lee's observatory at Hartwell, Bed-

fordshire, and thereafter (with the aid of his own seven-and-one-half-inch equatorial reflector) at his small private observatory in Waltham's Town, Essex, that he is now best remembered. As secretary of the Lunar Committee for Mapping the Surface of the Moon, set up by the British Association in 1865 to revise and supplement Beer and Mädler's lunar map, he wrote the annual reports up to 1869, introducing in them his own notation for the identification of such small features as craterlets, mountains, and rills.

As an aid to classifying the brightness of the lunar markings, Birt used a scale of lunar tints consisting of twenty-four shades of a single pigment—his homochromoscope—which he describes at the end of his monograph *Mare Serenitatis* (1869). His careful comparison and measurement of photograms and numerous telescopic observations by other leading selenographic experts strengthened his previous conviction that there was a "secular variation of tint" on the floor of the crater Plato, such as might have been caused by eruptive action or chemical activity on the moon. He was always very conscious, however, of the provisional nature of his conclusions, and later expressed the belief that any speculations on such physical changes would require the support of terrestrial analogies from chemistry, geology, and mineralogy.

After 1873 his health began to fail, and in 1877 he stopped observing altogether. Two years later he presented to the Royal Astronomical Society twelve manuscript volumes containing the portion of the lunar catalog that had been completed. He died, after a further rapid decline in his already poor health, at the age of seventy-seven.

BIBLIOGRAPHY

Among Birt's works are *Handbook on the Laws of Storms* (Liverpool, 1853) and *Mare Serenitatis* (London, 1869). Most of his publications are in the *Monthly Notices of the Royal Astronomical Society* (1859–1872), the *British Association Reports* (1859–1870), and the *Philosophical Magazine* (1846–1880). A detailed list, with an indication of each work's contents, is in Poggendorff, III (1898), 134. In addition, there are ninety-five letters from Birt to Sir John Herschel among the latter's unpublished correspondence at the Royal Society, London.

An obituary notice is in *Monthly Notices of the Royal Astronomical Society,* **42** (1882), 142–144.

ERIC G. FORBES

AL-BĪRŪNĪ (or Bērūnī), ABŪ RAYḤĀN (or Abu'l-Rayḥān) MUḤAMMAD IBN AḤMAD (*b.* Khwārazm [now Kara-Kalpakskaya A.S.S.R.], 4 September

973; *d.* Ghazna [?] [now Ghazni, Afghanistan], after 1050), *astronomy, mathematics, geography, history.*

Bīrūnī was born and grew up in the region south of the Aral Sea, known in ancient and medieval times as Khwārazm. The town of his birth now bears his name. The site was in the environs (*bīrūn,* hence his appellation) of Kāth, then one of the two principal cities of the region, located (in the modern Kara-Kalpakskaya A.S.S.R.) on the right bank of the Amu Dar'ya (the ancient Oxus) and northeast of Khīva. The second capital city of Khwārazm was Jurjāniyya (modern Kunya-Urgench, Turkmen S.S.R.), on the opposite side of the river and northwest of Khīva. There also Abū Rayḥān spent a good deal of time during the early part of his life. About his ancestry and childhood nothing is known. In verses ridiculing a certain poet (Yāqūt, p. 189; trans., *Beiträge,* LX, p. 62) he claims ignorance of his own father's identity, but the statement may have been rhetorical. He very early commenced scientific studies and was taught by the eminent Khwārazmian astronomer and mathematician Abū Naṣr Manṣūr. At the age of seventeen he used a ring graduated in halves of a degree to observe the meridian solar altitude at Kāth, thus inferring its terrestrial latitude (*Taḥdīd,* 249:7). Four years later he had made plans to carry out a series of such determinations and had prepared a ring fifteen cubits in diameter, together with supplementary equipment. There was, however, time only for an observation of the summer solstice of 995, made at a village south of Kāth and across the Oxus from it. At this time, civil war broke out. Bīrūnī went into hiding and shortly had to flee the country (*Taḥdīd,* 87:3, 109:6–110:11). "After I had barely settled down for a few years," he writes, "I was permitted by the Lord of Time to go back home, but I was compelled to participate in worldly affairs, which excited the envy of fools, but which made the wise pity me."

Since these "worldly affairs" essentially affected not only Bīrūnī's personal well-being but also his scientific work, it is necessary to introduce the names of six princely dynasties with which he became directly involved.

(1) The ancient title of Khwārazmshāh had long been held by the lord of Kāth, a member of the Banū 'Irāq. Abū Naṣr was a prince of this house (Krause, p. 3). In 995, however, the emir of Jurjāniyya attacked his suzerain, captured and killed him, and seized the title for himself (*Chahār Maqāla,* p. 241). It was this disturbance that caused Bīrūnī's flight.

(2) For well over a century the Khwārazmshāhs had been dominated by the Sāmānids, a royal house of Zoroastrian origin but early converted to Islam. The Sāmānid capital was in Bukhara, about two

hundred miles southeast of Khīva, from whence the dynasty ruled in its heyday an area comprising roughly all of present Afghanistan, Transoxiana, and Iran. In Bīrūnī's youth this empire was rapidly breaking up. Nevertheless, in a poem written much later (Yāqūt, p. 187; trans., *Beiträge,* LX, p. 61) he names as his first patron Manṣūr II, almost the last of the Sāmānid line, who reigned from 997 to 999.

(3) Much farther to the west flourished the Buwayhid dynasty, which had originated in the highlands south of the Caspian and extended its domain south to the Persian Gulf and, by 945, west over Mesopotamia.

(4) Set precariously between the Sāmānids and the Buwayhids was the Ziyārid state, based in Gurgān, a city just back of the southeast corner of the Caspian shore.

(5) All these competing dynasties were menaced, and eventually absorbed, by the swift expansion of another kingdom, that of the Ghaznavids, named from Ghazna, their base in east-central Afghanistan. Sultan Maḥmūd, son of a Turkish slave and the second and greatest of the line, was two years older than Bīrūnī. By 1020 he had carved out a realm extending a thousand miles north and south, and twice as far east and west.

(6) Over these kaleidoscopic shifts there presided at Baghdad the spectral figure of the Abbasid caliph, retaining only the shadow of power over these fragments of his ancestors' empire. Playing a role somewhat analogous to that of the medieval popes, he was accorded a strange religious respect by the temporal princes of Islam. Upon them the successive caliphs conferred prestige by investing them with honorific titles and robes of honor.

To which or from which of these kingdoms Bīrūnī fled in 995 is now uncertain. It may have been then that he went to Rayy, near modern Teheran. In the *Chronology* (p. 338) he quotes a ribald poem on the tribulations of penury, and to illustrate it states that he was once in Rayy, bereft of a royal patron and in miserable circumstances. A local astrologer chose to ridicule his views on some technical matter because of his poverty. Later, when his circumstances improved, the same man became friendly.

At the command of the Buwayhid prince, Fakhr al-Dawla, the astronomer al-Khujandī built a large mural sextant on a mountain above Rayy. With this Fakhrī sextant, named for the ruler, he observed meridian transits during 994. Bīrūnī wrote a treatise describing this instrument (*Sextant*) and a detailed account of the observations (*Taḥdīd,* 101:20–108:19). Part of his information was obtained from al-Khujandī in person, and since the latter died about

1000 (Suter, p. 74), the conversation between the two cannot have been long after the observations.

There is some reason for thinking that Abū Rayḥān also was in the Caspian province of Gīlān about this time. He dedicated a book (*RG* 7) to the Ispahbad (Persian for "ruler," or "commander") of Gīlān, Marzubān ibn Rustam, who was connected with the Ziyārids. In the *Chronology,* completed about 1000 (trans., pp. 47, 191), he mentions having been in the presence of this individual, perhaps the same Ispahbad who sheltered Firdawsī, the epic poet of Iran, from the wrath of Sulṭān Maḥmūd (Browne, pp. 79, 135).

Regardless of where he had been, Bīrūnī was back in Kāth by 997, for on 24 May of that year he observed a lunar eclipse there (Oppolzer 3403), having previously arranged with Abu'l-Wafā' that the latter should simultaneously observe the same event from Baghdad (*Taḥdīd,* 250:11, gives only the year; but Oppolzer 3404, on 17 November 997, was invisible from both cities). The time difference so obtained enabled them to calculate the difference in longitude between the two stations.

This year saw the beginning of the short reign of the Sāmānid Manṣūr II. If Bīrūnī ever resided at his court in Bukhara (as Bīrūnī's poem mentioned above may imply), it probably was at this time. Meantime, the ruler of Gurgān, the Ziyārid Qābūs, had been expelled from his lands, and at Bukhara he sought support for a return to power. He succeeded in reestablishing himself at Gurgān, and Bīrūnī either accompanied him or followed almost immediately thereafter, for about 1000 Bīrūnī dedicated to Qābūs his earliest extant major work, the *Chronology* (text, p. xxiv). This was by no means his first book, for in it he refers incidentally to seven others already completed, none of which are extant. Their titles indicate that he had already broken ground in the fields he later continued to cultivate, for one (*RG* 34) is on decimal computation, one (*RG* 46) on the astrolabe, one (*RG* 146) on astronomical observations, three (*RG* 42, 99, 148) on astrology, and two (*RG* 161, 162) are histories. By this time he also had engaged in an acrimonious correspondence with the brilliant Bukharan philosopher and physician Avicenna on the nature and transmission of heat and light. Bīrūnī refers to him (*Chronology,* text, p. 257) as "the youth." The appellation, coming from an individual still in his twenties, may seem less condescending when it is realized that the precocious Avicenna was still in his teens.

In the *Taḥdīd* (214:15–215:3), after describing the measurement of a degree along a terrestrial meridian made at the direction of the Caliph Ma'mūn, Bīrūnī

writes of his own abortive project to repeat the operation. A suitable tract of land was chosen between Gurgān and the land of the Oghuz Turks (in the deserts east of the Caspian?), but the patron, presumably Qābūs, lost interest.

The end of Abū Rayḥān's sojourn at the Ziyārid court can be fixed within precise limits, for in 1003 he observed two lunar eclipses from Gurgān, one on 19 February and the other on 14 August. On 4 June of the following year he observed a third lunar eclipse (*Canon,* pp. 740, 741), but this one from Jurjāniyya. Hence, sometime in the interim he had returned to his homeland, high in favor with the reigning Khwārazmshāh. This was now a certain Abu'l-'Abbās Ma'mūn, a son of the usurper to the title mentioned above. Both Ma'mun and a brother who preceded him on the throne had married sisters of the ever more powerful and truculent Sultan Maḥmūd of Ghazna.

The bounty of the shah enabled Bīrūnī to set up at Jurjāniyya an instrument, apparently a large ring fixed in the meridian plane, which in gratitude he called the Shāhiyya ring (*Canon,* 612:5). He reports in various places in the *Taḥdīd* and the *Canon* some fifteen solar meridian transit observations at Jurjāniyya, the first the summer solstice of 7 June 1016, the last on 7 December of the same year. It was probably during this interlude of prosperity and royal favor that he had a hemisphere constructed, ten cubits in diameter, to be used as a plotting device for the graphical solution of geodetic problems (*Taḥdīd,* 38:6).

Meanwhile, Khwārazmian political affairs, in which Bīrūnī was closely involved, had been building up to a climax. The Caliph Qādir conferred upon Ma'mūn an honorific title and dispatched an envoy bearing the insignia of the award. The shah was frightened lest Maḥmūd take offense at his accepting the honor conferred directly and not through Maḥmūd as implied overlord. Ma'mūn therefore sent Bīrūnī west into the desert to intercept the embassy, take delivery of the objects, and thus forestall a public investiture.

In 1014 Maḥmūd let it be understood to Ma'mūn that he wanted his own name inserted into the *khuṭba,* the Friday prayer for the faithful and for the reigning monarch. Ma'mūn convened an assembly of the notables, proposing that he accede to this demand, but the chiefs refused to allow him to do so, realizing that it meant the end of the region's autonomy. Ma'mūn then sent to them Bīrūnī, who, "with tongue of silver and of gold," convinced them that their liege was only testing them by his request and that the *khuṭba* would not be changed. At this,

Maḥmūd dispatched an insulting ultimatum to the shah, demanding that he keep his nobles in line, or he, Maḥmūd, would do it himself. The hapless Ma'mūn introduced the sultan's name into the *khuṭba* in the provincial mosques, but not those of Jurjāniyya and Kāth. Thereupon the Khwārazmian army revolted and killed Ma'mūn. This was all Maḥmūd needed. He marched into Khwārazm with ample forces, obtained the delivery of his sister, the Khwārazmshāh's widow, took Kāth, on 3 July 1017, cruelly executed the insurgent leaders, and set one of his officers on the throne. The surviving princes of the local dynasty were carried off to imprisonment in various parts of his domain (Barthold, pp. 275–279).

Much of our knowledge of these events is from Bīrūnī's extensive history of his native land, a work that has been lost except for fragments incorporated into other histories. As for Abū Rayḥān himself, he also was led off by the conqueror, partly, no doubt, to grace the sultan's court but also to remove an active partisan of the native rulers from the scene. He is next heard of in a village near Kabul, depressed and in miserable circumstances, but hard at work on the *Taḥdīd* (119:1–12). On 14 October 1018 he wanted to take the solar altitude, but had no instrument. He therefore laid out a graduated arc on the back of a calculating board (*takht*) and, with a plumb line, used it as an improvised quadrant. On the basis of the results obtained, he calculated the latitude of the locality.

The next firm date at our disposal is 8 April 1019, when he observed a solar eclipse from Lamghān (modern Laghman?), north of Kabul. He uses this, and the lunar eclipse mentioned below, to comment sarcastically upon the ignorance of the local astronomers.

Sachau has shown (*India*, trans., I, xi) that Bīrūnī's relations with Maḥmūd were never good, although the stories in the *Chahār Maqāla* (text, pp. 57–59) alleging cruel and arbitrary treatment of the savant by the sultan are doubtless apocryphal. It is evident that Abū Rayḥān received some sort of official support for his work, for in the *Canon* (p. 609) he writes of having determined the latitude of Ghazna by a series of observations carried out between 1018 and 1020 with an instrument he calls the Yamīnī ring. A title bestowed upon Sultan Maḥmūd by the caliph was Yamīn al-Dawla ("Right Hand of the State"). No doubt this ring was a monumental installation named, as was the custom, for the ruler patron.

It is also clear that Bīrūnī's interests in Sanskrit and in Indian civilization are due to his having become an involuntary resident of an empire that had by then expanded well into the Indian subcontinent. Already in 1002 Maḥmūd had conquered the district of Waihand, on the Indus east of Ghazna. By 1010 he had subjugated Multan and Bhatinda, the latter 300 miles east of the Indus. Twice repulsed (in 1015 and 1021) from the borders of Kashmir, by 1022 he had penetrated and subdued the Ganges valley to a point not far west of Benares. In 1026 Maḥmūd led a raid due south from Ghazna all the way to the Indian Ocean. From Somnāth, at the tip of the Kathiawar Peninsula, he carried off immensely valuable booty, as well as fragments of the phallic idol in the temple. One of the pieces was laid at the entrance to the Ghazna mosque, to be used as a footscraper by the worshipers (*India*, trans., II, 103; Nāẓim, ch. 8).

Abū Rayḥān profited from these events by travel and residence in various parts of India. The names of many of the places he saw are known, but no dates can be given for his visits. They were confined to the Punjab and the borders of Kashmir. Sachau (*India*, text, p. xii) lists some eleven Indian towns whose latitudes Bīrūnī reports as personally determined by him. Bīrūnī himself writes that while living (in detention?) at Nandana Fort, he used a nearby mountain to estimate the earth's diameter (*Taḥdīd*, 222:10). The installation at Nandana, taken by Maḥmūd in 1014, commanded the route by which he, the Moghuls after him, and Alexander the Great long before, penetrated the Indus valley. Bīrūnī's temporary residence overlooked the site where, in the face of King Poros and his elephants, Alexander effected his famous crossing of the Jhelum River, the classical Hydaspes (Stein).

It is also clear that Bīrūnī spent a great deal of time at Ghazna. The cluster of recorded observations made by him there commences with a series of meridian solar transits covering the summer solstice of 1019, and includes the lunar eclipse on 16 September of the same year (*Taḥdīd*, 291:9). He continued to observe equinoxes and solstices at Ghazna, the last being the winter solstice of 1021. In fact, this is the latest of Bīrūnī's observations that has been preserved. At about this time, according to Barani (*Canon*, III, vii), he completed his treatise on *Shadows*.

In 1024 the ruler of the Volga Turks sent an embassy to Ghazna. These people had trade relations with inhabitants of the polar regions, and Bīrūnī questioned members of the mission to supplement his knowledge of these lands. One of the ambassadors asserted in the sultan's presence that in the far north the sun sometimes did not set for days on end. Maḥmūd at first angrily put this down as heresy, but Abū Rayḥān convinced him that the report was both credible and reasonable (*Commemoration Volume*, p. 235; Yāqūt).

By the late summer of 1027 the treatise on *Chords* was completed (according to the Patna MS). During the same year a Chinese and Uighur Turkish embassy came to Ghazna, and from this mission Bīrūnī obtained geographical information on the Far East which he later incorporated into the *Canon* (*Commemoration Volume,* p. 234).

In 1030 Sultan Maḥmūd died, and the succession was disputed between two of his sons for a short period. Bīrūnī finished the *India* during this interim and, perhaps because of the uncertain political situation, refrained from dedicating it to any particular patron. Within the year Mas'ūd, the elder son, won the crown. His accession brought about a drastic improvement in the situation of his most famous scientist, and Bīrūnī named the *Canon* for the new ruler amid "a farrago of high-sounding words" in the preface (*India,* trans., I, xii).

Perhaps it was the change of regime that enabled him to revisit his native land. By whatever means, he made at least one trip back, for in the *Bibliography* he writes that for over forty years he had sought a certain Manichaean work, a copy of which he at length procured while in Khwārazm (*Chronology,* text, p. xxxvi). In the same source Bīrūnī relates that after he was fifty years old he suffered from a series of serious illnesses, and in his distress inquired of several astrologers concerning the length of his life. Their answers diverged wildly, and some were patently absurd. At the end of his sixty-first (lunar?) year he began improving, and had a dream in which he was seeking the new moon. As its crescent disappeared, a voice told him that he would behold 170 more of the same.

Mas'ūd was murdered by his officers and succeeded by his son Mawdūd in 1040. During Mawdūd's eight-year reign, Bīrūnī wrote the *Dastūr* (*RG* 167) and the *Gems.* Of his subsequent activities we have no knowledge, save that in the *Pharmacology* (p. 7) he notes having passed his eightieth (lunar?) year; his eyesight and hearing are failing, but he is still hard at work with the assistance of a collaborator. Thus the date of his death given by Ghaḍanfar as 13 December 1048 is incorrect; Bīrūnī outlasted his third Ghaznavid patron and achieved the life-span foretold in his dream.

When he was sixty-three years old, Bīrūnī prepared a bibliography of the works of the physician Muḥammad ibn Zakariyyā al-Rāzī, to which he appended a list of his own books. This runs to 113 titles (not counting twenty-five additional treatises written "in his name" by friends), partially arranged by subject matter and occasionally with a brief indication of the contents. Most of the entries also give the length of the particular manuscript in folios. The list is incomplete, for Abū Rayḥān lived at least fourteen years after this, working until he died. Moreover, seven additional works by him are extant and many more are named, some in his own writings and others in a variety of sources. All told, these come to 146. The reckoning is uncertain, for some titles counted separately may be synonyms, and additional items may well turn up in the future.

There is a wide range in size of the treatises. Several amount to only ten folios each, while, at the other extreme, three lost astronomical works run to 360, 550, and 600 folios respectively. Largest of all is the *India,* at 700 folios. The English translation of the latter, incidentally, takes up 654 pages of small type, so that one of Bīrūnī's folios is roughly equivalent to a modern printed page. The mean length of the seventy-nine books of known size is very nearly ninety folios. Assuming that the same holds for all 146 works, it follows that Bīrūnī's total output is on the order of 13,000 folios (or pages), consisting for the most part of highly technical material, including numerical tables, the results of involved computations, and analyses of materials from multifarious sources—a formidable accomplishment indeed.

The classification attempted in the table below is only approximate; for instance, a book placed in the geographical category could legitimately be classed as primarily geodetic, and so on. Practically nothing Bīrūnī wrote confines itself strictly to a single subject, and in many cases where the title alone survives, an informed guess is our only recourse. Nevertheless the table gives a reasonable breakdown of the man's activity. In the second column a "major work" has been taken arbitrarily as anything of 200 folios or more. The third and fourth columns show, respectively, the compositions known to exist in manuscript form and the numbers of these that have thus far been printed. Roughly four-fifths of Bīrūnī's work has vanished beyond hope of recovery. Of what has survived, about half has been published. Most of the latter (with the notable exception of the *Canon*) has been translated into other languages and has received some attention from modern scholars.

The table also clearly reveals both scope and areas of concentration. Bīrūnī's interests were very wide and deep, and he labored in almost all the branches of science known in his time. He was not ignorant of philosophy and the speculative disciplines, but his bent was strongly toward the study of observable phenomena, in nature and in man. Within the sciences themselves he was attracted by those fields then susceptible of mathematical analysis. He did serious work in mineralogy, pharmacology, and philology, subjects where numbers played little part; but about half his total output is in astronomy, astrology, and related subjects, the exact sciences par excellence of those days. Mathematics in its own right came next, but it was invariably applied mathematics.

CLASSIFICATION OF BĪRŪNĪ'S WORKS

	Works	Major Works	Extant	Published
Astronomy	35 ⎫	8	4	3
On astrolabes	4 ⎬ 62		2	
Astrology	23 ⎭	1	3	2
Chronology	5	1	1	1
Time measurement	2			
Geography	9 ⎫	1	1	1
Geodesy and Mapping Theory	10 ⎬ 19		1	
Mathematics				
Arithmetic	8 ⎫		1	1
Geometry	5 ⎬ 15		1	1
Trigonometry	2 ⎭		1	
Mechanics	2		1	
Medicine and Pharmacology	2	1	1	
Meteorology	1			
Mineralogy and Gems	2		1	1
History	4			
India	2	1	1	1
Religion and Philosophy	3		1	1
Literary	16			
Magic	2		1	
Unclassified	9	1	1	1
Total	146	14	22	13

Below are brief descriptions of most of Bīrūnī's works that are still available. They are our best sources for estimating the extent and significance of his accomplishments.

The *Chronology*. The day, being the most apparent and fundamental chronological unit, is the subject of the first chapter. Bīrūnī discusses the advantages of various calendric epochs—sunset or sunrise (horizon-based), noon or midnight (meridian-based) —and names the systems that use each. Next the several varieties of year are defined—lunar, solar, lunisolar, Julian, and Persian—and the notion of intercalation is introduced. Chapter 3 defines and discusses the eras of the Creation, the Flood, Nabonassar, Philip Arrhidaeus, Alexander, Augustus, Antoninus, Diocletian, the Hegira, Yazdigird, the Caliph Muʿtaḍid, the pre-Islamic Arabs, and Bīrūnī's native Khwārazm. Chapter 4 discusses the Alexander legend, giving sundry examples of pedigrees, forged

and otherwise. Next are lists of the month names, with variants, used by the Persians, Soghdians, Khwārazmians, Egyptians, Westerners (Spaniards?), Greeks, Jews, Syrians, pre-Islamic Arabs, Muslims, Indians, and Turks. In this chapter, the fifth, Bīrūnī commences his very extensive description of the Jewish calendar. (Except for the work of al-Khwārizmī, another Muslim, his is the earliest extant scientific discussion of this calendar.)

Chapter 6 culminates with a table (trans., p. 133) giving the intervals in days between each pair of the eras named above. This is preceded, however, by chronological and regnal tables in years (sometimes with months and days) for the Jewish patriarchs and kings; the Assyrians, Babylonians and Persians; the Pharaohs, Ptolemies, Caesars, and Byzantine emperors; the mythical Iranian kings; and the Achaemenid, Parthian, and Sasanian dynasties. Where tables from different sources conflict, all are given in full, and there are digressions on the length of human life and the enumeration of chessboard moves.

Chapter 7 continues the exhaustive discussion of the Jewish calendar, but includes a derivation of the solar parameters, a table of planetary names, and the Mujarrad table giving the initial weekdays of the mean (thirty-year cycle) lunar year.

Chapter 8 is on the religions of various pseudo prophets, the most prominent being the Sabians (or Mandaeans, alleged to be followers of Būdhāsaf = Bodhisattva!), Zoroastrians, Manichaeans, and adherents of Mazdak.

The remaining half of the book (save the last chapter) describes the festivals and fasts of the following peoples: Chapter 9, the Persians; 10, the Soghdians; 11 and 12, the Khwārazmians; 13, the Greeks (including material from Sinān ibn Thābit ibn Qurra on the parapegmatists); 14, the Jews; 15, the Melchite Christians; 16, the Jewish Passover and Christian Lent; 17, the Nestorian Christians; 18, the Magians and Sabians; 19, the pre-Islamic Arabs; 20, the Muslims. The concluding chapter, 21, gives tables and descriptive matter on the lunar mansions, followed by explanations of stereographic projection and other plane mappings of the sphere.

The *Astrolabe*. Amid the plethora of medieval treatises on the astrolabe, this is one of the few of real value. It describes in detail not only the construction of the standard astrolabe but also special tools used in the process. Numerical tables are given for laying out the families of circles engraved on the plates fitting into the instrument. Descriptions are also given of the numerous unusual types of astrolabes that had already been developed in Bīrūnī's time. As for the underlying theory, not only are the techniques and properties of the standard stereographic projection presented, but also those of certain nonstereographic and nonorthogonal mappings of the sphere upon the plane.

The *Sextant*. This two-page treatise describes the giant mural instrument for observing meridian transits built by al-Khujandī at Rayy for Fakhr al-Dawla, and perhaps seen by al-Bīrūnī, although he does not say so.

The *Taḥdīd*. The central theme is the determination of geographical coordinates of localities. In particular, Bīrūnī sets out to calculate the longitudinal difference between Baghdad and Ghazna. Several preliminary problems present themselves: latitude determinations, inclination of the ecliptic, the distribution of land masses and their formation, length of a degree along the terrestrial meridian, and differences in terrestrial longitudes from eclipse observations. Techniques and observations used by Bīrūnī and by others are reported. Application is made of a theorem of Ptolemy's that gives the longitudinal difference between two places in terms of the latitude of each and the great circle distance between them. The latter was estimated from caravan routes and lengths of stages. Successive computations then yield the differences in longitude between Baghdad, Rayy, Jurjāniyya, Balkh, and Ghazna, and likewise along a southern traverse including Shiraz and Zaranj. The final result is in error by only eighteen minutes of arc.

The *Densities*. By means of an ingenious form of balance exploiting Archimedes' principle, Bīrūnī worked out a technique for ascertaining the specific gravity of a solid of irregular shape. He reports very precise specific gravity determinations for eight metals, fifteen other solids (mostly precious or semiprecious stones), and six liquids.

The *Shadows*. As its full title indicates, this is a comprehensive presentation of all topics known to Bīrūnī to be connected with shadows. Of the total of thirty chapters, the first three contain philosophical notions about the nature of light, shade, and reflection. There are many citations from the Arabic poets descriptive of kinds of shadows.

Chapter 4 shows that the plane path traced in a day by the end point of a gnomon shadow is a conic. The next two chapters discuss the properties of shadows cast in light emanating from celestial objects. Chapters 7 and 8 define the shadow functions (tangent and cotangent) and explain the origins of the gnomon divisions used in various cultures: the Hellenistic 60, Indian 12, Muslim 7 or 6-1/2. The succeeding three chapters explain rules for converting between functions expressed in different gnomon lengths and for conversions into the other trigonometric functions (sine, secant, and their cofunctions, together with *their* various parameters), and vice versa. Chapter 12 gives tangent-cotangent tables for the four standard gnomon lengths and discusses interpolation. The next two chapters explain how to engrave the shadow functions on astrolabes. There follows, in Chapter 15, a discussion of gnomon shadows cast on planes other than horizontal, and on curved surfaces. Chapters 16 and 17 consider the effect of solar declination and local latitude on the meridian shadow length. A number of nontrigonometric approximate Indian rules are given. Chapters 18–21 list a variety of meridian-determination methods (including one from the lost *Analemma* of the first-century B.C. Diodorus). Chapter 22 is on daylight length and rising times of the signs as functions of the local latitude and the season. Here and in the next two chapters (on determining the time of day from shadows) rules are reproduced from numerous Indian, Sasanian, and early Islamic documents, many no longer extant. Some early Muslim rules are in Arabic doggerel written in imitation of Sanskrit *slokas*. Chapters 25 and 26 define the time of the Muslim daily prayers, some in terms of shadow lengths. Chapter 27 shows that in many situations on the celestial sphere, Menelaus' theorem gives relations between shadow functions. The concluding three chapters describe Indian and early Islamic techniques for calculating terrestrial and celestial distances by the use of shadows.

The *Chords*. The book begins by stating the following theorem: A, B, and C, three points on a circle, are so situated that $AB > BC$. From D, the midpoint of arc AC, drop a perpendicular, DE, to the chord AB. Then the foot of the perpendicular bisects the broken line ABC. There follow a number of proofs of this theorem, attributed to sundry Greek and Islamic mathematicians, some otherwise unknown to the literature. A second theorem, that in the configuration above, $\overline{AD}^2 = \overline{AB} \times \overline{BC} + \overline{BD}^2$, is also followed by a long series of proofs. The same thing is done for the expression $\triangle ADC - \triangle ABC = \overline{DE} \times \overline{EB}$. Then comes a set of metric relations between chords, based on the foregoing and leading up to propositions useful for calculating a table of chords (or sines).

The *Patañjali*. Cast in the form of a series of questions put by a hermit student and the answers given by a sage, this book deals with such philosophical and mystical topics as liberation of the soul and its detachment from the external world, the attributes of God, the power of spirit over the body, and the composition of the universe.

The *Tafhīm*. A manual of instruction in astrology,

well over half of the book is taken up with preliminaries to the main subject. Persian and Arabic versions are extant, both apparently prepared by Bīrūnī himself. It is arranged in the form of questions and answers. There are five chapters in all, the first (thirty-three pages in the Persian edition) on geometry, ending with Menelaus' theorem on the sphere. The second (twenty-three pages) is on numbers, computation, and algebra. Chapter 3, the longest (229 pages), deals with geography, cosmology, and astronomy. From it a complete technical vocabulary may be obtained, as well as sets of numerical parameters, some of them uncommon. The next chapter (thirty-one pages) describes the astrolabe, its theory and application. Only the last chapter (223 pages) is on astrology as such, but it is complete and detailed.

The *India.* The book commences with a prefatory chapter in which the author states that the subject is difficult because Sanskrit is not easy; there are extreme differences between Indians and non-Indians; and Indian fear and distrust has been exacerbated by Muslim conquests. The book will not be polemical and, when appropriate, Indian customs and beliefs will be compared with cognate ones of the Greeks.

Chapters 2–8 are on religion and philosophy: the nature of God, the soul, matter, mysticism, paradise, and hell. Chapters 9, 10, and 11 describe, respectively, the Hindu castes, laws concerning marriage, and the construction of idols. Chapters 12, 13, and 14 are on categories of literature: sacred, grammatical, and astronomical. The latter gives a table of contents of the *Brāhmasphuṭasiddhānta.* Chapter 15 presents tables of metrological units and gives various approximations to the number π. The next two chapters are on Indian systems of writing, number names, chess rules, and superstitions. Chapter 18 is geographical; in particular, sixteen itineraries are given with the distances in *farsakhs* between successive stages. Chapters 19–30 present astronomical and cosmological nomenclature, legends, and theories. Chapter 31 cites the geodetic parameters used by various astronomers, and the latitudes (observed by Bīrūnī) of a number of Indian cities. Chapters 32–53 are on Indian notions of time, including detailed definitions of the hierarchies of enormous cycles—the *yugas, kalpas,* and so on—interspersed with accounts of sundry religious legends. Calendric procedures are given in great profusion. Chapters 54–59 are astronomical, dealing with the computation of mean planetary positions, the sizes and distances of the planets, heliacal risings, and eclipses. The remainder of the book is largely astrological, but includes chapters on rites, pilgrimages, diet, lawsuits, fasts, and festivals.

The *Ghurra.* This is an example of an Indian *karaṇa,* a handbook enabling the user to solve all the standard astronomical problems of his time, with the emphasis on actual computation rather than on theory. Hence it resembles an Islamic *zīj* (astronomical handbook). Topics include calendric rules; length of daylight; determination of the astrological lords of the year, month, day, and hour; mean and true positions of the sun, moon, and planets; time of day; local latitude; solar and lunar eclipses; and visibility conditions for the moon and the planets. Bīrūnī has added worked-out examples, in particular, conversions from the Šaka calendar into the Hegira, Yazdigird, and Greek (so-called era of Alexander) calendars. Otherwise, he states, in his translation he has made no changes.

In general, the methods are those common to medieval Indian astronomy, but the parameters are not identical with any extant Sanskrit document. For instance, the radius of the defining circle for the sine function is 200 minutes, and the increment of arc, the *kardaja,* is ten degrees.

The *Canon.* This most comprehensive of Bīrūnī's extant astronomical works contains detailed numerical tables for solving all the standard problems of the medieval astronomer-astrologer. But it also has much more in the way of observation reports and derivations than the typical *zīj.* It is organized in eleven treatises (*maqāla*) that are further subdivided into chapters and sections.

Treatises 1 and 2 set forth and discuss general cosmological principles (that the earth and heavens are spherical, that the earth is stationary, etc.), units of time measurement, calendars, and regnal and chronological tables. This covers much of the ground gone over in the *Chronology,* but the chapter on the Indian calendar is additional.

Treatises 3 and 4 are on plane and spherical trigonometry respectively. There are tables of all the standard trigonometric functions, more extensive and precise than preceding or contemporary tables. Methods of solving many problems of spherical astronomy appear, together with tables of ancillary functions: oblique ascensions, declinations, and so on.

Treatise 5, on geodesy and mathematical geography, reworks much of the subject matter of the *Taḥdīd.* A table gives the geographical coordinates of localities.

Treatises 6 and 7 are on the sun and moon, respectively. Here (and with planetary theory farther on) the abstract models are essentially Ptolemaic, but many parameters are independently derived on the basis of all available observations (including Bīrūnī's own).

Treatise 8 treats of eclipse computations and the first visibility of the lunar crescent.

Treatise 9, on the fixed stars, includes a star table with 1,029 entries (cf. Ptolemy's 1,022). Magnitudes according to Ptolemy and to al-Ṣūfī are given.

The next treatise is on the planets, with tables and text for calculating longitudes, latitudes, stations, visibility, distances, and apparent diameters.

The concluding treatise is on astrological operations, describing various doctrines for calculating the astrological mansions, projection of the rays, the *taysīr,* the sectors (*niṭāqāt*), transits, and the curious cycles apparently developed by Abū Maʿshar.

The *Transits.* This book describes the various categories of astrological phenomena to which the term *mamarr* (transit or passage) was attached. One planet was said to transit another if it passed the other planet in celestial longitude, or celestial latitude, or in its relative distance from the earth. The notion seems to have been developed by astrologers using non-Ptolemaic astronomical doctrines described in documents no longer extant. Hence the main interest of the work is the assistance it gives toward the reconstruction of these lost Indian, Sasanian, and early Islamic theories.

The *Gems.* The work is organized in two parts, the first being on precious and semiprecious stones, the second on metals. Bīrūnī brings together material from Hellenistic, Roman, Syriac, Indian, and Islamic sources, supplemented by his own observations. In addition to descriptions of the physical properties of the various substances, there are very extensive etymological discussions of the technical terminology in many languages and dialects, and numerous illustrative quotations from Arabic poetry. The principal mines and sources of supply are cited. Relative weights of the metals with respect to gold are given, and there are tables showing the prices of pearls and emeralds as functions of size.

The *Pharmacology.* The book commences with an introduction in five chapters. The first presents an etymology for the Arabic word for druggist. The second gives technical terminology for categories of drugs. The next chapter is on the general theory of medicaments. In the fourth and fifth chapters Bīrūnī states his preference for Arabic over Persian as a language of science, and he names polyglot dictionaries available to him.

The main body of the work is an alphabetical listing of drugs comprising about 720 articles. For a typical entry the name of the substance is given in Arabic, Greek, Syriac, Persian, and an Indian language, and sometimes also in one or more less common languages or dialects: Hebrew, Khwārazmian, Tokharian,

Zabuli, and so on. There follows a full presentation of the Arabic variants and synonyms, liberally illustrated with quotations from the Arabic poets. The substance is described, its place or places of origin named, and its therapeutic properties given, although Bīrūnī disclaims medical competence on his own part. Sources are fully and critically mentioned.

Abū Rayḥān's dominant trait was a passion for objective knowledge. In pursuit of this he early began studying languages. His mother tongue was Khwārazmian, an Iranian language in which, he wrote, it would be as strange to encounter a scientific concept as to see a camel on a roof gutter (*mīzāb*) or a giraffe among thoroughbred horses (ʿirāb, an example of rhymed prose). Therefore he acquired a deep knowledge of both Arabic and Persian. The former, in spite of the ambiguity of its written characters, he esteemed a proper vehicle for the conveyance of science, whereas the latter he deemed fit only for the recital of bedtime stories (*al-asmār al-layliyya*) and legends of the kings (*al-akhbār al-kisrawiyya,* more rhymed prose; *Pharmacology,* p. 40). Of Greek, Syriac, and Hebrew he attained at least sufficient knowledge to use dictionaries in these languages. His command of Sanskrit, on the other hand, reached the point where, with the aid of *pandits,* he was able to translate several Indian scientific works into Arabic, and vice versa. He took obvious delight in Arabic poetry, composed verses himself, and liberally interlarded his writings with quotations from the classics.

Thus equipped, he made full use of all the documents that came to his hand (many of which have since disappeared), exercising a critical faculty that extended from the minutiae of textual emendations to the analysis of scientific theories. A strong sense of history permeates all his writings, making them prime sources for studying the work of his predecessors, as well as his own and that of his contemporaries.

Bīrūnī's pursuit of the truth was not confined to the written or spoken word. He had a strong penchant for firsthand investigation of natural phenomena, exercised at times under very trying circumstances. Along with this went an ingenuity in the devising of instruments and a flair for precision in observations. Because of this feeling for accuracy, and because of a well-founded fear of losing precision in the course of calculations, he tended to prefer observational methods that yielded direct results, as against techniques requiring extensive reduction by computation.

Speculation played a small role in his thinking; he was in full command of the best scientific theories of his time, but he was not profoundly original or a constructor of new theories. His attitude toward astrology has been debated. He spent a great deal of time in serious study of the subject, but Krause (p. 10) has collected passages in which Bīrūnī not only heaps ridicule upon ignorant or unscrupulous astrological practitioners, but indicates disbelief in the basic tenets of this pseudo science. Krause also reminds us that there were many centuries when the casting of horoscopes was the only way by which an astronomer could support himself in the exercise of his profession.

As for religion, Bīrūnī was doubtless a sincere Muslim, but there is no firm evidence of his having been an adherent of any particular sect within the faith. In the *Chronology* (trans., pp. 79, 326), written at the court of Qābūs, are passages that have been interpreted as betraying a Shī'i (hence anti-Arab and pro-Persian) bent. On the other hand, the *Pharmacology,* compiled under Ghaznavid patronage, represents the author as an orthodox Sunnī. Probably these two situations reflect no more than the fact that the two patrons were Shī'i and Sunnī, respectively. From time to time Bīrūnī inveighs harshly against various groups, but the criticism is of particular acts or attitudes, not of the group as such. Thus his strictures against the Arab conquerors of Khwārazm were called forth, not because they were Arab, or alien, but because they destroyed ancient books. Concerning the Christian doctrine of forgiveness he writes, "Upon my life, this is a noble philosophy, but the people of this world are not all philosophers. . . . And indeed, ever since Constantine the Victorious became a Christian, both sword and whip have ever been employed" (*India,* trans., II, 161).

In these, and in most matters, Bīrūnī had a remarkably open mind, but his tolerance was not extended to the dilettante, the fool, or the bigot. Upon such he exercised a broad and often crude sarcasm. Upon his showing an instrument for setting the times of prayer to a certain religious legalist, the latter objected that it had engraved upon it the names of the Byzantine months, and this constituted an imitation of the infidels. "The Byzantines also eat food," stated Abū Rayḥān. "Then do not imitate them in this!" and he ejected the fellow forthwith (*Shadows,* 37:9).

Such were the life, labors, and character of a man known to his contemporaries as the Master (*al-Ustādh*). Unknown in the medieval West, except perhaps by the garbled name Maître Aliboron, his name and fame have been secure in his own lands from his time until the present.

BIBLIOGRAPHY

The standard bibliographical work on Bīrūnī is D. J. Boilot, "L'oeuvre d'al-Beruni. Essai bibliographique," in *Mélanges de l'Institut dominicain d'études orientales,* **2** (1955), 161–256; and "Corrigenda et addenda," *ibid.,* **3** (1956), 391–396; no attempt has been made here to duplicate it. A good deal of material has, of course, appeared since it was published in 1955.

For points of view somewhat different from that expressed in the text, see Boilot's article on al-Bīrūnī in the new ed. of the *Encyclopaedia of Islam,* Krause's paper (cited below), and Sachau's prefaces to the text and to the translation of the *Chronology* and the *India. RG* stands for "Répertoire général," the numbered listing of Bīrūnī's works in Boilot.

I. ORIGINAL WORKS. Following are Bīrūnī's extant major works, listed alphabetically.

Astrolabe (*RG* 46). The Arabic title is *Kitāb fī istī'āb al-wujūh fī ṣan'at al-asṭurlāb.* Several MSS exist (see Boilot), but the text has not been published. Sections of it have, however, been translated and studied.

Bibliography (*RG* 168). Bīrūnī calls this *Risāla fī fihrist kutub Muḥammad b. Zakariyyā' al-Rāzī.* The text was published by Paul Kraus as *Épître de Bērūnī contenant le répertoire des Ouvrages de Muḥammad b. Zakarīyā ar-Rāzī* (Paris, 1936). The text of the part giving Bīrūnī's own bibliography appears in the text edition of the *Chronology,* pp. xxxviii–xxxxviii. It is translated into German in Wiedemann's "Beiträge," LX.

Canon (*RG* 104). The Arabic text has been published as *al-Qānūn al-Mas'ūdī* (Canon Masudicus), 3 vols. (Hyderabad-Dn., 1954–1956). References in the article are to page and line of the printed text, pagination of which is continuous, not commencing anew with each volume. A Russian translation, in preparation by P. G. Bulgakov, M. M. Rozhanskaya, and B. A. Rozenfeld, will be Vol. V of the *Selected Works.*

Chords (*RG* 64). There are three MS versions of this work: (1) Leiden Or. 513(5) = CCO 1012; (2) Bankipore Arabic MS 2468/42 = Patna 2,336,2519/40; (3) Murat Molla (Istanbul) 1396. The Leiden version has been published in translation and with a commentary, both by H. Suter, as "Das Buch der Auffindung der Sehnen im Kreise . . . ," in *Bibliotheca mathematica,* **11** (1910), 11–78. The text of version (2) has been published as the first of the four *Rasā'il* (Arabic for *treatises*). This contains, however, extraneous material, part of which is probably not by Bīrūnī, and part probably a fragment of *RG* 11. Many topics in (2) and (3) are missing from (1), and those parts that are in common are in drastically different orders. Two recensions by Bīrūnī himself are indicated. See H. Hermelink, in *Zentralblatt für Mathematik und ihre Grenzgebiete,* **54** (1956), 3; and A. S. Saidan, in *Islamic Culture,* **34** (1960), 173–175. Many of the additional sections in (2) and (3) are described by E. S. Kennedy and Ahmad Muruwwa in *Journal of Near Eastern Studies,* **17** (1958), 112–121. A composite Arabic text based on (2) and (3) was published by A. S. Demerdash as *Istikhrāj al-awtār fi'l-dā'ira* (Cairo, 1965). There is a Russian translation by C. A. Krasnova and L. A. Karpova, with commentary by B. A. Rosenfeld and C. A. Krasnova: *Iz istorii nauki i texniki v stranax Vostoka,* III (Moscow, 1963).

Chronology (*RG* 105). In Arabic this is *al-Āthār al-bāqiya min al-qurūn al-khāliya.* It was edited by E. Sachau as *Chronologie orientalischer Voelker von Albērūnī* (Leipzig, 1878, 1923; repr. Baghdad, 1963). The parts missing from Sachau's text are given by K. Garbers and J. Fück in J. Fück, ed., *Documenta Islamica inedita* (Berlin, 1952), pp. 45–98. It was translated into English by Sachau as *The Chronology of Ancient Nations* (London, 1879). The Russian translation by M. A. Sal'e, *Pamyatniki minuvshikh pokolenii,* is Vol. I of the *Selected Works* (Tashkent, 1957).

Densities (RG 63). This work's Arabic title is *Maqāla fi'l-nisab allatī bayn al-filizzāt wa'l-jawāhir fi'l-ḥajm* ("Treatise on the Ratios Between the Volumes of Metals and Jewels"). The text has never been published, but portions of it have been taken over by other authors and have been studied in modern times.

Gems (RG 156). Known as the *Kitāb al-jamāhir fī maʿrifat al-jawāhir,* this text was edited by F. Krenkow (Hyderabad-Dn., 1936). Krenkow also translated the text, but only the chapter on pearls has been published (see Boilot). There is, however, a translation by A. M. Belenskii—*Mineralogiya* (Moscow, 1963).

Ghurra. The *Ghurrat al-zījāt* is Bīrūnī's Arabic translation of the Sanskrit astronomical handbook called *Karaṇatilaka* (forehead caste mark of the Karaṇas), by one Vijayanandin or Vijaya Nanda. The original text is not extant, but a MS of the translation is in the Dargah Library of Pir Muhammad Shah, Ahmadabad. Portions of the Arabic text, with English translation, and a commentary were published in installments by Sayyid Samad Husain Rizvi in *Islamic Culture,* **37** (1963), 112–130, 223–245, and **39** (1965), 1–26, 137–180. Another text, translation, and commentary, by M. F. Qureshi, exist in typescript but have not been published.

India (RG 93). Also known as *Kitāb fī taḥqīq ma li'l-Hind . . . ,* this was edited by E. Sachau (London, 1888). A later edition has been published by the Osmania Oriental Publications Bureau (Hyderabad-Dn., 1958). Translated by E. Sachau as *Al-Beruni's India,* 2 vols. (London, 1910). Translated into Russian by A. B. Khalidov and Y. N. Zavadovskii as Vol. II of *Selected Works* (Tashkent, 1963).

Patañjali (RG 98). Bīrūnī's Arabic translation of this Sanskrit work is extant only in an incomplete MS edited by H. Ritter as "Al-Bīrūnī's Übersetzung des Yoga-Sūtra des Patañjali," in *Oriens,* **9** (1956), 165–200. See Boilot.

Pharmacology (RG 158). The Arabic title of this is *Kitāb al-ṣaydala fī ʾl-ṭibb.* There is no edition of the entire work. M. Meyerhof translated it into German, but of this only the introduction has been published, together with the corresponding part of the Arabic text and an extremely valuable foreword and commentary: "Das Vorwort zur Drogenkunde des Bērūnī," in *Quellen und Studien zur Geschichte der Naturwissenschaften,* **3** (1932), 157–208. A Russian translation, in preparation by U. I. Kazimov, will be Vol. IV of *Selected Works.*

Rasā ʾilu-l-Bīrūnī. This is the Arabic text of *RG* 64, 15, 45, and 38, published by Osmania Oriental Publications Bureau (Hyderabad-Dn., 1948).

Selected Works (Izbrannye proizvedeniya). Bīrūnī's extant works are being published in Russian by the Academy of Sciences of the Uzbek S.S.R. Volumes in print or in preparation are listed by individual titles.

Sextant (RG 169). The *Ḥikāyat al-ālāt al-musammāt al-suds al-fakhrī* ("Account of the Instrument Known as the Fakhrī Sextant") is MS 223, pp. 10–11, of the Univ. of St. Joseph, Beirut. It was edited by L. Cheikho in *Al-Mashriq,* **11** (1908), 68–69. With minor changes, this small treatise was copied without acknowledgment by Abu'l-Ḥasan al-Marrākushī as part of a larger work. Text and French translation appear in L. A. Sédillot, "Les instruments astronomiques des arabes," in *Mémoires . . . à l'Académie royale des inscriptions . . . ,* 1st ser., **1** (1844), 202–206.

Shadows (RG 15). The text has been published as the second of the *Rasā ʾil* with the title *Kitāb fī ifrād al-maqāl fī amr al-ẓilāl* ("The Exhaustive Treatise on Shadows"). An English translation has been made by E. S. Kennedy, but publication awaits completion of the commentary. References to the *Shadows* made in the article are to page and line of the published text.

Tafhīm (RG 73). This is the *Kitāb al-tafhīm li-awāʾil ṣināʿat al-tanjīm.* R. Ramsay Wright published an edition of the Arabic text with English translation as *The Book of Instruction in the Art of Astrology* (London, 1934). Bīrūnī's Persian version was published by Jalāl Humāʾi (Teheran, 1940).

Taḥdīd (RG 19). The Arabic title is *Taḥdīd nihāyāt al-amākin li-taṣḥiḥ masāfāt al-masākin,* and the work is extant in the unique Istanbul MS Fatih 3386. The Arabic text was published by P. Bulgakov as a special number of the Arab League journal, *Majallat maʿhad al-makhṭūṭāt al-ʿarabiyya* (Cairo, 1962). Translated into Russian by P. G. Bulgakov as *Geodeziya,* Vol. III of *Selected Works* (Tashkent, 1966). An English translation by Jamil Ali is *The Determination of the Coordinates of Cities, al-Bīrūnī's Taḥdīd al-Amākin* (Beirut, 1967). References in the article to the *Taḥdīd* are to page and line of the published text.

Transits (RG 45). In Arabic this is *Tamhīd al-mustaqarr li-taḥqīq maʿnā al-mamarr* ("Smoothing the Basis for an Investigation of the Meaning of Transits"). The text has been published as the third of the *Rasāʾil.* A translation by Mohammad Saffouri and Adnan Ifran, with commentary by E. S. Kennedy, is *Al-Bīrūnī on Transits* (Beirut, 1959).

II. SECONDARY LITERATURE. Works referred to parenthetically in the text, by author and page, are W. Barthold, *Turkestan Down to the Mongol Invasion,* 2nd ed. (London, 1928); E. G. Browne, *A Literary History of Persia,* II (Cambridge, 1928); *Chahār Maqāla of Aḥmad ibn ʿAli an-Niẓāmī al-ʿArūḍī as-Samarqandī,* Mirza Muḥammad ibn ʿAbd'l-Wahhāb, ed. (Leiden-London, 1910); Iran Society, *Al-Bīrūnī Commemoration Volume, A. H. 362–A. H. 1362* (Calcutta, 1951); Max Krause, "Al-Biruni. Ein iranischer Forscher des Mittelalters," in *Der Islam,* **26** (1940), 1–15; Muḥammad Nāẓim, *The Life and Times of Sulṭān Muḥmūd of Ghazna* (Cambridge, 1931); Aurel Stein, "The Site of Alexander's Passing of the Hydaspes and the Battle With Poros," in *Geographical Journal,* **80** (1932), 31–46; Heinrich Suter, "Die Mathematiker und Astronomen der

Araber . . .," in *Abhandlungen zur Geschichte der mathematischen Wissenschaften . . .*, X (Leipzig, 1900); Eilhard Wiedemann et al., "Beiträge zur Geschichte der Naturwissenschaften," in *Sitzungsberichte der Physikalisch-medizinischen Sozietät in Erlangen;* and Yāqūt al-Rūmī, Shihāb al-Dīn, Abū ʿAbdallāh, *Muʿjam al-udabāʾ* (= *Irshād al-arīb ilā maʿrifat al-adīb*), XVII (Cairo, 1936–1938).

E. S. KENNEDY

BISCHOF, CARL GUSTAV CHRISTOPH (*b.* Wörth, near Nuremberg, Germany, 18 January 1792; *d.* Bonn, Germany, 29 November 1870), *chemistry, geology.*

Bischof probably acquired his interest in natural sciences from his father, a teacher of natural history and geography. He attended the University of Erlangen, where he obtained the doctorate and became *Privatdozent* in chemistry and physics. He received much early encouragement and inspiration from Nees von Esenbeck and Goldfuss. With the latter he published a two-volume physical and statistical description of the Fichtelgebirge, a mountain range near Nuremberg (1817). His next work, written with Esenbeck and Rothe, dealt with the evolution of plants. His first independent book was the *Lehrbuch der Stöchiometrie* (1819). In the same year he was called to the newly founded University of Bonn, where he became professor of chemistry and technology.

For the rest of his life he concentrated on the chemical changes accompanying geological processes, first in the Rhineland and later in other German areas and even foreign regions. His main interest at first was the volcanic phenomena of the Eifel and neighboring areas—specifically, the springs in these areas, which he interpreted as being largely of volcanic origin. In 1824 he published *Die vulkanischen Mineralquellen Deutschlands und Frankreichs,* a work that aroused much interest and led to his being considered one of the main defenders of volcanistic theories (as opposed to the neptunistic). He corroborated his ideas on the origin of springs by a case study of the mineral spring of Roisdorf (1826).

The chief work of his volcanistic period was *Wärmelehre des Innern unseres Endkörpers* (1837). In this work he presented a critical compilation of all that was known at the time, together with many of his own observations on the thermal properties of the earth's surface, including observations made in mines. From these he derived his theories of thermal gradients, which were essentially correct, and his ideas on the origin of volcanism and the heat required for his kind of "metamorphic" transformation. He concluded

that the observed heat gradients explained satisfactorily all known volcanic activity, as well as springs and earthquakes. The evidence presented in this book was used immediately to support the plutonist theories dominant at the time. It also included experimental evidence; the volume reduction observed during the cooling of melted basalt inspired Élie de Beaumont to propose that folded mountain chains arose from wrinkling of the surface of the contracting earth, assuming that the earth had once been in a state of fusion.

Bischof had an interest in and talent for communicating his ideas to the general public. This is shown in his popular lectures, many of which are collected in *Populäre Vorlesungen über naturwissenschaftliche Gegenstände* (1842–1843) and *Populäre Briefe an eine gebildete Dame über das gesammte Gebiet der Naturwissenschaften* (1848–1849). Bischof was not only a gifted experimentalist; he also had a flair for translating scientific knowledge into practical use. For example he was the first to harness the HCO_3 springs in the volcanic areas of the Niederrhein for industrial purposes. He also promoted the recovery of copper from very low-grade ores by an inexpensive leaching and "cementation" method.

In 1848 Bischof began to publish his *Lehrbuch der chemischen und physikalischen Geologie,* the main source of his fame. The second edition, with a supplement, ran to 3,005 pages, and was published between 1863 and 1871. It was in many ways a continuation rather than a new edition. This enormous work soon became the standard geochemical text. It appeared to support a new school of thought, the "neoneptunistic." At the beginning of the first volume Bischof was still a plutonist and opposed neptunist views, although somewhat hesitantly. The intensive studies he made in connection with the *Lehrbuch,* however, convinced him more and more of the validity of the role of surface waters.

Bischof was and remained in many ways basically a laboratory chemist, despite his great interest in natural phenomena. This was his weakness in many instances, and the reason for his strong adherence to plutonism-volcanism until about 1846 and his fervent advocation of opposite views after this time.

Just as the exaggeration of the magmatic-hydrothermal theory of the formation of rocks and ore deposits was in part caused by one-sided experiments between 1900 and 1960, Bischof during his time exaggerated the role of water in his experiments, extrapolating from laboratory results to natural phenomena without adequate support from observations in nature. In this manner he assumed numerous transformations of sediments to crystalline schists, gneisses, and granites—and even basic igneous rocks—often without even discussing field relations. He rejected plutonic metamorphism and assumed that all metamorphic processes were caused by hydrochemical ("neptunic or katogene") reactions, i.e., changes at surface temperatures caused by a continuous flow of water through the rocks and introduction and subtraction of material. He was, in this respect, a forerunner of the extreme transformationists who, a century later, insisted upon similar transformations of sediments into various igneous rocks, usually without knowing of Bischof's work. He also believed that ore veins had been formed from descending solutions or by lateral secretion.

Bischof's work benefited several branches of geology and promoted a more scientific approach to many geological problems, such as the use of analogies with experiments (even though his geological theories were often proposed on the basis of laboratory evidence rather than field relationships). In 1849 he introduced the so-called oxygen coefficient into chemical comparisons of rocks by using the ratio between oxygen in bases and oxygen in SiO_2. He offered experimental evidence for causes of landslides in 1846 and 1863.

Bischof determined the relationship of gypsum and anhydrite and proposed a connection between crystallization and climate in the Dead Sea. He recognized that gypsum is not the end of salt deposition, but the beginning of a new sequence. He argued that since gypsum and halite are the first salts to precipitate during evaporation of seawater, calcareous sediments must have been formed through the action of organisms. He also recognized that dolomitization must have taken place and assumed magnesium bicarbonate to be a major cause. Bischof did not succeed in reproducing dolomitization in the laboratory, but was able to explain cavernous limestones and the lack of fossil shells in dolomites by leaching of dolomites. He also found, in 1864, that phosphoric acid accumulates in bones, shells, and the soft parts of animals. As early as 1829 Bischof had obtained melnikowite precipitates experimentally, and in 1863–1866 he discussed the different reactions by which gypsum or anhydrite forms in one case, and in another native sulfur is precipitated. Thus he contributed to the fundamental knowledge that decades later led to the suggestion that massive stratiform sulfide deposits may be sedimentary or exhalative-sedimentary.

BIBLIOGRAPHY

I. ORIGINAL WORKS. Bischof's major work is *Lehrbuch der chemischen und physikalischen Geologie,* 3 vols. (Bonn, 1846–1855; 2nd. ed., 3 vols. and supp., 1863–1871), trans. into English by B. H. Paul and J. Drummond as *Elements of Chemical and Physical Geology,* 3 vols. (London, 1854–1859). His other writings include *Physikalisch-statistische Beschreibung des Fichtelgebirges,* written with A. Goldfuss, 2 vols. (Nuremburg, 1817); with Nees von Esenbeck and Rothe, *Die Entwicklung der Pflanzensubstanz* (Erlangen, 1819); *Lehrbuch der Stöchiometrie* (Bonn, 1819); *Die vulkanischen Mineralquellen Deutschlands und Frankreichs* (Bonn, 1824); *Die Mineralquellen von Roisdorf* (Bonn, 1826); *Wärmelehre des Innern unseres Erdkörpers* (Bonn, 1837), also trans. into English (1844); and *Populäre Vorlesungen über naturwissenschaftliche Gegenstände* (Bonn, 1842–1843).

II. SECONDARY LITERATURE. Works on Bischof are F. Behrend and G. Berg, *Chemische Geologie* (Stuttgart, 1927); V. von Cotta, *Geologie der Gegenwart,* I (Leipzig, 1866), 61–62, 347–372; W. Fischer, *Gesteins- und Lagerstättenbildung im Wandel der wissenschaftlichen Anschauung* (Stuttgart, 1961); C. W. von Gümbel, in *Allgemeine Deutsche Biographie,* II, 665–669; Poggendorff, I, 202; and K. von Zittel, trans. by Maria M. Ogilvie-Gordon, *History of Geology and Paleontology* (London, 1901).

G. C. AMSTUTZ

BISCHOFF, GOTTLIEB WILHELM (*b.* Dürkheim an der Hardt, Germany, 21 May 1797; *d.* Heidelberg, Germany, 11 September 1854), *botany.*

Bischoff, who came from a family of pharmacists, was introduced to botany in Kaiserslautern by Wilhelm Koch, the author of *Synopsis florae Germanicae et Helveticae,* while he was studying graphic arts. In 1819 he entered the Academy of the Creative Arts at Munich, in order to perfect his drawing techniques; but in 1821, at the University of Erlangen, he turned to the study of botany and chemistry. Here he published his first work, *Die botanische Kunstsprache* (1822), in which his interest in terminology is apparent.

The botanist and scientific explorer Philipp von Martius encouraged Bischoff to continue his studies in Munich. In the first volume of Martius' *Nova genera et species plantarum* (1824), nearly all the drawings of plants, which Martius had brought back with him from his explorations in Brazil, were done by Bischoff. After completing his studies, Bischoff managed his father's pharmacy for about a year, but in 1824 he went to Heidelberg to study botany. By 1825 he had established himself there as a *Privatdozent;* in 1833 he became extraordinary professor, and in 1839 full professor of botany and director of the Botanical Garden of Heidelberg, which he completely reorganized.

Bischoff grew up in the era of *Naturphilosophie* in

German science, which still bore the imprint of Schelling, but he sought to dissociate himself from speculative discussion of nature. His investigations of cryptogams showed him to be an excellent observer, and his work on Characeae and on the Archegoniatae deserves special mention. He collected great amounts of the material that enabled Wilhelm Hofmeister to trace the development of lichens and ferns and to elucidate the relations between the life cycles and life histories of different plant phyla. In this connection his unfinished work *Die kryptogamischen Gewaechse* (1828), with its experiments on spores, must be mentioned because it prepared the way for Hofmeister's discovery of the alternation of generations. In *De hepaticis*, Bischoff described the reproductive organs of liverworts, calling the male sexual organs "antheridia" and the female ones "fruit-germs"; only later did he call the latter "archegonia." He also studied the Selaginellales and the Equisetales, which are interesting from the point of view of organic evolution.

In *Lehrbuch der Botanik* (1834–1840) Bischoff presented in detail the morphology and physiology of plants. He concurred with Goethe's assumption that all parts and organs of the plant originate from the leaf. The *Lehrbuch* contains a synopsis of plant pathology and one of the first histories of botany. In a clear and orderly fashion, Bischoff treats botanical knowledge up to 1837, when Matthias Schleiden's cell theory was published. His *Handbuch der botanischen Terminologie und Systemkunde* (1833–1844) is still of value as a general survey of the plant kingdom, for orientation on the development of botanical terminology, and for its discussion of numerous synonyms and the history of plant classification. Several of the nearly 4,000 figures that Bischoff himself drew for the book are still used in textbooks.

BIBLIOGRAPHY

I. ORIGINAL WORKS. A complete bibliography of Bischoff's works is in G. A. Pritzel, *Thesaurus literaturae botanicae,* new ed. (Leipzig, 1872), pp. 27–28. Among his works are *Die botanische Kunstsprache* (Nuremberg, 1822); *Die kryptogamischen Gewaechse,* 2 pts. (Nuremberg, 1828); *Handbuch der botanischen Terminologie und Systemkunde,* 3 vols. (Nuremberg, 1833–1844); and *Lehrbuch der Botanik,* 3 vols. (Stuttgart, 1834–1840).

II. SECONDARY LITERATURE. Works on Bischoff are *Botanische Zeitung,* **12** (1854), no. 39; Martin Möbius, *Geschichte der Botanik* (Jena, 1937), pp. 85, 122, 135, 152; *Neue deutsche Biographie,* II (Berlin, 1955), 263; Claus Nissen, *Die botanische Buchillustration,* 2 vols. (Stuttgart, 1951), see especially I, 217, and list of works illustrated by Bischoff in II, 16, nos. 165–167; 117, no. 1288;

M. Seubert, "G. W. Bischoff," in *Badische Biographien,* I (Heidelberg, 1875), 86; and E. Stübler, *Geschichte der medizinischen Fakultät der Universität Heidelberg* (Heidelberg, 1926), pp. 267, 274, 297.

JOHANNES STEUDEL

BISCHOFF, THEODOR LUDWIG WILHELM (*b.* Hannover, Germany, 28 October 1807; *d.* Munich, Germany, 5 December 1882), *comparative anatomy, physiology.*

Theodor's father, Ernst Christian Heinrich Bischoff, was a physician and a follower of Schelling's *Naturphilosophie.* He was a romantically stern and pious man. In 1806, after having served for several years as professor of physiology at the Medizinisch-Chirurgische Kollegium in Berlin, he divorced his first wife and married Juliane Hufeland, née Amelung, the wife of Christoph Wilhelm Hufeland. He then left Berlin and waited in Hannover for a new post. There Theodor, his only son by this second marriage, was born. After serving as a physician in Barmen-Elberfeld (now Wuppertal) and as an army physician during the "War of Liberation" against Napoleon (1813–1814), the elder Bischoff was appointed associate professor of pharmacology and forensic medicine at the reconstituted University of Bonn in 1818.

Theodor Bischoff was reared in a financially secure, cultured, and strict Protestant atmosphere. He attended the Gymnasium in Bonn and in 1825 passed the *Maturitätsprüfung.* After attending a special class in Gotha, he began his medical studies in Bonn (1826–1829). He attended the lectures given by Nees von Esenbeck, Friedrich Nasse, Philipp Franz von Walther, and Johannes Müller, all men with strong leanings toward speculative *Naturphilosophie.* This influence on Bischoff waned in 1830, when he continued his studies in Heidelberg under F. Carl Nägeli, Friedrich Tiedemann, and F. Arnold, and learned their preference for empirical research. His M.D. thesis (1832), completed under Tiedemann and Arnold, concerned the areas innervated by the *nervus accessorius willisii* in mammals, birds, and reptiles.

After passing the state medical examinations in Berlin, Bischoff interned at the University of Berlin's maternity clinic. He also attended lectures on comparative anatomy by Johannes Müller, who had taken over the Berlin chair of anatomy and physiology for the summer semester of 1833. Bischoff became lecturer in physiology at Bonn in September 1833. For the summer semester of 1836 he went to Heidelberg as lecturer in comparative and pathological anatomy. On 18 April 1839 he married the oldest daughter of Friedrich Tiedemann, his teacher in Heidelberg. In February 1843, he was appointed professor of anatomy and physiology at Heidelberg. From the fall of 1843 until 1854 he also taught in Giessen, first physiology and, from 1844, anatomy as well. In 1854, upon Liebig's recommendation, he received an invitation to teach the same subjects in Munich. He turned over his lectures in physiology to Carl Voit in 1863 and retired fifteen years later, at the age of seventy-one. He died 5 December 1882, after an intestinal perforation.

Bischoff received many decorations and honors. He was a member of the scientific academies of Berlin, Vienna, St. Petersburg, and Munich, the Royal Society of London, and the Kaiserlich Leopoldinischen Carolinischen Deutschen Akademie, as well as honorary member of many associations and societies.

Bischoff's scientific work began with zoological and botanical research. Next he wrote on physiological and physiological-chemical subjects. His most important works concerned the embryology of mammals and of man. While he worked in Munich, he stressed anthropological research. In addition, throughout his life he remained interested in general problems of natural philosophy and religion.

Bischoff's student papers on *Helix pomatia* and dragonflies were never printed, but his Ph.D. thesis on the spiral vessels of plants was published. His interest in physiological problems is shown in his treatises on the electric nerve currents (1841) and the reabsorption of narcotic toxins (1846). Also of interest is his attempt to determine the amount of blood in a fresh corpse (1856). In Heidelberg he conducted —jointly with P. G. von Jolly—the first, but relatively unsatisfactory, experiments concerning blood-bound oxygen and carbon dioxide.

Although Bischoff was neither inclined toward nor particularly gifted in vivisection, he developed an interest in embryology while an intern in Berlin. In this field he achieved excellent results. He began with research on the human fetal membrane and was able to demonstrate the existence of the decidual vessels and the amniotic epithelium. In Bonn he was the first to lecture before a large audience on the history of embryology. His interest in this subject had been aroused by the work of Karl Ernst von Baer, a disciple of Ignaz Döllinger, on the existence of the mammalian ovum in the graafian follicle (1827) and on the subsequent formation of embryonic epithelia through a process of segmentation.

In 1835 Bischoff showed the canine ovum moving through the fallopian tube. This achievement formed the starting point for a series of related research. At the Freiburg convention of natural scientists and physicians (1838) he reported on the presence of sperm in the peritoneal sac of the ovary of a bitch some twenty hours after copulation. He deduced that the follicle was made to burst by the entering sperm. Next, in answer to a contest problem posed by the Berlin Academy of Sciences, he investigated the first phases of mammalian development in the rabbit. Bischoff was the first to clarify the successive division of the mammalian ovum and the first subsequent segmentation processes. He also demonstrated that the embryonic vesicle consists of cells. This finding enabled him to establish the connection between embryology and the then new science of cytology.

In this work there arose controversies regarding the choice between epigenesis and evolution. Bischoff considered the embryo to be a liquid-filled vesicle, and attempted to derive the cellular substance of which the embryo is formed from the cellular beads of the morula. His history of the development of the rabbit egg was printed in 1842, that of the canine egg in 1845, of the guinea pig egg in 1852, and of the doe egg in 1854. His *Entwicklungsgeschichte der Säugetiere und des Menschen* was also translated into French, as were several other of his works.

At that time many scientists were doing research on embryology, with the result that all sorts of controversies and priority feuds arose. In 1843 Bischoff was compelled to correct his former views when it was found that ovulation occurs periodically, independent of copulation, and that subsequently the ovum commences its movement through the fallopian tube. His paper on this appeared in 1844 in German and in 1847 in English. His studies on the embryology of the guinea pig showed some remarkable differences from all prior observations. Of importance in this connection was Bischoff's clarification of the fertilization process in the doe: after being fertilized in August, the egg moves within a few days through the fallopian tube into the uterus and remains there for four and a half months without any further important development. In 1854 Bischoff had to correct his former views on one not unimportant point. It had been found, particularly by Barry (1843), that in the fertilization process the sperm penetrates the mammalian ovum. This had been disputed by Bischoff.

In 1859 Darwin's *On the Origin of Species* appeared. Bischoff then decided to change his field of research, and began to occupy himself more and more with anthropological investigations. While he approved the theory of selection in principle, he considered the general theory of the origin of species to be insufficiently substantiated, since it did not furnish any explanation for the general and individual origin of life. This criticism resulted from Bischoff's assumption that specific vital forces are active in development whereby "individual immortal basic causes" unite with matter. Although he closely related the activity of the soul with that of the brain, he nevertheless felt that the immortal basic cause of the individual continued to exist after death halted the soul's activity. Such ideas are also expressed in his posthumously published treatise *Gedanken eines Naturforschers über die Natur und über die Religion* (1878).

In connection with the question of man's place in the living world, Bischoff investigated the cerebral convolutions (1868) and the weight of the human brain (1880). He also studied the weight of the brain in relation to sex, body weight, body size, age, and race, and found no relationship between intelligence and brain weight. He did, however, consider the possibility of certain parallels. Bischoff's studies on the anatomy of the anthropoid apes also belong to this group of works.

Among Bischoff's physiological works particular mention should be made of those resulting from collaboration with or suggestions made by the great chemist Justus Liebig. In 1843, when Bischoff came to Giessen, Liebig's influential books *Die Chemie in ihrer Anwendung auf Agrikultur und Physiologie* (1840) and *Die Tierchemie . . .* (1842) had been published. The wealth of ideas formulated in these works stimulated Bischoff's interest in the metabolic processes. At that time scientists were beginning to investigate more closely the transformation of certain foods and their metabolic products. Liebig considered urea to be the measure of the protein metabolism in the tissue, whereas F. H. Bidder and Carl Schmidt interpreted it merely as the result of the actual amount of protein in the food. In Bischoff's *Der Harn als Maass des Stoffwechsels* (Giessen, 1853), which was dedicated to Liebig, the findings of Bidder and Schmidt are corroborated, but the production of urea is ascribed to the metabolism of nitrogen-rich substances. Liebig's theory of nitrogen-containing structural foodstuffs and respiratory nitrogen-free foods is substantiated. In Munich, Bischoff had Carl Voit as his collaborator. They jointly investigated nutrition in carnivores (1860) under conditions of starvation, an all-meat diet, and an all-fat diet, among others. Fat and similar substances were considered to be heat producers, nitrogen-containing substances to be energy producers. Subsequently, Voit founded the Munich school of metabolic physiology.

Bischoff had a gift for oratory and was a popular banquet speaker and eulogist. His eulogies of Johannes Müller and Friedrich Tiedemann and his address honoring Liebig's achievements in physiology are valuable documents in the history of natural science.

Somewhat peculiar is Bischoff's brusque rejection of women as university students in *Das Studium und die Ausübung der Medizin durch Frauen, beleuchtet durch Dr. Th. L. W. v. Bischoff* (1872). According to him, unqualified, half-trained female "artisans" impede and "most disastrously" disrupt the further development of medicine. Bischoff's life was filled with unflinching scientific labor, involving experiments, preparations, observations, comparisons, readings, and weighings. He investigated many subjects and left indelible marks on many areas. His vigor and his strong will, his firm character and integrity are testified to by all biographers.

BIBLIOGRAPHY

I. ORIGINAL WORKS. Complete bibliographies of Bischoff's works are in the biographies by Kupffer and Sudhoff (see below). Among his major writings are "Berichte über die Fortschritte der Physiologie," in Johannes Müller, ed., *Archiv für Anatomie, Physiologie und wissenschaftliche Medizin für die Jahre 1839–1847; Entwicklungsgeschichte des Kaninchens* (Brunswick, 1842); *Entwicklungsgeschichte der Säugetiere und des Menschen,* Vol. VII of Samuel Thomas von Sömmering's *Vom Baue des menschlichen Körpers,* new ed. (Leipzig, 1843); *Beweis der von der Begattung unabhängigen periodischen Reifung und Loslösung der Eier der Säugetiere und des Menschen* (Giessen, 1844); *Entwicklungsgeschichte des Hundeeies* (Brunswick, 1845); *Entwicklungsgeschichte des Reheies* (Giessen, 1854); *Die Gesetze der Ernährung des Fleischfressers durch neue Untersuchungen festgestellt* (Leipzig–Heidelberg, 1860), written with Carl Voit; "Über die Bildung des Säugetier-Eies und seine Stellung in der Zellenlehre," in *Sitzungsberichte der Königlichen Bayerischen Akademie der Wissenschaften zu München,* **1** (1863), 242; *Das Studium und die Ausübung der Medizin durch Frauen* (Munich, 1872); *Gedanken eines Naturforschers über die Natur des Menschen und über die Religion* (Bonn, 1878); and *Das Hirngewicht des Menschen. Eine Studie* (Bonn, 1880).

II. SECONDARY LITERATURE. Biographies of Bischoff with full bibliographies are Carl Kupffer, *Gedächtnisrede auf Theodor L. W. von Bischoff, 28.III.1884* (Munich, 1884); and Karl Sudhoff, "Bischoff, Theodor Ludwig Wilhelm (von)," in *Hessische Lebensbilder,* **3** (1928), 1–11. See also *Allgemeine Deutsche Biographie,* XLVI (1902), 570; *Almanach der Königlichen Bayerischen Akademie der Wissenschaften* (1875), pp. 182–187 (1878), pp. 133–134; *Biographisches Lexikon der hervorragenden Ärzte,* 2nd ed. (Berlin-Vienna, 1929–1935), II, 550–551; and *Index Catalogue of the Library of the Surgeon-General's Office, U.S. Army, Washington,* 1st ser., II (Washington, D.C., 1881), 72–73; 2nd ser., II (Washington, D.C., 1897), 353–354.

K. E. ROTHSCHUH

BISTERFELD, JOHANN HEINRICH (*b.* Siegen, Germany, *ca.* 1605; *d.* Weissenburg, Transylvania [now Alba Iulia, Rumania], 16 February 1655), *philosophy, theology.*

Bisterfeld's father, Johann, was a minister and professor of theology. He published a book on Ramist dialectics, and died while attending the Synod of Dort in 1619. The mother's maiden name was Schickard, and she appears to have been a sister of Martin Schickard, also of Siegen, professor of jurisprudence at Heidelberg and later at Deventer. As a student at the reformed University of Herborn, Bisterfeld studied under Comenius' teacher, Johann Heinrich Alsted, whose *Encyclopaedia* he is said to have known by heart at the age of sixteen. He may have studied in England in the middle 1620's, but in any case he matriculated at the University of Leiden on 3 November 1626, where he made the acquaintance of André Rivet, with whom he later corresponded. In 1628 Bisterfeld traveled in the Netherlands. He married Alsted's daughter Anna, but it is not known exactly when or where.

Early in 1629, Bisterfeld and Alsted were invited by Gabriel Bethlen, prince of Transylvania, to join the newly established (1622) academy in Weissenburg. Under the pressure of the dislocations caused by the Thirty Years' War in Nassau, they accepted the call to Transylvania, where Bisterfeld was professor of philosophy and theology until his death. His successor was the French-English traveler and divine Isaac Basire. During the late 1630's and the early 1640's, Bisterfeld also performed diplomatic duties for György Rákóczy I, in order to secure an alliance with France and Sweden against the Holy Roman Empire. Owing to the hesitation of Sweden, this alliance was not effected until 1643. In late July 1638, he arrived in Paris, where he conferred with Marin Mersenne. He spent the remainder of the year in western Europe, including Hamburg and Amsterdam.

Owing to the efforts of Rivet, Bisterfeld received a call to the University of Leiden, a position that would have satisfied his desire to return to "the more cultivated parts of Europe," but Rákóczy did not wish to lose so useful a man. Bisterfeld corresponded with Samuel Hartlib, John Dury, Theodore Haak, and others of their circle, and like them he looked forward to the union of the divided Protestant churches. A projected visit to Hartlib in London late in 1638 did not occur, but Bisterfeld's name figures in Hartlib's plans for an office of correspondence.

The philosophical basis of Bisterfeld's thought was the Ramism that reigned at the University of Herborn, and he also had much in common with Alsted and Comenius on other points: He shared their respect for Bacon, Ramón Lull, and Campanella, as well as their chiliasm and their belief in the universal harmony of all creation; universal knowledge, or pansophy, was their common aim. The Trinity was the source, norm, and end of all order. Philosophy was the pedagogue to theology, and Scriptures were the foundation of philosophy. Bisterfeld differed from Alsted and Comenius in his greater insight into the philosophical requirements of the system that would reveal the universal harmony and thus put man in control of nature. "Whatever is most true in philosophy," Bisterfeld said, "is also most useful in practice." He criticized Bacon and Campanella for failing to pay sufficient attention to Lull's *Ars magna,* and Comenius for ignoring metaphysics, for the lack of a strict method that would tie his system together.

Bisterfeld was strongly impressed by the need for a consistent terminology and precise definitions. It was not enough to "open the door to languages," as Comenius had done; Bisterfeld's nomenclature would be a "new door" ("nomenclator meus sit porta linguarum reformata"). On this point, Bisterfeld may have influenced projects for a philosophical language through his *Alphabeti philosophici libri tres* (1661). But he also saw the need to go beyond terminology. He realized more fully than his contemporaries the value of an *ars combinatoria,* or a logic of relations, as an Ariadne thread to serve as a guide in the labyrinth of the encyclopedia of knowledge. It was the chief aim of philosophy to reduce all the principles of particular areas of knowledge to the fewest possible common principles; it was the soul of practical theology to demonstrate that all things could be referred back to God.

This aspect of Bisterfeld's work had a strong effect on the young Leibniz, who read and commented upon Bisterfeld's most important philosophical writings during his student years at Leipzig. He noted that the *Philosophiae primae seminarium* was "a most brilliant little work whose equal in this kind I have not seen," and called the *Phosphorus catholicus, seu artis meditandi epitome* "a most ingenious little book." Together with the *Elementorum logicorum libri tres,* both were published at Leiden in 1657, but the *Phosphorus* had already been separately printed at Breda in 1649. In these works Leibniz seems first to have encountered the idea of universal harmony and the suggestion of a mathematical mode of logical calculation. Among the passages he especially noted was the statement that "logic is nothing but a mirror of relations." Leibniz remarked that "Bisterfeld proceeds in metaphysics almost like Bacon in physics," and he was fully aware of the affinity between Lull's and Bisterfeld's art of combinations. In his *De uno Deo, Patre, Filio ac Spiritu Sancto, mysterium pietatis* (Leiden, 1639; Amsterdam, 1645) Bisterfeld provided a detailed critique of Socinianism, directed against a work by Johannes Crellius.

BIBLIOGRAPHY

I. ORIGINAL WORKS. Bisterfeld's works are sparsely represented in even the largest libraries. His posthumous works were published as *Bisterfeldius redivivus,* 2 vols. (Leiden, 1661). Vol. I contains *Alphabeti philosophici.* Excerpts with Leibniz' comments are in Leibniz, *Sämtliche Schriften und Briefe,* 6th ser., *Philosophische Schriften,* I (Darmstadt, 1930), 151-161. An important letter to Hartlib is in J. Kvačala, ed., *Die pädagogische Reform des Comenius in Deutschland,* I, *Texte* (Berlin, 1903), 112-118 (*Monumenta Germaniae paedagogica,* XXVI).

II. SECONDARY LITERATURE. J. Kvačala, "Johann Heinrich Bisterfeld," in *Ungarische Revue,* **13** (1893), 40-59, 171-197, is diffuse and not entirely reliable. See also Kvačala, in *Die pädagogische Reform des Comenius in Deutschland,* II, *Historischer Überblick, Bibliographie, Namen und Sachregister* (Berlin, 1904), Index (*Monumenta Germaniae paedagogica,* XXXII). Interesting information about Bisterfeld in general and his work as a diplomat in particular is in I. Hudita, *Histoire des relations diplomatiques entre la France et la Transylvanie au XVIIᵉ siècle (1635-1683)* (Paris, 1927), esp. pp. 43-47, 57-58. See also Hudita, ed., *Répertoire des documents concernant les négociations diplomatiques entre la France et la Transylvanie au XVIIᵉ siècle (1636-1683)* (Paris, 1926), esp. pp. 61-68. Leroy E. Loemker offers a good account of Bisterfeld's philosophical position in "Leibniz and the Herborn Encyclopedists," in *Journal of the History of Ideas,* **22** (1961), 323-338. See also Paolo Rossi, *Clavis universalis* (Milan, 1960), pp. 197-200, 238-239. Much useful information can be gathered from letters and editorial notes in *Correspondance du P. Marin Mersenne,* Cornélis de Waard, ed. (Paris, 1932-   ), by tracing Bisterfeld through the indexes to VII (1962), VIII (1963), IX (1965), and X (1967), so far the last published.

HANS AARSLEFF

AL-BIṬRŪJĪ AL-ISHBĪLĪ, ABŪ ISḤĀQ, also

known as **Alpetragius** (his surname probably derives from Pedroche, Spain, near Cordoba; *fl.* Seville, *ca.* 1190), *astronomy, natural philosophy.*

Al-Biṭrūjī's only extant work is *De motibus celorum,* originally written in Arabic. He was a contemporary of Ibn Rushd (Averroës), and his astronomical system aroused much interest among such Christian natural philosophers as Albertus Magnus, Robert Grosseteste, and Roger Bacon. For a detailed study of his life and work, see Supplement.

BIZZOZERO, GIULIO CESARE (*b.* Varese, near Milan, Italy, 20 March 1846; *d.* Turin, Italy, 8 April 1901), *histology.*

Bizzozero was the son of Felice Bizzozero, a small manufacturer, and Carolina Veratti. After studying classics at Milan, he went to Pavia for medical study and received the M.D. in 1866. Upon graduation, Bizzozero enlisted in the army of Garibaldi as a military physician. The war against Austria ended within the year, and in 1867 he was appointed substitute professor of general pathology at the University of Pavia. He taught there until 1872; in that year Bizzozero became ordinary professor of general pathology at Turin. For almost thirty years he was a well-known teacher and researcher at Turin. Among the more illustrious of his pupils were Camillo Bozzolo, Camillo Golgi, Pio Foà, Gaetano Salvioli, and Cesare Sacerdotti. The school of Bizzozero in Turin and, later, the school of Alessandro Lustig in Florence were the first Italian teaching centers in general pathology.

A man of wide medical learning, Bizzozero was among the first to understand the importance to medicine of the microscope. In 1878 he instituted an annual course in clinical microscopy as an aid to the exhaustive study of sick persons. In 1879 he published his *Manuale di microscopia clinica,* later reprinted many times and translated into German. Three years before, Bizzozero had founded the *Archivio per le scienze mediche.* Stricken, after 1890, by a distressing debility of the right eye, he was unable to continue his own microscopical observations. He therefore devoted himself more and more to writing works that would develop an awareness of the need for public health measures. As early as 1883 Bizzozero set forth his program: the defense of mankind against infectious diseases. In 1890, he was appointed a senator.

Bizzozero was trained in scientific research by Eusebio Oehl, director of the laboratory of experimental physiology of Pavia University, and by Paolo Mantegazza, who in 1861 had founded the laboratory of general pathology at Pavia, the first in Italy. But the direction of Bizzozero's research was morphological. From his first paper in 1862 to his last paper in 1900, he was, essentially, a histologist. Bizzozero was so convinced of the importance of microscopical morphology that in 1880 he began, on his own initiative, to teach normal histology at Turin, a free course which he continued until his death.

Bizzozero was, undoubtedly, one of the outstanding histologists of his time. Of highest importance were his works on epithelial tissues—for instance, his studies of stratified squamous epithelium in 1870 and 1886—but even earlier there was his paper of 1864,

"Delle cellule cigliate del reticolo malpighiano dell'epidermide," in which he demonstrated the connections between the cells of the Malpighian layer. In collaboration with Gaetano Salvioli, Bizzozero defined the mesothelium of the great serous membranes (pleural and peritoneal) as a continuous layer, without stomata, separating the serous cavity from the lymphatic vessels. He also published studies (1888–1893) on the gastric and intestinal glands of mammals. Bizzozero thus contributed decisively to epithelial histology, fundamental knowledge of which had begun with the work of Jacob Henle.

Equally important were Bizzozero's observations on connective tissue: he illustrated (1865, 1872, 1873) the cells of the meninges and showed that tumors of the meninges (meningiomas) arise from the connective tissue cells of the meninges proper, not from the endothelial cells of blood vessels. In the structure of tendons he showed that the tendinous cells are in direct contact with the collagenous fibers. Special attention should be given to his work on the structure of the lymphatic glands. In 1872 Bizzozero clarified the peculiarity of cytoplasmatic relations between the cells and the fibers of the reticulum: "The cells are only applied on the reticulum, and they do not take integrated part in the constitution of reticulum." Bizzozero also anticipated actual knowledge of the "reticular cell," the staminal element of lymph nodes which he first called *cellula del reticolo*. He defined the important morphological problem of the sinuses of lymph nodes, demonstrating the existence of endothelial cells (reticuloendothelial cells) on the internal wall of sinuses. In 1868 Bizzozero demonstrated the erythrocytopoietic function of bone marrow, which he illustrated in several works, and in 1869 he discovered the megakaryocytes.

Bizzozero then undertook the solution of very important biological problems. In his first experimental work (1866) he demonstrated that granulation tissue originated as a consequence of the proliferative activity of mobile cells of loose connective tissue proper—cells which, for their high potentiality, he termed "embryonal cells" of loose connective tissue. Bizzozero also delineated the morphology of these "wandering polyblastic cells," knowledge of which was developed from 1902 to 1906 by the Russian histologist Alexander Maximov. Moreover, in this work Bizzozero demonstrated that in the neoproduction of granulation tissue there is also a neoproduction of capillaries; he described their development from compact cellular cordons in which a vascular cavity appears secondarily. This important observation was confirmed in 1871 by Julius Arnold in his *Experimentelle Untersuchungen über die Blutcapillaren.*

With his work on granulation tissue, Bizzozero was, with Virchow and Cohnheim, among the pioneers in the modern study of inflammation. Bizzozero's observations went further, however, for he first illustrated the power of ingestion (phagocytosis) as characteristic of the great mobile cells of loose connective tissue, of similar cells of bone marrow, and of the reticular cells of lymph nodes—a capacity to ingest damaged cells as well as the products of an inflammatory process: "The *celluliferous* cells [macrophages containing dead leukocytes] are large cells of connectival origin, which introduce into the proper contractile protoplasm the pus corpuscles [leukocytes]. . . . The finding of these celluliferous cells is not interpretable as a process of 'endogenesis' [as Rudolf Virchow then thought in his erroneous doctrine of endogenous cell formation], but as the effect of ingestion of pus corpuscles. . . . These great *celluliferous* cells unquestionably possess the power to devour pus corpuscles, erythrocytes, pigment granules."

In 1873 Bizzozero affirmed, ten years before Metchnikoff, that connective tissue cells (reticular cells of lymph nodes) act also against infection: "These cells, which contain granules of cinnebar or China ink 2–3 days after the injection in the subcutaneous connective tissue of those substances, constitute a very intricate labyrinth, through which the liquid carried from the lymphatic vessels is obliged to flow, and the corpuscles carried by the liquid, coming in contact with the protoplasm of reticular cells, are ingested by them. This fact is, perhaps, the cause of stoppage of some infections in the lymph nodes in which the lymphatic vessels arrive from the part overwhelmed by infection's products."

Although the name of Bizzozero is not linked with phagocytosis today, it is associated with the platelets. Knowing that Max Schultze in 1865 had described the presence, in the blood of healthy man, of irregular accumulations which he termed "granular formations," Bizzozero demonstrated in 1882 that they were normal elements of the blood and that they were linked to the phenomenon of thrombosis—hence their name of "thrombocytes."

BIBLIOGRAPHY

I. ORIGINAL WORKS. Bizzozero's works are collected in *Le opere scientifiche di Giulio Bizzozero,* 2 vols. (Milan, 1905), with a preface by Camillo Golgi, which contains all of Bizzozero's works, complete with original illustrations. For Bizzozero's research on thrombocytes, see especially his "Di un nuovo elemento morfologico del sangue e della sua importanza nella trombosi e nella coagulazione del sangue," in *Archives italiennes de biologie,* **2** (1882),

345–365; and "Ueber einen neuen Formbestandteil des Blutes, und dessen Rolle bei der Thrombose und der Blutgerinnung," in *Virchow's Archiv,* **90** (1882), 261–280. He also published a short book: *Di un nuovo elemento morfologico del sangue . . .* (Milan, 1883).

II. SECONDARY LITERATURE. Works on Bizzozero are R. Fusari, "Giulio Bizzozero," in *Monitore zoologico italiano,* **12** (1901), 103–107, a complete list of his work; and P. Franceschini, "La conoscenza dei tessuti connettivi nelle ricerche di Giulio Bizzozero," in *Physis,* **4** (1962), 227–267, which includes an extensive bibliography.

PIETRO FRANCESCHINI

BJERKNES, CARL ANTON (*b.* Christiania [later Kristiania, now Oslo], Norway, 24 October 1825; *d.* Kristiania, 20 March 1903), *mathematics, physics.*

Bjerknes was the son of Abraham Isaksen Bjerknes, a veterinarian, and Elen Birgitte Holmen. Both of his parents were of peasant stock, and throughout his life Bjerknes retained strong ties to his relatives in the country. The father, who as the youngest son did not inherit any land, died in 1838, leaving his widow and three children in straitened circumstances. In 1844 Bjerknes entered the University of Christiania and completed his undergraduate studies in 1848 with a degree in mining engineering. After several years at the Kongsberg silver mines (1848–1852) and as a mathematics teacher (1852–1854), he was awarded a fellowship that enabled him to study mathematics in Göttingen and Paris (1856–1857). The lectures of Dirichlet made a great impression on him and turned his interest to hydrodynamics, which later became the main subject of his research.

In 1859 Bjerknes married Aletta Koren, daughter of a minister. Two years later he was appointed lecturer in applied mathematics at the University of Christiania and was promoted to professor in 1866; in 1869 the professorship was converted to a chair of pure mathematics.

Bjerknes had a delightful personality and was an excellent teacher who was greatly respected by his students for his personal qualities and outstanding lectures. As the years passed, however, he showed an increasing tendency to professional isolation and a fear of publishing the results of his research, which was concerned mainly with hydrodynamic problems. Apart from the very close cooperation with his son Vilhelm, he lived for the most part in his own world. At one point Vilhelm had to extricate himself from this collaboration in order to avoid the danger of unproductive isolation. Nevertheless, in many fields he contributed to the elucidation and continuation of his father's theories.

Bjerknes had been particularly impressed by Dirichlet's demonstration that, according to the principles of hydrodynamics, a ball can move at a constant speed and without external force through ideal (frictionless) fluids, i.e., without the fluid's offering resistance to the ball's movement. Earlier, he had been greatly influenced by Leonhard Euler's *Lettres à une princesse d'Allemagne,* in which Euler opposed the concept of certain forces, such as Newtonian gravity, which are presumed to work at a distance rather than through an overall encompassing medium or ether. One of the strongest objections to the ether theory had always been the difficulty in understanding that according to the principle of inertia, a body not influenced by force should be able to move through such a medium without resistance, but in his lectures Dirichlet had proved that this was possible for movements in the frictionless fluids of hydrodynamics.

Slowly, Bjerknes developed the notion that it was possible, on the basis of hydrodynamics, to form a general theory of the forces active between the solid elements and the influence of the forces on the movements of those elements. First he studied the movement of a ball of variable volume through frictionless fluid according to the method of mathematical physics, and was thus led to further calculations of the simultaneous movements of two such balls. In this way he arrived at the historical conclusion, in 1875, that two harmoniously pulsating balls moving through frictionless fluid react as though they were electrically charged, i.e., they attract or repel one another with a force similar to that of Coulomb's law: they repulse one another when performing harmoniously pulsating oscillations in opposite phases (i.e., when one has maximum volume and the other's volume is minimal); conversely, they attract each other when oscillating in the same phase, thus attaining maximum or minimum volume at the same time.

This important discovery was followed by a number of tests that further stressed the analogy between the movement of bodies in frictionless fluids and the phenomena of electrodynamics. This research, which Bjerknes carried out in collaboration with his son, was substantiated by experiments that drew considerable attention at the electrical exhibition held in Paris in 1881.

Bjerknes' goal was now to develop this analogy to include Maxwell's general theory for electrodynamic phenomena, but despite his intensive efforts he did not attain this goal. His "hydrodynamic picture of the world" and his efforts to explain the electromagnetic forces through hydrodynamics are today more a fascinating analogy than a basic physical theory, yet through this research Bjerknes attained a great insight into hydrodynamic phenomena and thus anticipated later developments in several fields. It is especially noteworthy that through his efforts to describe the action of a magnetic field on an electric current he came to the conclusion that a cylinder rotating in a moving fluid is influenced by a force of the type that today is known as the hydrodynamic transverse force.

Shortly before his father's death Vilhelm Bjerknes published a work on long-range hydrodynamic forces as formulated in his father's theories. In it he explains and clarifies the important results of his father's research.

BIBLIOGRAPHY

I. Original Works. Among Bjerknes' writings are *Niels Henrik Abel, en skildring af hans liv og videnskabelige virksomhed* (Stockholm, 1880) and *Hydrodynamische Fernkräfte. Fünf Abhandlungen,* no. 195 in the series Ostwald's Klassiker der exakten Wissenschaften (Leipzig, 1915).

II. Secondary Literature. Works on Bjerknes are Vilhelm Bjerknes, *Vorlesungen über hydrodynamische Fernkräfte nach C. A. Bjerknes's Theorie,* 2 vols. (Leipzig, 1900–1902); "Til minde om professor Carl Anton Bjerknes," in *Forhandlinger i Videnskabs-selskabet i Kristiania,* no. 7 (1903), 7–24; *Fields of Force* (New York, 1906); *Die Kraftfelder* (Brunswick, 1909); and *C. A. Bjerknes. Hans liv og arbejde* (Oslo, 1925), translated as *Carl Anton Bjerknes. Sein Leben und seine Arbeit* (Berlin, 1933); Elling Holst, "C. A. Bjerknes som matematiker," in *Det Kongelige Frederika Universitet 1811–1911,* II (Kristiania, 1911); and Holtsmark, in *Norsk biografisk leksikon,* I, 581–583.

Mogens Pihl

BJERKNES, VILHELM FRIMANN KOREN (*b.* Christiania [later Kristiania, now Oslo], Norway, 14 March 1862; *d.* Oslo, 9 April 1951), *physics, geophysics.*

Bjerknes was the son of Carl Anton Bjerknes and Aletta Koren. His life and scientific activities were strongly influenced by his father; even in boyhood he became interested in the elder Bjerknes' hydrodynamic research, especially in the experimental verification of his father's discovery of the generation of forces between pulsating and rotating bodies in ideal (frictionless) fluids. His collaboration with his father was also necessary because the elder Bjerknes, who had never received any formal training in experimental physics, was rather impractical. It should be noted, however, that at an early age Bjerknes was able to give an independent, even critical, evaluation of his father's research. On the other hand, he defended his father's memory with great devotion and gave a clearer and more general explanation of his theoretical thinking in *Vorlesungen über hydrodynamische Fernkräfte nach C. A. Bjerknes' Theorie* and in *Die Kraftfelder.*

Bjerknes began his scientific studies at the University of Kristiania in 1880 and in 1888 received the M.S. During the last years of his studies he decided to cease collaborating with his father, a decision that must certainly have been very difficult to make but is a tribute to the maturity and independence with which Bjerknes regarded his possibilities for scientific research. In spite of his great devotion to his father, he was fully aware of the drawbacks to the elder Bjerknes' scientific isolation and one-sidedness, and feared that he himself could become a victim of the same circumstances. At this time he decided that after completing his education in mathematics and physics and obtaining a position that afforded him comparative peace and security, he would complete his father's work as far as possible.

After completing his studies, Bjerknes went to Paris on a state fellowship; there he attended Henri Poincaré's lectures on electrodynamics, during which Heinrich Hertz's studies on the diffusion of electrical waves were mentioned. He then went to Bonn, where he worked for nearly two years as Hertz's assistant and first scientific collaborator. For the rest of his life he remained a close friend of the Hertz family and helped Hertz's widow and daughter in 1933, when they had to flee the Nazis and seek refuge in England. This collaboration with Hertz resulted in some very important scientific publications on resonance in oscillatory circuits; and the theoretical and experimental resonance curves discovered by Bjerknes, along with a work by Poincaré, were of considerable importance for the understanding and final proof of Hertz's revolutionary experiments.

After his return to Norway, Bjerknes continued his studies, obtaining the Ph.D. in 1892 on the basis of the dissertation "Elektricitetsbevaegelsen i Hertz's primaere leder." It was his research in this field that especially qualified him for appointment as lecturer in applied mechanics at Stockholm's Högskola (School of Engineering) in 1893 and his appointment as professor of applied mechanics and mathematical physics at the University of Stockholm in 1895. Even though he abandoned experimental research in this field fairly soon, he retained a deep interest in the problems of electrodynamics for the rest of his life.

During the following years Bjerknes worked on his father's theories of hydrodynamic forces, which he succeeded in explaining in a simpler form than that based on his father's calculations of such specific examples as forces between pulsating balls in frictionless fluids. These investigations resulted in the two-volume work *Vorlesungen über hydrodynamische Fernkräfte nach C. A. Bjerknes's Theorie* (1900–1902). Later he often returned to the problem of force fields, which he treated in a simple, clear-cut fashion in two books published in 1906 and 1909.

During the period of his hydrodynamic studies, Bjerknes generalized on the well-known propositions of Lord Kelvin and Hermann Helmholtz concerning the so-called velocities of circulation and the conservation of the circular vortex. He then applied this generalization to the movements in the atmosphere and the ocean.

Bjerknes' generalization depended on the introduction of a broader interpretation of the concept of fluids than that normally used in classical hydrodynamic theory, which assumes that a unique relationship exists between pressure and the specific volume (the volume of a unit mass). He perceived the fluids as thermodynamic systems, which made it necessary to renounce such an unambiguous relationship, and was led to the formulation of the theory of physical hydrodynamics.

In this connection, however, reference should be made to the contribution made in 1896 by L. Silberstein, at that time unknown to Bjerknes, who developed one of Bjerknes' two circulation theorems without comprehending its far-reaching implications. The atmospheric movements that cause weather changes result from the radiation of heat from the sun, and the atmosphere thus works as a sort of thermodynamic heat engine that is constantly converting heat to mechanical energy; it also emits heat because of the friction resulting from atmospheric movements. It is therefore necessary, when atmospheric movements are described, to produce the synthesis of classical hydrodynamics and thermodynamics that results from the formulation of the theory of physical hydrodynamics.

Although he realized that it would not be completed in the near future, Bjerknes planned an ambitious program as the final goal of this research: he hoped to be able, with the help of the hydrodynamic and thermodynamic theories, to use knowledge of the present conditions of the atmosphere and hydrosphere to calculate their future conditions. During a visit to the United States in 1905 he presented these plans, and received from the Carnegie Foundation an annual stipend to support his research in this field. The grant continued until 1941.

During his period as professor at the University of Stockholm, Bjerknes began collaboration with various scientists, for which he was eminently suited because of his stimulating intellect and deep understanding of his associates' need for independent development and research. Of special importance was his collaboration with J. W. Sandström, with whom he wrote the first volume of *Dynamic Meteorology and Hydrography* (1910). The second volume (1911), dealing with kinematics, was written with Th. Hesselberg and O. Devik. The projected third volume, dealing with dynamics, was completed by associates, but he lived to see its publication in 1951. In 1933 he coauthored a book with his son, Jack, and a friend of the son, H. Solberg, *Physikalische Hydrodynamik mit Anwendung auf die dynamische Meteorologie.*

After his return from Stockholm in 1907 Bjerknes became professor of applied mechanics and mathematical physics at the University of Kristiania, where he collaborated with Sandström, Hesselberg, Devik, and H. U. Sverdrup in developing dynamic meteorology. In 1912, when he was offered the professorship of geophysics at the University of Leipzig and the chairmanship of the newly organized geophysical institute, he decided to accept the offer, in the hope of better prospects. The new institute was started under the best possible conditions: Hesselberg and Sverdrup followed him to Leipzig, and a few years later both his son and Solberg joined them.

A visit from Fridtjof Nansen resulted in an offer to Bjerknes to take over a professorship at the University of Bergen and to start a geophysical institute there. He decided to accept the offer after assuring himself that the institute in Leipzig would be carried on. Bjerknes was fifty-five when he started working in Bergen, and he remained there until 1926. His years in Bergen were perhaps the most productive of his life. His main collaborators were again his son and Solberg; later they were joined by S. Rosseland, T. Bergeron, E. Bjørkdal, C. Rossby, and E. Palmén. Bjerknes himself continued to play an active role in both the practical implementation of extensive meteorological services and the work on theoretical meteorological problems. From this period came his now classic work *On the Dynamics of the Circular Vortex With Applications to the Atmosphere and to Atmospheric Vortex and Wave Motion* (1921). One of his finest books, it contains a clear explanation of the most important basic ideas in his research.

After his appointment as professor of applied mechanics and mathematical physics at the University of Oslo in 1926, Bjerknes continued his studies in dynamic meteorology in cooperation with Solberg, J. Holmboe, C. L. Godske, and E. Høiland. He became involved in the teaching of theoretical physics, but remained within the limits of classical physics, and in 1929 he published a small book on vector analysis and kinematics as the first part of a textbook in theoretical physics. The next volume planned, which was to include an explanation of the elder Bjerknes' "hydromagnetic" theory, was never completed. Despite intensive efforts, Bjerknes and Høiland never succeeded in finding a satisfactory formulation of this theory, which had occupied Bjerknes from his earliest years. This was a problem from which he could not, and would not, disengage himself.

BIBLIOGRAPHY

I. ORIGINAL WORKS. A bibliography of Bjerknes' works is in *Geofysiske publikationer,* **24** (1962), 26–37. Among his writings are "Über die Dämpfung schneller electrischer Schwingungen," in *Annalen der Physik,* **44** (1891), 74–79; and "Über electrische Resonanz," *ibid.,* **55** (1895), 121–169; *Über die Bildung von Cirkulationsbewegungen und Wirbeln in reibungslosen Flüssigkeiten,* no. 5 in *Skrifter udgivet af Videnskabsselskabet i Christiania,* I (1898), 1–29; "Über einen hydrodynamischen Fundamentalsatz und seine Anwendung besonders auf die Mechanik der Atmosfäre und des Weltmeeres," in *Kungliga Svenska vetenskapsakademiens handlingar,* **31**, no. 4 (1898–1899), 1–35; *Vorlesungen über hydrodynamische Fernkräfte nach C. A. Bjerknes's Theorie,* 2 vols. (Leipzig, 1900–1902); *Fields of Force* (New York, 1906); *Die Kraftfelder* (Brunswick, 1909); *Dynamic Meteorology and Hydrography,* 2 vols. (Washington, D.C., 1910–1911), Vol. I written with J. W. Sandström and Vol. II with Th. Hesselberg and O. Devik, also translated as *Dynamische Meteorologie und Hydrographie,* 2 vols. (Brunswick, 1912–1913); *On the Dynamics of the Circular Vortex With Applications to the Atmosphere and to Atmospheric Vortex and Wave Motion* (Kristiania, 1921); *C. A. Bjerknes. Hans liv og arbejde* (Oslo, 1925), translated as *C. A. Bjerknes. Sein Leben und seine Arbeit* (Berlin, 1933); *Teoretisk fysik* (Oslo, 1929); and *Physikalische Hydrodynamik mit Anwendung auf die dynamische Meteorologie* (Berlin, 1933), written with J. Bjerknes, H. Solberg, and T. Bergeron, translated as *Hydrodynamique physique avec applications à la météorologie dynamique* (Paris, 1934).

II. SECONDARY LITERATURE. Works on Bjerknes are T. Bergeron, "Vilhelm Bjerknes," in *Småskrifter udgivet af Universitet i Bergen,* no. 11 (1962), 7–30; T. Bergeron, O. Devik, and C. L. Godske, "Vilhelm Bjerknes," in *Geofysiske publikationer,* **24** (1962), 6–25; T. Hesselberg, in *Norsk biografisk leksikon,* I, 584–588; and Harald Wergeland, "Vilhelm Bjerknes," in *Det kongelige Norske videnskabers selskabs forhandlinger,* **24,** no. 16 (1951), 74–78.

MOGENS PIHL

BJERRUM, NIELS JANNIKSEN (*b.* Copenhagen, Denmark, 11 March 1879; *d.* Copenhagen, 30 September 1958), *chemistry, physics, history of science.*

Bjerrum was the son of the well-known ophthalmologist and university professor Jannik Petersen Bjerrum and Anna Johansen, and the nephew of Kirstine Bjerrum Meyer, who edited the works of Oersted (1920) and wrote an important treatise on the history of the concept of temperature, *Temperaturbegrebets udvikling* (1909). He completed his doctorate at the University of Copenhagen in 1908 under S. M. Jørgensen with a dissertation entitled *Studier over basiske kromiforbindelser: Bidrag til hydrolysens teori* (Copenhagen, 1908). He had begun to lecture on elementary inorganic chemistry in 1907, and in 1914 he was made professor of chemistry at the Royal Veterinary and Agricultural College in Copenhagen, a post he held until his retirement in 1949. During the early years of his career he studied with Robert Luther in Leipzig (1905), Alfred Werner in Zurich (1907), Jean Perrin in Paris (1910), and Walther Nernst in Berlin (1911). In 1907 Bjerrum married Ellen Emilie Dreyer. Their son Jannik has been professor of chemistry at the University of Copenhagen since 1948. In many ways his work is an extension of his father's.

In 1928 Bjerrum was awarded the Oersted Medal. He was a member of the Carlsberg Foundation, the Rask–Oersted Foundation, and the Committee of the Solvay Institute for Chemistry, as well as the academies of science of Denmark, Norway, Sweden, Vienna, and New York. His honorary memberships were in the chemical societies of Belgium, the Netherlands, Sweden, and Switzerland.

Noteworthy for the historian of science, primarily because it presents the point of view of a prominent theoretical and experimental physical chemist, is Bjerrum's *Fysik og kemi* (in *Det nittende aarhundrede,* **18** [1925], 71–192). This volume gives his interpretation of various late nineteenth-century developments in atomic theory, thermodynamics, the electromagnetic theory of light, relativity and the physics of the ether, and the structure of the atom. In a lecture of 1922, "Kemiens udvikling i det 19. aarhundrede," Bjerrum emphasized the historical importance of the "mathematization" of chemistry, the exploitation of the atomic theory for stereochemical considerations, and the coordination of science and technology, of theory and practice.

Bjerrum's contributions to chemical physics, an outgrowth of his work with Nernst in Berlin, were made primarily in four papers (1911–1914). They deal with the application of the kinetic and quantum theories, and employ information obtained from absorption measurements in the infrared to elucidate the constitution and the optical and thermal properties of matter. His theoretical studies on specific heat as a function of temperature for gases represent advances over the specific heat studies that had been made for solids by Einstein, Nernst, and Lindemann. In this work Bjerrum succeeded in demonstrating the interdependence of specific heats and the spectrum as required by the quantum theory. The infrared absorption spectra of water vapor were further related, on the quantum hypothesis, to line broadening caused by molecular rotational frequencies that vary discontinuously and to radiating atoms that do not rotate—thus providing agreement with specific heat investigations which suggest that the rotational energy of atoms must be very small.

In a number of more general papers, such as "Nyere undersøgelser over atomernes bevaegelser med saerligt henblik paa kvantehypotesen" (1915) and "Moderne atomlaere og kvanteteori" (1919), Bjerrum revealed an extraordinarily keen appreciation of the significance of the quantum theory for atomic-molecular problems in general.

Physical chemistry, theoretical as well as analytical, was Bjerrum's lifelong interest and is the subject of the major part of his publications. As early as 1909 Bjerrum proposed a new form for the electrolytic dissociation theory. In 1916, at the sixteenth meeting of Scandinavian scientists in Kristiana (Oslo), he presented, in a most convincing form, his now-celebrated view on the dissociation of strong electrolytes—according to which some acids and hydroxyl compounds, and most salts, are almost completely dissociated into ions in the dissolved state. Arrhenius, who was chairman of the meeting, had won the Nobel Prize in chemistry in 1903 for his electrolytic theory of dissociation, and was not willing to accept this extension of his own theory. Bjerrum's view, according to which the "anomalous" behavior of strong electrolytes should be interpreted in terms of interionic forces, was extended in a second paper in 1916 and then explored in depth in a series of studies (1920–1932) on electrolytic dissociation theory. These studies also dealt with the activity and distribution coefficients of ions, osmotic pressure, association of ions, the Debye-Hückel theory, and the solubility of gases.

The currently accepted method of introducing activity coefficients into the expression for the velocity of a chemical reaction was published in 1923 by the Danish chemist J. N. Brønsted in a paper entitled "Zur Theorie der chemischen Reaktionsgeschwindigkeit." Bjerrum's papers on chemical kinetics and the discussions that took place between the two men appeared in the *Zeitschrift für Chemie* of 1923–1925. Bjerrum's view on how his own new theories regarding acids, bases, and salts developed within the context of the older views of Brønsted is treated admirably in a lecture delivered before the Danish Chemical Society in 1931 ("Syrer, salte og baser").

Bjerrum's joint paper on Brownian motion with Jean Perrin, "L'agitation moléculaire dans les fluides visqueux" (1911), is noteworthy for having demonstrated that the equilibrium distribution of particles is independent of the viscosity of the fluid in the gravitational field.

The study of buffer mixtures and indicators, and the measurement of the hydrogen ion concentration of solutions, was an early and continuing interest. In a paper of 1905 Bjerrum introduced his well-known extrapolation method for the elimination of the diffusion potential. The theory upon which this study rests was developed further and improved by E. A. Guggenheim, who worked with Bjerrum for a number of years. In his study of the theory and the sources of error in acidimetric and alkalimetric titrations and of buffer solutions (*Die Theorie der alkalimetrischen und azidimetrischen Titrierungen* [Stuttgart, 1914]), Bjerrum showed how to determine the end point of a titration and how to estimate the error that accompanies the choice of pH values associated with the use of a particular indicator.

Bjerrum's contributions to the theory of acids and bases include a novel method of using the experimentally determined strength constants of different acidic and basic groups in a molecule to establish the constitution and dissociation constants of ampholytes, particularly of amino acids. In a paper of 1923 he applied the notion of the different strength constants of polybasic acids to the determination of molecular distances. On the practical side, Bjerrum's contributions to the needs of a country where agriculture is of paramount importance are seen in his papers devoted to the factors that determine the pH, and therefore the reaction, of the soil, the hardness of water, and the general application of physicochemical measurements to agricultural problems.

In his study of the coordination chemistry of inorganic complexes, Bjerrum went beyond the classical methods of analysis and synthesis of his teacher Jørgensen by emphasizing the importance of physicochemical principles. In 1906 Bjerrum published a comprehensive 120-page study on the chromic chlorides (*Studier over kromiklorid*) that revealed the existence and mode of isolation of the previously unknown chromium monochloropentaquo complex $[\text{Cr Cl (H}_2\text{O)}_5]^{++}$. Two years later, in his doctoral dissertation on the theory of hydrolysis of chromium compounds, he investigated the formation and relation between "truly basic" and "latently basic" complexes. Bjerrum's papers on the complex chromium and gold salts span a period of more than forty years.

Bjerrum also made substantial contributions to colloid theory, concentrating on the study of substances with high molecular weights, their colloidal properties (e.g., charge), and the preparation of collodion membranes with reproducible permeabilities (1924–1927).

The function of the thiocyanate group as a ligand in chromium and gold compounds was the subject of two significant papers of 1915 and 1918. In the second paper Bjerrum and Aage Kirschner proposed a sequence of reactions that explained the overall complex kinetics of the aqueous decomposition of dithiocyanogen—a compound the preparation of which from nonaqueous solution was first accomplished by Erik G. Söderbäck in 1919. In 1949 Bjerrum investigated the gold chloride complexes.

During the last decade of his life, Bjerrum extended his interest in problems of molecular structure to the study of ice. This work, summarized in *Structure and Properties of Ice* (1951), treats the position of the hydrogen atoms and their zero-point entropy, changes in configuration, ionization and "molecular turns," and the proton-jump conductivity of ice and water.

On the frontier where physics and chemistry interact, Niels Bjerrum achieved world renown during the early decades of this century. He published about eighty scientific papers (not including translations) and ten books and monographs. Best known among the latter is his *Laerbog i uorganisk kemi* (1916–1917), which went through six editions and was translated into English, German, and Russian.

BIBLIOGRAPHY

Niels Bjerrum, *Selected Papers,* ed. by friends and co-workers on the occasion of his seventieth birthday (Copenhagen, 1949), contains, besides the 27 selected papers trans. into English, J. A. Christiansen, "A Survey of the Scientific Papers of Niels Bjerrum," a foreword by Niels Bohr, and a bibliography of Bjerrum's scientific publications, books, and papers (1903–1948), items 1–92; J. A. Christiansen, "Niels Bjerrum," in *Fysisk tidsskrift,* **57** (1959), 24–36, appends a list of Bjerrum's publications (items 93–103) that appeared after the publication of the papers listed in *Selected Papers;* Aksel Tovborg Jensen, "Niels Bjerrum," in *Oversigt over det Kongelige Danske Videnskabernes Selskabs Virksomhed* (1958/1959), 99–113, is an excellent short account of his life. See also Stig Veibel, "N. J. Bjerrum," in *Dansk biografisk leksikon,* III (1934), 183–185; and *Kemien i Danmark,* II, *Dansk kemisk bibliografi 1880–1935* (Copenhagen, 1943), 61–67, which contains a list of Bjerrum's 80 publications that appeared 1908–1935.

ERWIN N. HIEBERT

BLACK, DAVIDSON (*b.* Toronto, Canada, 25 July 1884; *d.* Peking, China, 15 March 1934), *anatomy, anthropology.*

By tradition Black's family followed the law (his father was Queen's Counsel), but early in life he showed a marked interest in biology and natural history. In 1903 he enrolled in the medical school of the University of Toronto, graduating in 1909 with M.D. and M.A. degrees. His first post was at Western Reserve University, Cleveland, Ohio, as anatomist; there he and T. Wingate Todd built up the museum of comparative anthropology and anatomy begun in 1893 by C. A. Hamann.

In 1914 Black went to Manchester, England, on sabbatical leave to study advanced anthropology under Grafton Elliot Smith. There he learned also to make casts, a skill that later proved valuable to him. Under Smith's auspices in London he met Arthur Keith, Arthur Smith Woodward, and Frederick Wood Jones. From London he went to Amsterdam to study neuroanatomy under C. V. Ariëns Kappers at the Central Institute of Brain Research. On his return to Cleveland he wrote his paper "Brain in Primitive Man" (1915).

Through his experience abroad and as the result of his intensive study of a treatise by William Diller Matthews, *Climate and Evolution,* Black became convinced that Asia had probably been the realm of early man and the center of dispersal of land mammals. In 1920 he had the opportunity to explore this theory when he accepted an appointment as anatomist and neurologist at the Peking Union Medical College. Always a tireless worker, in China, Black launched his brilliant career, teaching, writing, conducting field expeditions, and gathering about him as friends and co-workers such men as J. Gunnar Andersson, Wong Wen-hao, V. K. Ting, A. W. Grabau, C. C. Young, G. B. Barbour, and Teilhard de Chardin. His search for hominid fossils took him to eastern Mongolia, the Gobi Desert, Siam, Honan, and Kansu, and finally concentrated twenty-five miles from Peking at Chou K'ou-tien in the western hills. Here extensive excavations were undertaken by the archaeologists, and Black studied all fossil-bearing material in the laboratories of the Peking Union Medical College.

In 1927 a well-preserved left molar was recovered, and after study Black pronounced a new hominid genus, which he named *Sinanthropus pekinensis* Black and Zansky. Under the archaeologist W. C. Pei the site yielded numerous teeth and pieces of jawbone with teeth *in situ*. On 1 December 1929, in a cave seventy feet below working level, an almost complete skull cap was found in an environment of extinct animal bones, crudely chipped stones, and man-made fires. In 1930 a second skull was recovered. Black himself freed the skulls of their heavy coating of travertine, made casts, and wrote his series of reports on the discovery, morphology, and environment of *Sinanthropus pekinensis*. Among the scientists who flocked to Peking to consult with Black and to examine the fossils and the cave excavations were Henri Breuil, Walter Granger, Aleš Hrdečha, and G. Elliot Smith.

In 1934 he died suddenly while working on *Sinanthropus pekinensis*.

Black was a fellow of the Royal Society of London and of the Geological Society of America, and an honorary member of the National Academy of Sciences, Washington, as well as of other scientific organizations.

BIBLIOGRAPHY

Black's works include "Brain in Primitive Man," in *Cleveland Medical Journal,* **14** (Mar. 1915), 177–185; "On a Lower Molar Hominid Tooth From the Chou Kou Tien Deposit," in *Palaeontologia Sinica,* ser. D, **7,** fasc. 1 (Nov. 1927), 1–28; "*Sinanthropus pekinensis:* The Recovery of Further Fossil Remains of This Early Hominid From the Chou Kou Tien Deposit," in *Science,* **69,** no. 1800 (June 1929), 674–676; "Preliminary Notice of the Discovery of an Adult *Sinanthropus* Skull at Choukoutien," in *Bulletin of the Geological Society of China,* **8,** no. 3 (1930), 207–230; "Notice of the Recovery of a Second Adult *Sinanthropus* Skull Specimen," *ibid.,* **9,** no. 2 (1930), 97–100; "On an Adolescent Skull of *Sinanthropus pekinensis* in Comparison With an Adult Skull of the Same Species and With Other Hominid Skulls, Recent and Fossil," in *Palaeontologica Sinica,* ser. D, **7,** fasc. 2 (1931), 1–144; "Present State of Knowledge Concerning the Morphology of *Sinanthropus,*" in *Proceedings of the Fifth Pacific Science Congress* (Vancouver, B.C., 1933); "Fossil Man in China: The Choukoutien Cave Deposits With a Synopsis of Our Present Knowledge of the Late Cenozoic in China," in *Memoirs of the Geological Survey of China,* ser. A, no. 11 (1933), 1–168, written with Teilhard de Chardin, C. C. Young, and W. C. Pei; and "On the Discovery, Morphology and Environment of *Sinanthropus pekinensis,*" in *Philosophical Transactions of the Royal Society,* **B223** (1934), 57–120.

See also Dora Hood, *Davidson Black, a Biography* (Toronto, 1964).

DORA HOOD

BLACK, JAMES (*b.* Scotland, *ca.* 1787; *d.* Edinburgh, Scotland, 30 April 1867), *medicine, geology.*

During the Napoleonic Wars, Black was a naval surgeon and served in the West Indies. Subsequently he practiced as a physician in Newton Stewart, Bolton, Manchester (1839–1849), and again in Bolton, until his retirement to Edinburgh in 1856.

In the course of caring for his patients, Black made careful observations and collected data that he related, through his wide medical reading, to medical theory and to social conditions. *Capillary Circulation* (1825) reports his only experimental work, mainly on capillaries in the feet of ducks and frogs, in which he repeated the experiments of John Thomson. In this work, Black describes the blood as moving faster in the arteries than in the veins, the anastomoses, and the effects of ammonia in decreasing the diameter of the blood vessels and speeding the flow of blood— which is followed by passive dilation, congestion, and typical symptoms of inflammation. He further reviews the literature and discusses the nature of inflammation, its causes and conditions, its symptoms, and its relation to capillary circulation. Black's work was not highly regarded by his colleagues, but he continued it in 1826 with *The Nature of Fever,* which similarly reviewed alternative hypotheses and contemporary practice.

In the spring of 1829, Black visited the United States, where he studied medical practice and education and wrote the appreciative and critical sketch of the state of medicine in America, which included descriptions of the institutions that he had visited in New York and Philadelphia. On returning to Bolton, he embarked on an extensive survey of that town, relating the physical and social environment to health and habits and noting industrial changes; this was published in 1837 as "Sketch of Bolton."

Black was also a competent amateur geologist and paleontologist and published a number of papers on these subjects; they were mostly local and descriptive, but they also dealt with such topics as submerged forests and coal formation. A founding member of the council of the Manchester Geological Society, he delivered an address to it, "On Some Objects and Uses of Geological Research," in which he discussed the development of organisms toward perfection in terms of successive acts of a Creative Power, in relation to changes in the environment.

Black was active and well loved in many spheres. His family life seems to have been happy and devout, and one of his sons also became a naval surgeon. He was a founder-member of the British Association in 1831, lectured on geology at the Bolton Mechanics

Institute, and served on the committee whose work resulted in the establishment of one of the first municipal public libraries (in Bolton) in 1853. In 1854 a lithographed portrait of Black was published by public subscription.

BIBLIOGRAPHY

I. ORIGINAL WORKS. Black's medical works include *A Short Inquiry Into the Capillary Circulation of the Blood* . . . (London, 1825); *A Comparative View of the More Intimate Nature of Fever* . . . (London, 1826); "A Sketch of the State of Medicine, and of Medical Schools and Institutions, in the United States of America . . .," in *New England Medical and Surgical Journal,* **1** (1830–1831), 209–219, 301–313, 398–409; and "A Medico-topographical, Geological, and Statistical Sketch of Bolton and Its Neighbourhood," in *Transactions of the Provincial Medical and Surgical Association,* **5** (1837), 125–224 and map.

His geological works include "On Some Objects and Uses of Geological Research," in *Transactions of the Manchester Geological Society,* **1** (1841), 1–34; and *An Eclectic View of Coal Formation* (Manchester, 1847).

II. SECONDARY LITERATURE. There is an anonymous "Obituary" in *British Medical Journal,* **1** (25 May 1867), 623. Signed works on Black are A. Sparke, "James Black," in *Bibliographia Boltonensis* (Manchester, 1913), pp. 26–27; C. W. Sutton, "James Black," in *Dictionary of National Biography,* V (London, 1886), pp. 106–107, which gives additional references; and P. A. Whittle, "James Black," in *Bolton-le-Moors* (Bolton, 1855), p. 392.

DIANA SIMPKINS

BLACK, JOSEPH (*b.* Bordeaux, France, 16 April 1728; *d.* Edinburgh, Scotland, 6 December 1799), *chemistry, physics, medicine.*

A founder of modern quantitative chemistry and discoverer of latent and specific heats, Joseph Black, although born in France, was by blood a pure Scot. His father, John Black, was a native of Belfast; his mother, Margaret Gordon, was the daughter of an Aberdeen man who, like John Black, had settled in Bordeaux as a factor, or commission merchant, in the wine trade.

John Black and Margaret Gordon were married at Bordeaux in 1716, apparently in the Catholic faith. Joseph, fourth of their twelve children, was first educated by his mother. At the age of twelve he was sent to Belfast, where he learned the rudiments of Latin and Greek in a private school. About 1744 he crossed the North Channel to attend, as did so many Ulster Scots, the University of Glasgow. Here he followed the standard curriculum until, pressed by his father to choose a profession, he elected medicine. At this point he began the study of anatomy and

attended the lectures in chemistry recently inaugurated by William Cullen. These lectures were the decisive influence on Black's career; chemistry captivated him, and for three years he served as Cullen's assistant. So began a close friendship that lasted until Cullen's death.

In 1752 Black left Glasgow for the more prestigious University of Edinburgh, which boasted on its medical faculty the great anatomist Alexander Monro *primus,* the physiologist Robert Whytt, and Charles Alston, a botanist and chemist who lectured on *materia medica.* Black gained less, he said, from their lectures than from the bedside clinical instruction provided by the university's Royal Infirmary. Alston's lectures pleased him most, although he found him deficient in chemical knowledge, a matter of concern, for, as he wrote to Cullen, "no branch should be more cultivated in a medical college."[1]

In 1754 Black received the M.D. with his now historic dissertation *De humore acido a cibis orto et magnesia alba.* The next year, before the Philosophical Society of Edinburgh, he described the chemical experiments, considerably expanded, that had formed the second half of his dissertation. This classic paper—the chief basis of Black's scientific renown and his only major publication—appeared in 1756 in the Society's *Essays and Observations* under the title "Experiments Upon Magnesia Alba, Quicklime, and Some Other Alcaline Substances." Here Black demonstrated that an aeriform fluid that he called "fixed air" (carbon dioxide gas) was a quantitative constituent of such alkaline substances as *magnesia alba,* lime, potash, and soda.

The same year, 1756, brought Cullen to Edinburgh as professor of chemistry, and saw Black—at the age of twenty-eight Cullen's outstanding student—replace him in Glasgow. Here Black spent the next ten years. Although this period is sparsely documented, we know that he soon emerged as a gifted and effective teacher. His course in chemistry, launched in 1757–1758, proved so popular that many students, some with no particular relish for the subject, pressed to attend. Alongside his teaching, Black carried on an active and demanding medical practice; and since Glasgow, unlike Edinburgh, was administered by its faculty, he was constantly pressed upon by multifarious college duties. Yet it was at Glasgow that he developed his ideas about latent and specific heats—the second of his major scientific achievements—and carried out experiments, alone or with his students, to confirm his theories. These important discoveries he could never be induced to publish.

In 1766 Black received the call to Edinburgh. William Cullen relinquished the chair of chemistry to succeed Robert Whytt as Professor of the Institutes of Medicine, and Black took over Cullen's chair. At Edinburgh he was destined to remain. Although his duties were less onerous than at Glasgow—he limited his medical practice to the care of a few close friends like David Hume—his period of scientific creativity was at an end. Two short papers on insignificant subjects were his only publications. The teaching of chemistry now became his central concern; here, as at Glasgow, he became an idol to the medical students and to many others as well. Each year, from October to May, he delivered a series of more than a hundred lectures, and sometimes offered a course during the summer months.

Black's pedagogic achievement at least equals that of his great French contemporary, G.-F. Rouelle. Although he had no student of the stature of Lavoisier, there were many of great ability. His audience was surprisingly cosmopolitan; although French students were rare, men came from Germany, Switzerland, Scandinavia, and from as far away as Russia and America, attracted by the reputation of the Scotch medical schools and of Black himself. Lorenz Crell, known as editor of early chemical journals, was one of his German students. To Edinburgh from the American colonies came such men as James McClurg, later a successful Richmond physician, and the still more famous Benjamin Rush. Black's British students were no less gifted. At Glasgow there were John Robison, who was to bring out in 1803 his master's *Lectures on Chemistry,* and William Irvine, Black's collaborator in the work on specific heat. His Edinburgh students included Thomas Charles Hope, who succeeded him in 1797; Daniel Rutherford, the discoverer of nitrogen; and John McLean, who emigrated to America in 1795, where he became Princeton's first professor of chemistry. Among the last to hear Black lecture were Thomas Young, the versatile physician, physicist, and linguist; the elegant and prolific Henry Brougham; and Thomas Thomson, chemist and pioneer historian of chemistry.

There are several contemporary descriptions of the appearance, personality, and lecturing skills of this great teacher. On the platform he was an immaculate figure; his voice was low but so clear that he was heard without difficulty by an audience of several hundred. His style was simple, his tone conversational, far different from Rouelle's flamboyance. He spoke extemporaneously from the scantiest of notes; yet his lectures, of which numerous manuscript versions by his students have survived, were models of order and precision: the facts and experiments led a listener by imperceptible degrees to the theories and principles by which he explained them. Vivid accounts of his own discoveries, and demonstration experiments conducted with unvarying success were the highlights of his performance. He kept abreast of the progress of chemistry: through the years the outline of the lectures remained the same, but new material was added as chemistry, that "opening science," as he called it, steadily advanced; and Black told his students of new discoveries and theories, and of the men who had made them.

Black was a typical valetudinarian; never robust, he suffered all his life from chronic ill health, perhaps pulmonary in origin. With only limited reserves of energy, he nevertheless managed by careful diet and moderate exercise—hours of walking were part of his regimen—to husband his strength. In his prime, as the portrait by David Martin depicts him, he was a handsome man; and even in old age his appearance was impressive. Henry Cockburn, who saw Black in his last years, gives the following description:

> He was a striking and beautiful person; tall, very thin, and cadaverously pale; his hair carefully powdered, though there was little of it except what was collected in a long thin queue; his eyes dark, clear, and large, like deep pools of pure water. He wore black speckless clothes, silk stockings, silver buckles, and either a slim green silk umbrella, or a genteel brown cane. The general frame and air were feeble and slender. The wildest boy respected Black. No lad could be irreverent towards a man so pale, so gentle, so elegant, and so illustrious. So he glided, like a spirit, through our rather mischievous sportiveness, unharmed.[2]

And so we see him, on one of his increasingly rare strolls, pictured by the sharp eye of the caricaturist John Kay: slim, slightly stooped, an intent and pensive figure.

Black never married, but he was no recluse. Calm, self-possessed, gentle, and a trifle diffident, he nevertheless enjoyed conviviality. Until at last his health failed him, he frequented, besides the Philosophical Society and the Royal Society of Edinburgh which replaced it in 1783, those informal clubs for which Edinburgh was famous: the Select, the Poker, and the Oyster. The Oyster, a weekly dining club, was his favorite; indeed, with his two closest friends, Adam Smith and the geologist James Hutton, he had founded it. Other members were his cousin Adam Ferguson, William Cullen, Dugald Stewart, John Playfair, and James Hall: in a word, the scientific luminaries of that remarkable Scotch Renaissance. Since the rising industrialists of the region were often at table—John Roebuck, Lord Dundonald, for example, and visitors like Henry Cort—the Oyster might be compared with the famous Lunar Society of

Birmingham, for discussion often turned on the role of science in technological progress.

One after another Black's friends passed from the scene: Cullen in 1790 and William Robertson, principal of the University of Edinburgh, in 1793. Adam Smith was the first of the triumvirate to die, but increasing infirmity afflicted the two surviving members. Hutton, wasted by years and illness, fell gravely ill in the winter of 1796/97. Black, too, found his feeble strength waning. He gave his last full course of lectures in 1795–1796; but, aware of his debility, he chose Thomas Charles Hope as his assistant and eventual successor. The next year his health worsened, and Hope in effect took over. For a time Black's health improved slightly, and he lingered on two more years. The manner of his death was so peaceful, in a way so characteristic of his methodical and undramatic life, that it has been several times recounted. Curiously, the early authorities on Black's life are mistaken about the date of his death, variously given as November 26 (Adam Ferguson, John Robison, and Lord Brougham) and November 10 (Thomson, also quoted by his modern biographer, Sir William Ramsay). But a letter from Robison to James Watt settles the point: Black died on 6 December 1799, in his seventy-second year.[3]

By scrupulous frugality, Black had quietly amassed a substantial competence, something in excess of £20,000. In his will, this sum was divided among his numerous heirs according to an ingenious, and of course mathematical, plan. Black had a certain reputation for parsimony—it is said that he weighed on a balance the guineas his students paid to attend his course—and his biographers have felt obliged to set the record straight by citing instances of his generosity: the loans he made to friends, the poor patients he treated without charge, and even the spaciousness of his house and the plenty of his table, "at which he never improperly declined any company."[4] He was, at the very least, as methodical in his financial affairs as he was in his science, his teaching, and all the other aspects of his life.

Black's investigation of alkaline substances had a medical origin. The presumed efficacy of limewater in dissolving urinary calculi ("the stone") was supported by the researches of two Edinburgh professors, Robert Whytt and Charles Alston. It interested Cullen as well, and Black came to Edinburgh as a medical student with the intention of exploring the subject for his doctoral dissertation.

But at this moment Whytt and Alston were at loggerheads: they disagreed as to the best source, whether cockleshells or limestone, for preparing the quicklime. And they differed as to what occurs when mild limestone is burned to produce quicklime. Whytt accepted the common view that lime becomes caustic by absorbing a fiery matter during calcination, and thought he had proved it by showing that quicklime newly taken from the fire was the most powerful dissolvent of the stone. Alston, in an important experiment on the solubility of quicklime, showed that this was not the case, and that the causticity must be the property of the lime itself. Both men were aware that on exposure to the air quicklime gradually becomes mild, and that a crust appears on the surface of limewater. For Whytt, this resulted from the escape of fiery matter; but Alston, noting that the crust was heavier than the lime in solution, hinted that foreign matter, perhaps the air or something contained in it, produced the crust. Yet he was more disposed to believe that the insoluble precipitate formed when the quicklime combined with impurities in the water. Black, although he had criticized Alston as a chemist, was soon to profit from his findings.

Preoccupied at first with his medical studies, Black did not come to grips with his chosen problem until late in 1753. When he did so, he found it expedient to avoid any conflict between two of his professors; instead of investigating limewater, he would examine other absorbent earths to discover, if possible, a more powerful lithotriptic agent. He chose a white powder, *magnesia alba,* recently in vogue as a mild purgative. Its preparation and general properties had been described by the German chemist Friedrich Hoffmann; although it resembled the calcareous earths, *magnesia alba* was clearly distinguishable from them.

Black prepared this substance (basic magnesium carbonate) by reacting Epsom salts (magnesium sulfate) with pearl ashes (potassium carbonate). He treated the purified product with various acids, noting that the salts produced differed from the corresponding ones formed with lime. The *magnesia alba,* he observed, effervesced strongly with the acids, much like chalk or limestone.

Could a product similar to quicklime be formed by calcining *magnesia alba?* Would its solutions have the causticity and solvent power of limewater? Black's effort to test this possibility was the turning point of his research. When he strongly heated *magnesia alba,* the product proved to have unexpected properties. To be sure, like quicklime, this *magnesia usta* did not effervesce with acids. But since it was not sensibly caustic or readily soluble in water, it could hardly produce a substitute for limewater.

The properties of this substance now commanded Black's entire attention, notably the marked decrease in weight that resulted when *magnesia alba* changes into *magnesia usta.* What was lost? Using the balance more systematically than any chemist had done before him, he performed a series of quantitative experiments with all the accuracy he could command. Heating three ounces of *magnesia alba* in a retort, he determined that the whitish liquid that distilled over accounted for only a fraction of the weight lost. Tentatively he concluded that the major part must be due to expelled air. Whence came this air? Probably, he thought, from the pearl ashes used in making the *magnesia alba*; for Stephen Hales, he well knew, had shown long before that fixed alkali "certainly abounds in air."[5] If so, upon reconverting *magnesia usta* to the original powder, by combining it with fixed alkali, the original weight should be regained. This he proved to his satisfaction, recovering all but ten grains.

Magnesia usta, he soon found, formed with acids the same salts as *magnesia alba,* although it dissolved without effervescence. Only the presence or absence of air distinguished the two substances: *magnesia alba* loses its air on combining with acids, whereas the *magnesia usta* had evidently lost its air through strong heating before combining with acids.

Could the same process—the loss of combined air—also explain the transformation of lime into quicklime? Tentative experiments suggested something of the sort; but not until the work on magnesia was completed, late in 1753, did he examine this question. When he precipitated quicklime by adding common alkali, the white powder that settled out had all the properties of chalk, and it effervesced with acids. Early in 1754, Black wrote William Cullen that he had observed interesting things about the air produced when chalk was treated with acid: it had a pronounced but not disagreeable odor; it extinguished a candle placed nearby; and "a piece of burning paper, immersed in it, was put out as effectually as if it had been dipped in water."[6] This was an observation clearly worth pursuing. Nevertheless, he could no longer postpone the writing of his Latin dissertation and his preparation for his doctoral examination.

The dissertation is in two parts: the first, dealing with gastric acidity, was clearly added to give medical respectability to the work; Black was never happy about it, and hoped it would pass "without much notice."[7] The second set forth the experiments on *magnesia alba* and the tentative conclusions he drew from them. Nothing of significance was said about other alkaline substances or about what he was to call "fixed air."

The "Experiments," on the other hand, is a longer and more elaborate work. Like his dissertation, it is divided into two parts. In Part I, he recounts the experiments on *magnesia alba*; little or nothing is added, but now his theory is presented without equivocation: this substance he now describes as "a compound of a peculiar earth and fixed air."[8]

In Part II, Black describes experiments that enabled him to generalize the theory and to support his explanation of causticity. When lime is calcined, air is given off in abundance, and the caustic properties of the resulting quicklime do not derive from some fiery matter, but from the lime itself. He showed by experiment, in effect confirming what Alston had already done, that all of a given amount of quicklime, not merely a part of it, is capable of solution, if enough water is used. Thus the mysterious property of causticity is associated with a definite chemical entity having a definite solubility. As in the case of magnesia, he showed that calcareous earth combines with the same quantity of acid whether it is in the form of chalk (combined with air) or of quicklime. Again quicklime, made from a measured weight of chalk, when saturated with a fixed alkali can be converted into a fine powder nearly equal in weight to the original chalk. The quicklime was evidently saturated with air obtained from the alkali.

Black's theory also explained the production of strong or caustic alkalies (e.g., caustic potash) prepared by boiling quicklime with a solution of a mild alkali. What must occur is not, as chemists thought, that the acrimony of the potash is derived from the lime, but that fixed air is transferred from the mild alkali to the quicklime, thereby uncovering the inherent causticity of the alkali. Careful experiments confirmed this new extension of his doctrine.

A conclusive test of his theory of inherent causticity was Black's demonstration that both quicklime and *magnesia usta* could be produced by the "wet way," without the use of fire. He argued that if caustic alkali is caustic when not combined with "fixed air," it should separate magnesia from combination with acid and deposit it as *magnesia usta*. This he easily demonstrated. He performed a similar experiment with chalk.

An important collateral investigation stemmed from Black's experiments on the solubility of quicklime. Although he established to his satisfaction that it could be almost completely dissolved, he was puzzled not to find a larger residue of insoluble matter, for the air dissolved in water ought to combine with the quicklime to form a small amount of insoluble earth (carbonate). Perhaps the air had been driven off when the water was saturated with quicklime. The rough experiment to test this was performed after he had presented his major results to the Philosophical Society. In the receiver of an air pump, Black placed a small vessel containing four ounces of limewater; alongside it he put an identical vessel containing the same quantity of pure water. When the receiver was exhausted, the same amount of air appeared to bubble from both vessels. Clearly, the limewater contained dissolved air, but not of the kind that combined so readily with quicklime. In his "Experiments" he wrote: "Quicklime therefore does not attract air when in its most ordinary form, but is capable of being joined to one particular species only."[9] This he proposed to call "fixed air," preferring to use a name already familiar "in philosophy," rather than invent a new one. The nature and properties of this substance, he wrote, "will probably be the subject of my further inquiry."[10]

Black had shown that a particular kind of air, different from common air, can be a quantitative constituent of ordinary substances and must enter, as Lavoisier put it later, into their "definition." But he was not destined to make the investigation of such elastic fluids his "future inquiry." This was to be mainly the work of his British disciples—MacBride, Cavendish, Priestley, and Rutherford—and he published nothing further on the subject. Nevertheless, from his *Lectures* and other bits of evidence we learn that his discoveries did not end abruptly with the publication of his "Experiments." He knew that "fixed air" did not support combustion, that it had a density greater than common air, and that its behavior with alkaline substances resembled that of a weak acid. By experiments with birds and small animals, he soon demonstrated that this air would not support life. Using the limewater test, he showed that air expired in respiration consisted mainly of "fixed air"; and likewise that the elastic fluid given off in alcoholic fermentation, like that produced in burning charcoal, was identical with the "fixed air" yielded by mild alkalies when they effervesce with acids.

Black's doctrines did not have the prompt success on the Continent that they enjoyed in Britain. His influence on the early stages of the chemical revolution in France was far less than scholars have imagined; indeed, at first it was negligible. Before 1773 French chemists were unfamiliar with his "Experiments," which had appeared in English in an obscure publication. What they knew of his work derived largely from the arguments advanced against him by the German chemist J. F. Meyer, whose rival theory of *acidum pingue* was for a time widely credited. Black's case would surely have been strengthened had he published the simple experiment, performed at Glasgow in 1757 or 1758, of directly impregnating a solution of caustic alkali with the "fixed air" expelled from chalk or limestone, and so obtaining a product both effervescent and mild.

Black's discoveries concerning heat, the major achievement of his Glasgow period, were originally stimulated by William Cullen. In 1754 Cullen noted a striking phenomenon—the intense cold produced when highly volatile substances like ether evaporate—and he promptly wrote Black about his experiment. At about this time, Black set down in a notebook a curious observation made by Fahrenheit: water can be cooled below the freezing point without congealing; yet if shaken, it suddenly freezes and the thermometer rises abruptly to 32° on Fahrenheit's scale. This, Black speculated, might be due to "heat unnecessary to ice."

Fahrenheit's observation was recorded in Boerhaave's *Elementa chemiae,* a famous work that Cullen, and later Black, recommended in the English version of Peter Shaw to their students. This observation was hard to reconcile with the prevailing view that when water is brought near the freezing point, withdrawal of a small increment of heat must bring prompt solidification. But Fahrenheit's experiment showed that solidification (or liquefaction) required the transfer of substantial quantities of heat: of heat lying concealed and not directly detectable by the thermometer; of heat, to use Black's term, that was *latent.* Upon reflection, Black saw this notion to be quite consistent with commonly observed facts of nature. Snow, for example, requires a considerable time to melt after the surrounding temperature has risen well above the freezing point. A gradual absorption of heat must therefore be taking place, although the temperature of the snow remains unaltered.

Black became convinced of the reality of this latent heat through thoughtful reading and meditation on the familiar phenomena of change of state. He presented his doctrine in his Glasgow lectures, perhaps as early as 1757–1758, before he had performed any experiments of his own. Nor did his doctrine arise from any firmly held theory as to what heat might be.

Not until 1760 did Black carry out his earliest experiments on heat. The first fact to be ascertained was the reliability of the thermometer as a measuring tool. Would a thermometric fluid, having received equal increments of heat, show equal increments of expansion? Ingenious and simple experiments on mixing amounts of hot and cold water (*Lectures,* I, 56–58) convinced him that the scale of expansion of mercury, over that limited range, was indeed a reliable scale of "the various heats, or temperatures of heat."

Crucial to Black's experiments was his recognition of the distinction between *quantity of heat* and *temperature,* between what we sometimes describe as the *extensive* and *intensive* measures of heat. Although not the first to note this distinction, he was the earliest to sense its fundamental importance and to make systematic use of it. In his lectures, which always opened (after certain preliminaries) with a careful discussion of heat, he would tell his students:

> Heat may be considered, either in respect of its quantity, or of its intensity. Thus two lbs. of water, equally heated, must contain double the quantity that one of them does, though the thermometer applied to them separately, or together, stands at precisely the same point, because it requires double the time to heat two lbs. as it does to heat one.[11]

Temperature, of course, is read directly from the thermometer. But how to measure the *quantity* of heat? Black's answer is implied in the above quotation: the time required to warm or cool a body to a given temperature is related to the amount of heat transferred. This elusive quantity required a *dynamic* measurement: the heat gained or lost should be proportional to the temperature and the time of heat flow "taken conjointly."[12] Here, as so often in his career, the influence of Newton is quite apparent. In a famous paper of 1701, Newton had used a dynamic method to estimate temperatures beyond the reach of his linseed oil thermometer. Black in his lectures gave a clear account of Newton's experiments and how his law of cooling (as we now call it) was used to estimate relative temperatures above that of melting tin. Black's own experiments made use of the law of cooling, and it is not hard to imagine that Newton's dynamic method was the key to Black's.

Characteristically, Black was not satisfied to demonstrate qualitatively that there is such a thing as the latent heat of fusion: he proposed to measure it. The method occurred to him in the summer of 1761. First cooling a given mass of water to about 33°F., he would determine the time necessary to raise its temperature one degree, and compare this with the time required to melt the same amount of ice. Conversely, he would compare the time necessary to lower the temperature of a mass of water with the time necessary to freeze it completely. Assuming that both systems received heat from, or gave up heat to, the surrounding air at the same rate, as much heat should be given off in freezing a given amount of water as in melting the same amount of ice. Obliged to wait until winter, Black carried out the experiment in

December 1761 in a large hall adjoining his college rooms. The following April he described his results to his Glasgow colleagues and friends.

Black soon saw that latent heat must play a part in the vaporization of water as well as in the melting of ice. The analogy was so persuasive that as early as 1761—before testing his conjecture by experiment—he presented this version of his doctrine to his students. The success of the freezing experiments soon led him to investigate the latent heat of vaporization. But the method he first employed, a precise analogue of Fahrenheit's observation on supercooled water, was unsuited to measurement. A better method could be modeled on his freezing experiments. Tin vessels, containing measured amounts of water, would be heated on a red-hot cast iron plate. The time necessary to heat the water from 50°F. to the boiling point would be compared with the time necessary for the water to boil away. The chief obstacle was to find a source of heat sufficiently unvarying so that the absorption of heat could be safely measured by the time. A "practical distiller" informed Black that when his furnace was in good order, he could tell, to a pint, the quantity of liquor that he would get in an hour. When Black confirmed this by boiling off small quantities of water on his own laboratory furnace, he was ready for the experiments.[13] These he performed late in 1762. From the average of three experiments he calculated that the heat absorbed in vaporization was equal to that which would have raised the same amount of water to 810°, were this actually possible. This gives a figure of 450 calories per gram for the latent heat of vaporization of water, compared to a modern figure of 539.1 calories per gram. More accurate figures were obtained in later experiments, but several years elapsed before Black took up the subject again.

The second, and closely related, discovery made by Black concerning heat was that different substances have different heat capacities. It is commonly assumed that Black discovered *specific heats* before his work on latent heat. This is not the case. To be sure, the clue, once again, was found in Boerhaave's textbook; Fahrenheit had made certain experiments at his request and had obtained the surprising result that when he mixed equal quantities of mercury and water, each at a different temperature, the mercury exerted far less effect in heating or cooling the mixture than did the water. At first Black was puzzled; but he soon realized that mercury, despite its greater density, must have a smaller store of heat than an equal amount of water at the same temperature. If so, the capacities of bodies to store up heat did not vary with their bulk or density, but in a different fashion "for which no general principle or reason can yet be assigned."[14] Now Black could explain a peculiar effect reported twenty years earlier by George Martine, an authority on thermometers. Martine had placed equal volumes of water and mercury in identical vessels before a fire, and observed that the mercury increased in temperature almost twice as fast as the water. Black saw that since less heat was required to bring mercury up to a given temperature, a thermometer placed in it should rise more rapidly. Not until 1760 did Black perceive the significance of this effect, but he did not pursue the subject; he was principally absorbed with the more striking phenomena of changes of state. In 1764—a year that James Watt made memorable in the history of invention—Black returned to the study of heat. His experimental inquiry into specific heats, and his attempts to obtain a more accurate value for the latent heat of vaporization, were stimulated by the activities of Watt.

The year that Black began his Glasgow lectures, James Watt, a young man of nineteen, skilled in making mathematical instruments, was taken under the wing of the university as what we might today call a technician. He was soon called upon by Black to make things he needed for his experiments. Watt, in turn, after repairing the now-famous model of a Newcomen engine and undertaking experiments to improve its performance, turned to Black to explain an effect he could not comprehend. He was astonished at the large amount of cold water required to condense the steam in the engine cylinder, until Black explained his ideas about latent heat.

Watt was many months, and many experiments, away from hitting upon the historic invention of the separate condenser, and Black may be pardoned for believing that this disclosure inspired Watt's radical improvement of the steam engine, a claim advanced even more strongly by John Robison, who spoke of Watt as Dr. Black's most illustrious pupil. This, in a strict sense, Watt never was; and, despite his lifelong attachment to Black, he later insisted that the invention of the separate condenser had not been suggested by his knowledge of the doctrine of latent heat. But he readily credited Black with having clarified the problems he encountered and with teaching him "to reason and experiment in natural philosophy."[15]

On the other hand, Watt's ingenuity and questioning mind, and the practical problems he raised, revived Black's interest in heat. The problems he now investigated with John Robison and William Irvine were closely related to those Watt needed to elucidate. Irvine was set to work determining a more accurate value of the latent heat of steam. Using a common laboratory still as a water calorimeter, Irvine obtained improved values, although these were not high enough to be really accurate. Black, it should be remarked, never made or used the mythical ice calorimeter associated with his name, although it occurred to him in the spring or summer of 1764 that his knowledge of the latent heat of fusion of ice could be used to measure the latent heat of steam. Plans to put this to the test were set aside when Watt, late in 1764, began to obtain values that Black deemed sufficiently precise. Years later, Black gave the French scientists full credit for the independent invention and first use of an ice calorimeter.[16]

The measurements made at this time by Black, Irvine, and Watt on the specific heats of various substances are the earliest of which we have any trace. Watt seems to have been the first to stress the importance of investigating the subject systematically. He carried out experiments of his own, and Black put Irvine to work on the problem. Using the method of mixtures, Black and Irvine determined the heats communicated to water by a number of different solids. These joint experiments continued until Black left for Edinburgh. After Black's departure, Irvine continued these investigations, but his results were not published in his lifetime.

Joseph Black's view of chemistry, his chemical doctrines, can be derived from his single major paper and from the various versions of his lectures. Chemistry, to him, was a subject with wide practical application to medicine and to the progress of industry. But he insisted, as Cullen had done, that it is a science, albeit an imperfect one, not merely an art: "the study of the effects of heat and mixture, natural or artificial, with a view to the improvements of arts and natural knowledge."[17]

On the question of the "elements" or "principles" of bodies, Black showed a typical caution. He no longer credited the venerable doctrine of the four elements; little could be known about them, for there was no knowledge of the underlying constitution and forces of nature. It was more sensible to group into several classes, as Cullen did, those substances sharing certain distinguishable properties: the salts, earths, inflammable substances, metals, and water. These were not necessarily elementary; of earths there were several sorts that could not be decomposed further; water, Black believed, can on distillation be converted into earth; and there was reason to suspect that salts were not compounds of earth and water, but of an earth and some other unknown substance.

Black invariably devoted the early lectures of his course to the subject of heat, telling his students that Boerhaave, Robert Boyle, and Sir Isaac Newton followed Lord Bacon in believing that heat is caused by motion, and that the French thought heat to be the vibration of an imponderable, elastic fluid. The fluid theory was the one to which he quite definitely leaned, for it seemed to agree best with the phenomena; he could not, for example, readily conceive a motion of particles in dense, solid bodies. But such questions are involved in obscurity. And he told his students: "The way to acquire a just idea of heat is to study the facts."[18]

In discussing problems of combustion, fermentation, and the calcination of metals, Black—until the close of his career—presented a gingerly version of the phlogiston theory, although he generally avoided the term. Air, of course, was required for combustion; but like his contemporaries he invoked the property of elasticity to explain its role. Combustion was caused by the presence of an inflammable principle, for which different substances had a different "elective attraction." Inflammable and combustible substances, including the calcinable metals, were pervaded with this mysterious substance, the nature of which "we are still at a loss to explain." Although little could be said on the subject, heat and light appeared to be the principles of inflammability. There was, however, a fact that was hard to explain and was a strong objection to this theory. When it was possible to collect the product of combustion, or weigh a calcined metal, this product was heavier, despite the loss of the inflammable principle. Possibly this was a kind of matter that defied the general law of gravitation. Yet speculations of this sort were not Black's cup of tea. These doubts almost certainly prepared him to accept, in the main, Lavoisier's discoveries.

As late as 1785 Black was reluctant to adopt the new "French chemistry," a term he heartily disliked. The geologist Sir James Hall was the earliest of Black's circle to sense the winds of change. A visit to Paris in 1786 convinced him, and on his return to Scotland, in the course of long discussions, he brought Thomas Charles Hope around to his opinions. Early in 1788 Hall read before the Royal Society of Edinburgh a paper entitled "A View of M. Lavoisier's New Theory of Chemistry." Black may well have been present—we cannot be sure—but his intimate friend James Hutton was, and defended the phlogistic hypothesis with a paper of his own. Nevertheless, an Italian visitor to England, an admirer of Mme. Lavoisier, wrote her from London in 1788 that Black and Watt ("in my opinion the two best heads in Great Britain") were on the verge of being convinced by Lavoisier's antiphlogistic theory. Soon thereafter, Black began to mention the new doctrine

in his lectures; he wrote to Lavoisier, in a famous letter of October 1790, that he had begun to recommend the new system to his students as simpler, and more in accord with the facts, than the old. Robison's edition of Black's lectures, based on what Black was telling his students between 1792 and about 1796, amply confirms his statement. Yet it is clear that Black strongly disapproved of the new nomenclature, while recognizing that advances in chemistry made some such reform necessary. He objected to obliterating the work of the earlier chemists completely; he felt that the new terms were "evidently contrived to suit the genius of the French language," and he perceived in the new scheme a clever stratagem of the French chemists to give their doctrines "universal currency and authority."[19]

The most interesting and pervasive of Black's doctrines is the theory of chemical affinity. Here his debt to Cullen, and beyond Cullen to Newton's *Opticks,* is clearly evident. Chemical reactions result from the differential or "elective" attraction of chemical individuals for one another. Simple elective attractions are those produced by heat; "double elective attractions," reactions of double decomposition, are chiefly those that take place in solution. Black saw no reason for avoiding the term "attraction," as did the French chemists who spoke instead of "affinities" or "rapports." As Newton had insisted, "attraction" should be taken as a descriptive term, not a causal explanation.

Black's earliest use of this concept, and of Geoffroy's well-known table of affinities, appears in his "Experiments." He employs it to show the differential behavior of alkaline substances toward acids and "fixed air." For Black, as for Cullen, this became a centrally important pedagogical device; invariably he devoted several lectures to elective attractions, describing the table, and referring to it elsewhere when speaking of particular reactions. In the lectures of the early years Black set forth these reactions with the diagrams Cullen had invented, adding numbers to indicate the relative force of attraction between substances:

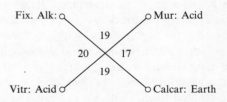

Later, he used a diagram consisting of segmented circles, but without numbers to indicate the relative attractions.[20] The following example illustrates what takes place when a compound of volatile alkali with any acid (e.g., ammonium chloride) reacts with a mild fixed alkali (e.g., sodium carbonate); here the "fixed air" or "mephitic air" represented by ⋈ combines with the volatile alkali, ♉; and the fixed alkali, ♐, joins itself to the acid, >:

Did Black wish to represent molecules in which the atomic partners are interchanged? Perhaps this occurred to him, but he probably conceived these diagrams primarily as what we call visual aids. Unlike his master, William Cullen, Black did not explicitly link his discussion of elective attractions with the corpuscular or atomic doctrine, about which he had little to say in his lectures.

Robison records that in an early conversation Black "gently and gracefully" checked his disposition to form theories and warned him to reject "even without examination, every hypothetical explanation, as a mere waste of time and ingenuity."[21] Like Newton, whom he so greatly esteemed—at least Newton as he understood him—Black chose not to "deal in conjectures."

In mid-career he told his students, well before the fulfillment of what we call the chemical revolution:

> Upon the whole, Chymistry is as yet but an opening science, closely connected with the usefull and ornamental Arts, and worthy the attention of a liberal mind. And it must always become more and more so: for though it is only of late, that it has been looked upon in that light, the great progress already made in Chymical knowledge, gives us a pleasant prospect of rich additions to it. The Science is now studied on solid and rational grounds. While our knowledge is imperfect, it is apt to run into errour: but Experiment is the thread that will lead us out of the labyrinth.[22]

NOTES

1. Thomson, *Cullen*, I, 573.
2. Henry Cockburn, *Memorials of his Times* (Edinburgh, 1856), pp. 48–49.
3. Muirhead, *Origin and Progress*, II, 261–263.
4. Ferguson, "Minutes," p. 116.
5. *Dissertatio*, p. 272, and "Experiments," p. 17. Compare *Lectures*, II, 63–64.
6. Thomson, *op. cit.*, I, 50.
7. Letter to Cullen, 18 June 1754, *ibid.*, pp. 50–51.
8. "Experiments," p. 25.
9. *Ibid.*, pp. 30–31.
10. *Ibid.*, p. 31.
11. Law, "Notes of Black's Lectures," I, 5.
12. *Ibid.*, p. 18.
13. *Lectures*, I, 157.
14. *Ibid.*, p. 79.
15. Muirhead, *op. cit.*, 264.
16. *Lectures*, I, 175.
17. Cochrane, "Notes From Black's Lectures, 1767/8," p. 3. Black saw no reason to change his definition: see *Lectures*, I, 12–13.
18. Law, *op. cit.*, I, 5. Compare *Lectures*, I, 35.
19. *Lectures*, I, 489–493.
20. Henry Guerlac, "Commentary on the Papers of Cyril Stanley Smith and Marie Boas," in Marshall Clagett, ed., *Critical Problems in the History of Science* (Madison, Wis., 1959), pp. 515–519. For a fuller treatment, see M. P. Crosland, "The Use of Diagrams as Chemical 'Equations' in the Lecture Notes of William Cullen and Joseph Black." Crosland argues that Black wished to illustrate the course of chemical reactions without implying mechanical explanations and that his symbols were generalized expressions for reactions of a similar type.
21. *Lectures*, I, vii.
22. Law, *op. cit.*, III, 88.

BIBLIOGRAPHY

I. ORIGINAL WORKS. Black's published writings are the following:

Dissertatio medica inauguralis . . . (Edinburgh, 1754). Reprinted in *Thesaurus medicus Edinburgensis novus*, II (Edinburgh–London, 1785). English translation by A. Crum Brown in *Journal of Chemical Education*, **12** (1935), 225–228, 268–273, with facsimile of title page and dedication.

"Experiments Upon Magnesia Alba, Quicklime, and Some Other Alcaline Substances," in *Essays and Observations, Physical and Literary. Read Before a Society in Edinburgh*, **2** (1756), 157–225. Republished, together with Cullen's "Essay on the Cold Produced by Evaporating Fluids" (Edinburgh, 1777; repr. 1782). Black's famous paper is most readily available as Alembic Club Reprints no. 1 (Edinburgh, 1898). The first French translation was "Expériences sur la magnésie blanche, la chaux vive, & sur d'autres substances alcalines, par M. Joseph Black, Docteur en Médecine," in *Observations sur la physique*, **1** (1773), 210–220, 261–275. A short summary of Black's work on magnesia had been published in the *Journal de médecine, chirurgie, pharmacie*, **8** (1758), 254–261.

"On the Supposed Effect of Boiling Upon Water in Disposing It to Freeze More Readily," in *Philosophical Transactions of the Royal Society of London*, **65** (1775), 124–129.

"Lettre de M. Joseph Black à M. Lavoisier," in *Annales de chimie*, **8** (1791), 225–229. The English original of Black's letter was printed by Douglas McKie in *Notes and Records of the Royal Society of London*, **7** (1950), 9–11.

"An Analysis of the Water of Some Hot Springs in Iceland," in *Transactions of the Royal Society of Edinburgh*, **3** (1794), 95–126.

Lectures on the Elements of Chemistry, John Robison, ed., 2 vols. (Edinburgh, 1803; American ed., 3 vols., Philadelphia, 1806–1807). Robison omitted Black's introductory lecture and much of the next two or three lectures. In a letter of 16 September 1802 to James Black, Joseph's brother, he tells of his difficulties in putting together, from Dr. Black's sparse notes, a coherent text. He even speaks of having to "manufacture" one lecture; obviously, although Robison's edition probably represents Black's opinions, the language may sometimes be Robison's. The text should be compared with the MS versions. See McKie, *Annals of Science,* **16** (1960), 131–134, 161–170.

"Case of Adam Ferguson, Drawn up by Joseph Black, M.D., in May, 1797," in *Medico-Chirurgical Transactions,* **8** (1816). Cited and summarized by Crowther.

"A Letter From Dr. Black to James Smithson, Esq. Describing a Very Sensible Balance," in *Annals of Philosophy,* n.s. **10** (1825), 52–54. Black's letter is dated 18 September 1790.

The earliest pictures of Black are two ink sketches made by Thomas Cochrane in his notes while attending Black's lectures in 1767–1768 in what appears to be an anatomical theater. Reproduced by McKie in *Annals of Science,* **1** (1936), 110, and in his edition of Cochrane's "Notes 1767/8."

Not much later (*ca.* 1770) is a fine oil by David Martin, the teacher of Sir Henry Raeburn (Collection of the University of Edinburgh). Published by Guerlac in *Isis,* **48** (1957) and by McKie as frontispiece to his edition of the Cochrane "Notes 1767/8."

The most familiar portrait of Black is by Raeburn (Collection of the University of Edinburgh), showing Black at about the age of sixty; often reproduced, sometimes (as in the frontispiece of Robison's edition of Black's *Lectures*) from an inferior engraving.

Roughly contemporaneous with the Raeburn portrait are the sketches of John Kay: one shows Black walking in the country; another places *en face* a birdlike Hutton and a pensive Black. The most interesting is a close view of Black lecturing, spectacles in hand, and before him a spate of scattered notes, a syphon, a burning candle, and a small bird in a cage, all to demonstrate the properties of "fixed air." See *A Series of Portraits and Caricature Etchings by the Late John Kay,* 2 vols. (Edinburgh, 1837), I, pt. 1, 52–57. Reproductions by Ramsay in his biography of Black and, more attractively, by John Read in *Humour and Humanism in Chemistry,* plates 41 and 44–45.

No published census of manuscript versions of Black's lectures exists, but a few may be mentioned, together with their present locations. The earliest is Thomas Cochrane's (Andersonian Library, University of Strathclyde, Glasgow); dating from Black's early teaching at Edinburgh, it is otherwise notable only for the caricatures of Black. Very sketchy, it has recently been published as *Notes from Doctor Black's Lectures on Chemistry 1767/8,* ed. with intro., by Douglas McKie (Cheshire, 1966).

More complete are the closely written set of 120 lectures recorded by James Johnson, 1770 (University of Edinburgh Library), and three volumes bearing the name of Joseph Freyer Rastrick and covering Black's lectures of 1769–1770 (History of Science Collections, Cornell University Library). A fine set is the Beaufoy MS, 1771/72 (University of Saint Andrews). Quite different from others is Alexander Law's "Notes of Doctor Black's Lectures on Chemistry" (University of Edinburgh Library), with fifty-seven lectures from 13 June to 22 December 1775, and elaborate notes

and appendices. For Black's later period there are the notes of George Cayley, 6 vols., 118 lectures, 1785–1786 (York Medical Society) and a similar set, without date or name of original owner, now at University College, London. McKie, in *Annals of Science* (1959), p. 73, believes this set to be contemporary with the Cayley notes.

II. SECONDARY LITERATURE. A brief, uninspired account of a visit to Black in 1784 (largely devoted to a description of Black's portable furnace) is given by the geologist Barthélemy Faujas de Saint-Fond, in his *Voyage en Angleterre et en Ecosse,* II (Paris, 1797), 267–272. The earliest biographical sketch is the short, anonymous account, probably by Alexander Tilloch, in *Philosophical Magazine,* **10** (1801), 157–158. But the most important source is Adam Ferguson, "Minutes of the Life and Character of Joseph Black, M.D.," in *Transactions of the Royal Society of Edinburgh,* **5** (1805), 101–117. Ferguson was Black's cousin and close friend. John Robison, "Editor's Preface," in *Lectures,* I, v–lxvi, draws heavily on Ferguson, yet adds much useful information. Thomas Thomson, *History of Chemistry,* I (London, 1830), ch. 9, relies on Ferguson and Robison, but adds personal impressions. Thomson also contributed short accounts of Black to the *Annals of Philosophy,* **5** (1815), 321–327, and the *Edinburgh Encyclopedia.* Lord Brougham, like Thomson one of Black's last students, devotes an interesting chapter to Black in his *Lives of Philosophers of the Time of George III* (London–Glasgow, 1855), pp. 1–24. George Wilson's brief note, in *Proceedings of the Royal Society of Edinburgh,* **2** (1849), 238, corrects the date of Black's death as given by Ferguson and Robison, citing newspaper accounts and Muirhead.

John Playfair's "Biographical Account of the Late Dr. James Hutton," in *Transactions of the Royal Society of Edinburgh,* **5,** pp. 39–99 of the "History of the Society," has references to Black. James Patrick Muirhead, *Origin and Progress of the Mechanical Inventions of James Watt,* 3 vols. (London, 1854), published numerous letters from Watt to Black, and one from Black to Watt. Also valuable is John Thomson's *Account of the Life, Lectures and Writings of William Cullen, M.D.,* 2 vols. (Edinburgh–London, 1859), with several early letters of Black to Cullen.

For Glasgow University in Black's time, see Henry G. Graham, *Social Life of Scotland in the Eighteenth Century,* II (London, 1899), chs. 12–13; W. Innes Addison, *Roll of Graduates of the University of Glasgow* (Glasgow, 1898) and *Matriculation Album of the University of Glasgow* (Glasgow, 1913). Worth consulting is W. R. Scott, *Adam Smith as Student and Professor* (Glasgow, 1937). Letters of Thomas Reid in *The Works of Thomas Reid, D.D.,* Sir William Hamilton, ed., 7th ed., I (Edinburgh, 1872), 39–50, describe Black's Glasgow lectures. For the chair of chemistry at Glasgow, see Andrew Kent, ed., *An Eighteenth Century Lectureship in Chemistry* (Glasgow, 1950). For Edinburgh, consult Alexander Bower, *History of the University of Edinburgh,* 2 vols. (Edinburgh, 1817); and Sir Alexander Grant, *Story of the University of Edinburgh,* 2 vols. (London, 1884).

Agnes Clarke's article on Black in the *Dictionary of*

National Biography is disappointing and sometimes inaccurate, but gives the correct date for Black's death. The most scientifically eminent of Black's modern biographers is Sir William Ramsay. He first discussed Black's work in his *Gases of the Atmosphere* (London, 1896), pp. 527–531, and again in his *Joseph Black, M.D., A Discourse* (Glasgow, 1904). His *Life and Letters of Joseph Black, M.D.* (London, 1918) is the only full-length biography; published posthumously, it is valuable chiefly for the use made of letters and papers of Black, including an autobiographical sketch, which have been otherwise inaccessible to scholars. Ramsay's book is unsatisfactory; when a scholarly biography is written, and one is badly needed, use will surely be made of Henry Riddell's "The Great Chemist, Joseph Black, His Belfast Friends and Family Connections," in *Proceedings of the Belfast Natural History and Philosophical Society,* 3 (1919/20), 49–88.

Black is, of course, discussed in the familiar histories or studies of early chemists. Most can be ignored; an exception is Max Speter's "Black," in G. Bugge, *Das Buch der grossen Chemiker,* 2 vols. (Weinheim, 1929), I, 240–252. J. R. Partington, *History of Chemistry,* III (London–New York, 1962), 131–143, appraises Black's proficiency as a chemist and gives detailed citations of the literature. John Read has a readable, if not wholly reliable, account of Black in his *Humour and Humanism in Chemistry* (London, 1947), ch. 8, and a brisk chapter in Kent's *Eighteenth Century Lectureship,* pp. 78–98. A longer and more informative account of Black, with new insights and some inaccuracies, is J. G. Crowther, *Scientists of the Industrial Revolution* (London, 1962), pp. 9–92. Archibald and Nan L. Clow, *The Chemical Revolution* (London, 1952), has a misleading title: it deals with the applications of chemistry to industry in the eighteenth and early nineteenth centuries, and is valuable for many passing references to Black's involvement in such matters.

Douglas McKie's paper on the Cochrane "Notes," in *Annals of Science,* 1 (1936), 101–110, has been superseded by his edition of that MS. But see his "Some MS Copies of Black's Chemical Lectures," *ibid.,* 15 (1959), 65–73; 16 (1960), 1–9; 18 (1962), 87–97; 21 (1965), 209–255; 23 (1967), 1–33. E. W. J. Neave, "Joseph Black's Lectures on the Elements of Chemistry," in *Isis,* 25 (1936), 372–390, merely outlines the contents of Robison's edition of Black's *Lectures.*

Black's influence on the progress of scientific medicine and biology is treated by Heinrich Buess, "Joseph Black und die Anfänge chemischer Experimentalforschung in Biologie und Medizin," in *Gesnerus,* 13 (1956), 165–189. Henry Guerlac, "Joseph Black and Fixed Air," in *Isis,* 48 (1957), 124–151, 433–456, attempts to clarify the chronology of Black's early life and to reconstruct the steps in his chemical investigations. Guerlac's *Lavoisier, The Crucial Year* (Ithaca, N.Y., 1962), pp. 8–35, 68–71, sees Stephen Hales, rather than Joseph Black, as the chief British influence on Lavoisier before 1773. M. P. Crosland has studied Black's teaching symbols in "The Use of Diagrams as Chemical 'Equations' in the Lecture Notes of William Cullen and Joseph Black," in *Annals of Science,* 15 (1959),

75–90. Twenty-six recently discovered letters by or concerning Black, including twenty-one written to his brother Alexander, have been published by Douglas McKie and David Kennedy, "Some Letters of Joseph Black and Others," in *Annals of Science,* 16 (1960), 129–170. Included is the important letter by John Robison on the problems encountered in publishing Black's *Lectures.*

For Black's work on heat, consult Ernst Mach, *Die Principien der Wärmelehre* (Leipzig, 1896), pp. 153–181; Douglas McKie and Niels H. de V. Heathcote, *The Discovery of Specific and Latent Heats* (London, 1935), pp. 1–53; and Martin K. Barnett, "The Development of the Concept of Heat From the Fire Principle of Heraclitus Through the Caloric Theory of Joseph Black," in *Scientific Monthly,* 42 (1946), 165–172, 247–257.

HENRY GUERLAC

BLACKMAN, FREDERICK FROST (*b.* Lambeth, England, 25 July 1866; *d.* Cambridge, England, 30 January 1947), *plant physiology.*

Blackman, whose father was a doctor, was the third child and eldest son in a family of eleven children. His interest in botany may have been started by a set of Sowerby's *British Botany* that belonged to his book-collecting father; it developed during his school days at Mill Hill, where he started a herbarium. His interest in the plant as a whole remained throughout his life. On leaving school in 1883, Blackman entered St. Bartholomew's Hospital to train as a doctor. Although his studies were highly satisfactory—he graduated B.Sc. in 1885—in 1887 he accepted an opportunity to read science at St. John's College, Cambridge, where he shared rooms with his younger brother, later Professor V. H. Blackman. In 1895 he was elected to fellowship of his college, which he retained until his death. Blackman played an active part in the life of St. John's, where he lived until his marriage in 1917, holding the office of steward from 1908 to 1914. As an undergraduate his interests included music and pictures, and the college later benefited from his advice in aesthetic matters.

Blackman was appointed a university demonstrator in botany in 1891, and continued as a member of the botany school until he retired from his readership in 1936. He assumed a full share of the administrative work of the department, including the extension of the buildings in 1933. Everything he did was done with meticulous care, and he inspired others to do likewise. When, in recognition of the active school of plant physiology that he had developed from the basis laid down by his predecessors S. H. Vines and Francis Darwin, a subdepartment of plant physiology was created in 1931 with the aid of a grant from the Rockefeller Fund, Blackman naturally became its head and, but for technicalities regarding retirement age (resulting from the university statutes of 1926), he would have become the first professor of plant physiology at Cambridge.

Blackman was elected a fellow of the Royal Society in 1908 and was awarded a Royal Medal in 1921. Outside the botany school he served the university in various ways, including many years as a member of the Fitzwilliam Museum Syndicate. From 1901 to 1936 he was a member of the board of the Cambridge Instrument Company, which was started by Horace Darwin, brother of Francis, who had preceded Blackman as reader in botany.

Blackman's published papers are not numerous. Although his mind was quick, he was not hurried over the planning of his experiments and the devising and perfecting of the apparatus; neither was he hurried in the contemplation of the results and the search for a just interpretation of them. He took great pains over the preparation of a paper; such was the standard he set himself that several papers, which in 1935 had reached a stage that would have satisfied many, were not published until after his death. Many papers by pupils in his laboratory bear his stamp if not his name.

Blackman's first two botanical papers appeared in the *Philosophical Transactions of the Royal Society* in 1895. They began a series entitled "Experimental Researches in Vegetable Assimilation and Respiration," which was continued by him and his pupils until 1933. As early as 1832 it had been suggested that most of the gaseous exchange between the leaves of a plant and the surrounding atmosphere takes place through the stomata. For a long time this was much disputed, and it was not accepted until convincing experimental evidence was produced by Blackman. The first paper described an apparatus for measuring the carbon dioxide in gaseous mixtures, of which Blackman said, "The *raison d'être* of the apparatus is to be found in the perfection of details and their adaptation so that all the various processes can be performed with the minimum of error, time, and labour . . ." (p. 487). This approach characterized all his designs.

Blackman was surprised by the high rate at which gases diffused through a septum with many small holes, as compared with that when there were fewer holes with the same total area. His correspondence with his friend R. A. Lehfeldt, a physical chemist, shows that the latter advised him that "The effectiveness of a stoma should be proportional to its diameter but if the stomata were very close more nearly proportional to the area."

In 1904 the third paper in the series, by Blackman's pupil G. L. C. Matthaei, demonstrated that temperature had little effect on the rate of carbon assimilation

at low intensities of illumination, while at high intensities the effect was comparable with that of many chemical reactions. This work directed Blackman's thoughts along lines that resulted in the publication of his classic paper "Optima and Limiting Factors" (1905). The terms "limiting factor" and "bottleneck" were not on the lips of biologists at that time. This paper is that of a pioneer in the application of physicochemical ideas to biological problems, a pioneer not unaware of the complexities of such problems. For instance, he says, "Physico-chemical finality is not to be attained in this matter, but special research might at least show how far the recorded optima are real metabolic truths and how far they are illusions of experimentation" (p. 286), and continues ". . . at present our science entirely lacks data that will stand critical analysis from the point of view indicated" (p. 295). The process limiting the rate of carbon assimilation at high intensities of illumination was later named the Blackman reaction by Otto Warburg.

These ideas were developed further in Blackman's presidential address to the Botany Section at the British Association meeting in 1908. It was a bold action to plead for the consideration of vital processes from the point of view of laws governing physicochemical processes at a time when, as he said, in consequence of the teaching of Pfeffer, "The notion that *every* change in which protoplasm takes part is a case of *'reaction' of an 'irritable' living substance to a 'stimulus'* overflowed its legitimate bounds and swamped the development of physical-chemical concepts" (p. 2), and continued, "No general treatment of the physiology of plants had yet been attempted in terms of reaction velocity" (p. 17).

Blackman later turned his attention to plant respiration. In 1928 three papers appeared dealing with part of the investigations his pupil P. Parija had made on the effect of the partial pressure of oxygen on the production of carbon dioxide by apples. Other papers were published with the assistance of a former pupil, J. Barker, after Blackman's death. The third paper of 1928, under Blackman's name, gives his interpretation of the complicated set of results analyzed in the previous papers. On the assumption that the products of glycolysis underwent fermentation to carbon dioxide and alcohol or complete oxidation to carbon dioxide and water, he deduced that glycolysis in air is more nearly complete than in nitrogen. Because the production of carbon dioxide in nitrogen was much more than one-third of that in air, he concluded there must be yet another fate for the products of glycolysis, which he called "oxidative anabolism."

His typical conclusion was that this schema provided a "plausible interpretation of all the quantitative variations of CO_2 production observed" (p. 521);

yet other data awaited similar analysis, "after which it may become necessary to take the present schema to pieces and reconstruct it . . ., but at least we shall have consolidated a mass of relations to which any future system must conform" (p. 522). This conclusion was based on an analysis of the behavior of more than twenty individual apples. Under Blackman's guidance his pupils carried out investigations on sugar content, rate of oxygen consumption, and composition of the atmosphere in the intercellular spaces of apples, in an attempt to complete the respiratory picture for this plant organ. Unfortunately, the work did not progress further than doctoral theses, now in the University Library at Cambridge.

Blackman's interests in botany were not confined to plant physiology. In his early years he lectured on the algae and later, with A. G. Tansley, his future brother-in-law, published "Classification of the Green Algae" in the first volume of the *New Phytologist* (1902). His other contribution to biology—certainly not the least—was the effect he had on many who attended his lectures. These were works of art, appreciated more on a second hearing, which they received from many of his research students. A mass of data collected from his wide reading or his own experiments was marshaled to point to his interpretation. The full discipline of Blackman's ways was experienced by those who had the privilege of starting research under his guidance. These students, many of whom proceeded to leading posts in British botany, carried the torch he lit.

BIBLIOGRAPHY

I. ORIGINAL WORKS. Blackman's writings include "Experimental Researches in Vegetable Assimilation and Respiration. I. On a New Method for Investigating the Carbonic Acid Exchange of Plants. II. On the Paths of Gaseous Exchange Between Aërial Leaves and the Atmosphere," in *Philosophical Transactions of the Royal Society,* **B186** (1895), 485–562; "III. On the Effect of Temperature on Carbon-dioxide Assimilation," ibid., **B197** (1904), 47–105 (by G. L. C. Matthaei); "Optima and Limiting Factors," in *Annals of Botany* (London), **19** (1905), 281–295; "The Manifestations of the Principles of Chemical Mechanics in the Living Plant," in *Transactions of Section K of the British Association Meeting* (London, 1908), pp. 1–18; "Analytic Studies in Plant Respiration. I. The Respiration of a Population of Senescent Ripening Apples [written with P. Parija]. II. The Respiration of Apples in Nitrogen and Its Relation to Respiration in Air [by Parija]. III. Formulation of a Catalytic System for the Respiration of Apples and Its Relation to Oxygen [by Blackman alone]," in *Proceedings of the Royal Society, B103* (1928), 412–513; and *Analytic Studies in Plant Respiration* (Cambridge, 1954).

II. SECONDARY LITERATURE. Articles on Blackman are G. E. Briggs, in *Obituary Notices of Fellows of the Royal Society,* **5** (May 1948), 651–657; and *Dictionary of National Biography,* supp. for 1941–1950.

G. E. BRIGGS

BLAEU, WILLEM JANSZOON (*b.* Alkmaar [?], Holland, 1571; *d.* Amsterdam, Holland, 21 October 1638), *cartography.*

Before beginning his scientific career, Blaeu was a carpenter and a clerk in the Amsterdam mercantile office of his patrician cousin Cornelius Pieterszoon Hooft. His main interests, however, were astronomy and navigation, so in 1595–1596 he worked with Tycho Brahe at the latter's observatory on the island of Hven, Denmark. He then settled in Amsterdam, where he married Marytje Cornelisdochter. In 1599 Blaeu bought a house on the Y, where he established himself as a merchant of maps and globes, in the making of which he soon became quite proficient.

In constant contact with merchants and navigators, Blaeu was well informed on their latest discoveries. At this time Holland was beginning to send its fleets to Asia, Africa, America, and the Arctic Ocean, and interest in navigation and cartography grew by leaps and bounds. Blaeu's first terrestrial globe dates from 1599; his first celestial globe, from 1602. In 1605 he published his first world map, *Nova universi terrarum orbis mappa;* his sea atlas, *Het Licht der Zeevaert,* appeared in 1608. He moved his shop to the Damrak "in de vergulde Sonnewyzer" ("at the sign of the gilded sundial"), where he also began to publish maps made by others, thus laying the foundation of his once-famous world atlas, *Novus atlas* (1634).

In 1633 Blaeu became the official cartographer of the Dutch East India Company. Four years later he moved his printing plant to the Bloemgracht, where, with its specially designed presses, its foundry of special types, and its rooms for engravers and collectors, it became a showplace.

After Blaeu's death the business was continued by his sons Joan and Cornelis. The Bloemgracht plant continued operations until 1650, and the bookstore at the Damrak remained open. In 1672 a fire destroyed its warehouse, but the firm was in the family until 1695–1696, under the management of Joan's sons Willem, Pieter, and Joan. The establishment was then taken over by J. Van Keulen.

BIBLIOGRAPHY

I. ORIGINAL WORKS. Blaeu's main works are *Nova universi terrarum orbis mappa* (Amsterdam, 1605); *Het Licht der Zeevaert* (Amsterdam, 1608); and *Novus atlas* (Amsterdam, 1634), trans. into Dutch as *Toonneel des*

Aerdrycks, 4 vols. (Amsterdam, 1635–1645), with various later eds. entitled *Atlas major, Le grand atlas,* and *Grooten Atlas,* in 9–12 vols. (Amsterdam, 1662–1665). The various known eds. are listed by Baudet and Stevenson (see below).

II. SECONDARY LITERATURE. Works on Blaeu are P. J. H. Baudet, *Leven en Werken van Willem Jansz. Blaeu* (Utrecht, 1871; supplement, 1872), and *Notice sur la part prise par W. J. Blaeu . . . dans la détermination des longitudes terrestres* (Utrecht, 1875); J. Keuning, "Blaeu's Atlas," in *Imago mundi,* **14** (1959), 74–89; H. Richter, "William Jansz. Blaeu With Tycho Brahe on Hven," *ibid.,* **3** (1939), 53–60; E. L. Stevenson, *William Janszoon Blaeu* (New York, 1914), with facsimile repro. of 1605 world map in 18 sheets, and *Terrestrial and Celestial Globes,* 2 vols. (New Haven, 1921).

D. J. STRUIK

BLAGDEN, CHARLES (*b.* Wooten-under-Edge, Gloucestershire, England, 17[?] April 1748; *d.* Arcueil, France, 26 March 1820), *physical chemistry.*

Virtually nothing is recorded of Blagden's family background or education. He studied medicine at Edinburgh and received the M.D. in 1768. He was elected a fellow of the Royal Society in 1772 and served as a medical officer in the British Army from about 1776 to 1780. From about 1782 to 1789 Blagden was Cavendish's assistant. Neither man ever revealed "the circumstances which brought them together or separated them" (G. Wilson, *Life of Cavendish,* p. 129). Cavendish settled an annuity on Blagden and left him a considerable legacy.

Blagden succeeded Paul Henry Maty as secretary of the Royal Society on 5 May 1784, at a time when the Society was sorely divided over the efficacy of the administration of its president, Sir Joseph Banks. Blagden, Banks's close friend for many years, was elected secretary by a large majority. Both in this capacity and as Cavendish's assistant he became involved in the prolonged "water controversy"—the question of priority in discovering the composition of water, claimed by both Cavendish and James Watt in England and by Lavoisier in France. Blagden admitted responsibility for conveying, quite well meaningly, word of the experiments and conclusions of both Watt and Cavendish to Lavoisier; and he seems to have been careless in overlooking errors of date in the printing of Cavendish's and Watt's papers. There appears, however, to be little ground for the charge, leveled by Muirhead and other supporters of Watt's claims, that Blagden deliberately falsified the evidence in favor of Cavendish.

Blagden's earliest published papers concerned experiments carried out on himself, Banks, and others, to determine the endurance of air temperatures of

up to 260° F.—he found the body temperature did not rise by more than one or two degrees. He also wrote a history of the attempts by Cavendish and others to determine the freezing point of mercury. A series of experiments on the supercooling of distilled water and solutions of salts led Blagden to study the effects of dissolved substances, beginning with common salt, on the freezing point of water. His conclusion that the salt lowers the freezing point in the simple inverse ratio of the proportion the water bears to it in the solution has come to be known as Blagden's law, although Richard Watson first discovered the relationship in 1771 (see J. R. Partington, *Text-book of Inorganic Chemistry* [London, 1921], p. 103; and Watson, in *Philosophical Transactions,* **61** [1771], 213–220). Nearly a century elapsed before his results could be integrated into a new theory of solutions initiated by the work of Raoult, Arrhenius, and van't Hoff; in the meantime, Blagden's work was virtually forgotten until Louis de Coppet drew attention to it in 1871.

Blagden spent much of his time in Europe, particularly in France—he was a close friend of Berthollet and other French scientists. Indeed, he had gone to live in Arcueil shortly before he died. He was knighted in 1792.

BIBLIOGRAPHY

I. ORIGINAL WORKS. Blagden published little outside the *Philosophical Transactions of the Royal Society.* Among his papers are "Experiments in a Heated Room," in *Philosophical Transactions,* **65** (1775), 111–128, 484–494; "History of the Congelation of Mercury," *ibid.,* **73** (1783), 329–397; "Experiments on the Cooling of Water Below Its Freezing Point," *ibid.,* **78** (1788), 125–146; and "Experiments on the Effect of Various Substances in Lowering the Point of Congelation of Water," *ibid.,* 277–312.

II. SECONDARY LITERATURE. A biography is F. H. Getman, "Sir Charles Blagden," in *Osiris,* **3** (1937), 69–87. The two sides of the "water controversy," giving diametrically opposed opinions respecting Blagden's integrity, are best studied in J. P. Muirhead, ed., *Correspondence of the Late James Watt on His Theory of the Composition of Water . . .* (London, 1846); and G. Wilson, *The Life of the Honourable Henry Cavendish, Including Abstracts of His Most Important Scientific Papers, and a Critical Inquiry Into the Claims of All the Alleged Discoverers of the Composition of Water* (London, 1851). The latter gives a useful bibliography of the subject and a biographical sketch of Blagden.

E. L. SCOTT

BLAINVILLE, HENRI MARIE DUCROTAY DE (*b.* Arques, France, 12 September 1777; *d.* Paris, France, 1 May 1850), *anatomy, zoology.*

Son of Pierre Ducrotay and Marie Pauger de Blainville, Henri grew up among the lesser but intensely proud Norman nobility. His schooling, interrupted by the French Revolution, recommenced in Rouen and Paris, where he at first studied music, art, and literature. There followed a brief but spectacular dissipation of his patrimony. Reforming himself and pursuing his ferocious desire to learn, Blainville turned to medicine (M.D., Paris, 1808) and then to natural history. Working in Cuvier's laboratory, he soon became an outstanding comparative anatomist and developed further as a remarkably independent thinker. In addition to anatomy, he lectured and published widely on descriptive and taxonomic invertebrate zoology (particularly malacology), comparative osteology, history of science, and the first principles of natural history. About 1810 he began formal instruction (as Cuvier's deputy) in various Parisian institutions (Athénée, Collège de France, Muséum d'Histoire Naturelle). He was named a professor at the Muséum in 1830 and in 1832 was appointed to Cuvier's vacant chair of comparative anatomy. In 1825 he was elected to the Académie des Sciences.

Blainville's lifelong objective in natural history was order. Order in the chaos of existence necessarily could derive only from clearly defined *principes*. These would follow inevitably from what Blainville called *la philosophie chrétienne*. Natural order was simply the unfolding of the Creator's design; that design in turn refocused our regard upon His wisdom and power. There were two roads to God, faith and knowledge, and for Blainville they merged into a single Christian philosophy. Blainville was a believing and, it appears, a practicing Roman Catholic. His religion, however, aimed less at spiritual experience than at an understanding of God's plan of creation, and thus was largely an elaboration on earlier objectives and beliefs of the deists.

God's plan for ordering animals and plants was the long-familiar scale of being, or *série*. Blainville vigorously defended the generalized *série* against Cuvier's attacks. Apparent gaps in the arrangement of existing organisms were nicely filled by fossil forms; Blainville carried out valuable paleontological research to support this proposition. Together, extinct and extant organisms testified to the original fullness, and hence rightness, of God's creation. Such change as occurred, possibly including that of species, was predicated by the divine plan.

Man stood both morally and physically at the summit of the *série*, presenting the standard by which the rank of all other forms was to be decided. Blainville followed Bichat in defining life as a general responsiveness of the organism to, and its persistence amid, ever-varying ambient conditions. This characteristic, *sensibilité*, was to biology what gravitation was to the Newtonian world machine; whether causal or not, it gave meaningful substance to the essential fact of *relation*. Organs of relation (principally the sensory and locomotory parts) thereupon assumed primacy and allowed Blainville to base his intricate and numerous classifications upon external features, those which mediated with the environment.

Blainville's influence was exerted principally through his famous lectures; he was a somewhat unsystematic author and brought few works to true completion. His extreme personal and family pride led him to bitter relations with contemporaries and an unsympathetic view of bourgeois France. Blainville's grand and enduring trinity was God, king, and France. His distaste for egalitarian society and contempt for Republican ideals led him to examine alternative social structures and to discuss favorably various utopian socialistic schemes. In 1813 he became a close acquaintance of Saint-Simon and, about 1824, the friend, disciple, and mentor of Comte, who carefully followed Blainville's most notable lecture series, that on physiology. F. L. P. Gervais, F. A. Pouchet, and H. C. M. Nicard were among Blainville's pupils.

BIBLIOGRAPHY

I. ORIGINAL WORKS. Blainville published over 150 articles and numerous monographs. A topical list of his writings is given in Flourens, pp. xliii–lx. His major publications are *De l'organisation des animaux, ou Principes d'anatomie comparée* (Paris, 1822); *Manuel de malacologie et conchyiologie,* 2 vols. (Paris–Strasbourg, 1825–1827); *Cours de physiologie générale et comparée professé à la Faculté des Sciences de Paris en 1829–1833,* Hollard, ed., 3 vols. (Paris, 1833); *Manuel d'actinologie et de zoophytologie,* 2 vols. (Paris, 1834); *Ostéographie ou description iconographique comparée du squelette et du système dentaire des cinq classes d'animaux vertébrés récents et fossiles pour servir de base à la zoologie et à la géologie* (Paris, 1839–1864)—24 fascicles were issued by Blainville between 1839 and 1850; the 25th was published, with a biographical notice of Blainville and indexes to all parts, by Nicard in 1864; *Histoire des sciences de l'organisation et de leurs progrès, comme base de la philosophie, rédigées d'après ses notes et ses leçons faites à la Sorbonne de 1830 à 1841, avec les développements nécessaires et plusieurs additions,* Maupied, ed., 3 vols. (Paris, 1845)—Maupied severely distorted Blainville's intention and arguments, and made him appear a shrill Catholic apologist (see Nicard, p. 149); *Sur les principes de la zooclassie ou de la classification des animaux* (Paris, 1847); and *Cuvier et [E.] Geoffroy Saint-*

Hilaire: Biographies scientifiques, H. C. M. Nicard, ed. (Paris, 1890), an angry polemic against Cuvier.

Blainville's papers passed to his student and biographer Nicard, and are today in the Bibliothèque Centrale, Muséum National d'Histoire Naturelle, Paris. These MSS include notes for lectures at the Muséum, drafts of published works, and occasional items of poetry and drama. (Information courtesy of Yves Laissus.) No collection of correspondence can be located.

II. SECONDARY LITERATURE. There exists neither a satisfactory study of Blainville's scientific work nor a detailed biography. The only comprehensive view of both is given in H. C. M. [Pol] Nicard, *Étude sur la vie et les travaux de M. Ducrotay de Blainville* (Paris, 1890). Nicard is at once hagiographer and confusing, quite unsystematic expositor. Nevertheless, he knew Blainville well and controlled his literary legacy; hence his volume is a major source and interpretation. In the preface, Nicard lists earlier biographical notices. M. J. P. Flourens wrote the official *éloge* for the Académie des Sciences: "Éloge historique de Marie-Henri [*sic*] Ducrotay de Blainville," in *Mémoires de l'Académie des Sciences, Paris,* **27** (1860), i–lx, also in Flourens's *Recueil des éloges historiques lus dans les séances publiques de l'Académie des Sciences* (Paris, 1856), pp. 285–341. Blainville's early physiological ideas are expounded in C. J. F. B. Dhéré, *De la nutrition considérée anatomiquement et physiologiquement dans la série des animaux, d'après les idées de M. Ducrotay de Blainville* (Paris, 1826). A brief but penetrating estimate of Blainville's religiophilosophical viewpoint is given in H. Gouhier, "La philosophie 'positiviste' et 'chrétienne' de H. de Blainville," in *Revue philosophique,* **131** (1941), 38–69. See also A. Comte, *Cours de philosophie positive,* III (Paris, 1838), leçon 40; P. Ducassé, *Méthode et intuition chez Auguste Comte* (Paris, 1939); and E. Littré, *Auguste Comte et la philosophie positive,* 2nd ed. (Paris, 1864), pp. 632–639, a discussion of Blainville and Maupied.

WILLIAM COLEMAN

BLAIR, PATRICK (*d.* Boston, England, 1728), *botany, biology, medicine.*

Reliable biographical information on Blair is scanty and contradictory; for example, the evidence for his death in 1728 is indirect—he had reached the letter H in his *Pharmaco-Botanologia,* and his death is assumed to have occurred when no further material appeared. Certainly he worked as a surgeon in Dundee, Scotland, for some years; and when, on 27 April 1706, a female Indian elephant died there, Blair dissected it. He presented his findings, with an extensive review of the literature, in a letter to the Royal Society in 1710; this communication was later published separately (1713). In 1712 Blair was elected a fellow of the Royal Society, and the same year was given an honorary M.D. by King's College, Aberdeen. Blair was a Jacobite, and was sentenced to death as

such on 7 July 1716; he was, however, pardoned after he successfully appealed to Sir Hans Sloane and others, such as Richard Mead, to intercede with the authorities on his behalf.

Blair appears to have been a practicing surgeon for most of his life, and in a communication to the Royal Society in 1717 he gave what Caulfield has called "probably the earliest description" of pyloric stenosis on record. But it is for his contributions to botany that Blair is most famous—not so much for his natural interest as a physician in the medicinal properties of plants (although this took up much of his time) but more for his work on plant sexuality. Although Sachs, in his *History of Botany,* felt that in this regard ". . . Patrick Blair . . . did nothing himself, but merely appropriated the general results of Camerarius' observations" (p. 391), Blair was only one of many—including Grew, Ray, Camerarius, and Bradley—who, according to Ritterbush, "escaped the consequences of plant sexuality for the scale of functions by ascribing hermaphroditic generation to plants, which they shared only with the lower animals" (*Overtures to Biology,* p. 117). Blair was an "ovulist" rather than a "pollenist."

Blair was something of a polemicist, and his unpublished manuscript preface bound with Bishop Rawlinson's copy of Bradley's *Philosophical Account of the Works of Nature* was, as Ritterbush has observed, "an exceptionally abusive attack upon Richard Bradley" (*op. cit.,* p. 96).

BIBLIOGRAPHY

I. ORIGINAL WORKS. In addition to several communications in the *Philosophical Transactions of the Royal Society,* Blair wrote the following: *Osteographia Elephantina: or, a Full and exact description of all the bones of an elephant, which died near Dundee, April the 27th. 1706. with their several dimensions. To which are premis'd, 1. An historical account of the natural endowments . . . of elephants . . . 2. A short anatomical account of their parts . . . In a letter to Dr. Hans Sloane* (London, 1713); *Miscellaneous Observations in the Practise of Physick, Anatomy and Surgery. With new and curious remarks in botany* (London, 1718); *Botanick Essays. In two parts. The first containing, the structure of flowers . . . and the second, the generation of plants, etc.* (London, 1720); and *Pharmaco-Botanologia: or, an Alphabetical and classical dissertation on all the British indigenous and garden plants of the new London Dispensatory . . . With many curious and useful remarks from proper observation* (London, 1723–1728).

One of the most important collections of Blair MSS is bound in with Bishop Richard Rawlinson's copy of Richard Bradley's *Philosophical Account of the Works of Nature,* now in the possession of the Bodleian Library, Oxford.

There are several Blair letters dated 1723–1724 as well as a 28-page preface to an apparently unfinished treatise.

II. SECONDARY LITERATURE. For an account of Blair's work on the elephant, see F. J. Cole, *A History of Comparative Anatomy* (London, 1944), pp. 325–328. A good general account of Blair's botanical contributions is P. C. Ritterbush, *Overtures to Biology* (New Haven, 1964), ch. 3. For general biographical information, Ernest Caulfield, "An Early Case of Pyloric Stenosis," in *American Journal of Diseases of Children,* **40** (1930), 1070–1077, is surprisingly informative. See also C. E. Raven, *John Ray* (Cambridge, 1950), pp. 185–186, for an account of Blair's attack on John Ray; and Julius von Sachs, *History of Botany* (Oxford, 1890), p. 391.

L. R. C. AGNEW

BLAISE. See **Blasius of Parma.**

BLANC, ALBERTO-CARLO (*b.* Chambéry, France, 30 July 1906; *d.* Rome, Italy, 3 July 1960), *prehistory, ethnology.*

Blanc was the son of Gian-Alberto Blanc, a distinguished naturalist and professor at the University of Rome and descendant of an old and prominent Savoyard family. When a part of the Duchy of Savoy voted for France in 1860, the Blancs chose to become Italian out of loyalty to the prince of Savoy. These origins endowed the Blanc family with a double culture, French and Italian. Like his father, Alberto-Carlo spoke and wrote the two languages with equal perfection. The family was affluent, owning extensive property, and like almost all Savoyard families they were Catholic. They were on friendly terms with the Abbé Breuil, the prehistorian. Sometimes, too, Cardinal Tisserant would accompany them into the field to take part in excavations in search of traces of prehistoric man.

After distinguishing himself as a student at the universities of Pisa and Rome, Blanc was appointed in 1938 to teach a course in geology at the former institution. He was attracted primarily by the most recent era, the Quaternary, in which man made his appearance. He married in 1939. One month later he wrote to André Cailleux:

> Forgive me for my somewhat tardy reply to your card of 21 February. In order to excuse myself at least partially, may I say that I was married on 20 February and that on the 25th of the same month I had the good luck to discover, in the midst of my honeymoon, a beautiful Neanderthal skull. Naturally, this upset all my plans and at the moment we, i.e., my wife and I, are in the process of digging in the new deposit here.

This letter was dated San Felice Circeo (Littoria), where the Blancs owned property. The Monte Circeo

skull, after thorough examination, quickly became a classic, since it is the most complete Neanderthal skull yet discovered.

Blanc was called to the University of Rome in 1939, where he taught ethnology and human paleontology. In 1957 he was appointed to the chair in paleoethnology. A member of numerous academies and scientific societies, he also was invited to lecture at more than twenty foreign universities. He was elected president of several international commissions and of the Sixth Congress of the International Union of Prehistoric and Protohistoric Sciences. He was the moving spirit behind the magazine *Quaternaria,* dedicated to the natural and cultural history of the Quaternary era.

Toward the end of 1958, while on a field trip in Apulia in southern Italy, Blanc experienced the first attacks of the disease that proved fatal. But to his very last hours, according to his pupil Georges Laplace, he "retained his extraordinary clarity of spirit, his marvelous smile, and the calm strength which he radiated."

An industrious and efficient worker, Blanc published 164 works in the span of twenty-six years. When he started his work in 1934, European prehistory was dominated by the great if somewhat authoritarian figure of the Abbé Breuil. With the latter's aid and advice, yet always preserving his independence, Blanc addressed himself first—and properly so—to the severe but beneficial school of empirical study. He participated in some hundred digs, most of which were performed under his direction. In Italy he discovered some fifty prehistoric deposits and six of the seven known human Neanderthal fossils of that country. Wisely, he studied the geology of these deposits with great care so as to be able to link up their history with that of the rest of Europe. The flora and fauna, which were interpreted by specialists, revealed changes during the course of time, a development to which Blanc turned his attention.

In 1939 Blanc was asked to give a course in the ethnology of presently existing populations, particularly the most primitive peoples. In comparing their type of life with that of prehistoric man of the advanced Paleolithic age, with which he was familiar, Blanc was struck by a clear deterioration in techniques and an ever-narrowing specialization as the transition from ancient to present times was followed. This led him to a new theory concerning the formation of ethnic groupings which he termed *ethnolysis:* starting from an ancient polymorphous ethnic grouping, present ethnic groupings are differentiated by a loss of characteristics:

". . . their centrifugal diffusion, which occurred in very special conditions varying for each people, resulted necessarily in widely differing specializations; certain cultural elements persisted (and developed) in certain peoples while disappearing in others, who in turn preserved certain elements which the former had lost. Thus, by alternative elimination, there occurred a separation, a segregation, a lysis of cultural elements which had coexisted originally [*L'évolution humaine*].

Blanc immediately recognized the potential affinities and generalizations of his idea. What he had assumed concerning ethnic groupings, he very soon extended to animal and plant associations, to the evolution of species, and in particular to the appearance of the human races: from ethnolysis he passed to *cosmolysis,* which embraced the entire physical, biological, and human universe:

Cosmolysis is that universal modality of evolution through which heterogeneous archaic entities and groupings, which in the state of primary blending contain a great number of characteristics and elements, are resolved into more and more homogeneous and distinct entities, through lysis (from the Greek *luo,* "I separate, dissolve") and segregation in each case of characters and elements which coexist in a mixed state in the above mentioned archaic entities and groupings [*Ibid.*].

Objections were raised to Blanc's views on the grounds that human prehistory, like the evolution of the species, shows inverse examples, where we pass from the simple to the complex and more varied elements. Indeed, Blanc himself recognized these phases of growing complexity, for instance, between the beginning and the last part of the Stone Age, between the Abbevillian and the upper Paleolithic periods. From the point of view of ethnology, he placed them within a two-phase cycle, i.e., complexification–simplification—the cycle that was to be repeated several times in the course of the ages. Evidently, however, he was far more interested in the second phase, that of simplification, or lysis, which he had invented himself. Even if, contrary to Blanc, it is supposed that the first phase, i.e., acquisition of new characters and their formation, plays just as important or even more important a role in the evolution of animal and especially plant species, we must recognize that the idea of cosmolysis explains certain facts.

But there was more to it. Like his contemporaries, Blanc saw clearly that his hypothesis and the facts supporting it agreed quite well with Neo-Darwinism, with the mutation-selection theory, and with the corpuscular theory of heredity that has been confirmed by so many other works since his death. In this respect, he was a precursor.

Given to bold generalizations, Blanc went even

further and speculated about the hydrogen atom and its components. Its then apparent simplicity seemed to him deceptive and he saw there "the simplified product of a history proceeding from a fundamental complexity of matter" (*Ibid.*). Even if one finds Blanc's theory of cosmolysis a less than complete explanation for the evolution of the cosmos, life, and mankind, Blanc's idea must still be given credit for its intrinsic strength and greatness.

BIBLIOGRAPHY

I. ORIGINAL WORKS. Blanc's writings include "Le glaciaire considéré au point de vue paléobiologique et géomorphologique," in *L'anthropologie,* **48** (1938); "Il Monte Circeo, le sue grotte paleolitiche ed il suo uomo fossile," in *Bollettino Società geografica italiana* (1939); "Etnolisi—Sui fenomeni di segregazione in biologia ed in etnologia," in *Rivista di antropologia,* **33** (1940); "Cosmolisi—Interpretazione genetico-storica delle entità e degli aggrupamenti biologici ed etnologici," *ibid.,* **34** (1941–1942); "Sviluppo per lisi delle forme distinte," in *Quaderni di sintesi,* **2** (1946); "I paleantropi di Saccopastore e del Circeo," in *Quartär,* **4** (1942); "Etnologia e paleontologia," in *Atti della Società italiana per il progresso delle scienze,* **41** (1943); "L'évolution humaine dans le cadre de la cosmolyse," in *Cahiers de la Faculté de Théologie de l'Université de Lausanne* (1946).

II. SECONDARY LITERATURE. A good account and a discussion of cosmolysis is in Piero Leonardi, *L'evoluzione dei viventi* (Brescia, 1957), also trans. into Spanish as *La evolución biológica* (Madrid, 1957); see pp. 265–276. For the life and works of Blanc, see the note by Georges Laplace in *Bulletin de la Société préhistorique française,* **58** (1961), 515–519.

ANDRÉ CAILLEUX

BLANCHARD, RAOUL (*b*. Orléans, France, 4 September 1877; *d.* Paris, France, 24 March 1965), *geography.*

Blanchard graduated from the École Normale Supérieure in 1900 and passed the *concours d'agrégation* in history and geography. At the time, geography was still mainly in a descriptive stage and an adjunct to history. His thesis on Flanders, presented at the University of Lille in 1906, was one of the first important works of regional geography based on research done *in situ.*

At the time of his appointment as lecturer in 1905, there was not a single student of geography at Grenoble. Through perseverance, teaching ability, and the novelty of his subject, he turned the university into one of the most active centers for geography in France. He later became a professor. In 1940 he was appointed dean of the Faculty of Liberal Arts and taught there until his retirement in 1948.

Blanchard was the creator of French Alpine geography, founding the *Revue de géographie alpine,* which published the first works on the French Alps. For the study of mountains he instituted field observation (he was an indefatigable hiker) together with rigorous arguments for studying structure, to which he gave priority (instead of erosion surfaces).

His twelve volumes on the French Alps are considered his chief work, but his range of interests was much greater. In human geography he produced important studies of cities, works that were novel at the time because they combined a study of the site with that of the development of the city. He prepared the volume on western Asia for the series Géographie Universelle (1929), and later published a general study of North America (1933). He knew North America well. He had been appointed instructor at Harvard in 1917 and was a full professor from 1928 to 1936. He also taught at Chicago, Columbia, and other schools in the United States as well as the universities of Montreal and Laval in Canada.

Blanchard was representative of his epoch in French geography. In time, of course, concepts and methods changed, and he was reproached by some for not having advanced his morphology beyond a somewhat oversimplified determinism.

BIBLIOGRAPHY

I. ORIGINAL WORKS. Blanchard's writings include *La Flandre . . .* (Dunkerque, 1906), his thesis; *Geography of France* (Chicago–New York, 1919), written with M. Todd; *Les Alpes françaises* (Paris, 1925); *L'Asie occidentale,* in the series Géographie Universelle, directed by P. Vidal de la Blache and L. Gallois (Paris, 1929); *L'Amérique du Nord: États-Unis, Canada et Alaska* (Paris, 1933); *Grenoble: Étude de géographie urbaine* (Grenoble, 1935); *Les Alpes occidentales,* 12 vols. (Grenoble, 1941–1958); and *A Geography of Europe* (New York, 1944), written with R. E. Crist.

II. SECONDARY LITERATURE. Biographies of Blanchard are J. Blache, in *Revue de géographie alpine,* 7 (1965), 361–370; P. Dagenais, in *Revue de géographie de Montréal,* 18 (1964), 133–135; D. Faucher, in *Revue de géographie des Pyrénées et du Sud-Ouest,* 13 (1965), 157; and A. Perpillou, in *Acta geographica* (Paris), no. 5 (1965), 1. See also *In Memoriam Raoul Blanchard,* prepared by the Association des Amis de l'Université de Grenoble (Grenoble, 1966).

JULIETTE TATON

BLASCHKE, WILHELM JOHANN EUGEN
(*b.* Graz, Austria, 13 September 1885; *d.* Hamburg, Germany, 17 March 1962), *mathematics.*

Blaschke's father, Josef Blaschke (1852–1917), was professor of descriptive geometry at the Landes-

Oberrealschule at Graz. Wilhelm inherited his father's predilection for the geometry of Jakob Steiner and his love of concrete problems. Josef also imparted to the boy a feeling for history and an open-mindedness toward foreign cultures that remained with him throughout his life.

Blaschke began his studies at the Technische Hochschule of Graz and earned his doctorate from the University of Vienna in 1908. For more than a decade afterward he traveled through Europe, seeking contact with many of the leading geometers of his day. He spent some months in Pisa with Luigi Bianchi and a semester in Göttingen, drawn there by Felix Klein, David Hilbert, and Carl Runge. He worked at Bonn with Eduard Study, whose main fields of research were geometry, kinematics, and the theory of invariants. Blaschke became *Privatdozent* at Bonn in 1910, but in the following year he went to the University of Greifswald to join Friedrich Engel, with whom he shared an admiration for the great Norwegian mathematician Sophus Lie.

In 1913 Blaschke accepted an extraordinary professorship at the Deutsche Technische Hochschule in Prague, and in 1915 he moved to Leipzig, where he became a close friend of Gustav Herglotz. Two years later he was made full professor at the University of Königsberg. After a short stay at Tübingen, Blaschke was called in 1919 to the full professorship of mathematics at the University of Hamburg, a position he retained until his retirement in 1953. He also held visiting professorships at Johns Hopkins University, at the University of Chicago, at the University of Istanbul, and at the Humboldt University in Berlin, and lectured at universities all over the world. He was married to Augusta Meta Röttger and had two children.

At Hamburg, Blaschke succeeded within a few years in gaining worldwide recognition for the department of mathematics of the newly founded university, for he was able to attract to Hamburg such well-known mathematicians as Erich Hecke, Emil Artin, and Helmut Hasse. Very soon Hamburg became a center of great mathematical activity and productivity, testimony to which is given by the *Abhandlungen aus dem mathematischen Seminar der Universität Hamburg* and the *Hamburger mathematische Einzelschriften,* both founded by Blaschke.

One of the leading geometers of his time, Blaschke centered most of his research on differential and integral geometry and kinematics. He combined an unusual power of geometrical imagination with a consistent and suggestive use of analytical tools; this gave his publications great conciseness and clarity and, with his charming personality, won him many students and collaborators.

Blaschke made "kinematic mapping" (discovered independently in 1911 by Josef Grünwald), which established a mapping between the group of isometries (motions) in the plane and the three-dimensional point space, a central tool in kinematics; and in an abstract turn given to it by Kurt Reidemeister, it proved very useful in the axiomatic foundation of several geometries. In *Kreis und Kugel* (1916), Blaschke investigated the isoperimetric properties of convex bodies, characterizing circles and spheres as figures of minimal properties. In this he was following methods suggested by Steiner, who had been criticized by Dirichlet for omitting an existence proof. This was first remedied by Weierstrass by means of the calculus of variation, but Blaschke supplied the necessary existence proofs in a fashion closer to the spirit of Steiner.

Blaschke's books on differential geometry soon gained worldwide recognition. The three-volume *Vorlesungen* (1921–1929) put into practice Felix Klein's "Erlangen Program" for differential geometry: Volume I was devoted to classical geometry, Volume II to affine differential geometry (a subject developed by Blaschke and his pupils), and Volume III to the differential geometry of circles and spheres, controlled by the transformation groups of Moebius, Laguerre, and Sophus Lie. (The treatment of projective differential geometry, however, was left to Blaschke's pupil Gerrit Bol.) Furthermore, Blaschke originated topological differential geometry, which studies invariants of differentiable mappings; he collected the results in his books *Geometrie der Gewebe* (1938) and *Einführung in die Geometrie der Waben* (1955). In 1950 Blaschke gave a new, concise exposition of differential geometry based on ideas of E. Cartan.

Inspired by Gustav Herglotz and by some classical problems of geometrical probability (Buffon's needle problem, Crofton's formulas), Blaschke began, about 1935, a series of papers on integral geometry. Because of its relations to convex bodies and kinematics, this field of research was especially to his liking; and many of his students continued his work in this area—Hadwiger, Wu, Chern, and Santaló.

Blaschke received honorary doctorates from the universities of Sofia, Padua, and Greifswald, and the Karlsruhe Technische Hochschule. He was elected corresponding or honorary member of about a dozen European scientific academies.

BIBLIOGRAPHY

I. ORIGINAL WORKS. Blaschke's works include *Kreis und Kugel* (Leipzig, 1916; Berlin, 1956), trans. into Russian (Moscow, 1967); *Vorlesungen über Differentialgeometrie,* 3 vols., I (Berlin, 1921, 1924, 1930, 1945), trans. into Russian (Moscow, 1935); II, rev. by Kurt Reidemeister (Berlin, 1923); III, rev. by G. Thomsen (Berlin, 1929); *Vorlesungen über Integralgeometrie,* 2 vols., I (Leipzig–Berlin, 1935, 1936, 1955), trans. into Russian (Moscow, 1938); II (Leipzig–Berlin, 1937; 3rd ed., 1955—together with Vol. I); *Ebene Kinematik* (Leipzig–Berlin, 1938); *Geometrie der Gewebe,* written with Gerrit Bol (Berlin, 1938); *Einführung in die Differentialgeometrie* (Berlin, 1950; 2nd ed., 1960), written with Hans Reichardt, trans. into Russian (Moscow, 1957); *Einführung in die Geometrie der Waben* (Basel–Stuttgart, 1955), trans. into Russian (Moscow, 1959), trans. into Turkish (Istanbul, 1962); *Ebene Kinematik,* written with H. R. Müller (Munich, 1956); *Reden und Reisen eines Geometers* (Berlin, 1957, 1961); and *Kinematik und Quaternionen* (Berlin, 1960).

II. SECONDARY LITERATURE. The following obituary notices describe Blaschke's life and work in greater detail: Werner Burau, "Wilhelm Blaschkes Leben und Werk," in *Mitteilungen der Mathematischen Gesellschaft in Hamburg,* **9,** no. 2 (1963), 24–40; Otto Haupt, "Nachruf auf Wilhelm Blaschke," in *Jahrbuch 1962 der Akademie der Wissenschaften und der Literatur zu Mainz* (Mainz–Wiesbaden, 1962), pp. 44–51; Erwin Kruppa, "Wilhelm Blaschke," in *Almanach der Österreichischen Akademie der Wissenschaften,* **112** (for 1962) (Vienna, 1963), 419–429; Hans Reichardt, "Wilhelm Blaschke †," in *Jahresbericht der Deutschen Mathematiker-Vereinigung,* **69** (1966), 1–8; and Emanuel Sperner, "Zum Gedenken an Wilhelm Blaschke," in *Abhandlungen aus dem Mathematischen Seminar der Universität Hamburg,* **26** (1963), 111–128 (with a bibliography by W. Burau, to which Reichardt gives an addition).

CHRISTOPH J. SCRIBA

BLASIUS OF PARMA (*b.* Parma, Italy, *ca.* 1345; *d.* Parma, 1416), *natural philosophy.*

Although presumably he was born in Parma, the first known reference to Blasius is found in the records for 1377 of the University of Pavia, where he took his doctorate, perhaps in 1374 (the latter date makes 1345 a plausible birth year). Listed as an examiner in March 1378, Blasius probably left Pavia by October of that year for the University of Bologna, where he remained at least until 1382 (for 1379–1380, he was officially described as a teacher of logic, philosophy, and astrology), and probably through 1383. On 20 May 1384, he agreed to teach at the University of Padua for four years; his name appears in the university records from February 1386 to 11 May 1387 and again on 16 December 1388 as the sponsor of a doctoral candidate who was represented by another scholar, probably because in 1387 Blasius had returned to Bologna as professor of philosophy and astrology for the period 1387–1388. On 29 July 1388, he was appointed a lecturer in natural philosophy at the University of Florence, where he remained until 1389.

During the next decade, when he reached the summit of his career, Blasius was again at Pavia as professor of "mathematical arts and both philosophies" (i.e., moral and natural). His whereabouts between 1400 and 1403 are unknown, but in subsequent years he taught at the University of Pavia (1403–1407) and the University of Padua (1407–1411). In October 1411 he was dismissed from the latter because he lacked students and was deemed no longer fit to teach, conditions that were probably caused by the infirmities of old age. He died five years later.

A sojourn in Paris, where he received his doctorate (so we are told in an explicit to his *Questio de tactu corporum duorum,* which was disputed at Bologna no later than 1388), is mentioned in his *Questiones super tractatum de ponderibus.*[1] It was probably while in Paris that he absorbed the new ideas of the Parisian Scholastics, ideas that he was to disseminate and popularize in Italy.

Blasius was not merely an Aristotelian commentator, but also wrote independent treatises on important scientific topics. Prior to 16 October 1396, when he was compelled to recant unspecified transgressions against the Church[2] (by this time he had probably written the bulk of his extant treatises), Blasius seems to have been a materialist and determinist, accepting as true certain articles condemned at Paris in 1277. In his *Questiones de anima* (Padua, 1385), he denied that the intellective soul was separable from the body, insisting that it was produced from transient matter. It was only by authority of the Church and faith—not by natural reason or evidence—that one ought to believe in its separability. Furthermore, he denied the immortality of the intellective soul while accepting the eternity of the world and a necessary determinism exerted by the celestial bodies and constellations on terrestrial and human events. Such opinions, characteristic of earlier Bolognese Averroists, were probably instrumental in provoking the ecclesiastical authorities. Blasius capitulated and complied swiftly. During 1396–1397, in lectures delivered at Pavia on the *Physics* of Aristotle, he repudiated all these views; and in 1405 he attacked astrological determinism (but not astrology) in his *Iudicium revolutionis anni 1405,* declaring that while the stars influenced men and events, the will of God and human free will could resist if they chose.

Of his numerous scientific treatises, only those on optics, statics, and intension and remission of forms have received more than cursory examinations, resulting in partial or complete modern editions. In addition to relevant discussions on optics in his *Questiones*

de anima and *Meteorologica,* Blasius also wrote *Quaestiones perspectivae* (dated 1390 in one manuscript), a lengthy commentary on some of the propositions of John Peckham's enormously popular thirteenth-century optical treatise, *Communis perspectiva.* Guided by an empiricist outlook derived ultimately from the optics of Ibn al-Haytham (Alhazen), and perhaps influenced by fourteenth-century nominalism, he made visual sensation the basis for human certitude and knowledge; consequently he placed heavy emphasis upon the psychology of perception. Traditional geometric optics was placed in the broader matrix of a theory of knowledge and cognitive perception based on vision.

Blasius composed at least two treatises on statics: one Scholastic, the other longer and non-Scholastic in form. The longer work, *Tractatus de ponderibus,* drew heavily on the thirteenth-century statical treatises associated with the name of Jordanus de Nemore. It was probably from the *Elementa Jordani super demonstrationem ponderum* that Blasius adopted the important concept of "positional gravity," which involved a resolution of forces where the effective "heaviness" or weight of a body in a constrained system is proportional to the directness of its descent as measured by the projection of an arbitrary segment of its path onto the vertical drawn through the fulcrum of a lever or balance. Ignoring straightforward and available definitions of positional gravity, Blasius presents the concept in Pt. I, Supps. 6 and 7, proving in the first of these that "in the case of equal arcs unequally distant from the line of equality (i.e., the line of horizontal balance) that which is a greater distance intercepts less of the vertical [through the axis]," and in the second that "one body is heavier than another by the amount that its movement toward the center [of the world] is straighter."[3] But the more of the vertical cut off by a projected arc, the straighter its descent and, therefore, the greater its positional gravity.

In Pt. II, Prop. 4 (probably based upon *Elementa Jordani,* Th. 2), Blasius misapplied the concept of positional gravity in demonstrating that "when the equal arms of a balance are not parallel with the horizon and equal weights are hung [on their ends], the beam assumes a horizontal position."[4] In Figure 1, let arms *AB* and *BC* be equal but not parallel to the horizon, *DF.* If equal weights are suspended at the ends of the equal arms, the latter would become parallel to the horizon, or *DF.* This will occur because, being heavy bodies, *a* and *c* will seek to descend, *c* to *F* and *a* to *G.* Assuming, quite improperly, that arcs *CF* and *AG* are equal, but unequally distant from *DF,* Blasius applies Pt. I, Supp. 6, to show that arc

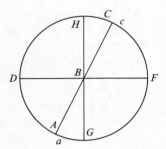

FIGURE 1

CF cuts off more of the vertical along *HG* than does arc *AG,* and concludes that *c*'s downward motion to *F* is more direct than *a*'s to *G.* Consequently (by Pt. I, Supp. 7, which is not cited but is clearly required), *c* is positionally heavier than *a* and will descend, forcing *a* upward until horizontal equilibrium is attained. The basic error in all this lies in assuming a simultaneous descent for *c* and *a,* instead of comparing the descent of *c* with the ascent of *a* and the ascent of *c* with the descent of *a.* The equality of these two ratios would have yielded the desired proof.

Positional gravity was more felicitously applied in proving the law of the lever (Pt. II, Prop. 10) and in demonstrating that equilibrium is attained on a bent lever when equal weights are suspended on its unequal arms, which terminate equidistantly from the axis of support (Pt. II, Prop. 11). A brief third part concerned the specific gravities of fluids and solids. Dynamic considerations played a role, since Blasius says (Pt. III, Prop. 1) that of two solid bodies descending in water, the heavier will descend more quickly. For comparison of liquids, a hydrometer was used, and its principle was utilized in the comparison of two solid, similarly shaped floating bodies, when Blasius advocated that each be divided into twelve equally spaced parts.

In one of two treatises on intension and remission of forms, *Questiones de latitudinibus formarum,* Blasius included both the English (arithmetic) and French (geometric) fourteenth-century versions of the mean speed theorem[5] that demonstrated the equality of the distances traversed during the same time by one body moving with uniform acceleration and another moving with a uniform speed equal to the velocity acquired by the body in uniform acceleration at the middle instant of its period of acceleration (i.e., $S = V_0 t + at^2/2$, where S is distance; V_0 initial velocity; a acceleration; and t time). Blasius may have introduced both versions into Italy.

Over a long career, Blasius discussed many traditional scientific concepts. Initially an apparent supporter of the impetus theory, he later denied, in his

Questiones super octo libros physicorum (1397), that it could explain acceleration in free fall or the rebound of bodies.[6] He accepted "Bradwardine's function,"[7] which described the relationship between the speeds of two bodies as $F_2/R_2 = (F_1/R_1)^{V_2/V_1}$, where F is motive power; $R,$ the resistive force of the body in motion; and $V,$ velocity. He also reflects common Parisian arguments when he denies the natural existence of vacuum inside or outside the cosmos[8] and then allows (contrary to Aristotle) that if a separate vacuum did exist, bodies could undergo motion and change[9] (in his *Questio de tactu corporum duorum,* Blasius holds that if a vacuum actually existed, many difficulties and contradictions involving the physical contact of two bodies could be resolved).[10]

Although not an original thinker, Blasius sympathetically absorbed the scientific ideas current among the "moderns" at the University of Paris during the fourteenth century. He helped disseminate these in Italy, where they were widely discussed until the time of Galileo.

NOTES

1. Quoted by Marshall Clagett in Marshall Clagett and E. A. Moody, *The Medieval Science of Weights,* pp. 413–414.
2. The brief document has been translated by L. Thorndike in *University Records and Life in the Middle Ages,* pp. 258–259.
3. Clagett and Moody, *op. cit.,* p. 243.
4. *Ibid.,* p. 251. The figure appears on p. 250.
5. Marshall Clagett, *Science of Mechanics,* pp. 402–403.
6. A. Maier, *Zwei Grundprobleme der scholastischen Naturphilosophie,* pp. 271–273.
7. *Questiones super tractatu De proportionibus Thome Berduerdini,* questions 10, 11 (MS Vat. lat. 3012, 151r–153v).
8. *Questiones super octo libros physicorum,* MS Vat. lat. 2159, 120v, c. 1.
9. *Ibid.,* 124r, c. 2–124v, c. 1.
10. G. F. Vescovini, "Problemi di fisica aristotelica in un maestro del XIV secolo: Biagio Pelacani da Parma," in *Rivista di filosofia,* **51** (1960), 196.

BIBLIOGRAPHY

I. ORIGINAL WORKS. All but a few of Blasius' works are unpublished. References to manuscripts of these treatises can be found in L. Thorndike and P. Kibre, "Blasius of Parma," in *A Catalogue of Incipits of Mediaeval Scientific Writings in Latin* (rev. and enl. ed., Cambridge, Mass., 1963), c. 1764; and, in an earlier but more conveniently arranged list, in L. Thorndike, *A History of Magic and Experimental Science,* IV (New York, 1934), app. 40, pp. 652–662.

Questions or commentaries on the following works of Aristotle are extant: *Questiones librorum de caelo et mundo* (Milan, Ambros. P. 120 Sup., 1–69; Bodleian Library, Canonicus Misc. 422, 1–52; Rome, Angelica 592 [F.6.4], 1–34; Rome, Angelica 595 [folio numbers unavailable];

Vienna, National Bibliothek, 2402, 1–63v); *Commentaria in Aristotelis de generatione et corruptione* (Vienna, National Bibliothek, 2402, 99r–123v); *Questiones de anima* (Vat. Chigi O IV 41, 112–217v; Vat. Urbinas lat. 1489, 74–[terminating folio number unavailable]; Bodleian Library, Canonicus Misc. 393, 1–78; Turin 1247 [folio numbers unavailable]); *Questiones in libros metheororum* (Vat. lat. 2160, 63–138v, which is immediately preceded by Blasius' *Conclusiones super libris methaurorum Aristotelis,* a work differing from the *Questiones;* Florence, Ashburnham 112, 1–60; Vat. Chigi O IV 41, 62–108v; University of Chicago 10, 39 ff.). On the *Physics* of Aristotle, Blasius left at least three versions: (1) *Expositio per conclusiones super octo libros physicorum Aristotelis* (Vat. lat. 2159, 1–98v); (2) *Questiones super octo libros physicorum,* preserved, with variant titles, in separate versions, one written in or before 1385 at Padua, of which only the first two books remain (Vat. Chigi O IV 41), and the other, copied in 1397 in Pavia, differing somewhat and embracing all eight books (Vat. lat. 2159, 61r–230r; despite an apparent overlap in pagination with the *Expositio,* it immediately follows the latter with independent pagination beginning with 61r); an incomplete and mutilated version of the Pavia copy is contained in Vat. lat. 3012, 2v–110v; and (3) an arrangement of Buridan's *Questiones super octo phisicorum libros Aristotelis* made around 1396 (Venice, S. Marco X, 103, 83–84).

The two works on statics are *Questiones super tractatum de ponderibus,* containing five questions and known only in a single manuscript (Milan, Ambros. F. 145 Sup., 18r–28r), edited and translated by Father Joseph Brown in a thesis, "The *Scientia de ponderibus* in the Later Middle Ages" (Univ. of Wis., 1967); and *Tractatus de ponderibus,* edited and translated by Marshall Clagett in Marshall Clagett and E. A. Moody, *The Medieval Science of Weights* (Madison, Wis., 1952), pp. 238–279. On intension and remission of forms, Blasius left two treatises, *De intensione et remissione formarum* and *Questiones super tractatu de latitudinibus formarum:* for manuscripts of both, see Marshall Clagett, *The Science of Mechanics in the Middle Ages* (Madison, Wis., 1959), pp. 404, 685–686; the second treatise was published in 1482 and 1486 at Padua and in 1505 at Venice, while part of the third and final question of the second treatise was edited and translated by Clagett in *Science of Mechanics,* pp. 402–408. On problems of motion, he wrote *Questiones super tractatu De proportionibus Thome Berduerdini* (i.e., Bradwardine); for manuscripts, see Marshall Clagett, *The Science of Mechanics in the Middle Ages,* p. 686; and *De motu iuxta mentem Aristotelis* (MS Vat. Barb. 357, 1–16v).

Of the three books and twenty-four questions of the *Quaestiones perspectivae,* Book I, quests. 1–10 were edited by F. Alessio as "Questioni inedite di ottica di Biagio Pelacani da Parma," in *Rivista critica di storia della filosofia,* **16** (1961), 79–110, 188–221; Book I, quests. 14 and 16, and Book III, quest. 3 (*ultima questio*), were edited by G. F. Vescovini as "Le questioni di 'Perspectiva' di Biagio Pelacani da Parma," in *Rinascimento,* **1** (1961), 207–243—the text is preceded by a lengthy discussion of the questions and their historical context on pp. 163–206.

The 1505 edition of *Questiones super tractatu de latitudinibus formarum* includes Blasius' *Questio de tactu corporum duorum,* which is summarized by G. F. Vescovini in "Problemi di fisica aristotelica in un maestro del XIV secolo: Biagio Pelacani da Parma," in *Rivista di filosofia,* **51** (1960), 179–200.

On astronomy, Blasius wrote *Questiones super tractatum sperae Johannis de Sacrobosco* (MS Parma 984) and a *Theorice planetarum* (Vat. lat. 4082, 47r–60v; Venice, S. Marco VIII.69, 175r–216v). The Latin text of the titles of the problems discussed by Blasius in the latter treatise was published by L. Thorndike in *Isis,* **47** (1956), 398–400. Thorndike mentions that the Latin texts of the first three problems and the last were published by G. Boffito and U. Mazzia in *Bibliofilia,* **8** (1907), 372–383, where they are mistakenly ascribed to Peter of Modena. In the same article, Thorndike (*Isis,* **47** [1956], 401–402) cites another astronomical work by Blasius, *Demonstrationes geometrice in theorica planetarum,* printed anonymously by Octavianus Scotus (Venice, 1518), fols. 143r–152v (a possible manuscript version of this treatise is Vat. lat. 3379, 52r–61r, which bears the slightly variant title *Blasii Parmensis demonstrationes geometrie in theoricam planetarum*). An astrological prediction constitutes Blasius' *Iudicium revolutionis anni 1405* (Bibliothèque Nationale MS 7443, 11v–17r).

The diverse treatises cited below conclude the list of Blasius' scientific and philosophic works known thus far: *Questiones super tractatus loyce* [i.e., *logice*] *magistri Petri Hyspani* [i.e., Peter of Spain] (Bodleian Library, Canonicus Misc. 421, 92–222); *Questiones undecim de locis* (Venice, S. Marco X, 208, 82–92); *Queritur utrum spericum tangat planum* (Bodleian Library, Canonicus Misc. 177, 153–154); *Questiones viginti sex predicamentis* (Venice, S. Marco X, 208, 43–82 and perhaps also Vat. Barberini 357); *De motu* (Vat. Barberini 357, 1–16v); *Elenchus questionum Buridani* (i.e., *A Refutation of Questions of Buridan;* Venice, S. Marco X, 103, 83–84); and a *De terminis naturalibus* (Bodleian Library, Canonicus Misc. 393, 78–83), of uncertain attribution. A theological work, *De predestinatione,* has also been preserved (Venice, Bibl. de' Santi Giovanni e Paolo 163).

II. SECONDARY LITERATURE. There is relatively little literature on Blasius. To what has already been cited, we may add L. Thorndike, *A History of Magic and Experimental Science,* IV, ch. 39; G. F. Vescovini, *Studi sulla prospettiva medievale* (Turin, 1965), ch. 12; A. Maier, *Die Vorläufer Galileis im 14. Jahrhundert* (Rome, 1949; 2nd ed., 1966), pp. 279–299, and *Zwei Grundprobleme der scholastischen Naturphilosophie,* 2nd ed. (Rome, 1951), pp. 270–274; and F. Amodeo, "Appunti su Biagio Pelacani da Parma," in *Atti del IV Congresso Internazionale dei Matematici,* **3** (Rome, 1909), 549–553.

EDWARD GRANT

BLAUW, WILLEM. See **Blaeu, Willem.**

BLAZHKO, SERGEI NIKOLAEVICH (*b.* Khotimsk-Mogilevskaya province, Russia, 17 November 1870; *d.* Moscow, U.S.S.R., 11 February 1956), *astronomy.*

The son of a merchant who had risen from the enserfed peasantry, Blazhko graduated from the Smolensk Gymnasium in 1888 and from the Physics and Mathematics Faculty of Moscow University in 1892. From 1894 to 1915 he was assistant at Moscow Observatory and from 1915 to 1918, an astronomer-observer there. In 1917 he married Maria Ivanovna Ushina, a teacher. In 1918 he became professor of astronomy at Moscow University and from 1920 to 1931 was, simultaneously, director of the observatory. From 1922 to 1931 he was also director of the university's Scientific Research Institute of Astronomy and Geodesy.

Blazhko's pedagogic career began in 1896, when he was entrusted with conducting exercises in practical astronomy at the university. From 1900 to 1918 he taught astronomy at the Women's Pedagogical College, and from 1909 to 1919 at the A. L. Shanyavsky People's University; from 1910 to 1918 he was *Privatdozent* and from 1918 professor at Moscow University; at the latter he held the chair of astronomy from 1931 to 1937 and the chair of astrometry from 1937 to 1953. In 1929 Blazhko was elected an associate member of the Academy of Sciences of the U.S.S.R. He received the title Honored Scientist of the R.S.F.S.R. in 1934 and was twice awarded the Order of Lenin and the Order of the Red Banner of Labor. He also belonged to numerous astronomical societies, both Russian and foreign.

Blazhko's primary sphere of scientific activity was the study of variable stars. In 1895 he began the systematic photographing of the heavens with a special "equatorial camera" built in Germany according to the design of V. K. Cerasky, director of the Moscow Observatory. He hoped, through comparison of plates taken at different times, to discover new variable stars. He also conducted visual observations of variable stars over several decades. Through these observations Blazhko discovered the periodic change of the periods and the shape of light curves of a number of short-period variable stars of the type RR Lyrae, a phenomenon that came to be called the "Blazhko effect." In all, Blazhko investigated more than 200 variable stars, and his valuable series of observations, which covered many years, is still used.

Blazhko's other scientific work involved photographing the sun with a photoheliograph in order to determine the period of its rotation according to the motion of its faculae (1895); obtaining spectra of two meteors in 1904 with an apparatus of his own construction; one of the first detailed investigations of meteor spectra (1907); and one of the first investigations of the spectrum of the eclipsing variable star U Cephei. Blazhko later obtained the spectrum of another meteor, and these three spectra were long among the first five known.

Blazhko devoted special attention to the study of eclipsing binary stars of the Algol type. In 1911, in his dissertation, "O zvezdakh tipa Algolya" ("On Stars of the Algol Type"), he was the first to give a general method for determining the elements of the orbits of eclipsing binaries. He also provided the first analysis of the influence of darkening toward the limb of a star's disk on the shape of the light curve. However, one must note that in 1912–1913 there appeared in the United States a series of articles by H. N. Russel and Harlow Shapley, who, independently of Blazhko, developed methods for studying eclipsing binary stars, not only of the Algol type but of other types as well (β Lyrae and W Ursae Majoris).

In 1919 Blazhko proposed an original photographic method for discovering minor planets—the method of triple exposure on one plate with intervals between exposures and with a shift in the declination of the telescope during the intervals. He devised a number of original instruments: a star spectograph, a blink-microscope, a special magnifying glass for reading the division marks of meridian circles, and a device for eliminating the "stellar magnitude equation" from the times of transit taken with meridian instruments.

BIBLIOGRAPHY

I. ORIGINAL WORKS. Principal works include "On the Spectra of Two Meteors," in *Astrophysical Journal*, **26**, no. 5 (1907), 341–348; "Über der Veränderlichensterne U Cephei," in *Astronomische Nachrichten*, **181** (1909), 295–298; "Étude de l'étoile RW Draconis à période variable et à courbe de la lumière variable," in *Russkii astronomicheskii zhurnal*, **1**, no. 2 (1924); *Kopernik* (Moscow-Leningrad, 1926); "Sur le variable XZ Cygni à période et à courbe de lumière variable," in *Annales de l'Observatoire astronomique de Moscou*, 2nd ser., **8** (1926), 23–41; "Photographische Aufnahmen der kleiner Planeten auf der Universitäts-Sternwarte zu Moskau," in *Astronomische Nachrichten*, **232** (1928), 131–134; "O spektre meteora 1907 g. avgusta 12" ("On the Spectrum of the Meteor of 12 August 1907"), in *Russkii astronomicheskii zhurnal*, **9**, nos. 3–4 (1932), 146–162; *Kurs prakticheskoy astronomii* ("Course of Practical Astronomy"; Moscow-Leningrad, 1938; 3rd ed., 1951); "Istoria Moskovskoy astronomicheskoy observatory v svyazi s istorey prepodavania astronomy v universitete (1824–1920)" ("History of the Moscow Astronomical Observatory in Connection with the Teaching of Astronomy at the University [1824–1920]"), in *Uchenye zapiski MGU*, jubilee ser., no. 58 (1940), 5–106; *Kurs obshchey astronomy* ("Course of General Astronomy";

Moscow–Leningrad, 1947); and *Kurs sfericheskoy astronomy* ("Course of Spherical Astronomy"; Moscow, 1948; 2nd ed., 1954).

II. SECONDARY LITERATURE. Works on Blazhko are B. V. Kukarkin, "Sergei Nikolaevich Blazhko (Necrolog)," in *Peremennye zvezdy*, **11**, no. 2 (1956), 63–64, with portrait; P. G. Kulikovsky, "50-letny yubiley S. N. Blazhko," in *Astronomicheskii kalendar na 1945 god* (Gorki, 1945), pp. 205–207; "Zasluzhenny deyatel nauki S. N. Blazhko. K 80-letiyu so dnya rozhdenia," in *Priroda* (1951), no. 8, 59–61; and "Sergei Nikolaevich Blazhko," in *Astronomicheskii kalendar na 1957 god* (Moscow, 1956), pp. 275–276, with portrait; the obituary "Sergei Nikolaevich Blazhko (1870–1956. Necrolog)," in *Astronomicheskii zhurnal*, **33**, no. 2 (1956), 278–280, with portrait; and V. V. Podobed, "S. N. Blazhko," in *Astronomicheskii tsirkular*, no. 168 (1956), 1–2.

P. G. KULIKOVSKY

BLICHFELDT, HANS FREDERICK (*b.* Illar, Denmark, 9 January 1873; *d.* Palo Alto, California, 16 November 1945), *mathematics.*

The son of Erhard Christoffer Laurentius Blichfeldt, a farmer who came from a long line of ministers, and Nielsine Maria Scholer, Blichfeldt showed unusual mathematical aptitude at an early age. He was assisted in his studies by his father, and in general he did well in all subjects. He passed the university entrance examinations with honors but did not attend because his parents were unable to afford it.

Fortunately for Hans, his family emigrated to the United States when he was fifteen. He spent four years as a laborer on farms and in sawmills in the Midwest and West and two years traveling about the country as a surveyor. His phenomenal ability to do all the surveying computations mentally so impressed his colleagues that they encouraged him to become a mathematician. He entered the recently founded Stanford University in 1894 and received his B.A. in 1896 and his M.A. in 1897. Not having enough money to go to Europe for a doctorate, as was the custom among the better-known mathematicians, he borrowed the money from a Stanford professor, Rufus L. Green, and enrolled in the University of Leipzig, where he studied under the famous mathematician Sophus Lie. In one year he received his doctorate *summa cum laude,* with the dissertation "On a Certain Class of Groups of Transformation in Three-dimensional Space."

During the year 1898 Blichfeldt was employed by Stanford as an instructor. He obtained the rank of full professor in 1913. He accepted the chairmanship of the mathematics department in 1927 and served in that capacity until his retirement in 1938. In addition, Blichfeldt served as a visiting professor at the University of Chicago in the summer of 1911 and at Columbia University during the summers of 1924 and 1925. He was professor emeritus at Stanford until his death.

Blichfeldt was extremely active in the American Mathematical Society and gave numerous talks in many parts of the country on his favorite topics, group theory and number theory. In 1912 he was elected vice-president of the Society.

Blichfeldt's contributions were primarily in the form of articles for the Society publications and European mathematics journals. His lifework was devoted to group theory and number theory. Some of the many topics that he covered were diophantine approximations, orders of linear homogeneous groups, theory of geometry of numbers, approximate solutions of the integers of a set of linear equations, low-velocity angle fire, finite collineation groups, and characteristic roots. In addition, he published the text *Finite Collineation Groups* and coauthored *Theory and Applications of Finite Groups* with G. A. Miller and L. E. Dickson.

During his life Blichfeldt received many honors. In 1920 he was elected to the National Academy of Sciences, which at the time was an achievement for a mathematician. From 1924 to 1927 he was a member of the National Research Council. After he retired from Stanford, the king of Denmark made him a Knight of the Order of the Dannebrog.

Blichfeldt's contributions in group theory and group characters are now of considerable importance because of recent applications of Lie groups in the sciences.

BIBLIOGRAPHY

Blichfeldt's works include "On a Certain Class of Groups of Transformation in Three-dimensional Space," in *American Journal of Mathematics,* **22** (1900), 113–120; "On the Determination of the Distance Between Two Points in *m* Dimensional Space," in *Transactions of the American Mathematical Society,* **3** (1902), 467–481; "On the Order of Linear Homogeneous Groups. I," *ibid.,* **4** (1903), 387–397; ". . . II," **5** (1904), 310–325; ". . . III," **7** (1906), 523–529; ". . . IV," **12** (1911), 39–42; "A Theorem Concerning the Invariants of Linear Homogeneous Groups With Some Applications to Substitution Groups," *ibid.,* **5** (1904), 461–466; "Theorems on Simple Groups," *ibid.,* **11** (1910), 1–14; "Finite Groups of Linear Homogeneous Transformations," Part II of *Theory and Applications of Finite Groups* (London–New York, 1916), pp. 17–390, written with G. A. Miller and L. E. Dickson; and *Finite Collineation Groups* (Chicago, 1917).

G. H. MILLER

BLISS, GILBERT AMES (*b.* Chicago, Illinois, 9 May 1876; *d.* Harvey, Illinois, 8 May 1961), *mathematics.*

Gilbert Ames Bliss, the son of George Harrison Bliss and Mary Maria Gilbert, devoted his life to the study of mathematics. Although his scientific interests ranged broadly over the field of analysis, with special emphasis on the basic existence theorems, the focal point of much of his work was the calculus of variations. Prior to World War I he wrote, with Max Mason and A. L. Underhill, on the application of the methods of Weierstrass to a number of problems in the latter subject. He worked in the ballistic laboratory at Aberdeen, Maryland, during the war, and used his knowledge of the calculus of variations to construct new firing tables. In the 1920's his papers encompassed the transformation of Clebsch, proofs of the necessity of the Jacobi condition, multiple integrals, and boundary value problems in his field.

His elementary Carus Monograph on the calculus of variations (1925) was followed, after some twenty years, by his definitive book: *Lectures on the Calculus of Variations* (1946). In this publication Bliss employed the scattered results of mathematicians of past decades, many of whom were his former students, to establish firmly the theoretical foundations of the calculus of variations. He approached his subject from the viewpoint of analysis and covered the use of existence theorems for implicit functions, differential equations, and the analysis of singular points for the transformations of the plane. He improved upon and extended the theories of the problems of Lagrange, Mayer, and Bolza and simplified the proofs of the necessary and sufficient conditions of these problems. He clearly presented the theory of the calculus of variations for cases involving no side conditions. Overall he gave a greater comprehensiveness and generality to the field than had previously existed. As a result of his earlier work as summarized in this book, Bliss may be judged one of the chief architects of the edifice of the calculus of variations.

Bliss's work represents a turning point in American mathematics. With his generation, American mathematics came of age. Previously, most American mathematicians had received their training in, and inspiration from, Europe. From the beginning of his career, Bliss was identified with the University of Chicago. He enrolled there in 1893, one year after the university opened its doors. He received his bachelor's degree in 1897, his master's in 1898, and his doctorate in 1900. Although he began his studies in mathematical astronomy, under the guidance of F. R. Moulton, he soon turned to the study of pure mathematics. E. H. Moore, Oskar Bolza—who aroused his

interest in the calculus of variations—and H. Maschke were his instructors.

Bliss spent his apprenticeship as a mathematics instructor at the universities of Minnesota (1900–1902) and Chicago (1903–1904). From 1902 to 1903 he did postgraduate work at the University of Göttingen. Bliss was assistant professor of mathematics at the University of Missouri (1904–1905) and at Princeton (1905–1908). In 1908 he returned to Chicago as an associate professor.

On 15 June 1912, Bliss married Helen Hurd (*d.* 1918). They had two children, Elizabeth and Gilbert, Jr. He married Olive Hunter 12 October 1920.

Bliss taught and worked at the University of Chicago from 1908 to 1941. He was associate professor until 1913, professor from 1913 to 1941, and professor emeritus from 1941. He succeeded Moore as chairman of the mathematics department in 1927 and was Martin A. Ryerson distinguished professor of mathematics from 1933 to 1941. Throughout his career at Chicago he was known for his lively sense of humor and for stressing the importance of a strong union between teaching and fundamental mathematical research.

From 1909 until his death, Bliss exerted a strong influence on the American mathematical scene. He was an associate editor of the *Transactions of the American Mathematical Society* from 1909 to 1916, and from 1921 to 1922 was president of the society. He was elected to the National Academy of Sciences in 1916, and in 1924, with G. D. Birkhoff and Oswald Veblen, he became a member of the awards committee of the newly instituted National Research Fellowships in mathematics. Bliss served on this committee until 1936. In 1925 he received the first Chauvenet Prize awarded by the Mathematical Association of America for his paper "Algebraic Functions and Their Divisors." The following year Bliss was elected a member of the American Philosophical Society. In 1935 he was made a fellow of the American Academy of Arts and Sciences. For many years Bliss served as chairman of the editorial committee established by the Mathematical Association of America for its Carus Monographs, a series of short expository books on mathematics for the layman.

BIBLIOGRAPHY

I. ORIGINAL WORKS. Bliss's books are *Fundamental Existence Theorems* (Princeton, 1913); *Calculus of Variations,* Carus Mathematical Monograph No. 1 (Chicago, 1925); *Algebraic Functions,* American Mathematical Society Colloquium Publications, XVI (New York, 1933); *Mathematics for Exterior Ballistics* (New York, 1944); *Lectures on the Calculus of Variations* (Chicago, 1946).

Bliss also wrote many articles: "The Geodesic Lines on the Anchor Ring" (doctoral dissertation), in *Annals of Mathematics,* **4** (1902), 1–21; "The Solutions of Differential Equations of the First Order as Functions of Their Initial Values," *ibid.,* **6** (1905), 49–68; "A Problem of the Calculus of Variations in Which the Integrand Is Discontinuous," in *Transactions of the American Mathematical Society,* **7** (1906), 325–336, written with Max Mason; "A New Proof of Weierstrass' Theorem Concerning the Factorization of a Power Series," in *Bulletin of the American Mathematical Society,* **9** (1910), 356–359; "Generalizations of Geodesic Curvatures and a Theorem of Gauss Concerning Geodesic Triangles," in *American Journal of Mathematics,* **37** (1914), 1–18; "A Note on the Problem of Lagrange in the Calculus of Variations," in *Bulletin of the American Mathematical Society,* **22** (1916), 220–225; "Integral of Lebesgue," *ibid.,* **24** (1917), 1–47; "Solutions of Differential Equations as Functions of the Constants of Integration," *ibid.,* **25** (1918), 15–26; "The Problem of Mayer With Variable End Points," in *Transactions of the American Mathematical Society,* **19** (1918), 305–314; "Functions of Lines in Ballistics," *ibid.,* **21** (1920), 93–106; "Algebraic Functions and Their Divisors," in *Annals of Mathematics,* **26** (1924), 95–124; "The Transformation of Clebsch in the Calculus of Variations," in *Proceedings of the International Congress of 1924 at Toronto,* **1** (1928), 589–603; "The Problem of Lagrange in the Calculus of Variations," in *American Journal of Mathematics,* **52** (1930), 673–744; "The Problem of Bolza in the Calculus of Variations," in *Annals of Mathematics,* **33** (1932), 261–274; "Mathematical Interpretations of Geometrical and Physical Phenomena," in *American Mathematical Monthly,* **40** (1933), 472–480; "The Calculus of Variations for Multiple Integrals," *ibid.,* **49** (1942), 77–89.

II. Secondary Literature. Articles on Bliss are L. M. Graves, "Gilbert Ames Bliss, 1876–1951," in *Bulletin of the American Mathematical Society,* **58** (1952), 251–264 (this article contains a bibliography of Bliss's publications); and Saunders MacLane, "Gilbert Ames Bliss (1876–1951)," in *Yearbook of the American Philosophical Society for 1951,* pp. 288–291.

Ronald S. Calinger

BLISTERFELD, J. H. See **Bisterfeld, Johann Heinrich.**

BLOMSTRAND, CHRISTIAN WILHELM (*b.* Växjö, Sweden, 20 October 1826; *d.* Lund, Sweden, 5 November 1897), *chemistry, mineralogy.*

The son of John Blomstrand, a teacher in a Gymnasium, and his wife Severina Rodhe, Blomstrand originally studied mineralogy at the University of Lund. His interest in chemistry began only after he had been awarded his doctorate (1850) and had been named the first recipient of the Berzelius scholarship. His *Habilitationsschrift* dealt with bromine and iodine compounds of tin. At the University of Lund, Blomstrand became adjunct in chemistry (1856) and later professor of chemistry and mineralogy (1862), a position that he occupied until his retirement (1895). He never married, and except for a brief period in 1861 when he served as mineralogist on an expedition to Spitzbergen, he remained at Lund.

Blomstrand's experimental inorganic research largely concerned the Group VB elements—the so-called earth acids (halides and oxyhalides of niobium, tantalum, molybdenum, and tungsten; heteropoly acids of iodic and periodic acid with chromic, molybdic, and tungstic acids). In addition to his strictly chemical work, he characterized and analyzed many minerals, especially those of the rarer elements or of unknown composition, such as monazite, ilmenite, tantalite, niobite, and euxenite.

Most of Blomstrand's theoretical works (such as those on azoammonium and chain theories) are polemical, but more often conciliatory than inflammatory in tone. Since he lived in Sweden during a period of transition between the older and newer chemistries and since he was a scientific as well as a political conservative, he sought to reconcile Berzelius' dualistic theory with the unitary and type theories. He was opposed to Kekulé's dogma of constant valence and strove to establish a sound and complete theory of variable valence. Blomstrand's chain theory, as modified and developed by Sophus Mads Jørgensen, was the most successful of the numerous attempts to explain the constitution of metalamines. It held sway for roughly a quarter century, until it was displaced by Alfred Werner's coordination theory in 1893.

BIBLIOGRAPHY

I. Original Works. "Zur Frage über die Constitution der Diazoverbindungen," in *Berichte der Deutschen chemischen Gesellschaft,* **8** (1875), 51–55; "Über die Metallammoniake oder die Metallamine," *ibid.,* **4** (1871), 40–52 (an English translation appears in G. B. Kauffman, ed., *Classics in Coordination Chemistry, Part II: Selected Papers* [*1798–1935*], New York [in press]); *Die Chemie der Jetztzeit vom Standpunkte der electrochemischen Auffassung aus Berzelius Lehre entwickelt,* Blomstrand's best-known work (Heidelberg, 1869) made his name known throughout Europe. A complete list of Blomstrand's publications can be found in *Svensk kemisk tidskrift,* **38,** no. 9 (1926), 235–238.

II. Secondary Literature. The entire Sept. 1926 issue of *Svensk kemisk tidskrift,* **38,** no. 9, 234–314, is devoted to articles on various aspects of Blomstrand's career; for obituaries, which include discussions of his works, see P. Klason, *Berichte der Deutschen chemischen Gesellschaft,* **30** (1897), 3227–3241; and E. von Meyer, *Journal für praktische Chemie,* **56** (1897), 397–400.

GEORGE B. KAUFFMAN

BLONDEL, ANDRÉ EUGÈNE (*b.* Chaumont, France, 28 August 1863; *d.* Paris, France, 15 November 1938), *physics, engineering.*

Blondel came from a family of Burgundian magistrates. His mother died when he was nine, and his education was directed entirely by his father. He completed his secondary studies in Dijon, entered the École Polytechnique in 1883, and then attended the École des Ponts et Chaussées. Upon graduation in 1888, he chose assignment to the Service Central des Phares et Balises. Blondel received his degree in mathematical sciences in 1885, and in physical sciences in 1889. He worked in Cornu's laboratory at the École Polytechnique in 1888–1889, and there acquired the knowledge that gave rise to his subsequent discoveries.

Blondel's very first projects drew attention to him, and in 1893 he became a professor of electrotechnology at both the École des Mines and the École des Ponts et Chaussées.

During the last few years of the century, Blondel, who until then had enjoyed excellent health, participated in sports, and traveled extensively, was stricken with paralysis of the legs, probably of psychosomatic origin. His father then settled near him in Paris. Bedridden, Blondel devoted himself wholeheartedly to his research and inspired a group of associates who worked in the research laboratory he had set up in Levallois.

His health improved somewhat around 1919, after the death of his father. His physical activity remained extremely limited, however, for the rest of his life.

Blondel indicated that all his work had been suggested by his research for the Service des Phares and his teaching of electrotechnology. This explains the tremendous variety of subjects he dealt with and the large number of his published works (more than 250).

His two main contributions are the oscillograph and the system of photometric units of measurement. Struck by the outdated units of measurement used in photometry, Blondel specified, in 1894, different units for this branch of optics. He introduced the fundamental concept of luminous flux and defined illumination according to the flux received by the unit surface. He thus established a coherent system of units, using as a basis the Violle candle and the meter. The

unit of flux, or lumen, was independent of the unit of length. This system was adopted in 1896 by the International Electrical Congress, meeting in Geneva, and it became the system used by the International Illumination Commission and the International Conference on Weights and Measures. It is also included, practically without change, in the international system adopted by the eleventh International Conference on Weights and Measures (1960).

Assigned to study the arc lamps used in lighthouses and their feed, he found deficiencies in the prevailing research methods, which did not allow a worker to see instantly the intensity of alternating currents. After a rather unsatisfactory test using a stroboscopic method (1891) he solved the problem by invention of the oscillograph (1893); he perfected two variations, a "soft iron" version and a bifilar one. For forty years these instruments were the most advanced and the most widely used in the study of variable electric phenomena. From the point of view of the moving band, they have been superseded by the cathode-ray tube oscilloscope, but they are no less valuable because of their simplicity and their small bulk.

BIBLIOGRAPHY

Blondel's oscillograph was patented in April 1897 (no. 266246); the original file is in the Institut National de la Propriété Industrielle, Paris. Among his writings is "La détermination de l'intensité moyenne sphérique des sources de lumière," in *L'éclairage électrique,* **2** (1895), 385–391; **3** (1895), 57–62, 406–414, 538–546, 583–586.

Works on Blondel are Louis de Broglie, *La vie et l'oeuvre d'André Blondel* (Paris, 1944), a lecture given at the annual meeting of the Académie des Sciences, 18 Dec. 1944; *Commemoration de la naissance d'André Blondel, 1863–1938* (Paris, 1963), a brochure published for the ceremony held 15 May 1963 at the Conservatoire National des Arts et Métiers, Paris; and *Commemoration de l'oeuvre d'André Eugène Blondel* (Paris, 1942), a collection of articles by Louis de Broglie, Camille Guitton, Joseph Béthenod, Eugène Darmois, Robert Gibrat, and others.

JACQUES PAYEN

BLONDEL, NICOLAS-FRANÇOIS (*b.* Ribemont, France [baptized there 15 June 1618]; *d.* Paris, France, 21 January 1686), *military engineering, architecture.*

Blondel was the eldest son of François-Guillaume Blondel, master of petitions to the queen mother and king's attorney at the bailiff's court of Vermandois, and of Marie de Louen. At seventeen he became an infantry cadet and fought against the Imperial forces in the Thirty Years' War. Between 1640 and 1652 he held a variety of positions, many of them in naval engineering. In July 1652 he became tutor to the son of Loménie de Brienne, secretary of state for foreign affairs, and spent the next three and a half years traveling through Europe with his pupil. Upon his return to Paris, Blondel succeeded Gassendi as lecturer in mathematics at the Collège Royal (now the Collège de France). From 1657 to 1662 Loménie de Brienne entrusted him with several diplomatic missions; when his period of service was over, he became commissioner general of the navy.

As a member of a commission seeking a harbor for the navy between the Loire and the Gironde, Blondel recommended the site of what is now Rochefort. He directed construction for the region and drew up plans for the town and its fortifications, and for restoration of the Saintes bridge and the Roman arch. Construction was not far advanced when Colbert sent him to the West Indies in July 1666, to look for harbors, make maps, and plan fortifications. The maps he made of Grenada (1:98,000) and Tortuga (1:76,500) in 1667 are in the Bibliothèque Nationale.

From 1640 on, when he was in Paris, Blondel never failed to attend the meetings held regularly by the scholars of the capital prior to the founding of the Royal Academy of Sciences. When he was unable to be present, he relied on correspondence to convey his passionate interest in theoretical discussions of any kind. Thus on 12 August 1657, he wrote at great length to Paul Wurz, one of his Swedish friends, to the effect that Galileo had erred in his *Discorsi e dimostrazioni matematiche* with respect to beams of equal resistance. Actually, the text that he criticized applied correctly to beams fixed at one end only, i.e., to brackets. (Also, he was wrong to claim that in Galileo's thinking beams resting on two supports were involved.)

In 1669 Colbert sponsored Blondel's admission to the Royal Academy of Sciences as a geometer, which in his case meant topographer. In 1671 he was appointed professor at, and director of, the Royal Academy of Architecture, which had just been founded. From then on, he attended the regular meetings of the two academies, gave a course in mathematics at the Collège Royal, and delivered public lectures at the Royal College of Architecture. His work increased in 1672, when Louis XIV put him in charge of public works for the city of Paris, and in 1673, when he was made mathematics tutor to the dauphin.

In the seventeenth century the profession of architect embraced subjects now considered a part of engineering. Blondel devoted part of his lectures at the Royal College of Architecture to geometry, arithmetic, mechanics, gnomonics, the art of fortification, and perspective and stereometry; but he did not feel it necessary to publish corresponding texts. In order to provide an architecture text, in 1673 he brought out a new edition, without the illustrations, of Louis Savot's *L'architecture françoise des bastimens particuliers* (first published in 1624). In his *Cours d'architecture* (1675–1683) he treated both decorative elements and such practical structures as bridges and aqueducts. He presented the concepts of the great architects since Vitruvius and shared the lessons he had learned from wide reading and many visits to most of the major monuments of antiquity, as well as his practical experience and his theories. The *Cours,* illustrated with many remarkable figures, remained the definitive reference work for French architects for more than a century.

While writing the portion of the *Cours* devoted to staircases, Blondel formulated the following rule, approved in 1675 by the Royal Academy of Architecture and still used today: "The length of the normal step of a man walking on level ground is two feet (Paris measure), and the distance between steps on a perpendicular ladder is one foot." From this he deduced that a staircase is well-balanced when $G + 2H =$ two feet (G is the tread of a step and H is the height of a step). This is the origin of the rule of art approved 28 January 1675 by the Royal Academy of Architecture and applied universally ever since; thus it would be proper to call it Blondel's rule.

In 1673, while editing his *Cours,* Blondel published the *Résolution des quatre principaux problèmes d'architecture.* The first problem concerns the sketching of columns; the second and the third, rampant arches. The fourth problem pertains to beams of equal resistance. Here Blondel reproduced his letter of 1657 addressed to Wurz, which he had printed in 1661, as well as his reply to a correspondent who had pointed out to him that his interpretation of Galileo's text was wrong. In his reply Blondel evinced an obstinacy worthy of a better cause and stuck to his criticism.

In 1676 Félibien, secretary of the Royal Academy of Architecture, published a work entitled *Des principes de l'architecture, de la sculpture, de la peinture et des autres arts qui en dependent; avec un dictionnaire des termes propres à chacun de ces arts* which Blondel recommended to his architectural course. Félibien's plates, remarkable in every respect, were to serve as models for the ones in the *Description des arts et métiers,* which was commissioned by order of the king on 16 June 1675. In turn they became the prototypes of the plates in the *Encyclopédie.*

During his infantry service, Blondel had been amazed at the crude methods of the French bombardiers. In 1637, during the siege of Landrecies, he had made the acquaintance of the English engineer Maltus, whom Louis XIII had summoned from Holland to teach his army the use of the mortar. Since Maltus fired by guesswork and then proceeded to make corrections, his first bombs at Landrecies at times fell on Frenchmen. In 1642, at the siege of Collioure, by sheer luck he had destroyed the water supply of the beleaguered Spaniards, who hastened to surrender; thus he appeared to have made progress. In order to improve this method, Blondel scrutinized all the publications on the subject, going even to the extent of reading the two chapters on fireworks inserted in Volume III of the *Cursus seu mundus mathematicus,* by the Jesuit Milliet de Chales. Galileo, who had overlooked air resistance, had demonstrated that the trajectory assumed the form of a parabola. Torricelli had indicated that it was sufficient to make a test shot under a predetermined angle by measuring the range obtained with a given charge and that a range was a function of the sine of the double angles of inclination of the mortar over the horizontal. Blondel too considered air resistance a negligible factor. Bent on arriving at a rule easy to apply, he presented the problem to the Royal Academy of Sciences on 6 March 1677. Buot came up with a solution on 10 March. Roemer offered an even simpler one on 20 March, and on 27 March he proposed to adopt a scaled half-circle as a sighting instrument. Finally, Philippe de La Hire, who did not yet hold membership in the Academy, communicated a third solution through Cassini as intermediary. Blondel used the three solutions for establishing the practical rules which he formulated in his *L'art de jetter les bombes,* the printing of which was delayed until 1683 by order of Louis XIV, who hardly cared to have the enemy profit by it. The French gunners, however, paid no attention to it and continued to use faulty firing tables until 1731 and the publication of the treatise by Belidor, under the title *Le bombardier françois, ou nouvelle methode de jetter les bombes avec precision.*

BIBLIOGRAPHY

I. ORIGINAL WORKS. Blondel's writings include *La solitude royalle ou description de Friderisbourg* (n.p., n.d.; dedicated to the king of Denmark, 5 Jan. 1653); *F. B. Epistola ad P. W., in qua famosa Galilaei propositio discutitur, circa naturam lineae qua trabes secari debent ut sint aequalis ubique resistentiae; et in qua lineam illam non quidem parabolicam, ut ipse Galilaeus arbitratus est, sed ellipticam esse demonstratur* (Paris, 1661); his ed. of Louis Savot's *L'architecture françoise des bastimens particuliers* (Paris, 1673; 2nd ed., enl., 1685), with illustrations and notes

by Blondel; *Comparaison de Pindare et d'Horace* (Paris, 1673); *Résolution des quatre principaux problèmes d'architecture* (Paris, 1673); *Cours d'architecture enseigné dans l'Académie Royale d'architecture,* 6 pts. (Paris, 1675–1683); *Histoire du calendrier romain, qui contient son origine et les divers changements qui luy sont arrivez* (Paris, 1682; The Hague, 1684); *L'art de jetter les bombes, et de connoitre l'etendue des coups de volée d'un canon en toutes sortes d'élevations* (Paris, 1683; Amsterdam, 1699); *Cours de mathematique contenant divers traitez composez et enseignez à Monseigneur le Dauphin* (Paris, 1683); and *Nouvelle maniere de fortifier les places* (Paris, 1683; The Hague, 1684, 1711), also trans. into Russian (Moscow, 1711).

II. SECONDARY LITERATURE. Archival sources are the Academy of Sciences, registers 5 (1669), 7 (1675–1679), 9 (1679–1683), and 11 (1683–1686); and the Collège de France, register of professorships. Published sources are Paul Bonnefon, ed., *Mémoires de Louis-Henri de Loménie, comte de Brienne, dit le jeune Brienne, publiés d'après le manuscrit autographe pour la Société d'Histoire de France,* 3 vols. (Paris, 1915–1919), *passim;* Harcourt Brown, *Scientific Organizations in Seventeenth Century France, 1620–1680* (Baltimore, 1934), pp. 12, 92; *Histoire de l'Académie Royale des Sciences,* I (Paris, 1733), 230–236; Henry Lemonnier, *Procès-verbaux de l'Académie Royale d'architecture 1671–1793,* I–II (Paris, 1911–1912), *passim;* Charles Lucas, "François Blondel à Saintes, à Rochefort et aux Antilles (1665–1667)," in *Congrès archéologique de France, LXIe session* (*La Rochelle-Saintes*), *1894* (Caen, 1897), pp. 326–341; and "Relation d'un voyage de Berlin à Constantinople par François Blondel, sieur des Croisettes et de Gallardon (novembre–décembre 1658)," in *Bulletin de géographie historique et descriptive, année 1899* (1900), 111–118; Louis-Placide Mauclaire and C. Vigoureux, *Nicolas-François de Blondel, ingénieur et architecte du roi (1618–1686)* (Laon, n.d. [1938]); and René Mémain, *Le matériel de la marine de guerre sous Louis XIV, Rochefort, arsenal modèle de Colbert (1666–1690),* thesis (Paris, 1936), commercially published without the first three words of the original title (Paris, 1937)—Mémain attributes to Blondel a monograph on the hot springs of Aix-la-Chapelle that was really the work of a contemporary physician of the same name.

ARTHUR BIREMBAUT

BLONDLOT, RENÉ-PROSPER (*b.* Nancy, France, 3 July 1849; *d.* Nancy, 24 November 1930), *physics.*

Son of Nicolas Blondlot, a renowned physiologist and chemist, René Blondlot spent nearly all his life in Nancy, where he taught physics at the local university. Although he was never a member of the Paris Academy of Sciences, he was named *correspondant* for the Section of General Physics in 1894. In addition, the Academy awarded him three of its most important prizes, chiefly for his experimental determinations of the consequences of Maxwell's theories of electromagnetism.

In 1875 John Kerr discovered that birefringence was produced in glass and in other dielectrics subjected to an intense electrical field. With the aid of a movable mirror Blondlot established that in the oscillating discharge of a condenser the time-lag between the electrical phenomenon and the appearance of the Kerr effect is less than 1/40,000 of a second. With Ernest Bichat he observed the same instantaneity for magnetic, rotatory polarization.

Using this same technique of a rapidly rotating mirror, Blondlot measured the velocity of electricity propagated through conducting wires. He sent simultaneous electrical charges through two wires, one of which was 1,800 meters longer than the other. By photographing the light from the resulting sparks successively reflected in a rotating mirror and then measuring the distance between the photographic images, Blondlot established that the speed of electricity in a conductor was nearly the same as that of light.

Blondlot received his greatest notoriety in the controversy over the existence of N rays. In the course of an attempt to polarize the newly discovered X rays, Blondlot claimed in 1903 to have found a new kind of invisible radiation, capable of being emitted not only from cathode ray tubes but also from many luminous sources, most notably from Auer burners. He named this new species of radiation N rays, in honor of the city of Nancy. No fewer than fourteen of his fellow scientists claimed also to have observed these N rays emanating from various animal and vegetable substances and, in the case of Jean Becquerel, from "anesthetized metals." Because of the difficulty of reproducing the experiments, many scientists came to doubt the existence of Blondlot's new ray. In 1904 the editors of the *Revue scientifique* undertook an examination of the entire matter and concluded that the positive experimental results had been the chimerical products of autosuggestion. Blondlot finally recanted and, probably as a result of the scandal, spent the rest of his life in relative obscurity.

BIBLIOGRAPHY

I. ORIGINAL WORKS. Blondlot's writings include *Recherches expérimentales sur la capacité de polarisation voltaïque* (Paris, 1881); *Introduction à l'étude de l'électricité statique* (Paris, 1885), written with Ernest Bichat; *Introduction à l'étude de la thermodynamique* (Paris, 1888); *Sur un électromètre astatique pouvant servir comme wattmètre* (Nancy, 1889), written with P. Curie; and *"N" Rays, A Collection of Papers Communicated to the Academy of Sciences,* J. Garcin, trans. (London, 1905).

II. SECONDARY LITERATURE. A brief *éloge* for Blondlot is in *Comptes rendus hebdomadaires des séances de l'Académie des sciences,* **191** (1 Dec. 1930), 80–81. For the N-ray controversy see *Revue scientifique,* **74,** no. 2 (July–Dec. 1904), 73–79, 545–552, 620–625, 705–709, 718–722, 783–785.

J. B. GOUGH

BLUMENBACH, JOHANN FRIEDRICH (*b.* Gotha, Germany, 11 May 1752; *d.* Göttingen, Germany, 22 January 1840), *natural history, anthropology, comparative anatomy.*

Blumenbach was born into a cultured, wealthy Protestant family. His father, Heinrich, was the assistant headmaster at the Gymnasium Ernestinum in Gotha; his mother, Charlotte Eleonore Hedwig Buddeus, was the daughter of a high government official in Gotha and the granddaughter of a Jena theologian. Thus, from a very early age, Blumenbach was exposed to both literature and natural science. After completing his Gymnasium studies in 1769, he studied at the universities of Jena and Göttingen, and received the M.D. in 1775 at the University of Göttingen.

At Jena, Blumenbach attended the lectures of the mineralogist Johann Ernst Immanuel Walch, the author of *Naturgeschichte der Versteinerungen,* which interested him in the study of fossils. In Göttingen, he studied under Christian W. Büttner, who lectured on natural history, beginning with man, and fascinated Blumenbach with vivid accounts of travel and foreign peoples, encouraged him to write his doctoral dissertation, and gave him the impetus to start his widely admired anthropological-ethnographic collection. His dissertation, *De generis humani varietate nativa liber,* which became world-famous and is considered one of the basic works on anthropology, was published for the first time in 1776 (and perhaps as early as 1775). In 1776 he was appointed curator of the natural history collection and extraordinary professor at Göttingen, and in 1778 he was named full professor of medicine.

Through his marriage in 1778 Blumenbach became the son-in-law of Georg Brandes, who held an influential position in the administration of the University of Göttingen, and a brother-in-law of Christian Gottlieb Heyne, the classics scholar. These connections helped strengthen Blumenbach's influence at the university. In 1816 he was appointed *professor primarius* of the Faculty of Medicine. In 1776 he had become a member of the Königliche Societät der Wissenschaften zu Göttingen, and in 1812 he became its permanent secretary. In addition, Blumenbach was either a regular or a corresponding member of more than seventy other academies and scientific organizations, including the Institut de France, the Royal Society and Linnean Society of London, the Königliche Akademie zu Berlin, the Imperial Academy of St. Petersburg, and the American Philosophical Society. He carried on extensive correspondence with scientists, the most noteworthy of whom were Albrecht von Haller, Peter Camper, and Charles Bonnet. He was unusually successful as a teacher, and many of his students who later became famous, such as Karl Ernst von Hoff, claimed that Blumenbach had given them the decisive impetus for the formation of their ideas.

Blumenbach's fame is based mainly on his role in the founding of scientific anthropology. He was one of the first scientists to view man as an object of natural history, and saw in him "the most perfect of all domesticated animals." On the other hand, he gave special emphasis to the gap between man and animal and attacked all political or social abuses of anthropological ideas, in particular the notion that black men were on a lower level of humanity than white men. In his dissertation one can find the first reliable survey of the characteristics and distribution of the human races; its most significant points were included in almost all later anthropological classifications.

Blumenbach's ideas on *Bildungstrieb* (*Nisus formativus*) made a great impression on his contemporaries (and later scientists as well). They are of historical significance because they offered some new arguments in favor of epigenesis to the conflict between it and preformation. However, they were very short-lived and did not exert any lasting influence.

Blumenbach's lectures and his textbook on comparative anatomy were epoch-making. Blumenbach believed that he was the first, at least in Germany, to lecture on comparative anatomy, and that his textbook was the first "to have appeared that dealt with the entire area of *anatome comparata*." This assumption was most probably correct, but one must not overlook the fact that his *anatome comparata* had less to do with homology than it did with *anatome animata comparata*, i.e., comparative physiological anatomy. Nevertheless, this textbook was without question a milestone in the history of this subject.

The *Handbuch der Naturgeschichte,* which went through many editions and was translated into many languages, exerted an even greater influence on the advancement of science. Although Blumenbach tended to follow the Linnaean system, this work ushered in a new era in natural history. It contains an abundance of new or hitherto insufficiently evaluated morphological and ecological findings, from which Blumenbach drew conclusions that led to a more modern (biological and evolutionary) concept of the plant and animal kingdoms. He concluded from the spread of certain parasites found only in the domestic pig that such parasites did not exist as long as pigs were not domesticated and that they could therefore not possibly have existed since the creation of the world. Such ideas, revolutionary in their day, were carefully presented in various places in the *Handbuch,* and were demonstrated by concrete examples.

In connection with the morphological analysis and geological dating of fossil plants and animals, Blumenbach developed ideas that were still unknown to most of the scientists of his day and were touched upon by only a few others, such as Soulavie. He came to the conclusion that there had been groups of plants and animals, now extinct, which could not be classified in the system of recent forms of life, and he even attempted to draw up a geological-paleontological time scale.

Blumenbach developed these ideas more deeply and in greater detail in his *Beyträge zur Naturgeschichte,* still a valuable source for historians of science. In addition to some interesting anthropological essays (e.g., on the alleged appearance of a *Homo ferus*), the *Beyträge* contains several essays on the "variability" of nature, a concept that was not understood very well. It also showed that the earth, with all its flora and fauna, had a very long history. Blumenbach was one of the earliest thinkers to recognize the "historicalness" of nature, and therefore occupies an important place in the history of evolution theory.

BIBLIOGRAPHY

I. Original Works. Blumenbach's major writings are *De generis humani varietate nativa liber* (Göttingen, 1776); *Handbuch der Naturgeschichte* (Göttingen, 1779; 12th ed., 1830); "Über den Bildungstrieb (*Nisus formativus*) und seinen Einfluss auf die Generation und Reproduction," in *Göttingisches Magazin der Wissenschaften,* **2** (1780), 240 ff.; "Über den Bildungstrieb und das Zeugungsgeschäft (Göttingen, 1781); *Geschichte und Beschreibung der Knochen des menschlichen Körpers* (Göttingen, 1786); *Handbuch der vergleichenden Anatomie* (Göttingen, 1805); and *Beyträge zur Naturgeschichte,* 2 vols. (Göttingen, 1806–1811).

II. Secondary Literature. Works dealing with Blumenbach are Walter Baron, "Evolutionary Ideas in the Writings of J. F. Blumenbach (1752–1840)," in *Ithaca 1962* (Paris, 1962), pp. 945–947; Walter Baron and B. Sticker, "Ansätze zur historischen Denkweise in der Naturforschung an der Wende vom 18. zum 19. Jahrhundert. I: Die Anschauungen Johann Friedrich Blumenbachs über die Geschichtlichkeit der Natur," in *Sudhoffs Archiv,* **47**

(1963), 19–26; K. E. A. von Hoff, *Erinnerung an Blumenbach's Verdienste um die Geologie bey der fünfzigjährigen Jubelfeyer seines Lehramtes am 24. Februar 1826* (Gotha, 1826); K. F. H. Marx, *Zum Andenken an Johann Friedrich Blumenbach, Eine Gedächtniss-Rede gehalten in der Sitzung der Königlichen Societät der Wissenschaften den 8. Februar 1840* (Göttingen, 1840); Hans Plischke, "Johann Friedrich Blumenbachs Einfluss auf die Entdeckungsreisen seiner Zeit," in *Abhandlungen der K. Gesellschaft der Wissenschaften zu Göttingen,* Phil. Hist. Kl. 3rd ser., no. 20 (Göttingen, 1937); and Johann St. Pütter, *Versuch einer academischen Gelehrten-Geschichte an der Georg-Augustus-Universität zu Göttingen,* pt. 2 (1788), pp. 148–149; pt. 3 (1820), pp. 303–307; pt. 4 (1838), pp. 421–424. See also *Allgemeine deutsche Biographie,* II (1875), 748–751.

WALTER BARON

BLYTH, EDWARD (*b.* London, England, 23 December 1810; *d.* London, 27 December 1873), *natural history.*

Like his father, a native of Norfolk, Blyth had a great love of nature and an extraordinary memory. When his father died in 1820, Blyth's mother took charge of the four children and immediately sent Edward, the oldest boy, to Dr. Fennell's school at Wimbledon. Although he displayed great intellectual ability, Blyth was frequently truant to go on scientific expeditions to the nearby woods; and in 1825 Dr. Fennell suggested that Mrs. Blyth, who had planned a university career and ultimately the ministry for her son, should send him to study chemistry in London with a Mr. Keating. Blyth thought the chemist was unsatisfactory, however, and upon coming of age, he invested in a small druggist's business in the town of Tooting, Surrey. This venture was doomed to failure because of his indifference: the real object of his affections was natural history. When not reading extensively in the British Museum, he collected butterflies, stuffed birds, or perhaps studied German—rising as early as three or four in the morning to do so.

While barely managing to exist, Blyth established an excellent reputation as a diligent and accurate naturalist. From 1833 until 1841, he contributed numerous notes and articles to scholarly journals, especially *The Magazine of Natural History.* In 1836 he published an edition of Gilbert White's *The Natural History and Antiquities of Selborne,* and he both translated and annotated the sections on mammals, reptiles, and birds for an edition of Georges Cuvier's *The Animal Kingdom* (1840). As a result of his scientific reputation (and perhaps as a result of an article on sheep in which he discussed Indian specimens), Blyth was offered a job as curator for the Royal Asiatic Society of Bengal. Despite the extremely low pay of 250 rupees per month,[1] he ac-

cepted the offer when his doctor advised him to seek a more salubrious climate for his delicate health. After arriving in Calcutta in September 1841, he worked with great industry for the society and published numerous reports, articles, and monographs, with particular emphasis on mammals and birds. The great English ornithologist John Gould observed that Blyth was "one of the first zoologists of his time, and the founder of the study of that science in India,"[2] and Allan Hume described him as "the greatest of Indian naturalists."[3]

In 1854 Blyth married Mrs. Sutton Hodges, a widow whom he had known in England, but this extremely happy marriage ended in December 1857, when his wife died. This great shock further weakened his chronically frail health, which led him to return to England in the summer of 1862, before learning whether he had received a government pension for his long and faithful service.[4] After returning to his homeland, in addition to his other scholarly works he contributed extensive notes and articles to *Land and Water* and *The Field* under the pseudonym "Zoophilus" or "Z." Unfortunately, Blyth found it extremely difficult, as his early rambling articles indicate, to complete his own longer works, for there were always more facts to be gathered and additional hypotheses to test. Some of these hypotheses were grandiose indeed, and in 1865 he attempted to explain, according to A. R. Wallace, *"everything* by the *Procession of the Equinoxes,"* which led Wallace to comment that Blyth was "certainly very queer."[5]

Nevertheless, his scientific abilities were recognized in 1865 by his election as honorary member of the Asiatic Society of Bengal. He was also a corresponding member of the Zoological Society of London and various other scientific academies and societies in Turin, Norway, Batavia, Moselle, and Philadelphia. He died from heart disease shortly after his sixty-third birthday.

At the time of his death, Blyth was preparing a work entitled "The Origination of Species." Although he was one of the very early converts to Darwin's theory of natural selection,[6] Blyth had long entertained ideas of his own on the species question. In 1835 he published the first of two excellent articles that discuss variation, the struggle for existence, sexual selection, and natural selection in terms that have a Darwinian sound.[7] Although Blyth was equivocal, he conceded that a better adapted organism might survive the struggle for existence and "transmit its superior qualities to a greater number of offspring"; that there is a decided tendency in nature for peculiarities to increase when two similar animals mate; that in human races if nontypical variations were propagated, they "would become the origin of a new race"; and that by selection man can produce breeds "very unlike the original type." But he also thought that the law allowing differences to be propagated "was intended by Providence to keep up the typical qualities of a species." Without man's intervention, domestic breeds would revert to the original type. In nature simple variations "are generally lost in the course of two or three generations" by the swamping effect of blending inheritance. He erroneously believed that the "original form of a species," not a subsequent modification, was "unquestionably" better adapted to its "natural habits." When he wrote these words, Blyth was not an evolutionist despite limited concessions that species may depart from the original type.[8]

On the other hand, Blyth's perceptive observations on variation in nature bear an interesting resemblance to Darwin's ideas, and, in fact, Darwin's copies of Blyth's articles in *The Magazine of Natural History* are heavily marked. While Blyth was in India, they corresponded frequently, and Blyth's lengthy letters were filled with detailed information, comments, and recommendations. One interesting example occurred in 1855 when he suggested that Darwin read his two papers of 1835 and 1837.[9] Although these articles were obviously germane to Darwin's work, and despite the fact that he had already read, marked, and taken notes on them, he apparently never cited them in print, which is one reason Darwin has been accused of plagiarizing the idea of natural selection from Blyth.[10] While the evidence indicates that Blyth probably did influence Darwin far more than most scholars have previously recognized, no one has established precisely when Darwin first read Blyth's works and what he found of interest there. Blyth no doubt provided Darwin with many insights and possibly reconfirmed certain ideas, but it was Darwin's *On the Origin of Species* which seems to have revolutionized Blyth's ideas on species, and not vice versa.[11] On the other hand, he was keenly aware of the issues in question and warmly recommended A. R. Wallace's first evolutionary paper, "On the Law Which Has Regulated the Introduction of New Species" (Sept. 1855), to Darwin; this was perhaps Darwin's first clear warning of Wallace's work on evolution.[12] Blyth's influence on Darwin, however, does not affect the epochal importance of *On the Origin of Species*.

NOTES

1. Allan Hume was especially bitter about Blyth's low pay. "In Memoriam," in *Stray Feathers*, **2** (1874), n.p.
2. John Gould, *The Birds of Asia* (London, 1850–1853), III, pt. 26, pl. 41.
3. *Op. cit.*
4. His request was at first denied, but through the efforts of Sir P. Cautley and Dr. Falconer, he finally received a pension of £150 per year. See Grote, p. xii.
5. Letter, Alfred Russel Wallace to Alfred Newton, 9 November 1865, at the Balfour Library, Cambridge. The italics are Wallace's. I wish to thank A. J. R. Wallace and R. R. Wallace for permission to quote from their grandfather's MSS.
6. The Asiatic Society of Bengal received a copy of Darwin's *Origin* in February or March 1860. Shortly thereafter Blyth commented favorably on Darwin's views, and at the meetings of November 1860 he staunchly defended his ideas. See *Journal of the Asiatic Society of Bengal,* **29** (1860), 86, 283, 383, 385, 428–438, esp. 436–438.
7. These two articles were published in three parts each in *The Magazine of Natural History*. The first had a different title for each part: pt. 1, "An Attempt to Classify the 'Varieties' of Animals, With Observations on the Marked Seasonal and Other Changes Which Naturally Take Place in Various British Species and Which Do Not Constitute Varieties," in **8** (1835), 40–53; pt. 2 "Observations on the Various Seasonal and Other External Changes Which Regularly Take Place in Birds, More Particularly in Those Which Occur in Britain; With Remarks on Their Great Importance in Indicating the True Affinities of Species; And Upon the Natural System of Arrangement," in **9** (Aug. 1836), 393–409; pt. 3, "Further Remarks on the Affinities of the Feathered Race; and Upon the Nature of Specific Distinctions," *ibid.* (Oct. 1836), 505–514. The second article, "On the Psychological Distinctions Between Man and All Other Animals; And the Consequent Diversity of Human Influence Over the Inferior Ranks of Creation From Any Mutual and Reciprocal Influence Exercised Among the Latter," appeared in three consecutive parts all under the same title, *ibid.*, n.s. **1** (Jan. 1837), 1–9; (Feb. 1837), 77–85; (Mar. 1837), 131–141. Loren Eiseley has reprinted these articles in "Charles Darwin, Edward Blyth, and the Theory of Natural Selection," in *Proceedings of the American Philosophical Society,* **103** (Feb. 1959), 94–158; see 114–150.
8. Blyth (1835), pp. 41, 46–49.
9. The books and MSS referred to are at the University Library, Cambridge. For Blyth's remark see the Darwin Papers, Box 98, MSS headed "Notes on Lyell, Vol. 2, Edit. 1832" (1855), p. 48.
10. See Eiseley, *op. cit.,* 102–103. His arguments are repeated and elaborated in "Darwin, Coleridge, and the Theory of Unconscious Creation," in *Daedalus,* **94,** no. 3 (Summer 1965), 588–602.
11. Darwin to Sir Charles Lyell, (1 June 1860), in *The Life and Letters of Charles Darwin,* II (1887), 314–316; see 316.
12. Letter, Blyth to Darwin, 8 Dec. 1855, Darwin Papers, Box 98, Cambridge University. The letter probably arrived in England about Feb. 1856.

BIBLIOGRAPHY

I. ORIGINAL WORKS. In addition to the articles referred to in the Notes, Blyth wrote an enormous number of notes, articles, and monographs. Many of these are listed by A. Grote with his memoir of Blyth prefaced to "Catalogue of Mammals and Birds of Burma," in *Journal of the Asiatic Society of Bengal,* pt. 2, extra no. (Aug. 1875), iii–xxiv, esp. xvii–xxiv; reprinted without bibliography in Eiseley (1959). Since Grote used Blyth's letters (then in the possession of his sister but now missing) as well as his own recollections, his biography of Blyth is the most valuable one available. Some of Blyth's letters to Darwin are in the Darwin Papers, Cambridge University, but his handwriting was frequently very poor, and these valuable letters have not yet been fully utilized.

II. Secondary Literature. Other than Grote's biographical sketch, the obituaries of Blyth—such as those in *Nature,* **9** (1874), 191, and *The Field* (3 Jan. 1874), 3—are of little value. H. D. Geldart's "Notes on the Life and Writings of Edward Blyth" (read 28 Oct. 1879), in *Transactions of the Norfolk and Norwich Naturalists Society,* **3** (1884), 38–46, used Grote exclusively, except for excerpts from and comments on Blyth's 1835 article which Grote omitted. H. M. Vickers also cited this perceptive article by Blyth in "An Apparently Hitherto Unnoticed 'Anticipation' of the Theory of Natural Selection," in *Nature,* **85** (16 Feb. 1911), 510–511. Recently, attention has been directed to Blyth by Eiseley (1959). Perhaps the tenor of the replies to Eiseley has been established by Theodosius Dobzhansky, "Blyth, Darwin, and Natural Selection," in *The American Naturalist,* **93** (1959), 204–206. He stresses that Darwin's thinking processes were not totally free from "subconscious components" and asked, "Might not even Darwin have been mistaken about the sources of some of his ideas?" Eiseley replied in 1965 (see n. 10).

H. Lewis McKinney

BOAS, FRANZ (*b.* Minden, Germany, 9 July 1858; *d.* New York, N.Y., 21 December 1942), *anthropology.*

Boas exercised considerable influence in the "historical" and "scientific" reorientation of anthropology from about 1890 to 1925, especially in the United States. He made significant contributions to formulation of problems and methods in human growth, linguistics, folklore, art, and the ethnology of the Indians of the Northwest Coast.

Franz was one of six children of Meier Boas, a moderately successful merchant, and Sophie Meyer, who founded a Froebel-type kindergarten in Minden. At an early age he expressed an interest in traveling to far-off lands to study the life and customs of exotic peoples, but as he pursued his studies at the Gymnasium in Minden, mathematics and physics claimed his attention and remained the focus of his graduate work at Heidelberg, Bonn, and Kiel. At twenty-three Boas received a doctorate in physics, but during his university career his desire to travel and to understand "nature as a whole" was renewed, probably by the inspiration of the naturalist and geographer Alexander von Humboldt. A friendship with the geographer Theobald Fischer also influenced the turn to anthropology.

In the fall of 1882 Boas attended meetings of the Berlin Anthropological Society, where he sought out Adolf Bastian, the foremost German ethnologist, and Rudolf Virchow, the famous anthropometrist. From Virchow he received anthropometric training, while Bastian gave him "good advice," encouragement, and

friendly assistance. By June 1883 Boas was on his way to Cumberland Sound, Baffin Island, on the polar research schooner *Germania.*

Before setting out for the Arctic, Boas read widely on Eskimo culture and studied the language, apparently intending to gather both geographic and ethnographic materials. He had every reason to be satisfied with his geographic researches, completed in 1884, for he had corrected many misconceptions about Baffin Island and had established the presence of two large lakes (not one) in the interior. He had also charted some 250 miles of coastline, often at great discomfort and hazard to his life. The expedition was crucial in turning Boas to anthropology, for he not only came to admire the Arctic people but also observed firsthand that geographic forces were not the prime determinants of human behavior. Obviously the source of these determinants must be sought elsewhere, and Boas elected to follow Bastian in focusing on mental processes. By the time Boas published *The Central Eskimo* in 1888, ethnological contributions were outrunning the geographic.

On Boas' return to Germany, Bastian found him a position in the Museum für Völkerkunde as an assistant, and in 1886 he became lecturer in geography at the University of Berlin. At the time he was undecided about pursuing a career in Germany, for he felt frustrated by the discrimination and insults to which he had been subject because of his Jewish origins. Still fresh from the Arctic adventure, he was excited by the visit of some Bella Coola Indians "on exhibit" in Berlin. Boas interviewed them and threw himself into the task of ordering the museum's collection of Northwest Coast materials. He soon had managed a shaky financing that would enable him to live among the Indians of the Northwest Coast for a few months. This was the first of thirteen field trips to the area (the last was in 1931). Altogether he spent some two and a half years among the coastal Indians.

Contact with F. W. Putnam during a meeting of the American Association for the Advancement of Science in Buffalo, New York, developed into an enduring association; it provided new opportunities for Boas and influenced his decision to remain in the United States. Putnam arranged for Boas to become a foreign associate member of the Association and in 1887, when Boas appeared at the New York office of *Science* to present an article, he was asked to become assistant editor. This provided a small income, whereupon Boas married Mary Krackowizer of New York, whom he had met in Germany.

A chance meeting with G. Stanley Hall led to an invitation to become a lecturer in anthropology at Clark University, a position Boas held until 1892, when he accepted Putnam's invitation to become his anthropological assistant in charge of exhibits for the Columbian Exposition in Chicago. In that same year, under Boas' direction, the first Ph.D. in anthropology in North America was conferred on A. F. Chamberlain, who became his successor at Clark. Boas stayed with Putnam during the formative years of the Field Museum, which had been founded to house some of the riches of the ethnological exhibits of the Columbian Exposition. When Putnam left in 1894, Boas became curator of anthropology, but difficulties already afoot soon provoked his resignation. Boas was virtually destitute until 1896, when Putnam offered him the post of curator of ethnology and somatology at the American Museum of Natural History. The museum appointment led to a lectureship in physical anthropology at Columbia University, followed by a professorship in 1899 (he retired in 1937). Putnam left the museum in 1901, and Boas assumed the post of curator of anthropology, resigning in 1905.

Boas made a number of basic assumptions about the nature of reality which guided his approach to the phenomenon of man and dictated his contributions to anthropology. The heart of his position was the assumption that reality is structured. It has an inner core that remains relatively stable in the face of altered conditions and an outer form that changes in response to alterations in conditions. The scientific problem lay in uncovering the inner core and in finding to what extent it was affected by variations in external form and vice versa. The only way to uncover this hidden reality, in Boas' view, was to study the variations, and when the variable aspects of range and nature had been determined, it would be possible to describe the inner form with confidence. This empirical-inductive position was not novel, however; it echoed the usual approach of natural scientists at that time. However, the application of an inductive orientation to the "evolutionary" anthropology of the day was bound to produce profound alterations in problem definition, methodology, and results.

Boas' most general and signal contributions to anthropology stem from his earnest desire to make the discipline a rigorous and exact science. No anthropologist at the time seems to have understood so well as Boas the full implications of the inductive position and why the path of deduction then followed in anthropology must lead to erroneous conclusions and perpetuation of a quasi-science. No one pressed more vigorously for abandonment of uncritical inferences and comparisons than Boas, as he systematically destroyed the popular and "scientific" myths of the day. Except for his ethnographic texts, which presented material with little commentary, he used every

review, public lecture, article, introduction, and analytical monograph to rephrase problems and to point out the complex logical and technical operations involved in achieving precise controls and conclusions. Most of the rephrasings picked up the complexities glossed over by uncritical classification: What criteria shall be used when we say that a culture or a custom is simple in comparison with another? How does one classify cultures that are simple in technology, yet complicated in social organization? How can the criteria employed be freed from subjective bias traceable to the relativistic categories of thought found in one's own culture?

Boas has been cited as a destroyer of the "evolutionist" position, but as a scientist, he was the opponent of any kind of speculation. "Evolutionary" anthropology, dominant when Boas entered the discipline, operated deductively with a number of unproved assumptions. It was therefore necessary to replace this pseudo anthropology and its uncritical "comparative method" with a "scientific" anthropology grounded in a critical use of detailed factual materials. Attention should be directed to process—how forms change.

In the course of unseating "evolutionary" anthropology, Boas contributed some basic principles to practice. (1) All classifications are relative, and the scientist must realize this when he seeks to conceptualize his findings. The error of forcing the logic of one's own categories of thought on the "primitive" must be avoided, or the product of research will be useless. (2) Classification is no substitute for process—for what actually happens. Data must be collected in such detail that the operation will record variations in forms and the causes of these variations, thereby offering clues to process. (3) For items to be comparable, they must show similarities not only in outward form but also in their histories. One must beware of using functional analogies produced by convergence as if they were homologies—which alone can pass muster for scientific comparison. (4) Coincidence must not be taken for causal connection. Boas' classic target here was the alleged relation linking race, language, and culture. With well-known historic illustrations, supplemented by examples out of his own fieldwork, Boas was able to show that race, language, and culture varied independently of each other. (5) No system of explanation can account for everything, yet there can be no scientific explanation at all without accounting for the variations insofar as objective controls can be brought to bear. (6) Valid interpretations are possible only when derived from a relevant context. To seek the source of religious behavior in a "contemplation" of nature is suspect because more likely sources for religious ideas are the "feelings" and "imaginative play" accompanying "social experience." (7) The data compared must be quantified before "laws" can be extracted.

The determination to reorient anthropology came gradually, as Boas developed field experience and began to analyze his Northwest Coast materials, especially myths and legends, in the light of their geographic distributions. He paid special tribute to the geographer Friedrich Ratzel in supplying this methodological lead. As early as 1888 he called attention to the great importance of "cultural contact" for the cultural development of "primitive" societies, but he was nevertheless willing to admit that comparative evolutionary studies were sound enough to allow the conclusion that the "human mind develops everywhere according to the same laws." By 1896, however, Boas was convinced that the "vain endeavor to construct a uniform systematic history of the evolution of culture" with the aid of the traditional "comparative method" had to be renounced if anthropology were to become a science. The method he advocated was the "historical."

The historical method would uncover process through a meticulous consideration of individual forms and their variations. By plotting culture "elements" in space, historic relations could be outlined and psychological processes recovered, as one noted alterations in form and meaning made by individual peoples when reinterpreting borrowed traits according to their own social traditions. Properly applied, the historical method would disclose how diverse elements had been accumulated and ordered in a kind of unity not only within particular tribes but also within areas where they seemed to be especially characteristic. Once the variations had been disposed of, the local culture base would be recognizable. In applying the historical method, it was best to begin with a limited area and gradually extend one's controlled comparisons outward. Certain uniformities could be found in the cultures of societies located in geographic areas suggesting a kind of natural culture region with which to begin.

At all times the investigator must stay within the limits of his data and avoid inferences that have not been checked against facts. The occurrence of similar forms in adjacent tribes usually indicated that diffusion had taken place, but the researcher must consider other contingencies. Likewise, a wide and continuous distribution would suggest an ancient history for the culture element in question, but an age-area principle could not be applied to ethnographic facts as a blanket rule, because historic exceptions were known. To hold that distant tribes with similar customs were

linked historically would not be reasonable unless a more or less continuous chain of distribution of elements held in common could be traced, or migration were likely. Boas thus admitted that parallel developments in widely separated areas could occur and that such might owe their similarities to identical psychological processes. In this regard he noted how language elements were distributed so irregularly throughout the world that some phonetic, morphological, and classificatory features must owe their similarities to "psychological causes" operating in the context of a limited number of alternatives. Such an admission would not lend wholehearted support to a unilinear type of development, however. Boas' viewpoint stressed a generalized psychological base, an impulse as it were, that could be expressed in any number of ways. Therefore, differentiation was more expectable than restriction to a single response. It followed that no unilinear parallelism based on identical psychological processes could be granted until the strictures of historic contact, migration, and convergence had been satisfied. The inner form thus would stand in relief only as the variations had been accounted for.

By the time Boas wrote the introduction to the *Handbook of American Indian Languages* (1911), he was able to outline the essentials of his position. He intended to establish the "historical method" and then move on to "problems of cultural dynamics, of integration of culture and of the interaction between individual and society." All these efforts were programmed to uncover the ultimate anthropological reality—the psychological laws governing human behavior.

Once convinced that he was on the track of a scientific anthropology, Boas drove himself tirelessly and systematically toward the goal. He preferred to operate in the context of problems and methods rather than to formulate neat definitions for the classification and manipulation of data. In consequence, the conceptual language of anthropology owes little to Boas, who rarely offered a definition of culture, the alleged hallmark of anthropology. He was, however, a prime contributor to the emergence of the culture concept, stressing the weight of "social tradition" as a molding force in human behavior. Boas thus was in the vanguard of those who recognized that what individuals experienced and learned as members of a society represented a basic problem for social science investigation, and that the key to human behavior would be found in sociopsychological processes rather than in common human psychological tendencies stressed by evolutionists when reconstructing the stages of culture growth.

From his field experience Boas was convinced that the sociopsychological processes linking primitive men to social tradition were basically little different from those of civilized societies. By 1930 two of his students, Ruth Benedict and Margaret Mead, were breaking new ground in learning how cultures stimulate the development of unique personality types.

Boas distinguished three important problems to which anthropology must be directed: "reconstruction of human history"—biological, linguistic, and social; "determination of types of historical phenomena and their consequences"; and the "dynamics of change." In starting with problems and methods, it is apparent that Boas wished to reorient his readers to the intricate processes involved in human phenomena. Aware of his own deficiencies in ethnographic details, he had no wish to forestall a scientific advance by presenting an elaborate explanatory system. Classifications and explanations must come later—after full description of the phenomena. Ultimate understandings would emerge as psychological processes came to light, but Boas wanted to make it clear that anthropology, since it dealt with "secondary [historic] features," could not use psychology as a jumping-off point. Rather, "The psychological problem [of inner form] is contained in the results of the historic inquiry."

When casting about for the most sensitive indicators of psychological processes, Boas was drawn to language, for in the "linguistic categories" of specific languages he hoped to uncover the "unconscious" impulses that had given rise to the "fundamental ideas of language." Since ethnology could be considered the "science dealing with mental phenomena of the life of the peoples of the world," the two stood to gain by mutual cooperation, and Boas encouraged the thought that linguistics would make a greater contribution to anthropology as a part of ethnology than were it to go its own way. The study of folklore was selected as the second center of investigation because Boas had observed that "nothing seems to travel as readily as fanciful tales." Some elements were widely distributed throughout North America, and there were obvious connections between the mythology of northeast Asia and that of the Northwest Coast. Boas labored for thirty years to produce a compilation of folklore elements from throughout the Northwest Coast area and from which he could extract the psychological processes by which they had been altered during their spread and reinterpretation. Many of the conclusions advanced in the voluminous quantitative study *Tsimshian Mythology* (1916) had been foreshadowed in shorter papers on how folklore traits drawn from a number of sources accumulated gradually and were integrated into the folklore traditions and narrative styles of a particular tribe.

Boas' theory of culture history, and his view of the integration of culture, owed much to his pursuit of mythological elements on the Northwest Coast. Since mythic elements could be disengaged from narratives and plots and widely diffused, he became convinced that culture seldom, if ever, diffused as a complex and unified whole. He therefore opposed the *Kulturkreislehre,* who assembled disparate elements into "culture complexes" and treated them as if they had diffused *en bloc.* Again he found confirmation for his notion that any cultural tradition was a complicated product of intricate historical and psychological processes rooted in the "social life of the people." Under such circumstances one could hardly expect mythology to be a "direct reflex of the contemplation of nature" and to present a uniform "organic growth" expressing uniformities in the human mind. It was true that incidents and actors in folktales had a way of becoming associated with natural phenomena (stars, animals, mountains, trees), but these were secondary symbolizations projected through the "play of imagination with the events of human life." In Boas' historical view, individual cultures might develop some tendencies toward becoming a unity, but none could become a thoroughly consistent and integrated whole.

Myths also proved a useful touchstone for language studies, literary analysis, and world view. When they were dictated by the informant and recorded phonetically in text, a corpus of materials was available for linguistic analysis. Myths often contained theological, philosophical, and scientific explanations, and thus provided an important channel to primitive thought. But although Boas was aware of the uses to which myths could be put in understanding the psychology of a people in their choice of metaphor, in the symbolism expressed in the personalities of the actors, and in explanations of events, he never explored these dimensions in any depth.

Art was the third medium Boas used to demonstrate that human phenomena are highly variable and have complex historic, social, and psychological roots. He confounded those who interpreted the history of art as an evolution from a realistic to an abstract representation by pointing out that within any society there may be found examples of both realistic and geometric design. Actually, an utterly realistic treatment did not occur in primitive art. The intent might be representative, but "symbolic forms" or conventions representing heads, legs, and other body details normally were used, and the primitive artist knew very well that he had not succeeded in duplicating what he portrayed. The imaginative stimulus the artist received from materials and tools while approaching the task within a traditional context provided the key to much of the variation in the artistic expression of any tribe, and Boas cautioned against assuming that conventionalization was so rigid that no variations could occur in primitive art.

Stress on the interplay of tradition, material, tool, and technical virtuosity channeled Boas' focus on process in art, and helped him explain why individual variations and stylistic conventionalizations must occur. Only the total context of any art could provide relevant and valid source materials for scientific generalization. The elements of art could be explained much better by the rhythmic and alternating movements involved in technical operations than by contemplation of nature's analogues. Uniformities found in any art were a product of stylistic traditions, which limited human inventiveness, and not the consequence of uniform responses by the human mind.

Physical anthropology constituted Boas' fourth instrument to promote a scientific anthropology. It seemed highly probable to him that the predominance of heredity over environment assured a great permanence of human types. However, the problem of physical variability had to be dealt with first because variability was not a matter of biology but the result of unknown influences on the more permanent characteristics. The plotting of human types according to their geographic distribution therefore must be the first order of business, paying due attention to variations stemming from "mixture," the fixing of types through inbreeding and isolation, and differentiations that followed natural tendencies for succeeding generations to vary from parental stems. Subtle physiological changes induced by nutrition and mode of life could not be ignored, because man, like other domesticated species, was not impervious to such influences. The races that anthropologists so easily assumed to be homogeneous and stable in type actually masked a considerable heterogeneity that would become apparent—and significant—as the complex histories of the "genetic lines" of which they were composed came to the surface. When the historic analysis had revealed the range and sources of variations, the permanent features would stand clear and would allow definition of local "genetic" types instead of "ecotypes." Boas was soon convinced that historic complexities in anatomical variation were such that it would be futile to expect to find any "pure races" or an original race from which a rigid genealogy could be plotted.

Boas set out to document physical variation by investigating alterations that might be due to rates of growth, intermixture, and mode of life. Knowing individuals differed in their maturational rates, he asked how these uneven rates influenced distributions and classifications. He admitted that development of a dynamic set of growth statistics would increase the complexities of research problems, but a vast and interesting array of challenging questions would open up as "physiological changes in the individual and the types and variabilities of these changes become accessible to investigation."

Measurement of nearly 18,000 immigrants in New York provided Boas with a controversial study in physical variation. In the New World urban setting, round-headed east European Jews became more long-headed, while south Italians, long-headed to begin with, became more short-headed. Two ethnic groups with differing head shapes thus tended to converge in a new urban environment. The changes were registered in children, and native-born children registered a greater shift in stature and in head form than did foreign-born. The study excited anthropometrists, who had viewed physical types as quite stable and had relied on head form as a special index for racial classification and history. Although Boas drew on his data to emphasize the "plasticity" of human types, he realized that genetic organization had not been altered. Nonetheless the study called attention to the dynamic relation linking type and environment, and cautioned against the ready acceptance of external form as a mirror image of genetic type.

Stimulated by an experimental study in which "pure lines" of beans had shown variations apparently traceable to both inheritance and environment, Boas attempted to determine the relative importance of these variables for human physical types. By statistical correlation of variance "averages" among "fraternities" comprising a line of descent, he hoped to measure the heterogeneity of the line. Boas was sufficiently knowledgeable in mathematics to attempt innovations in correlational procedures to suit his anthropometric data, but these *ad hoc* efforts had no lasting effect, for Pearson and Fisher developed more sophisticated techniques.

With variations the key to his initial scientific purpose, Boas turned to controlled observation and recording of detailed information as prerequisites to the critical and "exhaustive" analysis that must take place. There could be no substitute for facts, which alone could lead to the understanding of forms and processes. Hence, the somewhat natural history approach of Boas to the collection of anthropological data. The anthropologist must be a fieldworker, but he could not approach his task with preconceived ideas. A properly trained anthropologist would observe, but above all he would depend on the people he was studying to supply their own categories of thought for sifting the phenomena. It followed that the interview would not be directed, except incidentally. The informant would be presented with a problem, but he then would be left free to develop his narrative and to follow the lead of his own interests. A fieldworker should strive for language mastery, but in the absence of the language skill, texts dictated by the informant in his own language could be recorded phonetically.

Boas recommended the collection of comparable materials from several informants, but he made no real effort to increase the number of his informants in the hope of increasing reliability. Instead, he customarily sought control through numbers by expanding the list of elements. The historic emphasis tended to focus attention on issues other than the determination of culture patterns or literary style, but Boas' treatment invariably turned to the presence or absence of literary expression in riddles, moralizing fables, epic poetry, and the like to show that primitive literature had a history and was not a natural and spontaneous product of common human mental processes.

In reviewing Boas' substantive contributions to anthropology, it is apparent that the key to his success lay in a determined massing of data, a quick grasp of the ramifications of problems, and a perceptive utilization of leads furnished by investigators in related fields.

A restrained and businesslike tone governed Boas' relations with his Indian informants, preventing him from probing their offbeat habits, but his methodical record established a platform upon which subsequent investigators could build. His publications, often with ethnographic notes, concerned a remarkable number of Pacific Coast and inland tribes: Northern and Southern Kwakiutl, Bella Coola, Tsimshian, Chinook, Tillamook, Kathlamet, Kutenai, and a Keresan-speaking pueblo of the Southwest.

In his search for the inner world of the primitive, Boas pioneered in using those who had been raised among the Indians or who were their close associates. He went to some pains to train George Hunt, a mixed-blood Tlingit reared among the Kwakiutl, in phonetic transcription, and Hunt rewarded him with many pages of text, including mythology, potlatch narratives, and Kwakiutl recipes. James Teit, a sheepherder, also was encouraged to publish extensively on the Thompson and other Indians of the plateau region.

Boas was largely responsible for conduct of the Jesup North Pacific Expedition (1897–1900), which sought answers to cultural relations linking Siberian and Northwest Coast peoples. His efforts to establish an international school of American archaeology and ethnology dedicated to research in Mexico ultimately failed as a result of the revolution that erupted in 1910, but during his directorship (1911–1912), Boas was able to acquaint the school and the Mexican appointee, Manuel Gamio, with the uses of stratigraphy and typology in formulating a sequence of cultures for the Valley of Mexico. The interest Boas generated in folklore was passed on to students and associates, including William Jones, George A. Dorsey, Edward Sapir, Pliny E. Goddard, Robert H. Lowie, Melville J. Herskovits, Gladys Reichard, and Melville Jacobs. During his editorship (1908–1924) of the *Journal of American Folk-Lore*, Boas assured an outlet for the texts and translations he had inspired. Publications of the American Ethnological Society and of the Columbia University series Contributions to Anthropology also were utilized for folklore works until 1940.

In linguistics, Boas' accomplishments parallel his achievements in folklore. A self-taught linguist, he used his editorship of the *Handbook of American Indian Languages* (1911–1941) to outline a proper study of language and to provide "grammatical sketches" that would serve as models for future research. His intent was to achieve uniform presentations, treating the grammar "as though an intelligent Indian was going to develop the forms of his own thoughts by analysis of his own form of speech." In 1917 Boas took the initiative in launching the *International Journal of American Linguistics,* which he not only edited until his death but also maintained with personal funds.

In physical anthropology, Boas' pioneer efforts led to discovery of individual variability in "tempo of growth." He was the first to initiate human growth studies in North America, and his was the first chart of standardized heights and weights for American children according to chronological age, corrected statistically to give the standard deviation or variance at each half-year interval. Boas also pointed out the close correlation between the rate of physiological development and mental development; physiologically advanced subjects made better scores in school work and on psychological tests than did physiologically retarded subjects of the same age.

Boas has been criticized for impeding the progress of American anthropology for two or more decades by training a generation of students antagonistic to evolutionary problems and by exercising his commanding influence in publication and organizational channels. Such an accusation is difficult to evaluate, but the existence on the Continent of a similar antievolutionary drive leaves the charge open to doubt. The basic limitations of Boas' approach stem from his determined efforts to overturn "speculative" evolutionary theories of the origin and development of human thought and culture. He concentrated on investigation of "mental phenomena" in art, language, and mythology and thus was diverted from the study of cultures in their organizational and functional operations. Preoccupation with historic processes also led to an indifference to the processes of change then taking place in Indian cultures. His methodological practice of reducing larger culture units to elemental parts in order to trace historic relations prevented full appreciation of the stylistic integration that cultures might exhibit. Once Boas developed his position, he was little inclined to change course or to go beyond the scientific boundaries he had outlined. This inflexibility is apparent in an inclination to press more rigorous and searching methods upon unfinished research rather than to open up new problems.

Besides holding honorary and regular memberships in many national anthropological organizations in Europe and in the United States, Boas held a number of presidencies, including those of the American Anthropological Association (1907, 1908), New York Academy of Science (1910), American Folklore Society (1931), and American Association for the Advancement of Science (1931). From 1901 to 1919 he served as honorary philologist to the Bureau of American Ethnology.

BIBLIOGRAPHY

I. ORIGINAL WORKS. A select list of papers (some revised or condensed) assembled by Boas in *Race, Language and Culture* (New York, 1940) offers an excellent introduction to the range of his activities and his theoretical position. This can be supplemented with such reprints as *The Central Eskimo* (1888; repr. Lincoln, Neb., 1964); *The Mind of Primitive Man* (1911; repr. New York, 1963); and *Primitive Art* (1927; repr. New York, 1955). In *Kwakiutl Ethnography* (Chicago, 1966), Helen Codere has added a number of published selections to an unfinished manuscript in order to furnish a representative account of Boas' description of this people. The raw data for Boas' study of bodily changes in immigrants was published as *Materials for the Study of Inheritance in Man* (New York, 1928). He was also contributing editor of the *Handbook of American Indian Languages*, 4 vols. (Washington, D.C.–New York, 1911–1941). A full bibliography is in Memoir 61 (see below).

II. SECONDARY LITERATURE. Two sympathetic views of Boas appeared as memoirs of the *American Anthropologist: Franz Boas, 1858–1942,* Memoir 61 (Menasha, 1943), with contributions by A. L. Kroeber, Ruth Benedict, and others; and Walter Goldschmidt, ed., *The Anthropology of Franz Boas: Essays on the Centennial of His Birth,* Memoir 89 (Menasha, 1959). In June Helm, ed., *Pioneers of American Anthropology,* American Ethnological Society, Monograph 43 (Seattle, 1966), Ross Parmenter describes the friendship of Boas and Zelia Nuttall, the celebrated Mexican researcher, and Robert Rohner presents diary and correspondence material relevant to Boas' fieldwork on the Northwest Coast. M. J. Herskovits, *Franz Boas: The Science of Man in the Making* (New York, 1953), offers the appreciative reflections of a student, viewing Boas as teacher, scientist, and citizen of the world. More critical treatments can be found in Leslie White, *The Ethnography and Ethnology of Franz Boas,* Texas Memorial Museum Bulletin 6 (Austin, Tex., 1963), and *The Social Organization of Ethnological Theory,* Rice University Studies, Monograph in Cultural Anthropology, **52,** no. 4 (Houston, Tex., 1966). For Boas' contribution to the concept of culture, see George Stocking, Jr., "Franz Boas and the Culture Concept in Historic Perspective," in *American Anthropologist,* **68,** no. 4 (1966), 867–882.

FRED W. VOGET

BOBILLIER, ÉTIENNE (*b.* Lons-le-Saulnier, France, 17 April 1798; *d.* Châlons-sur-Marne, France, 22 March 1840), *geometry, mechanics.*

Étienne Bobillier was the second son of Ignace Bobillier, a merchant, who died when Étienne was seven years old. He and his brother Marie André were raised by their mother, a wallpaper merchant. Étienne attended the local secondary school and seemed inclined toward literary studies, in which he won awards. Until he was sixteen, he showed no interest in mathematics, but then his brother, a student at the *lycée* of Besançon, was accepted by the École Polytechnique. Étienne resolved to follow this example and, shutting himself up with the books left behind by his brother and aided from time to time by advice from him, he completed the course in special mathematics. He then presented himself for the competitive entrance examination in 1817. The examiner, well known for his severity, put Étienne first on his list. He was admitted to the École Polytechnique as fourth in rank.

Bobillier finished his first year eighth out of sixty-four students. Because of financial needs, he took a leave of absence from the École Polytechnique in October 1818, in order to become an instructor in mathematics at the École des Arts et Métiers at Châlons. The young instructor soon showed a remarkable gift for teaching; exhibiting a rapid judgment, lively mind, lucid language, and strength of character that impressed, captivated, and subdued his students.[1] He taught trigonometry, statics, analytic geometry, descriptive geometry, practical mechanics, physics, and chemistry.

In 1829 Bobillier, who saw no future where he was, applied for a university post and, upon Poisson's recommendation, he became professor of special mathematics at the Collège Royal of Amiens. The minister of commerce, however, who had authority over all Écoles des Arts et Métiers, named him director of studies at the École of Angers. He took up his post there on 1 January 1830. After the July Revolution, civil war broke out again in the west and Bobillier, a volunteer in the National Guard of Angers, fought in a rather hard month-long campaign against the Chouans.

In 1832 his post as director of studies was abolished, and Bobillier returned to Châlons as instructor-in-chief in mathematics. By 1834 he was full professor, a rank he retained until his death. He also held a professorship of special mathematics at the municipal high school. Bobillier was named Chevalier of the Legion of Honor in 1839.

In 1836 he became seriously ill; but the following year he married. In spite of a recurring illness, Bobillier refused to interrupt his work, even though he finally was confined to bed. Imprudently, he resumed his teaching and other activities too soon—a decision that hastened his death in 1840.

Bobillier became known to the scientific world particularly through his contributions to the *Annales de Gergonne.*[2] The first, in August 1826, was a modest solution of certain problems posed to the readers by the editor. In April 1830 he went on to demonstrate the principle of virtual velocities for machines in equilibrium. He also contributed to Quetelet's *Correspondance mathématique et physique,*[3] to the *Mémoires de l'Académie de Caen,*[4] and to a few provincial journals[5]—probably a total of some forty writings. He also edited for his students a book of elementary algebra and a complete course in geometry. His courses in mechanics and physics were written out in autograph.[6]

At the time of his death, Bobillier was working on a dissertation concerning the geometric laws of motion[7] that he meant to present as a report before the Académie des Sciences. Some of the passages in his course in geometry are probably an early outline for this.

Because of his isolation in the provinces, Bobillier had few direct contacts with the scientific world of his time. His premature departure from the École Polytechnique prevented him from forming the lasting friendships that are one of the principal hallmarks of that famous school.

He knew Poncelet, however, through correspondence and a close relationship that began in 1828–1829.[8] Unfortunately, their correspondence seems to have been lost. Bobillier never met J. D. Gergonne, the editor of the *Annales,* nor Adolphe Quetelet and Michel Chasles. In spite of the coincidence of their statements and interests, and of the fact that questions of priority arose between them, they do not seem to have corresponded directly. In fact, in the notice that Chasles wrote on Bobillier, he made a serious error as to the date of his death.[9]

There is even more reason to think that Bobillier had neither contact nor correspondence with Jakob Steiner and Julius Plücker, his emulators on the staff of the *Annales.* It should be noted that Gergonne often edited the articles of his collaborators to suit himself, which makes it difficult to judge them definitively.

Loyal to Gaspard Monge's ideas, Bobillier treated geometric problems in a way akin to both analytic geometry and projective geometry. He first set up a problem in the form of an equation in a particular case, simple enough so that the analytic geometry of his time could deal with it. Then, through a transformation by reciprocal polars, he obtained the dual. In this respect he was a disciple of Gergonne.

Such a method was hardly suitable for treating metric proportion. In 1824 Poncelet presented to the Académie des Sciences a report in which he solved the difficulty by taking the sphere as the quadric of reference.[10] Since his report had not been published, he then, at Gergonne's insistence, gave a somewhat sybilline sketch of it in the *Annales.*[11] Upon reading this, Chasles and Bobillier rediscovered Poncelet's method; and Bobillier was first to publish it.[12]

In his course in geometry Bobillier was the very first to use transformation by reciprocal polars relative to a circle in order to provide an elementary study of conic sections. For a more sophisticated point of view of the same field, his following proposition may be cited: The polar circles of a fixed point of a conic section, relative to all the triangles inscribed in the curve, meet at the same point.[13]

Bobillier is best known, however, for his studies of successive polars of curves or algebraic surfaces, and for his abridged notation. He stated, following Monge, that the tangents drawn from a point to a plane curve of order m have their points of contact on a curve of order $m - 1$, which he called the polar of the point. He made analogous statements concerning space.

In a series of studies[14] Bobillier showed that the polars of collinear points have $(m - 1)^2$ points in common. The polars of a point relative to a linear pencil (an expression that came into use after his time) of curves of order m form a pencil of order $(m - 1)$. If the point describes a straight line, the $(m - 1)^2$ points at the base of this pencil describe a curve of order $2(m - 1)$.

In considering the successive polars of the same points that are of order $(m - 1)$, $(m - 2) \cdots 1$, one is led to the following theorem: The polar of order n of a point P is the locus of all points whose polars of order $(m - n)$ pass through P. Plücker agreed with Bobillier in stating this theorem, which he had mentioned to Gergonne without any proof.

In May 1828 there appeared in the *Annales* Bobillier's essay on a new mode of research on the properties of space.[15] The method of research that he expounded was, he stated, susceptible to various applications, which he hoped to publish in successive issues.

With A a linear function of two coordinates and a a constant, $A = 0$ is the equation of a straight line. $ABC = 0$ is the equation of the extensions of the sides of a triangle, known as the equation of the triangle; and $aBC + bCA + cAB = 0$ is the general equation of a conic section circumscribed about the triangle. Its tangents at the vertices are $bC + cB = 0$; $cA + aC = 0$; $aB + bA = 0$. In fact, the straight line $bC + cB = 0$ meets the conic only at the point $B = 0$, $C = 0$. The triangle circumscribed about the conic, the points of contact being the vertices of the first triangle, has for its "equation" $(bC + cB)(cA + aC)(aB + bA) = 0$. The straight line passing through the three points of intersection of the tangents with the corresponding sides of the original triangle is $bcA + caB + abC = 0$. The lines of junction of the corresponding vertices of the two triangles— $cB - bC = 0$; $aC - cA = 0$; $bA - aB = 0$—are concurrent. It is then a trivial matter to show that this point and this line are pole and polar of each other in relation to the conic section in question.

Bobillier showed by a similar and clever process that, in space, if a tetrahedron is inscribed in a quadric, then another tetrahedron can be circumscribed about the same quadric so that the points of contact of its faces are the vertices of the original tetrahedron. The oppositely placed faces of the two tetrahedrons cut each other in four lines, and their oppositely placed vertices are joined by four other lines. The straight lines of each group belong to the same quadric.

Aware of the value of his method, Bobillier applied it in the 1 June 1828 number of the *Annales* to some elementary geometric propositions.[16] In particular, he obtained from it the known proposition concerning the chords common to a circle and a conic section, and the theorems of Pascal and C. J. Brianchon. The efficacy of the method may be judged by these simple examples.

In statics, in which Bobillier was particularly concerned with catenaries, his report "De l'équilibre de la chaînette sur une surface courbe"[17] should be mentioned. This problem was taken over by F. Minding in 1835, by C. Gudermann in 1834 and 1846, by P. Appell in 1885, and by A. G. Greenhill in 1897. In spite of a few minor errors in computation, the work remains most elegant.

Bobillier's demonstration of the principle of virtual velocities[18] consisted in substituting "for any ordinary machine, whose character can be changed in an infinite number of ways, the winch, whose conditions of equilibrium are so well known and that, at least for the infinitely small deviation that we can estimate in its equilibrium, remains. exactly the same." His method is extremely clever.

In kinematics there seem to be no known traces of the work Bobillier was doing toward the end of his life, although the passages in his book on geometry that treat this subject are still extant.[19] Two theorems and one problem are particularly in evidence: All movement of a triangle on a plane can be produced by rolling a certain line over another fixed line, the triangle being invariably linked to the first line. If a triangle, *abc*, moves in such a fashion that the sides *ab* and *ac* constantly touch two circles, the envelope of the third side is also a circle; and the centers of the three envelopes determine a new circle that includes all the instantaneous centers of rotation. Bobillier then went on to pose the problem of how to determine the corresponding center of curvature in the path of the third vertex, *c*, when given the centers of curvature at points *a* and *b* of the paths described by vertices *a* and *b* of triangle *abc*. The construction he gave of this center is known as the Bobillier construction.

NOTES

1. Obituary, in *Almanach du département de la Marne* (1841), pp. 316–320.
2. In vols. **17–20.**
3. Vol. **4** (1828).
4. "De la courbe nommée chaînette," 1831.
5. E.g., *Recueil des travaux de la Société d'agriculture, commerce, sciences et arts de la Marne:* "Notes sur les puits à bascule" (1826) and "Note sur le principe de Roberval" (1834).
6. From the obituary of 1841.
7. From the obituary. However, Bobillier notes this memoir in the 10th ed. of the *Géométrie,* p. 208.

8. Poncelet, *Applications d'analyse et de géométrie*, II, 486. Poncelet calls Bobillier "an intelligent and singularly active mind."

9. *Rapport sur les progrès de la géométrie*, pp. 65–68. "We owe remarkable researches to Bobillier, a distinguished geometer who gave hopes of great achievements for mathematical sciences, from which he was snatched in 1832 at the age of thirty-five."

10. See, e.g., *Applications*, p. 529.

11. Vol. **17**, pp. 265–272; see also vol. **18**, pp. 125–149.

12. *Annales*, **18**, pp. 185–202, "Démonstration de divers théorèmes de géométrie." "In writing the above article we have used only the contents of M. Poncelet's letter" (the letter in vol. **17**). On p. 269 of vol. **18**, Chasles said: "It was only yesterday evening that your number of January 1828 reached me. I have read M. Bobillier's report with considerable eagerness . . . but I must say that the special case in which a sphere is taken . . . has come to me only through the reading of the analysis in the report" (report by Poncelet, vol. **17**, p. 265).

13. "Mémoire sur l'hyperbole équilatère."

14. *Annales*, vol. **18**, pp. 89, 157, 253; vol. **19**, pp. 106, 138, 302.

15. Vol. **18**, pp. 321–339.

16. "Philosophie mathématique. Démonstration nouvelle de quelques propriétés des lignes du second ordre."

17. *Annales*, vol. **20**, pp. 153–175.

18. *Ibid.*, pp. 285–288.

19. *Cours de géométrie*, 10th ed., pp. 204–208.

BIBLIOGRAPHY

I. ORIGINAL WORKS. Among Bobillier's writings are "Notes sur les puits à bascule," in *Recueil des travaux de la société d'agriculture, commerce, sciences et arts de la Marne* (1826); material in *Correspondance mathématique et physique*, **4** (1828); "De la courbe nommée chaînette," in *Mémoires de l'Académie de Caen* (1831); "Note sur le principe de Roberval," in *Recueil des travaux . . .* (1834); *Cours de géométrie* (10th ed., Paris, 1850); and *Principes d'algèbre* (6th ed., Paris, 1865).

Many of his articles were published in the *Annales de mathématiques pures et appliquées:* "Démonstration de divers théorèmes de géométrie," **18**, 185–202; "En rédigeant l'article qu'on vient de lire . . . ," *ibid.*, 269; an article on polars of collinear points, *ibid.*, 89, 159, 253, and **19**, 106, 138, 302; an article on new methods of research on the properties of space, **18**, 321–339; "Philosophie mathématique. Démonstration nouvelle de quelques propriétés des lignes du second ordre," *ibid.*, 359–367; "Mémoire sur l'hyperbole équilatère," **19**, 349–359; "De l'équilibre de la chaînette sur une surface courbe," **20**, 153–175; and an article on the principle of virtual velocity, *ibid.*, 285–288.

II. SECONDARY LITERATURE. Works providing more information on Bobillier and his accomplishments are Michel Chasles, *Rapport sur les progrès de la géométrie* (Paris, 1870), pp. 65–68, excellent from a mathematical standpoint; J. L. Coolidge, *A History of Geometrical Methods* (Oxford, 1940; New York, 1963), p. 143, which perpetuates Chasles's error on the date of Bobillier's death; and Poncelet's *Applications d'analyse et de géométrie* (Paris, 1864), II, 486, 529; and an article on the sphere as the quadric of reference, in *Annales de mathématiques pures et appliquées*, **17**, 265–272, and **18**, 125–149. There is an obituary of Bobillier in *Almanach du département de la Marne* (1841), 316–320.

J. ITARD

BOCHART DE SARON, JEAN-BAPTISTE-GASPARD (*b.* Paris, France, 16 January 1730; *d.* Paris, 20 April 1794), *astronomy.*

Bochart, whom Laplace aptly described as an enlightened amateur scientist, followed family tradition by choosing a legal career and by having a keen interest in astronomy. His prominent name, his scientific competence, and his generosity to academicians (e.g., he financed the publication of Laplace's *Théorie du movement et de la figure élliptique des planètes*) led to his election, in 1779, as an honorary member of the Académie des Sciences and to his appointment, after the death of Camus, as one of the directors of Jacques Dominique Cassini's project, the Carte de France. He approached science with concrete images rather than with abstractions, through mechanics rather than through mathematics, and with practical interests rather than with theoretical ones.

At an early age Bochart successfully tried his hand at making reflecting telescopes, and astronomical instruments then became his passion. He spared neither his free time nor his wealth in creating one of Europe's largest and finest collections. Renowned craftsmen constructed his instruments: for example, John Dolland made an early achromatic telescope for him, and Jesse Ramsden, a very accurate degree-cutting machine. Bochart placed his collection at the disposition of the academicians: Jean Delambre, Pierre Méchain, Guillaume Le Gentil, Achille Dionis du Séjour, and Charles Messier.

Bochart calculated the orbits of comets on the basis of observations furnished by his long-time collaborator, Messier. The observed positions were few and close together; this presented special difficulties for Bochart, who used Boscovich's method, which he simplified and mechanized in his calculations. His predictions vastly aided Messier in finding the comets after they had disappeared behind the sun. The supposition that Bochart was forced to make when trying to calculate the orbit of Herschel's comet—discovered in 1781—played an important role in identifying it as the planet Uranus. He supposed that it followed a circular orbit with a radius equal to twelve times the distance of Saturn from the sun. This proved accurate, and Laplace then calculated the precise elliptical orbit. Bochart, who became the First President of the Parliament of Paris a few months before the outbreak of the French Revolution, lost his head during the reign of terror of the Committee of Public Safety.

BIBLIOGRAPHY

I. ORIGINAL WORKS. Bochart's astronomical observations are in *Mémoires de l'Académie Royale des Sciences, année 1769,* 421, 429; *ibid., année 1770,* 232; *ibid., année 1774,* 19; *ibid., année 1775,* 217; and *ibid., année 1776,* 450. An orbital calculation is "Comète observée en 1779," in *Connaissance des Temps pour . . . 1782* (Paris, 1779), 395.

II. SECONDARY LITERATURE. More information on Bochart and his work may be found in Jacques Dominique Cassini, "Découverte de la planète Herschel," in *Connaissance des temps . . . 1786* (Paris, 1783), 3–4; Cassini published his eulogy of Bochart separately and in *Mémoires pour servir à l'histoire des sciences* (Paris, 1810), 373–391; J.-J. DeLalande, "Histoire de l'astronomie pour 1794," in *Connaissance des temps . . . pour l'année sextile VIIe* (Paris, 1797), 282–318, esp. 310–311 for a eulogy of Bochart, which was also published in DeLalande's *Bibliographie astronomique* (Paris, 1803), 752–754. Boscovich gives his method in "De orbitis cometarum determinandis, ope trium observationum parum a se invicem remotarum," in *Mémoires de mathématique et de physique* (Académie des Sciences), VI (Paris, 1774), 198–215, 401–434. Detailed information on Bochart's family is given in P. Humbert, "Les astronomes français de 1610 à 1667," in Société d'Études Scientifiques et Archéologiques de Draguignan, *Mémoires,* **63** (1942), 1–72; L. Moréri, *s.v.* Bochart, *Le grand dictionnaire historique* (Paris, 1759).

ROBERT M. MCKEON

BÔCHER, MAXIME (*b.* Boston, Massachusetts, 28 August 1867; *d.* Cambridge, Massachusetts, 12 September 1918), *mathematics.*

Maxime Bôcher was the son of Ferdinand Bôcher, the first professor of modern languages at the Massachusetts Institute of Technology, and Caroline Little, of Boston. He entered Harvard in 1883, specializing in mathematics and natural science under W. E. Byerly, B. O. Peirce, and J. M. Peirce. He was elected to Phi Beta Kappa upon his graduation in 1888. Bôcher then went to Göttingen as a traveling fellow to audit the lectures of Felix Klein, Schönflies, Schur, Schwarz, and Voigt. Encouraged by Klein, he wrote a tract that won the prize in a competition sponsored by the Philosophical Faculty at Göttingen in 1891. It also served as his doctoral dissertation (1891), and was published as a book (1894) with an introduction by Klein.

In 1891 Bôcher returned to Harvard as an instructor in mathematics, and rose through the ranks to a professorship in 1904. In 1913 he was an exchange professor at the Sorbonne for a three-month period beginning in November.

He served the mathematical community unstintingly as a member of the editorial staff of the *Annals of Mathematics* in 1896–1900, 1901–1907, and 1911–1914; as vice-president, in 1902, and as president, in 1909 and 1910, of the American Mathematical Society; and as editor of the Society's *Transactions* in 1908, 1909, and 1911–1913. Under Klein's leadership as president of the International Commission on the Teaching of Mathematics, Bôcher served as chairman of the American Committee on Graduate Work in Universities, which published the report "Graduate Work in Mathematics in Universities and in Other Institutions of Like Grade in the United States" in the *Bulletin of the U.S. Bureau of Education,* no. 6 (1911). He was an invited speaker at the St. Louis Congress of Mathematicians in 1904 and at the Fifth International Congress of Mathematicians, Cambridge, England, in 1912, where his paper dealt with boundary problems in one dimension.

Bôcher was a prolific contributor to mathematical journals on the theory of differential equations and related questions. His research topics included systems of linear differential equations of the first order, singular points of functions satisfying partial differential equations of the elliptic type, exposition of the work of Jacques Sturm on algebraic and differential equations, boundary problems, and George Green's functions for linear differential and difference equations, and the theorems of oscillation of Sturm and Klein.

He was a member of the National Academy of Sciences and the American Philosophical Society, and was a fellow of the American Academy of Arts and Sciences.

BIBLIOGRAPHY

I. ORIGINAL WORKS. Bôcher's books are *Über die Reihenentwickelungen der Potentialtheorie* (Leipzig, 1894), his doctoral thesis; *Introduction to Higher Algebra* (New York, 1907); *An Introduction to the Study of Integral Equations,* Cambridge Tracts in Mathematics and Mathematical Physics, no. 10 (Cambridge, 1909); *Plane Analytic Geometry With Introductory Chapters on the Differential Calculus* (New York, 1915); *Trigonometry With the Theory and Use of Logarithms* (New York, 1915), written with H. D. Gaylord; *Leçons sur les méthodes de Sturm dans la théorie des équations différentielles linéaires et leurs développements modernes,* delivered at the Sorbonne in 1913–1914, G. Julia, ed. (Paris, 1916), in the Borel series.

His numerous papers are listed in Poggendorff, V, 129. A more complete list is found in G. D. Birkhoff, "The Scientific Work of Maxime Bôcher," in *Bulletin of the American Mathematical Society,* **25,** no. 5 (1919), 197–216.

II. SECONDARY LITERATURE. Further biographical detail may be found in W. F. Osgood, "The Life and Services of Maxime Bôcher," in *Bulletin of the American Mathematical Society,* **25,** no. 8 (1919), 337–350; in "Maxime

Bôcher," in *Science,* n.s. **48,** no. 1248 (29 Nov. 1918), 534–535, repr. by the National Academy of Sciences in its *Annual Report* for 1918, pp. 49–50, and also by *The Harvard University Gazette* (22 Oct. 1918), p. 14; in the *Lebenslauf* in his doctoral thesis (gift copy presented by Bôcher to Widener Library, Harvard University, 19 Sept. 1891); in *Who's Who in Science* (1912), p. 53; in *American Men of Science* (1910), p. 47; and in the "Reports of Meetings," in *Bulletin of the American Mathematical Society,* **17** (1910–1911), 77, 277, 507.

Carolyn Eisele

BOCK, JEROME (*b.* Heidesbach, or Heidelsheim, Germany, 1498; *d.* Hornbach, Germany, 21 February 1554), *botany.*

Bock (also known as Hieronymus Tragus) was one of the three "German fathers of botany." Along with Otto Brunfels and Leonhard Fuchs, he represented the transition from late medieval botany, with its philological scholasticism, to early modern botany, with its demand that descriptions and illustrations be derived from nature.

Melchior Adam, Bock's first biographer, provides the earliest, and in some cases the only, information on his career. His birthplace is debatable, but internal evidence indicates that his adult life was spent in the Saar. His parents, Heinrich and Margarethe (maiden name unrecorded), apparently wished their son to enter a cloister. Where he received his early schooling is unknown. He may have attended the University of Heidelberg; but whether he studied medicine, philosophy, or theology is uncertain, for there is no record that he received a degree. In January 1523 Bock accepted a position in Zweibrücken; and on 25 January 1523 he married Eva, daughter of Heinrich and Margarethe Victor. He remained in Zweibrücken until 1533, when he accepted a canonry at the Benedictine church of St. Fabian in nearby Hornbach. The growing religious unrest forced Bock, who had become a follower of Luther, to leave Hornbach in August 1550. For a short period he acted as personal physician to the Landgraf Philipp II of Nassau, whose garden he is said to have supervised and to whom his *Kreuterbuch* was dedicated. In 1551 he returned to Hornbach, where he died three years later, probably of consumption. Bock's memorial tablet at St. Fabian's, where he was buried, was later discovered by Adam, who preserved a transcript of it.

The first result of Bock's botanizing excursions, dating from his years at Hornbach and conducted, he states, while dressed as a peasant, is the short tract *De herbarum quarundam nomenclaturis.* As the title suggests, it is concerned primarily with nomenclature—more specifically, with relating Greek and Latin names to local plants. Despite the lexicographical

orientation, the brief entries indicate a personal acquaintance with plants, and Bock is not afraid to admit that he has never seen some of the plants mentioned by the ancients.

The appearance of Bock's *Neu Kreütterbuch* (1539) marked a new beginning in botany. It was some time, however, before his departure from tradition found general acceptance. Written in the vernacular, lacking illustrations, and sandwiched between the better-known writings of Brunfels and Fuchs, it was soon lost from sight. Only with the publication in 1546 of the first illustrated edition, and bolstered by the Latin translation of 1552, did Bock's position become assured. As the first to describe the local flora, Bock has been credited with discovering many new species. The lack of illustrations turned out to be a blessing in disguise, for it forced Bock to describe plants in such a manner that they could be recognized by a reader whose botanical knowledge was limited to local species and their vernacular names.

Bock's lasting contributions to botany, commemorated by Charles Plumier, who named the genus *Tragia* (*Euphorbiaceae*) in his honor, were the result of a happy union of talent and perseverance. By combining personal observation and precise description with an attempt to establish taxonomic relationships on a new basis, Bock broke sharply with the past. Being neither a physician, at least in the ordinary sense, nor a university scholar, he looked at plant life with the eyes of a true amateur, unencumbered by the necessity of finding a therapeutic rationale or a classical antecedent for every plant.

The third German edition (1551), from which the Latin translation was made, may be considered Bock's final statement. Despite such additions as a preface and an index, the text and illustrations remained essentially unaltered in successive editions. It will be convenient first to note the general format of the *Kreuterbuch.* The descriptions of approximately seven hundred plants and trees are arranged in three parts. The first two deal with herbs, monocotyledons, and cryptogams, while the third part treats of shrubs and trees. Each of the more than four hundred chapter divisions follows a set formula: "On Names," "On the Power and Effect," "Internal Uses," and "External Uses." Prior to the section on nomenclature, which contains Greek, Latin, and Arabic synonyms, there is an untitled section in which the plant is described. It is this material upon which Bock's reputation depends. Innocent of the sexuality of plants and the taxonomic significance of the reproductive organs, Bock necessarily based the descriptions upon the morphological characteristics of the vegetative portions. The descriptions usually contain the following information: the general aspect, including height, sometimes expressed in the form of a comparison with another, better-known plant; remarks on the foliage, including any noteworthy shape, texture, odor, or color; and miscellaneous observations concerning root systems, time of flowering, and economic uses. By establishing marks useful for field identification—the presence of milky sap or stipules, the distinction between various underground parts or between terete and quadrangular stems—Bock was the first modern botanist to teach the importance of fine structure. Although this momentarily diverted attention from the potential significance of floral organs, it stimulated inquiry until optical aids changed the conception of plant anatomy.

Floral structure was not ignored, however, and it is here that Bock's powers of observing and recording details are most apparent. He described the stamen, noting that it was typically composed of two parts, the filament and anther, and that while the number of stamens varied, their number was constant for a given species. This description, one of the earliest in botanical literature, is matched by his account of the pistil, which he correctly noted was composed of stigma and style. Another remarkable observation was his recognition that species of the birch family (*Betulaceae*) have, in addition to the familiar, tassel-like aments, other, quite inconspicuous flower clusters. In neither case, however, was Bock able to identify them with the staminate catkins or the pistillate inflorescence recognized today.

Passing from the blossom to the subsequent seed or fruit, another side of Bock's ability is revealed. As the first to describe the lily of the valley (*Convallaria majalis* L.), his account is the more noteworthy because it calls attention to the fruit, which he likens to red coral (fol. 204v, 1577 ed.). Ever searching for more accurate information or a confirmation of his suspicions, he planted the downy catkins of a willow. He was pleased to see them germinate, which demonstrated that they were seeds (fol. 380v). An even more determined effort was his nightly vigil to collect seeds from a fern (*Osmunda regalis* L.). Naturally he failed, but by collecting some of the ejected sporangia without resorting to incantations or other superstitious practices (fol. 194v), he made a major, if unappreciated, step forward.

The larger, drupaceous fruits, which served many domestic purposes, did not require so exacting a description. On the other hand, in order to illustrate a fruit-bearing tree in the same naturalistic manner as herbs, a different technique was demanded. In conjunction with David Kandel, the Strasbourg artist whom Bock employed, a workable solution was found for some thirty trees. The woodcuts depict the characteristic leaf, the shape of the fruit (often disproportionately enlarged and placed in inset), and various genre scenes representing the symbolic value or economic use of the tree in question.

In his efforts to observe native plants, Bock traveled widely in the Rhineland and elsewhere, often supplying the names of towns where he encountered unusual plants. He recorded such ecological and phenological data as would provide a more accurate account, including habitat, occurrence of weeds, and time of budding. Not all of his observations were made in the field, however, for he mentions his friends' gardens, some of which he visited or from some of which he received specimens.

As a consequence of his wide knowledge, it was inevitable that Bock made some effort at classification. Expressly rejecting an alphabetical arrangement, he made the fullest possible use of relating plants in terms of similarity of form, corolla shape, and formation of seed capsules. Because of his ignorance of plant sexuality, his efforts have only historical interest today. Nevertheless, by indicating a method based upon more than one criterion, he provided guidelines for succeeding generations of taxonomists.

By focusing attention on the plants themselves and by daring to question the high authority of Dioscorides and other classical writers, Bock laid down methodological canons whose future importance transcended even his own accomplishments. The rapid development of botany in the latter half of the sixteenth century owed much to the schoolteacher from Zweibrücken who led the exodus from the library into the fields.

BIBLIOGRAPHY

I. ORIGINAL WORKS. Because of serious discrepancies in the accounts of Nissen, Pritzel, and Roth (1899), and in the absence of any bibliography of Bock's published writings, the following list may be useful.

Bock's major work is, of course, the *Kreuterbuch*. It first appeared as *Neu Kreütterbuch von Underscheydt, Würckung und Namen der Kreutter, so in teutschen Landen wachsen . . .* (Strasbourg, 1539). The second German ed., the first to be illustrated, was *Kreuterbuch. Darin Underscheid, Würckung und Namen der Kreuter, so in deutschen Landen wachsen . . .* (Strasbourg, 1546); there was an enlarged edition entitled *Kreuterbuch, darinn Underscheidt, Namen und Würckung der Kreuter, Stauden, Hecken und Beuman, sammt ihren Früchten, so in deutschen Landen wachsen . . .* (Strasbourg, 1551, 1556, 1560, 1565, 1572, 1574). Melchior Sebizius edited *Kreütterbuch, darin Underscheidt, Nammen und Würckung der Kreütter . . .* (Strasbourg, 1577, 1580, 1586, 1587, 1595, 1630; facsimile reprint, Munich, 1964, essentially a reprint of the 1551 ed.). The

Speisskammer has been added as pt. 4, and there is new material in the preliminary leaves.

Others works by Bock are *De herbarum quarundam nomenclaturis,* in Otto Brunfels, *Herbarum vivae eicones ad naturae imitationem . . .,* II (Strasbourg, 1531–1532), the ninth of twelve tracts appearing under the title *De vera herbarum cognitione appendix* (the pagination varies with the ed. of Brunfels); *Hieronymi herbarii Apodixis Germanica, ex qua facile vulgares herbas omnes licebit perdiscere, ibid.,* the last tract of the collection *De vera herbarum . . .*—although sometimes ascribed to Bock, it may well be the work of Hieronymus Brunschwig (1450–1512); *Der vollen brüder ordern. Diss buchlein zeyget an was der wein würcke inn denen so ihn missbrauchen* (Strasbourg, ca. 1540); *Kurtz regiment für das grausam Haupt, wehe und breune, vor die Gemein und Armes heuflin hin und wider im Wasgaw und Westereich . . .* (Strasbourg, 1544); *Regiment für alle zufallende kranckheit das Leibs auch wie man die Leibsgebrechen so jetzund vorhanden sol abschaffen* (n. p., 1544; *vide* Roth [1899], p. 67, no. 3); *Regiment für das Hauptweh,* in *Artzneybuch köstlich für mancherley Kranckheit des gantzen Leibs . . .* (Erfurt, 1546; Frankfurt, ca. 1549; Nuremberg, 1549 [the title of the collection is different]; Königsberg, 1565); *Bader Ordnung . . . aufs den Hochgelerten Hippocrate und Barptholomeo Montagnana, sampt andern auffs kürtzest, allen frommen Badern zu Trost, ins Teutsch gestelt* (Strasbourg, 1550); *Teutsche Speisskammer* (Strasbourg, 1550, 1555); *Verae atque ad vivum expressae imagines omnium herbarum, fructicum et arborum . . .* (Strasbourg, 1550, 1553); *De stirpium maxime earum quae in Germania nostra nascuntur . . . interprete Davide Kybero . . .* (Strasbourg, 1552), a translation of the 1551 edition of the *Kreuterbuch* that also contains tracts by Conrad Gesner and Benedict Textor; *Artzneibüchlin,* in Johannes Dryander, *New Artznei und Practicierbüchlin* (Frankfurt, 1557, 1572).

II. SECONDARY LITERATURE. Works concerning Bock are Melchior Adam, *Vitae Germanorum medicorum* (Heidelberg, 1620), pp. 67–72; J.-E. Gérock, "Les illustrations de David Kandel dans le *Kreuterbuch* de Tragus," in *Archives alsaciennes d'histoire de l'art* (1931), 137–148, with eleven figures; Edward Lee Greene, *Landmarks of Botanical History,* Smithsonian Miscellaneous Collections, LIV (Washington, D.C., 1909), 220–262; Heinrich Marzell, "Das Buchsbaum-bild im Kräuterbuch (1551) des Hieronymus Bock," in *Sudhoffs Archiv,* **38** (1954), 97–103; Louis Masson, "Le 'Livre de plantes' de Tragus," in *Aesculape,* **24** (1934), 301–310, ten figures; Ernst H. F. Meyer, *Geschichte der Botanik,* IV (Königsberg, 1857), 303–309; Claus Nissen, *Die botanische Buchillustration,* II, nos. 182–184 (Stuttgart, 1951); Georg A. Pritzel, *Thesaurus literaturae botanicae,* 2nd ed. (Milan, 1950), facsimile reproduction of Leipzig 1872 ed., nos. 864–868; F. W. E. Roth, "Hieronymus Bock, genannt Tragus (1498–1554)," in *Botanisches Centralblatt,* **74** (1898), 265–271, 313–318, 344–347; and "Hieronymus Bock, genannt Tragus, Prediger, Arzt und Botaniker 1498 bis 1554," in *Mitteilungen des historischen Vereins der Pfalz,* **23** (1899), 25–74; Kurt Sprengel, *Geschichte der Botanik,* I (Altenberg–Leipzig,

1817), 269–272, which contains a list of 109 plants first described by Bock.

JERRY STANNARD

BODE, JOHANN ELERT (*b.* Hamburg, Germany, 19 January 1747; *d.* Berlin, Germany, 23 November 1826), *astronomy.*

Bode, the son of a commercial accounting teacher and the nephew of the well-known writing master and mathematic master Jürgen Elert Kruse of Hamburg, had a great love for practical calculations throughout his life. This, with his pedagogical abilities, made him an excellent teacher of astronomy. He studied astronomy by himself and was strongly stimulated in his studies by the Hamburg scholars J. A. Reimarus and J. G. Büsch, as well as by the poet Friedrich Klopstock. They encouraged the nineteen-year-old to publish his famous *Anleitung zur Kenntnis des gestirnten Himmels* (1768), which was in print for nearly a hundred years and won innumerable adherents to astronomy.

In 1772 Johann Lambert summoned Bode to the astronomical observatory of the Berlin Academy as an arithmetician, to help in the publication of accurate ephemerides. The sale of astronomical almanacs was one of the chief sources of income for the Academy; because of their low degree of accuracy, however, the almanacs were not selling well. The new *Astronomisches Jahrbuch für 1776* was compiled under Bode's direction and published in 1774. He continued to do the calculations for and publish each successive annual volume until that of 1829 (published in 1826). Bode's almanacs were soon greatly esteemed. Aside from the ephemerides, the *Jahrbücher* also contained scientific news on observations and discoveries around the world.

In 1786 Bode was appointed royal astronomer, director of the astronomical observatory, and member of the Berlin Academy. He was active in these positions for nearly forty years, until his retirement in 1825. In spite of the renovations which he arranged, the observatory, situated on the roof of a five-story tower of the Academy building, could not compete with those of Paris and London; it was equipped only for modest investigations of comets, planets, double stars, and so forth.

Bode's literary activity more than made up for the observatory's deficiencies. Besides his tables, his two sky atlases were for a long time indispensable tools for astronomers: the *Vorstellung der Gestirne,* which, according to the example set by John Flamsteed's atlas, contained more than 5,000 stars; and the *Uranographia,* which surpassed all its predecessors by listing over 17,000 stars and containing, for the first time, the nebulae, star clusters, and double stars discovered by William Herschel.

Bode was almost the only writer to support the then not widely known ideas of Kant, Lambert, and Herschel on the infinity of space, the infinite number of inhabited worlds, and the continuous birth and passing away of stars according to natural laws. He also made public in 1772 the relation first established by the Wittenberg professor Johann Daniel Titius, the Titius-Bode series, according to which the distances between the large planets are in a nearly regular geometric progression. The minor planets, unknown at that time, and the planet discovered in 1781 by Herschel fit well into this series. (If one substitutes for Venus, Earth, Mars, Jupiter, and Saturn the numbers $n = 0, 1, 2, 4, 5$, then the distance is obtained from the relation $A = 0.4 + 2^n \cdot 0.3$ [astronomical units]. For Mercury the last member is zero, for the minor planets $n = 3$, for Uranus $n = 6$.) Bode gave the name Uranus to Herschel's newly discovered planet.

Bode married three times: his first two wives were nieces of the Berlin astronomer Christine Kirch; the third was the niece of the chemist Andreas Marggraf. He was a member of the Royal Society of London, as well as of the academies of Berlin, St. Petersburg, Stockholm, Copenhagen, and Göttingen.

BIBLIOGRAPHY

I. ORIGINAL WORKS. Bode's writings include *Anleitung zur Kenntnis des gestirnten Himmels* (Hamburg, 1768; 11th ed., Berlin, 1858); *Sammlung astronomischer Tafeln* (Berlin, 1776); *Kurzgefasste Erläuterung der Sternkunde* (Berlin, 1778; 3rd ed., Berlin, 1808); *Dialogen über die Mehrheit der Welten* (Berlin, 1780; 3rd ed., Berlin, 1798), a translation of Fontenelle's *Entretiens sur la pluralité des mondes; Vorstellung der Gestirne auf 34 Kupfertafeln nebst Fixsternverzeichnis* (Berlin–Stralsund, 1782; 2nd ed., Berlin, 1805); *Allgemeine Betrachtungen über das Weltgebäude* (Berlin, 1801; 3rd ed., Berlin, 1807); and *Uranographia sive astrorum descriptio* (Berlin, 1801), 20 folios with the catalog *Allgemeine Beschreibung und Nachweisung der Gestirne*.

II. SECONDARY LITERATURE. Biographical material on Bode is in Encke, an obituary speech, in *Abhandlungen* of the Berlin Academy (1827); Poggendorff, I; *Allgemeine deutsche Biographie*, III, 1; and Schroeder, *Lexikon der hamburgischen Schriftsteller*, I (Hamburg, 1851), 282 ff., with an extensive list of his works.

BERNHARD STICKER

BODENHEIMER, FRITZ SIMON (*b.* Cologne, Germany, 6 June 1897; *d.* London, England, 4 October 1959), *entomology, zoology, history of science.*

The son of Max Yitshaq Bodenheimer and Rosa Dalberg, Bodenheimer studied zoology in Frankfurt and subsequently specialized in agricultural entomology. In 1921 he received his doctorate from the University of Bonn and in 1922 emigrated to Palestine, to become head of the department of entomology at the agricultural experiment station of the Jewish Agency. He moved to The Hebrew University in Jerusalem in 1928; he was promoted to professor in 1931 and remained there until his retirement in 1953. Bodenheimer also served as adviser on applied entomology in Europe, the Near East, South Africa, and Australia.

Bodenheimer contributed significantly to knowledge of the Palestinian fauna, with emphasis on insects. At the time, his *Animal Life in Palestine* (1935) was the generally accepted survey of the subject, but his main interest was the ecological relations of animals, chiefly moles, insect pests, and parasitic insects. He correlated variations in dormancy and rhythms of development, and in the population of pests, parasites, and hosts, with a wide range of climatic and biotic environmental factors in the widely divergent climates of Palestine. In collaboration with many others, Bodenheimer studied particular adaptations to different habitats, and it was one of his major accomplishments that he stimulated the interest of so many. In animal ecology he was a pioneer of more than regional importance, giving particular attention to theoretical concepts. Bodenheimer's special interest in citrus, the major crop of Israel, is reflected in his exhaustive *Citrus Entomology in the Middle East* (1951).

Beginning with his two-volume study *Materialien zur Geschichte der Entomologie* (1928–1929), Bodenheimer showed great interest in the history of biology. His numerous studies emphasized early Hebrew works and the biology and biologists of the Near East. Major works in this field are *Animal Life in Bible Lands* (1949–1956) and *History of Biology* (1958). In all of these a very wide range of relevant source material is brought together, but the final version lacks lucidity and polish.

From 1947 Bodenheimer was increasingly active in organizations related to the history of science. From 1950 to 1953 he was vice-president, and from 1953 to 1956 president, of the Académie Internationale d'Histoire des Sciences.

BIBLIOGRAPHY

Bodenheimer's writings include *Materialien zur Geschichte der Entomologie bis Linné*, 2 vols. (Berlin, 1928–1929); *Die Schädlingsfauna Palästinas* (Berlin, 1930); *Animal Life in Palestine* (Jerusalem, 1935); *Animal Life in Bible Lands,* 2 vols. (Jerusalem, 1949–1956); *Citrus Entomology in the Middle East* (The Hague, 1951); *Précis d'écologie animale* (Paris, 1954); *Animal Ecology To-day* (The Hague, 1958); *History of Biology* (London, 1958); and his autobiography, *A Biologist in Israel* (Jerusalem, 1959), which includes a bibliography of 420 items.

JACOB LORCH

BODENSTEIN, ADAM OF. See **Adam of Bodenstein.**

BOË, FRANZ DE LA. See **Sylvius, Franciscus.**

BOEHME, JACOB (*b.* Alt Seidenberg, near Görlitz, Germany, 1575; *d.* Görlitz, 17 November 1624), *theology, mysticism.*

Boehme was the fourth child of Jacob and Ursula Boehme. The father belonged to a well-to-do, old family of German-speaking farmers. A prominent man in the village, he held lay offices in the local church. As a boy Boehme herded cattle with neighboring farm boys, attended the village school, and was given a Lutheran upbringing. At fourteen he was apprenticed to the village cobbler, perhaps owing to his delicate health, and three years later he set out on his journeyman travels. Around 1595 he returned to Görlitz, where in 1599 he became a citizen of the town, set up as a master cobbler, and married Catharina Kuntzschmann, with whom he had four sons. Her father was a butcher, and her family was prosperous and influential in city affairs. Boehme was now enabled to buy a house in Görlitz, where he spent the remainder of his life, interrupted only by visits to his spiritual friends among the nobility of the region and by travels on business to the Leipzig fair and to Prague. In 1613 he gave up cobbling and entered the cloth trade, but his later years were clouded by financial distress caused by inflation and the beginning of the Thirty Years' War.

In 1600 occurred the decisive event in Boehme's life. Through the chief pastor of Görlitz, Martin Moller, he had recently been exposed to the great tradition of German mysticism: to Johann Tauler, Heinrich Suso, and Jan Van Ruysbroeck, among others. He went through a period of anxious search for insight. The result was the profound mystical experience that shaped his life and inspired the writings that form the culmination of the German mystical tradition. One day while sitting in his room in a state of melancholy, his eyes by chance caught the sunlight reflected from a pewter dish. His soul was immediately ushered into a mystical vision, and he maintained that the innermost part of the secrets of

nature as well as the true nature of good and evil were revealed to him. In a quarter of an hour, he saw and knew more than he could have learned by years of study in the universities. At first full of doubt, he soon became convinced that he had received the gift of vision. When it was upon him, he could penetrate into the very heart and being of all things in creation. But it was twelve years before Boehme recorded this experience and its fruits in his first work, *Aurora oder Morgenröthe im Aufgang.* Meant only as a private record, and left unfinished, it soon began to circulate in manuscript copies among his friends and thus came to the attention of the local church authorities, who took a hostile view of the work and enjoined him to desist from any further writing.

Devout and humble, Boehme did not write until 1618, when the spirit again urged him so strongly that he could no longer remain silent. The rest of his works, amounting to more than thirty items, were written during the remaining years of his life—some short, some long, many as responses to questions from friends or as polemics against opponents. He was again called to account by the authorities, but no action was taken, and he died quietly in his house in Görlitz as a member of the Lutheran church to which he had belonged all his life. Among his most important works are *Von den drei Principien Göttliches Wesens, Vom dreifachen Leben des Menschen, De signatura rerum oder von der Geburt und Bezeichnung aller Wesen, Mysterium magnum oder Erklärung über das erste Buch Mosis, Der Weg zu Christo* (the only work published [1624] during Boehme's lifetime), and *Von der Gnaden-Wahl oder von dem Willen Gottes über die Menschen,* which Boehme considered his greatest work.

In all his works Boehme spoke as a prophet; he believed that God had chosen him to reveal to mankind what lay hidden. Convinced that he wrote under direct inspiration, he claimed that he changed nothing once it was written. The obscurity of his style is the expression of his mode of insight—full of bold metaphors, alchemical terms, number symbolism, and Neoplatonic conceptions—and reveals his background in Luther, Paracelsus, Kaspar Schwenckfeld, and Valentin Weigel. Boehme deprecated book learning, distrusted reason and the disputes of the theologians, and was fond of saying, as did Weigel, that all knowledge was revealed within him as in a book, even the Bible, so long as he had Christ's spirit in him. All the same, it is evident that Boehme was by no means unfamiliar with the thought of his spiritual forerunners, whose work he no doubt knew both from his own reading and from conversations with his visionary friends. Having had only elementary schooling, Boehme was largely self-taught. Later in life he often voiced regret that he had not learned Latin, and his writing in German earned him the title of *teutonicus philosophus.* His friend and first biographer, Abraham von Frankenberg, observed that Boehme's eyes were sky-blue and shone like the windows of Solomon's Temple.

Boehme's philosophy cannot be reduced to brief, systematic statement; it was not conceived in terms that would permit such reduction, and his own conceptions shifted in the course of time—the *Aurora,* he later said, was a work of his spiritual childhood. An understanding of his philosophy can, however, be gained by noting a few of its fundamental concerns. Boehme's initial problem was the existence of evil and the concealment of God from the world of man. His answer revealed a cosmic drama, with opposition of light and dark, spirit and body, love and wrath, joy and pain, eternity and time. All things visible were emanations of things invisible; the hidden God lay revealed under the visible creation. The "out-breathed" or "outspoken" invisible power, the Word, had called forth creation. Nature is the language of God to man, if only man will read it aright. The undifferentiated *Ungrund,* or nothingness (in the English translations, the "abyss"), is like an eye that seeks an object in order to become aware of itself, a mirror of images whose possibilities suggest the actualities of nature. By a repeated process of reflecting, willing, and creating, God's self-knowledge finds expression in nature, which is thus ordered according to the heavenly wisdom, the eternal Sophia.

Placed in time and body after the Fall, man's path to regeneration is renewed revelation of the secrets of nature. Adam's first and decisive fall occurred when he fell asleep and lost the direct insight into creation that he had hitherto possessed, being purely spiritual and ever awake. Sinfulness is caused by a perverse imagination, whose consequence is inadequate or false knowledge. The promise of again placing good over evil, light over dark, was given in the obedience and suffering of Christ, a reversal of Adam's course into time, history, and body. By placing cosmogony at the center of his theology, Boehme reveals his debt to the Lutheran tradition, and especially to Paracelsus and the Protestant mystics of the sixteenth century. But he is more explicit and detailed than his predecessors. One far-reaching effect of this theology was profound reverence for nature and closeness to it. Nature is given positive reality; its study gains justification; its observation—if rightly used as an avenue to the invisible realm beyond it—is an act of devotion. To the seventeenth century this view was more widely derived from Boehme rather

than directly from Paracelsus. To Boehme a meadow in bloom with flowers was a mystical opening.

Adam, the first man, was created in the image of God; as the microcosm, he had the macrocosm in him. Although not original with Boehme, this view is prominent in his philosophy. It was in this sense that he wrote out of the book "which I myself am," not from other books or the instruction of the learned. He also claimed another special gift, direct insight into the language of nature, the language Adam spoke when he named the animals in the Garden of Eden. He even felt that he had direct access to new truths through his God-given insight into the interpretation of the sounds and forms of his own language, which, like all other languages, reveals the divine plan to the truly inspired mind. The language of nature had been adumbrated before Boehme, but he carried his doctrine on this point far beyond any previous speculation. This doctrine proved especially influential during the seventeenth century, often occurring in isolation from his theology. The observation was made more than once that the hoped-for philosophical language would copy the function of Adam's language, thus recapturing a measure of the insight into nature and the unity of knowledge that had been lost. Boehme was a mystic, but his mysticism did not advocate withdrawal from the world; on the contrary, his way was spiritual immersion in it.

After his death, Boehme's manuscripts were carefully collected and taken to Holland, where the first published versions appeared. From Holland his works, printed or in manuscript copies, passed into England, where they were all published in English versions between 1644 and 1663, many for the first time in any language. Thus Boehme was first discovered in England, where he had a wide and varied influence, most clearly among the Quakers. In Germany he did not gain prominence until he was taken up by the Pietists during the eighteenth century. He had a strong impact on German Romantic thought and later gained a position of eminence in post-Kantian idealism, in large measure through the French translations of Louis-Claude de Saint-Martin (1743–1803). Boehme has also had a strong and enduring influence on Russian writers.

BIBLIOGRAPHY

I. ORIGINAL WORKS. The MSS are described in Werner Buddecke, *Verzeichnis von Jakob Böhme-Handschriften* (Göttingen, 1934) (= *Hainbergschriften,* 1). The German eds. are listed in Buddecke, *Die Jakob Böhme-Ausgaben. Ein beschreibendes Verzeichnis,* pt. 1 (Göttingen, 1937) (= *Hainbergschriften,* 5), and the translations in pt. 2

(Göttingen, 1957) (= *Arbeiten aus der Staats- und Universitätsbibliothek,* Göttingen, N.F. 2). The best collected edition is *Theosophia revelata,* J. W. Ueberfeld, ed., 21 pts. (Amsterdam, 1730); repr. in 11 vols., Will-Erich Peuckert, ed. (Stuttgart, 1955–1961). K. W. Schiebler's edition of *Jakob Böhme's Sämmtliche Werke,* 7 vols. (Leipzig, 1831–1847), has a poor text and cannot be used for serious work.

The recently discovered autograph copies of Boehme MSS have been ed. by Werner Buddecke in Jacob Böhme, *Die Urschriften,* 2 vols. (Stuttgart, 1963–1966). The first collected English edition is *The Works of Jacob Behmen,* G. Ward and T. Langcake, eds., 4 vols. (London, 1764–1781), usually called William Law's edition. With the exception of *Der Weg zu Christo* (from the 1775 version of G. Moreton), this ed. reprints the seventeenth-century versions of J. Sparrow, J. Ellistone, and H. Blunden.

II. SECONDARY LITERATURE. There has been a continual flow of Boehme literature since the 1640's; only the most important can be mentioned here: Gottfried Arnold, *Unparteyische Kirchen- und Ketzer-Historie,* 2 vols. in 4 pts. (Frankfurt, 1699–1700), pt. 2, 656–682; Franz von Baader, "Vorlesungen über J. Böhme's Theologumena und Philosopheme," in *Gesammelte Schriften zur Naturphilosophie,* Franz Hoffmann, ed. (Leipzig, 1852), pp. 357–432; and *Vorlesungen und Erläuterungen zu Jacob Böhmes Lehre,* Julius Hamberger, ed. (Leipzig, 1855)—Vols. III and XIII, respectively, in Franz von Baader, *Sämmtliche Werke,* Franz Hoffman and Julius Hamberger, eds., 16 vols. (Leipzig, 1851–1860); R. Jecht, "Die Lebensumstände Jacob Böhmes," in his ed. of *Jacob Böhme, Gedenkgabe der Stadt Görlitz* (Görlitz, 1924), pp. 7–75; and Will-Erich Peuckert, *Das Leben Jacob Böhmes,* 2nd ed., rev., in Vol. X of the reprint edition of *Theosophia revelata* listed above. The best full exposition is A. Koyré, *La philosophie de Jacob Boehme* (Paris, 1929). On particular aspects of Boehme, the following works are useful: Ernst Benz, *Der Vollkommene Mensch nach Jacob Böhme* (Stuttgart, 1937); *Der Prophet Jakob Boehme, ein Studie über den Typus nachreformatorischen Prophetentums* (Akademie der Wissenschaften und der Literatur. Mainz. Abhandlungen der Geistes- und Sozialwissenschaftlichen Klasse, 1959, no. 3); "Zur metaphysischen Begründung der Sprache bei Jacob Böhme," in *Dichtung und Volkstum,* **37** (1936), 340–357; "Zur Sprachalchimie der deutschen Barockmystik," *ibid.,* 482–498; "Die Sprachtheologie der Reformationszeit," in *Studium Generale,* **4** (Apr. 1951), 204–213; "Die Geschichtsmetaphysik Jakob Böhmes," in *Deutsche Vierteljahrsschrift für Literaturwissenschaft und Geistesgeschichte,* **13** (1935), 421–455; M. L. Bailey, *Milton and Jakob Boehme* (New York, 1914); Heinrich Bornkamm, *Luther und Böhme* (Bonn, 1925); Emanuel Hirsch, *Geschichte der neuern evangelischen Theologie im Zusammenhang mit den allgemeinen Bewegungen des europäischen Denkens,* II (Gütersloh, 1951), 208–255; Serge Hutin, *Les disciples anglais de Jacob Boehme aux XVIIᵉ et XVIIIᵉ siècles* (Paris, 1960); Wolfgang Kayser, "Böhmes Natursprachenlehre und ihre Grundlagen," in *Euphorion,* **31** (1930), 521–562, an especially useful and stimulating study; Peter

Schäublin, *Zur Sprache Jakob Boehmes* (Winterthur, 1963); Wilhelm Struck, *Der Einfluss Jakob Boehmes auf die englische Literatur* (Berlin, 1936); and Nils Thune, *The Behemenists and the Philadelphians, a Contribution to the Study of English Mysticism in the 17th and 18th Centuries* (Uppsala, 1948). The following three works offer good introductions: Howard H. Brinton, *The Mystic Will* (New York, 1930); Rufus M. Jones, *Spiritual Reformers in the 16th and 17th Centuries* (New York, 1914; Beacon Paperback, 1959); and John Joseph Stoudt, *Sunrise to Eternity, a Study in Jacob Boehme's Life and Thought* (Philadelphia, 1957).

HANS AARSLEFF

BOERHAAVE, HERMANN (*b.* Voorhout, Netherlands, 31 December 1668; *d.* Leiden, Netherlands, 23 September 1738), *medicine, botany, chemistry.*

Boerhaave was the son of the Reverend Jacobus Boerhaave and of his second wife, Hagar Daelder. The boy's mother died when he was five years old; his father then married Eva Dubois, the daughter of a Leiden clergyman, who proved to be a devoted stepmother. The elder Boerhaave personally saw to his son's upbringing, supervising his physical, as well as moral and intellectual, education. Boerhaave also spent three years in the grammar school in Leiden.

Boerhaave's father died in 1683; in accordance with his wish, Boerhaave applied himself to the study of theology and philosophy upon his matriculation at the University of Leiden in 1684. As a student, Boerhaave distinguished himself by a series of five disputations, three of which dealt with the human mind. He also delivered an oration on Cicero's view of Epicurus' concept of the *summum bonum,* for which the governors of the university awarded him a gold medal. He earned a degree in philosophy in 1690 with a thesis on the distinction of mind from body.

Upon graduation, Boerhaave continued to study theology. At the same time, however, his interest began to turn to medicine. He attended the yearly public dissections conducted by Anton Nuck and independently studied the works of Hippocrates, Vesalius, Fallopio, Bartholin, and Sydenham. In 1693 he took a medical degree at the academy of Harderwijk, having presented a thesis, *De utilitate explorandorum in aegris excrementorum ut signorum.*

Unfounded rumors had raised the suspicion that Boerhaave was a secret adherent of Spinoza; since such an allegation could only damage his ecclesiastical career, he turned definitely to a medical one. He settled in Leiden, augmenting the income from his small practice by giving lessons in mathematics. In 1701 he was appointed a lecturer in medicine by the University of Leiden; in his inaugural public address he advocated the study of the works of Hippocrates. He lectured on the *institutiones medicae* at the university, and gave private lectures on the theory and practice of medicine (for which he was paid by his students). In addition, he began to lecture on chemistry at the request of foreign (probably English) students.

Boerhaave restored the declining prestige of the Faculty of Medicine at Leiden, and in 1703 he was offered a professorship at the University of Groningen. He rejected the offer, and the governors of Leiden, anxious to retain him, promised him the first chair to become vacant there. At the same time, he was authorized to give an academic oration. This address, *De usu ratiocinii mechanici in medicina,* was his iatromechanistic credo.

Boerhaave's lectures became the basis for several textbooks. His *Institutiones medicae* was published in 1708 and his *Aphorismi de cognoscendis et curandis morbis* appeared in 1709. These books were largely responsible for Boerhaave's European reputation; indeed, pirated editions appeared both in the original Latin and in modern languages.

In 1709 the chair of botany and medicine fell vacant at Leiden, and Boerhaave was immediately appointed to it. He thus entered into a new field of science. As professor of botany, he was ex officio supervisor of the university's botanical garden and was given an official residence and an allowance for foreign correspondence and the exchange of seeds and plants. He hastily drew up a new catalog of plants for the garden (*Index plantarum,* 1710)—the previous list dated from 1687. During the next ten years, Boerhaave made extensive additions to the botanical garden, and the second edition of his catalog (*Index alter,* 1720) listed 5,846 species, more than 2,000 more than his earlier index. Although he was totally untrained in botany, Boerhaave recognized the need for a new system of classification; he was aware of his own limitations, however, and made no attempt to provide one. Rather, he helped Linnaeus in every way that he could.

On 14 September 1710 Boerhaave married Maria Drolenvaux, the daughter of a rich merchant. They had four children, of whom one daughter, Maria Joanna, lived to adulthood.

In 1714 Boerhaave was appointed vice-chancellor of the university, a position that he again filled in 1730. The same year he was, perhaps by his own request, charged with clinical teaching, which in Leiden had been practiced since 1637 but had fallen into neglect. Boerhaave revivified bedside teaching (for which two six-bed wards, one for men and one for women, of the Caecilia Hospital were reserved) and raised it to new heights, attracting students from all over Europe. His oration *De comparando certo in physicis,* made 8 February 1715, marked the end of his first term as vice-chancellor.

When Le Mort, the professor of chemistry, died in 1718, Boerhaave was chosen to succeed him, and for the next ten years he held simultaneously three of the five chairs that constituted the whole of Leiden's Faculty of Medicine. Boerhaave assumed his new duties with the oration *De chemia suos errores expurgante.* He lectured with extraordinary zeal and energy, four or five hours a day, until he was halted by a severe, painful illness (which he himself diagnosed as *lumbago rheumatica,* as described by Sydenham) that confined him to bed for five months in 1722. In January 1723 the students and citizens of Leiden celebrated his recovery and return to teaching with illuminations of the university building and a large part of the city.

Boerhaave was undeniably a great teacher. His lecture room was crowded with students from several countries (all lectures were given in Latin, of which Boerhaave had an easy mastery). Often many students had to stand, and some young noblemen were known to hire men to get to the classroom early to reserve their seats. Haller called Boerhaave *communis Europae praeceptor;* in the years of his tenure, 1,919 students were enrolled in the Medical Faculty, of whom 659 came from English-speaking countries. Many of his students copied out their lecture notes at home, to be copied by others in some instances; several exercise books containing unpublished lectures are thus extant, in addition to his lectures as published by some pupils.

Boerhaave's influence spread throughout Europe. His textbooks were published in Great Britain, France, Germany, and Italy, among other countries, and his students transmitted his teachings (even to later generations, since after Boerhaave's death Haller published a seven-volume edition of the *Institutiones,* and Gerard van Swieten published a five-volume commentary on his *Aphorismi*). The medical faculties of the universities of Vienna, Göttingen, and Edinburgh were begun or reformed after the system that Boerhaave instituted at Leiden. Indeed, the modern medical curriculum—with its emphasis on natural science, anatomy, physiology, pathology, and, in particular, clinical training—owes much to Boerhaave. His little book *Atrocis, nec descripti prius, morbi historia* (1724) made a twofold contribution to medicine. In this case history—that of Baronet Wassenaer, Admiral of the Republic, who ate a heavy meal, experienced severe chest pains, and died the next day—Boerhaave, who performed the postmortem examination himself, made the first diagnosis of a spontaneous rupture of the esophagus. Moreover, in his presentation, he established the classic form for a morbid history—anamnesis, physical examination, diagnosis, history of the disease, and autopsy findings.

Boerhaave's interest in, and influence on, systematism extended to the synthesis of older and newer theories of medicine. Medical science was in a state of confusion at the beginning of the eighteenth century; the heritage of old Greek medicine was still honored, but no attempt had been made to reconcile it with the medical discoveries of the previous century. Boerhaave attempted to build a comprehensive medical doctrine. To this end he published a new edition of the works of Aretaeus of Cappadocia, which he furnished with a valuable critical apparatus, and reedited or wrote new prefaces for editions of the works of Prospero Alpini, Eustachius, Bellini, Carolus, and Nicholas Piso. With his younger colleague B. S. Albinus he reedited the *Opera omnia* of the great anatomist Vesalius. Another work on anatomy is his *Opusculum anatomicum de fabrica glandularum* (1722), in which he defended Malpighi's concept of the structure of the glands against that of Fredrik Ruysch.

He further collected the iatromechanical theories of the late seventeenth century—most notably those of Willis, Baglivi, Borelli, and Bellini—and merged them into a creative synthesis. For example, Boerhaave, like Baglivi, stressed the pathological and therapeutic significance of mechanically deranged body fibers, but at the same time he joined Borelli's and Bellini's iatromechanical theories to Willis' detailed discussions of nervous disorders. In attempting to develop a satisfactory theory of a self-regulating bodily machine, Boerhaave manipulated the older ideas—without, however, entire success.

Accepting Leeuwenhoek's faulty interpretation of the process of hemolysis, he held that, in the blood, the red globules could be broken up into six yellow globules, which in turn consisted of six very small pellucid spherules, thought to be made up of particles too small to be visible through the microscope. Boerhaave made appropriate distinction of orders of vessels into sanguiferous arteries, of which the smallest would admit one red globule; serous capillaries, of which the smallest would admit one yellow globule; lymphatic vessels, which would admit nothing larger than the pellucid spherules; and a series of still smaller vessels, in descending order of diameter, which would admit specific particles. In his attempt to explain the vital phenomena, Boerhaave rejected the hypotheses of the iatrochemical school and used hydraulic and mechanical principles, taking into account the velocity of the blood, the angle and diameter of the vessels, the size and shape of the particles, the viscosity of the blood, and so forth. He interpreted inflammation, for example, as the result of stagnation of the blood in the smallest capillaries combined with an increased velocity of the blood, leading to increased pressure on the obstructing matter. Moreover, the smallest elements of the walls of the vessels might be too rigid and stiff or too weak and lax, which could produce pathological conditions. (Since Boerhaave could not know of the microbiological causes of disease, he attributed many of them to insufficient digestion of food, from which an acid or alkaline putrid acrimony might arise, for which he advised proper therapeutic measures.) Thus he devised a doctrine that was generally accepted for some time—although it failed him as an explanation for specific secretion of the glands.

Boerhaave belongs, with Stahl and Hoffmann, to the great systematists of the early eighteenth century. Apparently there was a demand for a comprehensive and consistent medical system for the mass of new facts and observations that he had scrupulously collected and attempted to arrange appropriately.

How much his system was appreciated by his pupils may be gathered from the words of one of them, his biographer W. Burton: "It will now perhaps be universally granted that our professor has indeed supplied us with the best system from an unparallel'd fund of medical learning happily digested."

Boerhaave was influenced by the philosophy of Descartes, but more so by the great English scientists Boyle and Newton. He accepted the corpuscular theory of the structure of matter. In accordance with this, his system was essentially mechanistic, although he acted eclectically and introduced chemical and other viewpoints. Nevertheless, although he avoided the extreme one-sidedness of the iatrochemical school, against which he campaigned, he tried to understand the vital processes and phenomena in the body, using an inanimate model.

In this respect he was in direct opposition to the animistic organicism of his contemporary Stahl, who understood the distinction between an organism and a mechanism better than Boerhaave. (Boerhaave never entered into a discussion with Stahl and he did not even mention Stahl's well-known phlogiston theory in his chemical textbook.)

The inconsistencies of Boerhaave's system generated discussion that eventually led, however, to the statement of the problems of animal heat and irritability. Boerhaave's contribution to physiology thus came as an almost accidental side effect; but there is no doubt that his work served as the stimulus to physiological research of the latter half of the eighteenth century, and that he contributed significantly to the discussion of the important problems that his work raised. Boerhaave's lasting influence on medicine does not lie so much in his system, or in new discoveries, but in his teaching. In his clinical instruction he indoctrinated his pupils with the old Hippocratic method of bedside observation and taught them to act methodically in the examination of their patients.

Boerhaave's most important contributions to science, perhaps, were made in chemistry—paradoxically, since his medical system was mainly based on mechanics and he did not think that chemistry was yet an adult science. He introduced exact, quantitative methods into chemistry by measuring temperature and using the best available balances made by Fahrenheit; indeed, he may be considered the founder of physical chemistry as well as a contributor to pneumatic chemistry and biochemistry. He was an indefatigable experimenter, exhibiting an unbelievable tenacity in his experiments on mercury. He introduced biochemical demonstrations into his chemical courses for medical students.

Boerhaave was the first to obtain urea, by a procedure that took more than a year, and to discover its diuretic properties, as well as its cooling effect when dissolved in water. He demonstrated that water could be obtained by condensation from burning alcohol, and described a rapid method of making vinegar—sometimes called Boerhaave's method.

Boerhaave's attitude toward alchemy was somewhat ambiguous; he did not dogmatically deny a priori the possibility of the transmutation of metals, but examined it in a series of painstaking experiments that lasted over a period of many years. He purified his mercury specimens by forcing them through leather and then washing them in seawater. In one experiment, he used a fulling mill to shake a specimen of mercury, enclosed in a glass bottle, for a period of eight and one-half months; he then distilled it sixty-one times. Other specimens of mercury were variously heated for fifteen and one-half years, boiled 511 times, or mixed with gold and then distilled 877 times. Gold remained gold, and mercury, mercury; he did, however, obtain mercury with the specific weight of 14.1 as the result of one of these year-long experiments. These experiments were published in the *Philosophical Transactions of the Royal Society of London* (1734–1736).

After his illness of 1722, Boerhaave realized he must take care of his health. In 1724 he bought an estate near Leiden, where he spent his leisure time arranging a great private botanical garden. He pub-lished, at the dying author's request, a splendid edition of Sebastian Vaillant's *Botanicon Parisiense* in 1727. In 1729 he resigned his professorships of botany and chemistry; on this occasion he made a public oration in which he took a retrospective view on his career and thanked many botanists throughout Europe who had helped him in enriching the garden. He continued, however, to lecture on the theory and the practice of medicine and to give clinical demonstrations until the year of his death. When a spurious edition of his chemical lecture notes was published in 1724 as *Institutiones et experimenta chemiae* (translated into English by Shaw and Chambers under the captivating title *The New Chemistry*), he felt impelled to publish a textbook on chemistry, the *Elementa chemiae,* which was later translated into English and French and remained the authoritative chemical manual for decades. In addition he published the papers of Jan Swammerdam, which he had bought in Paris, in both Dutch and Latin, as *Biblia naturae* (2 volumes, 1737–1738).

His popularity was now at its highest; he was created a foreign member of the Académie Royale des Sciences of Paris (1728) and elected a fellow of the Royal Society of London (1730); the czarina of Russia invited him to become her court physician, and royalty and members of the nobility sought his advice. He was now the most famous man of science in Europe and was considered an oracle. The secret of his influence lay in the conjunction of a universal scholarship with a cheerful personality and impeccable character.

In autumn 1737 Boerhaave began to show symptoms of serious heart failure. Dyspnea forced him to interrupt a bedside lecture in April 1738; he made his will, advised the governors of the university about the choice of his successor, and died in his house in Leiden, after an illness of several months. He was buried in St. Peter's Church, and the whole scholarly community of Europe mourned him. On 4 November 1738 his friend Albertus Schultens delivered a eulogy based, in part, upon autobiographical notes left by Boerhaave.

BIBLIOGRAPHY

I. Original Works. Boerhaave's *Atrocis, nec descripti prius, morbi historia,* a facsimile of the first edition (1724) and first French translation, with an introduction by G. A. Lindeboom, appeared as the ninth volume in the series Dutch Classics in the History of Science (Nieuwkoop, 1964).

A complete list of all works written, edited, or provided with a preface by Boerhaave, as well as of the works based on his textbooks, lectures, etc., is in G. A. Lindeboom, *Bibliographia Boerhaaviana* (Leiden, 1959). See also Lindeboom, ed., *Boerhaave's Correspondence,* 2 vols. (Leiden, 1962–1964).

II. SECONDARY LITERATURE. Further works on Boerhaave are [W. Burton] *An Account of the Life and Writings of Herman Boerhaave* (London, 1743); F. W. Gibbs, "Boerhaave and the Botanists," in *Annals of Science,* **13** (1957), 47–61, and "Boerhaave's Chemical Writings," in *Ambix,* **6** (1958), 117–135; F. R. Jevons, "Boerhaave's Biochemistry," in *Medical History,* **6** (1962), 343–362; Lester S. King, *The Medical World of the Eighteenth Century* (Chicago, 1958), chs. 3 and 4, and *The Growth of Medical Thought* (Chicago, 1963), pp. 177–185; G. A. Lindeboom, *Iconographia Boerhaavii* (Leiden, 1963), and *Herman Boerhaave. The Man and His Work* (London, 1968); M. Maty, *Essai sur le caractère du grand médecin ou Éloge de Mr. Herman Boerhaave* (Cologne, 1747); and D. Schoute et al., *Memorialia Hermanni Boerhaave* (Haarlem, 1939), lectures given at the 1938 international Boerhaave commemoration.

G. A. LINDEBOOM

BOETHIUS, ANICIUS MANLIUS SEVERINUS (*b.* Rome [?], *ca.* 480; *d.* near Pavia, Italy, 524/525), *logic, mathematics, music, theology, philosophy.*

Very little is known of Boethius' life before his downfall, imprisonment, and execution (522–525). He belonged to one of the more eminent families of the Roman aristocracy, the Anicii, to which two emperors and perhaps also Pope Gregory the Great belonged. Manlius Boethius, consul for 487, may have been his father, and a prefect of the *praetorium* for 454 may have been his grandfather. Indirect evidence suggests an approximate date for Boethius' birth: he was younger than the writer Ennodius (*b.* 475), his distant relative and friend; he considered himself not old in 523; and he achieved public eminence in 510. His appointment to the honorific title of consul in 510, while he was writing a commentary on Aristotle's *Categories;* his presence in Rome in 522, when he delivered a speech in the Senate before King Theodoric, who had just made Boethius' two sons consuls; his imprisonment in or near Pavia in 522/523; and his death there two years later are well documented. All other chronological data are hypothetical, including his appointment to one of the highest offices in the Roman Gothic kingdom, the *magisterium officiorum,* which gave him some measure of control over state affairs.

For a long time it was taken for granted that Boethius studied in Athens because of a statement made in Theodoric's name by Cassiodorus that in fact suggests a contrary conclusion: "You [Boethius] have penetrated *from a distance* the schools of Athens"

(italics author's).[1] Many now accept the view that he studied under Ammonius in Alexandria; the hypothesis is based on a vague possibility that a prefect of Alexandria *ca.* 476 named Boetios was Boethius' father and on the close connection of many passages in the two philosophers' works.[2] But common doctrines most often derive from common sources, and books travel more easily than men. There is no reason to believe that Boethius ever left Italy.

When still young Boethius lost his father, but acquired the powerful and inspiring protection of Q. Aurelius Memmius Symmachus, a member of an eminent Roman family that combined public authority with great culture. Symmachus may well have provided Boethius with his first knowledge of fourth-century Greco-Latin learning and with the encouragement to bring it up to date. Symmachus' daughter, Rusticiana, became Boethius' wife and bore him two sons, Boethius and Symmachus. Theodoric flattered him for his learning, and asked his advice when the king of France wanted a harper and when the king of Burgundy wanted a water clock and a sundial. Whether Theodoric appointed him to high office because of his special abilities or in order to strengthen his hold on the Roman nobility we cannot know; but he certainly did not take into account Boethius' solidarity with other members of the Senate and his attachment to the idea of the Roman Empire and Roman "freedom," nor did he realize that collaboration does not necessarily mean submission and renunciation. In 522, when Boethius defended Albinus against the charge of betraying the Gothic king for the Roman emperor, Theodoric took his revenge: he ordered Boethius' imprisonment and death.

Boethius left no perceptible mark on politics and statesmanship. His death inspired many to consider him a martyr,[3] but hagiography does not lead to proper appreciation of a man's work. On the other hand, centuries after his death Boethius was responsible for what he probably achieved in a very small measure during his lifetime: the spread of encyclopedic learning. He became the broadcaster of much Greek knowledge to many generations who used Latin and, through them, to many others. Several factors converged to produce this result: basic among them are the body of works that he translated, elaborated, or adapted from the Greek and his own writings, in which he probably exercised somewhat more independent judgment.

Here again we must be cautious. Much has been made of Boethius' grand plan to leave behind, in Latin, the achievements of the Greek past, but he did not outline any such plan. His interests were varied; he had some acquaintance with the general scheme of the lay encyclopedia of knowledge dominating the Greek schools and cultural life of his time, and with the new developments of Christian doctrine. However, for two areas of knowledge he outlined a vague scheme. The first was the basic doctrines of philosophy: "I shall translate and comment upon as many works by Aristotle and Plato as I can get hold of, and I shall try to show that their philosophies agree."[4] This echoes a plan first suggested by Plotinus' forerunner Ammonius Saccas and partly carried out by Plotinus' faithful pupil Porphyry. It is particularly important because it can be shown more than once that Boethius is repeating his source almost literally, even where the translation is disguised; and Porphyry was often his source. It must also be noted that Boethius speaks of writings of which he can "get hold," thus hinting that he was not working where works of Aristotle and Plato were easily obtained.

Another partial plan is suggested by the introductory section of Boethius' *Arithmetic,* dedicated to his father-in-law.[5] There he says that he intends to produce a handbook for each of the four mathematical disciplines—arithmetic, music, geometry, astronomy—which he calls the *quadrivium,* probably the first time this word was used. This led, by analogy, to the term *trivium* for the disciplines dealing with words instead of with numbers or magnitudes. Here again one ought to be cautious and not interpret the intention as a definite plan: the four disciplines were linked in the Greek tradition from which Boethius drew his material.[6] Nor should one be drawn by the flattering letter of Theodoric/Cassiodorus (*ca.* 507–513) into believing that what is written there described works already composed rather than Boethius' knowledge and an ability to discuss matters contained in Greek works.

We know too little about schools and intellectual life when Boethius was young to be able to infer what he learned from whom, or how and where he learned it. We can only try to find out from his works what may have contributed to their composition. The two elements that seem to emerge from such an inquiry are the Roman intellectual life of the latter fourth century and the Greek scholastic tradition as it appeared in the fifth century.

A few books, possibly very few, written in fourth-century Rome had come into Boethius' hands: books of logic or on the line between logic and rhetoric. He may have learned more from his father-in-law, one of whose ancestors had been a member of the learned circles of *ca.* 360–380. Representing that period in Boethius' works are Marius Victorinus, African and pagan by birth, Roman and Christian by adoption; Vettius Agorius Praetextatus, the leader of the pagan revival; Albinus; and Themistius, the eminent Greek rhetorician, philosopher, and teacher of many Romans, including Agorius, in Constantinople. Cicero should be added, because he was the great Roman of that period, master and inspirer of these revivalists.

Boethius possessed, at least in part, Victorinus' Latin adaptation of Porphyry's *Isagoge* and used it for his shorter commentary, in dialogue form, on this work. Victorinus may even have encouraged him to present as his original work what he was actually adapting from the Greek: Victorinus had done this in the *Isagoge* and Boethius did it in several of his "original" works of logic and, perhaps, of theology. Victorinus may also have been the source for other writings by Boethius, if we accept as authentic one of the two basic versions of Cassiodorus' *Institutiones:* there[7] Victorinus is credited with a translation of Aristotle's *Categories* and *De interpretatione,* commentaries on the *Categories* and Cicero's *Topica,* and a *De syllogismis hypotheticis.* In any case, Victorinus provided an example of how to spread Greek culture among Latin-speaking people.

Boethius may have known one work by Agorius Praetextatus: his Latin version of Themistius' paraphrase of Aristotle's *Analytics,* but he is rather ambiguous: he may simply have known that such a version existed. Of Albinus, Boethius knew that he had written something on logic. It may be suspected that Albinus was in fact responsible for the Latin version of Themistius' exposition of the *Categories,* which, from *ca.* 780, was ascribed to St. Augustine;[8] but Boethius was not familiar with it. The connection with Themistius appears to be indirect. Apart from Agorius' (and Albinus'?) dependence on Themistius, this idea seems to be confirmed by the place that Themistius' doctrines concerning the "topics," or types of logical and rhetorical arguments, have in Boethius' work; Themistius' classification of topics is discussed by Boethius as a parallel to Cicero's classification and analysis of them.

Greece and the Greek world still had active and organized centers of higher studies and well-stocked libraries. Boethius may never have gone near them, but he could try to obtain some of the books used there, most probably in Athens, by students and teachers. There is no mention in his works[9] of contemporary Greek scholars or philosophers, nor of those of the two or three previous generations. The most modern man he mentions is Proclus' teacher Syrianus (first half of the fifth century). More than once mention is made of Iamblichus, a Neoplatonist of the first half of the fourth century, whose intellectual legacy passed, after three generations, to Proclus, a Constantinopolitan who headed the Athenian school in the decades immediately preceding Boethius' birth. Recent studies have strengthened the hypothesis that the few books from which Boethius derived his knowledge of Greek philosophy and science came from Athenian circles.

When it is maintained, with a great wealth of quotations and parallel passages, that Boethius was a pupil of Ammonius,[10] master in Alexandria, nothing more is shown than that what Ammonius had learned from his masters in Athens, especially from Proclus, had also reached Boethius. The detailed analysis of the Porphyrian and Aristotelian commentaries of Boethius made by J. Shiel leaves little doubt that his conclusions are right: Boethius possessed one volume of the Greek *Organon,* in which the logical texts of Porphyry and Aristotle were surrounded by a rich collection of passages extracted from the main commentaries of the third and fourth centuries. All the quotations from and references to Porphyry, Iamblichus, Themistius, and Alexander of Aphrodisias are secondhand. Wherever it is possible to check, they are also found in the corresponding extant Greek commentaries. Even quotations from other works of Aristotle, not commented upon by Boethius, come from these selections of Greek commentaries.

In general, considering the nature of most of Boethius' writings, one would do well to discount even internal references to "past" works: some of these references may come from the original Greek works[11] or—as happens with many writers—may be expressions based on the author's wishful thought that, by the time one work is finished, others will also be completed, so that the reader will be able to take the whole series of works in a definite systematic order linked by cross-references. Consequently, it is reasonable to consider as works surely written by Boethius those which are extant and cannot easily be denied as his. Doubts still remain regarding the actual "Boethian" form of several of these works: double recensions suggest that early editors took more freedom than we should like in reshaping the works of the man they intended to glorify. This might even lead us to suggest that Boethius' name was soon added to works not his own, as was done in later times.

The existing works include a considerable body of logical writings: translations, commentaries, and independent treatises.[12] We still have the translations of (1) Porphyry's *Isagoge* (*ca.* 507), in two slightly different versions; (2) Aristotle's *Categories* (before 510), in one uniform, quite polished recension and in a mixture of parts of this recension with parts of a

rougher rendering (perhaps Boethius' own, incompletely preserved); (3) Aristotle's *De interpretatione* (before 513), in three slightly different forms; (4) Aristotle's *Prior Analytics* (before 520), like the *Categories,* in one polished recension and in a mixture of parts of this with parts of a more primitive (perhaps Boethius' original) rendering; (5) Aristotle's *Topics* (before 520), in a uniform, unpolished edition and one small section from a more finished text; (6) Aristotle's *Sophistical Refutations* (before 520), in one recension (another existing recension is probably the result of the mixture of the usual recension by Boethius with some elements of a twelfth-century translation or revision by James of Venice). The suggestion that a Latin collection of passages from Greek commentaries on *Prior Analytics* was also translated by Boethius may have to be discarded, and there is only scanty evidence that he translated the *Posterior Analytics.* The translations, especially if one considers only the less finished recensions as undoubtedly authentic, suggest that Boethius' knowledge of Greek was by no means excellent.

The logical works commented upon by Boethius are (1, 2) Porphyry's *Isagoge:* one commentary (*ca.* 505), in the form of a dialogue, is based on some sections of Victorinus' adaptation, and another (*ca.* 508), in five books, is based on Boethius' own translation; (3) Aristotle's *Categories* (509–511), on the basis of Boethius' translation, with a second commentary perhaps intended but probably never written;[13] (4, 5) Aristotle's *De interpretatione* (513–516), a shorter commentary in two books and a longer one in six, both based on Boethius' translation; (6) Cicero's *Topics* (*ca.* 522), preserved incomplete, in seven books. A commentary on Aristotle's *Topics* is mentioned by Boethius, but it is not known whether it was ever written.

The "independent" logical works are (1) *On Categorical Syllogism* (*ca.* 505–506), in two books; (2) *On Division* (*ca.* 507); (3) *On Hypothetical Syllogisms* (*ca.* 518), in three books; (4) *Prolegomena* (*ca.* 523), known in the Middle Ages as *Antepraedicamenta* and, from 1492 on, as *Introductio in syllogismos categoricos;* and (5) *De differentiis topicis* (*ca.* 523). (*On Definitions,* a treatise ascribed to Boethius from the twelfth to the nineteenth centuries, is the work of Marius Victorinus. Small rhetorical treatises published as independent works are extracts or adaptations from the *De differentiis topicis.*)[14]

Two works by Boethius on disciplines of the *quadrivium* still exist: the *Arithmetic,* in two books, and the *Music,* in five. No agreement has been reached by scholars on the status of the various recensions of a *Geometry* that bear Boethius' name in many manuscripts and editions and were quoted as his for several centuries; it is quite possible that they include at least some sections originally written by him as translations of and adaptations from Euclid. None of the texts on astronomy that have been tentatively connected with Boethius can be ascribed to him unless new evidence comes to light.

Boethius' writings on theology are confined to two short pamphlets, *On the Trinity* and *On the Two Natures and One Person of Christ,* and the briefly argued answers to two questions, *Are "Father," "Son," "Holy Spirit" Predicated Substantially of "God"* and *How Can Substances Be Good in Virtue of Their Existence, Without Being "Goods" qua Substances (Quomodo Substantiae . . .,* often known as *De hebdomadibus).*[15]

All these writings are obviously didactic or scholastic. The same character is shared, but veiled in a literary form, by Boethius' one personal, original, and attractive work, the *Consolation of Philosophy* (523–524), written in verse and prose while he was awaiting execution.

Among the books most frequently—and erroneously—ascribed to him are Dominic González' (or Gundissalinus') *De unitate et uno* (twelfth century) and Thomas of Erfurt's *De disciplina scholarium* (thirteenth century). Translations from Aristotle (*Metaphysics, Ethics,* etc.) made in the twelfth century were occasionally attributed to Boethius from the twelfth to the sixteenth centuries; more persistent was the attribution, from 1510 to the early twentieth century, of the translation by James of Venice of the *Posterior Analytics* (*ca.* 1140).

Originality is rare in Boethius' works. Even where the sources of the doctrines expounded cannot be traced back exactly to a particular author, it can easily be assumed that he was following a definite model. It is also clear, especially in advanced logic, mathematics, and theology, that his preparation, and possibly his linguistic knowledge, was not sufficient for him to pass on all the best that was available to him. But, considering the enormous influence that his works exerted on the revival of learning from the late eighth to the thirteenth centuries, it is important to delineate the doctrines he expounded. We shall not include, however, those contained in those works of Aristotle that he translated.

Two points from the commentaries on Porphyry—which go back mainly to the commentaries of the Porphyrian school itself as it continued, particularly in Athens—deserve special mention. One concerns the Aristotelian divisions of philosophy, and more especially the general plan of logic.[16] Boethius' texts contributed more than anything else to popularization of those divisions. Philosophy, as the encyclopedia of knowledge, is divided into two parts: the theoretical (speculative) sciences and the practical sciences. The first is tripartite: it contains the sciences of nature that consider things material and changeable (physical sciences in a wide sense); those that consider the same things abstracted from movement and matter (mathematical, or "intelligible," sciences); and those that consider things immaterial and unchangeable ("theology" or, later, metaphysics). The second part contains the sciences that deal with action, in relation either to the individual (ethics), or to the family ("economics"), or to social life (politics). Logic is the science of persuasive argument, composed of several propositions; it is the science of syllogism in its general form, or in its applications in common discussion, or in its application to demonstration. This main part of logic must be preceded by a study of individual propositions, and this, in its turn, by the study of individual terms or classes of terms.

The other point concerns what came to be known as the problem of universals.[17] Porphyry had only mentioned its difficulties; Boethius treated some of them and suggested solutions. Especially important are his distinction between "things as they are" and "things as they are conceived" and his mention of the theory of *indifferentia,* a half-way solution that simultaneously allows for and denies the presence of, in things outside the mind, the common element that characterizes universality. This became the doctrine of one of the main schools of thought of the early twelfth century.

In the commentary to the *Categories,* derived largely from the two commentaries by Porphyry, one finds such statements as "A sign of continuity in a body is this: if one part of it is put in motion, the whole body is put in motion, and, if a body which is a whole is moved, at least other parts near those which are set in motion will be moved; as if I push a stick touching one extreme, the other parts of the stick will be moved as that extreme."[18] The commentaries on *De interpretatione* contain interesting analyses of the meanings of necessity[19] and—a source of interminable meditation and discussion—the different aspects of the so-called problem of future contingents:[20] Is a future event, which is not foreseeable on the basis of a known law of nature, such that a proposition describing it is bound to be true or false?

The *De divisione,* covering one of the main sections of logic as detailed by Porphyry at the beginning of the *Isagoge* and possibly based on a similar treatise of the Roman or Athenian school of the fourth or fifth century, contains a classification and partial analysis of the kinds of distinctions that must be considered when inquiring into one's subject matter. It propounds the elements for a methodical approach to scientific inquiry. Four kinds of "division" are listed: (1) division of a genus according to fundamental, substantial, different features and according to species, which are determined by at least some of these differences—this is indispensable for achieving satisfactory definitions; (2) division of a whole into its constituent parts, so that precision in accounting for the nature and structure of the whole may be attained; (3) "division of words," i.e., classification of the different meanings or functions of individual words, in order to avoid confusion and sophistry; and (4) "division of accidents," i.e., classification of some feature that may belong, but not essentially, to many different things or kinds of things (the blue of the sea, the blue of a wall, etc.), which will aid in understanding the relationship between accidental features and the essential nature of things.

The *Prolegomena* (*Introductio ad syllogismos categoricos*), which may go back, directly or indirectly, to a similar introduction by Porphyry and is mentioned by Boethius in his first commentary on the *Isagoge,*[21] restates and expands Aristotelian doctrines on noun and verb, but concentrates mainly on the relationships between propositions that are quantified in the subject and either positive or negative in the subject and/or the predicate. This is a later and more extensive treatment of what had appeared as the first book of *De syllogismis categoricis,* the second book of which is a rather poor synthesis, with the addition of a few mechanically constructed combinations, of the first part of Aristotle's *Prior Analytics.* This work most probably also reflects an elementary textbook of Porphyrian origin.

In *De syllogismis hypotheticis* the basic formulation of the Theophrastian syllogism ("If A then B; if B then C; therefore, if A then C") is played upon through a multiplication of formulas resulting from the insertion of the negative at different places in the premise. The importance of this is limited because A, B, C, must stand for nouns; thus, we fall directly back into the nonhypothetical syllogism. The Stoic hypothetical syllogism had its role in this work, as well as in the commentary on the *Topics* of Cicero, but with no original contribution. The one element that may be useful for an analysis of scientific method is the distinction between accidental connection or coincidence ("Fire being warm, the heavens are spherical") and natural connection ("There being man, there is animal" and, more compelling, "If the Earth comes in between, there follows an eclipse of the moon"), technically termed by Boethius *consequentia secundum accidens* and *consequentia naturae* (the latter being either *non per positionem terminorum* or *per positionem terminorum*).

The commentary on Cicero's *Topics* and the *De differentiis topicis* deal with the kinds of arguments used to persuade, either in a purely theoretical context or in a practical one, i.e., in dialectical or rhetorical arguments. The second work includes most that is important, from a methodological point of view, in the first. It is a systematic exposition of the nature of individual propositions (categorical and hypothetical), questions, theses, and rhetorical "hypotheses," and of connected propositions (such as syllogisms); and then of the headings under which arguments can be classified according to Themistius and Cicero. The importance of such a work lies mainly in its provision of the tools for a critical evaluation of arguments used in discussion and exposition of theories and facts. Thus, distinctions are made between arguments based on definitions, on descriptions, on similarities, on different interpretations of words, on assertions valid for whole classes (and therefore for subclasses), on regular causality, on contradiction, on authority, and on parallelism of situations.

The theological treatises must be considered here because of their role in training several generations, from the ninth century to the thirteenth, to apply the concepts developed by philosophy as a basis for clear thinking to fields where acceptance of dogmatic statement would have appeared more apposite. In *On the Trinity* and, within narrower limits, in the question on the predication of the three Persons to the subject "God," Boethius tries to explain the apparently absurd equation "one = three" by using the distinctions of Porphyry's (and Aristotle's) classes of predicates (genus, species, difference, accident, property) and the ten Aristotelian categories (substance, quantity, quality, relation, etc.). He was, of course, not the inventor of rational theology: *On the Trinity,* which reflects one of the revolutionary trends in Greek theology, is perhaps no more than a disguised translation. But his exposition of the problem and the attempt to locate the absurdity, or possibly the validity, of a statement within the intellectual framework of his time give him an eminent position in the progress toward clarity and exercise of critical power.

The short work on goodness of beings (*Quomodo substantiae . . .*) also claims more than an antiquarian interest. In this writing Boethius set out to solve an eminently nonmathematical problem with something of a mathematical method, and thereby, through many centuries, trained students to organize their thoughts and apply their powers of deduction: "Just as is the custom in mathematics and other disciplines, I begin with a series of definitions and axioms or postulates, from which all the rest will be derived."[22] The *Quomodo* is also important for the neat distinction between essence (*esse*) and existence (*quod est*), which may have a distant echo in the distinction between hypothesis and verification.

The treatise *Two Natures and One Person in Christ* provides us with, among other things, an analysis of the meanings that *natura* has in different contexts. The four meanings are set forth in these formulas: "Nature is to be found in things that can somehow be grasped by our mind"; "Nature (of substances) is what can bring about or be the recipient of an effect"; "Nature (of bodily substances) is the principle of movement per se, not accidentally"; and "Nature is the specific difference giving a definite thing its form." With the definition of *persona*—which became traditional in theology and is at the basis of most of our usages of "person"—Boethius also contributed to the establishment of the technical distinction between *personalis* and *confusa* in the context of the development of the medieval and modern theory of "supposition." For this second purpose, Boethius' definition ("Person is the individual substance of a rational nature") lost the connotation "rational," preserving above all the element of individuality.

The mathematical works by Boethius reproduced Greek works. Although it is not as clear as it has been thought, partly on the basis of what Boethius himself says, exactly which Greek works were reproduced,[23] it is clear that the neo-Pythagorean theory of number as the very divine essence of the world is the view around which the four sciences of the quadrivium are developed. Number, qua multitude considered in itself, is the subject matter of arithmetic; qua multitude applied to something else (relations between numbers?), the subject matter of music; qua magnitude without movement, of geometry; and qua magnitude with movement, of astronomy. The *Arithmetic* develops here and there what was too concise in Nicomachus and abbreviates what was too diffuse. Further, it passes on to the Latin reader many of the basic terms and concepts of arithmetical theory: prime and composite numbers, proportionality, *numeri figurati* (linear, triangular, etc.; pyramidal and other solid numbers), and ten different kinds of *medietates* (arithmetical, geometrical, harmonic, counterharmonic, etc.). His interest in proportions is perhaps connected with the story according to which, while in prison, he thought out a game based on number relations. Here it is noticeable, however, that his understanding of arithmetic, and possibly of Greek, was limited: the more advanced propositions and proofs in Nicomachus, such as the proposition that cubic numbers can be expressed as the successive

sums of odd numbers and the proposition expressing the relation between triangular numbers and the polygonal numbers of polygons with *n* sides, are missing from the *Arithmetic*. He does not, however, miss such elementary things as the multiplication table up to ten.

The *Music* is a continuation of the *Arithmetic,* which contains several elements and terms more appropriate for the treatment of speculative, purely arithmetical music. But, before he comes to this, the very essence of the second science of the quadrivium, Boethius reminds us of the Platonic view that, unlike the other "mathematical sciences," which have only a theoretical value, music has a moral value as well. He also distinguishes the three kinds of music in which number relationships express themselves: the music of the universe (each of the heavens has its special chord), the music of human nature (which harmonizes man's bodily and psychic activities), and the music of some instruments. The third is the only one that, although deteriorated because of its involvement in matter, can be heard. Most of the book is devoted to a lengthy catalog of somewhat classified number relations, most of them with their technical terms and with some description of the nature of the sounds corresponding to them. But, music being considered as science, most of what the musicologist, the artistic composer, and the practicing player would consider essential to the understanding of what music is, is beyond Boethius' grasp.

Boethius' *Geometry,* which is mentioned in Cassiodorus' *Institutiones,* may well have been very different from any of the texts, varied in extent and, in many cases, with different contents, that appeared under his name during the Middle Ages. There is very little more of a geometrical nature in the most ancient manuscripts ascribed to Boethius than Euclid's definitions (from Book I) and some propositions (from Books III and IV) without the proofs. But, as part of the *Geometry,* there is the description of the abacus, the elementary computer based on a decimal system with the individual numbers classified under the headings *numeri incompositi*—the *digiti* (1–9) and the *articuli* (10, 20, $\cdots$, 100, etc.)—and *compositi* (11–19, 21–29, $\cdots$, 101–109, etc.), and there are rules for multiplication and division.

One additional contribution to mathematics that reached the Middle Ages through Boethius is in his commentaries to Porphyry (a sign that his knowledge of such matters is secondhand): the formula $\frac{n(n-1)}{2}$ for the number of possible combinations of two elements in a class of *n* elements.[24]

The *De consolatione philosophiae,* considered from

the doctrinal point of view, is on the whole a restatement of the eclectic Neoplatonic cosmology. Three aspects may be usefully emphasized, because this book contributed in large measure to impressing them into the minds of philosophers and scientists, and of the world at large. (1) Independently of any revelation, the mind can achieve certainty about the existence of God, his goodness, and his power of ruling over the universe. (2) The universe is ordered according to unbroken chains of causes and effects, where necessity, under supervision and determination by God, would be apparent to an all-knowing mind and where chance is nothing more than the coincidental intersection of distinct lines of causation. (3) The order of the universe includes a descent from the first cause to the lowest effects and a return from the lowest ends to the highest beginning. Causality, in the more restricted modern sense, and teleology have preserved a stronger hold on the minds of many generations because of the enormous popularity, until the sixteenth century, of the *Consolatio.* But Boethius' insistence on the possibility of combining freedom of the will with God's eternally present knowledge of the order he willed engaged scholars in theological subtleties more than in a scientific approach to research or organization of knowledge.

NOTES

1. Cassiodorus, *Variae* I.45.3.
2. P. Courcelle, *Les lettres grecques,* p. 299, n. 1.
3. E.g., Dante, *Divine Comedy, Paradiso* X.124–129.
4. *Second Commentary on De interpretatione,* Meiser, ed., pp. 79–80.
5. *Arithmetic,* Friedlein, ed., p. 3.
6. See esp. Iamblichus' *Commentary on Nicomachus' Arithmetic,* E. Pistelli, ed. (Leipzig, 1894), pp. 5–8.
7. Cassiodorus, *Institutiones* I.iii.18, R. A. B. Mynors, ed. (Oxford, 1937), p. 128.
8. *Categoriae,* in *Aristoteles Latinus* I.1–5 (Bruges, 1961), p. lxxviii.
9. There is no foundation for the view held by Courcelle in *Les lettres grecques* (p. 278) that *audivimus* in Boethius' *Second Commentary,* Meiser, ed., p. 361, line 9, should be read "Ammonius."
10. Courcelle, pp. 270–277.
11. See J. Shiel, "Boethius' Commentaries on Aristotle," *passim.*
12. For the dates of the logical works I follow De Rijk, "On the Chronology." Some of the views I express here on the question of second recensions are at variance with hypotheses I put forward in the past.
13. But see P. Hadot, in *Archives d'histoire doctrinale et littéraire du moyen âge.*
14. A. Mai "discovered" these texts in MS Vat. lat. 8591; they are part of a collection of Boethian logical texts made in Constantinople *ca.* 530, of which many copies exist.
15. Views have been expressed by competent scholars both for and against the authenticity of a fifth theological text, the *De fide Catholica,* which seems to have intruded itself, anonymously, at some later stage into the collection of the other four. The arguments in favor seem unsatisfactory.
16. G. Schepss and S. Brandt, eds., pp. 7–10.

17. *Ibid.,* pp. 23–32, 159–167.
18. *Patrologia Latina,* LXIV, cols. 204–205.
19. E.g., in the *Second Commentary on the De interpretatione,* Meiser, ed., pp. 241 ff.
20. *Ibid.,* pp. 190–230.
21. Schepss and Brandt, p. 15.
22. H. F. Stewart and E. K. Rand, eds., p. 40.
23. Very close similarities can be noticed between Boethius and Nicomachus' commentator Iamblichus.
24. Schepss and Brandt, pp. 118–120, 319–321.

BIBLIOGRAPHY

I. ORIGINAL WORKS. The first ed. meant to contain all the works of Boethius was brought out by Iohannes and Gregorius de Gregoriis, with the scholarly collaboration of Nicolaus Iudecus (Venice, 1491–1492; repr. 1498–1499); it did not include the translations of *Prior Analytics, Topics,* and *Sophistical Refutations* but did contain the pseudepigrapha *On Definition, De unitate et uno,* and *De disciplina scholarium.* A complete ed. (Basel, 1546, 1570), with the pseudepigrapha and the non-Boethian translation of *Posterior Analytics* includes the translations missing from the Venice collection reproduced from a text rev. by Jacques Lefèvre d'Étaples (Paris, 1503), which was based on the Greek, under the supervision and with the collaboration of Heinrich Lorit; for the logical works (except the uncommented translations) and for the theological treatises this ed. depends on Giulio Marziano Rota's ed. (Venice, 1537). J. P. Migne, ed., *Patrologia Latina,* LXIII and LXIV, contains all the works of the 1570 ed., some of them from more recently published texts, and some fragments wrongly thought to be new discoveries. Both the Corpus Scriptorum Ecclesiasticorum Latinorum and the Corpus Christianorum include complete editions of Boethius in their plans. In Vol. 48 of the former (Vienna, 1906), G. Schepss and S. Brandt edited the two *Commentaries on Porphyry,* and in Vol. 67 (Vienna, 1934), W. (Guillelmus) Weinberg edited the *Consolatio philosophiae;* in Vol. 94 of the latter (Turnhout, Belgium, 1957), L. Bieler edited the *Consolatio.*

Critical editions of the translations are being done by L. Minio-Paluello, partly with the collaboration of B. G. Dod, as part of the *Aristoteles Latinus,* a section of the Corpus Philosophorum Medii Aevi (Bruges–Brussels–Paris): I, pts. 1–2, *Categoriae* (1961); III, pts. 1–2, *Analytica priora* (1962); II, pt. 1, *De interpretatione* (1965); I, pt. 6, Porphyry's *Isagoge* (1966); V, pts. 1–2, *Topica* (1969); and VI, pt. 1, *Elenchi sophistici* (in preparation).

Among the earliest eds. are *Consolatio philosophiae* (Savigliano, *ca.* 1471)—at least sixty-two Latin eds. of the work were printed before 1501; *Analytica priora* (Louvain, 1475); *Second Commentary on Porphyry, Commentary on Categories,* text of *De interpretatione* (Naples, *ca.* 1476); all the translations (Augsburg, 1479); *De differentiis topicis* and *In Ciceronis Topica commentarium* (Rome, 1484); *De institutione arithmetica* (Augsburg, 1488); *De Trinitate, Utrum Pater . . ., Quomodo substantiae* (Venice, 1489); and the doubtful *De fide Catholica* (Leiden, 1656).

Among the recent eds. not mentioned above, the following are important: *In Ciceronis Topica commentarium,*

I. G. Baiter, ed., in Cicero's *Opera,* I. C. Orelli and I. G. Baiter, eds., I (Zurich, 1833)—this ed. also contains the short section discovered and published by C. B. Hase in *Johannis Laurentii Lydi, De ostentis* (Paris, 1823), pp. 341–356; *De institutione arithmetica, De institutione musica, Geometria,* G. Friedlein, ed. (Leipzig, 1867); *Opera theologica,* R. Peiper, ed. (Leipzig, 1871); *Commentaries on the De interpretatione,* C. Meiser, ed. (Leipzig, 1877–1880); *De divisione,* in an appendix to L. Davidson, *The Logic of Definition* (London, 1885); *The Theological Tractates,* with English translation by H. F. Stewart and E. K. Rand, and *The Consolation of Philosophy,* with English translation by I. T. [John Thorpe?], rev. by H. F. Stewart (London–Cambridge, Mass., 1936). A fragment, believed by the ed. to come from Boethius' *Second Commentary to the Categories,* was published by P. Hadot in *Archives d'histoire doctrinale et littéraire du moyen âge,* **34** (1960), 10–27.

II. Secondary Literature. Extensive bibliographies on Boethius can be found in L. Bieler's ed. of the *Consolatio* (see above), pp. xvi–xxvi; P. Courcelle, *Les lettres grecques en occident de Macrobe à Cassiodore,* 2nd ed. (Paris, 1948), pp. 401–415, and *La consolation de philosophie dans la tradition littéraire* (Paris, 1967), pp. 383–402 and, for the commentaries on the *Consolatio,* pp. 403–438; M. Cappuyns, "Boèce," in *Dictionnaire d'histoire et de géographie ecclésiastique,* IX (1937), cols. 349–380; B. Geyer, *Die patristische und scholastische Philosophie,* Vol. II of Friedrich Ueberweg's *Grundriss der Geschichte der Philosophie,* 11th ed. (Berlin, 1928), pp. 133, 669–670; C. Leonardi, L. Minio-Paluello, U. Pizzani, and P. Courcelle, "Boezio," in *Dizionario biografico degli italiani,* XII (in press); and A. Momigliano, "Cassiodorus and Italian Culture of His Time," in *Proceedings of the British Academy,* **41** (1955), 227–245.

Besides the above-mentioned works by Cappuyns, Courcelle (*Les lettres . . .*), and Momigliano, see the following on Boethius' life and work in general: H. M. Barrett, *Boethius, Some Aspects of His Times and Works* (Cambridge, 1940); M. Grabmann, *Geschichte der scholastischen Methode,* I (Freiburg, 1909), 148–177; M. Manitius, *Geschichte der lateinischen Literatur des Mittelalters,* I (Munich, 1911), 22–36; A. Momigliano, "Gli Anicii e la storiografia latina del VI secolo," in *Rendiconti dell'Accademia nazionale dei Lincei, classe scienze morali,* 8th ser., **9** (1956), 279–297; B. G. Picotti, "Il Senato Romano e il processo di Boezio," in *Archivio storico italiano,* 7th ser., **15** (1931), 205–228; E. K. Rand, *Founders of the Middle Ages* (Cambridge, Mass., 1928), pp. 135–180; and H. Usener, *Anecdoton Holderi* (Bonn, 1877).

On the influence of Boethius see R. Murari, *Dante e Boezio* (Bologna, 1905); and H. R. Patch, *The Tradition of Boethius: A Study of His Importance in Mediaeval Culture* (New York–Oxford, 1935).

On Boethius' logical works (sources, chronology, translations, theories, influences) see L. Bidez, "Boèce et Porphyre," in *Revue belge de philologie et d'histoire,* **2** (1923), 189 ff.; I. M. Bocheński, *Formale Logik* (Freiburg–Munich, 1956), translated by I. Thomas (Notre Dame, Ind., 1961); L. M. De Rijk, "On the Chronology of Boethius's Works on Logic," in *Vivarium,* **2** (1964), 1–49, 125–162, which supersedes all previous studies on the subject; K. Dürr, *The Propositional Logic of Boethius* (Amsterdam, 1951); W. Kneale and M. Kneale, *The Development of Logic,* (Oxford, 1962), pp. 189–198; L. Minio-Paluello, "Iacobus Veneticus Grecus, Canonist and Translator of Aristotle," in *Traditio,* **8** (1952), 265–304, and "Les traductions et les commentaires aristotéliciens de Boèce," in *Texte und Untersuchungen zur Geschichte der altchristlichen Literatur,* Vol. 64 of Studia Patristica (1957), pp. 358–365; C. Prantl, *Geschichte der Logik im Abendlande,* I (Leipzig, 1855; repr. Graz, 1955), 679–721; A. N. Prior, "The Logic of Negative Terms in Boethius," in *Franciscan Studies,* **13** (1953), 1–6; J. Shiel, "Boethius' Commentaries on Aristotle," in *Mediaeval and Renaissance Studies,* **4** (1958), 217–244; and A. Van de Vyver, "Les étapes du développement philosophique du haut moyen âge," in *Revue belge de philologie et d'histoire,* **8** (1929), 425–452.

Also see the prefaces to Minio-Paluello's eds. of Boethius' works listed above; however, some of the views expressed in this article are new, and will be discussed in future writings. The previous literature on the authorship of the translations is discussed in full in these prefaces.

For the theological treatises see, besides Usener's *Anecdoton Holderi,* V. Schurr, *Die Trinitätslehre des Boethius im Lichte der skytischen Kontroversen* (Paderborn, 1935). The latest discussion of the authenticity of *De fide Catholica,* with references to the previous works on the subject, is W. Bark, "Boethius's Fourth Tractate: The So-called 'De Fide Catholica,'" in *Harvard Theological Review,* **59** (1946), 55–69. For the influence of the treatises in the Middle Ages, see M. Grabmann, *Die theologische Erkenntnis- und Einleitungslehre des heiligen Thomas auf Grund seiner Schrift In Boethium De Trinitate* (Fribourg, 1948); and N. M. Haring's editions of *A Commentary on Boethius' De hebdomadibus by Clarenbaldus of Arras* and *The Commentaries of Gilbert, Bishop of Poitiers on the Two Boethian Opuscula Sacra on the Holy Trinity,* in *Nine Mediaeval Texts,* Vol. I of Studies and Texts, published by the Pontifical Institute of Mediaeval Studies (Toronto, 1955), pp. 1–96.

On the mathematical works, including the *De musica,* see M. Cantor, *Vorlesungen über Geschichte der Mathematik,* 3rd ed., I (Leipzig, 1907), 573–585, which contains references to previous works, especially Friedlein's; J. L. Heiberg, in *Philologus,* **43,** 507–519; F. T. Koppen, "Notiz über die Zahlwörter im Abacus des Boethius," in *Bulletin de l'Académie des sciences de St. Pétersbourg,* **35** (1892), 31–48; O. Paul, *Boethius, fünf Bücher über die Musik aus dem lateinischen . . . übertragen und . . . sachlich erklärt* (Leipzig, 1872); G. Pietzsch, *Die Klassifikation der Musik von Boetius bis Ugolino von Orvieto* (Halle, 1929); U. Pizzani, "Studi sulle fonti del *De institutione musica* di Boezio," in *Sacris erudiri,* **16** (1965), 5–164; H. Potiron, *Boèce théoricien de la musique grecque* (Paris, 1961); P. Tannery, "Notes sur la pseudo-géométrie de Boèce," in *Bibliotheca mathematica,* **3** (1900), 39–50; and R. Wagner, "Boethius," in *Die Musik in Geschichte und Gegenwart,* II (Kassel–Basel, 1952), cols. 49–57.

All the relevant bibliography for the *De consolatione*, its sources, doctrines, diffusion, and influence, is in the edition by Bieler and in Courcelle's *La consolation*.

A good source for recent bibliography is Menso Folkerts' critical edition of the two-book version of Boethius' *Geometry, Boethius Geometrie II: Ein mathematisches Lehrbuch des Mittelalters* (Göttingen, 1967), doctoral dissertation.

LORENZO MINIO-PALUELLO

BOETIUS DE BOODT, ANSELMUS. See **Boodt, Anselm de.**

BOETTGER, RUDOLPH CHRISTIAN VON. See **Böttger, Rudolf Christian von.**

BOGUSLAVSKY, PALM HEINRICH LUDWIG VON (*b.* Magdeburg, Prussia, 7 September 1789; *d.* Breslau, Prussia, 5 June 1851), *astronomy.*

The son of a Prussian captain, Boguslavsky attended the Dom School in Magdeburg, then entered the Prussian military service; after military training he took part in the campaign against Napoleon in 1813–1815. After his discharge he lived on his estate in Silesia, where, as an amateur, he occupied himself with astronomical observations. In 1831 he became a senior astronomer at the astronomical observatory in Breslau; in 1836 he was appointed extraordinary professor at the University of Breslau, and in 1843 became director of the astronomical observatory there. He was concerned primarily with the observation and orbit computation of comets, meteor groups, planets, and solar eclipses, and he also contributed to the *Berliner academischen Sternkarten*.

His son Heinrich Georg (1827–1884) was an oceanographer and hydrographer in Berlin.

BIBLIOGRAPHY

Biographical articles on Boguslavsky are in *Allgemeine deutsche Biographie*, III, 58; and Poggendorff, I, 225.

BERNHARD STICKER

BÖHEIM, MARTIN. See **Behaim, Martin.**

BOHL, PIERS (*b.* Walka, Livonia [now Latvian S.S.R.], 23 October 1865; *d.* Riga, Latvia, 25 December 1921), *mathematics.*

The son of George Bohl, a merchant, Piers Bohl first studied in his native city and then at a German Gymnasium in Viljandi, Estonia. In 1884 he entered the department of physics and mathematics at the University of Dorpat, Estonia, from which he grad-

uated in 1887 with a candidate's degree in mathematics (equivalent to a master's degree in the United States), having won a gold medal for a competitive essay on the theory of invariants of linear differential equations (1886). Bohl defended dissertations in applied mathematics for his master's degree in 1893 (equivalent to a doctorate in the United States) and for his doctorate in 1900. (The doctorate, a degree that can be gained only after the candidate has done outstanding work in his chosen field, allows the holder to be called professor.) He received both of these advanced degrees from Dorpat. From 1895 Bohl taught at Riga Polytechnic Institute (from 1900 with the rank of professor); and when the institute was evacuated to Moscow at the beginning of World War I, he accompanied it. He returned to Riga in 1919 and was appointed professor at the University of Latvia, which had been founded that year. Two years later he died of a cerebral hemorrhage.

In his master's dissertation, Bohl was the first to introduce and to study that class of functions (more general than ordinary periodic functions) which in 1903 were named quasi-periodic by the French mathematician E. Esclangon, who discovered them later than, but independently of, Bohl. Finite sums of periodic functions with, generally speaking, incommensurable periods (of the type $\sin x + \sin \sqrt{2}x + \sin \sqrt{3}x$) are an example. Harald Bohr's concept of almost-periodic functions is the further generalization of this class.

In his doctoral dissertation, Bohl, following Henri Poincaré and A. Kneser, presented a new development of topological methods of systems of differential equations of the first order. To the investigation of the existence and properties of the integrals of these systems, he applied a series of theorems, which he developed and proved, concerning points that remain fixed for continuous mappings of *n*-dimensional sets of points. L. Brouwer's famous theorem on the existence of a fixed point under the condition of the mapping of a sphere onto itself is easily obtained as a consequence of one of the propositions completely demonstrated in Bohl's "Über die Bewegung. . . ." Bohl's topological theorems did not, however, attract the attention of contemporary mathematicians.

Studying one problem of the theory of secular perturbations (1909), Bohl encountered the question of the uniform distribution of the fractional parts of functions satisfying certain conditions. The theorem he developed was also developed independently by H. Weyl and W. Sierpinski; it was generalized by Weyl in 1916. Later the theory of the distribution of fractional parts of functions became a large part of number theory.

BIBLIOGRAPHY

I. Original Works. For Bohl's early work, see *Theorie und Anwendung der Invarianten der linearen Differentialgleichungen* (Dorpat, 1886), which manuscript is in the Historical Archive of the Estonian S. S. R., Tartu; and *Über die Darstellung von Funktionen einer Variablen durch trigonometrische Reihen mit mehreren einer Variablen proportionalen Argumenten* (Dorpat, 1893), his master's dissertation. His doctoral dissertation, "O Nekotorykh Differentsialnykh Uravneniakh Obshchego Kharaktera, Primenimykh v Mekhanike" ("On Some Differential Equations of a General Character, Applicable in Mechanics;" Yurev, 1900), is also available in French as "Sur certaines équations différentielles d'un type général utilisables en mécanique," in *Bulletin de la Société mathématique de France,* **38** (1910), 1–134. See also "Über die Bewegung eines mechanischen Systems in der Nähe einer Gleichgewichtslage," in *Journal für reine und angewandte Mathematik,* **127** (1904), 179–276; and "Über ein in der Theorie der säkularen Störungen vorkommendes Problem," *ibid.,* **135** (1909), 189–283.

II. Secondary Literature. For further information on Bohl, see A. Kneser and A. Meder, "Piers Bohl zum Gedächtnis," in *Jahresbericht der Deutschen Mathematikervereinigung,* **33** (1925), 25–32. A complete bibliography of Bohl's work and of literature devoted to him appears in A. D. Myshkis and I. M. Rabinovich, eds., *P. G. Bohl. Izbrannye Trudy* ("P. G. Bohl, Selected Works"; Riga, 1961), biography and analysis of scientific activity, pp. 5–29.

A. P. Youschkevitch

BOHN, JOHANNES (*b.* Leipzig, Germany, 20 July 1640; *d.* Leipzig, 19 December 1718), *physiology, medicine.*

Bohn was the son of a wealthy merchant family. He studied medicine in Jena and Leipzig and about 1665 received the doctorate from the medical school of Leipzig. From 1663 to 1665 he traveled through Denmark, Holland, England, Switzerland, France, and possibly Italy. In 1668 he was named professor of anatomy and surgery at Leipzig; in 1690 he became municipal physician; and the following year he was appointed professor of practical medicine. Bohn was a critical, truth-loving man who was so careful of his scientific reputation that on his deathbed he arranged for the destruction of all his unpublished writings.

Bohn's accomplishments are in three areas: anatomy and physiology, iatrochemistry, and forensic medicine. His twenty-six *Exercitationes physiologicarum* appeared at irregular intervals from 1668 on; these are doctoral dissertations, written by Bohn and disputed by various candidates for the doctorate. Most of the *Exercitationes* appeared in 1668; the rest appeared from time to time until about 1677. They

were later reprinted as a whole in a pirated edition. Only a few copies of the work are available. Bohn later reworked these dissertations into a completely new composition which appeared in 1680 as *Circulus anatomicus-physiologicus seu Oeconomia corporis animalis,* and was dedicated to Malpighi.

The *Exercitationes* and the *Circulus* show Bohn to have been an expert on the then new anatomical and physiological discoveries. He cites contemporary authors almost exclusively and thereby proves himself one of the innovators in physiology who completely forsook the Galenic tradition. He describes and discusses all major functions of the body. He complements the knowledge gained from the literature with numerous firsthand experiments, for example, experiments on bile and the biliary tract, lymph ducts, heart contractions, pancreatic secretion, on the conjectured swelling of ligated nerves, and artificial perfusion of an excised kidney.

Bohn's basic attitude was mechanistic in that he gave predominantly physical interpretations of vital processes. He especially esteemed Malpighi, Borelli, and Boyle. Bohn had an excellent knowledge of iatrochemistry as well, but he maintained a critical position against this doctrine. He condemned the ancient theory of qualities as unsuitable to the explanation of chemical processes. Wherever possible, he referred to Jan van Helmont's theories of the *fermentum* and to those of Sylvius on the *acidum* and the *alcali.* In his opinion, the process of digestion cannot be explained without the theories of iatrochemistry; with the help of *spiritus* and *sal volatile,* a fermentative transformation of food into chyle takes place. But he opposed a general explanation of physiological findings and clinical observations exclusively by these theories, and especially in his *De alcali et acidi insufficientia* (1675) he explicates this attitude.

Bohn contributed several significant works to forensic medicine. He is considered one of the founders of this discipline and one of the initiators of forensic autopsy.

BIBLIOGRAPHY

I. Original works. Bohn's works on forensic medicine are not mentioned here. Among his other works are *Disputatio de sudore* (Leipzig, 1661), his dissertation, sponsored by Johannes Michaelis; *Exercitationum physiologicarum XXVI* (Leipzig, 1668–1677); *Circulus anatomicus-physiologicus, seu Oeconomia corporis animalis, hoc est cogitata functionum animalium, notissimarum formalitatem et causas concernantia* (Leipzig, 1680, 1686), dedicated to Malpighi and consisting of thirty progymnasmata and eleven other dissertations; *Observationes quaedem anatomica circa structuram vasorum biliarum et motuum bilis spectantes* (Leipzig, 1682); *Dissertationes chymico-physicae, chymiae finem, instrumenta et operationes frequentiones explicantes . . .* (Leipzig, 1685, 1696); and *De duumviratu hypochondriacorum* (Leipzig, 1689), a polemic against Sylvius.

II. SECONDARY LITERATURE. There is no biography of Bohn, but further information on him and his work may be found in A. von Haller, *Bibliotheca anatomica,* I (1774), pp. 497–499; M. Neuburger, "Deutsche Experimentalphysiologen des 17. Jahrhunderts," in *Deutsche medizinische Wochenschrift,* **23** (1897), 483–486; and J. C. Rosenmüller, *De viris quibusdam in Academia Lipsiensi Anatomes peritia in clavuerunt,* III (1816), 7–9.

Also see *Allgemeine deutsche Biographie,* III (Leipzig, 1876), 81–99, with an incomplete bibliography; A. von Haller, *Bibliotheca medicinae practicae,* 4 vols., III (Basel, 1778), 87–88, with a list of forty-two dissertations; *Biographie médicale,* I (Paris, 1855), 539–540; *Biographie universelle ancienne et moderne,* IV (Paris, 1843), 553; and *Biographische Lexikon des hervorragenden Ärzte aller Zeiten und Länder,* 2nd ed., I (Berlin–Vienna, 1929), 606–607.

K. ROTHSCHUH

BOHR, HARALD (*b.* Copenhagen, Denmark, 22 April 1887; *d.* Copenhagen, 22 January 1951), *mathematics.*

Bohr's father was the distinguished physiologist Christian Bohr; his mother, a daughter of the prominent financier, politician, and philanthropist D. B. Adler. In the home he and his elder brother Niels imbibed a deep love of science. At the age of seventeen Bohr entered the University of Copenhagen. Of his teachers, he felt the closest kinship to H. G. Zeuthen, but the most decisive factor in his development as a mathematician was his study of Jordan's *Cours d'analyse* and Dirichlet's *Vorlesungen über Zahlentheorie* with Dedekind's supplements. In his later student years, his interests centered on analysis. After his master's examination he went to study with Landau in Göttingen. This center of mathematics became like a second home to Bohr, and he returned there often. During the years before World War I, he also came into close contact with Hardy and Littlewood, and he often went to Cambridge and Oxford to study.

After obtaining his doctor's degree in 1910, Bohr joined the faculty of the University of Copenhagen. In 1915 he was appointed professor at the College of Technology, a position he retained until returning in 1930 to the University of Copenhagen, where he headed the newly founded Institute of Mathematics. Bohr was one of the leading analysts of his time, and he exerted an extraordinary influence both in inter-

national mathematical circles and in the academic life of his own country. As a teacher he was greatly admired and loved. When the rise of Nazism in Germany in 1933 endangered the academic community, among others, Bohr was among the first to offer help. His close personal relations with colleagues in many countries enabled him to help in finding new homes for those scientists who were either forced to leave Germany or who chose to do so, and he turned all his energies to this task. He himself did not escape exile in the latter part of World War II, when he was compelled to take refuge in Sweden.

Bohr's contribution to mathematics is one of great unity. His first comprehensive investigation, which formed the subject of his doctor's thesis, was concerned with the application of Cesàro summability to Dirichlet series. In a number of later papers he studied other aspects of the theory of Dirichlet series, in particular the distribution of the values of functions represented by such series. His method consists in a combination of arithmetic, geometric, and function-theoretic considerations. His collaboration with Landau was concentrated mainly on the theory of the Riemann zeta-function. It culminated in the so-called Bohr-Landau theorem (1914), concerning the distribution of its zeros. In later papers Bohr gave a detailed study of the distribution of its values in the half plane to the right of the critical line.

The problem of which functions may be represented by Dirichlet series led Bohr to his main achievement, the theory of almost periodic functions, on which the greater part of his later work is concentrated. If a Dirichlet series is considered on a vertical line in the complex plane, it reduces to a trigonometric series. It was therefore natural to consider more generally the problem of which functions of a real variable can be represented by such a series, i.e., can be formed by superposition of pure oscillations. In the special case where the frequencies of the oscillations are integers, the answer is given in the classical theory of Fourier series of periodic functions. Whereas hitherto in the theory of Dirichlet series one had always worked with frequencies forming a monotonic sequence, Bohr discovered that in order to obtain an answer to the problem one would have to consider series with quite arbitrary frequencies. The answer was obtained by introducing the notion of almost periodicity. The theory was published in three papers in *Acta mathematica* (1924–1926), and numerous mathematicians joined in the work on its simplification and extension. Thus Weyl and Wiener connected it with the classical theories of integral equations and Fourier integrals, and Bochner developed a summation method for Bohr-Fourier series generalizing Fejér's theorem. Stepanoff, Wiener, and Besicovitch studied generalizations depending on the Lebesgue integral. Other aspects of the theory were studied by Favard, Wintner, and many others. In the 1930's Von Neumann succeeded in extending the theory to functions on arbitrary groups, and it thus found a central place in contemporary mathematics.

BIBLIOGRAPHY

Bohr's *Collected Mathematical Works,* 3 vols. (Copenhagen, 1952), contain all his mathematical writings, with the exception of elementary articles and textbooks in Danish. An English translation of an autobiographical lecture appears as a preface to this edition.

Obituaries of Bohr include those by S. Bochner, in *Bulletin of the American Mathematical Society,* **58** (1952), 72–75; B. Jessen, in *Acta mathematica,* **86** (1951), i–xxiii, repr. as supp. S. 25 in Bohr's *Collected Mathematical Works,* III, supp. 163–176; O. Neugebauer, in *Year Book 1952 of the American Philosophical Society* (1953), pp. 307–311; N. E. Nørlund, in *Oversigt over det Kongelige Danske Videnskabernes Selskabs Virksomhed, 1950–1951* (1951), pp. 61–67, in Danish; O. Perron, in *Jahresbericht der Deutschen Mathematiker-vereinigung,* **55** (1952), pt. 1, 77–88; and E. C. Titchmarsh, in *Journal of the London Mathematical Society,* **28** (1953), 113–115.

BØRGE JESSEN

BOHR, NIELS HENRIK DAVID (*b.* Copenhagen, Denmark, 7 October 1885; *d.* Copenhagen, 18 November 1962), *atomic and nuclear physics, epistemology.*

A tradition common to many pioneers in science has been the combination of achievement in actual discovery of natural laws with philosophical reflection on the nature of scientific thinking and the foundations of scientific truth. This combination is essential to such scientists in the sense that epistemological considerations played a decisive part in the success of their investigations and that, conversely, the results of the latter led them to deeper understanding of the theory of knowledge. Niels Bohr in particular was very conscious of this twofold aspect of his scientific activity, deep-rooted as it was in the environment in which he grew up and received his education.

The family in which Bohr was the second of three children belonged to the well-to-do intellectual circles of Copenhagen; his father, Christian Bohr, was a talented professor of physiology at the University of Copenhagen; his mother, Ellen Adler, came from a wealthy Jewish family that was prominent in such varied activities as banking, politics, classical philology, and progressive pedagogy. The parents allowed the children's native gifts the fullest development, and

formal education was supplemented at every stage by example and encouragement at home. Niels was not as brilliant a pupil as his younger brother Harald, who became an eminent mathematician; they both, however, showed interests in other fields, including sports. At the University of Copenhagen, Niels stood out as an unusually perceptive investigator. His first research project, a precision measurement of the surface tension of water by the observation of a regularly vibrating jet, was completed in 1906, when he was still a student, and it won him a gold medal from the Academy of Sciences. It is a mature piece of work, remarkable for the care and thoroughness with which both the experimental and theoretical parts of the problem were handled.

Bohr's doctoral dissertation, *Studier over metallernes elektrontheori* (1911), was a purely theoretical work that again exhibited a mastery of the vast subject he had chosen, the electron theory of metals. This theory, which pictures the metallic state as a gas of electrons moving more or less freely in the potential created by the positively charged atoms disposed in a regular lattice, accounted qualitatively for the most varied properties of metals; but it ran into many difficulties as soon as a quantitative treatment was attempted on the basis of then accepted principles of classical electrodynamics.

In order to throw light on the nature of these difficulties, Bohr developed general methods allowing him to derive the main features of the phenomena from the fundamental assumptions in a very direct way. He could thus clearly exhibit the fundamental nature of the failures of the theory, which were in fact attributed to an insufficiency of the classical principles themselves. Thus, he showed that the magnetic properties of the metals could in no way be derived from a consistent application of these principles. The rigor of his analysis gave him, at this early stage, the firm conviction of the necessity of a radical departure from classical electrodynamics for the description of atomic phenomena.

The study of physics, even carried to such unusual depth, did not absorb all of Bohr's energy; his intellectual curiosity knew no bounds. With his characteristic earnestness and thoroughness he took up the hints that circumstances offered as starting points for highly original philosophical reflections. His father's scientific work concentrated on the quantitative analysis of physical processes underlying the physiological functions; the school which he founded and which was brilliantly continued by his pupils still flourishes in modernized form. The type of problem that Christian Bohr was investigating required the closest attention to the elaboration of refined techniques of physical measurement, and simultaneously raised profound philosophical questions about the relationship between physical and biological phenomena.

During Niels's adolescence, the philosophical trend in scientific circles was a reaction against the mechanistic materialism of the preceding generation. In the liberal atmosphere surrounding Christian Bohr's friends, a group to which the philosopher Harald Höffding belonged, this reaction took a moderate and thoughtful form, however. Bohr, the master of the investigation of the physical basis of the physiological processes, insisted on the practical necessity of considering these processes also from the teleological point of view in order to arrive at a complete description. Niels and Harald Bohr were admitted as silent listeners to the philosophical conversations of their father and his friends, and this first confrontation with the epistemological problem of biology, in which apparently conflicting views were found equally indispensable for a full understanding of the phenomena, made a lasting impression upon Niels's mind.

He also soon came to share the negative attitude of the progressive bourgeoisie, to which his family belonged, toward the church and religious beliefs in general; but it is characteristic of his independence of judgment that he arrived at this conclusion only after he had convinced himself that the church upheld doctrines that were logically untenable and shunned the pressing task, at the time preoccupying all liberal minds, of alleviating a still widespread pauperism. His approach to social and philosophical questions, even at such an early stage, was marked by the same logical rigor and breadth of vision as his scientific thinking.

It was in the course of his meditations on the human condition that, considering the role of language as a means of communication, he first came across a situation of great generality whose recognition was the source of his later decisive contribution to the epistemology of physics. He was struck by the fact that the same word is currently used to denote a state of consciousness and the concomitant behavior of the body. In trying to describe this fundamental ambiguity of every word referring to mental activity, Bohr had recourse to an analogy drawn from the mathematical theory of multivalued functions: each such word, he said, belongs to several "planes of objectivity," and we must be careful not to allow them to glide from one plane of objectivity to another. However, it is an inherent property of language that there is only one word for the different aspects of a given psychical activity. There is no point in trying to remove such ambiguities; we must recognize their existence and live with them.

After finishing his studies in Copenhagen, Bohr went to Cambridge, hoping to pursue his work on electron theory under the guidance of J. J. Thomson. Unfortunately, Thomson had lost interest in the subject, and failed to appreciate the importance of Bohr's dissertation, which the latter showed him in an English translation he had been at great pains to make; this was turned down by the Cambridge Philosophical Society as too long and too expensive to print, and Bohr's further attempts to get it published were equally abortive.

This grievous disappointment did not prevent Bohr from making the most of his stay in Cambridge, but as soon as he conveniently could, he moved to Manchester, where Ernest Rutherford had established a flourishing laboratory. There, from March to July 1912, working with utmost concentration, he laid the foundations of his greatest achievement in physics, the theory of atomic constitution. It would be difficult to imagine two temperaments more different than those of Bohr and Rutherford; but this first contact initiated, besides a new epoch in science, a lifelong friendship, compounded of filial affection on Bohr's part and of warm cordiality, tinged with respect, on the part of the jovial New Zealander. With his shrewd judgment of people, Rutherford soon sensed the genius in the shy, unassuming young man, and his immense strength, imaginative insight, and directness of approach were an inspiration to Bohr.

Toward the end of 1910, Rutherford had proposed a "nuclear" model of the atom in order to account for the large-angle scattering of α rays observed in his laboratory. Since the discovery of the electron as a carrier of an elementary unit of negative electric charge, the atom was thought of as a system of a certain number of electrons, kept together by an equivalent positive charge, somehow attached to the massive substance of the atom (the electron itself being nearly two thousand times lighter than the lightest atom). If this positive charge were spread over the whole atom, the α rays, or positively charged helium atoms, impinging upon it would generally undergo small deviations from their courses; the frequent occurrence of large-angle deviations suggested direct collisions with a strongly concentrated positive substance. A quantitative check fully confirmed this inference and revealed that the massive, positively charged nucleus of the atom had linear dimensions a hundred thousand times smaller than those of the whole atomic structure.

Bohr eagerly took up the new model and soon recognized its far-reaching implications. In particular, he pointed out that the nuclear model of the atom implied a sharp separation between the chemical properties, ascribed to the peripheral electrons, and the radioactive properties, which affected the nucleus itself. This immediately suggested a close relation between the atomic number, which indicates the position of an element in Mendeleev's periodic table, and the number of its electrons, or its nuclear charge, which should thus be more fundamental than its atomic weight. Indeed, the periodic table showed one or two irregularities in the sequence of atomic weights, and it became increasingly difficult to accommodate in it the newly discovered radioactive products; Bohr showed how all these anomalies could be eliminated if one admitted the occurrence of atomic nuclei of the same charge but different mass, so that there could be more than one species of atom occupying the same place in the periodic table. Somewhat later, the name "isotope" was given to these chemically indistinguishable atomic species of different weights.

According to the nuclear model, radioactive transformations had to be conceived as actual transmutations of the atomic nucleus. Thus, Bohr argued, by the emission of an α ray, the nucleus lost two units of charge and became an isotope of the element two places back in the periodic table. In β decay, on the other hand, the emission of an electron resulted in the gain of one unit of charge, and the product nucleus occupied the next higher place in the periodic table. Simple as it may seem, the inference leading to these "displacement laws" of radioactive elements was far from obvious at that time.

The only person in the laboratory who followed Bohr's thoughts with deep interest and genuine understanding, and who was able to help him in the discussion of the empirical information, was a young Hungarian chemist, Georg von Hevesy, who was himself on the verge of discovering the use of isotopes as tracers, which brought him fame. Indeed, Rutherford himself, insensible to the logical cogency of Bohr's argument, dissuaded him from publishing such hazardous deductions from his own atomic model, to which he was not prepared to ascribe the fundamental significance that Bohr gave it; and when, a few months later, the displacement laws could be discerned by mere inspection of the accumulated experimental evidence, Kasimir Fajans (one of those who then enunciated them) so little understood their meaning that he actually presented them as evidence against the Rutherford atomic model.

Bohr's survey of the implications of Rutherford's atomic model did not stop at the recognition of the existence of a relation between the atomic number (which summarizes the whole physicochemical behavior of the element) and the number of electrons in the atom. He resolutely attacked the much harder problem of determining the exact nature of this relation, which amounts to a dynamic analysis of the atomic structure represented by the nuclear model. Following J. J. Thomson's example, Bohr assumed that the electrons would be symmetrically distributed around the nucleus in concentric circular rings. He had then to face the problem, not present in Thomson's model, of how to account for the stability of such ring configurations, which could not be maintained by the electrostatic forces alone.

Bohr had become convinced, from his study of the behavior of electrons in metals, that the validity of classical electrodynamics would be subject to a fundamental limitation in the atomic domain, and he had no doubt that this limitation would somehow be governed by Planck's quantum of action; he knew already how to quantize the motion of a harmonic oscillator, i.e., to select from the infinity of possible motions a discrete series characterized by energy values increasing by finite steps of magnitude $h\nu$, where h is Planck's universal constant and ν the frequency of the oscillator. One could try to apply a similar quantization to the motions of an atom's electrons, whose frequencies might be identified with the resonance frequencies observed in the scattering of light by the atom.

Thus, an allowed state of motion characterized by a frequency ω_n would have a binding energy of the form $W_n = Knh\omega_n$, where n is an integer numbering the state and K is some numerical factor that could possibly depend on the type of motion. Such a formula could be combined with the relation given by the classical theory between the binding energy and the amplitude of the motion, in order to obtain a relation between the amplitude of motion, whose order of magnitude is known from various evidence about the atomic dimensions, and the corresponding resonance frequency, which is obtained from optical measurements. It was easy to ascertain that the numerical value of Planck's constant, entering such a relation, did lead to the expected orders of magnitude; but this rough check, however encouraging, was clearly insufficient to establish the precise form of the quantum condition.

At this juncture, Bohr obtained a much deeper insight into the problem by a brilliant piece of work, which he—working, as he said, "day and night"—completed with astonishing speed. The problem was one of immediate interest for Rutherford's laboratory: in their passage through a material medium, α particles continually lose energy by ionizing the atoms they encounter, at a rate depending on their velocity. This energy loss limits the depth to which the particles can penetrate into the medium, and the relation between this depth, or range, and the velocity offers a way of determining this velocity. What Bohr did was to analyze the ionizing process on the basis of the Rutherford model of the atom and thus express the rate of energy loss in terms of the velocity by a much more accurate formula than had so far been achieved—a formula, in fact, to which modern quantum mechanics adds only nonessential refinements.

Bohr's interest in atomic collision problems never faltered. In the early 1930's, when the modern theory of these processes was being elaborated, especially by Hans Bethe, Felix Bloch, and E. J. Williams, he took an active part in the work, a good deal of which took place in Copenhagen; and as late as 1948 he wrote a masterly synthesis of the whole subject, in which one still finds, in modernized form, the arguments of his early analysis.

The success of this analysis showed him, however, that the classical theory, while completely failing to account for the stability of the periodic motions of the atomic electrons, could deal with undiminished power with the aperiodic motions of charged particles traversing a region in which there is an electric field. This means that, however radical the break with classical ideas implied by the existence of the quantum of action, one must expect a gradual merging of the quantum theory into the classical one for motions of lower and lower frequencies. Moreover, one may expect that the effect of a very slow and gradual modification of the forces acting on or within an atomic system will be correctly estimated by the classical theory.

These were shrewd points, which Bohr used skillfully and which he eventually developed into powerful heuristic principles. An immediate application of the second principle helped him to discuss simple models of atomic and molecular structures, which reproduced, at least in order of magnitude, a number of features derived from various experiments and thus further illustrated the fruitfulness of the Rutherford atomic model. Indeed, this model was the first to permit a clear-cut distinction to be made between atom and molecule—a molecule being defined as a system with more than one nucleus—and thereby to open the way to an understanding of the nature of chemical binding. The models studied by Bohr were characterized by the arrangement of the electrons in one or more ring configurations, disposed around the nucleus as the common center in an atom, or symmetrically with respect to the nuclei in molecules. While the absolute dimensions of these configurations depended on quantum conditions that he could only roughly guess, their stability, owing to the argument

mentioned above, could be examined by classical methods; thus, he could explain why hydrogen could form a diatomic molecule, while helium could not.

Although these considerations were crude—and are completely superseded by the modern conceptions—they were remarkably successful; in fact, they do embody an important feature of the chemical bond that is part of the modern theory: the fact that this bond is due to the formation of a configuration of electrons shared by the combining atoms. The hydrogen molecule, for instance, was well represented by a ring of two electrons perpendicular to the line joining the two nuclei.

With regard to the determination of the states of motion allowed by the quantum condition mentioned above, Bohr found that the Rutherford model leads to remarkably simple results, at least for the type of configuration he considered. In general, the classical theory of the motion furnishes an additional relation between the binding energy and the frequency, which allows one to eliminate the frequency from the quantum condition and thus obtain for the binding energy W_n an expression depending only on the integer n, with a coefficient that, besides Planck's constant, contains the parameters characterizing the system and the type of motion. Thus, to take the simplest example of the hydrogen atom, consisting of a singly charged nucleus and an electron of mass m and charge e, the classical theory shows that there is proportionality between W_n^3 and ω_n^2; this leads, for the allowed states of binding, to the very simple law $W_n = A/n^2$, and the precise value of the coefficient A is $\pi^2 e^4 m/2K^2 h^2$; only the numerical factor K remains in doubt.

When he left Manchester in July 1912, Bohr was filled with ideas and projects for further exploration of this world of atoms that was displaying such wide prospects; but he had another reason to be in high spirits. Since 1911, shortly before his departure for England, he had been engaged to Margrethe Nørlund, a young woman of great charm and sensibility. The marriage took place in Copenhagen on 1 August 1912 and was a happy and harmonious union. Margrethe's role was not an easy one. Bohr was of a sensitive nature, and constantly needed the stimulus of sympathy and understanding. When children came —six sons, two of whom died young—Bohr took very seriously his duties as paterfamilias. His wife adapted herself without apparent effort to the part of hostess, and evenings at the Bohr home were distinguished by warm cordiality and exhilarating conversation.

In the autumn of 1912, Bohr took up the duties of assistant at the University of Copenhagen; he fulfilled them conscientiously, and used the privilege extended to holders of the doctorate of giving a free course of lectures. At the same time, he started to write up the account of his Manchester ideas. Then, at the beginning of 1913, the orientation of his thought took a sudden turn toward the problem of atomic radiation, which rapidly led him to the decisive step in the process of incorporating the quantum of action into the theory of atomic constitution. The rest of the academic year was spent reconstructing the whole theory upon the new foundation and expounding it in a large treatise, which was immediately published, in three parts, in the *Philosophical Magazine.*

It had been known since Kirchhoff's pioneering work that the spectral composition of the light emitted by atoms is characteristic for the chemical species; a whole science of spectroscopy had developed on this principle and a great deal of extremely accurate material had been accumulated. Obviously, the tables of wavelengths of the characteristic spectral lines must contain very precise information on the structure of the emitting atoms; but since atomic spectra consist of apparently capricious sequences of thousands of lines, it seemed hopeless to try to decipher such complicated codes. It therefore came as a great surprise to Bohr to learn from a casual conversation with a colleague that spectroscopists had managed to discover regularities behind the chaos.

In particular, J. R. Rydberg, of the nearby University of Lund, had found a very simple and remarkable formula expressing the frequencies of several "series" of spectral lines which recurred, with different values of the parameters, in the spectra of different atoms. The striking feature of Rydberg's formula was that the frequencies were represented by differences of two terms, each of which depended in a simple way on a number which could take a sequence of integral values; a series corresponded to the sequence obtained by keeping one of the terms fixed and varying the other.

Thus, the frequencies ν_{nm} of the lines of the hydrogen spectrum could be represented in the simplest possible form in terms of two integers as

$$\nu_{nm} = R\left(\frac{1}{n^2} - \frac{1}{m^2}\right),$$

with a single parameter, R, of accurately known numerical value. As soon as Bohr saw this formula, he immediately recognized that it gave him the missing clue to the correct way to introduce the quantum of action into the description of atomic systems.

The formal similarity between the terms of the Rydberg formula R/n^2 and the expression for the energies $W_n = A/n^2$ of the possible stationary states of the atom suggested to him, in the spirit of Planck's conception of the quanta of radiation, that the emission by the atom of light of frequency ν_{nm} occurred in the form of single quanta of energy $h\nu_{nm}$; Rydberg's formula then indicated that in this process the atom passed from an initial stationary state W_n to another stationary state, W_m. An immediate control of this interpretation offered itself: according to it, the value of Rydberg's constant should be given by $Rh = A$, that is, by $R = \pi^2 e^4 m/2K^2 h^3$. Inserting in this expression the known values of e, m, and h, and taking the value $1/2$ for K (which would give the correct binding energy W_n for a harmonic oscillator of frequency ω_n), Bohr obtained a value of R as near the experimental one as the errors in the determinations of the other constants allowed.

However convincing such a stringent quantitative test could appear, there was in this new conception of the radiation process a feature that must be considered so unusual as to be almost unthinkable: the frequencies ν_{nm} of the emitted light did not coincide with any of the allowed frequencies of revolution ω_n of the electrons or their harmonics—a feature of the classical theory of radiation so immediate and elementary that it seemed impossible to abandon it.

That Bohr was not deterred by this consideration was due essentially to the dialectical turn of mind he had acquired in his youthful philosophical reflections. The conflict between the classical picture of the atomic phenomena and their quantal features was so acute that no hopes (such as those Planck was still expressing) could be entertained of solving it by reducing the latter to the former; one had, rather, to accept the coexistence of these two aspects of experience, and the real problem was to integrate them into a rational synthesis. Bohr later said that the clue offered by Rydberg's formula was so transparent as to lead uniquely to the quantal description of the radiation process he proposed; this gave him the conviction that it was right, in spite of the radical break with classical ideas that it implied.

In order to clinch the argument, however, Bohr went a very important step further. He knew that the quantal behavior of a system, whatever it was, had to satisfy the requirement of going over to the corresponding classical behavior in the limiting case of motions involving large numbers of quanta of action. Applying this test to his interpretation of Rydberg's formula, Bohr found that the condition could be fulfilled only by ascribing the value $1/2$ to the numerical coefficient K, for which the right value of Rydberg's constant was obtained. Indeed, for large values of the number n, the frequencies $\nu_{n,n+p}$ are then seen to tend to the values of the frequency of revolution, $\omega_n = 2R/n^3$, and its successive harmonics, $p\omega_n$. Thus, as Bohr expressed it, "the most beautiful analogy" was established—in the sense just indicated—between classical electrodynamics and the quantum theory of radiation.

In his great papers of 1913, Bohr presented his theory as being founded upon two postulates, whose formulation he refined in later papers. The first postulate enunciates the existence of stationary states of an atomic system, the behavior of which may be described in terms of classical mechanics; the second postulate states that the transition of the system from one stationary state to another is a nonclassical process, accompanied by the emission or absorption of one quantum of homogeneous radiation, whose frequency is connected with its energy by Planck's equation. As for the principle by which the possible stationary states are selected, Bohr was still very far from a general formulation; indeed, he was keenly aware of the necessity of extending the investigation to configurations other than the simple ones to which he had restricted himself. The search for sufficiently general quantum conditions defining the stationary states of atomic systems was going to be a major problem in the following period of development of the theory.

A statement in Bohr's first paper gave rise to a controversy that soon ended in triumph for the new theory and in no small degree contributed to its swift acceptance. On the strength of his interpretation of Rydberg's formula, Bohr had pointed out that a certain series of lines attributed to hydrogen ought actually to be ascribed to helium: it had been fitted to the formula for hydrogen with half-integral values of the numbers n,m; in Bohr's view, which required integral values for these numbers, this could only mean that the Rydberg constant for this series was four times that for hydrogen, corresponding to a doubly charged nucleus. The experienced spectroscopist Alfred Fowler received the suggestion with understandable skepticism, but control experiments, which were at once performed in Rutherford's laboratory, confirmed Bohr's prediction. Fowler's last-ditch resistance, in the form of the pointed objection that Rydberg's coefficient for the contested series was not exactly $4R$ (R being the hydrogen value), was brilliantly countered by Bohr: he showed that the slight difference was to be expected as an effect of the motion of the nucleus, which he had neglected in his first approximation.

There is no doubt that this dramatic incident was decisive in convincing Rutherford and Fowler that there was something after all in this young foreigner's theorizing. This was also James Jeans's attitude when, in the report of Bohr's work he gave at the British Association meeting at Birmingham in September 1913, he pointed out that the only justification of Bohr's postulates "is the very weighty one of success." At Göttingen, that center of mathematics and physics, where the sense of propriety was strong, the prevailing impression was one of scandal, or at least bewilderment, in the face of the undeserved success of such high-handed disregard of the canons of formal logic; but the significance of Bohr's ideas did not escape those who had themselves most searchingly pondered the problems of quantum theory, Albert Einstein and Arnold Sommerfeld.

No one realized more keenly than Bohr himself the provisional character of his first conclusions, and above all the need for a deeper analysis of the logical relationship between the classical and quantal aspects of the atomic phenomena that were embodied in the two postulates. At the same time, he was faced with an overwhelming program of generalizing the theory and unfolding all its consequences. He was naturally more and more dissatisfied with his job at the university, which left him little time for research and (since he had mainly to deal with medical students) little hope of turning out pupils able to assist him in his work.

The academic authorities were slow in realizing that an exceptional situation had arisen, and when Rutherford offered him a lectureship in Manchester, Bohr was glad to avail himself of the opportunity to pursue his work under the most favorable conditions. He remained in Manchester for two years. In the meantime, the Danish authorities had moved to offer Bohr a professorship, which he accepted; and three years later, thanks to the active intervention of a group of friends, who donated the ground, they were at last persuaded to build Bohr a laboratory: this was the famous Institute for Theoretical Physics, of which he was director for the rest of his life. The founding of the institute came just in time to keep Bohr in his native country, for Rutherford, who had just been called to the directorship of the Cavendish Laboratory in Cambridge, had already invited Bohr to join him.

The new institute was meant to be primarily a physical laboratory; what was termed "theoretical physics" would now be called "fundamental physics." Bohr did not draw any sharp distinction between theoretical and experimental research; on the contrary, he visualized these two aspects of research as supporting and inspiring each other, and he wanted the laboratory equipped so as to make it possible to test new theoretical developments or conjectures by appropriate experiments. He managed to put this conception into effect; the experimental investigations carried out at the institute have not been numerous, but have always been of high quality—some of them, indeed, of pioneering importance—and all have been directly relevant to the theoretical questions under consideration. In order to keep up with the changing outlook of current theory, it was imperative to expand and even to renew the experimental equipment in order to adapt it to entirely new lines of research; this Bohr did with remarkable foresight as well as persuasive tenacity in securing the necessary funds.

Bohr's atomic theory inaugurated two of the most adventurous decades in the history of science, a period in which the efforts of the elite among the younger generation of physicists were concentrated on the numerous problems raised by the theory and on experimental investigations that further stimulated the theoretical developments or provided the required proof of theoretical predictions. Three experimental advances that furthered the progress of the theory were made as early as 1913 and 1914. The domain of X-ray spectroscopy was opened up by H. G. J. Moseley's brilliant work in Manchester, and its significance for atomic theory, on the basis of Bohr's ideas, was pointed out by Walther Kossel. The experiments of James Franck and Gustav Hertz on the excitation of radiation from atoms by collisions with electrons, and those of Johannes Stark on the modification of the atomic spectra by strong electric fields, offered a new approach to the study of the dynamical behavior of atomic systems; their interpretation was soon outlined by Bohr himself.

Optical spectroscopy, whose importance had been suddenly enhanced, was actively developed, especially by the school established at Tübingen under Friedrich Paschen's leadership; with his collaborators Ernst Back, Alfred Landé, and others, Paschen analyzed in great detail the fine structure of the line spectra and the further splitting of the lines under the action of magnetic fields of increasing strength, and he formulated the regularities obeyed by the frequencies and intensities of the lines in terms of sets of quantum numbers attached to the spectroscopic terms and taking integral or half-integral values.

On the theoretical side, too, the scene was rapidly changing. The isolation in which Bohr had hitherto found himself gave way to a lively collaboration with a growing number of fellow workers all striving toward the common goal, freely exchanging ideas, discussing results and conjectures, sharing the thrill of success and the expectation of further progress. By tacit consent, Bohr was the leader to whom all turned for guidance and inspiration. There were other great schools of theoretical physics, the foremost being those newly established by Sommerfeld in Munich and by Max Born in Göttingen; they pursued their own lines of research, always keeping in close contact with the Copenhagen group. The first to join Bohr in Copenhagen was a young Dutchman, H. A. Kramers, who arrived in 1916 and for the next ten years was Bohr's tireless assistant and talented collaborator. During this period, many others came to Bohr's institute; among them was Bohr's faithful friend Hevesy, as well as younger men—Oskar Klein, Wolfgang Pauli, and Werner Heisenberg.

The first of the main problems requiring consideration was the generalization of the quantum conditions defining the stationary states. Bohr did not at first attempt to make use of the general methods of classical mechanics; this was not his way of tackling problems. He preferred to handle concrete cases and to develop ingenious arguments which, although lacking generality, had the advantage of clearly bringing out the physical features of essential importance. In the present instance, he again started from the premise that slow deformations of a system would not change its quantal state, and developed it into a principle of mechanical transformability, which proved quite efficient within a limited scope. The idea was to transform one type of motion continuously into another by slow variation of some parameter; if the determination of the stationary states had been accomplished for one of the two motions, one could derive stationary states, by such a transformation, for the other. To this end, one could take advantage of the existence of dynamical quantities, the adiabatic invariants, which have the property of remaining unchanged under slow mechanical transformations.

As early as 1911, Paul Ehrenfest had emphasized the important role played by adiabatic invariants in the quantum theory of radiation in thermodynamic equilibrium; but neither he nor Bohr at first succeeded in extending this conception to modes of motion more complicated than simple periodic ones. Decisive progress in this problem was made by Sommerfeld, who at the end of 1915 succeeded in formulating a full set of quantum conditions for the general Keplerian motion, including even the relativistic precession of the elliptic trajectory. Sommerfeld's work not only supplied an explanation (a partial one as it turned out) of the fine doublet structure of the lines of the hydrogen spectrum, but showed the way to the desired generalization of the rules of quantization to more complex atomic systems, whose motions were not simply periodic.

Bohr eagerly followed this new line of attack; he now made full use of the powerful methods of Hamiltonian dynamics, especially in the form adapted to the wide class of motions known as multiply periodic, to which the motions of the electrons in atoms belonged. It was fortunate that Kramers, skilled in the relevant techniques, was at hand to help him; even so, it took years of strenuous effort to bring the work to completion. In their general form, the quantum conditions stated that a certain set of adiabatic invariants should be integral multiples of Planck's constant; but in the process of establishing this result, a formidable hurdle was the occurrence of "degeneracies" of the motions into simple periodic ones, which led to ambiguities in the formulation of the corresponding quantum conditions. This difficulty was eventually overcome by another ingenious application of the principle of mechanical transformability.

The theory of multiply periodic systems offered the possibility of a more rational treatment of the question which Bohr had tackled in his very first reflections on the nuclear atomic model: the gradual building up of atoms of increasing complexity and the origin of the periodicities in the atomic structures revealed by Mendeleev's table. The starting point was the consideration of the individual stationary orbits of each single electron in the electrostatic field of the nucleus, "screened" by the average field of the other electrons; the residual interaction of the electrons could then be treated by the perturbation methods originally developed for use by astronomers. For those spectra originating from quantum transitions of a single electron, usually the most weakly bound one, the quantum conditions provided a characterization directly comparable with the specification of the spectroscopic terms by quantum numbers.

The confrontation of the theory with the relevant spectroscopic evidence led to partial success: the main features of the empirical term sequences were well reproduced by the theory, and the spectroscopic quantum numbers on which these features depended accordingly acquired a simple mechanical interpretation (except for the occurrence of half-integral values, which appeared as an arbitrary modification of the quantum conditions); but the finer structure of the term sequences presented a complexity for which the atomic model offered no mechanical counterpart.

In spite of this imperfection, the model could be expected to give reliable guidance at least in the investigation of the broader outlines of atomic structures. The primitive ring configurations of Bohr's previous attempt were now replaced by groupings of individual electron orbits in "shells" specified by definite sets of quantum numbers, according to rules that were inferred from the spectroscopic data. This conception of the shell structure of atomic systems did

not merely account for the main classification of the stationary states; its scope could be extended to include the interpretation of the empirical rules established by the spectroscopists for the intensities of the quantal transitions between these states. This was a much more difficult problem than that of the formulation of quantum conditions for the stationary states; the complete breakdown of classical electrodynamics, reflected in Bohr's quantum postulates, seemed at first to remove the very foundation on which a comprehensive theory of atomic radiation could rest. It was in taking up this challenge that Bohr was led to one of his most powerful conceptions: the idea of a general correspondence between the classical and the quantal descriptions of the atomic phenomena.

Bohr seized upon the only link between the emission of light in a quantal transition and the classical process of radiation: the requirement that the classical description should be valid in the limiting case of transitions between states with very large quantum numbers. If the atom were treated as a multiply periodic system, its states of motion could be represented as superpositions of harmonic oscillations of specified frequencies and their integral multiples, each occurring with a definite amplitude; it was indeed possible to verify that the frequencies of quantal transitions between states of very large quantum numbers tended to become equal to those multiples of the classical frequencies given by the differences between these quantum numbers; in the limit of large quantum numbers, then, the classical amplitudes could be used directly to calculate the intensities of the quantal transitions. Bohr boldly postulated that such a correspondence should persist, at least approximately, even for transitions between states of small quantum numbers; in other words, the amplitudes of the harmonics of the classical motion should in all cases give an estimate of the corresponding quantal amplitudes.

The power of this correspondence argument was immediately illustrated by the application Kramers made of it, in a brilliant paper, to the splitting of the hydrogen lines in an electric field. Not only did the correspondence argument, for want of a more precise formulation, play an indispensable part in the interpretation of the spectroscopic data, but it eventually gave the decisive clue to the mathematical structure of a consistent quantum mechanics.

By 1918 Bohr had visualized, at least in outline, the whole theory of atomic phenomena, whose main points have been presented in the preceding sections. He of course realized that he was still very far from a logically consistent framework wide enough to incorporate both the quantum postulates and those aspects of classical mechanics and electrodynamics that seemed to retain some validity. Nevertheless, he at once started writing up a synthetic exposition of his arguments and of all the evidence upon which they could have any bearing; in testing how well he could summarize what was known, he found occasion to check the soundness of his ideas and to improve their formulation. In the present case, however, he could hardly keep pace with the growth of the subject; the paper he had in mind at the beginning developed into a four-part treatise, "On the Theory of Line Spectra," publication of which dragged over four years without being completed; the first three parts appeared between 1918 and 1922, and the fourth, unfortunately, was never published. Thus, the full impact of Bohr's views remained confined to the small but brilliant circle of his disciples, who indeed managed better than their master to make them more widely known by the prompter publication of their own results.

Bohr's theory of the periodic system of the elements, based essentially on the analysis of the evidence of the spectra, renewed the science of chemistry by putting at the chemists' disposal rational spectroscopic methods much more refined than the traditional ones. This was dramatically illustrated in 1922, by the identification, at Bohr's institute, of the element with atomic number 72. This discovery was made by Dirk Coster and Hevesy, under the direct guidance of Bohr's theoretical predictions of the properties of this element; they gave it the name "hafnium," from the latinized name of Copenhagen. The conclusive results were obtained just in time to be announced by Bohr in the address he delivered when he received the Nobel Prize in physics for that year.

There was never any question of Bohr's resting on his well-deserved laurels. He did not allow the apparent triumph of the quantum theory of atomic systems to mislead him into believing that the model used to describe these systems—simple point charges interacting by electrostatic forces according to the laws of classical mechanics—bore any close resemblance to reality. In fact, the fine structure of the spectroscopic classification manifested an essential insufficiency of this model, whose nature was not yet elucidated; but above all, the peculiar character of the correspondence between the quantal radiation processes and their classical counterpart strongly suggested that the classical model was no more than an auxiliary framework in the application of quantum conditions and correspondence considerations.

After Kramers had succeeded in extending the scope of the correspondence argument to the theory of optical dispersion—thus rounding off a treatment of the interaction of atomic systems with radiation that accounted for all emission, absorption, and scattering processes—Bohr ventured to propose a systematic formulation of the whole theory, in which what he called the virtual character of the classical model was emphasized. In this he was aided by Kramers and a young American visitor, J. C. Slater, and the new theory was published in 1924 under the authorship of all three. The most striking feature of this remarkable paper, "The Quantum Theory of Radiation," was the renunciation of the classical form of causality in favor of a purely statistical description. Even the distribution of energy and momentum between the radiation field and the "virtual oscillators" constituting the atomic systems was assumed to be statistical, the conservation laws being fulfilled only on the average. This was going too far: the paper was hardly in print before A. H. Compton and A. W. Simon had established by direct experiment the strict conservation of energy and momentum in an individual process of interaction between atom and radiation. Nevertheless, this short-lived attempt exerted a profound influence on the course of events; what remained after its failure was the conviction that the classical mode of description of the atomic processes had to be entirely relinquished.

This conviction was strengthened by the outcome of the other line of investigation most actively pursued in Copenhagen in these years, the search for the missing dynamic element of the atomic model. Pauli approached this arduous problem by trying to unravel the spectroscopic rules governing the fine structure of the terms and the splitting of the spectral lines in an external magnetic field—the anomalous Zeeman effect. He at length recognized that the entire problem could be simplified by attributing to the individual stationary states of each electron an additional quantum number, susceptible to two values only and combining with the other quantum numbers according to definite rules.

This conclusion at once threw light on the systematics of the shell structure of the elements, which Bohr had left incomplete, but which had lately been improved by E. C. Stoner. In fact, Pauli was able, in 1925, to formulate the simple underlying principle of this systematics: each stationary state—including the specification of the new quantum number—cannot be occupied by more than one electron. This exclusion principle has since received considerable extension, and has in fact turned out to be one of the most fundamental in nature. In the same year, decisive progress was made in the interpretation of the new quantum number by two of Ehrenfest's young pupils, S. A. Goudsmit and G. E. Uhlenbeck: they pointed out that the new quantum number could be ascribed to a proper rotation, or spin, of the electron, and that an intrinsic magnetic moment, related to the spin, could then account for the anomalous Zeeman effect. However, the quantization of the spin was at variance with that expressed by the quantum conditions; this circumstance, as well as the exclusion principle, which obviously was quite unaccountable in classical terms, showed in the most striking fashion that not only the radiation field but also the atomic constituents were out of reach of the conceptions of classical physics.

The crisis to which the attempt to treat the atom as a classical dynamic system had led did not last long. By the summer of 1925 Heisenberg had found the clue to the construction of a consistent mathematical scheme embodying the quantum postulates. This momentous progress was the direct outcome of the investigation of the optical dispersion theory initiated by Kramers. Heisenberg had taken an active part in this work and had been much impressed by the stand taken by Bohr, Kramers, and Slater. If classical conceptions could no longer be relied upon to supply at least a framework for the quantum theory, he concluded, what must be looked for is an abstract formal scheme expressing only relations between directly observable quantities, like the stationary states and the amplitudes whose absolute squares should express the probabilities of quantal transitions between these states. The correspondence between classical and quantal amplitudes established in the theory of dispersion, envisaged from this point of view, took the shape of a set of algebraic rules that these quantal amplitudes had to obey and that defined an algorism adapted to the rational formulation of laws of motion and quantum conditions, as well as the precise calculation of radiation amplitudes.

Heisenberg's program was eagerly taken up in Göttingen, where Born immediately recognized that the noncommutative algebra involved in Heisenberg's relations was the matrix calculus; at the same time, a young Cambridge physicist, P. A. M. Dirac, was developing even more abstract and elegant methods. While in the high places of mathematics the formal scheme of the new quantum mechanics was thus being built up, a more critical attitude prevailed in Copenhagen. Pauli pointed out that by limiting the observable quantities to stationary states and radiation amplitudes, Heisenberg was unduly restricting the scope of the theory, since it was an essential part of the correspondence argument that the new theory should contain as limiting case, for large quantum

numbers, the more detailed description of the motion in classical terms.

The fulfillment of this essential requirement necessitated a considerable extension of the mathematical framework of the theory, allowing it to accommodate both discontinuous and continuous aspects of the atomic phenomena. The decisive contribution was unexpectedly made by the "outsiders," Louis de Broglie and Erwin Schrödinger, who were exploring the conjecture that the constituents of matter might, like radiation, be governed by a law of propagation of continuous wave fields.

Although the idea in this one-sided form was at once seen to be untenable, it nevertheless provided the missing element; as Born especially emphasized, the wave fields associated with the particles give the probability distributions of the variables specifying the state of motion of these particles. Thus, the required formal completion of quantum mechanics could be carried out at the beginning of 1927, when Dirac indicated the most general representation of the operators belonging to the physical quantities, and the way to pass at will from any representation to any other according to definite prescriptions which guaranteed the fulfillment of all correspondence requirements. However, such classical features of the motion of particles as a sequence of positions forming a uniquely determined trajectory appeared only as a limiting case of a more general mode of description that was essentially statistical.

The quantum conditions were found to impose a peculiar restriction on the statistical distributions of the values of physical quantities. If, as a consequence of these conditions, the operators representing two such quantities do not commute, the average spreads in the assignment of the values they may take under given circumstances are reciprocal; their product exceeds a limit that depends on the degree of noncommutation and is proportional to Planck's constant. Thus, if in definite experimental circumstances the position of an electron, relative to some fixed frame of reference, is confined within narrow limits, its momentum will have a correspondingly wide range of possible values, each with its definite probability of occurrence, depending on the experimental conditions.

Heisenberg, who in 1927 discovered these remarkable indeterminacy relations, realized their epistemological significance. In fact, the novelty of quantum mechanics in this respect is that it allows for the possibility of using all classical concepts, even though their precise determinations may be mutually exclusive—as is the case with the concept of a particle localized at a point in space and time, and that of a wave field of precisely given momentum and energy, whose space-time extension is infinite. Indeterminacy relations between such concepts, then, indicate to what extent they may be used concurrently in statistical statements. Heisenberg saw that the origin of these reciprocal limitations must lie in quantal features of the processes in which the quantities in question are observable, and he attempted to analyze such idealized processes of observation from this point of view.

This was the occasion for Bohr to reenter the scene. His role so far had been to inspire and orient the creative efforts of the younger men, especially Heisenberg and Pauli, and he could legitimately consider the new theory as the attainment of the goal toward which he had so long been striving. On the one hand, the radical break with classical physical theories, which he had felt to be inescapable from the very beginning, was now formally accomplished by the substitution of abstract relations between operators for the simple numerical relations of classical physics. On the other hand, the abstract character of the new formalism made it at last possible to fulfill the requirement he had always emphasized: not to sacrifice any aspect of the phenomena, but to retain every element of the classical description within the limits suggested by experience.

The peculiar form of limitation of the validity of classical concepts expressed by the indeterminacy relations demanded a more thorough analysis than that which Heisenberg had initiated, however. For this challenging task Bohr was, of course, not unprepared. The occurrence of conflicting, yet equally indispensable, representations of the phenomena evoked the ambiguities of mental processes over which he had pondered in his student days. Now, however, similar dilemmas confronted him in an incomparably simpler form, for the description of atomic phenomena operated with only a few physical idealizations. Bohr hoped that the study of such a transparent case would lead him to a formulation of the epistemological situation that was sufficiently general to be applicable to the deeper problems of life and mind, and he devoted all his energy to it. Although he very soon was able to elucidate the essential features, he spent most of the following decade patiently refining the formulation of the fundamental ideas and exploring all their implications.

In any investigation of the scope of physical concepts, the method to follow is prescribed by the nature of the problem; one has to go back to the definition of the concepts by means of apparatus—real or idealized—suited to the measurement of the physical quantities they represent. The analysis of such mea-

suring operations should then reveal any limitation in the use of these concepts resulting from the laws of physics. This had been the method followed by Einstein in establishing the relativity of simultaneity; the same method was followed by Heisenberg and Bohr to elucidate the indeterminacy relations. It emerged from Bohr's analysis that the decisive element brought in by the quantum of action is what he called the individual character of quantal processes: any such process—for instance, the emission of radiation by an atom—occurs as a whole; it is well defined only when it is completed, and it cannot be subdivided like the processes dealt with in classical physics, which involve immense numbers of quanta, into a sequence of gradual changes of the system.

In particular, the measurement of a physical quantity pertaining to an atomic system can be regarded as completed only when its result has been recorded as some permanent mark left upon a registering device. Such a recording cannot be performed without some irreversible loss of control of the quantal interaction between the atomic system and the apparatus. Thus, if we record the position of an electron by a spot on a rigidly fixed photographic plate, we lose the possibility of ascertaining the exchange of momentum between the electron and the plate. Conversely, an apparatus suited to the determination of the momentum of the electron must include a mobile part, completely disconnected from the rigid frame of spatial reference, whose position, when it exchanges momentum with the electron, therefore necessarily escapes our control. Here is the root of the mutual exclusion of the application of such concepts as position and momentum in the extreme case of their ideally precise determination. More generally, by relaxing the accuracy requirements, it is possible to limit the reciprocal exclusion to the extent indicated by the indeterminacy relations, thus allowing for the concurrent use of the two concepts in a description that is then necessarily statistical.

It thus appears that in order to reach full clarity in such a novel situation, the very notion of physical phenomenon is first of all in need of a more careful definition that embodies the individuality or wholeness typical of quantal processes. This is achieved by inserting in the definition the explicit specification of all the relevant experimental arrangement, including the recording devices. Between phenomena occurring under such strictly specified conditions of observation, there may then arise the type of mutual exclusion for which an indeterminacy relation is the formal expression.

It is this relationship of mutual exclusion between two phenomena that Bohr designated as complementarity; by this he wanted to stress that two complementary phenomena belong to aspects of our experience which, although mutually exclusive, are nevertheless indispensable for a full account of experience. The introduction of the notion of complementarity finally solved the problem of the consistent incorporation of the quantum of action into the conceptual framework of physics—the problem with which Bohr had struggled so long. Complementarity was not an arbitrary creation of Bohr's mind, but the precise expression, won after patient efforts demanding a tremendous concentration, of a state of affairs entirely grounded in nature's laws, one that, according to Bohr's familiar exhortation, had to be learned only from nature. It consecrated the recognition of a statistical form of causality as the only possible link between phenomena presenting quantal individuality, but made it plain that the statistical mode of description of quantum mechanics was perfectly adapted to these phenomena and gave an exhaustive account of all their observable aspects.

From the epistemological point of view, the discovery of the new type of logical relationship that complementarity represents is a major advance that radically changes our whole view of the role and meaning of science. In contrast with the nineteenth-century ideal of a description of the phenomena from which every reference to their observation would be eliminated, we now have the much wider and truer prospect of an account of the phenomena in which due regard is paid to the conditions under which they can actually be observed—thereby securing the full objectivity of the description, since the description is based on purely physical operations intelligible and verifiable by all observers. The role of the classical concepts in this description is obviously essential, since those concepts are the only ones adapted to our capabilities of observation and unambiguous communication.

In order to establish a link between these concepts and the behavior of atomic systems, we have to use measuring instruments composed—like ourselves—of large numbers of atoms, and this requirement unavoidably leads to complementary relations and a statistical type of causality. These are the main lines of the new structure of scientific thought that gradually unfolded itself as Bohr, with uncompromising consistency, pursued his epistemological analysis to its limits. That some of the greatest representatives of the type of physical thinking with which he was so decisively breaking refused to follow him is understandable; that Einstein should be among them was always a matter of surprise and regret to Bohr. On the other hand, the progress of his work owed much

to Einstein's opposition; indeed, its successive stages are marked by the refutation of Einstein's subtle objections. Bohr himself retraced the dramatic course of this long controversy in an article of 1949, which marks the nearest he ever came to a systematic exposition of his argumentation.

The role of complementarity in quantum mechanics is above all to provide a logical frame sufficiently wide to ensure the consistent application of classical concepts whose unrestricted use would lead to contradictions. Obviously, such a function is of universal scope, and an occasion soon presented itself to put its usefulness to the test. In the early 1930's the extension of the mathematical methods of quantum mechanics to electrodynamics was beset with considerable formal difficulties, which raised doubts regarding the possibility of upholding the concept of the electromagnetic field in quantum theory.

This was clearly a point of crucial importance, since it bore upon the fundamental issue of a possible limit to the validity of the correspondence argument, hitherto unchallenged. According to Bohr's point of view, one had to inquire whether every component of the electromagnetic field could, in principle, be measured with unlimited accuracy, and whether the measurements of more than one component were subject only to the reciprocal limitations resulting from their complementary relationships. Bohr took up this investigation, which occupied him and Leon Rosenfeld during most of the period from 1931 to 1933. He succeeded in devising idealized measuring procedures, satisfying all requirements of relativity, by means of which all consequences of the quantization of the electromagnetic field could be confirmed. In view of the significance of the issue at stake, this work had a wider repercussion than its immediate effect of establishing the consistency of quantum electrodynamics: it showed how essential a part Bohr's epistemological standpoint played in the conception of the quantum phenomena.

By the middle 1930's the main interest had shifted, in Copenhagen as elsewhere, to the rapidly expanding field of nuclear physics. On the theoretical side, the results of the experiments on the reactions induced by the impact of slow neutrons on nuclei, carried out by Enrico Fermi and his school at Rome, created a critical situation. In discussing the processes involving the impact of charged particles, α particles or protons, on a nucleus, it had been found sufficient to represent the effect of the forces acting between the nucleus and the impinging particle schematically by an attractive potential well extending over the volume of the nucleus; to this was added the repulsive electrostatic potential, forming a coulomb barrier around the nucleus. It was therefore natural to analyze the neutron reactions with the help of the same potential, without the coulomb barrier; and it was a surprise that this model did not even qualitatively account for the observed effects. In particular, it was impossible on this basis to understand the very large probabilities with which the capture of the neutron by the nucleus occurred for a sequence of resonance energies.

Faced with this puzzling problem, Bohr proceeded to look for cases of capture processes occurring under a simpler form than in the range of low energies, in which they appeared to be tied to resonance conditions. As it happened, he had only to return to James Chadwick's earliest experiments, performed with neutrons of higher energy; he noticed that the different reactions induced by these neutrons all occurred at any energy with about the same probability, whose order of magnitude indicated that almost every neutron hitting the nucleus was captured by it. This strikingly simple result suggested to him a reaction mechanism radically different from the distortion of neutron waves by a potential well; indeed, in contrast with the quantal character of the latter model, the analogy Bohr proposed was completely classical. He visualized the nucleus as an assembly of nucleons held together by short-range forces, and thus, in effect, behaving like the assembly of the molecules forming a droplet of liquid.

The energy of a particle impinging upon such a system of similar particles moving about and continually colliding with each other will be rapidly distributed among all of them, with the result that none has enough energy to leave the system: the impinging neutron is captured, and a "compound nucleus" is thus formed in a state of high excitation. This state will subsist during a time that is long on the nuclear scale, i.e., which corresponds to many crossings of the nuclear volume by any single nucleon. It will decay as soon as some random fluctuation in the energy distribution has concentrated a sufficient amount of energy on some nucleon, or group of nucleons, to allow it to escape, a process comparable to evaporation from the heated droplet. It was also easy to understand that the density of possible states of the compound nucleus would rapidly increase with the energy of excitation; this explained the absence of resonance effects at high energies as well as their presence in the low-energy range.

Bohr's "droplet model" of nuclear reactions, refined in various ways since it was proposed in 1936, still holds as the adequate mode of description of one of the most important types of nuclear processes. It is of course an idealized model, and its basic assumptions are not always sufficiently fulfilled to ensure its

validity. Thus, another type of reaction has been found to occur, in which the interaction of the impinging particle with a single mode of motion of the target nucleus leads directly to a transfer of energy large enough to complete the process, without formation of a compound nucleus; these "direct interaction" processes are successfully treated with the help of the old method of the potential well, in which provision is made for the possibility of capture by a formal trick imitating the way in which the absorption of light is taken into account in classical optics. Compound nucleus and "optical" potential have now shed all apparent opposition and are blended into a comprehensive theory.

The most important application of Bohr's theory was the interpretation of nuclear fission. This is a type of reaction that may be initiated by impact of a neutron on a very heavy nucleus: the compound nucleus formed by the capture of the neutron has so little stability that it can split into two fragments of about the same mass and charge. It was Otto Hahn's and Fritz Strassmann's chemical identification of such fragments as decay products of uranium under neutron bombardment that led O. R. Frisch and Lise Meitner to recognize that the fission mechanism was the only conceivable interpretation.

The first experiments actually showing the emission of the fragments were performed in Copenhagen by Frisch in January 1939. By then Bohr had left for the United States, where he had been invited to spend a few months at Princeton. It was on his departure that he had heard of Frisch's idea and project; during the voyage and shortly after his arrival, also in January 1939, he outlined the whole theory of the process. In the following months, this theory was refined and elaborated in great detail, with J. A. Wheeler's collaboration.

A point that at first seemed surprising was that such a splitting of the nucleus into two parts, obviously initiated by a relative oscillation of these parts with increasing amplitude, could occur with a probability comparable to that of more familiar processes, such as the emission of a γ ray, which results from a stable motion affecting only a very few nucleons. As Bohr pointed out, however, this is a direct consequence of the statistical law of energy distribution among the various modes of motion of the compound nucleus. It seemed harder to explain the differences in the efficacy of slow and fast neutrons in inducing fission in different nuclei, but Bohr solved this problem as soon as he was confronted with the experimental data. By one of his most brilliant feats of rigorous induction from experiment, he unraveled the complex case of uranium, concluding that only the rare isotope of mass number 235 was fissile by slow neutrons, while the abundant isotope of mass 238 was not; and he showed by a very simple argument that this difference of behavior was due solely to the fact that the numbers of neutrons in the two isotopes were odd and even, respectively.

The discovery that the highly unstable fission fragments emitted neutrons immediately raised the question of the possibility of a chain reaction leading to the liberation of huge amounts of energy of nuclear origin. The answer to this question was soon found, and, coming as it did at a critical moment in the social and political evolution of the world, the unfolding of its consequences was precipitated with unprecedented violence. If this was a fateful development in the history of mankind, it also deeply affected Bohr's individual fate.

The work with fission, continued after his return to Copenhagen during the first three years of World War II, was the last piece of research he carried to completion in the quiet and serene atmosphere he had himself done so much to create. Only much later, during the last two summers of his life, did he for a while manage to concentrate again on a phenomenon very near to those with which he had started his scientific career: the superconductivity of metals, in which the quantum of action manifests itself, so to speak, by macroscopic effects. He tried, without success, to put the somewhat abstract theory of these effects on a more physical basis. In 1943, however, he was dragged into the turmoil of the war, and when he later came back to Copenhagen, he had to cope with profoundly changed conditions of scientific work that banished from his institute the intimacy of bygone years.

Bohr did not fare well among statesmen. In their eyes his candor and directness appeared strange and suspicious, and his clearsightedness was beyond their grasp. The physicists who were desperately striving, under great moral and intellectual stress, toward the dark goal of the nuclear weapon, felt the need of calling Bohr to their support. Bohr was transported in 1943 from Copenhagen to England, through Sweden, not without danger to his life, and was suddenly faced, to his surprise and dismay, with the advanced stage of a project he had deemed beyond the realm of technical accomplishment. Although he did take part, both in England and in the United States, in discussions of the physical problems related to the development of nuclear weapons, his main concern was to make the statesmen, as well as the physicists, aware of the political and human implications of the new source of power.

It is a striking example of his optimism that, besides the obvious dangers, he also stressed the potential advantages of the situation: the existence of a weapon equally threatening to all nations, he argued, offered a unique opportunity for reaching a universal agreement never to use it, which could become the foundation of an era of lasting peace. The condition for setting up such an agreement, he added with his customary logic, was universal knowledge of the issue. More concretely, he urged the Western leaders to initiate contacts with the Russians, with the view of creating a climate conducive to the establishment of peaceful relations and mutual confidence between the West and the East. Although these thoughtful considerations were appreciated by some of the men in key positions, his attempts to put them before Roosevelt and Churchill ended in failure. The fulfillment of his darkest predictions in the following years did not prevent him from persevering, and in 1950 he decided to publish an open letter to the United Nations, in which he repeated his plea for an "open world" as a precondition for peace. The timing of such an appeal was the worst possible; but it is now as relevant as ever, and may still perhaps find a response some day.

Apart from this unhappy excursion into the realm of world politics, Bohr devoted much time and energy to the more immediate tasks he was called upon to fulfill. In Denmark, the expansion of his institute occupied him to the last, and he also took a leading part in the foundation and organization, in 1955, of a Danish establishment for the constructive application of nuclear energy. When the European Center for Nuclear Research was founded in 1952, its theoretical division was installed in Bohr's institute, until it could move nearer the experimental divisions at Geneva in 1957; it was then replaced in Copenhagen by a similar institution of more restricted scope, the Nordic Institute for Theoretical Atomic Physics, created with Bohr's participation by the five Nordic governments to accommodate young theoretical physicists from those countries. In these years of unprecedented expansion of scientific research all over the world, Bohr's advice and support were sought on many occasions, and never in vain. He was more than ever a public figure, and honors were conferred on him from every quarter.

Unaffected by this lionization, Bohr made the best of it. An invitation to give a lecture was the occasion for him to orient his thought toward the particular aspect of science that would be familiar to his audience, and to reflect on the possible bearing on it of the new epistemological conceptions he had developed in quantum theory. Thus, in the 1930's he had given a lecture entitled "Light and Life" before a congress of phototherapists, and had spoken of the complementary features of human cultures in an assembly of anthropologists. In the postwar period, he went on in this vein and expressed thoughts about the human condition which for him were inseparable from a proper understanding of the aim and meaning of science. His writings on such topics were collected in three books, published in 1934, 1958, and 1963. These have been translated into several languages, and one must hope that in spite of the difficulty of style they may exert the same influence on the philosophical attitude of coming generations as on the minds of those who heard Bohr himself.

In fact, the form of publication of Bohr's essays is not felicitous. The books contain some repetition, especially in elementary expositions of the physical background, and the main points are often suggested to the reader rather than plainly stated. Involved sentences try to embrace all the shades of an uncommonly subtle dialectical form of thinking. Such obstacles ought not to deter those who are genuinely concerned with the problems, but the unprepared audiences to whom the message was addressed have too often failed to appreciate its true character. Bohr put an enormous amount of work into the composition of his essays, and they contain the most carefully weighed expression of his philosophy.

Bohr's essays strikingly illustrate the continuity of his thought. He was striving all the time to find more precise formulations and to disclose new aspects of the complementary relationships he was exploring, but the basic conception remained the same in all essentials from his youth to his last days. Critics endeavoring to trace foreign influences on his thinking are quite misguided: he was no doubt interested when analogies were pointed out to him between his own conceptions and those of others, but such comparisons never led to any modification of his argumentation—this argumentation, in contrast with the other, was so solidly founded in the analysis of the clear and precise situation offered by the development of quantum theory that there was no need for any firmer foundation. Indeed, Bohr repeatedly stressed the fortunate circumstance that the simplicity of the physical issue made it possible for him to arrive at an adequate formulation of the relations of complementarity he perceived in all aspects of human knowledge.

The domain in which complementary situations manifest themselves most immediately is the realm of psychical phenomena—which had been the starting point for Bohr's early observations. He was now able to express in terms of complementarity the peculiar relation between the description of our emotions as revealed by our behavior and our consciousness of

them; in such considerations he liked to imagine (on slender evidence, it must be said) that sayings of ancient philosophers and prophets were groping expressions for complementary aspects of human existence.

In the development of human societies, Bohr emphasized the dominant role of tradition over the complementary aspect of hereditary transmission in determining the essential elements of what we call culture; this he held in opposition to the racial theories then propagated in Germany. Nearer to physics, he pointed out that the two modes of description of biological phenomena which were usually put in absolute opposition to each other—the physical and chemical analysis on the one hand, the functional analysis on the other—ought to be regarded as complementary. Altogether, he saw in complementarity a rational means of avoiding the exclusion of any line of thought that had in any way proved fruitful, and of always keeping an open mind to new possibilities of development.

In his last years, he followed with the deepest satisfaction the spectacular advance of molecular biology. In the last essay he wrote, "Light and Life Revisited," he made it clear that in upholding the use of functional concepts in biology, he did not have in mind any insuperable limitation of the scope of the physical description; on the contrary, he saw in the recent progress the unlimited prospect of a full account of biological processes in physical terms, without prejudice to an equally full account of their functional aspect.

The origin of Bohr's epistemological ideas in a purely scientific situation confers on them the character of scientific soundness and certainty. Bohr was always careful to stress both the necessity, in epistemological investigations, of divesting oneself of all preconceived opinions and of seeking guidance exclusively in the data of experience and the equally stringent necessity of recognizing in every case the limitations inherent in the concepts used in the account of the phenomena. In order to understand the unique significance of his contribution to epistemology, it is necessary to realize that complementarity is a logical relationship, referring to our way of describing and communicating our experience of a universe in which we occupy the singular position of being at the same time, and inseparably, spectators and actors. Far from excluding any aspect of the universe from our reach, complementarity enables us, so far as we can judge, to account for all aspects of the phenomena—comprehensively, rationally, and objectively. By the rigor of his rational thinking, the universality of his outlook, and his deep humanity, Bohr ranks among the fortunate few to whom it has been given to help the human mind take a decisive step toward a fuller harmony with nature.

BIBLIOGRAPHY

This biography is based mainly on personal experience and conversations with Niels Bohr and his closest collaborators, as well as on the correspondence and documents in the Niels Bohr Archive in Copenhagen. Detailed biographical material is published in *Niels Bohr, His Life and Work as Seen by His Friends and Colleagues,* S. Rozental, ed. (Amsterdam, 1967). See also the report of the Niels Bohr Memorial Session held in Washington, D.C., on 22 April 1963 in *Physics Today,* **16,** no. 10 (Oct. 1963), 21–62; and an earlier essay of a more personal character: L. Rosenfeld, *Niels Bohr: An Essay* (Amsterdam, 1945; rev. ed., 1961). There is much autobiographical material in Bohr's Rutherford memorial lecture, "Reminiscences of the Founder of Nuclear Science and of Some Developments Based on His Work," in *Proceedings of the Physical Society of London,* **78** (1961), 1083–1115.

A full bibliography of Bohr's publications may be found in *Nuclear Physics,* **41** (1963), 7–12. The main items are the following: *Studier over metallernes elektrontheori* (Copenhagen, 1911); *On the Constitution of Atoms and Molecules,* papers of 1913 reprinted from the *Philosophical Magazine* with an introduction by L. Rosenfeld (Copenhagen, 1963); "On the Quantum Theory of Line Spectra," pts. I–III, in *Det Kgl. Danske Videnskabernes Selskabs Skrifter, naturvidenskabelig-matematisk Afdeling,* **4,** no. 1 (1918–1922); "The Structure of the Atoms," his Nobel lecture, in *Nature,* **112** (1923), 29–44; "The Quantum Theory of Radiation," with H. A. Kramers and J. C. Slater, in *Philosophical Magazine,* **47** (1924), 785–802; "Zur Frage der Messbarkeit der elektromagnetischen Feldgrössen," with L. Rosenfeld, in *Det Kgl. Danske Videnskabernes Selskab, matematisk-fysiske Meddelelser,* **12,** no. 8 (1933); "Neutron Capture and Nuclear Constitution," in *Nature,* **136** (1936), 344–348, 351; "The Mechanism of Nuclear Fission," with J. A. Wheeler, in *Physical Review,* **56** (1939), 426–450; and "The Penetration of Atomic Particles Through Matter," in *Det Kgl. Danske Videnskabernes Selskab, matematisk-fysiske Meddelelser,* **18,** no. 8 (1948).

The three volumes of collected essays are *Atomic Theory and the Description of Nature* (Cambridge, 1934; repr. 1961); *Atomic Physics and Human Knowledge* (New York, 1958); and *Essays 1958–1962 on Atomic Physics and Human Knowledge* (New York, 1963).

LEON ROSENFELD

BOISBAUDRAN, PAUL ÉMILE LECOQ DE (called **François**) (*b.* Cognac, France, 18 April 1838; *d.* Paris, France, 28 May 1912), *chemistry.*

Boisbaudran's family belonged to the ancient Protestant nobility of Poitou and Angoumois, and had been wealthy prior to the religious persecutions of the seventeenth and eighteenth centuries. When Boisbaudran was born, however, his father and uncle were coproprietors of a wine business at Cognac. His mother, daughter of an army officer, was a learned woman who taught her son classics, history, and foreign languages. Although he had no formal schooling, Boisbaudran worked through the course books of the École Polytechnique, performing experiments in a home laboratory equipped by his uncle.

At the age of twenty, Boisbaudran began to work for the family company, traveling through the Continent and England on business. He continued to study chemistry and physics in his spare time; as business prospered, he was allowed to spend more time on scientific work. His early research concerned supersaturation of salt solutions, conditions of crystallization, and crystalline shapes.

Boisbaudran is best known for his work on spectroscopic methods of elementary analysis. In a volume entitled *Spectres lumineux* (1874), he reported the results of extensive and refined spectral examinations of thirty-five elements. This work was undertaken to test several generalizations relating spectral wavelength to atomic weight. In this work, Boisbaudran held that the various kinds of spectra for the elements were related to the various motions (rotation, vibration, and translation) of the molecules. He believed, however, that the displacement of the lines in related elements did not correspond to the magnitude of the molecular forces (as some chemists held) but to the mass of the molecules.

In 1875 Boisbaudran spectroscopically discovered a new element, gallium, which he found in zinc blende from a mine in Hautes-Pyrénées. Continuing his work in Wurtz's laboratory in Paris, he was able to obtain the free metal by electrolysis of a solution of the hydroxide in potassium hydroxide. Gallium, Boisbaudran realized, was the "eka-aluminum" predicted by Mendeleev, and was the first of Mendeleev's predicted elements to be isolated. Boisbaudran's finding thus provided valuable evidence for the validity of Mendeleev's periodic classification of the elements.

In 1879 Boisbaudran began spectroscopic experimentation with the rare earth elements, research that he pursued for several decades. Collaborating with John Lawrence Smith, he showed that didymium from cerite differed from that coming from samarskite. This discrepancy led to the discovery of samarium. In 1885 the elements that have since been named dysprosium, terbium, and europium were identified from their phosphorescent spectra. Such phosphorescent bands were produced by making the liquid under consideration the positive pole, instead of the negative pole, when a line spectrum is formed. In 1886 a new element, later called gadolinium, was detected in earths yielding samarium. In 1904 Boisbaudran used "Z" to denote an element contained in earth separated from impure terbium and subsequently identified as pure terbium.

After 1895 Boisbaudran's scientific work decreased considerably because of failing health and family and business concerns. He married late in life, but no further information about his family can be found. Boisbaudran was a winner of the Cross of the Legion of Honor, the 1879 Davy Medal (for his discovery of gallium), and the Prix Lacaze. He was a corresponding member of the chemistry section of the French Academy of Sciences, and a foreign member of the Chemical Society of London.

BIBLIOGRAPHY

I. ORIGINAL WORKS. Among Boisbaudran's writings are *Spectres lumineux: Spectres prismatiques et enlonguers d'ondes destinés aux recherches de chimie minérale,* 2 vols. (Paris, 1874), and an article on gallium, in E. Fremy, ed., *Encyclopédie chimique,* XVI (Paris, 1884), 201–222. The discovery of gallium is reported in *Comptes rendus de l'Académie des sciences,* **81** (1875), 493–495; *Philosophical Magazine,* 5th ser., **2** (1876), 398–400; and *Annales de chimie et de physique,* **10** (1877), 100–141. A crucial work is *Analyse spectrale appliquée aux recherches de chimie minérale,* 2 vols. (Paris, 1923), written with A. Gramont, which contains a biographical sketch of Boisbaudran and a complete bibliography, pp. xi–liv; most of his publications are also listed in Poggendorff.

II. SECONDARY LITERATURE. Works on Boisbaudran are M. A. Gramont, "Lecoq de Boisbaudran: Son oeuvre et ses idées," in *Revue scientifique,* **51,** pt. 1 (25 Jan. 1913), 97–109; W. Ramsay, obituary, in *Journal of the Chemical Society,* **103** (1913), 742–746; Urbain, obituary, in *Chemische Zeitung,* **36** (1912), 923–933; and Mary Elvira Weeks, *Discovery of the Elements,* 6th ed. (Easton, Pa., 1956), esp. chs. 25, 26.

SUSAN G. SCHACHER

BOISLAURENT, FRANÇOIS BUDAN DE. See **Budan de Boislaurent, François.**

BOLK, LODEWIJK, usually called **LOUIS** (*b.* Overschie, the Netherlands, 10 December 1866; *d.* Amsterdam, the Netherlands, 17 June 1930), *anatomy.*

Bolk's parents wanted him to study for the ministry, but he preferred to attend medical school, which they could not afford. In 1888 he managed, with financial aid, to matriculate as a medical student at Amsterdam University, where he became an assistant to Georg Ruge, professor of human anatomy, after he had passed his final medical examination in October 1896. When Ruge retired, Bolk was appointed his successor in February 1898, because he had proved himself an exponent of functional, as against descriptive, anatomy.

In the anatomical periodical *Petrus Camper,* which Bolk and Winkler started in 1900, Bolk published on the comparative anatomy of the cerebellum and its nerves. The localization of muscle coordination in the cerebellum proved to have clinical implications. Leiden University awarded him an honorary doctorate in 1902, but he refused the professorship of anatomy there—Amsterdam University had started to build a new anatomical institute adapted to his needs and ideas.

The removal of an old graveyard near the institute induced Bolk to study human skulls and teeth. His research dealt with the ontogény of the teeth, left-handedness and right-handedness, the length of the body in different races (Nordic and Alpine in the Netherlands), color of the eyes and hair, endocrinology, and general ontogeny.

Bolk was knighted (1918) while *rector magnificus* of Amsterdam University. Here, for the first time, he put forward his ideas of "fetalization." The theory was fully expounded during the Anatomical Congress in Freiburg (1926) and was published as "Das Problem der Menschwerdung." It considers man to be a neotenic ape and states that the retention of many fetal characters in the adult is caused by the endocrine glands. The theory indicates that, in a way, apes are more specialized from an evolutionary point of view than man is.

On the occasion of his silver jubilee as professor, Bolk was made a Commander in the Order of Orange-Nassau, and in 1927 he received the Swedish Retzius Medal for his work on the cerebellum. At the time of his death all professors of anatomy in the Netherlands and the East Indies had been his pupils.

BIBLIOGRAPHY

I. ORIGINAL WORKS. For a nearly complete list of Bolk's 179 publications, see A. J. P. Van Den Broek, "Louis Bolk," in *Gegenbaurs morphologisches Jahrbuch,* **65** (1931), 497–516. Additional papers are nos. 1, 3, 11, 12, 21, 24, 44, 47, and 67 in the list in A. J. Van Bork-Feltkamp, "Anthropological Research in the Netherlands," in *Verhandelingen van de Koninklijke Nederlandse Akademie van Wetenschappen, afdeling Natuurkunde,* **37** (1938), 1–166, list on 137–139. Bolk's earlier works include papers on the problems of segmental anatomy, in *Morphologisches Jahrbuch* (1894–1900); "Das Cerebellum der Säugetiere," in *Petrus Camper,* **3** and **4,** also published separately (1906); and *Odontologische Studien,* 2 vols. (1913–1914). The "fetalization theory" is in *Hersenen en Cultuur* (1918; 3rd ed., 1932); "The Part Played by the Endocrine Glands in the Evolution of Man," in *The Lancet* (10 September 1921); and "Das Problem der Menschwerdung," in *25sten Versammlung der anatomischen Gesellschaft in Freiburg* (Jena, 1926). A posthumous work is his contribution to *Handbuch der vergleichenden Anatomie der Wirbeltiere* (Berlin–Vienna, 1931).

II. SECONDARY LITERATURE. The best biography is that of A. J. P. Van Den Broek (see above). Additional data are in Van Bork-Feltcamp (see above). Obituaries are C. U. Ariëns Kappers, in *Psychologische en Neurologische Bladen,* **4** (1930), 1–6; J. A. J. Barge, in *Jaarboek van de Maatschappy de Nederlandsche Letterkunde* (1935–1936); Brouwer, *Verslagen der Koninklijke Nederlandsche Akademie van Wetenschappen,* **6** (1930); *Gedenkboek Universiteit van Amsterdam* (Amsterdam, 1932), pp. 188, 554; W. A. Mijsberg, in *Geneeskundig Tijdschrift voor Nederlandsch-Indië,* **2** (1930), 737–738; C. A. J. Quant, in *The Lancet* (12 July 1930), 76; A. J. P. Van Den Broek, in *Nederlandsch Tijdschrift voor Geneeskunde* (1930); and F. A. F. C. Went, "In Memoriam Lodewijk Bolk," in *Verslagen der Koninklijke Nederlandsche Akademie van Wetenschappen,* **39** (1930), 1–7.

H. ENGEL

BOLOS OF MENDES, also known as **Bolos the Democritean** (*b.* Mendes, Egypt; *fl. ca.* 200 B.C.), *biology.*

The dates of Bolos of Mendes cannot be established with certainty, and nothing seems to be known of his life. The extent of his influence cannot be estimated easily because of his deliberate policy of passing off his writings under Democritus' name. Obvious pseudo-Democritean writings, in turn, were later attributed to Bolos. Together these writings, none of which has survived, constitute a complex literary tradition in which the original contributions cannot be disentangled from later additions. Bolos was widely read in antiquity, when his reputation rivaled that of Aristotle as an authority in natural history. Judging from the titles of his lost writings, he wrote on a wide range of subjects. Some evidence exists that he was one of the principal early sources for the later encyclopedic tradition in which natural history and the lore of marvels are indistinguishable. Only a few fragments actually bear his name, thus precluding a detailed reconstruction of any of his writings. It is doubtful that he was systematic in collecting his data or that he made original contributions. The evidence suggests, rather, that he collected a large and diverse body of information, largely supernatural in nature, that could be put to the various purposes suited to the exploitation of the irrational in Hellenistic times.

Bolos' best-known and most influential work was entitled Φυσικὰ δυναμερά ("Natural Properties"). Sometimes known as Περὶ συμπαθειῶν καὶ ἀντιπαθειῶν ("On Sympathies and Antipathies"), it was an attempt to categorize observed biological and ecological relationships and to explain them in terms of the supposed, conscious "loves and hates" existing between the entities in question. Animals, plants, and minerals, each associated with its particular astral god, were believed to be invested with miraculous powers. As a result, magical ritual and religious invocations tended to take the place of causal explanation based on empirical observation and description. Bolos' influence is seen most clearly in Aelian, Pliny, and the anonymous Hermetic writers.

Other works ascribed to Bolos include Χειρόκμητα ("Things Made or Performed by Hand"), which is usually cited under the name of Democritus. It dealt with medical and magical herbs and various agricultural practices. His Περὶ λιθῶν ("On Stones") was a catalog of precious and semiprecious stones in which their supernatural powers were described in a manner foreshadowing the later lapidaries. Another of his writings, Περὶ γεωργίας ("On Farming"), was known to Columella and was frequently consulted by the writers of the *Geoponica.* Two other writings ascribed to him, but whose precise titles and meaning are unclear, are "Concerning Miracles" and an astrological tract, "On the Signs of the Sun and Moon." Portions of late magical papyri containing alchemical texts and directions for technological processes, some of which have been attributed to Pseudo-Democritus, may derive ultimately from Bolos' lost Βαφικά ("Things Dyed or Gilded"). He is also credited with separate writings on medicine, magical herbs, military tactics, and ethics, and Περὶ Ἰουδαίων ("History of the Jews"), but few identifiable fragments remain.

BIBLIOGRAPHY

Further discussion of Bolos or his work can be found in Hermann Diels, *Antike Technik,* 2nd ed. (Leipzig, 1920), pp. 127–138; Wilhelm Kroll, "Bolos und Demokritos," in *Hermes,* **69** (1934), 228–232; E. H. F. Meyer, *Geschichte der Botanik,* I (Königsberg, 1854), 277–284; Eugen Oder, "Beiträge zur Geschichte der Landwirthschaft bei den Griechen," in *Rheinisches Museum für Philologie,* **45** (1890), 58–99; and Max Wellmann, "Bolos aus Mendes," in Pauly-Wissowa, *Real-Encyclopädie,* III, cols. 676–677; "Die Georgika des Demokritos," in *Abhandlungen der Preussischen Akademie der Wissenschaft, Philosophisch-Historische Klasse,* no. 4 (1921), which contains an edition of the eighty-two fragments surviving from Bolos' writings on agriculture; and "Die ΦΥΣΙΚΑ des Bolos Demokritos und der Magier Anaxilaos aus Larissa," *ibid.*, no. 7 (1928), the fundamental study.

JERRY STANNARD

BOLOTOV, ANDREI TIMOFEEVICH (*b.* Dvoryaninovo, Tula oblast, Russia, 18 October 1738; *d.* Dvoryaninovo, 15 October 1833), *agronomy, biology.*

Bolotov's father was an army officer, and in 1755 Bolotov, too, entered military service. From 1757 to 1761 he was a translator attached to the Russian military governor at Königsberg, and in 1761–1762 he was adjutant to the St. Petersburg chief of police. Bolotov retired in 1762, moved to the country, and devoted himself to agronomy and botany, especially horticulture.

Characteristic of Bolotov's work was a striving not only to explore a given problem and to explain a given phenomenon arising from his practical experience and experimentation, but also to discover general biological laws and to find means of influencing the development of plants for practical purposes.

Bolotov's most noteworthy achievement was the defense and further development, during a period when the humus theory of soil fertility reigned supreme, of the theory that plants need mineral nourishment. Following Linnaeus, Camerarius, Koelreuter, and Christian Sprengel, Bolotov advocated, developed, and propagandized the field concept at a time when the majority of botanists approached it with distrust or completely ignored it as unfounded.

Bolotov considered the union of male and female sexual elements as the condition of fertilization and development of a new plant from a seed bud. He noted the quantity of pollen necessary for normal fertilization, the widespread occurrence in nature of cross-pollination, and the role of wind and insects in the latter process. His research on these questions covered the period 1778 to 1823. In 1778, fifteen years before Sprengel, Bolotov gave a sufficiently precise description of dichogamy—the maturation of the pistil and the stamen of bisexual plants at different times, which ensures cross-pollination in these plants.

In an article on the hazel nut (1804) and in several earlier works, such as "O semenakh" ("On Seeds," 1780), he noted the role of multiple pollination in increasing the fitness for survival of a species; thus, he anticipated the general features of Thomas Knight's discovery, which later received an explanation in the works of Darwin and of I. V. Michurin. Bolotov saw in cross-pollination and intraspecific and interspecific hybridization some of the sources of the multiplicity of forms in nature. Much attention is given in his works to the formative influence of environmental conditions; in many of these works elements of an ecological approach to the analysis of phenomena in the plant world are clearly shown.

Bolotov was the author of more than 300 works, a prodigious output.

BIBLIOGRAPHY

Many of Bolotov's works were brought together in *Izbrannye sochinenia po agronomy, pludovodstvu, lesovodstvu, botanike* ("Selected Works on Agronomy, Fruit Growing, Forestry, and Botany," Moscow, 1952).

Works on Bolotov are A. P. Berdyshev, *A. T. Bolotov—perv russky ucheny agronom* ("A. T. Bolotov—The First Russian Agronomist," Moscow, 1949); *Istoria estestvoznania v Rossy* ("The History of Natural Science in Russia"), I, pt. 1 (Moscow, 1957), 475–478; I. M. Polyakov, "Istoria otkrytia dikhogamy i rol russkikh uchenykh v etom otkryty" ("History of the Discovery of Dichogamy and the Role of Russian Scientists in This Discovery"), in *Uspekhi sovremennoi biologii*, **30**, no. 2 (1950), 291–306; and I. M. Polyakov and A. P. Berdyshev, "A. T. Bolotov i ego trudy v oblasti selskokhozyaystvennoy i biologicheskoy nauki" ("A. T. Bolotov and His Works in the Fields of the Agricultural and Biological Sciences"), in Bolotov's *Izbrannye sochinenia*.

S. R. MIKULINSKY

BOLTWOOD, BERTRAM BORDEN (*b.* Amherst, Massachusetts, 27 July 1870; *d.* Hancock Point, Maine, 14/15 August 1927), *radiochemistry.*

Scientists spent the first several years following Henri Becquerel's discovery of radioactivity in 1896 largely in studying the physical properties of the radiations. By 1904, however, enough radioelements had been found to shift their interest to the bodies emitting these radiations. In the chemical identification of the radioelements and in positioning them in proper sequence in the decay series, Boltwood was an equal among such first-generation radiochemists as Otto Hahn, Frederick Soddy, Friedrich Giesel, and Herbert N. McCoy.

Boltwood's paternal ancestors came to America from Great Britain in the mid-seventeenth century. They settled in New England, where for several generations they were farmers, millers, and blacksmiths. One was able to work his way through Williams College, graduating in 1814 and later becoming a lawyer in Amherst, Massachusetts. This was Lucius Boltwood, Bertram's grandfather, who was active in the founding of Amherst College and served as its secretary from 1828 to 1864. He also was a candidate for the governorship of Massachusetts in 1841. Bertram's father, Thomas Kast Boltwood, graduated from Yale College in 1864, received a degree from the Albany Law School in 1866, and practiced his profession until his untimely death in 1872. Bertram, an only child, thereafter was raised entirely by his mother, Margaret Van Hoesen Boltwood, in her native village of Castleton-on-Hudson, New York. The Van Hoesens, of Dutch stock, were among the early settlers of Rensselaer County during the seventeenth century.

Bertram Boltwood grew up in comfortable surroundings, attended a private school, and from 1879 to 1889 prepared at the Albany Academy for Yale. The intellectual stature of his family, represented by cousin Ralph Waldo Emerson and uncle Charles U. Shepard, a professor of mineralogy at Amherst, presumably had great influence on him, although his childhood was characterized more by fun and practical jokes than by scholarship. Nevertheless, he entered Yale's Sheffield Scientific School in 1889, majoring in chemistry. Upon completion of the three-year course, Boltwood took highest honors in his subject and then departed for two years of advanced study at the Ludwig-Maximilian University in Munich. The training he received there under Alexander Krüss in special analytical methods and in the rare earths was to prove valuable in later years.

Boltwood returned to Yale in 1894 as a laboratory assistant in analytical chemistry and also to pursue graduate research. His work on double salts was accomplished under the direction of Horace L. Wells, who became his thesis adviser. In 1896 Boltwood spent a semester at the University of Leipzig, where he studied physical chemistry in Ostwald's laboratory, and then returned to Yale, where he received the Ph.D. in June 1897. A strong attachment brought Boltwood back to Europe several times in later years; his exuberant personality, his lifelong bachelorhood, and his height—well over six feet—made him both distinctive and welcome there.

Following graduation, Boltwood remained at the Sheffield Scientific School as an instructor in analytical chemistry, a position he had assumed a year earlier; later he was an instructor in physical chemistry. Until 1900, when he established a private laboratory as a consulting chemist, Boltwood devoted himself to perfecting laboratory apparatus and techniques and supplying teaching materials for students. He devised a simple automatic Sprengel pump, a new form of water blast, a lead fume pipe for the Kjeldahl nitrogen determination apparatus, and, somewhat later, Boltwax, a wax with low melting point, useful

for vacuum seals. He also translated German texts on physical chemistry and quantitative analysis by electrolysis. Boltwood's eager acquisition of new techniques made him a storehouse of information upon which his colleagues often drew. In later years he conducted demonstration classes in laboratory arts for research students.

In 1900 Boltwood left Yale and, with Joseph Hyde Pratt, also a Sheffield graduate, established a partnership: Pratt and Boltwood, Consulting Mining Engineers and Chemists. Pratt worked in the field, mostly in the Carolinas, and sent ore samples for analysis to Boltwood's private laboratory in downtown New Haven. Many of these samples contained rare earth elements and uranium and thorium, with which they commonly are associated. In 1896 Becquerel had discovered the radioactivity of uranium, and in 1898 Gerhard C. Schmidt and Marie Curie independently found thorium to be radioactive. It was perhaps inevitable that Boltwood's interest would turn in this direction, considering his early training in the analysis of rare earths, his inclination toward analytical and physical chemistry, his current familiarity with such ores as monazite and uraninite, and the challenge offered to his laboratory skill by work in radioactivity. He was not a total stranger to radioactivity, moreover, for in a senior thesis written under his direction in 1899, a student had repeated the Curies' separation process for radium and had narrowly missed the discovery of actinium in the pitchblende residues. Upon André Debierne's announcement of this new radioelement, Boltwood tested his student's substance and confirmed actinium's presence.

In April 1904, Boltwood began research on radioactivity. Not long before, Ernest Rutherford and Frederick Soddy had advanced a revolutionary new interpretation of this phenomenon: that radioactive atoms decay and transmute into other elements. While the evidence supporting this theory already was impressive, Boltwood reasoned that he could more strongly confirm it by showing a constant ratio between the amounts of radium and uranium in unaltered minerals. Such uniformity in composition would have to be accepted as proof of a genetic relationship, wherein the uranium decayed in several steps to form radium, which in turn decayed to form a series of several daughter products.

Boltwood quickly saw that the minute traces of radium, with chemical properties of its own, would be difficult to separate and test quantitatively. He therefore chose to measure radium's first daughter product, emanation, as an indication of the amount of radium present. Emanation, being chemically inert and a gas, required only mechanical separation; its activity thus was easier to measure. Within a few months, Boltwood's gas-tight gold-leaf electroscope yielded data showing that the activity of radium emanation was directly proportional to the amount of uranium in each of his samples. Rutherford, delighted with this news, encouraged Boltwood to perform the same tests on minerals with much smaller percentages of uranium. Yet even with this further confirmation in hand, Boltwood decided that direct proof that uranium decays into radium was desirable—he would try to "grow" radium.

One of the steps in this effort was to determine the equilibrium amount of radium. Boltwood's voluminous correspondence with Rutherford had ripened into a warm friendship; and the two collaborated, by mail, in the 1906 announcement that "the quantity of radium associated with one gram of uranium in a radio-active mineral is equal to approximately 3.8×10^{-7} gram." (The figure accepted today is 3.42×10^{-7} gram.) But Boltwood's attempts to grow radium were unsuccessful. Only one product between uranium and radium was then known; this was uranium X, whose short half-life should allow detectable quantities of radium to form within reasonable time limits. Yet even after more than a year, he was unable to observe any radium emanation in his uranium solution. Since Boltwood's faith in the disintegration theory did not waver, he concluded that there must be a long-lived decay product between uranium X and radium that was preventing the rapid accumulation of the daughter product.

Boltwood's search for this "parent of radium" was interrupted by his appointment as assistant professor of physics at Yale College. During the summer of 1906 he moved his apparatus into the Sloane Physics Laboratory and prepared to undertake his new academic duties. These responsibilities proved more extensive than anticipated, since, owing to the illness of the laboratory's director, Boltwood's close friend Henry A. Bumstead, he was left in charge of extensive renovations in the old building. Resumption of the search led him to Debierne's actinium, and Boltwood indeed believed for a while that he had properly placed actinium in the decay series. Among others, Soddy in Glasgow was working on the same problem, and the two carried on a heated controversy in the pages of *Nature*. Rutherford also was disinclined to accept actinium as the parent of radium and based his objection on the relative activities of actinium's products, a field in which Boltwood and McCoy had done basic work. The activities of many radioelements had been determined, relative to that of uranium, and

if those of actinium and its products were added to those of uranium, uranium X, radium, radium emanation, radium A, B, and so on, the total would be far greater than that of the mineral which supposedly contained them all in secular equilibrium.

Further investigation showed Boltwood that his difficulty lay in accepting Debierne's work on actinium as correct. In fact, there were other constituents in the Frenchman's radioelement, one of them having chemical properties similar to those of thorium. It was this substance, named "ionium" by Boltwood in 1907, that was the immediate parent of radium. He had now proved that ionium grows radium; that uranium grows ionium had still to be shown to complete the direct proof of this relationship. Tests a few years later were unsuccessful due to the small quantity of ionium accumulated. Finally, in 1919, Soddy conclusively proved this relationship, using uranium purified many years earlier.

An outgrowth of this work was a superior method for the determination of the half-life of radium. Under Boltwood's direction during the 1913–1914 academic year, a Norwegian chemist, Ellen Gleditsch, who had previously worked in Madame Curie's laboratory, obtained a value of slightly under 1,700 years. Another result of this intensive study of the chemistry of the radioelements was the realization that many of these substances, which differed in type and intensity of radiation, nevertheless could not be separated chemically. Thus, beginning about 1907, Boltwood, as well as Hahn, McCoy, and most other radiochemists, recognized the inseparability of, for example, thorium, radiothorium, ionium, and uranium X. But it was not until 1913 that Kasimir Fajans and Soddy declared them to be chemically identical isotopes, and explained the decay sequence by the group displacement laws.

Just as the radioelements were related, Boltwood's research activities bore logical connections. His first foray into the intricacies of the radioactive decay series in 1904 soon led him to examine the question of the inactive end products. Earlier analyses of uranium minerals showed that lead invariably appeared with the uranium. Between 1905 and 1907 Boltwood extended these observations and noted further that the geologically older minerals contained higher proportions of lead, as would be expected if this end product were accumulating over the ages. The thorium series was less well understood, and Boltwood at first doubted that it ended in lead, while actinium was not then recognized as forming part of a distinct series.

A direct result of this work was a striking application of science, the method of radioactive dating of rocks. If the rate of formation of an inactive decay product could be determined, the total amount found in a mineral would immediately yield its age. Both lead and helium (believed by most to be the alpha particle) were seen as suitable elements and, indeed, served in radioactive dating techniques. The helium method, pioneered in England by R. J. Strutt (later the fourth Baron Rayleigh), could not, however, give more than a minimum age because a variable portion of the gas would have escaped from the rock. But the lead method, developed by Boltwood in 1907, proved satisfactory and is still in use today. In effect, Boltwood reversed his procedure of confirming the accuracy of lead:uranium ratios by the accepted geological ages of the source rocks, and used these ratios to date the rocks. Because most geologists, under the influence of Lord Kelvin's nineteenth-century pronouncements, inclined toward an age of the earth measured in tens of millions of years, Boltwood's claim for a billion-year span was met with some skepticism. However, the subsequent work of Arthur Holmes, an understanding of isotopes, and the increasing accuracy of decay constants and analyses finally brought widespread acceptance of this method in the 1930's.

Boltwood's major contributions lay in the understanding of the uranium decay series. Still, he was able to suggest, with Rutherford in 1905, that actinium is genetically related to uranium, though not in the same chain as radium, while in the thorium series he almost beat Hahn to the discovery of mesothorium in 1907. His other significant service to the study of radioactivity was to bring greater precision and advanced techniques into the laboratory, as in his insistence that only by complete dissolution and boiling of the mineral could all the emanation be extracted from radioactive bodies.

Boltwood remained at Yale the rest of his life, except for the academic year 1909–1910, when he accepted an invitation to Rutherford's laboratory at the University of Manchester. Yale, fearing that he would remain in England indefinitely, offered Boltwood a full professorship in radiochemistry. This appointment brought him back to New Haven, but it also marked the end of his research career. Heavy academic duties, including supervision of construction of the new Sloane Physics Laboratory and unsuccessful efforts to obtain large quantities of radioactive minerals for research, seem to have taken all his time and energy. His stature as the foremost authority on radioactivity in the United States brought him membership in the National Academy of Sciences, the American Philosophical Society, and other organizations, but it also brought him numerous requests from

prospectors, mine owners, speculators, chemical refiners, and wholesalers to analyze samples, devise separation processes, and find financial backing (from wealthy Yale alumni) for various projects. These efforts probably helped stimulate the production of radium, in which the United States led the world by about 1915, although they did not appreciably aid the progress of science.

In 1918 Boltwood was appointed director of the Yale College chemical laboratory and presided over the consolidation of the Yale and Sheffield chemistry departments. To cement this union, the new Sterling Chemistry Laboratory was proposed, and Boltwood was placed in charge of its design. He completed it successfully, but the strain of this effort caused a breakdown in his health from which he never fully recovered. Periods of severe depression alternated with his more customary cheerful spirits, and resulted in his suicide during the summer of 1927.

Boltwood's influence in radioactivity was widespread—through his published papers, correspondence, and personal contacts, for he trained surprisingly few research students. Part of his success stemmed from his close association with Rutherford, but like Rutherford's other chemical collaborators, Soddy and Hahn, he was eminently capable of major contributions in his own right.

BIBLIOGRAPHY

I. ORIGINAL WORKS. A reasonably complete list of Boltwood's publications is in Alois F. Kovarik's sketch of him in *Biographical Memoirs of the National Academy of Sciences,* **14** (1930), 69–96. His unpublished correspondence, papers, and laboratory notebooks are preserved in the Manuscript Room, Yale University Library. His extensive correspondence with Rutherford is in the Rutherford Collection, Manuscript Room, Cambridge University Library.

II. SECONDARY LITERATURE. In addition to Kovarik's memoir (see above), the following obituary notices offer information about Boltwood: *Yale Alumni Weekly,* **37** (7 Oct. 1927), 65; Kovarik, in *Yale Scientific Magazine,* **2** (Nov. 1927), 25, 44, 46; Rutherford, in *Nature,* **121** (14 Jan. 1928), 64–65; Kovarik, in *American Journal of Science,* **15** (Mar. 1928), 188–198.

LAWRENCE BADASH

BOLTZMANN, LUDWIG (*b.* Vienna, Austria, 20 February 1844; *d.* Duino, near Trieste, 5 September 1906), *physics.*

Boltzmann's father, Ludwig, was a civil servant (*Kaiserlich-Königlich Cameral-Concipist*); his mother was Katherina Pauernfeind. He was educated at Linz and Vienna, receiving his doctorate in 1867 from the

University of Vienna, where he had studied with Josef Stefan. Boltzmann held professorships at the universities of Graz, Vienna, Munich, and Leipzig. In 1876 he married Henrietta von Aigentler, who bore him four children.

Distribution Law. The first stimulus for Boltzmann's researches came from teachers and colleagues at the University of Vienna, especially Stefan and Josef Loschmidt. In a lecture Stefan suggested the problem in electrical theory whose solution constituted Boltzmann's first published paper (1865);[1] he also published a few papers on kinetic theory and did important experimental work on gases and radiation that provided the basis for some of Boltzmann's theories. Loschmidt (also in 1865) accomplished the first reliable estimate of molecular sizes with the help of the Clausius-Maxwell kinetic theory. Although Loschmidt was later to dispute Boltzmann's interpretation of the second law of thermodynamics, the problem of finding quantitative relations between atomic magnitudes and observable physical quantities was a common interest of both men.

Boltzmann began his lifelong study of the atomic theory of matter by seeking to establish a direct connection between the second law of thermodynamics and the mechanical principle of least action (1866). Although Clausius, Szily, and others later worked along similar lines, and Boltzmann himself returned to the subject in his elaboration of Helmholtz' theory of monocyclic systems (1884), the analogy with purely mechanical principles seemed insufficient for a complete interpretation of the second law. The missing element was the statistical approach to atomic motion that had already been introduced by the British physicist James Clerk Maxwell.[2] Boltzmann's first acquaintance with Maxwell's writings on kinetic theory is indicated by his paper on thermal equilibrium (1868). In this paper, he extended Maxwell's theory of the distribution of energy among colliding gas molecules, treating the case when external forces are present. The result was a new exponential formula for molecular distribution, now known as the "Boltzmann factor" and basic to all modern calculations in statistical mechanics. To understand how Boltzmann arrived at this result, we must first review the work of Maxwell on which it is based.

Maxwell, in his first paper on kinetic theory (1859), had pointed out that the collisions of gas molecules would not simply tend to equalize all their speeds but, on the contrary, would produce a range of different speeds. Most of the observable properties of a gas could be calculated if one knew, instead of the positions and velocities of all the molecules at any

given time, only the average number of molecules having various positions and velocities. In many cases it seems reasonable to assume that the gas is spatially uniform, that is, the average number of molecules is the same at different places in the gas. The problem is then to determine the velocity distribution function $f(v)$, defined so that $f(v)\,dv$ is the average number of molecules having speeds between v and $v + dv$.

Maxwell argued that $f(v)$ should be a function that depends only on the magnitude of v, and that the velocity components resolved along the three coordinate axes should be statistically independent. Hence, he inferred that

$$f(v) = (N/\alpha^3\pi^{3/2})e^{-(v^2/\alpha^2)}, \qquad (1)$$

where N is the total number of molecules, and α^2 is inversely proportional to the absolute temperature.

In his long memoir of 1866, Maxwell admitted that the assumptions used in his previous derivation of the distribution law "may appear precarious"; he offered another derivation in which the velocities of two colliding molecules, rather than the velocity components of a single molecule, were assumed to be statistically independent. This means that one can express the joint distribution function for the probability that molecule 1 has velocity v_1, while at the same time molecule 2 has velocity v_2, as the product of the probabilities of these two separate events:

$$F(v_1, v_2) = f(v_1)f(v_2). \qquad (2)$$

To derive the distribution function itself, Maxwell argued that the equilibrium state would be reached when the number of collisions in which two molecules with initial velocities (v_1, v_2) rebound with final velocities (v_1', v_2') is equal to the number of collisions in which two molecules with initial velocities (v_1', v_2') rebound with final velocities (v_1, v_2); from this condition it follows that

$$F(v_1, v_2) = F(v_1', v_2'). \qquad (3)$$

By combining this equation with that for the conservation of energy (in the case when no forces act),

$$\frac{1}{2}m_1v_1{}^2 + \frac{1}{2}m_2v_2{}^2 = \frac{1}{2}m_1v_1'{}^2 + \frac{1}{2}m_2v_2'{}^2, \quad (4)$$

Maxwell deduced (as before) that

$$f(v_1) = (N/\alpha^3\pi^{3/2})\,e^{-(v^2/\alpha^2)}. \qquad (5)$$

This type of reasoning about velocity distribution functions was repeatedly used and generalized by Boltzmann in his own works on kinetic theory. He began, in his 1868 paper, by considering the case in which one of the particles of a system is acted on by a force with a corresponding potential function,

$V(x)$. The condition of conservation of energy would then be

$$\frac{1}{2} m_1 v_1{}^2 + V(x_1) + \frac{1}{2} m_2 v_2{}^2$$

$$= \frac{1}{2} m_1 v_1'{}^2 + V(x_1') + \frac{1}{2} m_2 v_2'{}^2, \quad (6)$$

and Boltzmann could then apply Maxwell's procedure to deduce the distribution function

$$f(v) = (\text{const.})\, e^{-h(mv^2/2 + V[x])}. \quad (7)$$

The constant factor h could be related to the absolute temperature of the gas, as Maxwell and Clausius had done, by comparing the theoretical pressure of the gas with the experimental relation between pressure and temperature (Gay-Lussac's law). In modern notation, h is equivalent to $1/kT$, where k is a constant, now called Boltzmann's constant, and T is the absolute temperature on the Kelvin scale.

The physical meaning of the Maxwell-Boltzmann distribution law is that the energy ($E = mv^2/2 + V[x]$) of a molecule is most likely to be roughly equal to kT; much larger or much smaller energies occur with small but finite probability.

In the same paper of 1868, Boltzmann presented another derivation of the Maxwell distribution law that was independent of any assumptions about collisions between molecules. He simply assumed that there is a fixed total amount of energy to be distributed among a finite number of molecules, in such a way that all combinations of energies are equally probable. (More precisely, he assumed uniform distribution in momentum space.) By regarding the total energy as being divided into small but finite quanta, he could treat this as a problem of combinatorial analysis. He obtained a rather complicated formula that reduced to the Maxwell velocity-distribution law in the limit of an infinite number of molecules and infinitesimal energy quanta.

The device of starting with finite energy quanta and then letting them become infinitesimal is not essential to such a derivation, but it reveals an interesting feature of Boltzmann's mathematical approach. Boltzmann asserted on several occasions that a derivation based on infinite or infinitesimal quantities is not really rigorous unless it can also be carried through with finite quantities. While this prejudice kept him from appreciating and using some of the developments in pure mathematics that appeared toward the end of the nineteenth century, it also had the curious effect of making some of his equations for energy distribution and transfer look similar to those of modern quantum theory. (This is perhaps not quite

accidental, since Planck and other early quantum theorists were familiar with Boltzmann's works and used many of his techniques.)

Transport Equation and H-theorem. Although Maxwell and Boltzmann had succeeded in finding the correct distribution laws by assuming that the gas is in an equilibrium state, they thought that the kinetic theory should also be able to show that a gas will actually tend toward an equilibrium state if it is not there already. Maxwell had made only fragmentary attempts to solve this problem; Boltzmann devoted several long papers to establishing a general solution.

Approach to equilibrium is a special case of a general phenomenon: dissipation of energy and increase of entropy. It was Boltzmann's achievement to show in detail how thermodynamic entropy is related to the statistical distribution of molecular configurations, and how increasing entropy corresponds to increasing randomness on the molecular level. This was a peculiar and unexpected relationship, for macroscopic irreversibility seemed to contradict the fundamental reversibility of Newtonian mechanics, which was still assumed to apply to molecular collisions. Boltzmann's attempts to resolve this contradiction formed part of the debate on the validity of the atomic theory in the 1890's. Seen in this context, the proof of the distribution law has even more significance than the law itself.

Boltzmann's major work on the approach to equilibrium (and on transport processes in gases in general) was published in 1872. This paper, like that of 1868, took Maxwell's theory as the starting point. Boltzmann first derived an equation for the rate of change in the number of molecules having a given energy, x, resulting from collisions between molecules. He considered a typical collision between two molecules with energies x and x' before the collision, and energies ξ and $x + x' - \xi$ after the collision. Such a collision reduces by one the number of molecules with energy x; the number of such collisions is assumed to be proportional to the number of molecules with energy x, and also to the number of molecules with energy x'. Boltzmann used here, without any comment, Maxwell's assumption of statistical independence of the velocities of two colliding molecules (eq. 2); later it was recognized that there might be valid grounds for objecting to this assumption.[3] With this assumption, the decrease in $f(x)$ will be equal to the product, $f(x)f(x')$, multiplied by an appropriate factor for the collision probability and integrated over all values of x'. Similarly, the increase in $f(x)$ may be attributed to inverse collisions in which the molecules have energies ξ and $x + x' - \xi$ before the collision, and x and x' after the collision. By such arguments Boltzmann arrived at the equation

$$\frac{\partial f}{\partial t} = \int_0^\infty \int_0^{x+x'} \left[\frac{f(\xi,t)f(x+x'-\xi,t)}{\sqrt{\xi}\sqrt{x+x'-\xi}} - \frac{f(x,t)f(x',t)}{\sqrt{x}\sqrt{x'}} \right]$$
$$\sqrt{xx'}\psi(x,x',\xi)\, dx'\, d\xi. \quad (8)$$

(This is a special case of the general Boltzmann transport equation [eq. 9]; terms describing the effect of external forces and nonuniformities on the change of f are here omitted. The square root expressions in the denominators, which do not appear in the form of the equation generally used, result from the fact that energy rather than velocity is the variable.)

One additional assumption involved in this derivation should be mentioned: the collision probability function, $\psi(x, x', \xi)$, is the same for both the direct and inverse collisions; that is, the collision is perfectly reversible.

Following Maxwell's 1866 development of the transport equations, Boltzmann showed how the diffusion, viscosity, and heat conduction coefficients of a gas could be calculated by solving the general transport equation

$$\frac{\partial f}{\partial t} + \xi\frac{\partial f}{\partial x} + \eta\frac{\partial f}{\partial y} + \zeta\frac{\partial f}{\partial z} + X\frac{\partial f}{\partial \xi} + Y\frac{\partial f}{\partial \eta}$$
$$+ Z\frac{\partial f}{\partial \zeta} + \int d\omega_1 \int b\, db \int d\phi V(ff_1 - f'f_1') = 0, \quad (9)$$

where (ξ,η,ζ) are components of the velocity of a particle and (X,Y,Z) are components of the force acting on it, and V, ϕ, b, and ω_1 are variables characterizing the relative motion of the two molecules during a collision. (Values of the function f for velocities of the two molecules before and after the collision are indicated by f, f_1, f', and f_1'.)

It is difficult to obtain exact solutions of Boltzmann's transport equation except when the molecules interact with inverse fifth-power forces, a case for which Maxwell had found an important simplification.[4] Boltzmann made several attempts to develop accurate approximations for other force laws, but this problem was not satisfactorily solved until the work of S. Chapman and D. Enskog in 1916–1917. Boltzmann's equation is now frequently used in modern research on fluids, plasmas, and neutron transport.

If the velocity distribution function is Maxwellian, then the integral on the right-hand side of eq. 8 vanishes identically for all values of the variables, and we find $\partial f/\partial t = 0$. In other words, once the Maxwellian state has been reached, no further change in the velocity distribution function can occur.

So far this is simply an elaboration of the previous arguments of Maxwell and of Boltzmann himself, but now, with an explicit formula for $\partial f/\partial t$, Boltzmann was able to go further and show that $f(x)$ probably tends toward the Maxwell form. He did this by introducing a function, E, depending on $f(x)$

$$E = \int_0^\infty f(x,t)\left\{ \log\left[\frac{f(x,t)}{\sqrt{x}}\right] - 1 \right\} dx \quad (10)$$

and showing that E always decreases unless f has the Maxwellian form:

$$\frac{dE}{dt} < 0 \text{ if } f \neq (\text{const.})\sqrt{x}e^{-hx},$$
$$\frac{dE}{dt} = 0 \text{ if } f = (\text{const.})\sqrt{x}e^{-hx}. \quad (11)$$

(The proof is straightforward and relies simply on the fact that the quantity $(a - b)\log b/a$ is always negative if a and b are real positive numbers.) Boltzmann also noted that in the Maxwellian state E is essentially the same as the thermodynamic entropy (aside from a constant factor). Thus Boltzmann's "H-function" (the notation was changed from E to H in the 1890's) provides an extension of the definition of entropy to nonequilibrium states not covered by the thermodynamic definition.

The theorem that H always decreases for nonequilibrium systems was called "Boltzmann's minimum theorem" in the nineteenth century, and now goes by the name "Boltzmann's H-theorem." (It has not yet been proved rigorously except with certain specializing assumptions.)

Reversibility and Recurrence Paradoxes. The H-theorem raised some difficult questions about the nature of irreversibility in physical systems, in particular the so-called "reversibility paradox" and "recurrence paradox." (The modern terminology goes back only to the Ehrenfests' 1911 article, in which the words *Umkehreinwand* and *Wiederkehreinwand* were introduced.) The reversibility paradox, first discussed by Lord Kelvin (1874) and brought to Boltzmann's attention by Loschmidt, is based on the apparent contradiction between one of the basic premises of Boltzmann's derivation—the reversibility of individual collisions—and the irreversibility predicted by the theorem itself for a system of many molecules. Of course there must be such a contradiction between any molecular theory based on Newtonian mechanics and the general principle of dissipation of energy, but Boltzmann's work was the first to reveal this inconsistency explicitly.

Boltzmann's initial response (1877) to the reversibility paradox was the suggestion that the irreversibility of processes in the real world is not a consequence of the equations of motion and the form of the intermolecular force law but, rather, seems to be a result of the initial conditions. For some unusual initial conditions the system might in fact decrease its entropy (increase the value of H) as time progresses; such initial conditions could be constructed simply by reversing all the velocities of the molecules in an equilibrium state known to have evolved from a nonequilibrium state. But, Boltzmann asserts, there are infinitely many more initial states that evolve with increasing entropy, simply because the great majority of all possible states are equilibrium states. Moreover, the entropy would also be almost certain to increase if one picked an initial state at random and followed it backward in time instead of forward.

The recurrence paradox arises from a theorem in mechanics first published by Poincaré in 1890. According to this theorem, any mechanical system constrained to move in a finite volume with fixed total energy must eventually return to any specified initial configuration. If a certain value of the entropy is associated with every configuration of the system (a disputable assumption), then the entropy cannot continually increase with time, but must eventually decrease in order to return to its initial value. Therefore the H-theorem cannot always be valid.

Poincaré, and later Zermelo (1896), argued that the recurrence theorem makes any mechanical model, such as the kinetic theory, incompatible with the second law of thermodynamics; and since, it was asserted, the second law is a strictly valid induction from experience, one must reject the mechanistic viewpoint.

Boltzmann replied that the recurrence theorem does not contradict the H-theorem, but is completely in harmony with it. The equilibrium state is not a single configuration but, rather, a collection of the overwhelming majority of possible configurations, characterized by the Maxwell-Boltzmann distribution. From the statistical viewpoint, the recurrence of some particular initial state is a fluctuation that is almost certain to occur if one waits long enough; the point is that the probability of such a fluctuation is so small that one would have to wait an immensely long time before observing a recurrence of the initial state. Thus the mechanical viewpoint does not lead to any consequences that are actually in disagreement with experience. For those who are concerned about the cosmological consequences of the second law—the so-called "heat death" corresponding to the final attainment of a state of maximum disorder when all irreversible processes have run their course —Boltzmann suggested the following idea. The universe as a whole is in a state of thermal equilibrium, and there is no distinction between forward and

backward directions of time. However, within small regions, such as individual galaxies, there will be noticeable fluctuations that include ordered states corresponding to the existence of life. A living being in such a galaxy will distinguish the direction of time for which entropy increases (processes going from ordered to disordered states) from the opposite direction; in other words, the concept of "direction of time" is statistical or even subjective, and is determined by the direction in which entropy happens to be increasing. Thus, the statement "Entropy increases with time" is a tautology, and yet the subjective time directions in different parts of the universe may be different. In this way local irreversible processes would be compatible with cosmic reversibility and recurrence. (Boltzmann's concept of alternating time directions has recently been revived in connection with theories of oscillating universes.)

Statistical Mechanics and Ergodic Hypothesis. Having followed Boltzmann's work on irreversible processes into some of the controversies of the 1890's, let us now return to his contributions to the theory of systems in thermal equilibrium (for which the term "statistical mechanics" was introduced by J. Willard Gibbs).

It would be possible (as is in fact done in many modern texts) to take the Maxwell-Boltzmann distribution function (eq. 7) as the basic postulate for calculating all the equilibrium properties of a system. Boltzmann, however, preferred another approach that seemed to rest on more general grounds than the dynamics of bimolecular collisions in low-density gases. The new method was in part a by-product of his discussion of the reversibility paradox, and is first hinted at in connection with the relative frequency of equilibrium, as opposed to nonequilibrium, configurations of molecules: "One could even calculate, from the relative numbers of the different distributions, their probabilities, which might lead to an interesting method for the calculation of thermal equilibrium."[5] This remark was quickly followed up in the same year (1877) in a paper in which the famous relation between entropy and probability,

$$S = k \log W,$$

was developed and applied. In this equation, W is the number of possible molecular configurations ("microstates," in modern terminology) corresponding to a given macroscopic state of the system.[6] (To make this expression meaningful, microstates have to be defined with respect to finite cells in phase space; the size of these cells introduces an arbitrary additive constant in S which can be determined from quantum theory.)

The new formula for entropy—from which formulas for all other thermodynamic quantities could be deduced—was based on the assumption of equal a priori probability of all microstates of the system (that is, all microstates that have the same total energy). As noted above, Boltzmann had already proved in 1868 that such an assumption implies the Maxwell velocity distribution for an ideal gas of noninteracting particles; it also implies the Maxwell-Boltzmann distribution for certain special cases in which external forces are present. But the assumption itself demanded some justification beyond its inherent plausibility. For this purpose, Boltzmann and Maxwell introduced what is now called the "ergodic hypothesis," the assumption that a single system will eventually pass through all possible microstates.

There has been considerable confusion about what Maxwell and Boltzmann really meant by ergodic systems. It appears that they did not have in mind completely deterministic mechanical systems following a single trajectory unaffected by external conditions; the ergodic property was to be attributed to some random element, or at least to collisions with a boundary. In fact, when Boltzmann first introduced the words *Ergoden* and *ergodische,* he used them not for single systems but for collections of similar systems with the same energy but different initial conditions. In these papers of 1884 and 1887, Boltzmann was continuing his earlier analysis of mechanical analogies for the second law of thermodynamics and also developing what is now (since Gibbs) known as ensemble theory. Here again, Boltzmann was following a trail blazed by Maxwell, who had introduced the ensemble concept in his 1879 paper. But while Maxwell never got past the restriction that all systems in the ensemble must have the same energy, Boltzmann suggested more general possibilities and Gibbs ultimately showed that it is most useful to consider ensembles in which not only the energy but also the number of particles can have any value, with a specified probability.

The Maxwell-Boltzmann ergodic hypothesis led to considerable controversy on the mathematical question of the possible existence of dynamical systems that pass through all possible configurations. The controversy came to a head with the publication of the Ehrenfests' article in 1911, in which it was suggested that while ergodic systems are probably nonexistent, "quasi-ergodic" systems that pass "as close as one likes" to every possible state might still be found. Shortly after this, two mathematicians, Rosenthal and Plancherel, used some recent results of Cantor and Brouwer on the dimensionality of sets of points to prove that strictly ergodic systems are

indeed impossible. Since then, there have been many attempts to discover whether physical systems can be ergodic; "ergodic theory" has become a lively branch of modern mathematics, although it now seems to be of little interest to physicists.

After expending a large amount of effort in the 1880's on elaborate but mostly fruitless attempts to determine transport properties of gases, Boltzmann returned to the calculation of equilibrium properties in the 1890's. He was encouraged by the progress made by Dutch researchers—J. D. van der Waals, H. A. Lorentz, J. H. van't Hoff, and others—in applying kinetic methods to dense gases and osmotic solutions. He felt obliged to correct and extend their calculations, as in the case of virial coefficients of gases composed of elastic spheres. The success of these applications of kinetic theory also gave him more ammunition for his battle with the energeticists (see below).

Other Scientific Work. Although Boltzmann's contributions to kinetic theory were the fruits of an effort sustained over a period of forty years, and are mainly responsible for his reputation as a theoretical physicist, they account, numerically, for only about half of his publications. The rest are so diverse in nature—ranging over the fields of physics, chemistry, mathematics, and philosophy—that it would be useless to try to describe or even list them here. Only one common characteristic seems evident: most of what Boltzmann wrote in science represents some kind of interaction with other scientists or with his students. All of his books originated as lecture notes; in attempting to explain a subject on the elementary level, Boltzmann frequently developed valuable new insights, although he often succumbed to unnecessary verbosity. He scrutinized the major physics journals and frequently found articles that inspired him to dash off a correction, design a new experiment, or rework a theoretical calculation to account for new data.

Soon after he started to follow Maxwell's work on kinetic theory, Boltzmann began to study the electromagnetic theory of his Scottish colleague. In 1872, he published the first report of a comprehensive experimental study of dielectrics, conducted in the laboratories of Helmholtz in Berlin and of Töpler in Graz. A primary aim of this research was to test Maxwell's prediction that the index of refraction of a substance should be the geometric mean of its dielectric constant and its magnetic permeability ($i = \sqrt{\epsilon\mu}$). Boltzmann confirmed this prediction for solid insulators and (more accurately) for gases. He also confirmed the further prediction that if the speed of light (and hence the index of refraction) varies with direction in an anisotropic crystal, then the dielectric constant must also vary with direction.

During the next few years, Boltzmann began experimental work in diamagnetism while continuing his theoretical research in kinetic theory. He proposed a new theory of elastic aftereffects, in which the stress on a material at a given time depends on its previous deformation history.

In 1883, as a result of preparing an abstract of H. T. Eddy's paper (on radiant heat as a possible exception to the second law of thermodynamics) for Wiedemann's *Beiblätter,* Boltzmann learned of a work by the Italian physicist Adolfo Bartoli on radiation pressure. Bartoli's reasoning stimulated Boltzmann to work out a theoretical derivation, based on the second law of thermodynamics and Maxwell's electromagnetic theory, of the fourth-power law previously found experimentally by Stefan:

(radiation energy) $\propto$ (absolute temperature)^4.

Although at the time the "Stefan-Boltzmann law" for radiation seemed to be an isolated result with no further consequences, it did at least show a possible connection between thermodynamics and electromagnetism that was exploited in the later quantum theory. In the 1920's it was applied by Eddington and others in explaining the equilibrium of stellar atmospheres.

In the 1890's Boltzmann again revived his interest in electromagnetic theory, perhaps as a result of Hertz's experiments, which he repeated before a large audience in Graz. He published his *Vorlesungen über Maxwells Theorie . . .* in 1891 and 1893, along with some papers in which he suggested new mechanical models to illustrate the field equations. In 1895 he published an annotated German edition of Maxwell's paper "On Faraday's Lines of Force" in Ostwald's Klassiker der exakten Wissenschaften. Boltzmann was partly responsible for the eventual acceptance of Maxwell's theory on the Continent, although he did not advance the theory itself as much as did Lorentz, nor did he grapple with the difficult problems that ultimately led to Einstein's theory of relativity.

Defense of the Atomic Viewpoint. Throughout his career, even in his works on subjects other than kinetic theory, Boltzmann was concerned with the mathematical problems arising from the atomic nature of matter. Thus, an early paper with the title "Über die Integrale linearer Differentialgleichungen mit periodischen Koeffizienten" (1868) turned out to be an investigation of the validity of Cauchy's theorem on this subject, which is needed to justify the application of the equations for an elastic continuum to a crystalline solid in which the local properties vary

periodically from one atom to the next. Every time someone published new data on the specific heats of gases, Boltzmann felt obliged to worry again about the distribution of energy among the internal motions of polyatomic molecules.

Until the 1890's, it seemed to be generally agreed among physicists that matter *is* composed of atoms, and Boltzmann's concern about the consistency of atomic theories may have seemed excessive. But toward the end of the century, the various paradoxes—specific heats, reversibility, and recurrence—were taken more seriously as defects of atomism, and Boltzmann found himself cast in the role of principal defender of the kinetic theory and of the atomistic-mechanical viewpoint in general. Previously he had not been much involved in controversy—with the exception of a short dispute with O. E. Meyer, who, ironically, had accused Boltzmann of proposing a theory of elasticity that was inconsistent with the atomic nature of matter. But now Boltzmann found himself almost completely deserted by Continental scientists; his principal supporters were in England.

In retrospect it seems that the criticisms of kinetic theory in this period were motivated not primarily by technical problems, such as specific heats of polyatomic molecules but, rather, by a general philosophical reaction against mechanistic or "materialistic" science and a preference for empirical or phenomenological theories, as opposed to atomic models. The leaders of this reaction, in the physical sciences, were Ernst Mach, Wilhelm Ostwald, Pierre Duhem, and Georg Helm. Mach recognized that atomic hypotheses could be useful in science but insisted, even as late as 1912, that atoms must not be considered to have a real existence. Ostwald, Duhem, and Helm, on the other hand, wanted to replace atomic theories by "energetics" (a generalized thermodynamics); they denied that kinetic theories had any value at all, even as hypotheses.

In the first volume of his *Vorlesungen über Gastheorie* (1896), Boltzmann presented a vigorous argument for the kinetic theory:

Experience teaches that one will be led to new discoveries almost exclusively by means of special mechanical models. . . . Indeed, since the history of science shows how often epistemological generalizations have turned out to be false, may it not turn out that the present "modern" distaste for special representations, as well as the distinction between qualitatively different forms of energy, will have been a retrogression? Who sees the future? Let us have free scope for all directions of research; away with all dogmatism, either atomistic or anti-atomistic! In describing the theory of gases as a mechanical *analogy,* we have already indicated, by the choice of this word, how far removed we are from that viewpoint which would see in visible matter the true properties of the smallest particles of the body [Brush trans., p. 26].

In the foreword to the second volume of this book (1898), Boltzmann seemed rather more conscious of his failure to convert other scientists to acceptance of the kinetic theory. He noted that attacks on the theory had been increasing, but added:

I am convinced that these attacks are merely based on a misunderstanding, and that the role of gas theory in science has not yet been played out. The abundance of results agreeing with experiment which van der Waals has derived from it purely deductively, I have tried to make clear in this book. More recently, gas theory has also provided suggestions that one could not obtain in any other way. From the theory of the ratio of specific heats, Ramsay inferred the atomic weight of argon and thereby its place in the system of chemical elements— which he subsequently proved, by the discovery of neon, was in fact correct. . . .

In my opinion it would be a great tragedy for science if the theory of gases were temporarily thrown into oblivion because of a momentary hostile attitude toward it, as was for example the wave theory because of Newton's authority.

I am conscious of being only an individual struggling weakly against the stream of time. But it still remains in my power to contribute in such a way that, when the theory of gases is again revived, not too much will have to be rediscovered. . . [Ibid., pp. 215–216].

Boltzmann and Ostwald, although on good personal terms, engaged in bitter scientific debates during this period; at one point even Mach thought the argument was becoming too violent, and proposed a reconciliation of mechanistic and phenomenological physics.[7] While teaching at Leipzig with Ostwald during the period 1900–1902, Boltzmann was undergoing periods of mental depression and made one attempt at suicide. He returned to Vienna in 1902, where he succeeded himself as professor of theoretical physics and also lectured on the philosophy of science, replacing Ernst Mach, who had to retire for reasons of health. In 1904 he went to the United States to attend the World's Fair at St. Louis, where he lectured on applied mathematics, and also visited Berkeley and Stanford. He later described his experiences on this trip in a satirical article, "Reise eines deutschen Professors ins Eldorado." But despite his travels and discussions with scientific colleagues, he somehow failed to realize that the new discoveries in radiation and atomic physics occurring at the turn of the century were going to vindicate his own theories, even if in somewhat altered form. The real cause of Boltzmann's

suicide in 1906 will never be known; but insofar as despair over the rejection of his lifework by the scientific community may have been a contributing factor (as has sometimes been suggested without much evidence), it is certainly one of the most tragic ironies in the history of science that Boltzmann ended his life just before the existence of atoms was finally established (to the satisfaction of most scientists) by experiments on Brownian motion guided by a kinetic-statistical theory of molecular motion.

NOTES

1. All of Boltzmann's publications for which only the year is given may be found in his *Wissenschaftliche Abhandlungen.*
2. See *The Scientific Papers of James Clerk Maxwell* (Cambridge, 1890). The 1859 and 1866 papers of Maxwell, together with other papers by Clausius, Boltzmann, Kelvin, Poincaré, and Zermelo (cited by year in this article) may be found in S. G. Brush, ed., *Kinetic Theory,* 2 vols. (Oxford, 1965–1966).
3. See Boltzmann, *Vorlesungen über Gastheorie,* I, §3; P. and T. Ehrenfest, "Begriffliche Grundlagen der statistischen Aufassung in der Mechanik."
4. It was in reference to this result of Maxwell's that Boltzmann wrote his oft-quoted comparison of styles in theoretical physics and styles in music, dramatizing the almost magical disappearance of V from the integrand of eq. 9 when the words "let $n = 5$" were pronounced (*Populäre Schriften,* p. 51).
5. Brush, *Kinetic Theory,* II, 192.
6. This formula for S is clearly related to Boltzmann's earlier expression for the H-function (eq. 9). If we know that the system has probability W_i of being in macrostate i, with given values of W_i for all i, then the expectation value of the entropy can be calculated from

$$S = k \sum W \, log \, W$$

with an appropriate interpretation of the summation or integration.
7. *Die Principien der Wärmelehre, historisch-kritisch entwickelt* (Leipzig, 1896), pp. 362 ff.

BIBLIOGRAPHY

I. ORIGINAL WORKS. The technical papers that originally appeared in various periodicals have been reprinted in Boltzmann's *Wissenschaftliche Abhandlungen,* F. Hasenöhrl, ed., 3 vols. (Leipzig, 1909). Lectures and articles of general interest are collected in *Populäre Schriften* (Leipzig, 1905). A review article written with J. Nabl, "Kinetische Theorie der Materie," was published in *Encyklopädie der mathematischen Wissenschaften,* V, pt. 1 (Leipzig, 1905), art. V8. Other works are *Vorlesungen über Maxwells Theorie der Elektrizität und des Lichtes,* 2 vols. (Leipzig, 1891–1893); his ed. of Maxwell's "On Faraday's Lines of Force," *Ueber Faraday's Kraftlinien* (Leipzig, 1895), with 31 pages of notes by Boltzmann; *Vorlesungen über Gastheorie,* 2 vols. (Leipzig, 1896–1898), trans. by S. G. Brush, with introduction, notes, and bibliography, as *Lectures on Gas Theory* (Berkeley, 1964); *Vorlesungen über die Principe der Mechanik,* 3 vols. (Leipzig, 1897–1920); and

Über die Prinzipien der Mechanik, Zwei akademische Antrittsreden (Leipzig, 1903). Books based on Boltzmann's lectures are Charles Emerson Curry, *Theory of Electricity and Magnetism* (London, 1897), with a preface by Boltzmann; and Hugo Buchholz, *Das mechanische Potential,* published with *Die Theorie der Figur der Erde* (Leipzig, 1908).

II. SECONDARY LITERATURE. Works on Boltzmann are Engelbert Broda, *Ludwig Boltzmann: Mensch, Physiker, Philosoph* (Berlin, 1955); S. G. Brush, "Foundations of Statistical Mechanics 1845–1915," in *Archive for History of Exact Sciences,* **4** (1967), 145–183; René Dugas, *La théorie physique au sens de Boltzmann et ses prolongements modernes* (Neuchâtel, 1959); P. and T. Ehrenfest, "Begriffliche Grundlagen der statistischen Auffassung in der Mechanik," in *Encyklopädie der mathematischen Wissenschaften,* IV, pt. 32 (Leipzig, 1911), trans. by M. J. Moravcsik as *The Conceptual Foundations of the Statistical Approach in Mechanics* (Ithaca, N.Y., 1959); and G. Jaeger, "Ludwig Boltzmann," in *Neue Österreichische Biographie 1815–1918,* pt. 1, *Biographien,* II (Vienna, 1925), 117–137. Other articles on Boltzmann are listed in the bibliography of the Brush trans. of *Lectures on Gas Theory.*

STEPHEN G. BRUSH

BOLYAI, FARKAS (WOLFGANG) (*b.* 9 February 1775, Bolya [German, Bell], near Nagyszeven [German, Hermannstadt], Transylvania, Hungary [now Sibiu, Rumania]; *d.* 20 November 1856, Marosvásárhely, Transylvania, Hungary [now Târgu-Mureş, Rumania]), *mathematics.*

Farkas Bolyai was the son of Gáspár (Kasper) Bolyai and Christina Vajna (von Páva) Bolyai. Bolya was the hereditary estate of the noble family of Bolyai de Bolya, which was mentioned as early as the thirteenth and fourteenth centuries. By the time of Gáspár it had been reduced to a small holding, but Gáspár added another holding (which belonged to his wife's family) in Domáld, near Marosvásárhely. He enjoyed a reputation as an industrious and intelligent landholder of strong character.

Young Farkas received an education at the Evangelical-Reformed College in Nagyszeven, where he stayed from 1781 to 1796. He excelled in many fields, especially in mathematics, and showed interest in theology, painting, and the stage. In 1796, he traveled to Germany, going first to Jena and then, with a fellow student at Nagyszeven, Baron Simon Kemény, entered the University of Göttingen, where he studied until 1799. Among his teachers were the astronomer Felix Seyffen and the mathematician Abraham Gotthelf Kästner. It was at this time that Bolyai began his lifelong friendship with Carl Friedrich Gauss, also a student at Göttingen, who already was intensely engaged in mathematical research. From this period dates Bolyai's interest in the foundations of geometry, especially in the so-called Euclidean or parallel axiom, to which Kästner and Seyffer, as well as Gauss, were devoting attention. Bolyai maintained a correspondence with Gauss that, with interruptions, lasted all their lives.

After his return to Transylvania, Bolyai became a superintendent in the house of the Keménys in Koloszvár (German, Klausenburg; now Cluj, Rumania). In 1801 he married Susanna von Árkos, the daughter of a surgeon. His wife was talented but sickly and nervous, and the marriage was not a happy one. The couple settled in Domáld, where Bolyai farmed from 1801 to 1804. In 1802 their son, János, was born, at the von Árkos home in Koloszvár.

In 1804, Farkas accepted the position of professor of mathematics, physics, and chemistry at the Evangelical-Reformed College at Marosvásárhely, where he taught until his retirement in 1853. During this half century he was known as a patient and kind teacher, but one who lacked the faculty of easily transmitting to others his own scientific enthusiasm, despite the emphasis he placed on correct mathematical education. Meanwhile, he continued his research, concentrating on the theory of parallels. He sent a manuscript on this subject, *Theoria parallelarum,* with an attempt to prove the Euclidean axiom, to Gauss in 1804. The reasoning, however, satisfied neither Gauss nor himself; and Bolyai continued to work on it and on the foundations of mathematics in general.

The Euclidean axiom, which appears as the fifth postulate in Book I of Euclid's *Elements,* is equivalent to the statement that through a given point outside a given line only one parallel can be drawn to the line. It is also equivalent to the statement that there exists a triangle in which the sum of the three angles is equal to two right angles and, hence, that all triangles have this property. Attempts to prove this axiom—that is, to deduce it from other, more obvious, assumptions—began in antiquity. These attempts were always unsatisfactory, however, and the nature of the axiom had remained a challenge to mathematicians. Bolyai, working in almost total scientific isolation, often despaired while trying to understand it.

During such moments of discouragement, he sought consolation in poetry, music, and writing for the stage. In 1817, his *Öt Szomorujátek, Irta egy Hazafi* ("Five Tragedies, Written by a Patriot") was entered in a contest. The following year, another play, *A Párisi Par* ("The Paris Process"), appeared. Bolyai's wife died in 1821, and in 1824 he married Theresia Nagy, the daughter of an iron merchant in Marosvásárhely. They had one son, Gregor.

Farkas began to interest himself in mathematics

again when his son János evinced unusual mathematical talent. In 1829 Bolyai finished his principal work, but because of technical and financial problems it was not published until 1832–1833. It appeared in two volumes, with the title *Tentamen juventutem studiosam in elementa matheseos purae, elementaris ac sublimioris, methodo intuitiva, evidentiaque huic propria, introducendi, cum appendice triplici* ("An Attempt to Introduce Studious Youth Into the Elements of Pure Mathematics, by an Intuitive Method and Appropriate Evidence, With a Threefold Appendix"). While writing the *Tentamen,* Bolyai had his first difficulties with his son János. In spite of warnings from his father to avoid any preoccupation with Euclid's axiom, János not only insisted on studying the theory of parallels, but also developed an entirely unorthodox system of geometry based on the rejection of the parallel axiom, something with which his father could not agree. However, despite misgivings, Bolyai added his son's paper to the first volume and thus, unwittingly, gave it immortality. In 1834, a Hungarian version of Volume I was published.

The *Tentamen* itself, the fundamental ideas of which may date back to Bolyai's Göttingen days, is an attempt at a rigorous and systematic foundation of geometry (Volume I) and of arithmetic, algebra, and analysis (Volume II). The huge work shows the critical spirit of a man who recognized, as did few of his contemporaries, many weaknesses in the mathematics of his day, but was not able to reach a fully satisfactory solution of them. Nevertheless, when it is remembered that Bolyai worked in almost total isolation, the *Tentamen* is a most remarkable witness to the sharpness of his mind and to his perseverance. In many respects, he can be taken as a precursor of Gottlob Frege, Pasch, and Georg Cantor; but, as with many pioneers, he did not enjoy the credit that accrued to those who followed him.

The *Tentamen* was almost totally unappreciated by Bolyai's contemporaries, although Gauss expressed his pleasure at finding "everywhere thoroughness and independence." Disappointed and again a widower, the sensitive man found little consolation in the equally disappointed János, who after his retirement from military service had come to live in Marosvásárhely. The two men often clashed. In 1837 both entered a contest on complex numbers sponsored by the Jablonow Society in Leipzig. The elder Bolyai's contribution was taken essentially from his *Tentamen.* When no prize was awarded to either of them, their disillusionment grew; but whereas the son sank more and more into melancholy, the father—poetic, musical, and venerable—remained an outstanding, although somewhat eccentric, citizen of the provincial

town, who was often consulted on technical questions. Both men also wrote much on a theory of salvation for mankind, and both returned occasionally to mathematics. Besides some elementary books, Bolyai published a summary of his *Tentamen* in German as *Kurzer Grundriss eines Versuches* (1851); after retiring from college teaching, and after having heard of Gauss's death, he wrote *Abschied von der Erde.* He died after suffering several strokes.

BIBLIOGRAPHY

I. ORIGINAL WORKS. Among Bolyai's works are *Az arithmetica Eleje* ("Elements of Arithmetic," Marosvásárhely, 1830); *Ürtan elemei kerdóknek* ("Elements of the Theory of Space for Beginners," Marosvásárhely, 1850–1851); and *Kurzer Grundriss eines Versuches* (Marosvásárhely, 1851). His major work, the *Tentamen,* was published in Latin in 2 vols. (Marosvásárhely, 1832–1833); 2nd ed., Vol. I (Budapest, 1897), Vol. II (Budapest, 1904), with an additional volume of figures.

II. SECONDARY LITERATURE. For information on Bolyai, see P. Stäckel, *W. und J. Bolyai, Geometrische Untersuchungen,* 2 vols. (Leipzig, 1913): the first volume is biographical; the second contains German translations of the theory of parallels of 1804, parts of the *Tentamen,* and the *Kurzer . . . Versuches.* The correspondence between Bolyai and Gauss is found in *Briefwechsel zwischen C. F. Gauss und W. Bolyai* (Leipzig, 1899). Further biographical material may be found in L. David, *A két Bólyai élete és munkássága* ("Life and Work of the Two Bolyais," Budapest, 1923) and "Die beiden Bolyai," supp. to *Elemente der Mathematik,* no. 11 (1951). A memorial work, *Bolyai Farkas 1856–1956,* was published in Târgu-Mureş in 1957. A stage play by Lászlo Németh, "A két Bólyai" ("The Two Bolyais") was first produced in 1962, and is collected in the author's *Változatok egy témara* (Budapest, 1961). See also K. R. Biermann, "Ein Brief von Wolfgang Bolyai," in *Mathematische Nachrichten,* **32** (1966), 341–346.

D. STRUIK

BOLYAI, JÁNOS (JOHANN) (*b.* 15 December 1802, Koloszvár [German, Klausenburg], Transylvania, Hungary [now Cluj, Rumania]; *d.* 27 January 1860, Marosvásárhely, Hungary [now Târgu-Mureş, Rumania]), *mathematics.*

The son of Farkas (Wolfgang) Bolyai and Susanna von Árkos Bolyai, János Bolyai received his early education in Marosvásárhely, where his father was professor of mathematics, physics, and chemistry at Evangelical-Reformed College. The precocious lad was first taught by his father and showed early proficiency not only in mathematics but also in other fields, such as music. He mastered the violin at an early age. From 1815 to 1818, he studied at the college where his father taught. The elder Bolyai had hopes that the son would go on to Göttingen to study with his friend Gauss, but he did not. In 1818 János entered the imperial engineering academy in Vienna, where he received a military education; he remained there until 1822.

From his father, János had inherited an interest in the theory of parallels; but in 1820 his father warned him against trying to prove the Euclidean axiom that there can be only one parallel to a line through a point outside of it:

> You should not tempt the parallels in this way, I know this way until its end—I also have measured this bottomless night, I have lost in it every light, every joy of my life— . . . You should shy away from it as if from lewd intercourse, it can deprive you of all your leisure, your health, your peace of mind and your entire happiness.— This infinite darkness might perhaps absorb a thousand giant Newtonian towers, it will never be light on earth, and the miserable human race will never have something absolutely pure, not even geometry . . . [Stäckel, pp. 76–77].

In the same year, however, János began to think in a direction that led him ultimately to a non-Euclidean geometry. He profited by conversations with Karl Szász, governor in the house of Count Alexis Teleki. In 1823, after vain attempts to prove the Euclidean axiom, he found his way by assuming that a geometry can be constructed without the parallel axiom; and he began to construct such a geometry. "From nothing I have created another entirely new world," he jubilantly wrote his father in a letter of 3 November 1823. By this time János had finished his courses at the academy and had entered upon a military career, beginning as a sublieutenant. His duties took him first to Temesvár (now Timişoara, Rumania), in 1823–1826, then to Arad (Rumania), in 1826–1830, and finally to Lemberg (now Lvov, W. Ukraine), where in 1832 he was promoted to lieutenant second class. During his military service, he was often plagued with intermittent fever, but he built up a reputation as a dashing officer who dueled readily. In 1833 he was pensioned off as a semi-invalid, and he returned to his father's home in Marosvásárhely.

While visiting his father in February 1825, János had shown him a manuscript that contained his theory of absolute space, that is, a space in which, in a plane through a point P and a line l not through P there exists a pencil of lines through P which does not intersect l. When this pencil reduces to one line, the space satisfies the Euclidean axiom. Farkas Bolyai could not accept this geometry, mainly because it depended on an arbitrary constant, but he finally decided to send his son's manuscript to Gauss. The first letter (20 June 1831) went unanswered, but Gauss

did answer a second letter (16 January 1832). In this famous reply, dated 6 March 1832 and directed to his "old, unforgettable friend," Gauss said:

> Now something about the work of your son. You will probably be shocked for a moment when I begin by saying *that I cannot praise it,* but I cannot do anything else, since to praise it would be to praise myself. The whole content of the paper, the path that your son has taken, and the results to which he has been led, agree almost everywhere with my own meditations, which have occupied me in part already for 30–35 years. Indeed, I am extremely astonished. . . .

Further on, after mentioning that there had been a time when he had been inclined to write such a paper himself, Gauss continued, "Hence I am quite amazed, that now I have been saved the trouble, and I am very glad indeed that it is exactly the son of my ancient friend who has preceded me in such a remarkable way." Gauss ended with some minor remarks, among them a challenge to János to determine, in his geometry, the volume of a tetrahedron, and a critique of Kant's theory of space.

It is now known from Gauss's diaries and from some of his letters that he was not exaggerating; but for János the letter was a terrible blow, since it robbed him of the priority. Even after he became convinced that Gauss spoke the truth, he felt that Gauss had done wrong in remaining silent about his discovery. Nevertheless, he allowed his father to publish his manuscript, which appeared as an appendix to the elder Bolyai's *Tentamen* (1832), under the title "Appendix scientiam spatii absolute veram exhibens" ("Appendix Explaining the Absolutely True Science of Space"). This classic essay of twenty-four pages, which contains János' system of non-Euclidean geometry, is the only work of his published in his lifetime. Gauss's letters had such a discouraging influence on him that he withdrew into himself more and more, and for long periods he did hardly any mathematics. Disappointment grew when his essay evoked no response from other mathematicians.

After his retirement from the army, János lived with his father, who was then a widower. This arrangement lasted only a short time, however. Tension grew between father and son, who were both disappointed at the poor reception given their work, and János withdrew to the small family estate at Domáld, visiting Marosvásárhely only occasionally. In 1834 he contracted an irregular marriage with Rosalie von Orbán. The couple had three children, the first born in 1837.

In an attempt to reestablish themselves in mathematics, both father and son participated in the Jablonow Society prize contest in 1837. The subject was the rigorous geometric construction of imaginary quantities, at that time a subject to which many mathematicians (for example, Augustin Cauchy, W. R. Hamilton, and Gauss) were paying attention. The Bolyais' solutions were too involved to gain a prize, but János' solution resembled that of Hamilton, which was published about the same time, although in simpler terms, and which considered complex numbers as ordered pairs of real numbers. Again the Bolyais had failed to obtain due recognition. János continued to do mathematical work, however, some of it strong and some, because of his isolation, very weak. His best work was that on his absolute geometry, on the relation between absolute trigonometry and spherical trigonometry, and on the volume of the tetrahedron in absolute space. On the last subject, there are notes written as late as 1856. Nikolai Lobachevski's *Geometrische Untersuchungen zur Theorie der Parallellinien* (1840), which reached him through his father in 1848, worked as a powerful challenge, for it established independently the same type of geometry that he had discovered. In his later days he occasionally worried about the possibility of contradictions in his absolute geometry—a real difficulty that was not overcome until Beltrami did so later in the nineteenth century. János also worked on a salvation theory, which stressed that no individual happiness can exist without a universal happiness and that no virtue is possible without knowledge.

János' father died in 1856 and his relationship with Rosalie ended at about the same time, thus depriving him of two of his few intimate contacts. However, in the four years left to him, he did have his good moments. He could write enthusiastically about the ballet performances of the Vienna Opera and compose some beautiful lines to the memory of his mother. He died after a protracted illness, and was buried in the Evangelical-Reformed Cemetery in Marosvásárhely.

The "Appendix" was practically forgotten until Richard Baltzer discussed the work of Bolyai and Lobachevski in the second edition of his *Elemente der Mathematik* (1867). Jules Houel, a correspondent of Baltzer's, then translated Lobachevski's book into French (1867) and did the same with Bolyai's "Appendix" (1868). Full recognition came with the work of Eugenio Beltrami (1868) and Felix Klein (1871).

BIBLIOGRAPHY

In addition to the works cited in the article on Farkas Bolyai, see the English translation of the "Appendix," with an introduction, by G. B. Halsted (Austin, Texas, 1891; new ed., Chicago–London, 1914), reprinted in R. Bonola, *Non-Euclidean Geometry* (reprinted New York, 1955). There are accounts of Bolyai's geometry in the many books on non-Euclidean geometry. See D. M. Y. Sommerville, *Bibliography of Non-Euclidean Geometry* (London, 1911). Further material may be found in I. Tóth, *Bolyai János élete és miive* ("Life and Work of Johann Bolyai," Bucharest, 1953); *János Bolyai Appendix* (Bucharest, 1954), in Rumanian.

E. Sarlóska, "János Bolyai, the Soldier," in *Magyar tudományos akadémia Matematikai eś fizikai osztályanak kőzleményei,* **15** (1965), 341–387, contains a documentary study of Bolyai's army life.

D. J. Struik

BOLZA, OSKAR (*b.* Bergzabern, Germany, 12 May 1857; *d.* Freiberg im Breisgau, Germany, 5 July 1942), *mathematics.*

Bolza's principal mathematical investigations covered three topics: the reduction of hyperelliptic integrals to elliptic integrals, elliptic and hyperelliptic functions, and the calculus of variations. On the first two topics Bolza proved an able follower of his teachers Karl Weierstrass and Felix Klein. In the realm of reduction problems he worked chiefly on third-degree and fourth-degree transformations. He stressed elliptic theory and often reformulated it as a special case of the hyperelliptic theory in his papers on hyperelliptic θ, σ, and ζ functions. On the third topic his book *Lectures on the Calculus of Variations* (1904) presented the most recent contributions of Weierstrass, Adolf Kneser, and David Hilbert, as well as his own comments. In this book and other writings he added to the theory in the plane and the problem of Lagrange with fixed end points. He extended and applied existence theorems for implicit functions and for solutions to differential equations. Bolza's most significant single contribution was the unification of the problems of Lagrange and Mayer into his more general problem of Bolza. This problem was the fifth, classical necessary condition for a minimum to appear. Leonhard Euler, Adrien-Marie Legendre, Karl Jacobi, and Karl Weierstrass had formulated the previous four. The problem of Bolza in parametric form is to find in a class of arcs $y_i(x)$, where ($i = 1, \cdots, n; x_0 < x < x_1$) which satisfy equations of the form

$$\phi_\beta(y, y') = 0 \qquad (\beta = 1, \cdots, p)$$
$$\psi_\mu(y) = 0 \qquad (\mu = 1, \cdots, q)$$

and end conditions of the form

$$J_\gamma[y(x_0), y(x_1)] = 0 \qquad (\gamma = 1, \cdots, r),$$

one that minimizes a sum of the form

$$I = G[y(x_0), y(x_1)] + \int_{x_0}^{x_1} f(y, y') \, dx.$$

In this formulation the problem of Mayer with variable end points is the problem of Bolza with its integrand function f identically zero, while the problem of Lagrange with variable end points is the case when G is absent from I.

The son of Emil Bolza and Luise König, Bolza displayed a variety of interests during his youth. At the Gymnasium in Freiburg, he eagerly studied languages and comparative philology, but when he entered the University of Berlin in 1875, he decided to study physics under Kirchhoff and Helmholtz. After tiring of experimental work, in 1878 Bolza switched to the study of pure mathematics. The chief mentor for his mathematical studies at Berlin was Weierstrass, who was particularly interested in the calculus of variations and strongly influenced the course of Bolza's research. From 1878 to 1880 Bolza's studies led him from Berlin to Strasbourg, back to Berlin, and then to Göttingen. After deciding that he wanted to teach, either in a Gymnasium or a university, he interrupted his mathematical studies from 1880 to 1883 in order to prepare for and pass the Staatsexamen, a prerequisite for Gymnasium teaching. From 1883 to 1885 Bolza returned to his mathematical studies, working privately on his doctoral dissertation at the University of Freiburg. After Felix Klein accepted his dissertation on hyperelliptic integrals, he received his doctorate from Göttingen in June 1886. He followed this with a year's private seminar with Klein in Göttingen.

After completing his studies, two reasons prompted Bolza to abandon his teaching plans and go to the United States. Friends complained of the lack of time allowed for research in German schools; second, he was not robust and feared that Gymnasium teaching would be too strenuous for him. He had been rejected for military service in 1887. Bolza arrived in the United States in 1888, and in January 1889 he became reader in mathematics at Johns Hopkins University. In October of that same year he advanced to associate professor in mathematics at Clark University. On 1 January 1893, Bolza became associate professor of mathematics at the newly founded University at Chicago. He advanced to full professor in the following year.

After 1898 Bolza felt a growing desire to return to Germany. In 1908 the death of Heinrich Maschke, an old college friend and a colleague at Chicago, severed perhaps the strongest bond that kept him in America. In addition, he felt that America had made great strides in the training of scholars and believed that he should step aside for the increasing number of young American-trained teachers. In 1910, when he left the University of Chicago, he was given the title of nonresident professor of mathematics.

Upon his return to Germany, Bolza studied various subjects. He accepted the position of honorary professor of mathematics at the University of Freiburg, but in a few years World War I turned his prime interest from mathematics to religious psychology and languages, especially Sanskrit. He had grown up in a pre-World War I Europe in which people believed no major war could occur again: all problems would be resolved by reason. The trauma of World War I shook the foundations of thought for many, including Bolza; he turned to religious psychology and Sanskrit in search of answers on how to establish a better society. Bolza studied Sanskrit so that he could read firsthand the literature concerning the religious systems of India. His new interests prompted him to interrupt his mathematical research in 1922 and his class lectures in 1926. Bolza became more and more engrossed in psychological research, and he devoted full time to it from 1926 until 1929. The result of this work was *Glaubenlose Religion,* which he published in 1931 under the pseudonym F. H. Marneck.

In his final years Bolza remained an active academician. He returned to lecturing on mathematics at the University of Freiburg from 1929 to 1933, when he retired. After his retirement he continued to publish papers on mathematics and religious psychology. At the request of friends he wrote a brief autobiography, *Aus meinen Leben.* As late as 1939 Bolza wrote to friends of his interest in studying the foundations of geometry.

BIBLIOGRAPHY

I. ORIGINAL WORKS. Books by Bolza include *Lectures on the Calculus of Variations* (Chicago, 1904); *Vorlesungen über Variationsrechnung, Umgearbeitete und stark Vermehrte deutsche Ausgabe der "Lectures on the Calculus of Variations"* (Leipzig, 1908); "Gauss und die Variationsrechnung," in Gauss's *Werke,* X, pt. 2, 5 (Göttingen, 1922); *Aus meinen Leben* (privately published, 1936); *Glaubenlose Religion* (Munich, 1931), published under the pseudonym F. H. Marneck; *Meister Eckehart als Mystiker, eine religions-psychologische Studie* (Munich, 1938). See also "Elliptic Functions," a handwritten record of a course given at the University of Chicago, probably in the winter quarter, 1901; and "Lectures on Integral Equations," in W. V. Lovitt, *Linear Integral Equations* (New York, 1924).

For articles by Bolza see "Über die Reduction hyperelliptischen Integrale erste Ordnung und erster Gattung auf elliptische durch eine Transformation vierten Grades," in *Mathematical Annals,* **28** (1887), 447–456; "On Binary

Sextics With Linear Transformations Into Themselves," in *American Journal of Mathematics,* **10** (1888), 47–70; "The Elliptic Function Considered as a Special Case of the Hyperelliptic Function," in *Transactions of the American Mathematical Society,* **1** (1900), 53–65; "Weierstrass' Theorem and Kneser's Theorem on Transversals for the Most General Case of an Extremum of a Simple Definite Integral," *ibid.,* **7** (1906), 459–488; "Die Lagrangeschen Multiplikatorenregel in die Variationsrechnung für den Fall von gemischten Bedingung bei variabeln Endpunkten," in *Mathematical Annals,* **64** (1907), 370–387; "Heinrich Maschke, His Life and Work," in *Bulletin of the American Mathematical Society,* **15** (1908), 85–95; "Über den Hilbertischen Unabhangigkeitssatz beim Lagrangeschen Variationsproblem," in *Rendiconti del Circolo matematico di Palermo,* **31** (1911), 257–272; "Über zwei Eulersche Aufgaben aus der Variationsrechnung," in *Annali di matematica pura ed applicata,* **20** (1913), 245–255; "Einführung in E. H. Moore's *General Analysis* und deren Anwendung auf die Verallgemeinerung der Theorie der linearen Integralgleichungen," in *Jahrbuch Deutschen Mathematische Verein,* **23** (1914), 248–303; "Der singuläre Fall der Reduction hyperelliptische Integrale erster Ordnung auf elliptische durch Transformation dritten Grades," in *Mathematical Annals,* **111** (1935), 477–500.

II. SECONDARY LITERATURE. An article on Bolza is G. A. Bliss, "Oskar Bolza—In Memoriam," in *Bulletin of the American Mathematical Society,* **50** (1944), 478–489, which contains a chronological list of Bolza's writings.

RONALD S. CALINGER

BOLZANO, BERNARD (*b.* Prague, Czechoslovakia, 5 October 1781; *d.* Prague, 18 December 1848), *philosophy, mathematics, logic, religion, ethics.*

Bolzano was born in one of the oldest quarters of Prague and was baptized Bernardus Placidus Johann Nepomuk. His mother, Caecilia Maurer, daughter of a hardware tradesman in Prague, was a pious woman with an inclination to the religious life. At the age of twenty-two she married the elder Bernard Bolzano, an Italian immigrant who earned a modest living as an art dealer. The father was a widely read man with an active social conscience, and felt responsible for the well-being of his fellow men. He put his ideas into practice and took an active part in founding an orphanage in Prague.

Bernard was the fourth of twelve children, ten of whom died before reaching adulthood. Of delicate health, he had a quiet disposition, although he was easily irritated and very sensitive to injustice.

From 1791 to 1796 he was a pupil in the Piarist Gymnasium, and in 1796 he entered the philosophical faculty of the University of Prague, where he followed courses in philosophy, physics, and mathematics. His interest in mathematics was stimulated by reading A.

G. Kästner's *Anfangsgründe der Mathematik,* because Kästner took care to prove statements which were commonly understood as evident in order to make clear the assumptions on which they depended.

The benevolence of the environment in which Bernard Bolzano was reared, both at home and in school, influenced his entire life. In fact, he raised to the supreme principle of moral conduct the precept always to choose that action, of all possible actions, which best furthers the commonweal.

After having finished his studies in philosophy in 1800, Bolzano entered the theological faculty. These studies did not strengthen his belief or resolve his doubts concerning the truth and divinity of Christian religion, but he found a solution in his professor's statement that a doctrine may be considered justified if one is able to show that faith in it yields moral profit. This made it possible for Bolzano to reconcile religion with his ethical views and to consider Catholicism the perfect religion.

In 1805 Emperor Franz I of Austria, of which Czechoslovakia was then a part, decided that a chair in the philosophy of religion would be established in each university. The reasons for this were mainly political. The emperor feared the fruits of enlightenment embodied in the French Revolution, and therefore was sympathetic to the Catholic restoration that joined issue with the spirit of freethinking which had spread over Bohemia. Bolzano, who had taken orders in 1804, was called to the new chair at the University of Prague in 1805.

Spiritually, Bolzano belonged to the Enlightenment. Both his religious and social views made him quite unsuitable for the intended task, and difficulties were inevitable. His appointment was received in Vienna with suspicion, and it was not approved until 1807.

Bolzano's lectures, in which he expounded his own views on religion, were enthusiastically received by his students; in particular, his edifying Sunday speeches (*Erbauungsreden,* in *Gesammelte Schriften,* I) to the students were warmly applauded. He was respected by his colleagues, and in 1815 became a member of the Königlichen Böhmischen Gesellschaft der Wissenschaften and, in 1818, dean of the Prague philosophical faculty.

In the struggle between the Catholic restoration and the Enlightenment action against Bolzano was postponed until 1816, when a charge was brought against him at the court in Vienna; his dismissal was issued on 24 December 1819. He was forbidden to publish and was put under police supervision. Bolzano repeatedly refused to recant the heresies of which he was accused, and in 1825 the action came to an end through the intervention of the influential nationalist leader J. Dobrovsky.

From 1823 on, Bolzano spent summers on the estate of his friend J. Hoffmann, near the village of Těchobuz in southern Bohemia. He lived there permanently from 1831 until the death of Mrs. Hoffmann in 1842. Then he returned to Prague, where he continued his mathematical and philosophical studies until his death.

Though Bolzano's career was concerned mainly with social, ethical, and religious questions, he was irresistibly attracted by philosophy, methodology of science, and especially mathematics and logic. His philosophical education—which acquainted him with the Greeks and with Wolff, Leibniz, and Descartes—convinced him of the necessity of forming clear concepts and of sound reasoning, starting from irreducible first principles and using only intrinsic properties of defined concepts. Such methods could not take into account properties alien to their definition, such as geometrical evidence (see *Beyträge*). On occasion he applied these principles with remarkable results; on other occasions, however, his philosophical approach, particularly to mathematics, led him to introduce insufficiently founded and incorrect assumptions. Such was the case in *Die drey Probleme,* which was explicitly intended to lead to a completely new theory of space—which, of course, it failed to do. In the domain of mathematical analysis, however, Bolzano's struggle for clear concepts did lead to profound results that, unfortunately, did not attract the attention of the mathematical world or influence the development of mathematics.

Around the turn of the nineteenth century, mathematicians in Europe were concerned with two major problems. The first was the status of Euclid's parallel postulate, and the second was the problem of providing a solid foundation for mathematical analysis, so as to remove the so-called scandal of the infinitesimals. Bolzano tried his hand at both problems, with varying success.

In 1804 he published his *Betrachtungen über einige Gegenstände der Elementargeometrie,* in which he tried to base the theory of triangles and parallels on a theory of lines, without having recourse to theorems of the plane. The full development of this theory of lines was postponed—and although Bolzano often returned to the theory of parallels (without success), his linear theory was never completed.

In the course of the following years, Bolzano became acquainted with the extensive work done in the theory of parallels, such as that of A. M. Legendre and F. K. Schweikart. There are no indications that he ever knew of the final breakthrough to non-

Euclidean geometry by Nikolai Lobachevski and János Bolyai, although the latter's work was published in 1832 in Hungary. Bolzano's own manuscript "Anti-Euklid" follows a different line of thought and is devoted mainly to methodological criticism of Euclid's *Elements.* In fact, in his methodological principles he went so far as to require definitions of such geometrical notions as those of (simple closed) curve, surface, and dimension (see *Die drey Probleme; Ueber Haltung;* "Geometrische Begriffe"; and E. Winter, *Die historische Bedeutung*), and to require proofs of such seemingly evident statements as "A simple closed curve divides the plane into two parts," which is now known as the Jordan curve theorem. Indeed, the discussion in "Anti-Euklid" confirms the opinion held by H. Hornich that Bolzano was the first to state this as a theorem (requiring proof). The problems raised in this connection by Bolzano found their final solution at the end of the nineteenth century and the beginning of the twentieth in that branch of mathematics called topology (for a discussion of these matters, see Berg, *Bolzano's Logic*).

It should be emphasized that Bolzano was not the only one, or even the first, to be concerned with the problem of rigorous proofs in mathematics. A curious fact, however, is that although many of the mathematicians actively interested in the problem of the foundation of mathematical analysis surpassed him in mathematical skill, Bolzano overcame them decisively in the foundation of analysis, in which as early as 1817 (see *Rein analytischer Beweis*) he obtained fundamental results, which were completed in 1832–1835 in his theory of real numbers (see Rychlík, *Theorie der reellen Zahlen*).

The introduction of infinitesimals by Newton and Leibniz in the seventeenth century met with violent resistance from philosophers and mathematicians, and vivid discussions on infinitesimal quantities went on throughout the eighteenth century. Bishop Berkeley's attack in *The Analyst* (1734) is well known. Although Leibniz himself did not consider the existence of infinitesimals to be well founded, and held that their use could be avoided, he admitted them as ideal quantities, which could be handled in calculations like ordinary quantities (except that they equal their finite multiples). These arithmetical properties, however, formed the weak point in the theory of infinitesimals because of the lack of an exhaustive description of the real number system, which was accomplished only in the second half of the nineteenth century. How badly the general laws of arithmetic were understood may be illustrated by the problem of division by zero. This problem kept Bolzano busy from 1815 on, and he never fully got to the bottom of it, as can be seen, for instance, in §34 of his *Paradoxien des Unendlichen,* where he admits identities of the form $A/0 = A/0$, despite his knowledge of Ohm's solution.

To overcome the difficulties presented by infinitesimals, Lagrange proposed to base analysis on the existence of Taylor's expansion for functions, and this attitude was widely accepted for a time. Bolzano did not escape its influence, and made extensive studies on Taylor's theorem (see *Der binomische Lehrsatz* and "Miscellanea mathematica").

A different position was held by d'Alembert, who proposed to found differential calculus on the notion of limit and contended that differential calculus does not treat of infinitely small quantities, but of limits of finite quantities.

Certainly d'Alembert's opinion impressed his contemporaries, and many attempts, such as Lagrange's, were made to free differential calculus from infinitesimals. The first successful attempt was made by Bolzano in his *Rein analytischer Beweis* (1817), which is devoted to a proof of the important theorem which states that if for two continuous functions f and ϕ we have $f(\alpha) < \phi(\alpha)$ and $f(\beta) > \phi(\beta)$, then there is an x between α and β such that $f(x) = \phi(x)$.

Bolzano argues that a sound proof of this theorem presupposes a sound definition of continuous function. In his introduction he gives such a definition, which is important because it is the first that does not involve infinitesimals, and is, essentially, the one used up to now. In the more accurate formulation of Volume I of the *Functionenlehre,* it reads: If $F(x + \Delta x) - Fx$ in absolute value becomes less than an arbitrary given fraction $1/N$, if one takes Δx small enough, and remains so, the smaller one takes Δx, the function Fx is said to be continuous (in x). Bolzano also distinguishes between right and left continuity.

It should be noted that in 1821 Cauchy, in his *Cours d'analyse,* adopted a different definition: $f(x + \alpha) - f(x)$ infinitely small for all infinitely small α. Because of its elegance, this definition was generally accepted.

In his proof of the theorem in the *Rein analytischer Beweis,* Bolzano uses a lemma that later proved to be the cornerstone of the theory of real numbers. He was fully aware of the paramount importance of this theorem, and he formulated it with great generality, as follows: If a property M does not hold for all values of a variable x, but does hold for all x less than a certain u, then there is a quantity U, which is the greatest of all those for which it holds that all x less than it have property M.

In modern terminology, U is the greatest lower bound of the (nonempty) set of x for which M does not hold.

Though the two theorems mentioned above already bear witness to the outstanding content of the *Rein analytischer Beweis,* it contains another theorem of equal importance, which is known as Cauchy's condition of convergence. Bolzano devotes a whole section to it and proves that if a sequence $F_1(x)$, $F_2(x)$, $F_3(x)$, $\cdots$, $F_n(x)$, $\cdots$, $F_{n+r}(x)$ is such that the difference between the nth term $F_n(x)$ and every later one $F_{n+r}(x)$ remains less than any given quantity if only n has been taken large enough, then there is a fixed quantity, and only one, to which the terms approach—as near as one likes, if one continues the sequence far enough.

The proofs of these theorems are incomplete, and were bound to be so, because complete proofs would require a precise notion of quantity (real number), which Bolzano did not have at that time. He was aware of at least some of the difficulties involved, because his methodology, as expounded in the *Beyträge,* demanded the systematic development of a theory of real numbers that should logically precede his theory of real functions.

A fairly complete theory of real functions is contained in Bolzano's *Functionenlehre,* including many of the fundamental results that were rediscovered in the second half of the nineteenth century through the work of K. Th. Weierstrass and many others.

In the first part, concerning continuous functions, it is shown that a function Fx which is unbounded on the closed interval $[a, b]$ cannot be continuous on $[a, b]$. The proof uses the so-called Bolzano-Weierstrass theorem that a bounded infinite point set has an accumulation point. For this theorem Bolzano refers to his own work, in which up to now it has not been found.

Functions continuous on a closed interval attain there a maximal and a minimal value. Bolzano sharply distinguishes between continuity and the property of assuming intermediate values, and proves that continuous functions assume all values intermediate between any two function values, while the converse is shown not to be true.

In §13 Bolzano notices a property of continuous functions which is rather close to uniform continuity, a notion which is due to E. Heine (1870, 1872). In connection with the function

$$Fx = \frac{1}{1 - x},$$

which is continuous on (0, 1), he observes that though a function may be continuous on the open interval (a, b), it does not follow that a real number e, independent of x in (a, b), exists, such that one need not choose $\Delta x < e$ in order that $F(x + \Delta x) - Fx < 1/N$. Indeed, if in the example x approaches 1, the Δx has to be taken increasingly smaller in order that $F(x + \Delta x) - Fx < 1/N$.

As K. Rychlík has pointed out in his commentary in Volume I of the *Schriften,* the said property is weaker than uniform continuity. One may be tempted, however, to assume that Bolzano intended uniform continuity and that only the formulation is defective. The more so, when in "Verbesserungen und Zusätze" we find the correct theorem: If the function Fx is continuous on the closed interval $[a, b]$, then there exists a (real) number e such that for all x in $[a, b]$ the Δx need not be chosen $< e$ in order that $F(x + \Delta x) - Fx <$ a given number $1/N$. Further reading reveals, however, that Bolzano had no clear notion of uniform continuity after all.

Careful attention is paid to the connection between monotonicity and continuity. Thereby the following correction to §79 of the *Functionenlehre* in "Verbesserungen und Zusätze" should not remain unnoticed: If the (real) function Fx increases (or decreases) steadily on the closed interval $[a, b]$, then Fx is continuous on $[a, b]$, with the exception of a set of isolated values of x which may be infinite or finite.

The most remarkable result of the *Functionenlehre,* however, is the construction in §75 of the so-called Bolzano function. There Bolzano constructs a function as the limit of a sequence of continuous functions which is continuous on the closed interval $[0, 1]$ such that it is in no subinterval monotone. The importance of this function, however, derives from another property—its nondifferentiability.

The second part of the *Functionenlehre* is devoted to derivatives. Particular emphasis is laid on the distinction between continuity and differentiability. Bolzano shows that the above-mentioned function, though continuous in $[0, 1]$—which is not proved— fails to be differentiable on an everywhere dense subset of $[0, 1]$. In fact, the function is nowhere differentiable on $[0, 1]$. This example preceded by some forty years that of Weierstrass, who in 1875 published a different example of a nowhere differentiable continuous function which roused wide interest and even indignation.

Bolzano erroneously believed that his function was continuous because it was the limit of continuous functions; in explanation it may be remarked that Cauchy made the same error. Apparently Bolzano was not aware of a counterexample given by N. H. Abel in 1826.

Though the second part of the *Functionenlehre*

contains many interesting results, it contains as many errors, such as the statement that the derivative of an infinite series is the sum of the derivatives of its terms, and the conclusion that the limit of a sequence of continuous functions again is a continuous function. Both errors tie up with the notion of uniformity and therefore are explainable; the following error is less easy to understand. In 1829 Cauchy put forward the function

$$C(x) = e^{-1/x^2} \text{ (to be completed by } C[0] = 0)$$

as an example of a function, different from zero for all $x \neq 0$, having all its derivatives zero for $x = 0$ and, hence, not admitting a Taylor expansion in the neighborhood of $x = 0$. Bolzano knew of this example in 1831 (see "Miscellanea mathematica," p. 1999), yet in the *Functionenlehre,* §89, we find the following theorem:

If $F^{n+r}a = 0$ for $r > 0$, then

$$F(a + h) = Fa + h \cdot F'a + \frac{h^2}{2} F''a + \cdots +$$

$$\frac{h^n}{2.3 \cdots n} F^n a,$$

which is clearly refuted by Cauchy's example.

The firm base on which the theory of functions was to rest, according to Bolzano's methodology—the theory of quantities (real numbers)—was completed in 1832–1835. Like most of Bolzano's mathematical work, it remained in manuscript and was published for the first time only in 1962 (see Rychlík, *Theorie der reellen Zahlen*). As a result, this bold enterprise failed to exercise any influence on the development of mathematics, which in the second half of the nineteenth century independently took the same course.

Real numbers occur in Bolzano's writings under the name of measurable infinite number-expressions. They make their appearance in "Miscellanea mathematica," pt. 22, p. 2000–2001 (1832), in connection with the geometric progression, which has inspired many interesting ideas. The representation of the sum S of an infinite geometric progression as given in the footnote to §18 of the *Paradoxien des Unendlichen* is paradigmatic.

Bolzano's idea is that descriptions of (real) numbers make sense only if they permit determination of the numbers described with an arbitrarily high degree of precision by means of rational numbers. In general, these descriptions require an infinite number of arithmetical operations to be carried out—for instance, the sum S of a geometric progression. These are the infinite number expressions with which Bolzano is concerned. If the results obtained by carrying out only a finite number of operations is always positive, the number expression is called positive.

An infinite number expression S is called measurable (or determinable by approximation) if to any natural number q there is an integer p, such that

$$S = \frac{p}{q} + P_1 = \frac{p+1}{q} - P_2,$$

where P_1 and P_2 are positive (infinite) number expressions.

Infinitely small numbers are those for which all $p = 0$, i.e., those S for which

$$S = P_1 = \frac{1}{q} - P_2,$$

as well as their opposites.

An essential requirement is that measurable numbers differing in an infinitesimal number have to be considered as equal. Therefore, equality is defined by equality of p for all q in the above representation of infinite number expressions. On the basis of these definitions, Bolzano completed his systematic exposition of the theory of real numbers and, thereby, of mathematical analysis.

The elaboration is not quite satisfactory because of many errors due to his insufficient mathematical skill (for interpretations and evaluation of Bolzano's theory, see Laugwitz, "Bemerkungen"; van Rootselaar, "Bolzano's Theory of Real Numbers"; Rychlík, *Theorie der reellen Zahlen*).

The essential differences between Bolzano's incomplete theory of real numbers and those of, for instance, Weierstrass and Georg Cantor are marked by the shift from intensional meaning, in Bolzano's work, toward a general tendency to extensionality, and, above all, by the possibility of creating new mathematical objects by means of definition by abstraction, based on equivalence relations, of which Bolzano was unaware. These differences also appear clearly in his *Paradoxien des Unendlichen,* which contains many interesting fragments of general set theory.

The existence of infinite sets is proved in a way similar to that followed by Richard Dedekind in his memoir *Was sind und was sollen die Zahlen* (1887). Most noteworthy, however, is that in §20 of *Paradoxien des Unendlichen* Bolzano is at the border of cardinal arithmetic, a border which he is unable to cross. There he notices a property of infinite sets: that they may be brought into one-to-one correspondence with a proper subset. In fact, he observes that this will always be the case with infinite sets. That two sets may be brought into one-to-one correspondence is no reason for him to consider them to be composed of the same number of elements (*Paradoxien des Unendlichen,* §21), however, and he sees no reason to consider such sets as equal. On the contrary, in order for two sets to be considered as equal, he argues, they must be defined on the same basis (*gleiche Bestimmungsgründe haben*). Needless to say, this is too vague to be dealt with mathematically. Here again, we see that Bolzano halts at a point where application of the method of definition by abstraction would have opened entirely new fields of knowledge.

Precisely that property of infinite sets noticed by Bolzano was afterward used by Dedekind as a definition of the infinite (1882). The introduction of equivalence classes of sets under one-to-one correspondence was fully exploited by Cantor in his theory of cardinals, a very important chapter of general set theory.

Bolzano planned to elaborate the methodology begun in his *Beyträge* and to develop it into a complete theory of science, of which a treatise on logic was to form the cornerstone. From 1820 on, he worked steadily on it, and his four-volume treatise *Wissenschaftslehre* appeared in 1837. The plan of the *Wissenschaftslehre* appears clearly from the following subdivision (see Kambartel, *Bernard Bolzano's Grundlegung der Logik,* pp. 14–17):

(1) Fundamental theory: proof of the existence of abstract truths and of the human ability to judge.

(2) Elementary theory: theory of abstract ideas, propositions, true propositions, and deductions.

(3) Theory of knowledge: condition of the human faculty of judgment.

(4) Heuristics: rules to be observed in human thought in the search for truths.

(5) Proper theory of science: rules to be observed in the division of the set of truths into separate sciences and in their exposition in truly scientific treatises.

The work did not induce a complete revision of science, as Bolzano hoped, but, on the contrary, remained unnoticed and did not exercise perceptible influence on the development of logic. Some of the innovations in logic contained in the first two volumes did attract attention, as well as excessive praise— notably from Edmund Husserl and Heinrich Scholz (see Berg, *op. cit.*; Kambartel, *op. cit.*; and the literature cited in them).

The rise of logical semantics, initiated by Alfred Tarski in the 1930's, has led to a revival of the study of Bolzano's logic in the light of modern logic (see Berg, *op. cit.*) and of his theory of an ideal language.

The heart of Bolzano's logic is formed by his concepts of (abstract) proposition (*Satz an sich*), abstract idea (*Vorstellung an sich*), truth, and the notions of derivability (*Ableitbarkeit*) and entailment (*Abfolge*).

These notions may be explained with the help of Bolzano's example:

(*a*) Cajus is a human being.

(*b*) All human beings have immortal souls.

(*c*) Cajus has an immortal soul.

First of all, (*a*) expresses an abstract proposition, which in itself has no real existence, but is something to which (*a*) refers and which is either true or false. An abstract proposition may be expressed in many ways linguistically, and it is said to be true if it asserts something as it actually is (*"so wie es ist,"* *Wissenschaftslehre*, §25).

Bolzano argues that any proposition may be expressed in the normal form "*A* has *b*." For instance,

(*a'*) Cajus has human existence

is the normal form of the proposition expressed by (*a*).

Parts of propositions which are not themselves propositions are (abstract) ideas; for example, in (*a'*) the expression "human existence" refers to an abstract idea.

Between abstract propositions there exist relations, among which those of consistency and derivability are of paramount importance. Propositions *A*, *B*, *C*, ⋯ are called consistent with respect to the common ideas *i*, *j*, ⋯ if there are ideas *i'*, *j'*, ⋯ which, after substitution for *i*, *j*, ⋯ turn the propositions *A*, *B*, *C*, ⋯ into simultaneously true propositions *A'*, *B'*, *C'*, ⋯. Propositions *A'*, *B'*, *C'*, ⋯ are called derivable from *A*, *B*, *C*, ⋯ with respect to the ideas *i*, *j*, ⋯ whenever *A*, *B*, *C*, ⋯, *A'*, *B'*, *C'*, ⋯ are consistent with respect to *i*, *j*, ⋯ and if any substitution *i'*, *j'*, ⋯ for *i*, *j*, ⋯ that turns *A*, *B*, *C*, ⋯ into true propositions also turns *A'*, *B'*, *C'*, ⋯ into true propositions. According to Bolzano, (*c*) is derivable from (*a*) and (*b*).

The relation of entailment (*Abfolge*) may subsist between true propositions, and refers to the situation that *A* is true because $A_1, A_2, \cdots$ are true. The treatment of this notion, however, is rather unsatisfactory (see Berg, *op. cit.;* Buhl, *Ableitbarkeit und Abfolge;* Kambartel, *op. cit.* for details).

The resemblance that many of the concepts introduced by Bolzano bear to modern logic has led to the opinion that Bolzano may be considered a true precursor of modern logic. (For a detailed account, consult Berg, *op. cit.;* and Kambartel, *op. cit.;* for Bolzano's philosophy, Fujita, *Borutsāno no tetsugaku* ["Bolzano's Philosophy"]).

BIBLIOGRAPHY

I. Original Works. Bolzano's published works include the following: *Betrachtungen über einige Gegenstände der*

Elementargeometrie (Prague, 1804; repr. *Schriften*, V); *Beyträge zu einer begründeteren Darstellung der Mathemàtik* (Prague, 1810; new ed. by H. Fels, Paderborn, 1926); *Der binomische Lehrsatz und als Folgerung aus ihm der polynomische und die Reihen, die zur Berechnung der Logarithmen und Exponentialgrössen dienen, genauer als bisher erwiesen* (Prague, 1816); *Die drey Probleme der Rectification, der Complanation und der Cubirung, ohne Betrachtung des unendlich Kleinen, ohne die Annahmen des Archimedes, und ohne irgend eine nicht streng erweisliche Voraussetzung gelöst; zugleich als Probe einer gänzlichen Umstaltung der Raumwissenschaft, allen Mathematikern zur Prüfung vorgelegt* (Leipzig, 1817; repr. *Schriften*, V); *Rein analytischer Beweis des Lehrsatzes, dass zwischen je zwey Werthen, die ein entgegengesetztes Resultat gewähren, wenigstens eine reelle Wurzel der Gleichung liege* (Prague, 1817; new ed. in Ostwald's Klassiker der exakten Wissenschaften, no. 153 [Leipzig, 1905]; also in Kolman, *Bernard Bolzano*).

Also *Lebensbeschreibung des Dr. Bernard Bolzano mit einigen seiner ungedruckten Aufsätze und dem Bildnisse des Verfassers,* ed. M. J. Fesl (Sulzbach, 1836; repr. Vienna, 1875), an autobiography; *Wissenschaftslehre, Versuch einer ausführlichen und grösstentheils neuen Darstellung der Logik mit steter Rücksicht auf deren bisherigen Bearbeiter,* 4 vols. (Sulzbach, 1837; new ed. by A. Höfler and W. Schultz, 4 vols. [Leipzig, 1914–1931]; also in *Gesammelte Schriften*); *Paradoxien des Unendlichen,* ed. F. Přihonsky (Leipzig, 1851; English ed. by D. A. Steele, *Paradoxes of the Infinite* [New Haven, 1950]); *Ueber Haltung, Richtung, Krümmung und Schnörkelung bei Linien sowohl als Flächen sammt einigen verwandten Begriffen* (ed. in *Schriften*, V).

There are two collections of Bolzano's works. One is *Gesammelte Schriften,* 12 vols. (Vienna, 1882); the contents are as follows: I: *Erbauungsreden;* II: *Athanasia oder Gründe für die Unsterblichkeit der Seele;* III–VI: *Lehrbuch der Religionswissenschaft;* VII–X: *Wissenschaftslehre;* XI: *Dr. Bolzano und seine Gegner;* XII: *Bolzano's Wissenschaftslehre und Religionswissenschaft in beurteilender Übersicht.* The other is *Bernard Bolzano's Schriften,* 5 vols., ed. Königlichen Böhmischen Gesellschaft der Wissenschaften (Prague, 1930–1948), which contains the following: I: *Functionenlehre,* ed. K. Rychlik (1930); II: *Zahlentheorie,* ed. K. Rychlik (1931); III: *Von dem besten Staate,* ed. A. Kowalewski (1932); IV: *Der Briefwechsel B. Bolzano's mit F. Exner,* ed. E. Winter (1935); V: *Mémoires géometriques,* ed. J. Vojtech (1948).

Additional works are in manuscript: "Anti-Euklid" (fragment), in Österreichische Nationalbibliothek, Vienna, Handschriftensammlung, Series Nova, 3459, section 5 (also edited in Večerka, "Bernard Bolzano's Anti-Euklid"); "Geometrische Begriffe, die jeder kennt und nicht kennt," in Österreichische Nationalbibliothek, Vienna, Handschriftensammlung, Series Nova, 3459, sections 3b and 3c; "Miscellanea mathematica," 1–24, in Österreichische Nationalbibliothek, Vienna, Handschriftensammlung, Series Nova, 3453–3455; and "Verbesserungen und Zusätze zu dem Abschnitt von der Differenzialrechnung," in Österreichische Nationalbibliothek, Vienna, Handschriftensammlung, Series Nova, 3472, section 7.

II. SECONDARY LITERATURE. Works on Bolzano include J. Berg, *Bolzano's Logic* (Stockholm, 1962), which has an extensive bibliography; and "Bolzano's Theory of an Ideal Language," in R. E. Olson, ed., *Contemporary Philosophy in Scandinavia* (Baltimore, in press); G. Buhl, "Ableitbarkeit und Abfolge in der Wissenschaftstheorie Bolzanos," in *Kantstudien,* **83** (1961); H. Fels, *Bernard Bolzano, sein Leben und sein Werk* (Leipzig, 1929), which includes a Bolzano bibliography; I. Fujita, *Borutsāno no tetsugaku* ("Bolzano's Philosophy") (Tokyo, 1963); H. Hornich, "Ueber eine Handschrift aus dem Nachlass von B. Bolzano," in *Anzeiger. Osterreichische Akademie der Wissenschaften,* mathematische-naturwissenschaftliche Klasse, no. 2 (1961); F. Kambartel, *Bernard Bolzano's Grundlegung der Logik* (Hamburg, 1963), which includes selections from Wissenschaftslehre I and II and an excellent introduction; A. Kolman, *Bernard Bolzano* (Berlin, 1963), which has an extensive bibliography; D. Laugwitz, "Bemerkungen zu Bolzanos Grössenlehre," in *Archive for History of Exact Sciences,* **2** (1964), 398–409; B. van Rootselaar, "Bolzano's Theory of Real Numbers," in *Archive for History of Exact Sciences,* **2** (1964), 168–180; K. Rychlik, *Theorie der reellen Zahlen im Bolzanos handschriftlichen Nachlasse* (Prague, 1962); K. Večerka, "Bernard Bolzano's Anti-Euklid," in *Sborník pro dějiny přírodních věd a teckniky* (*Acta historiae rerum naturalium nec non technicarum,* Prague), **11** (1967), 203–216; E. Winter, *Leben und geistige Entwicklung des Sozialethikers und Mathematikers B. Bolzano 1781–1848,* Hallische Monographien, no. 14 (Halle, 1949), which has a Bolzano bibliography; *Die historische Bedeutung der Frühbegriffe B. Bolzano's* (Berlin, 1964); and *Wissenschaft und Religion im Vormärz. Der Briefwechsel Bernard Bolzanos mit Michael Josef Fesl 1822–1848* (Berlin, 1965); and E. Winter, P. Funk, J. Berg, *Bernard Bolzano, Ein Denker und Erzieher in Österreichischen Vormärz* (Vienna, 1967).

B. VAN ROOTSELAAR

BOMBELLI, RAFAEL (*b.* Bologna, Italy, January 1526; *d.* 1572), *algebra.*

Rafael Bombelli's family came from Borgo Panigale, a suburb three miles north of Bologna. The original family name was Mazzoli. The Mazzolis, who seem to have been small landowners, adopted the name Bombelli early in the sixteenth century. Some of them were supporters of the Bentivoglio faction. An unsuccessful conspiracy to restore the Bentivoglio *signoria* in 1508 resulted in the execution of seven men, among whom was Giovanni Mazzoli, Rafael Bombelli's great-grandfather. Giovanni Mazzoli's property was confiscated but was later restored to his grandchildren. One of them was Antonio Mazzoli, alias Bombelli, who later became a wool merchant and moved to Bologna. There he married Diamante Scudieri, the daughter of a tailor. Six children were born to this marriage, of whom the eldest son was Rafael Bombelli.

All that is known about Bombelli's education is that his teacher (*precettore*) was Pier Francesco Clementi of Corinaldo, an engineer-architect. It has been suggested that Bombelli might have studied at the University of Bologna, but this seems unlikely when one considers his family background and the nature of his profession. He spent the greater part of his working life as an engineer-architect in the service of his patron, Monsignor Alessandro Rufini, a Roman nobleman. Rufini was *cameriere* and favorite of Pope Paul III, and later was bishop of Melfi. The major engineering project on which Bombelli was employed was the reclamation of the marshes of the Val di Chiana. It was at a time when the reclamation work had been suspended that he wrote his treatise on algebra in the peaceful atmosphere of his patron's villa in Rome. His professional engagements seem to have delayed the completion of the book, but the more important part of it was published in 1572. His death soon afterward prevented the publishing of the remainder of the work. It was not published until 1929.

Bombelli's teacher, Pier Francesco Clementi, was employed by the Apostolic Camera (*ca.* 1548) in draining the marshes of the Topino River at Foligno (100 miles from Rome). It is not known whether Bombelli himself worked in Foligno; but by 1551 he had begun to work for Rufini in the reclamation of the Val di Chiana marshes. Rufini began to take an interest in this project in 1549, when the rights of reclamation of that part of the marshes which belonged to the Papal States were obtained by his nominee. Evidence of Bombelli's activity is found in the record relating to the marking out and settlement of the boundaries of the reclaimed land. The work of reclamation was interrupted sometime between 1555 and 1560. By 1560 Bombelli had returned to the Val di Chiana, and his work there ended in that year. In 1561 he was in Rome, where he took part in the unsuccessful attempt to repair the Ponte Santa Maria, one of the bridges over the Tiber.

Bombelli's work in the Val di Chiana earned him a reputation as an engineer, and led to his being one of the consultants on a proposed project for draining a part of the Pontine Marshes during the reign of Pius IV (1559–1565). The historian Nicolai, in his *De' bonificamenti delle Terre Pontine* (1800), says that the work was to have been directed by Rafael Bombelli, "famous among hydraulic engineers for having successfully drained the marshes of the Val di Chiana." The project was not realized, however.

Rafael Bombelli grew up in an Italy that was active in the production of works on practical arithmetic. Luca Pacioli, author of the *Summa di arithmetica, geometria, . . .* (1494), had lectured at Bologna at the beginning of the century. So had Scipione dal Ferro, a citizen of Bologna and one of the foremost mathematicians of the time. Their successors, Cardano, Tartaglia, and Ferrari, who were attempting the solution of the cubic and biquadratic equations, lived and worked in the neighboring cities of northern Italy. Cardano's *Practica arithmeticae* was published in 1539 and was followed in 1545 by his great treatise on algebra, the *Ars magna,* which gave the methods of dal Ferro and Ferrari for solving the cubic and biquadratic equations, respectively. In 1546 the controversy between Cardano and Tartaglia became public with the appearance of the latter's *Quesiti et inventioni diverse.* Copies of the *Cartelli di matematica disfida* (1547–1548), exchanged between Ferrari and Tartaglia, were circulated in the principal cities of Italy. Such was the climate in which Bombelli conceived the idea of writing a treatise on algebra. He felt that none of his predecessors except Cardano had explored the subject in depth; but Cardano, he thought, had not been clear in his exposition. He therefore decided to write a book that would enable anyone to master the subject without the aid of any other text. The work, written between 1557 and 1560, was a systematic and logical exposition of the subject in five parts, or books. In Book I, Bombelli dealt with the definitions of the elementary concepts (powers, roots, binomials, trinomials) and applications of the fundamental operations. In Book II he introduced algebraic powers and notation, and then went on to deal with the solution of equations of the first, second, third, and fourth degrees. Bombelli considered only equations with positive coefficients, thus adhering to the practice of his contemporaries. He was therefore obliged to deal with a large number of cases: five types of quadratic equations, seven cubic, and forty-two biquadratic. For each type of equation, he gave the rule for solution and illustrated the rule with examples. Bombelli feared that the examples given in Book II would not be sufficient for a beginner who wished to master the subject, so he decided to include in Book III a series of problems by which the student would be taken, in stages, through the various operations of algebra. For this purpose he chose problems that were common to books on practical arithmetic of his day. Many of them were "applied problems"— that is, problems that had denominate numbers— and not mere exercises in manipulating symbols. They were often woven into incidents that could have occurred in the marketplace or tavern. Books IV and V formed the geometrical portion of the work. Book IV contained the application of geometrical methods to algebra, *algebra linearia,* and Book V was devoted to the application of algebraic methods to the solution of geometrical problems. Unfortunately, Bombelli was unable to complete the work as he had originally planned, in particular Books IV and V.

He had the opportunity, however, of studying a codex of Diophantus' *Arithmetic* in the Vatican Library during a visit to Rome. It was shown to him by Antonio Maria Pazzi, *lector ad mathematicam* at the University of Rome. They set out to translate the manuscript, but circumstances prevented them from completing the work. The changes that Bombelli made in the first three books of his *Algebra* show evidence of the influence of Diophantus. At the end of Book III, Bombelli said that the geometrical part, Books IV and V, was not yet ready for the publisher, but that it would follow shortly. His death prevented his keeping the promise. It was only in 1923 that the manuscript of the *Algebra* was rediscovered by Ettore Bortolotti in the Biblioteca Comunale dell'Archiginnasio in Bologna.

In his *Algebra,* Bombelli gave a comprehensive account of the existing knowledge of the subject, enriching it with his own contributions. Cardano had observed that the general rule given by dal Ferro could not be applied in solving the so-called irreducible case of the cubic equation, but Bombelli's skill in operating with "imaginary numbers" enabled him to demonstrate the applicability of the rule even in this case. Because of the special nature and importance of these imaginary quantities, he took great care to make the reader familiar with them by introducing them early in his work—at the end of Book I. He said he had found "un altra sorte di radice cuba legata" ("another kind of cube root of an aggregate") different from the others. This was the cube root of a complex number occurring in the solution of the irreducible case of the cubic equation. He called the square roots of a negative quantity *più di meno* and *meno di meno* (that is, *p. di m.* 10, *m. di m.* 10 for $+\sqrt{-10}$, $-\sqrt{-10}$). Having pointed out that the complex root is always accompanied by its conjugate, he set out the rules for operating with complex numbers and gave examples showing their application. Here he showed himself to be far ahead of his time, for his treatment was almost that followed today. Bombelli also pointed out that the problem of trisecting an angle could be reduced to that of solving the irreducible case of the cubic equation (this was illustrated in Book V). Although he made no significant contribution to the solution of the biquadratic equation, he showed the application of Ferrari's rule to every possible case.

In Book III of the printed version of the *Algebra* one finds no trace of the influence that practical arithmetics originally had on Bombelli. He said in the preface that he had deviated from the custom of those authors of arithmetics who stated their problems in the guise of human actions; his intention was to teach the "higher arithmetic." The problems of applied arithmetic that were originally included in Book III were left out of the published work; by doing so, Bombelli helped to raise algebra to the status of an independent discipline. In place of these applied problems he introduced a number of abstract problems, of which 143 were taken from the *Arithmetic* of Diophantus. Although Bombelli did not distinguish Diophantus' problems from his own, he acknowledged that he had borrowed freely from the *Arithmetic*. He was in fact the first to popularize the work of Diophantus in the West.

Apart from the solution of the irreducible case of the cubic equation, the most significant contribution Bombelli made to algebra was in the notation he adopted. He represented the powers of the unknown quantity by a semicircle inside which the exponent was placed: $\cup\!\!\!\!1$ for the modern x, $\cup\!\!\!\!2$ for x^2, and $5\cup\!\!\!\!1$ or $5\!\!\!\overset{\cup\!\!\!\!1}{}$ for $5x$. In the printed work the semicircle was reduced to an arc: $\underset{1}{\cup}$, $\underset{2}{\cup}$, $5\!\!\!\overset{1}{}$. The zero exponent, $\underset{0}{\cup}$, was used in the manuscript, $48\,\underset{0}{\cup}$ for 48, but was omitted from the published work. The notation $\text{R}\underline{\quad}$ was used in the manuscript in applying the radical to the aggregate of two or more terms: $\text{R}\lfloor 4p\text{R}6\rfloor$ for $\sqrt{4+\sqrt{6}}$. He even used the radical sign as a double bracket: $\text{R}^3\lfloor 2p\text{R}\lfloor 0m121\rfloor\rfloor$ for $\sqrt[3]{2+\sqrt{0-121}}$. In the printed work the horizontal line was broken, and R, R^3 became Rq, Rc: for example, $Rc\lfloor 2pRq\lfloor 0m121\rfloor\rfloor$.

Although incomplete, Books IV and V of the *Algebra* reveal Bombelli's versatility as a geometer. He had reduced some of the arithmetical problems of Book III to an abstract form and had interpreted them geometrically. He did not feel obliged to give geometrical proofs for the correctness of the results that he had obtained by algebraic methods. In doing so, he had broken away from a long-established tradition. The linear representation of powers, the use of the unit segment, and the representation of a point by "orthogonal coordinates" are some of the noteworthy features of this part of the work.

Bombelli was the last of the algebraists of Renaissance Italy. The influence that his *Algebra* had in the Low Countries is attested to by Simon Stevin and Adrien Romain. In the course of a short historical survey of the solution of equations, in his *Arithmetique,* Stevin referred to Bombelli as "great arithmetician of our time." He used a slightly modified form of Bombelli's notation for the powers of the unknown. While giving Bombelli due credit, he stressed the superiority of his notation to that of the Cossists. About a century later Leibniz, while teaching himself mathematics, used Bombelli's *Algebra* as a guide to the study of cubic equations. His correspondence with Huygens shows the keen interest these two men took in the work of the Italian mathematicians of the Renaissance. In the words of Leibniz, Bombelli was an "outstanding master of the analytical art."

BIBLIOGRAPHY

I. ORIGINAL WORKS. Versions of the *Algebra* are *L'algebra di Rafaello Bombello, cittadino bolognese,* in Biblioteca Comunale dell'Archiginnasio in Bologna, Codex B.1569; *L'algebra* (Bologna, 1572); and Ettore Bortolotti, ed., *L'algebra, opera di Rafael Bombelli da Bologna, Libri IV e V* (Bologna, 1929).

II. SECONDARY LITERATURE. For references to earlier literature, see S. A. Jayawardene, "Unpublished Documents Relating to Rafael Bombelli in the Archives of Bologna," in *Isis,* **54** (1963), 391–395, and "Rafael Bombelli, Engineer-Architect: Some Unpublished Documents of the Apostolic Camera," *ibid.,* **56** (1965), 298–306.

S. A. JAYAWARDENE

BONANNI, FILIPPO. See **Buonanni, Filippo.**

BONAPARTE, LUCIEN JULES LAURENT, called **Charles Lucien** (*b.* Paris, France, 24 May 1803; *d.* Paris, 29 July 1857), *zoology.*

Bonaparte was the son of Napoleon's younger brother, Lucien (1775–1840). His mother was Alexandrine de Bleschamp. In 1822 Bonaparte married his cousin Zénaïde Charlotte Julie, the daughter of the king of Naples and Spain. They had twelve children.

Soon after his marriage Bonaparte went to the United States, where he started a brilliant career as a naturalist. At twenty-five he returned to Europe and settled in Italy, beginning his great political activity. He advocated the organization of scientific congresses, which in Italy also served as the opportunity for meetings of independents and reformers. Upon the accession of Pope Pius IX, Bonaparte became a member of the pope's party. Next he was a member of the Radical party and of the supreme junta that seized power in the Roman states. After the pope's flight to Gaeta in November 1848, Bonaparte became a deputy from Viterbo; having been made vice-president of the Assemblée Nationale Romaine, he was also on the commission to draw up the constitution. When the Italian republic fell and French troops marched into Rome, he left Italy and went to France. He was not allowed to remain in Marseilles and therefore continued his trip. In Orléans he was arrested but released, then fled to Le Hâvre, where he took a boat for England. In 1850, once again allowed to live in Paris, Bonaparte left politics and turned exclusively to his scientific work. He had begun with a few essays in botany, but his zoological research became very important. While in the United States he had published numerous ornithological notes in the *Journal of the Philadelphia Academy of Sciences* and applied himself to the continuation of Wilson's work on birds.

As early as 1831 Bonaparte became interested in the great principles of classification and was critical of Cuvier's concepts. He classified the Insectivora before the Rodentia and separated the Chiroptera from the Primates. Besides the morphological characteristics, he considered the physiological data, such as, in the case of birds, "the perfect or imperfect condition" of the chicks at birth. Bonaparte raised the Batrachia to the rank of a subclass. He then united the saurians and the ophidians (Reptilia), placing the iguanodons at the head, as "the most perfect of cold-blooded and air-breathing animals."

In ichthyology Bonaparte made use of the location, the structure, and the relationships of the branchiae in the classification of fishes. He made a distinction between two new "sections," the Physostomi and the Physoclisti, according to whether or not the alimentary canal (the branchiae, according to Bonaparte) communicates with the air bladder. In general classifications, Bonaparte carefully reconstituted the synonymy of a species, minutely described its coloration (often illustrated by beautiful plates), and considered both its behavior and its geographic distribution.

Bonaparte tried to establish our knowledge of various zoological groups once and for all, and published numerous synopses, conspectuses, and catalogs. He urged zoologists to study local fauna and conceived the writing of a general work on the fauna of France, *Histoire naturelle générale et particulière des animaux qui vivent en France.* This was to be carried out in collaboration with Victor Meunier, and its prospectus is dated 1857. Bonaparte's death prevented the realization of the project. He had visited many museums in the United States and Europe and was deeply interested in the Muséum d'Histoire Naturelle. He hoped for the creation of a special gallery in which to exhibit the native fauna, with an accompanying professorship for its study. The teaching of natural sciences, according to him, should affect the study of agriculture and be conceived so as "to reach those who do not have the time to study."

Bonaparte had many friends abroad. In the United States he had known Audubon, and in Leiden he was friendly with J. C. Temminck and H. Shlegel. He was also a member of numerous learned societies and academies: the Philadelphia Academy of Natural Sciences, the Academy of Sciences and Literature of Baltimore, the Academy of Sciences of Berlin, and the Royal Academy of Turin. In 1839 Agassiz defeated Bonaparte for election to corresponding membership of the Académie des Sciences de Paris by one vote, but Bonaparte was elected on 18 March 1844.

Bonaparte left his personal library to the Muséum d'Histoire Naturelle. It contains works on the natural sciences, meteorology, history, and politics. It also includes his extensive correspondence, not yet cataloged.

BIBLIOGRAPHY

I. ORIGINAL WORKS. Bonaparte's writings include *American Ornithology or the Natural History of Birds Inhabiting the United States,* 4 vols. (Philadelphia, 1825–1833); *Observations on the Nomenclature of Wilson's Ornithology* (Philadelphia, 1826); "The Genera of North American Birds and a Synopsis of the Species to Be Found Within the Territory of the United States," in *Annales du Lycée New-York,* **11** (1826–1828); "Tableau comparatif des ornithologies de Rome et de Philadelphie," in *Nouveau journal des savants* (1827); "*Fauna Italica,*" *Iconographia della fauna italica per le quattro classi degli animali vertebrati,* 3 vols. (Rome, 1832–1841); "Amphibia Europaea ad systema nostrum vertebratorum ordinata," in *Memorie della Accademia delle scienze di Torino* (1840), 385–456; "Monographia leuciscorum Europaeorum," in *Actes du Congrès zoologique Pisa* (1840), p. 150; "Systema vertebratorum," in *Transactions of the Linnean Society of London,* **18** (1840), 247–305; *Catalogo metodico degli ucelli europei* (Bologna, 1842); *Catalogo metodico dei mammiferi europei* (Milan, 1845); *Catalogo metodico dei pesci europei* (Naples, 1846); *Conspectus systematis erpetologiae et amphibiologiae* (Leiden, 1850); *Conspectus systematis ornithologiae* (Leiden, 1850; rev., enl. ed., 1854); *Monographie des Loxiens* (Leiden–Düsseldorf, 1850), written with H. Schlegel; *Conspectus generum avium,* 2 vols. (Leiden, 1850–1857); *Discours, allocutions et opinions de Charles Louis Prince Bonaparte dans le Conseil des Députés et l'Assemblée Constituante de Rome en 1848 et 1849* (Leiden, 1857); and *Iconographie des pigeons non figurés par Madame Knip* [Mlle. Pauline de Courcelles], 2 vols. (Paris, 1857).

II. SECONDARY LITERATURE. Works on Bonaparte are Élie de Beaumont, *Notice sur les travaux scientifiques de S. A. le Prince Charles Louis Bonaparte (Réflexions sur ce travail par M. Richard du Cantal)* (1886); *Biographie du Prince Charles Bonaparte, Prince de Canino, fils de Lucien,* J. P. Jules Pautet, trans.; and the article in *Dictionnaire de biographie française,* VI (Paris, 1954). There is also an anonymous notice on Bonaparte's works in *Revue et magazine de zoologie,* **11** (1850).

G. PETIT

BONAVENTURA, FEDERIGO (*b*. Ancona, Italy, 24 August 1555; *d*. Urbino [?], Italy, March 1602), *meteorology.*

Bonaventura was the son of Pietro Bonaventura, an officer in the army of the duke of Urbino and a poet, and of Leonora Landriani of Milan. Upon his father's death in 1565 Federigo, supported by the duke of Urbino, went to Rome, where he was educated with Francesco Maria della Rovere at the house of Cardinal Giulio della Rovere. At the age of eighteen he returned to Urbino. Following the accession of Duke Francesco Maria II in 1574, Federigo met with even greater favor. He continued his studies at Urbino, particularly Greek mathematics and natural philosophy. In addition to his scholarly activities, Bonaventura served as Urbino's ambassador to several European courts. His marriage to Pantasilea, countess of Carpegna, in 1577 produced twelve children, including Pietro, who became bishop of Cesena, and Francesco Maria, who wrote several literary works.

Bonaventura's most important scientific writings deal with meteorology. As yet they have not been carefully studied, nor has their significance in sixteenth-century meteorological thought been determined. They include *De causa ventorum motus* (1592), in which he argues, in opposition to many later interpreters, that there is no basic disagreement between the theory of winds of Aristotle and that of Theophrastus; *Pro Theophrasto atque Alexandro Aphrodisiensi . . . apologia* (1592), in which he again attempts to defend the ancient Peripatetic meteorological theories against such modern interpreters as Francesco Vimercato; *Anemologiae pars prior* (1593), which is essentially a Latin translation of Theophrastus' *De ventis* and *De signis,* with long and detailed commentaries on the two works; and *Quomodo calor a sole corporibus coelestibus producatur secundum Aristotelem* (1627), in which he argues that Aristotle held that the sun's heat is transferred to other bodies through motion, rather than through light.

All of Bonaventura's writings on meteorology are marked by an attempt to determine the precise meaning of the ancient texts through philological techniques, with apparently little effort being made to utilize experience and observation to verify their truth. He also wrote works on medical subjects (especially *De natura partus octomestris* [1596]) and

political philosophy, and translated into Latin works of Themistius and of Ptolemy (*Inerrantium stellarum apparitiones ac significationum collectio* [1592]).

BIBLIOGRAPHY

I. ORIGINAL WORKS. Lists of Bonaventura's published works are available in Mazzuchelli, Narducci, and Vecchietti (see below). See also the following MSS: Biblioteca Ambrosiana, Milan, Q. 118 sup., and S. 87 sup.; Biblioteca Oliveriana, Pesaro, 1494, 1500, 1503, 1509; and Vat. urb. lat. 1333, 1349. Among his published works are *De causa ventorum motus* (Urbino, 1592; Venice, 1594); *Inerrantium stellarum apparitiones ac significationum collectio* (Urbino, 1592), a Latin translation of the work by Ptolemy, with a long commentary; *Pro Theophrasto atque Alexandro Aphrodisiensi . . . apologia* (Urbino, 1592; repr. Venice, 1594); *Anemologiae pars prior* (Urbino, 1593), repr. as *Meteorologicae affectiones* (Venice, 1594); *De natura partus octomestris* (Urbino, 1596, 1600; Frankfurt, 1601, 1612; Venice, 1602); and a collection of *Opuscula* (Urbino, 1627), which contains, among others, *Quomodo calor a sole corporibus coelestibus producatur secundum Aristotelem.*

II. SECONDARY LITERATURE. Writings on Bonaventura or his work are Giammaria Mazzuchelli, *Gli scrittori d'Italia,* II (Brescia, 1760), 1563–1564; M. Michaud, *Biographie universelle,* 2nd ed. (Paris, 1880), IV, 687; Enrico Narducci, *Giunte all'opera . . . del . . . Mazzuchelli* (Rome, 1894), p. 95; and P. Vecchietti and T. Vecchietti, *Biblioteca picena,* III (Osimo, 1796), 1–6.

See also *Degli uomini illustri di Urbino commentario del P. Carlo Grossi con aggiunte scritte dal conte Pompeo Gherardi* (Urbino, 1856), pp. 72–78.

CHARLES B. SCHMITT

BONCOMPAGNI, BALDASSARRE (*b*. Rome, Italy, 10 May 1821; *d*. Rome, 13 April 1894), *history of mathematics, history of physics.*

The son of Luigi Boncompagni, prince of Piombino, and of Maria Maddalena Odelscalchi, Baldassarre was a student of Barnaba Tortolini, the noted mathematician. In 1843 *Crelle's Journal* published the results of mathematical analyses obtained by Boncompagni, who afterward concentrated mainly on the history of mathematics and of physics. His works in this field include one on the development of the study of physics in Italy during the sixteenth and seventeenth centuries, as well as publications concerning Guido Bonatti, Plato of Tivoli, Gerard of Cremona, and Gerard of Sabbionetta.

From these studies, Boncompagni was led to examine the works of Leonardo Fibonacci, about whom little was known at that time. By means of numerous accurate works, he made known Fibonacci's importance in the history of mathematics, illustrating his life and works in the accurate edition of the *Scritti di Leonardo Pisano* (1857–1862).

In order to meet the requirements of his scientific publications, Boncompagni established his own printing plant, called "delle Scienze Matematiche e Fisiche." For forty years he assumed full financial responsibility for the entire cost of its operation, freely granting to other scientists the privilege of using its facilities. The plant published important documents on the history of science, such as the papers on challenging mathematics between Ferrari and Tartaglia and the unpublished letters of Lagrange and Gauss. In order to have a specialized journal for his favorite studies, in 1868 Boncompagni undertook the publication of *Bullettino di bibliografia e di storia delle scienze matematiche e fisiche.* Known as *Bullettino Boncompagni,* it ceased publication in 1887.

Boncompagni was among the first thirty members of the Pontifical Academy of the New Lincei, which was founded in 1847 by Pope Pius IX, who desired to reactivitate the academy founded by Federico Cesi, of which Galileo had also been a member. He published the transactions of the Academy, from volume XXIV to volume XLVII, at his own expense. He was faithful to it even after the Italian government established the Lincei Academy. Boncompagni came to the assistance of needy scholars and students, assigning them to well-paying tasks in transcription and in translation, thus leaving behind him the memory of an enlightened and generous patronage.

BIBLIOGRAPHY

I. Original Works. There are 209 works listed in "Catalogo degli scritti del Principe D. Baldassarre Boncompagni," I. Galli, ed., in *Atti dell'Accademia Pontificia dei nuovi Lincei,* **47** (1893–1894), 171–186. Among these works are "Recherches sur les intégrales définies" in *Crelle's Journal,* **25** (1843); "Studi intorno ad alcuni avanzamenti della fisica in Italia nei secoli XVI e XVII," in *Giornale Arcadico di scienze, lettere ed arti* (1846); "Della vita e delle opere di Guido Bonatti astrologo ed astronomo del secolo decimo terzo," *ibid.* (1851); "Delle versioni fatte da Platone Tiburtino traduttore del secolo duodecimo," in *Atti dell'Accademia Pontificia dei nuovi Lincei,* **4** (1850–1851), 247–286; "Della vita e delle opere di Gherardo Cremonese traduttore del secolo duodecimo e di Gherardo da Sabbionetta astronomo del secolo decimoterzo," *ibid.,* 387–493; and *Saggio intorno ad alcune opere di Leonardo Pisano* (Rome, 1854).

II. Secondary Literature. Works on Boncompagni are M. S. De Rossi, "Commemorazione del socio ordinario Principe D. Baldassarre Boncompagni," in *Atti dell'Accademia Pontificia dei nuovi Lincei,* **47** (1893–1894), 131–134; A. Favaro, "Don Baldassarre Boncompagni e la storia delle Scienze Matematiche e Fisiche," in *Atti del R. Istituto veneto di scienze, lettere ed arti,* 7th ser., **6** (1894–1895), 509–521; and I. Galli, "Elogio del Principe Don Baldassarre Boncompagni," in *Atti dell'Accademia Pontificia dei nuovi Lincei,* **47** (1893–1894), 161–170.

Ettore Carruccio

BOND, GEORGE PHILLIPS (*b.* Dorchester, Massachusetts, 20 May 1825; *d.* Cambridge, Massachusetts, 17 February 1865), *astronomy.*

The third son of William Cranch Bond and Selina Cranch, George Bond grew up in an environment focused on Harvard Observatory, where his father was the first director. The scientific collaboration with his father began so early that it is often difficult to separate their contributions. At the age of twenty-three he assisted in the observations of Saturn that led to his discovery of the satellite Hyperion. Two years later, he found Saturn's crepe ring. Hence Bond was the natural choice for director of Harvard Observatory when his father died in 1859.

The selection was not unchallenged, however, for Benjamin Peirce, the top mathematical astronomer in the country, also aspired to the directorship. The resulting antagonism with Peirce and his scientific clique hampered Bond in many ways and embittered his career. A serious and uncompromising man, Bond believed that this rivalry cost him a place when the National Academy of Sciences was incorporated in 1863.

Bond's principal observations were carried out with the observatory's 15-inch refractor, which, until it was surpassed in 1862, ranked with the Pulkovo instrument as the largest refractor in the world. His comprehensive and handsomely illustrated monograph on Donati's Comet of 1858, in *Annals of the Harvard College Observatory* (1862), won widespread acclaim and in 1865 brought him the gold medal of the Royal Astronomical Society, the first ever awarded to an American.

George Bond directed the observatory a scant six years—he died of tuberculosis at the age of thirty-nine. He had undertaken an intense investigation of the Orion Nebula, but his health broke before he could complete it. The memoir was published posthumously. His remarkable drawing of the nebula can be favorably compared with modern photographs. In 1860 Bond reported on the comparative brightness of the sun, moon, and Jupiter, a fundamental research that has placed "Bond albedo" in the contemporary astronomical vocabulary.

Bond's most enduring fame, however, rests on his enthusiastic experimentation with stellar photography and his perceptive anticipation of its potential; in

1857 he wrote, "There is nothing, then, so extravagant in predicting a future application of photography on a most magnificent scale. . . . What more admirable method can be imagined for the study of the orbits of the fixed stars and for resolving the problem of their annual parallax?" His pioneering daguerreotype work, undertaken from 1847 to 1851 in cooperation with his father, resulted in the first photograph of a star, Vega. Bond's 1857 experiments with wet collodion photography achieved still greater success. With considerable justification Edward S. Holden called him "the father of celestial photography."

BIBLIOGRAPHY

I. ORIGINAL WORKS. Among his writings are "Account of the Great Comet of 1858," in *Annals of the Harvard College Observatory,* **3** (1862); "Observations upon the Great Nebula of Orion," *ibid.,* **5** (1867). Selections from Bond's diaries during his trips abroad in 1851 and 1863, and from his correspondence, as well as an extensive bibliography, appear in Edward S. Holden, *Memorials of William Cranch Bond and George Phillips Bond* (San Francisco, 1897); bound copies of the Bond correspondence used by Holden are in the Lick Observatory Library. See also "Diary of the Two Bonds: 1846–1849," Bessie Z. Jones, ed., in *Harvard Library Bulletin,* **15** (1967), 368–386, and **16** (1968), 49–71, 178–207,

II. SECONDARY LITERATURE. An extensive evaluation of Bond's scientific work is given in the Royal Astronomical Society presidential address by Warren De La Rue, in the Society's *Monthly Notices,* **35** (1865), 125–137. See also Dorrit Hoffleit, *Some Firsts in Astronomical Photography* (Cambridge, Mass., 1950).

OWEN GINGERICH

BOND, WILLIAM CRANCH (*b.* Falmouth [now Portland], Maine, 9 September 1789; *d.* Cambridge, Massachusetts, 29 January 1859), *astronomy.*

His father, William Bond, a fiery Cornishman, and his strict, forceful mother, Hannah Cranch, emigrated to Massachusetts in 1786; soon after William Cranch Bond's birth, their lumber export business failed and the family moved to Boston, where they opened a clockmaking shop. Bond's youth was spent in the hardship of poverty, and he was obliged to leave school at an early age. His rare mechanical ability proved invaluable in the shop, where he constructed a chronometer at the age of fifteen.

A total solar eclipse in 1806 fixed Bond's attention on astronomy, and at the age of twenty-one he independently found the Comet of 1811. The parlor of the first house he owned, in Dorchester, was converted into an observatory complete with granite pier and, in the ceiling, a meridian opening. As an expert clockmaker, he rated the chronometers for numerous expeditions to determine longitudes in the eastern United States. Bond married his cousin Selina Cranch in 1819; she bore him four sons and two daughters. After her death in 1831, Bond married her elder sister, Mary Roope Cranch.

In 1815, when Bond traveled to Europe, he was commissioned by Harvard to examine instruments and observatories in England. Proposals for a meteorological and astronomical observatory at Harvard came to naught, however, until 1839, when Bond was invited to transfer his own equipment to Dana House in Cambridge and to serve (without salary) as astronomical observer to Harvard University.

The great sun-grazing comet of 1843 aroused an immense latent interest in astronomy, and some ninety societies and individuals subscribed $25,730 for the building of a large telescope at Harvard. A 15-inch refractor, equal in size to the largest in the world, was ordered from Munich and mounted in Cambridge in June 1847. Bond's mechanical ingenuity manifested itself in the construction of the dome, in the remarkable observing chair, and in the regulating device that made the chronograph a precision instrument.

With the 15-inch telescope Bond undertook elaborate studies of the Orion Nebula and of the planet Saturn, and during his administration the daguerreotype process was first used to photograph stars. Bond was a modest, retiring, and deeply religious man. An accurate evaluation of his abilities was given by Benjamin Peirce: "In his original investigations he naturally restrained himself to those forms of observation which were fully within reach of his own resources. . . . He consequently availed himself less of the remarkable capacity of his instrument for delicate and refined measurements than of its exquisite optical qualities."

BIBLIOGRAPHY

Bond's writings include "History and Description of the Astronomical Observatory of Harvard College," in *Harvard College Observatory Annals,* **1,** pt. 1 (1856); "Observations on the Planet Saturn," *ibid.,* **2,** pt. 1 (1857); and "Diary of the Two Bonds: 1846–1849," Bessie Z. Jones, ed., in *Harvard Library Bulletin,* **15** (1967), 368–386, and **16** (1968), 49–71, 178–207. An extensive bibliography and much original material are given in Edward S. Holden, *Memorials of William Cranch Bond and George Phillips Bond* (San Francisco, 1897). An early photographic portrait appears as the frontispiece of *Harvard College Observatory Annals,* **7** (1871).

OWEN GINGERICH

BONNET, CHARLES (*b.* Geneva, Switzerland, 13 March 1720; *d.* Geneva, 20 May 1793), *natural history, biology, philosophy.*

Bonnet was the son of Pierre Bonnet, whose family lived at Thônex, near Geneva, and of Anne-Marie Lullin. A mediocre student, he was gifted neither in languages nor in mathematics; moreover, he was hindered by increasing deafness, which exposed him to the taunts of his playmates. His father decided to engage a private tutor, a Dr. Laget, who played a prominent part in stimulating the boy's early interest in the natural sciences. In 1736, Bonnet avidly read Pluche's study *Le spectacle de la nature.* The following year, he read the memoirs of René Réaumur and began a correspondence with the great scientist. These were decisive steps. In 1738 he submitted an essay on entomology to the Academy of Sciences of Paris. His father, however, looked unfavorably upon a career in the natural sciences, and Bonnet agreed to study law instead. In 1744 he received a doctorate in law. He married Jeanne-Marie de La Rive in 1756 and retired to his wife's estate at Genthod, near Geneva. All his life Bonnet had to contend with precarious health. In addition to being deaf, he became, while still young, almost completely blind, then began to suffer severe asthma attacks.

Bonnet is considered one of the fathers of modern biology. He is distinguished for both his experimental research and his philosophy, which exerted a profound influence upon the naturalists of the eighteenth and nineteenth centuries.

Bonnet was twenty-six when he made his first and greatest discovery, the parthenogenesis of the aphid. He very carefully raised a female spindle-tree aphid, then observed that she produced ninety-five offspring without mating. Virginal generation was therefore possible. Bonnet wrote a note for the Academy of Sciences, which, on Bernard de Fontenelle's recommendation, appointed Bonnet a corresponding member. Then, taking up Réaumur's (1712) and Abraham Trembley's (1740) research on regeneration, Bonnet began his observation of rainwater worms of the species *lumbriculus.* He demonstrated that one of these worms, cut into twenty-six pieces, would become twenty-six perfectly constituted new worms. In 1745, he published several monographs on this subject. Bonnet devoted another work to the regeneration of a snail's head (1769), and in 1777 he dealt with regeneration of the limbs of a triton.

Bonnet's research induced him to study the breathing of caterpillars and the locomotion of ants. In 1745 he published the comprehensive *Traité d'insectologie,* a work that entitles him to consideration as an early exponent of experimental entomology. After 1750 Bonnet published only a few studies on zoology; henceforth, his research was in plant physiology. In the preface to a remarkable work entitled *Recherches sur l'usage des feuilles dans les plantes* (1754), Bonnet wrote:

> Insects held my attention for some years. The strenuousness with which I worked on this study strained my eyes to such an extent that I was forced to interrupt it. Deprived thus of what had so far been my greatest pleasure, I tried to console myself by changing subjects. I then turned toward the physics of plants—a matter less animated, less fertile in discoveries but of a more generally recognized usefulness.

In the *Recherches,* Bonnet grouped five memoirs, all of which were of prime importance for plant biology: He precisely described the characteristics of the nutrition of leaves and of their transpiratory phenomena. Although he did not know the kinds of gases (oxygen and carbon dioxide) produced and absorbed by green leaves exposed to light, Bonnet made very careful observations on their production. For his masterly experimentation, Bonnet should be considered one of the first naturalists to investigate experimentally the question of photosynthesis. He studied the movement of leaves and discovered the epinastic phenomena; he observed the position of leaves on the axis of the stalk and collected a great many anatomic facts; he returned to experiments on etiolation, on the movement of the sap, and on teratology. Bonnet could no longer observe with his own eyes, so he surrounded himself with collaborators, all of whom later became distinguished naturalists—for example, François Huber, the bee specialist, and Jean Sénebier, famous for his research on photosynthesis. The collaborators performed innumerable tests on hybridation of corn, wheat, and darnel. Bonnet was opposed to the theory of transmutation of the species and may rightly be considered a forerunner of Lamarckism through his definition of his original concept of the "chain of beings"—parts of which, it is true, he had borrowed from Leibniz.

Next Bonnet turned to philosophy and methodology. A true theoretician of biology, he exercised an enormous influence in this field and maintained a correspondence with almost all the scientists of his time. He published works that caused a considerable stir—among them *Essai de psychologie* (1754) and *Essai analytique sur les facultés de l'âme* (1759). Bonnet then returned to theoretical biology, publishing *Considérations sur les corps organisés* (1761), *Contemplation de la nature* (1764), *Palin-*

génésie philosophique (1769), and *Recherches philosophiques sur les preuves du christianisme* (1771).

Bonnet was an enthusiastic champion of preformation, the theory postulating that the animal already existed in miniature in the germ cell. His discovery of parthenogenesis was, to him, proof that the female germ cell contains the preformed individual. Thus Bonnet became a fervent partisan of ovism. Many other naturalists, such as Albrecht von Haller, supported this thesis—a surprising one nowadays—of preformation. Yet Bonnet was less doctrinaire than his colleagues; he supported, for example, a very elastic thesis of the germ cell, which, according to him, was not only "an organized body reduced in size . . ." but "every kind of original preformation out of which may result an organic whole, as of his immediate principle." This theory, which Bonnet christened "palingenesis," set forth the functional and structural notion of the cell, which was not stated formally until a hundred years later.

Bonnet was not only a remarkable experimentalist in his younger years and a theoretician with fertile ideas: he was the instigator of a whole series of fundamental experiments. His extraordinary imagination suggested projects that his poor eyesight prevented him from carrying out; he treated these projects in numerous works, and above all he discussed them with his many correspondents. For instance, he suggested to Lazzaro Spallanzani that he carry out experiments on artificial insemination.

Mention must be made of the importance of Bonnet's methodological work. Of course he was—particularly in his more important writings—a theoretician, but a theoretician who experimented widely. Every observed fact, every proposed theory, gave Bonnet the opportunity to suggest the technique best suited for progress toward a solution. In his voluminous correspondence (he purportedly wrote over 700 letters annually), philosophical treatises, notes submitted to the Academy, and his most important monographs, he showed himself constantly preoccupied with methodological problems. Well before Claude Bernard, Bonnet attributed a preponderant role in scientific research to the "art of observing." The quality of his work fluctuates greatly, so it is not surprising that Bonnet is not appreciated without reservations. He sought after truth with courage and perseverance, was distrustful of his own hypotheses, and was ready to accept the conclusions of his strongest adversaries, if convinced that they were right. The personal qualities of Charles Bonnet, as much as his writings, justify the extraordinary reputation that he enjoyed in his lifetime and that survives today.

BIBLIOGRAPHY

I. ORIGINAL WORKS. Bonnet's writings include *Traité d'insectologie* (Paris, 1745); *Essai de psychologie* (Leiden, 1754); *Recherches sur l'usage des feuilles dans les plantes* (Leiden, 1754); *Essai analytique sur les facultés de l'âme* (Copenhagen, 1760); *Considérations sur les corps organisés* (Amsterdam, 1762); *Contemplation de la nature,* 2 vols. (Amsterdam, 1764); *La palingénésie philosophique* (Geneva, 1769); *Recherches philosophiques sur les preuves du christianisme* (Geneva, 1771); and *Oeuvre d'histoire naturelle et de philosophie,* 8 vols. in 4°, 18 vols. in 8° (Neuchâtel, 1779–1783).

II. SECONDARY LITERATURE. Works on Bonnet include G. Bonnet, *Charles Bonnet* (Paris, 1929), a thesis; R. de Caraman, *Ch. Bonnet, philosophe et naturaliste, sa vie et ses oeuvres* (Paris, 1859); E. Claparède, *La psychologie animale de Ch. Bonnet* (Geneva, 1909); J. Rostand, *Esquisse d'une histoire de la biologie: Un préformationniste—Ch. Bonnet* (Paris, 1945), pp. 65–80, and *Hommes d'autrefois et d'aujourd'hui: Ch. Bonnet* (Paris, 1966), pp. 7–45; R. Savioz, *La philosophie de Ch. Bonnet de Genève* (Paris, 1948), and *Mémoires autobiographiques de Ch. Bonnet de Genève* (Paris, 1948); A. Schubert, *Die Psychologie von Bonnet und Tetens* (Zurich, 1909), a thesis; and J. Trembley, *Mémoire pour servir à l'histoire de la vie et des ouvrages de M. Ch. Bonnet* (Bern, 1794).

P. E. PILET

BONNET, PIERRE-OSSIAN (*b.* Montpellier, France, 22 December 1819; *d.* Paris, France, 22 June 1892), *mathematics.*

Bonnet was the son of Pierre Bonnet, *commis banquier,* and Magdelaine Messac. After attending the College of Montpellier, he in 1838 entered the École Polytechnique in Paris, where he studied at the École des Ponts et des Chaussées. After graduation, however, he declined an engineering position, preferring teaching and research. In 1844 he became *répétiteur* at the École Polytechnique, augmenting his income by private tutoring. In a paper of 1843 he published convergence criteria of series with positive terms, among them logarithmic criteria. Another paper on series was honored by the Brussels Academy of Sciences and was published in 1849. By that time Bonnet had, starting in 1844 with the paper "Sur quelques propriétés générales des surfaces," begun to publish that series of papers on differential geometry on which his fame is based. The merit of this work was recognized by the Académie des Sciences when it elected Bonnet to membership in 1862 to replace Biot.

In 1868 Bonnet became Michel Chasles's *suppléant* at the École Polytechnique in the latter's course on higher geometry, and in 1871 he became director of studies there. He also taught at the École Normale Supérieure. In 1878 he obtained a chair at the Sorbonne, succeeding the astronomer Leverrier, and in 1883 he succeeded Liouville as a member of the Bureau des Longitudes. Married and the father of three sons, he always lived the quiet and unpretentious life of a scholar.

Bonnet's favorite field was the differential geometry of curves and surfaces, a field opened by Euler, Monge, and Gauss, but at that time lacking systematic treatment and offering wide fields of research. Between 1840 and 1850 this challenge was taken up by Bonnet and a group of younger French mathematicians—Serret, Frenet, Bertrand, and Puiseux—but it was Bonnet who most consistently continued in this field. In the "Mémoire sur la théorie générale des surfaces," presented in 1844 to the Académie, Bonnet introduced the concepts of geodesic curvature and torsion, and proved a series of theorems concerning them. One of these is the formula for the line integral of the geodesic curvature along a closed curve on a surface, known as the Gauss-Bonnet theorem (Gauss had published only a special case). Bonnet also showed the invariance of the geodesic curvature under bending of the surface.

From 1844 to 1867 Bonnet wrote a series of papers on differential geometry of surfaces. Special attention should be given to the "Mémoire sur la théorie des surfaces applicables sur une surface donnée" (1865–1867), written as a solution for a prize contest announced by the Académie in 1859: i.e., to find all surfaces of a given linear element. The problem is sometimes associated with Edouard Bour, who wrote a competing memoir (1862). The third entrant was Delfino Codazzi. Bonnet, in his contribution, showed the importance of certain formulas introduced in 1859 by Codazzi, formulas now taken as part of the so-called Gauss-Codazzi relations. He also showed the role these formulas play in the existence theorem for surfaces, if first and second fundamental forms are given. Bour, in his paper, came to similar conclusions.

In these and other papers Bonnet stressed the usefulness of special coordinate systems on a surface, such as isothermic and tangential coordinates; studied special curves, such as lines of curvature with constant geodesic curvature (1867); and investigated the conditions under which geodesic lines are the shortest connection between two points on a surface. He also paid much attention to minimal surfaces—for instance, those applicable on each other—and surfaces of constant total and constant mean curvature (1853).

Bonnet also published works on geodesy and cartography, theory of series (convergence criteria), al-

gebra, rational mechanics, and mathematical physics. In 1871 he gave a definition of the limit for functions of a real variable.

BIBLIOGRAPHY

I. ORIGINAL WORKS. Among Bonnet's papers are "Note sur la convergence et divergence des séries," in *Journal de mathématiques pures et appliquées,* **8** (1843), 73–109; "Sur quelques propriétés générales des surfaces et des lignes tracées sur les surfaces," in *Comptes rendus de l'Académie des Sciences,* **14** (1844); "Mémoire sur la théorie générale des surfaces," in *Journal de l'École Polytechnique,* **32** (1848), 1–46; "Sur la théorie des séries," in *Mémoires couronnés de l'Académie de Bruxelles,* **22** (1849); "Mémoire sur l'emploi d'un nouveau système de variables dans l'étude des propriétés des surfaces courbes," in *Journal de mathématiques pures et appliquées,* ser. 2, **5** (1860), 153–266; and "Mémoire sur la théorie des surfaces applicables sur une surface donnée," in *Journal de l'École Polytechnique,* **41** (1865), 201–230, and **42** (1867), 1–151.

Bonnet's most important papers are mainly in the *Journal de l'École Polytechnique,* the *Journal de mathématiques pures et appliquées,* and the *Comptes rendus de l'Académie des Sciences.* He also wrote a *Mécanique élémentaire* (Paris, 1858). Bonnet's papers have never been collected, but the essence of his work on the theory of surfaces can be found in Gaston Darboux's *Leçons sur la théorie générale des surfaces,* 4 vols. (Paris, 1887–1896), *passim.*

II. SECONDARY LITERATURE. Works on Bonnet are P. Appell, "Notice sur la vie et les travaux de Pierre Ossian Bonnet," in *Comptes rendus de l'Académie des Sciences,* **117** (1893), 1013–1024; Michel Chasles, *Rapport sur les progrès de la géometrie en France* (Paris, 1870), pp. 199–214; and A. Franceschini, "Bonnet," in *Dictionnaire de biographie française,* Vol. VI (Paris, 1954).

D. J. STRUIK

BONNEY, THOMAS GEORGE (*b.* Rugeley, England, 27 July 1833; *d.* Cambridge, England, 10 December 1923), *geology.*

One of the last links with the heroic age of geology, Bonney was contemporary with Sedgwick, Murchison, Lyell, and Darwin during his early professional life; his pupils included Sollas, Marr, Watts, Teall, and Strahan.

The eldest of ten children born to Rev. Thomas Bonney, headmaster of the Rugeley grammar school, and his wife, the daughter of Edward Smith, Bonney graduated from St. John's College, Cambridge, as Twelfth Wrangler in the Mathematical Tripos in 1856 and obtained a second-class in the Classical Tripos; illness frustrated his intention to sit for the Theological Tripos as well. After five years as mathematics master at Westminster School, during which time he was ordained a priest and elected to a fellowship at St. John's, Bonney was recalled to the college as junior dean in 1861, becoming tutor in 1868 and also college lecturer in geology, a subject in which he was until then a self-taught amateur. At that time there were no university lectureships, but Bonney shouldered the main responsibility for university as well as college teaching in the subject during Sedgwick's declining years and exerted a powerful influence in molding the Cambridge school of geology.

Surprisingly, Bonney was not elected to succeed Sedgwick, and in 1877 he accepted the Yates-Goldschmidt professorship of geology at University College, London. At first conducting his part-time professorial duties from Cambridge, he became secretary of the British Association for the Advancement of Science in 1881, and this brought with it a sufficient increase of income for him to set up housekeeping in London with his sister. As secretary of the Association, Bonney organized its first meeting outside Britain (in Montreal), and during his London residence he became president of its Geological Section. (In 1910 he became president of the Association.) He also served, successively, as secretary and president of the Geological Society of London, and president of the Mineralogical Society. The Royal Society elected him a fellow in 1878; and he also became honorary canon of Manchester, Whitehall Preacher (at the Chapel Royal), and a Hulsean and Rede's lecturer at Cambridge. Bonney resigned his chair in 1901, but remained "doing fairly lucrative work" as one of the regular writers for a newspaper, the *Standard,* until 1905, when he returned to Cambridge.

Lack of formal education in geology may have contributed to that independence of outlook which constantly questioned dogma, and his insistence on proof may be attributed to his mathematical training. Bonney would accept no theory until it was exhaustively proved, and he inevitably became a formidable controversialist in nineteenth-century geology: "Fine phrases unsupported by facts prove to be no better than cheques without a balance at the bank." He was profoundly impressed by the *Origin of Species,* and in one of his presidential addresses lamented that the science of mineralogy "still needs its Darwin"; nevertheless, many contemporary theories and hypotheses came under his stricture.

Bonney's interest in glaciology was lifelong; it was the subject of his second paper in the *Geological Magazine* and of his presidential address to the British Association in 1910. Observations on valley glaciers made during his frequent visits to Switzerland caused him to dispute the efficacy of ice as an erosive agent,

and he remained unconvinced of the formation of cirques by plucking action or of more than superficial modification of river valleys by moving ice. While tarns and lakelets might be formed by glacial excavation, he could not accept the latter as the origin of larger lakes. Neither could he believe that the Scandinavian ice sheet ever reached the shores of Britain; he contended, *inter alia,* that the deep coastal trough bordering Norway must have afforded an easy path to the Arctic Ocean. His final presidential address, on the British "drift," marshaled his difficulties in accepting the land-ice hypothesis without venturing an alternative explanation.

Bonney was a leading figure in the early days of British petrography, following closely in the wake of Zirkel and Rosenbusch. Important studies on basic and ultrabasic igneous rocks led naturally to his demonstration of the true character of British serpentines, and in one of his numerous papers on these rocks he strongly contested Sterry Hunt's views of their sedimentary origin. As an authority on the Archaean rocks of England and Wales, Bonney became involved in the heated discussions of the age of the Eastern Gneiss (Moinian) of the northwest Highlands of Scotland, and of the age and relations of the metamorphic rocks of the Alps. Rocks for identification and analysis were sent to him from all over the world, and several of his later papers concern the parent rock (eclogite) of the diamond in South Africa. His petrological interests were not, however, confined to igneous rocks, and one of his presidential addresses (British Association, 1886), "The Application of Microscopic Analysis to Discovering the Physical Geography of Bygone Ages," is a remarkable pioneering achievement in what is now called sedimentology. Bonney was also chairman of the Coral Reef Committee of the Royal Society, which organized and reported on the Funafuti boring.

Bonney was by training and by temperament an exceedingly versatile man: geologist, mathematician, theologian, and classicist; an alpine traveler and a noted climber; a journalist and writer on architecture and scenery; and a draftsman of great merit. But above all, he was an outstanding teacher, and it was through teaching as much as through his prolific writings that he exercised such influence upon nineteenth-century geology. He was one of the first to introduce the examination of thin slices of rocks under the microscope, to lay emphasis on practical work in the laboratory and in the field, and, by his severely critical attitude, to compel his students to seek the facts and the evidence underlying any theory. As a teacher, he put out all his talents at compound interest.

BIBLIOGRAPHY

I. ORIGINAL WORKS. Bonney was the author of more than 200 scientific papers; a dozen books on geology, travel, architecture, and theology; several volumes of sermons; and a great many newspaper articles. The majority of his scientific papers are in *Quarterly Journal of the Geological Society of London, Geological Magazine,* and *Mineralogical Magazine.* His books include *The Story of Our Planet* (London, 1893); *Charles Lyell and Modern Geology* (London, 1895); *Ice Work Past and Present* (London, 1896); *Volcanoes* (London, 1899); *The Building of the Alps* (London, 1912); and *Memories of a Long Life* (Cambridge, 1921).

II. SECONDARY LITERATURE. Articles on Bonney are "Eminent Living Geologists: The Rev. Professor T. G. Bonney," in *Geological Magazine,* **38** (1901), 385–400, which contains a full catalog of his scientific papers to 1901; and W. W. Watts, an obituary notice in *Proceedings of the Royal Society,* **B99** (1926), xvii–xxvii.

O. M. B. BULMAN

BONNIER, GASTON (*b.* Paris, France, 1853; *d.* Paris, 30 December 1922), *botany.*

During the last half of the nineteenth century, botany changed from a descriptive science to an experimental one; Gaston Bonnier was one of the botanists responsible for this transformation. A fervent advocate of the experimental approach, he made several discoveries that, although not revolutionary, were of considerable importance to the growth of the science.

Bonnier's father and grandfather were both professors of law, but he seems to have been interested in botany from the very beginning of his academic career. He was a student at the École Normale in Paris and taught there for several years before succeeding to the chair of botany at the Sorbonne in 1887.

In 1879, Bonnier received the D.S.N. upon publication of his thesis, an anatomical and physiological study of the nectary organs. This thesis earned him the Prix de Physiologie Expérimentale of the Paris Academy of Sciences (of which he was made a member in 1896). Traditionally the nectary organs had been one of the best weapons in the arsenal of teleology; it was said that they existed solely to produce nectar, which itself existed solely to attract bees, the agents of cross-fertilization. Bonnier demonstrated the absurdity of this argument by proving that in many species of plants a bee can easily collect nectar without going near the pollen-carrying stamens. He proved that the nectaries are important to the plant chiefly because they store the excess sugar that is needed during periods of increased physiological activity, nectar being only an incidental by-product of transpiration.

The decade after the publication of his thesis was the most productive period of Bonnier's career. Between 1880 and 1882 he studied (in collaboration with Philippe van Tieghem) the physiological activity of seeds, grains, and bulbs and discovered that they are not physiologically "dead," as had been thought. From 1883 to 1885, he published several lengthy papers on plant respiration in collaboration with Louis Mangin. At that time botanists had just begun to realize that respiration and photosynthesis are different processes. Bonnier and Mangin were particularly interested in the relationship between respiration and various environmental conditions. Of their many discoveries, the most crucial was the fact that respiration proceeds most rapidly in the absence of light. They also developed an apparatus for determining the ratio of carbon dioxide discharged to oxygen absorbed at any given moment and demonstrated that this ratio remains constant for each species, no matter what the respiration rate may be at any given time. Finally, toward the end of this decade, Bonnier branched out into an entirely different field—lichenology—and settled a long-standing botanical debate by proving that lichens are composed of two symbiotic forms, an alga and a fungus, the latter reproducing by means of spores.

Bonnier became increasingly involved in administrative affairs. He was deeply concerned about the development of botany as a discipline, and he had helped to organize a separate faculty in natural sciences while at the École Normale. Botanical facilities were inadequate at the Sorbonne, and in 1889 Bonnier was able to remedy that situation by founding and directing the Laboratoire de Biologie Végétale at Fontainebleu. In 1890 he took on the additional burden of editing a new botanical journal, *Revue générale de botanique.* He continued in that post, as well as in the others, until his sudden death.

From 1890 to 1922, most of Bonnier's scientific work was concerned with the relationship between structure and environment. In this connection he studied the differences between alpine and arctic plants, and attempted to find correlations with differences in their habitats. He also undertook studies of heat production and pressure transmission in plants. During this time he wrote extensively, producing several botanical handbooks, a few popularizations, a basic text, and, finally, his twelve-volume masterpiece, *Flore complète . . . de France, Suisse et Belgique,* some of which was published posthumously.

BIBLIOGRAPHY

Articles by Bonnier include "Les nectaires," in *Annales des sciences naturelles (botanique)*, 6th series, **8** (1879), 5–212, and "Recherches sur la vie ralentie et sur la vie latente," in *Bulletin de la Société Botanique de France*, **27** (1880), 83–88, 116–122; **29** (1882), 25–29, 149–153. A summary of the work done by Bonnier and Mangin can be found in "La fonction respiratoire chez les végétaux," in *Annales des sciences naturelles (botanique)*, 7th series, **2** (1885), 365–380; the original papers are in *Annales*, 6th series, **17** (1884), 210–306; **18** (1884), 293–381; **19** (1885), 217–255. A representative article of several on alpine and arctic plants is "Les plantes arctiques comparées aux mêmes espèces des Alpes et des Pyrennées," in *Revue générale de botanique*, **6** (1894), 505–527. Of his books, other than practical guides such as *Nouvelle flore pour la détermination facile des plantes* (Paris, 1887), the most important are his text, *Cours de botanique*, 2 vols. (Paris, 1901), and his *Flore complète illustrée et en couleurs de France, Suisse et Belgique*, 12 vols. (Paris, 1912–1934).

For a discussion of Bonnier's work, see M. H. Jumelle, "L'oeuvre scientifique de Gaston Bonnier," in *Revue générale de botanique*, **36** (1924), 289–307.

Ruth Schwartz Cowan

BONOMO, GIOVAN COSIMO (*b.* Leghorn, Italy, 30 November 1666; *d.* Florence, Italy, 13 January 1696), *medicine.*

Bonomo received the doctorate in philosophy and medicine at the University of Pisa on 22 June 1682. The following year, on 18 December, he passed the qualifying examination to practice his profession in Tuscany. He often served as physician in the galleys of Grand Duke Cosimo III, which had Leghorn as their home port.

Bonomo belonged to the biological school that originated with Galileo. Inspired by the research that had enabled his teacher Francesco Redi to disprove the theory of the spontaneous generation of insects in 1668, and availing himself of Giacinto Cestoni's skill with the microscope, Bonomo, in his *Osservazioni intorno a' pellicelli del corpo umano* (1687), affirmed that scabies is caused by mites. As a matter of fact, the mites of patients suffering from scabies had been known for some time, but they were considered a consequence and not a cause of the disease.

With the aid of the microscope, it was demonstrated that this arachnid reproduces by means of eggs and that it possesses an oral apparatus with which it penetrates the skin. Hence, Bonomo resolved to adopt local therapy aimed at killing the mites, instead of the general therapy that had previously been used. The results thus obtained enabled him to conclude that the mites were the cause of the disease. It fol-

lowed that scabies is transmitted by the mites from a victim to a healthy person. Therefore, it is a "live" infection, of which Bonomo's work constituted the first clinical and experimental proof.

In April 1691, the grand duke appointed Bonomo physician to his daughter Anna Maria Luisa, who had married the elector of the Rhenish Palatinate, Johann Wilhelm. In this capacity he accompanied her to Düsseldorf and remained there until the end of 1694 or the beginning of 1695, when he was obliged, for reasons of health, to return to Florence.

BIBLIOGRAPHY

Bonomo's major work is *Osservazioni intorno a' pellicelli del corpo umano* (Florence, 1687).

Works on Bonomo are Luigi Belloni, "Le 'contagium vivum' avant Pasteur," in *Les conférences du Palais de la Découverte* (Paris, 1961), pp. 10–11; "La medicazione topica nella scoperta della etiologia acarica della scabbia," in *Simposi clinici*, **1** (1964), xxi–xxvi; "I secoli italiani della dottrina del contagio vivo," *ibid.*, **4** (1967), liii; Ugo Faucci, "Contributo alla storia della scabbia," in *Rivista di storia delle scienze mediche e naturali*, **22** (1931), 153–170, 198–215, 257–371, 441–475; and C. Lombardo, "Giovan Cosimo Bonomo a Pisa," *ibid.*, **29** (1938), 97–121.

Luigi Belloni

BONVICINO (also known as **BONVOISIN** or **BUONVICINO**), **COSTANZO BENEDETTO** (*b.* Centallo, near Cuneo, Piedmont, 1739; *d.* Turin, Italy, 25 January 1812), *chemistry.*

The comfortable circumstances of Bonvicino's family enabled him to attend the University of Turin, from which he received his degree in medicine on 14 April 1764. In 1778 he was admitted to the College of Physicians. Bonvicino devoted himself almost entirely to chemistry, however, at first under the guidance of V. A. Gioanetti, and acquired considerable scientific prestige. In 1783 he became a member of the Academy of Sciences of Turin, of which he was president in 1801–1802. In 1800 he was made professor of pharmaceutical chemistry and of the natural history of drugs at the University of Turin.

Bonvicino's first scientific work dealt with a qualitative and a partially quantitative analysis of a Piedmontese mineral called *pierre hydrophane,* known for its characteristic of losing its opacity when immersed in water. A similar mineral had previously been examined by Torbern Bergman.

Bonvicino's activity in the Academy of Sciences of Turin during the reign of the house of Savoy (1783–1798) was in analytical and industrial chemistry. He was placed in charge of the Academy's laboratory and of the analysis of mineral waters and waters used by dyers. He also supervised the production and control of common salts and wrote reports on new proposals dealing largely with the textile and dye industries and with metallurgy.

In opposition to the views held by Lavoisier, in November 1787 Bonvicino requested the Turin Academy to take an official position against the chemical nomenclature proposed by the French scientist. This occurred at a time when the Academy was totally dedicated to a defense of the theories of Stahl. On 12 February 1792 Bonvicino reported to the Academy on some experiments he had performed in support of the phlogiston theory. His scientific production during this period achieved some noteworthy results that are recorded in all the chemistry manuals of the period. His memoir on the isolation of phosphoric acid from calcium phosphate by means of ammonium carbonate dates from 1784–1785; previously, oxalic acid, which gave only a partial purification, had been used.

The writings that give us a truer measure of Bonvicino's scientific achievements are those related to the analysis of water and salts. The predominance of the experimental aspect freed the scientist from the rigid interpretative schemes that were based on preconceived theories.

In his carefully conducted studies, Bonvicino made use of a technique that aimed at the solution of problems of quantitative determination, that is, problems that dealt with the loss of weight, due to mechanical and physical factors, of substances being examined. The results yielded a great mass of data that appeared in scientific publications during the second half of the eighteenth century while being subjected to further experimental verification. From these studies he wrote his *Elementi di chimica,* a rich compendium of his university courses.

During the Napoleonic period (1798–1812), Bonvicino was especially interested in a more rational exploitation of the mineral resources of the Piedmont, a problem he tackled from all points of view: the importance of the mineral wealth (the survey and analysis of minerals were the chief objects of his studies during this period); the development of the industries that processed the minerals (to be achieved by the gradual replacement of the miners, who used crude techniques, by students who had been trained in technical schools, the establishment of which Bonvicino strongly advocated); the updating of mining legislation (still on a feudal basis, mining laws presented a serious obstacle to free enterprise); and combustibles (besides the traditional source, wood, he also searched for coal deposits).

BIBLIOGRAPHY

I. ORIGINAL WORKS. A fairly complete bibliography of Bonvicino's published works may be found in G. G. Bonino, *Biografia medica piemontese* (see below), II, 593–596. Books not included by Bonino are *Sulle cagioni recenti della minor produzione in bozzoli e in sete nel Piemonte e sui mezzi di rimediarvi* (Turin, 1802); *Elementi di chimica farmaceutica e di storia naturale e preparazione de' rimedi,* 2 vols. (Turin, 1804–1810); *Pensieri sulla cura dell'epizozia che regna ora in Piemonte* (Turin, 1805); *Storia di quattro persone che morirono avvelenate dai funghi* (Turin, n.d.); *Mémoire présenté à la Commission du Grand Conseil d'Administration de l'Université de Turin nommée pour examiner tout ce qui a rapport aux examens de médecine* (Turin, n.d.); and *Memorie ed istruzioni sui mezzi di minorare i danni delle carestie nel Piemonte per mezzo della dilatata coltura dei pomi di terra, volgarmente detti tartifle* (Turin, n.d.). Articles omitted by Bonino are "Rouissage du chanvre," in *Memorie dell'Accademia delle scienze di Torino,* **10** (1793), xxxii–xxxix; "Note sur la diopside," in *Journal des mines,* **20**, no. 115 (1812), 65 ff.; and "Sur la formation de l'hydrophane et du cacholong," *ibid.,* no. 118 (1812), 305 ff.

Unpublished memoirs and MSS of Bonvicino, preserved in the library of the Academy of Sciences of Turin, are "Sulla maniera di trarre il sale catartico dal scisto delle montagne di Sallances" (1784), MS collection 485; "Analisi di alcune acque naturali relativamente alle tinture" (1790), MS collection 540; "Analyse de la teinture tonique dite les Gouttes de Bestouscheff" (1791), MS collection 443–445; and "Parere su un saggio di Vitriolo della nuova fabbrica eretta in Carouge dal sig. De Voiseray" (1791), MS collection 2331.

Also preserved in the same library are reports prepared by Bonvicino and the commissions of which he was a member at the request of private industry, and six letters from Bonvicino to colleagues in the Academy. Bonvicino's activity in the Academy of Sciences is recorded in its MS minutes, preserved in its library.

II. SECONDARY LITERATURE. An obituary notice on Bonvicino is A. Garmagnano, *Clarissimi Benedicti Bonvicini chimiae pharmaceuticae professoris medicae facultatis praesidis laudatio* (Turin, 1812). A longer sketch of his life is G. G. Bonino, in his *Biografia medica piemontese,* II (Turin, 1825), 585–596. Its information was republished in a biography of Bonvicino by I. Guareschi, in *Supplemento annuale alla Enciclopedia di chimica* (Turin, 1910), pp. 445–453. For information on the scientific milieu in which Bonvicino worked, the only worthwhile work is still that of I. Guareschi, "La chimica in Italia dal 1750 al 1800," in *Supplemento annuale alla Enciclopedia di chimica* (Turin, 1909), pp. 327–378.

GIORGIO PEDROCCO

BOODT, ANSELMUS BOETIUS DE (*b.* Bruges, Belgium, *ca.* 1550; *d.* Bruges, 21 June 1632), *mineralogy.*

Boodt was the son of Willem de Boodt and Johanna Voet, daughter of a famous lawyer. The Boodts were a noble Roman Catholic family, and Anselmus was destined for a career in the administration of his native town. He probably took his first university degree in civil and canon law at Louvain. After this he studied medicine under Thomas Erastus at Heidelberg and obtained his M.D. in Padua.

From 1583 Boodt lived in Bohemia as physician to Wilhelm Rosenberg, the burgrave of Prague. He was on very friendly terms with the imperial physician, Thadeus Hayek, a well-known Bohemian naturalist and historian. With Hayek and Nicolas Barnaud he made some alchemical experiments that are mentioned in Barnaud's "In aenigmaticum"; however, he was critical of alchemy and a decided opponent of Paracelsus. Besides being a polyglot and poet, Boodt drew and painted flowers, animals, and minerals. He made many mineralogical excursions in Germany, Silesia, and Bohemia.

On 11 February 1584, while he was in Prague, Boodt was appointed canon of St. Donat's Church in Bruges; he held this post until 1595 without leaving Prague. On 1 January 1604 he was nominated physician in ordinary to Rudolf II and retained this position until the death of the emperor in 1612. Under the influence of Rudolf, a devoted collector of all curiosities, Boodt began in 1604 to write his chief work, *Gemmarum et lapidum historia* (1609).

In 1612 Boodt returned to Bruges, where he spent the rest of his life as a town, councillor. He never married. On 17 October 1630 he made his will, bequeathing to the Jesuits of Bruges the sums that Rudolf II owed him. His next of kin received his books, pictures, instruments, and collections of minerals.

In his *Gemmarum et lapidum historia* Boodt made the first attempt at a systematic description of minerals, dividing the minerals into great and small, rare and common, hard and soft, combustible and incombustible, transparent and opaque. He uses a scale of hardness expressed in three degrees and notes the crystalline forms of some minerals (triangular, quadratic, and hexangular). Boodt criticizes some of the views of Aristotle, Pliny, Paracelsus, and others, but accepts the existence of the four elements and three principles, although he also mentions atoms. He enumerates about 600 minerals that he knows from personal observation, and describes their properties, values, imitations, and medical applications. There are also tables of values of diamonds according to their size and a short description of the polishing of precious stones. Boodt cites nineteen authors and, besides the minerals known to him, gives a list of 233 minerals whose names he knows from Pliny and Bartholomeus Anglicus, among others.

BIBLIOGRAPHY

I. ORIGINAL WORKS. Boodt's only published work is *Gemmarum et lapidum historia* (Hanau, 1609); 2nd ed., prepared by Adrianus Toll, M.D. (Leiden, 1636); the 3rd ed., also prepared by Toll (Leiden, 1649), has as supplement John de Laet's *De gemmis et lapidibus librii II et Theophrastus' Liber de lapidibus Graece et Latine cum brevibus notis* (1647). The *Gemmarum* was translated into French by Jean Bachou as *Le parfaict joaillier, ou histoire des pierreries* (Lyons, 1644, 1649).

II. SECONDARY LITERATURE. Writings on Boodt or his work are Nicolas Barnaud, "In aenigmaticum quoddam epitaphium Bononiae," in *Theatrum chemicum,* III (Strasbourg, 1613), 787; O. Delepierre, *Biographie des hommes remarquables de la Flandre occidentale,* I (Bruges, 1843), 31–35; G. Dewalque, *Biographie nationale de Belgique,* IV, 814–816; F. M. Evans, *Magic Jewels* (Oxford, 1922), p. 154; F. V. Goethals, *Lectures relatives à l'histoire des sciences, des arts, des lettres, des moeurs et de la politique en Belgique* (Brussels, 1838), pp. 98–105; J. E. Hiller, in *Annales Guebhard-Severine,* 11 (1935), 74; in *Archeion,* 15 (1933), 348–368; in *Quellen und Studien zur Geschichte der Naturwissenschaften und der Medizin,* 8 (Berlin, 1942), 1–125; and in *Fortschritte der Mineralogie, Krystallographie und Petrographie* (Stuttgart), 17 (1932), 418–419; E. Hoefer, ed., *Nouvelle biographie universelle,* VI (Paris, 1853), 665; F. M. Jaeger, in *Chemisch Weekblad,* 15 (1918), 628, and in *Historische Studiën. Bijdragen tot de Kennis van de Geschiedenis der Natuurwetenschappen in Nederlanden gedurende de 16e en 17e Eeuw* (Groningen, 1919), pp. 99–149; *Nieuw Nederlands biografisch Woordenboek,* VI, 151–152; Oesterreichische Nationalbibliothek, Vienna, MS 14724, p. 133; J. R. Partington, *A History of Chemistry,* II (London, 1961), 101–102; "Testament olographe d'Anselme de Boodt, conseiller-pensionnaire de Bruges, 1630," in *Annales de la Société d'émulation,* 2nd ser., 11 (1861), 370–383; and A. J. J. Van de Velde, "*Rede op de hulde Anselmus Boetius de Boodt de Brugge op 20 november 1932,* names de Academie," in *Koninklijke Vlamsche Academie voor Wetenschappen, Letteren en Schoone Kunsten van België, Klasse der Wetenschappen. Verslagen en Mededeelingen* (Brussels, Nov. 1932), pp. 1505–1507.

WŁODZIMIERZ HUBICKI

BOOLE, GEORGE (*b.* Lincoln, England, 1815; *d.* Cork, Ireland, 1864), *mathematics.*

George Boole was the son of John Boole, a cobbler whose chief interests lay in mathematics and the making of optical instruments, in which his son learned to assist at an early age. The father was not a good businessman, however, and the decline in his business had a serious effect on his son's future. The boy went to an elementary school and for a short time to a commercial school, but beyond this he educated himself, encouraged in mathematics by his father and helped in learning Latin by William Brooke, the proprietor of a large and scholarly circulating library. He acquired a knowledge of Greek, French, and German by his own efforts, and showed some promise as a classical scholar; a translation in verse of Meleager's "Ode to the Spring" was printed in a local paper and drew comments on the precocity of a boy of fourteen. He seems to have thought of taking holy orders, but at the age of fifteen he began teaching, soon setting up a school of his own in Lincoln.

In 1834 the Mechanics Institution was founded in Lincoln, and the president, a local squire, passed Royal Society publications on to the institution's reading room, of which John Boole became curator. George, who now devoted his scanty leisure to the study of mathematics, had access to the reading room, and grappled, almost unaided, with Newton's *Principia* and Lagrange's *Mécanique analytique,* gaining such a local reputation that at the age of nineteen he was asked to give an address on Newton to mark the presentation of a bust of Newton, also a Lincolnshire man, to the Institution. This address, printed in 1835, was Boole's first scientific publication. In 1840 he began to contribute to the recently founded *Cambridge Mathematical Journal* and also to the Royal Society, which awarded him a Royal Medal in 1844 for his papers on operators in analysis; he was elected a fellow of the Royal Society in 1857.

In 1849, Boole, on the advice of friends, applied for the professorship of mathematics in the newly established Queen's College, Cork, and was appointed in spite of his not holding any university degree. At Cork, although his teaching load was heavy, he found more time and facilities for research. In 1855 he married Mary Everest, the niece of a professor of Greek in Queen's College and of Sir George Everest, after whom Mount Everest was named.

Boole was a clear and conscientious teacher, as his textbooks show. In 1864 his health began to fail, and his concern for his students may have hastened his death, since he walked through rain to a class and lectured in wet clothes, which led to a fatal illness.

Boole's scientific writings consist of some fifty papers, two textbooks, and two volumes dealing with mathematical logic. The two textbooks, on differential equations (1859) and finite differences (1860), remained in use in the United Kingdom until the end of the century. They contain much of Boole's original work, reproducing and extending material published in his research papers. In the former book, so much use is made of the differential operator D that the method is often referred to as Boole's, although it is in fact much older than Boole. Both books exhibit a great technical skill in the handling of operators: in the volume on finite differences, an account is given of the operators π and ρ, first introduced in Boole's Royal Society papers. The basic operators of this calculus, Δ and E, are defined by the equations

$$\Delta u_x = u_{x+1} - u_x, \; E\, u_x = u_{x+1};$$

Boole then defines his new operators by the operational equations

$$\pi = x\Delta, \; \rho = xE,$$

and shows how they can be used to solve certain types of linear difference equations with coefficients depending on the independent variable. These operators have since been generalized by L. M. Milne-Thomson.

In papers in the *Cambridge Mathematical Journal* in 1841 and 1843, Boole dealt with linear transformations. He showed that if the linear transformation

$$x = pX + qY, y = rX + sY$$

is applied to the binary quadratic form

$$ax^2 + 2hxy + by^2$$

to yield the binary quadratic form

$$AX^2 + 2HXY + BY^2,$$

then $\qquad AB - H^2 = (ps - qr)^2 (ab - h^2).$

The algebraic fact had been partly perceived by Lagrange and by Gauss, but Boole's argument drew attention to the (relative) invariance of the discriminant $ab - h^2$, and also to the absolute invariants of the transformation. This was the starting point of the theory of invariants, so rapidly and extensively developed in the second half of the nineteenth century; Boole himself, however, took no part in this development.

Other papers dealt with differential equations, and the majority of those published after 1850 studied the theory of probability, closely connected with Boole's work on mathematical logic. In all his writings, Boole exhibited considerable technical skill, but his facility in dealing with symbolic operators did not delude him into an undue reliance on analogy, a fault of the contemporary British school of symbolic analysis. E. H. Neville has remarked that mathematicians of that school treated operators with the most reckless disrespect, and in consequence could solve problems beyond the power not merely of their predecessors at the beginning of the century but of their inhibited successors at the end of the century, obtaining many remarkable and frequently correct formulas but ignoring conditions of validity.

Boole greatly increased the power of the operational calculus, but seldom allowed himself to be carried away by technical success: at a time when the need for precise and unambiguous definitions was often ignored, he was striving, although perhaps not always with complete success, to make his foundations secure. There is a clear and explicit, although later, statement of his position in his *Investigation of the Laws of Thought;* there are, he says, two indispensable conditions for the employment of symbolic operators: "First, that from the sense once conventionally established, we never, in the same process of reasoning, depart; secondly, that the laws by which the process is conducted be founded exclusively upon the above fixed sense or meaning of the symbols employed." With the technical skill and the desire for logical precision there is also the beginning of the recognition of the nonnumerical variable as a genuine part of mathematics. The development of this notion in Boole's later and most important work appears to have been stimulated almost accidentally by a logical controversy.

Sir William Hamilton, the Scottish philosopher (not to be confused with the Irish mathematician Sir William Rowan Hamilton), picked a logical quarrel with Boole's friend Augustus De Morgan, the acute and high-minded professor of mathematics at University College, London. De Morgan's serious, significant contributions to logic were derided by Hamilton, on the grounds that the study of mathematics was both dangerous and useless—no mathematician could contribute anything of importance to the superior domain of logic. Boole, in the preface to his *Mathematical Analysis of Logic* (1847), demonstrated that, on Hamilton's own principles, logic would form no part of philosophy. He asserted that in a true classification, logic should not be associated with metaphysics, but with mathematics. He then offered his essay as a construction, in symbolic terms, of logic as a doctrine, like geometry, resting upon a groundwork of acceptable axioms.

The reduction of Aristotelian logic to an algebraic calculus had been more than once attempted; Leibniz had produced a scheme of some promise. If the proposition "All A is B" is written in the form A/B, and "All B is C" in the form B/C, then it is tempting to remove the common factor B from numerator and denominator and arrive at A/C, to be correctly interpreted as the conclusion "All A is C." Any attempt

to extend this triviality encountered difficulties: Boole's predecessors had tried to force the algebra of real numbers onto logic, and since they had not envisaged a plurality of algebras, it was believed that only if the elementary properties of the symbols implied formal rules identical with those of the algebra of real numbers could the subject be regarded as a valid part of mathematics. Boole recognized that he had created a new branch of mathematics, but it is not clear whether he appreciated that he had devised a new algebra. He appears not to have known that geometries other than Euclidean could be constructed; but he knew of Rowan Hamilton's quaternions, an algebra of quadruplets in which products are noncommutative, for one of his minor papers (1848) deals with some quaternion matters. Grassmann's similar, if more general, work in the *Ausdehnungslehre* (1844) seems to have been unknown. Boole, then, knew of an algebra similar to, but not identical with, the algebra of real numbers.

If we consider a set U, the universal set or the universe of discourse, often denoted by 1 in Boole's work, subsets can be specified by elective operators $x, y, \cdots$, so that xU is the subset of U whose elements have the property defining the operator x. Thus, if U is the set of inhabitants of New York, we can select those who are, say, male by an elective operator x and denote the set of male inhabitants of New York by xU. Similarly, the left-handed inhabitants of New York may be denoted by yU, and blue-eyed inhabitants by zU, and so on. The elective operators may be applied successively. Thus we may first select all the males and from these all the left-handers by the symbolism $y(xU)$; if we first select all the left-handers and from these all the males, we have the symbolism $x(yU)$. Since in each case the final set is the same, that of all left-handed males, we can write $y(xU) = x(yU)$, or, since the universe of discourse U is understood throughout, simply write $yx = xy$. The analogy with the commutative algebraic product is clear. The associative law for products, $x(yz) = (xy)z$, can be verified at once in this interpretation, since each side denotes the set of those who are at once male, left-handed, and blue-eyed; Boole uses this without bothering to give any explicit justification. He was careful, however, to remark that although an analogy exists, the evidence on which the laws are based in his work is not related to the evidence on which the laws of the algebra of real numbers are based. To select the set of males from the set of males is merely to arrive at the set of males; thus the definition of the operator x leads to the idempotent law $x(xU) = xU$, or $x^2 = x$, the first break with ordinary algebra.

The product or intersection operation can also be regarded as a symbolic expression of the logical concept of conjunction by means of the conjunctive "and," since xy will denote the set of those inhabitants of New York who are at once male *and* left-handed.

If xU is the subset of males in the universal set U, it is natural to write the set of nonmales, that which remains when the set of males is subtracted from U, as $U - xU$, or, briefly, $1 - x$. This set, the complement of x relative to U, which Boole for brevity denoted by $\bar{x}$, can be regarded as arising from the application of the logical negation "not" to the set x. Addition has not yet been defined, but Boole did not hesitate to rewrite the equation $\bar{x} = 1 - x$ in the form $x + \bar{x} = 1$, implying that the universal set is made up of the elements of the subset x or of the subset not-x; this suggests that the sign $+$ is the symbol for the connective "or." But the word "or" in English usage has an inclusive and an exclusive sense: "either . . . or . . . and possibly both" and "either . . . or . . . but not both." Boole chose the exclusive sense, and so did not allow the symbolism $x + y$ unless the sets x, y were mutually exclusive.

Modern usage takes $x + y$ for the union or logical sum, the set of elements belonging to at least one of x, y: this union Boole included in his symbolism as $x + \bar{x}y$. Kneale suggests that Boole's choice of the exclusive sense for the symbol $+$ was caused by a desire to use the minus sign $(-)$ as the inverse of the plus sign $(+)$. If y is contained in x, $x - y$ can consistently denote those elements of x which are not elements of y—the complement of y relative to x—but if $+$ is used in the inclusive sense, then the equations $x = y + z$, $x = y + w$ do not imply $z = w$, so that $x - y$ is essentially indeterminate. Alternately, a use of the idempotent law implies that

$$(x - y)^2 = x - y,$$

and a further application of this law suggests that from

$$x^2 - 2xy + y^2 = x - y$$

it follows that

$$x - 2xy + y = x - y$$

and, hence, that $y = xy$; this is a symbolic statement that y is a subset of x. Boole was thus led to the use of the sign $+$ in the exclusive sense, with the sign $-$ as its inverse.

The idempotent law $x^2 = x$ is expressed in the form $x(1 - x) = 0$, but it is not altogether clear whether Boole regarded this as a deduction or as a formulation of the fundamental Aristotelian principle that a prop-

osition cannot be simultaneously true and false. Some of the obscurity is due to the fact that Boole does not always make clear whether he is dealing with sets, or with propositions, or with an abstract calculus of which sets and propositions are representations.

Much of the 1847 tract on the mathematical analysis of logic is devoted to symbolic expressions for the forms of the classical Aristotelian propositions and the moods of the syllogism. The universal propositions "All X's are Y's," "No X's are Y's" take the forms $x(1 - y) = 0$, $xy = 0$. The particular propositions "Some X's are Y's," "Some X's are not Y's" do not take what might appear to be the natural forms $xy \neq 0$, $x(1 - y) \neq 0$, possibly because Boole wished to avoid inequalities and to work entirely in terms of equations. He therefore introduced an elective symbol, v; any elements common to x and y constitute a subset v; which, he says, is "indefinite in every respect but this"—that it has some members. The two particular propositions he wrote in the forms $xy = v$, $x(1 - y) = v$. This ill-defined symbol needs careful handling when the moods and figures of the syllogism are discussed. Thus the premises "All Y's are X's," "No Z's are Y's" give the equations $y = vx$, $0 = zy$, with the inference $0 = vzx$ to be interpreted as "Some X's are not Z's." Boole explains that it would be incorrect to interpret $0 = vzx$ as "Some Z's are not X's" because the equation $y = vx$ fixes the interpretation of vx as "Some X's" and "v is regarded as the representation of 'Some' only with respect to the class X."

A similar obscurity is encountered when an attempt is made to define division. If $z = xy$, what inferences can be drawn about x, in the hope of defining the quotient z/y? Since z is the intersection of x and y, and thus is contained in y, $yz = z$; thus x, which contains z, contains yz. Any other element of x that is not in z cannot be in y, and hence x is made up of yz and an indeterminate set of which all that can be said is that its elements belong neither to y nor to z, and thus belong to the intersection of $1 - y$ and $1 - z$. Thus

$z/y = yz +$ an indefinite portion of $(1 - y)(1 - z)$.

Boole gave this result as a special case of his general expansion formula, and his argument is typical of that used to establish the general theorem. From $y + \bar{y} = 1$, $z + \bar{z} = 1$, it follows that $yz + y\bar{z} + \bar{y}z + \bar{y}\bar{z} = 1$, that is, the universe of discourse is the sum of the subsets yz, $y\bar{z}$, $\bar{y}z$, $\bar{y}\bar{z}$. Hence, any subset whatsoever will be at most a sum of elements from each of these four subsets; thus

$$z/y = Ayz + By\bar{z} + C\bar{y}z + D\bar{y}\bar{z},$$

with coefficients A, B, C, D to be determined. First, set $y = 1$, $z = 1$, so that $\bar{y} = \bar{z} = 0$; then $A = 1$. Next, set $y = 1$, $z = 0$, so that $\bar{y} = 0$, $\bar{z} = 1$; then $B = 0$. Third, set $y = 0$, $z = 1$, so that $\bar{y} = 1$, $\bar{z} = 0$; if the term in $\bar{y}z$ were present, then C would have to be infinite; hence, the term in $\bar{y}z$ cannot appear. Finally, if $y = z = 0$, the coefficient D is of the form $0/0$, which is indeterminate. This asserts the possible presence of an indefinite portion of the set $\bar{y}\bar{z}$. Thus, as before,

$$z/y = yz + \text{ an indefinite portion of } \bar{y}\bar{z},$$

or, as Boole frequently wrote it,

$$\frac{z}{y} = yz + \frac{0}{0}(1 - y)(1 - z).$$

Schröder showed that the introduction of division is unnecessary. But the concept of the "development" of a function of the elective symbols is fundamental to Boole's logical operations and occupies a prominent place in his great work on mathematical logic, the *Investigation of the Laws of Thought*. If $f(x)$ involves x and the algebraic signs, then it must denote a subset of the universe of discourse and must therefore be made up of elements from x and $\bar{x}$. Thus

$$f(x) = Ax + B\bar{x},$$

where the coefficients A and B are determined by giving x the values of 0 and 1. Thus

$$f(x) = f(1)x + f(0)(1 - x),$$

which in the *Mathematical Analysis of Logic* Boole regards as a special case of MacLaurin's theorem, although he dropped this analogy in the *Investigation of the Laws of Thought*. A repeated application of this method to an expression $f(x,y)$ containing two elective symbols yields

$$f(x,y) = f(1,1)\,xy + f(1,0)\,x(1 - y) \\ + f(0,1)(1 - x)y + f(0,0)(1 - x)(1 - y),$$

and more general formulas can be written down by induction. Logical problems which can be expressed in terms of elective symbols may then be reduced to standard forms expediting their solution.

Boole's logical calculus is not a two-valued algebra, although the distinction is not always clearly drawn in his own work. The principles of his calculus, as a calculus of sets, are nowhere set out by him in a formal table, but are assumed, sometimes implicitly, and are, save one, analogous to the algebraic rules governing real numbers:

$$xy = yx \\ x + y = y + x \\ x(y + z) = xy + xz \\ x(y - z) = xy - xz.$$

If $x = y$, then

$$xz = yz \\ x + z = y + z \\ x - z = y - z.$$

$$x(1 - x) = 0.$$

Of these, only the last has no analogue in the algebra of real numbers. These principles suffice for the calculus of sets. But Boole observes that in algebra the last principle is an equation whose only roots are $x = 0$, $x = 1$. In the calculus of sets this would assert that any set is either the null set or the universal set. Boole added this numerical interpretation in order to establish a two-valued algebra, of which one representation would be a calculus of propositions in which the truth of a proposition X is denoted by $x = 1$ and its falsehood by $x = 0$: the truth-value of a conjunction "X and Y" will be given by xy, and of an exclusive disjunction "X or Y" by $x + y$. The distinction between propositions and propositional functions, not drawn by Boole, was made later by C. S. Peirce and Schröder.

The use of $x + y$ to denote the exclusive sense of "or" led to difficulties, such as the impossibility of interpreting $1 + x$ and $x + x$, which Boole surmounted with considerable ingenuity. But Jevons, in his *Pure Logic* (1864), used the plus sign in its inclusive (and/or) sense, a use followed by Venn and C. S. Peirce and since then generally adopted. Peirce and Schröder emphasized that the inclusive interpretation permits a duality between sum and product, and they also showed that the concepts of subtraction and division are superfluous and can be discarded. With the use of $x + y$ to denote "either x or y or both," the expression $x + x$ presents no difficulty, being just x, while $1 + x$ is the universal set 1. The duality of the two operations of sum and product exemplified by the equations $xx = x$, $x + x = x$ can now be carried further: the formulas

$$xy + xz = x(y + z), \qquad (x + y)(x + z) = x + yz$$

are duals, since one can be derived from the other by an interchange of sum with product. This duality is clearer if these operations are denoted by the special symbols $\cap$, $\cup$ now in general use for product and sum, that is, for intersection and union. In this notation, the preceding equations are written

$$(x \cup y) \cap (x \cup z) = x \cup (y \cap z), \\ (x \cap y) \cup (x \cap z) = x \cap (y \cup z).$$

With the inclusive interpretation, the system can now be shown to obey the dual rules of De Morgan:

$$\overline{xy} = \bar{x} + \bar{y}, \qquad \overline{x + y} = \bar{x}\bar{y}.$$

In the *Investigation of the Laws of Thought*, the calculus is applied to the theory of probability. If $P(X) = x$ is the probability of an event X, then if events X, Y are independent, $P(X \text{ and } Y) = xy$, while if X and Y are mutually exclusive, $P(X \text{ or } Y) = x + y$. The principles laid down above are satisfied, except for the additional numerical principle in which the allowable values of x are 0 and 1, which is not satisfied. A clear and precise symbolism enabled Boole to detect and correct flaws in earlier work on probability theory.

E. V. Huntington in 1904 gave a set of independent axioms on which Boole's apparatus can be constructed, and various equivalent sets have been exhibited. One formulation postulates two binary operations $\cup$, $\cap$ (union and intersection) which have the commutative and distributive properties:

$$x \cup y = y \cup x, \qquad x \cap y = y \cap x,$$
$$x \cup (y \cap z) = (x \cup y) \cap (x \cup z),$$
$$x \cap (y \cup z) = (x \cap y) \cup (x \cap z);$$

further, there are two distinct elements, 0 and 1, such that for all x

$$x \cup 0 = x, \qquad x \cap 1 = x;$$

also, for any x, there is an element $\bar{x}$ (the complement) for which

$$x \cup \bar{x} = 1, \qquad x \cap \bar{x} = 0.$$

The system so defined is self-dual, since the set of axioms remains unchanged if $\cup$ and $\cap$ are interchanged when 0, 1 are also interchanged. The associative laws for union and intersection are not required as axioms, since they can be deduced from the given set.

If intersection and complement are taken as the basic operations, with the associative law $x \cap (y \cap z) = (x \cap y) \cap z$ now an axiom and the relation between the basic operations given by the statements

if $x \cap \bar{y} = z \cap \bar{z}$ for some z, then $x \cap y = x$,
if $x \cap y = x$, then $x \cap \bar{y} = z \cap \bar{z}$ for any z,

then union can now be defined in terms of intersection and complement by the equation

$$x \cup y = \overline{\bar{x} \cap \bar{y}},$$

0 can be defined as $x \cap \bar{x}$, and 1 as the complement of 0. The two systems are then equivalent.

The theory of lattices may be regarded as a generalization. A lattice is a system with operations $\cup$, $\cap$ having the commutative, distributive, and associative properties. Thus every Boolean algebra is a lattice; the converse is not true. The lattice concept is wider than the Boolean, and embraces interpretations for which Boolean algebra is not appropriate.

Boole's two-valued algebra has recently been applied to the design of electric circuits containing simple switches, relays, and control elements. In particular, it has a wide field of application in the design of high-speed computers using the binary system of digital numeration.

BIBLIOGRAPHY

I. ORIGINAL WORKS. Boole's papers include "Researches on the Theory of Analytical Transformations, With a Special Application to the Reduction of the General Equation of the Second Order," in *Cambridge Mathematical Journal,* **2** (1841), 64–73; "On a General Method in Analysis," in *Philosophical Transactions of the Royal Society of London,* **134** (1844), 225–282. *An Address on the Genius and Discoveries of Sir Isaac Newton* was published in Lincoln in 1835.

His textbooks are *Treatise on Differential Equations* (Cambridge, 1859, and later editions); a posthumous *Supplementary Volume* (Cambridge, 1865), compiled from Boole's notes by Isaac Todhunter, and containing a list of Boole's publications; *Treatise on the Calculus of Finite Differences* (Cambridge, 1860, and later editions).

On mathematical logic: *The Mathematical Analysis of Logic, Being an Essay Towards a Calculus of Deductive Reasoning* (Cambridge, 1847; repr. Oxford, 1948, and in Boole's *Collected Logical Works,* I, Chicago–London, 1916); *An Investigation of the Laws of Thought, on Which Are Founded the Mathematical Theories of Logic and Probability* (London, 1854; repr. New York, 1951, and in Boole's *Collected Logical Works,* II, Chicago–London, 1916).

II. SECONDARY LITERATURE. E. V. Huntington, "Sets of Independent Postulates for the Algebra of Logic," in *Transactions of the American Mathematical Society,* **5** (1904), 208–309; E. V. Huntington, "Postulates for the Algebra of Logic," in *Transactions of the American Mathematical Society,* **35** (1933), 274–304; W. Kneale, "Boole and the Revival of Logic," in *Mind,* **57** (1948), 149–175, which contains a useful bibliography; W. Kneale, "Boole and the Algebra of Logic," in *Notes and Records of the Royal Society of London,* **12** (1956), 53–63; Sir Geoffrey Taylor, "George Boole, 1815–1864," *ibid.,* 44–52, which gives an account of Boole's life by his grandson.

T. A. A. BROADBENT

BORCH, OLUF. See **Borrichius, Olaus.**

BORCHARDT, CARL WILHELM (*b.* Berlin, Germany, 22 February 1817; *d.* Rudersdorf, near Berlin, 27 June 1880), *mathematics.*

BORCHARDT

The son of Moritz Borchardt, a wealthy and respected Jewish merchant, and Emma Heilborn, Borchardt had among his private tutors the mathematicians J. Plücker and J. Steiner. From 1836 he studied at the University of Berlin with Dirichlet, and from 1839 at the University of Königsberg with Bessel, F. Neumann, and Jacobi. In his doctoral thesis (1843; unpublished and now lost), written under the supervision of Jacobi, he dealt with certain systems of nonlinear differential equations. In 1846–1847 he was in Paris, where he met Chasles, Hermite, and Liouville. Borchardt became a *Privatdozent* at the University of Berlin in 1848, and a member of the Berliner Akademie der Wissenschaften in 1855. He married Rosa Oppenheim. Very poor health interrupted his teaching for years; nevertheless, from 1856 to 1880 he edited, as Crelle's successor, Volumes **57–90** of the celebrated *Crelle's Journal für die reine und angewandte Mathematik,* upholding its high standard of mathematical scholarship.

Borchardt became known as a mathematician through his first publication (1846), in which he generalized a result obtained by Kummer concerning the equation that determines the secular disturbances of the planets (characteristic equation, or secular equation). By means of determinants Borchardt proved that in this case Sturm's functions can be represented as a sum of squares. From this it follows that the roots of the characteristic equation are real. In several further papers Borchardt applied the theory of determinants to algebraic questions, mostly in connection with symmetric functions, the theory of elimination, and interpolation. Another group of his papers dealt with the arithmetic-geometric mean (AGM). Gauss and Lagrange had established its connection with the complete elliptic integral of the first class. Borchardt, starting from the functional equation for the limit value of the AGM, derived a linear differential equation of the second order, the differential equation of the complete, first-class elliptic integral. He also studied a variant process of the AGM connected with the circular functions, and the generalization of the AGM to four elements and its relation to hyperelliptic integrals. Other papers dealt with problems of maxima and the theory of elasticity.

BIBLIOGRAPHY

I. ORIGINAL WORKS. Borchardt's *Gesammelte Werke,* G. Hettner, ed. (Berlin, 1888), contains 25 papers and some short communications. His works are listed in Poggendorff, I, 238; III, 162; IV, 158.

II. SECONDARY LITERATURE. Works on Borchardt are Maurice d'Ocagne, "C. W. Borchardt et son oeuvre," in *Revue des questions scientifiques* (Jan. 1890), also repr. separately (Brussels, 1890); and Max Steck, in *Neue deutsche Biographie,* II (Berlin, 1955), 456.

CHRISTOPH J. SCRIBA

BORDA

BORDA, JEAN-CHARLES (*b.* Dax, France, 4 May 1733; *d.* Paris, France, 19 February 1799), *physics, mathematics.*

Borda was the tenth child and the sixth son of the sixteen children of Jean-Antoine de Borda and Jeanne-Marie-Thérèse de Lacroix. His parents were both of the nobility, and his parental ancestors had been in the military since the early seventeenth century. Borda began his studies at the Collège des Barnabites at Dax, then continued at the Jesuit Collège de la Flèche. He entered the École du Génie de Mézières in 1758 and finished the two-year course in one year. Borda scorned religion, at least in his youth, and he never married. While commanding a flotilla of six ships in the Antilles in 1782, Borda was taken prisoner by the English. After this misfortune, his health declined steadily. He was elected a member of the Paris Académie des Sciences in 1756 (and of its successor, the Institut de France), the Académie de Bordeaux in 1767, the Académie de Marine in 1769, and the Bureau des Longitudes in 1795. Borda is a major figure in the history of the French navy. He attained the rank of *capitaine de vaisseau,* participated in several scientific voyages and in the American Revolution, and in 1784 was named *inspecteur des constructions et de l'École des Ingénieurs de vaisseau.*

Borda's most important contributions are his work in fluid mechanics and his development and use of instruments for navigation, geodesy, and the determination of weights and measures. In a series of theoretical and experimental memoirs he studied fluid flow reactions and fluid resistance as applied to artillery, ships, scientific instruments, and hydraulic wheels and pumps. Specifically, he demonstrated that Newton's theory of fluid resistance was untenable and that the resistance is proportional to the square of the fluid velocity and to the sine of the angle of incidence. He introduced the Borda mouthpiece and calculated the coefficient of fluid contraction from an orifice. Borda's use of the principle of conservation of *vis viva* was important as a precursor of Lazare Carnot's work in mechanics.

Borda's development of a surveying instrument, the *cercle de réflexion,* contributed to the French success in measuring the length of the meridional arc. He participated in the work on a standard system of weights and measures, and designed the platinum standard meter and the standard seconds pendulum. He contributed memoirs on the calculus of variations and, in connection with his *cercle de réflexion,* developed a series of trigonometric tables. Borda's importance to science lies in his skillful use of calculus and experiment, unifying them in diverse areas of physics. This led Biot to state that one owes to Borda and Coulomb the renaissance of exact physics in eighteenth-century France.

BIBLIOGRAPHY

I. ORIGINAL WORKS. A complete bibliography of Borda's memoirs is contained in Mascart (see below). His various papers on fluid mechanics are contained in the *Mémoires de l'Académie des sciences* for the years 1763 and 1766–1769. For a description of his *cercle de réflexion,* see *Description et usage du cercle de réflexion avec différentes méthodes pour calculer les observations nautiques, par le Chevalier de Borda* (Paris, 1787; 4th ed., 1816).

II. SECONDARY LITERATURE. The most important treatment of Borda's work is the massive 800-page study by Jean Mascart, *La vie et les travaux du Chevalier Jean-Charles de Borda,* published as a volume of the *Annales de l'Université de Lyon,* n.s., **2,** Droit, Lettres, fasc. 33 (Lyons-Paris, 1919). The best contemporary essay is S. F. Lacroix, *Éloge historique de Jean-Charles Borda* (Paris, *ca.* 1800). For a recent summary of Borda's work in fluid mechanics, see R. Dugas, *Histoire de la mécanique* (Paris, 1950), pp. 292–300.

C. STEWART GILLMOR

BORDET, JULES (*b.* Soignies, Belgium, 13 June 1870; *d.* Brussels, Belgium, 6 April 1961), *bacteriology, immunology.*

Bordet established the basis of humoral immunity and founded serology. The second son of a schoolteacher, he was an outstanding student at the Athénée Royal of Brussels and received the M.D. from the University of Brussels in 1892. He had begun his research even before finishing his medical studies.

In 1894, thanks to a scholarship awarded by the Belgian government, Bordet went to Paris to work in Élie Metchnikoff's laboratory at the Institut Pasteur. It was there, between the ages of twenty-five and thirty, that he made his principal discoveries in humoral immunity.

Married in 1899, he had two daughters and one son, Paul, who also worked in experimental medicine.

In Metchnikoff's laboratory Bordet studied the mechanics of bacteriolysis, a phenomenon consisting in the lysis of cholera vibrios injected into the peritoneum of immunized animals and recently discovered by R. Pfeiffer and Issaeff (1894). Bordet reached the conclusion that bacteriolysis was due to the action of two substances: a specific antibody that he called the sensibilizer, which was resistant to heat of 55°C. and present in serum from immunized animals, and a nonspecific, thermolabile substance, which is found in serum from both unvaccinated and vaccinated animals. He identified this substance as Büchner's "alexin," which later became known as "complement." Bordet then demonstrated that the mode of action of the hemolytic serums is absolutely analogous to that of the bacteriolytic ones.

As early as 1895 Bordet underscored the specific character of the agglutination of the *Vibriocomma* (Asiatic cholera bacillus) through anticholeric immunoserum. By using hemolytic serums, he extended the idea of antigenic specificity to the constitution of the cells, and by using precipitating serums, to the proteins of the various animal species.

Famous at thirty, Bordet in 1901 accepted the directorship of the Institut Antirabique et Bactériologique, which had just been founded in Brussels and which in 1903 was renamed the Institut Pasteur du Brabant. There he continued his research on immunity and demonstrated that if an antibody has the ability to unite with an antigen, the alexin can be absorbed only by the complex antigen-antibody, that is, the antigen "sensitized" by the antibody. This complex antigen-antibody can bring about the fixation of the alexin of fresh serum, and because of this, the alexin can no longer cause the lysis of red corpuscles sensitized by the hemolysin. This is the alexin-fixation reaction (the complement-fixation reaction), which Bordet and his brother-in-law Octave Gengou applied in 1901 to the serodiagnosis of typhoid fever, carbuncle, hog cholera, and other diseases and which makes it possible to trace the antibody in the patient's serum. This reaction was taken up again by Wassermann in the diagnosis of syphilis, and more recently has been used in the diagnosis of virus infections.

In his interpretation of the mechanism of the union of antigen and antibody, Bordet compared this union to adsorption phenomenon, while Ehrlich defended the theory of a union by definite proportions. The further work of Heidelberger and his school confirmed Bordet's concept.

In 1906, while carrying out research in different directions, Bordet and Gengou discovered the whooping cough bacillus and extracted an endotoxin, prepared a vaccine, and, with Sleeswijk, studied the antigenic variability of the bacillus. In 1909 Bordet isolated the germ of bovine peripneumonia and that of avian diphtheria. From 1901 to 1920 he studied blood coagulation and, from 1920 on, bacteriophages.

All of his research was conducted while Bordet bore

the heavy duties of directing the Institut Pasteur du Brabant (until 1940, when his son Paul succeeded him) and teaching at the Faculty of Medicine of the Free University of Brussels, where he occupied the chair of bacteriology from 1907 to 1935. Besides this, he went to Paris every year to lecture on immunity in the microbiology course at the Institut Pasteur, where he was made president of the Conseil Scientifique in 1935.

Bordet's work on humoral immunity, which made possible the application of serological techniques to diagnosis and control of infectious diseases, brought him many international awards, including the Nobel Prize in medicine for 1919, as well as the highest academic distinctions and honors.

BIBLIOGRAPHY

I. ORIGINAL WORKS. Most of Bordet's papers were published in *Annales de l'Institut Pasteur.* His major work is *Traité de l'immunité dans les maladies infectieuses* (Paris, 1920, 1939). Many documents, such as laboratory notebooks, are preserved in the Musée Jules Bordet, at the Institut Pasteur du Brabant, in Brussels.

II. SECONDARY LITERATURE. Works on Bordet are J. Beumer, "Jules Bordet 1870–1961," in *Journal of General Microbiology,* **29** (1962), 1–13; Paul Bordet, "Jules Bordet," in *Florilège des sciences en Belgique pendant le XIX siècle et le début du XXe* (Brussels, 1968), pp. 1036–1067; A. M. Dalcq, "Notice biographique sur J. Bordet," in *Bulletin de l'Académie royale de médecine de Belgique,* 7th ser., **1** (1961), 352–365; and "Jules Jean Vincent Bordet," in Blakiston's *New Gould Medical Dictionary,* N. L. Hoerr and Arthur Osol, eds., 2nd ed. (New York–Toronto–London, 1956). Also of value is the "Volume jubilaire de Jules Bordet," *Annales de l'Institut Pasteur,* **79,** no. 5 (1950), 479–520.

JEAN VIEUCHANGE

BORDEU, THÉOPHILE DE (*b.* Izeste, France, 22 February 1722; *d.* Paris, France, 23 November 1776), *medicine.*

The son and grandson of Béarnese physicians, Bordeu studied medicine at Montpellier, where he received his medical degree on 10 November 1743. He returned to Montpellier for further study in 1745 and in 1746 went to Paris, where he devoted his time particularly to the clinical examination of patients at La Charité hospital. He returned to Béarn, to Pau, in 1749. There he held, in succession, the posts of intendant and superintendent of the mineral waters of Aquitaine, drawing attention to their therapeutic value through a newspaper that he had founded. His reputation led to his appointment as a corresponding member of the Royal Academy of Sciences of Paris in 1747.

In 1752 Bordeu went again to Paris, with the intention of practicing medicine, but he had to observe the regulation that only graduates of the Paris Faculty of Medicine could practice in the capital. He renewed his studies and was again graduated M.D. on 7 October 1754. At this time he became an attending physician at La Charité. Very soon he attracted a large practice, which aroused jealousy. As the result of a conspiracy organized by Michel-Philippe Bouvart, his name was removed from the list of Paris physicians in 1761, an act that had the effect of preventing him from practicing. Bordeu defended himself vigorously and was reinstated in 1764. His success with patients continued, and he cared for many important persons, among them Madame Du Barry.

The part that Bordeu played in the history of thermalism has caused him to be considered the founder of modern hydrotherapy. It was through him that the baths of the Pyrenees became known throughout the south of France and even in Paris. His *Journal de Barèges* and his *Recherches sur les maladies chroniques* (1775) are among his most important contributions to this field.

Bordeu also studied anatomy. In 1747 he published "Recherches anatomiques sur les articulations des os de la face," which won him membership in the Academy of Sciences. He had already written a treatise on the formation of chyle, *Chylificationis historia* (1742), that foreshadowed his important work on the glands, *Recherches anatomiques sur les différentes positions des glandes et sur leur action* (1752). In the latter he announced the double innervation (trophic and functional) of glands and organs, thus proving the existence of secretory nerves. He offered in evidence a local increase in the circulation when a gland is in action and, while emphasizing the influence of the imagination, showed that excretion is due to the gland itself and not the surrounding muscles. This shows the importance of Bordeu as a precursor in the science that in the twentieth century came to be distinguished as endocrinology. Finally, he demonstrated that secretion is the active elaboration of a new product separate from the constituents of the blood. Bordeu completed this sequence with his famous *Recherches sur le tissu muqueux* (1767), in which he described connective tissue—under the name of mucous tissue—showing its role in exchanges, the phenomena of nutrition, and the mechanical equilibrium of organs and tissues.

Semeiology also interested Bordeu. His "Recherches sur les crises" appeared in Diderot's *Encyclopédie,* as did his "Recherches sur le pouls par rapport aux crises." Both mark him as a clinician of the first order who knew how to obtain a large number of diagnostic and prognostic facts from an examination. Since Bordeu, physicians take the pulse by applying the tips of the four fingers to the hollow of the radius.

Bordeu played a great role in the history of medical theories. His thesis at Montpellier, *De sensu generice considerato* ("On the Senses, Considered Generically," 1742), suggested the direction in which he was heading. His other works demonstrated that he considered each organ as having its own life and believed that life was the sum of all these "little lives" of the organs. Coordination among them was due to the mucous tissues. The organs and glands were set in motion by an irritation termed "sensibility." These ideas opened the way for vitalism, a doctrine of which the school of Montpellier became the champion.

BIBLIOGRAPHY

I. ORIGINAL WORKS. Works by Bordeu are *Chylificationis historia* (Montpellier, 1742); *De sensu generice considerato* (Montpellier, 1742); "Recherches anatomiques sur les articulations des os de la face," in Académie Royale des Sciences, *Mémoires des savants étrangers,* II (Paris, 1747); *Recherches anatomiques sur les différentes positions des glandes et sur leur action* (Paris, 1752); *Recherches sur le tissu muqueux* (Paris, 1767); and *Recherches sur les maladies chroniques* (Paris, 1775). His works are collected in A. Richerand, ed., *Oeuvres complètes de Théophile de Bordeu, précédées d'une notice sur sa vie et ses ouvrages,* 2 vols. (Paris, 1818).

Many of Bordeu's previously unpublished works have been brought to light by Lucien Cornet: *Théophile de Bordeu* (Bordeaux, 1922); "Une consultation médicale au XVIIIᵉ siècle," in *Bulletin de la Société des Sciences, Lettres et Arts de Pau,* 3rd ser., **10** (1949), 44–50; "Le procès de Théophile de Bordeu, documents inédits," *ibid.,* **14** (1953), 139–143; "Lettres inédites de Théophile de Bordeu, présentées et commentées par le Dr. Lucien Cornet," *ibid.,* **15** (1954), 24–29; "Nouvelles lettres inédites de Théophile de Bordeu (1753)," *ibid.,* **18** (1957), 65–70; "Lettres inédites de Théophile de Bordeu (1746)," *ibid.,* **20** (1959), 49–67; "Un ami de Théophile de Bordeu: Le médecin Jean de Brumont-Disse," *ibid.,* **21** (1960), 39–52; "Lettres inédites de Théophile de Bordeu (1746). Deuxième séjour à Montpellier," in *Journal de médecine de Bordeaux,* no. 136 (May 1960), 501–520; "Lettres inédites de Théophile de Bordeu (1747). Premier séjour à Paris," *ibid.,* no. 137 (September-November 1960), 1302–1404; "Lettres inédites de Théophile de Bordeu (1748). L'année de Versailles," *ibid.,* no. 138 (May 1961), 1475–1483; "Lettres de Théophile de Bordeu (1749). Fin du séjour à Versailles et retour à Pau," *ibid.,* no. 140 (February 1963), 328–337; "Lettres inédites de Théophile de Bordeu (1749)," in *Journal de médecine de Bordeaux,* no. 10 (October 1963); "Théophile de Bordeu et Madame de Sorbério," in *Revue régionaliste des Pyrénées,* no. 161-162 (January-June 1964), 6–22;

"Lettres inédites de Théophile de Bordeu (1750). Deuxième séjour à Pau et tournée d'inspection en Bigorre," in *Revue régionaliste des Pyrénées,* no. 59 (1964), 155–164, and no. 60 (October-December 1964), 277–287; and "Théophile de Bordeu, le biologiste," in *Bulletin de la Société des Sciences, Lettres et Arts de Pau,* 4th ser., **1** (1966), 123–125.

II. SECONDARY LITERATURE. Works on Bordeu are E. Forgue, *Théophile de Bordeu, fondateur de l'hydrologie, précurseur de la biologie moderne (1722–1776)* (Paris, 1937); J. J. Gardane, *Éloge historique de Bordeu* (Paris, 1777); F. Granel, *Un médecin du XVIIIᵉ siècle aux conceptions biologiques modernes: Théophile de Bordeu (1722–1776), docteur de Montpellier et de Paris* (Montpellier, 1964); and P. Roussel, *Éloge historique de Théophile de Bordeu* (Paris, 1778).

LOUIS DULIEU

BORDONE DELLA SCALA, GIULIO. See **Scaliger, Julius Caesar.**

BOREL, ÉMILE (FÉLIX-ÉDOUARD-JUSTIN) (*b.* Saint-Affrique, Aveyron, France, 7 January 1871; *d.* Paris, France, 3 February 1956), *mathematics.*

Borel's father, Honoré, son of an artisan, was a Protestant village pastor. His mother, Émilie Teissié-Solier, came of a local merchant family. In 1882, already known as a prodigy, he left his father's school for the *lycée* at nearby Montauban. In Paris as a scholarship student preparing for the university, he entered the family circle of G. Darboux through friendship with his son, saw the "good life" of a leading mathematician, and set his heart on it. In 1889, after winning first place in the École Polytechnique, the École Normale Supérieure, and the general competitions, Borel chose the gateway to teaching and research, in spite of the blandishments of a special representative of the École Polytechnique.

Fifty years later Borel's colleagues celebrated the jubilee of his entrance to the École Normale, rightly considering that as the beginning of his scientific career. Indeed, he published two papers during his first year and appears to have established there his lifetime pattern of intensely serious and well-organized activity. He embraced an agnostic, scientific, and rational outlook that implied a responsible interest in all aspects of human affairs, and the extensive friendships of his undergraduate days helped make possible his broad cultural and political influence in later life. First in the class of 1893, he was promptly invited to teach at the University of Lille, where he wrote his thesis and twenty-two papers in three years before being called back to the École Normale, where publications, honors, and responsibilities piled up rapidly.

In 1901 Borel married Paul Appell's eldest daughter, Marguerite, who had interested him for some time but had only then turned seventeen. She wrote more than thirty novels (as Camille Marbo), was president of the Société des Gens de Lettres, and both assisted and complemented her husband's many-sided activity. They had no children but adopted Fernand Lebeau, son of the older of Borel's two sisters, after the early death of his parents. In 1906 they used money from one of Émile's prizes to launch *La revue du mois,* which appealed successfully to a very broad circle until the war and economic crisis killed it in 1920. During this period Borel's publications and activities showed a progressive broadening of interest from pure mathematics to applications and public affairs. Without seeming to diminish his mathematical creativity, he wrote texts and popularizations, edited several distinguished series of books, contributed to popular magazines and the daily press, played leading roles in professional and university affairs, and maintained acquaintances ranging from poets to industrialists.

Such an implausible level of activity was possible because Borel's uncommon intelligence and vigor were accompanied by efficient organization and self-discipline. He could be kind and generous of his time and energy in meeting his official or self-imposed obligations. He was even ready to risk his status for a good cause. But he had no time for "small talk" or trivial activity, seemed formidable and even rude to outsiders, and with increasing age grew more impatient with would-be wasters of his time. His lectures displayed his mind at work rather than a finished exposition, and his teaching consisted primarily in directing his students' efforts.

In 1909 Borel occupied the chair of theory of functions, newly created for him at the Sorbonne, and began thirty-two years on the University Council, representing the Faculty of Science. In 1910 he entered what he called the happiest time of his life as vice-director of the École Normale in charge of science students, but World War I cut it short. His service in sound location at the front (while Marguerite headed a hospital), and in organizing research and development in the War Office under his old friend Paul Painlevé, turned his interests more than ever toward applications. After the war he could not be happy again at the École Normale. There were "too many ghosts in the hallways," including that of his adopted son. At his request he moved to the chair of probability and mathematical physics at the Sorbonne and maintained only honorary connections with the École Normale. The era was closed by the longest of his many trips abroad, including five months in China

with Painlevé, and by his election to the Academy in 1921.

While continuing his flow of publications and his lectures in mathematics, Borel now moved rapidly into politics as mayor of Saint-Affrique (with Marguerite presiding over the Jury Femina), councillor of the Aveyron district, Radical and Radical-Socialist member of the Chamber of Deputies (1924–1936), and minister of the navy (1925). Important scientific legislation, the founding of the Centre National de la Recherche Scientifique, and several ships named after mathematicians are traceable to his initiative. He helped plan and raise funds for the Institut Henri Poincaré and served as director from its founding in 1928 until his death.

Retired from politics in 1936 and from the Sorbonne in 1940, Borel still had the vigor to produce more than fifty additional books and papers, to participate in the Resistance in his native village, to which he returned after a brief imprisonment by the Germans in 1940, and to travel extensively. The breadth of his services was recognized by such honors as the presidency of the Academy (1934), the Grand Cross of the Legion of Honor (1950), the first gold medal of the Centre Nationale de la Recherche Scientifique (1955), the Croix de Guerre (1918), and the Resistance Medal (1945). A fall on the boat while returning from giving a paper at a meeting of the International Institute of Statistics in Brazil in 1955 hastened his death the following year at eighty-five.

Borel's undergraduate publications showed virtuosity in solving his elders' problems rather than great originality, but a "big idea" was incubating. Already in 1891 he was "extrêmement séduit" by Georg Cantor, whose "romantic spirit" mixed explosively with Borel's rigorous training in classical analysis and geometry. By sensing both the power and danger of set concepts, Borel anticipated the unifying themes of his lifework and of much mathematics in the twentieth century. In his thesis of 1894, which Collingwood rightly calls "an important mathematical event," can be found the ideas with which he initiated the modern theories of functions of a real variable, measure, divergent series, nonanalytic continuation, denumerable probability, Diophantine approximation, and the metrical distribution theory of values of analytical functions. All are related to Cantorian ideas, especially to the notion of a denumerable set. This is obvious for the two most famous results in the thesis, the Heine-Borel covering theorem (misnamed later by Schoenflies) and the proof that a denumerable set is of measure zero. The first asserted that if a denumerable set of open intervals covers a bounded set of points on a line, then a finite subset of the intervals is sufficient to cover. The second involves implicitly the extension of measure from finite sets of intervals to a very large class of point sets, now known as Borel-measurable sets.

Borel exploited his first insights in many directions. His *Leçons* of 1898 and other works laid the basis of measure theory so solidly that in that field the letter *B* means Borel. In 1905 he noticed that probability language was convenient for talking about measure of point sets, and in 1909 he introduced probability on a denumerable set of events, thus filling the gap between traditional finite and "geometrical" (continuous) probability. In the same paper he proved a special case of his strong law of large numbers. But Borel remained skeptical of the actual infinite beyond the denumerable and of nonconstructive definitions. Much of his work was motivated by finitistic ideas, and his last book (1952) discussed his observation that most real numbers must be "inaccessible," since with a finite alphabet we can name at most a denumerable subset. By this caution he avoided some of the pitfalls into which others fell, but he also was barred from the fruits of greater daring. It was Lebesgue, Baire, Fréchet, and others who pushed set and measure theoretic ideas more boldly and so opened the way to the abstract analysis of the mid-twentieth century.

Other motivations are visible in Borel's work: the challenge of unsolved classical problems and visible gaps, an early and increasing admiration for Cauchy, an interest in physical and social problems, all tinged strongly with French patriotism. Often his solutions opened whole fields for exploitation by others. His "elementary" proof of Picard's theorem in 1896 not only created a sensation because the problem had resisted all attacks for eighteen years, but also established methods and posed problems that set the theme of complex function theory for a generation. Borel's work on divergent series in 1899 filled the gap between convergent and divergent series. His work on monogenic functions (summed up in his monograph of 1917) showed the primacy of Cauchy's idea of the existence of the derivative over the Weierstrassian notion of series expansion and filled the gap between analytic and very discontinuous functions.

Before World War I, Borel had worked out most of his original ideas, and thereafter his scientific publications were largely the development and application of earlier ideas and the solution of minor problems. A major exception is the series of papers on game theory (1921–1927) in which he was the first to define games of strategy and to consider best strategies, mixed strategies, symmetric games, infinite games, and applications to war and economics. He proved the minimax theorem for three players, after

some doubts for five and seven, and finally (1927) conjectured its truth a year before John von Neumann independently first took up the subject and proved the general theorem. Although Borel's papers were overlooked until after von Neumann's work was well known, he must be considered the inventor, if not the founder, of game theory.

Borel's innovations are essential in twentieth-century analysis and probability, but his research methods belong rather to the nineteenth. He abjured generalization except when it was forced on him. He was motivated by specific problems and applications. He disliked formalism ("pure symbolism turning about itself"), logicism, and intuitionism (both too removed from the physical reality that he thought should guide mathematics). Borel was the most successful mathematician of his generation in using specific problems and results as scientific parables pointing the way to broad theories that still remain fertile.

BIBLIOGRAPHY

I. Original Works. A complete scientific bibliography to 1939 appears in *Selecta. Jubilé scientifique de M. Émile Borel* (Paris, 1940), and is extended to 1956 in the biographies by Collingwood and Fréchet, which also analyze Borel's work in detail. The papers in the *Selecta* are in part more representative of the commentators' interests than of Borel's most significant work, but a complete collected works is in preparation. His writings on philosophical questions, pedagogy, and social problems are well covered in *Émile Borel, philosophe et homme d'action. Pages choisies et presentées par Maurice Fréchet* (Paris, 1967). Borel's own analysis of his work appears in his *Notice sur les travaux scientifiques* (Paris, 1912) and his *Supplément (1921) à la Notice (1912)*, in the *Selecta*. Very revealing also are his "Documents autobiographiques," in *Organon* (Warsaw), **1** (1936), 34–42, repr. in *Selecta,* and "Allocution," in *Notices et discours de l'Académie des Sciences,* **2** (1949), 350–359.

Of more than 300 scientific publications the most notable are his thesis, "Sur quelques points de la théorie des fonctions," in *Annales de l'École Normale,* 3rd ser., **12** (1895), 9–55; "Démonstration élémentaire d'un théorème de M. Picard sur les fonctions entières," in *Comptes rendus de l'Académie des Sciences,* **122** (1896), 1045–1048; "Fondements de la théorie des séries divergentes sommables," in *Journal de mathématique,* 5th ser., **2** (1896), 103–122; "Sur les zéros des fonctions entières," in *Acta mathematica,* **20** (1897), 357–396; *Leçons sur la théorie des fonctions* (Paris, 1898; 4th ed., 1950), his most influential book; "Mémoire sur les séries divergentes," in *Annales de l'École Normale,* 3rd ser., **16** (1899), 9–131, which won a grand prize of the Academy and led to over 200 papers by others during the following two decades; *Leçons sur les fonctions entières*

(Paris, 1900; 2nd ed., 1921), an exposition of the work growing out of his paper on the Picard theorem; *Leçons sur les séries divergentes* (Paris, 1901; 2nd ed., 1928); *Leçons sur les fonctions de variables réeles et les développements en séries de polynomes* (Paris, 1905; 2nd ed., 1928); "Les probabilités dénombrables et leurs applications arithmétiques," in *Rendiconti del Circolo Matematico di Palermo,* **27** (1909), 247–270; *Le hasard* (Paris, 1914), probably his best popularization; "I. Aggregates of Zero Measure. II. Monogenic Uniform Non-analytic Functions," in *Rice Institute Pamphlet,* 4th ser., **1** (1917), 1–52; *Leçons sur les fonctions monogènes uniformes d'un variable complexe* (Paris, 1917), the definitive exposition of his work in this area; "La théorie du jeu et les équational intégrales à noyau symétrique," in *Comptes rendus de l'Académie des Sciences,* **173** (1921), 1302–1308—this and two later notes (1924, 1927) on game theory appear in translation with commentary by Fréchet and von Neumann in *Econometrica,* **21** (1953), 95–125; *Méthodes et problèmes de la théorie des fonctions* (Paris, 1922), a collection winding up his work in that area; *La politique républicaine* (Paris, 1924), his most substantial political work; *Principes et formules classiques du calcul des probabilités* (Paris, 1925), the first fascicle of the Traité; *Valeur pratique et philosophique des probabilités* (Paris, 1939), the last fascicle of the Traité; *Théorie mathématique du bridge à la portée de tous* (Paris, 1940), written with A. Cheron; *Le jeu, la chance et les théories scientifiques modernes* (Paris, 1941); "Sur l'emploie du théorème de Bernoulli pour faciliter le calcul d'une infinité de coefficients—Application au problème de l'attente à un quichet," in *Comptes rendus de l'Académie des Sciences,* **214** (1942), 425–456, his last original contribution to probability theory; *Les probabilités et la vie* (Paris, 1943), another fine popularization with later editions and translations; *Éléments de la théorie des ensembles* (Paris, 1949), a summation containing some new results; and *Les nombres inaccessibles* (Paris, 1952), his last book.

Series that he edited (always contributing substantially also) include Collection de Monographies sur la Théorie de Fonctions (Paris, 1898–1952)—sometimes called the Borel tracts, this totaled over fifty volumes, ten by Borel himself—and Cours de Mathématiques (Paris, 1903–1912), a series of elementary texts designed to cover various curricula, usually written with collaborators. Other series include La Nouvelle Collection Scientifique (1910–1922), thirty-five popularizations; Bibliothèque d'Éducation par la Science (Paris, 1924–1946), high-level popularizations for the educated layman; Traité de Calcul des Probabilités et de Ses Applications (Paris, 1925–1938), eighteen fascicles in four volumes, intended to cover the whole field as it had developed since 1875; Collection de Physique Mathématique (Paris, 1928–1950); and Collection de Monographies des Probabilités et de Leurs Applications (Paris, 1937–1950), seven volumes intended to supplement the Traité by current research.

II. Secondary Literature. Along with the material in the *Selecta* and Borel's autobiographical writings cited above, the best sources are "Jubilé scientifique de M. Émile Borel . . . 14 janvier 1940," in *Notices et discours de l'Académie des Sciences,* **2** (1949), 324–359; L. de Broglie, *ibid.,* **4** (1957), 1–24; E. F. Collingwood, in *Journal of the London Mathematical Society,* **34** (1959), 488–512, and **35** (1960), 384; M. Fréchet, "La vie et l'oeuvre d'Émile Borel," in *Enseignement mathématique,* 2nd ser., **11** (1965), 1–95; M. Loève, "Integration and Measure," in *Encyclopaedia Britannica* (1965); and P. Montel, in *Comptes rendus de l'Académie des Sciences,* **242** (1965), 848–850.

Kenneth O. May

BOREL, PIERRE (*b.* Castres, Languedoc, France, *ca.* 1620; *d.* Paris, France, 1671), *history, medicine, chemistry.*

Borel studied at Montpellier and returned to Castres as an M.D. in 1641. Besides practicing medicine, he collected rarities, plants, antiquities, and minerals from the town and countryside of Castres. In 1645 he published a catalog of his collection and expanded it in 1649 to include the history and Roman inscriptions of the area.

About the end of 1653 Borel moved to Paris, where he received the title of *médecin ordinaire du roy.* Again, he became very active as a collector. He assembled some 4,000 manuscripts and books of the Hermetic philosophers or chemists and published a catalog in Paris in 1653. A collection of linguistic antiquities listed in alphabetical order (1655) was the basis for Favre's greatly enlarged *Dictionnaire du vieux François,* published in 1882. Borel also studied reports about the telescope; in his book of 1656 he cites Zacharias Janssen (1590) as the first inventor and Hans Lipperhey (1608) as the second. He also describes a "polemoscope," a 1637 invention designed for looking around corners, which is particularly useful in warfare. He appended to this book an account of a hundred medicophysical observations with the microscope.

Among his original contributions to medicine are the statement that cataract is a darkening of the crystalline lens and the recommendation of the use of concave mirrors in the diagnostic examination of the nose and throat. Borel is credited with the first description of brain concussions.

His last work seems to have been a *Hortus* (1667), which listed plants with known uses in medicine.

BIBLIOGRAPHY

I. Original Works. *Catalogue des raretés du cabinet de P. Borel* (Castres, 1645); *Les antiquités, raretés, plantes, minéraux et autres choses considérables de la ville et comté de Castres, d'Albigeois, et des lieux qui sont à ses environs etc.* (Castres, 1649); *Bibliotheca chimica, seu catalogus librorum philosophicorum hermeticorum, in quo quatuor millia circiter auctorum chimicorum . . . usque ad annum 1653 continentur* (Paris, 1654); *De vero telescopii inventore, cum brevi omnium conspicillorum historia etc., accessit etiam centuria observationum microscopicarum* (The Hague, 1655, 1656); *Hortus, seu armamentarium simplicium plantarum et animalium ad artem medicam spectantium, cum brevi eorum etymologia, descriptione, loco, tempore et viribus* (Castres, 1667); *Petri Borelli historiarum et observationum medico-physicarum centuriae IV* (Frankfurt–Leipzig, 1676), with additions by Arnold de Boot and L. Cattier.

II. SECONDARY LITERATURE. See articles by R. P. Niceron, in *Mémoires pour servir à l'histoire des hommes illustres dans la république des lettres avec un catalogue résumé de leurs ouvrages,* XXXVI (Paris, 1736), 218–224 (Niceron gives certain biographical dates that have been proved wrong); August Hirsch, ed., *Biographisches Lexikon der hervorragenden Ärzte,* 2nd. ed., I (Berlin, 1929), 632; and Mme. Puech-Milhau, in *Revue du Tarn,* 4th ser., no. 7 (1936), 279–280.

EDUARD FARBER

BORELLI, GIOVANNI ALFONSO (*b.* Naples, Italy, January 1608; *d.* Rome, Italy, 31 December 1679), *astronomy, epidemiology, mathematics, physiology (iatromechanics), physics, volcanology.*

Borelli is not as widely known or appreciated as perhaps he should be. What reputation he has is based upon his mechanics, including celestial mechanics, and his physiology or iatromechanics. The former, unfortunately, was quickly and completely overshadowed by the work of Isaac Newton; and his iatromechanics, although important and influential, was too much informed by what proved to be a relatively sterile systematic bias to bear much immediate fruit. Accordingly historians have undervalued his place in the development of the sciences in the seventeenth century, and they have paid little attention to his career or his personality. (There has been no lengthy treatment of his life since the eighteenth century, and important and elementary biographical information is still hard to come by.) But he was highly respected by his contemporaries. He read widely, and he drew his scientific inspiration from a broad spectrum of the heroes and near-heroes of the early seventeenth century: such men as Galileo Galilei, William Harvey, Johannes Kepler, and Santorio Santorio. He worked on many problems, contributed significantly to all the topics he touched, and in fact played an important part in establishing and extending the new experimental-mathematical philosophy. He was brilliant enough scientifically to be very much ahead of his time, even if he was not quite brilliant enough nor free enough from other commitments to produce general synthetic solutions in his fields of interest which would be either successful or entirely convincing.

During the century prior to Borelli's birth, Italians had been in the forefront of the late Renaissance effort to translate and master the Alexandrian astronomers, mathematicians, and physiologists. By the end of that century many had learned all they could from the past and had begun to strike out on their own. Galileo's telescopic discoveries only dramatically underscored the fact that major innovations were underway in all fields of natural philosophy. And they also indicated that the Italians could be expected to continue playing a leading role in these new enterprises. But during Borelli's lifetime the world saw Galileo condemned for his innovations, the Lincei persecuted, the Cimento disbanded, and the Investiganti of Naples suspended. It also saw the death, in the decade of the 1640's, of many of Galileo's most talented disciples: Benedetto Castelli, Bonaventura Cavalieri, Vincenzo Renieri, and Evangelista Torricelli. Borelli's Italy rejoiced over the conversion of Queen Christina of Sweden and perhaps was as much interested in the fact of Nicholas Steno's conversion as in his scientific accomplishments. Moreover, it was a politically fragmented Italy, portions of which were absorbed in struggles to throw off oppressive foreign domination. And later on its best investigators, for example, Marcello Malpighi and Gian Domenico Cassini, had to find recognition and support north of the Alps. In sum, the new philosophy faced distracting competition and even open hostility from several quarters, and in the long run the Italians could find neither the wherewithal nor the enthusiasm to support science in the ways it was beginning to be supported elsewhere. Borelli's career, then, is an illuminating record of an original scientist who was also politically active in Counter-Reformation Italy. Borelli himself ended his life in political exile in Rome—poverty stricken, teaching elementary mathematics.

Borelli's birth was not auspicious. As part of their rule of southern Italy at the turn of the century, the Spanish maintained military garrisons in the three principal fortresses of Naples. On 28 January 1608, a Spanish infantryman, Miguel Alonso, stationed at Castel Nuovo, witnessed the baptism of his first son, Giovanni Francesco Antonio. The mother was a local woman by the name of Laura Porrello (variously spelled in the records as *porrello, porrella, borrella, borriello, borrelli*). The couple went on to have one daughter and four more sons, including a Filippo baptized 9 March 1614. In later years both Giovanni and Filippo used Borelli as a family name; Giovanni dropped two of his baptismal names but retained an

Italianized version of his father's name in their place. Why they did this perhaps can be guessed from the circumstances of their early years.

In November 1614 Tommaso Campanella was returned to Castel St. Elmo, where he had previously been confined. Meanwhile Miguel Alonso had been ordered to Castel St. Elmo. Just after Campanella's return, Miguel became implicated in some serious offense and was arrested along with several other persons. Although it is not known for certain what the alleged crime was, responsible sources suggest that there may have been a conspiracy to free Campanella. In any case the interrogations and trial took place in secret, and during the summer of 1615 Miguel was found guilty and sentenced to the galleys. Upon his certification that he was unable to serve in the galleys the sentence was commuted to exile. Miguel seems to have gone to Rome, and it has usually been supposed that this was the occasion for young Borelli's presence there and eventual contact with Benedetto Castelli. But now we know that Miguel did not remain in exile. He appealed his case and was exonerated. In April 1617 he returned to duty at Castel St. Elmo, where he stayed until he died in 1624. Laura Porrello possibly remained attached to Castel St. Elmo in some capacity, for at her death in 1640 she was buried, as Miguel had been, at the church serving the fortress.

We can guess that sometime before 1626 young Borelli came to the attention of Campanella; there was no lack of opportunity. In 1616 the latter was given a few months of at-large detention in Castel Nuovo (he may have written his *Defense of Galileo* at this time), but he was back in the dungeon of Castel St. Elmo when Miguel returned from exile. In May 1618 he was again sent to Castel Nuovo, where he had a relatively easy imprisonment; he was able to write, see friends, and even have students. It is possible that Borelli was among these, and it is also possible that Borelli received some medical training at the University of Naples in this period, although we have no published records to that effect. In 1626 Campanella was taken to Rome, where he was fully liberated in 1628. Five years later a disciple, under duress, implicated Campanella in a plot to assassinate the Spanish viceroy in Naples. Under great pressures Campanella fled Italy for Paris, in 1634, taking Filippo Borelli with him. There Filippo helped to edit and publish various of Campanella's works, and in at least one he appears as *nipote ed amanuense dello autore*. What happened to Filippo later is not known, but a letter of another of Campanella's disciples in 1657 connects Giovanni Alfonso with information concerning several hundred copies of Campanella's

books left at the Dominican convent of Santa Maria Sopra Minerva and also indicates that Giovanni had a brother, a "P. Tomaso filosofo." It has been suggested that on Campanella's death, in 1639, Filippo entered orders and took the name Tommaso.

We do not know when Borelli himself went to Rome. Anytime after 1628 he could have resumed whatever relationship he had established in Naples with Campanella; and it is quite possible that Campanella in turn introduced him to Castelli. In any case he became a student of Castelli along with Torricelli. He must have been in Rome through the period of the publication of Galileo's *Dialogo* and the subsequent trial. Although he did not meet Galileo, he probably had access to all the ins and outs of the affair through both his mentors. And possibly it was during this period that he acquired a copy of calculations or tables made by Galileo concerning the Medici planets (the moons of Jupiter), calculations which were not among the papers inherited by Vincenzo Viviani at Galileo's death and which Viviani requested a copy of in 1643. After Campanella left Rome, Borelli continued for a while with Castelli. In 1635, or shortly thereafter, Castelli's recommendation obtained for Borelli the public lectureship in mathematics in Messina, Sicily. And Castelli continued to look after Borelli's welfare. In 1640, when the mathematics chair at the University of Pisa became vacant, he wrote two letters to Galileo praising Borelli very highly, calling him in one *huomo di grandissimo ingegno e sapere, versatissimo nelle dottrine di V.S. molto Ill.re e tutto tutto* NOSTRI ORDINIS. Galileo's choice, however, was Vincenzo Renieri who then held the position until his death in 1647. Borelli would eventually obtain the post, but not until 1656.

Meanwhile Borelli made his way in Messina. The city had had little to boast of since the death of Francesco Maurolico in 1575. In the 1630's, however, there was an effort toward a political and intellectual revival which included an attempt to improve substantially the city's university. The people backing these moves were among the same who formed the Accademia della Fucina in 1639, a group of the young, enlightened nobility and merchant class, jealous of its political rights and beginning to grow restless under the restrictions of Spanish rule. The Fucina itself became a forum for both political and intellectual discussion, and in 1642 it came under the direct protection of the Messinese senate. It is not clear when Borelli became a member, but his talents as a public lecturer of mathematics were already highly appreciated. In 1642 the senate provided him with ample funds and sent him on a mission to leading universities to hire away good teachers, especially in law and medicine. We can guess that on this trip Borelli stopped in Naples to see Marco Aurelio Severino, perhaps renewing an old association. He must have visited Castelli in Rome. We know that he visited Tuscany, but unfortunately too late to see Galileo. But he did spend some time in Florence, and while there he met both Viviani and Prince Leopold, the youngest brother of the grand duke. After Florence he went on to Bologna where he very favorably impressed Bonaventura Cavalieri. Then he was off to Padua and eventually Venice where he planned to catch a ship back to Messina. Among the topics of discussion in Florence must have been the work of Santorio, for in Venice he bought a copy of *De statica medicina* and mailed it back to Viviani along with other items of scientific interest. By 1643, then, even though he had not yet published, he was beginning to be known in Italy, and what evidence we have indicates that he had already exposed himself to the studies that were to concern him for the rest of his life: mathematics, physiology, and planetary astronomy.

From 1643 to 1656 Borelli remained in Sicily, so far as we know; he published two works and possibly had a hand in a third. The first developed out of a dispute that may have had some polemic roots in the political and intellectual rivalry between Messina and Palermo. In 1644 a Pietro Emmanuele of Palermo published a *Lettera intorno alla soluzione di un problema geometrico*. This was attacked, so he followed it a year later with a *Lettera in difesa di un problema geometrico*. In the second, at least, Borelli's reputation was impugned, and Borelli replied in the *Discorso del Signor Gio: Alfonso Borelli, accademico della Fucina e professore delle scienze matematiche nello Studio della nobile città di Messina, nel quale si manifestano le falsità, e gli errori, contenuti nella difesa del Problema Geometrico, risoluto dal R. D. Pietro Emmanuele* (Messina, 1646). The Fucina also reacted to protect both itself and Borelli by encouraging the publication of several pamphlets. In one of them, Daniele Spinola's *Il Crivello* (Macerata, 1647), the resolution of the original problem was provided by Giovanni Ventimiglia, a student and a friend of Borelli.

As this controversy died down, Sicily was invaded by an epidemic of fevers. Messina was especially hard hit and the senate encouraged its local *dotti* to try to discern its causes. One study that resulted was Borelli's *On the causes of the malignant fevers of Sicily in the years 1647 and 1648 . . .*; to which he added a section entitled *And at the end the digestion of food is treated by a new method* (Cosenza, 1649). During his investigation of the epidemic Borelli had visited other cities, observed autopsies, and noted in detail

the circumstances under which the disease was prevalent. He concluded that in no way were the fevers caused by meteorological conditions or astrological influences, but were probably caused by something getting into the body from the outside. Since this thing seemed to be chemical, Borelli prescribed a chemical remedy, sulfur, and for this recommendation he acknowledged the counsel of his friend and colleague Pietro Castelli (*d.* 1661). In the addendum he again disclosed a chemical approach; he characterized digestion as the action of a *succo acido corrosivo* turning food into a liquid form. Borelli would repeat and expand this particular inquiry during his stay in Pisa.

In 1650 Borelli was considered for the chair of mathematics at Bologna. Cavalieri had died in 1647 and the authorities there wished to fill the post with someone equally able. Accordingly they made inquiries concerning Borelli and received strong endorsements for him as the best mathematician in Italy after Cavalieri. They also learned that Borelli was a trifle capricious and had a leaning toward the "moderns," Copernicus and Galileo (*il Gubernico et il Galileo*). Whether or not this latter was a factor, Borelli was passed over and the chair went to Gian Domenico Cassini. So Borelli remained in Messina and was there when Maurolico's *Emendatio et restitutio conicorum Apollonii Pergaei* was finally published in 1654. The original of the *Conics* of Apollonius had contained eight books, but the sixteenth century possessed only the texts of the first four. Maurolico had attempted to reconstruct Books V and VI. The extent of Borelli's connection with this project is not certain. We do know that he had composed a digest of the first four books before he left Messina. On this account alone he would have been prepared for an opportunity that presented itself when he later arrived in Pisa. Sometime previously the Medici had acquired an Arabic manuscript which seemed to contain all the original eight books. As early as 1645 Michelangelo Ricci had corresponded with Torricelli about the possibility of translating and publishing it, but with no results. Somehow Borelli had learned of it, however, for just a month after his inaugural lecture at Pisa, in the spring of 1656, he wrote to Leopold suggesting that with the aid of someone who knew Arabic he could edit these "most eagerly awaited" last four books. This led, in 1658, to a long summer's collaboration in Rome with the Maronite scholar Abraham Ecchellensis during which the two substantially completed an edition of Books V, VI, and VII. (It turned out that Book VIII was missing from the manuscript.) After many frustrating delays the work finally saw print in 1661 along with an appended Archimedean *Liber assumptorum* taken from another manuscript.

We must presume that in the years before Borelli left Messina he was already in touch with what would become a very important group in Naples. Tommaso Cornelio and Leonardo Di Capoa had both studied with Marco Aurelio Severino. On Severino's urging Cornelio had traveled for several years and had studied with such leading innovators of northern Italy as Ricci, Torricelli, and Cavalieri. When he came back to Naples in 1649 he brought with him the works of Galileo, Descartes, Gassendi, Bacon, Harvey, and Boyle, among others; and he and a lawyer named Francesco d'Andrea started an informal gathering which met to hear the results of its members' investigations. As it gained notoriety, the group faced various pressures, among them political, and in 1663 expediency compelled it to organize formally as the Accademia degli Investiganti under the protection of Andrea Concublet, the marchese d'Arena. All the while it pursued its physical, chemical, and physiological inquiries; corresponded with individuals and groups in other cities; and from time to time received distinguished visitors. Marcello Malpighi, for instance, had been at Pisa from 1656 to 1659 and then went to Bologna. In 1662 Borelli recommended him for the chair that had become vacant with the death of Pietro Castelli in Messina, and on his way south in the fall of that year Malpighi was warmly entertained by Cornelio and Di Capoa. From at least the time of his return to Naples, Cornelio had devoted himself to physiological experimentation in the new mathematical-mechanical manner. He became a professor of mathematics at the University of Naples in 1653. By 1656 his old teacher Severino had persuaded Cornelio to publish his investigations and speculations; delays occurred, unfortunately, but when his *Progymnasmata physica* appeared in 1663 one section of it carried a dedication to Borelli. For Borelli's part, almost immediately upon his arrival in Pisa he established a flourishing anatomical laboratory in his own house. Here he collaborated with and taught many talented students of the various disciplines of anatomy from Marcello Malpighi, at the beginning of his stay, to Lorenzo Bellini and Carlo Fracassati, in his last few years. Here also he nurtured his great iatromechanical project, a work on the movements of animals. He probably had had such an endeavor in mind before he came; in 1659 he could already complain of having to put it aside because of the work on Apollonius. By 1659, of course, Borelli had become involved in many things, not the least of them the experimental investigations of the Accademia del Cimento.

One year after Borelli arrived in Tuscany the Accademia del Cimento held its first session; the year Borelli left, the Cimento quietly died. Indeed, Borelli seems to have been the principal animus of the academy, but lest he appear the sole mover, we should recall the documentation, especially for the extensive experimental work performed during this Galilean epoch, in Giovanni Targioni Tozzetti's *Atti e memorie inedite dell'Accademia del Cimento e notizie aneddote dei progresse delle scienze in Toscana.* In fact the Tuscan court had been thoroughly infected by Galileo's ideas and those of his pupils. Grand Duke Ferdinand II, from the time of his accession to power in 1628 until his death in 1670, maintained a personal laboratory as did Prince Leopold. From the time of the death of the Master, Galileo, informal gatherings met at the court and presented and discussed experiments. At first Torricelli was the most prominent figure; after his death in 1647 Viviani presided over the activities.

Then, possibly under the crystallizing influence of Borelli, Leopold asked for and received permission from Ferdinand to organize formally an academy for purely experimental research. Under Leopold's aegis it met for the first time in June of 1657. Among its more distinguished members, besides Borelli and Viviani, were Antonio Oliva (*d.* 1668), Carlo Rinaldini (*d.* 1698), and Francesco Redi (*d.* 1697). Nicholas Steno arrived in Florence in 1666 and soon thereafter joined the group. Lorenzo Magalotti, after attending the University of Pisa as a student, was appointed secretary in 1660. The Cimento had adopted a policy of submerging the identities of its members and presenting itself as a group. Accordingly, when Magalotti brought out the *Saggi di naturali esperienzi fatte nell'Accademia del Cimento* in 1666–1667, it appeared anonymously and refrained from identifying the individual contributions of the members. Actually the *Saggi* presented only part of the work performed; it tended to emphasize the identification and description of physical phenomena and the perfecting of measuring techniques. It failed to present other interesting investigations, including some potentially controversial observations and discussions of comets.

During the life of the Cimento dissension appeared among the membership; Borelli may have originated some of it. He seems to have chafed under the requirement of anonymity, and by all accounts he was a touchy person to get along with under any circumstances. In any case, toward the end of 1666 and just after the publication of his important work on the theory of the motions of the moons of Jupiter, Borelli made his decision to leave Tuscany and return to Messina. In 1667 Leopold was created a cardinal and thus had some of his energies diverted. Rinaldini moved on to the University of Padua, and Antonio Oliva went to Rome where he came under the suspicion of the Inquisition and died by throwing himself from a window of one of its prisons. In December of 1667 Steno converted to Catholicism and shortly thereafter set out on a series of journeys. How or whether any of these events may have been connected is not known with any degree of certainty. But at this point the Cimento effectively ceased to function, even though it apparently was not formally dissolved, and even though Prince, now Cardinal, Leopold continued to direct some experimental work until he died in 1675. As far as Borelli was concerned, he had been, and afterward remained, on excellent terms with Leopold; and Leopold maintained his high regard for Borelli.

Besides his involvement with the Cimento and his own laboratory, Borelli had had other things to keep him busy during these years in Tuscany, among them his teaching duties. He was by no means the usual sort of professor. Nor did he bother to cultivate the finer graces of that calling. His first lectures at Pisa, for instance, were something of a disaster. He lacked any particular eloquence and was long-winded and dull. The students reacted with catcalls and agitation, once forcing him to stop before finishing his lesson. Very quickly, however, he demonstrated his capabilities, and his lack of Tuscan oratorical polish probably became less of a barrier. Then, in connection with his post, he prepared for publication of his *Euclides restitutus.* Not one to be overawed by canonical texts, he frankly stated that although Euclid had done an excellent job in compiling his *Elements,* these nevertheless could be repetitive and prolix, and it was time to put the material together in a clearer and more concise package. While he was about it, Borelli took the opportunity not only to reexamine the parallel postulate and propose his own version but also to try to establish the theory of proportions on firmer grounds. The Latin edition of this work appeared in 1658. Five years later his student Domenico Magni undertook the task of providing a "Euclid for the layman" by editing out most of Borelli's technical commentary and shortening and translating the remainder into Italian. Both works apparently were very well received. In subsequent editions of the Latin version, Borelli's short summary of Apollonius and other brief analyses appeared.

One of the more notable events during Borelli's stay in Pisa had been the appearance of a comet in late 1664. Borelli immediately took up the vigil and kept very close track of it throughout December and until the beginning of February 1665. Out of this came

a small paper, which he published in the form of a letter addressed to Stefano degli Angeli, a mathematician at the University of Padua. Borelli showed that, no matter which interpretation one preferred, Ptolemaic, Tychonic, or Keplerian, one had to admit that the comet changed in its absolute distance from the earth. This fact raised obvious difficulties for the first two systems, and Borelli argued that it presented difficulties for the Keplerian also. He went on to show that his parallax measurements proved the comet to be above the moon, at least toward the end of the observations presented here. This was touchy material, and Borelli published under the pseudonym of Pier Maria Mutoli. His interest in comets continued into the spring. In early May he wrote Leopold that he believed that the true motion of a comet *then* visible could in no ways be accounted for by means of a straight line but rather by a curve very similar to a parabola. And he proposed to demonstrate it, not only by calculation, but also with some kind of mechanical device. Borelli apparently built this instrument; unfortunately, neither it nor any description of it remains.

During the summer of 1665 Borelli established an astronomical observatory in the fortress of San Miniato, a pleasant site on a hill a short distance from Florence. Here he used an excellent Campani telescope and some instruments of his own design to try to determine with extreme accuracy the motions of Jupiter's satellites. From this work came his *Theoricae mediceorum planetarum ex causis physicis deductae* (1666), in which, among other things, he explained how the elliptical orbits of planetary bodies could be understood in terms of three types of action. In the first place, a planetary body has a tendency toward a central body and would move toward that central body if no other factors intervened. Then, a central body, such as the sun, sends out rays and as that body rotates the rays also rotate. The cumulative effect of the impacts of these seemingly corporeal rays is to impart to the planet a motion around the central body. This motion in revolution thus produces a centrifugal tendency which balances the original centripetal one and thereby establishes the planet in a given mean orbit. Small self-correcting fluctuations account qualitatively for the observed ellipses. There are some obvious difficulties in accommodating these proposals to the satellites of the major planets, and it is clear that Borelli had much more in mind than just explaining the motions of the moons of Jupiter. The Copernican implications of his scheme, however, could be masked by seeming to focus attention on Jupiter.

Meanwhile, as time allowed, Borelli continued his

anatomical research. He collaborated with Lorenzo Bellini in an investigation of the structure of the kidney, and in 1664 this resulted in a short piece entitled *De renum usu judicum.* And he also produced two major studies which were not only exercises in pure mechanics but also, in the eyes of Borelli himself, necessary introductions to what he would consider to be his most important work, the *De motu animalium.* Respectively, these were *De vi percussionis* (1667) and *De motionibus naturalibus a gravitate pendentibus* (1670). Both cover considerably more subject matter than their titles indicate. In the first, for instance, Borelli discusses percussion in detail, some general problems of motion, gravity, magnetism, the motion of fluids, the vibrations of bodies, and pendular motion, to cite just a few items. Likewise, in the second, he argues against positive levity, discusses the Torricellian experiment, takes up siphons, pumps, and the nature of fluidity, tries to understand the expansion of water while freezing, and deals with fermentation and other chemical processes. When we consider that all this was the product of years of experimental and theoretical investigation, we should not wonder that he objected to giving it over to be brought out anonymously by the Cimento just because he happened to present a good deal of it before that society. To the apparent displeasure of Leopold, Borelli published *De vi percussionis* in Bologna. And in the early summer of 1667 he set out once more to Messina.

On the way he passed through Rome and stopped for the summer in Naples. While there he was the guest of the Investiganti for whom he repeated many of the experiments he had performed at the Cimento. And he also repeated for his own edification some work that the Investiganti had accomplished independently. As a result of this visit, Concublet provided for the publication of *De motionibus naturalibus,* for which Borelli reciprocated by writing a warm dedication to him. Back in Messina, Borelli resumed his chair in mathematics. Stefano degli Angeli had raised some objections to parts of *De vi percussionis,* so in 1668 Borelli wrote the short *Risposta;* one of the problems concerned the deviation toward the east of a body dropped from a tower. In 1669 there occurred a major eruption of Etna and Borelli took the occasion to observe it closely, making notes on the topography of the mountain, the locations of the flows, and the nature of the various materials ejected, and offering some reasoned speculations of the sources of the heat powering the display. These he published in the *Historia et meteorologia incendii Aetnaei anni 1669.* Meanwhile he tried to return to his long delayed *De motu animalium.*

Borelli did not confine himself only to the sciences.

He had always taken a great interest in the public affairs of Messina. For example, while he was in Tuscany he helped to procure a copy of a manuscript the Messinese wished to publish. The work in question was the *Storia della guerra di Troja* by Guido Giudici delle Collone. A Latin version had been found among the papers of Maurolico, but it was known that the Accademia della Crusca had cited an Italian translation in Florence. At the request of the Messinese senate and with the aid of Borelli a copy was made in 1659. The Fucina published it in 1665 with a dedication to the senate. When Borelli returned from Pisa, then, he was coming home. And even though he was nearing sixty, he seems to have taken up an active political role. Agitation had been growing between the local citizens and their Spanish overlords. This led in 1674 to an open revolt. With some assistance from the French the struggle continued until 1678 when the French decided to leave the city, taking with them many of the city's leaders and (among other things) ensuring the closing of the Fucina. But trouble had brewed even before 1674. Borelli himself was thought to have provided the ideological inspiration for a party of republicans. In 1672 the Spanish Conservatore del Regno managed to stir up riots against the party, during which the home of Carlo Di Gregorio, which served as the meeting place for the Fucina, was burned. Borelli was declared a rebel and a price was placed on his head. He left very quickly and seems to have gone directly to Rome. One of his current projects also became a casualty. He had been into the papers of Maurolico and was publishing the latter's edition of the works of Archimedes when in 1672 the Spanish confiscated the nearly completed printing.

When Borelli arrived in Rome he was by no means unknown to that city. Besides his years of study there and several visits during the intervening period, he also knew and had corresponded frequently with Michelangelo Ricci and from its beginning the *Giornale de' Letterati* had published news of his scientific accomplishments: abstracts of his longer works and complete versions of a few shorter pieces. It is not surprising, then, that he would come to the attention of Queen Christina and come under her somewhat erratic patronage. Christina had been the only legal offspring of Gustavus Adolphus of Sweden. She had received an excellent education and undertook many projects, among them the creation of a learned academy in Stockholm. One of her first acts after her spectacular conversion to Catholicism was to attempt to start an academy in Rome, this in early 1656. Unfortunately, political and financial problems occupied her attention for many years. Finally, in

1674, she launched her Accademia Reale. Borelli appeared twice before it in 1675—in February when he spoke on the construction of the triremes of the ancients and again in April when he discussed Etna, this time including considerations resulting from a climb to the rim of the volcano in 1671. Christina also patronized another, more scientific group, known variously as the Accademia dell'Esperienza or the Accademia Fisica-matematica. It was organized in July of 1677 under the leadership of Giovanni Giustino Ciampini, who was also connected with the *Giornale de' Letterati.* Its membership included Borelli and an old friend and disciple, Lucantonio Porzio. But recognition apparently did not entail too much tangible support, and Borelli began to look farther afield for that. Cassini had been in Paris for several years and had become a member of the Royal Academy of Sciences. In 1676 Borelli wrote him complaining of the extreme circumstances to which he had been reduced by his enemies and the lack of quiet which was interfering with the completion of his works; he hinted that he too would like to serve the Most Christian King. By February 1677, negotiations were under way. A year later he had hopeful news, but he wrote that he was too old to travel to Paris. Instead he would send his work on the motion of animals to be printed there with a dedication to the king. In May of 1678 he still hoped for his election to the Royal Academy, but since he did not wish to trust his only copy of *De motu animalium* to the mails, he wrote that he needed time to have another made. Actually it is unlikely that he ever was elected to the Academy. A short time previously he had been robbed of all his possessions by a servant. Lacking adequate means, he had accepted the hospitality of the fathers of the Casa di S. Pantaleo and had entered their house on 13 September 1677. For the last two years of his life he taught mathematics at its Scuole Pie. Apparently he never sent a copy of his manuscript to Paris. Then in late 1679 Queen Christina agreed to bear the printing costs and Borelli dedicated the *De motu animalium* to her. He died in December, however, and his benefactor at the convent, P. Giovanni di Gesù, accepted the responsibility of seeing this last and most important work through the press. Volume I, treating of external motions, or the motions produced by the muscles, appeared in 1680. Volume II, dealing with internal motions, such as the movements of the muscles themselves, circulation, respiration, the secretion of fluids, and nervous activity, appeared in late 1681. A simple stone in the wall of the Church of S. Pantaleo recalls: *Joh. Alphonso Borellio, neapolitano, philosopho medico et matematico, clarissimo, . . .*

BIBLIOGRAPHY

I. ORIGINAL WORKS. Borelli's major writings are *Discorso . . . nel quale si manifestano le falsità e gli errori contenuti nella difesa del problema geometrico risoluto dal R. D. Pietro Emmanuele* (Messina, 1646); *Delle cagioni delle febbri maligne di Sicilia negli anni 1647 e 1648, . . . Ed in fine si tratta della digestione di cibi con nuovo metodo* (Cosenza, 1649); *Euclides restitutus* (Pisa, 1658); *Apollonius Pergaeus Conicorum lib. v. vi. vii. paraphraste Abalphato Asphahanensi nunc primum editi. Additus in calce Archimedis assumptorum liber, ex codicibus Arabicis m. ss. . . . Abrahamus Eccellensis. . . latinos reddidit* (Florence, 1661); *Euclide rinnovato* (Bologna, 1663); *Del movimento della cometa apparsa il mese di Dicembre 1664* (Pisa, 1665); *Theoricae mediceorum planetarum ex causis physicis deductae* (Florence, 1666); *De vi percussioni liber* (Bologna, 1667); *Risposta . . . alle considerazioni fatte sopra alcuni luoghi del suo libro della forza della percossa del R. P. F. Stefano de gl' Angeli* (Messina, 1668); *De motionibus naturalibus a gravitate pendentibus, liber* (Regio Iulio [Reggio di Calabria], Bologna, 1670); *Istoria et meteorologia incendii Aetnaei anni 1669 . . . accessit. Responsio ad censuras Rev. P. Honorati Fabri contra librum auctoris De vi percussionis* (Regio Iulio [Reggio di Calabria], 1670); *Elementa conica Apollonii Pergaei, et Archimedis opera, nova et breviori methodo demonstrata* (Rome, 1679); *De motu animalium . . . Opum Posthumum. Pars prima* (Rome, 1680), *Pars altera* (Rome, 1681); and "Discorso sopra la laguna di Venezia. Relazione sopra lo stagno di Pisa. Supplemento da aggiungersi alla proposizione seconda del secondo libro del P. Castelli, ecc.," in *Raccolta d'autori che trattano del moto dell'acque,* IV (Florence, 1765), 15–63.

Shorter tracts and less important works appeared in various issues of *Giornale de' Letterati;* Borelli, et al., *Tetras anatomicarum epistolarum de lingua, et cerebro* (Bologna, 1665); Marcello Malpighi, *Opera posthuma* (London, 1697); and Giovanni Targione Tozzetti, *Atti e memorie inedite dell' Accademia del Cimento,* 3 vols. (Florence, 1780).

The collections of the libraries of Florence, especially the Galileiana of the Biblioteca Nazionale, contain a great deal of unpublished correspondence to, from, and relating to Borelli. Other Italian libraries, and perhaps French and English ones, must still have a great deal of unrecognized and unpublished Borelli materials. The following have made many Borelli letters available: Howard B. Adelmann, *Marcello Malpighi and the Evolution of Embryology,* 5 vols. (Ithaca, N. Y., 1966); Giovanni Arenaprimo di Montechiaro, "Gio: Alfonso Borelli a Marcello Malpighi," in *Studi di medicina legale e varii . . . in onore di Giuseppe Ziino ecc.* (Messina, 1907), pp. 467–475; Vincenzo Busacchi and Giordano Muratori, "Giovanni Alfonso Borelli e lo Studio di Bologna," in *Bollettino delle scienze mediche* [Società di Bologna], **136** (1964), 86–90; Modestino Del Gaizo, *Alcune lettere di Giovanni Alfonso Borrelli, dirette una al Malpighi, le altre al Magliabechi* (Naples, 1886); "Contributo allo studio della vita e delle opere di Giovanni Alfonso Borrelli," *Atti dell'Accademia Pontaniana, Napoli,*

20 (1890), 1–48; "Una lettera di G. A. Borelli ed alcune indagini di pneumatica da lui compiute," in *Memorie della Pontificia Accademia Romana dei Nuovi Lincei*, 21 (1903), 61–78; "Note di storia della vulcanologia," *Memoria* no. 5 in *Atti dell'Accademia Pontaniana, Napoli*, 36 (1906); "Evangelista Torricelli e Giovanni Alfonso Borrelli. Appunti raccolti nel compiersi il terzo secolo dalla loro nascita," in *Rivista di fisica, matematica e scienze naturali* (Pavia), 17 (1908), 385–402; "L'opera scientifica di G. A. Borelli e la Scuola di Roma nel secolo XVII," in *Memorie della Pontificia Accademia Romana dei Nuovi Lincei*, 27 (1909), 275–307; and "Di una lettera inedita di G. A. Borelli diretta a M. Malpighi," in *Atti dell'Accademia Pontaniana, Napoli*, 49 (1919), 29–40; Tullio Derenzini, "Alcune lettere di Giovanni Alfonso Borelli ad Alessandro Marchetti," in *Physis*, 1 (1959), 224–243; and "Alcune lettere di Giovanni Alfonso Borelli a Gian Domenico Cassini," *ibid.*, 2 (1960), 235–241; Angelo Fabroni, *Lettere inedite di uomini illustri*, 2 vols. (Florence, 1773–1775); Giovanni Giovannozzi, "La versione borelliana dei *Conici* di Apollonio," in *Memorie della Pontificia Accademia Romana dei Nuovi Lincei*, 2nd ser., 2 (1916), 1–32; *Lettere inedite di Giovanni Alfonso Borelli al P. Angelo [Morelli] di S. Domenico sulla versione di Apollonio* (Florence, 1916); "Carte Borelliane nell' Archivio Generale delle Scuole Pie a Roma," in *Atti della Pontificia Accademia Romana dei Nuovi Lincei*, 72 (1918–1919), 81–86; and "Una lettera di Famiano Michelini a Giovanni Alfonso Borelli," *ibid.*, 80 (1926–1927), 315–319; Ugo Morini and Luigi Ferrari, *Autografi e codici di lettori dell'Ateneo Pisano esposti in occasione dell' XI congresso di medicina interna* (Pisa, 1902), pp. 19–23; Giuseppe Mosca, *Vita di Lucantonio Porzio pubblico primario cattedratico di Notomia* (Naples, 1765); Luigi Tenca, "Le relazioni fra Giovanni Alfonso Borelli e Vincenzio Viviani," in *Rendiconti dell'Istituto Lombardo di scienze e lettere, Milano*, 90 (1956), 107–121; and Giambatista Tondini, *Delle lettere di uomini illustri* (Macerata, 1782).

Among the translations of portions of the *De motu animalium* are Max Mengeringhausen, *Die Bewegung der Tiere*, no. 221 in *Ostwald's Klassiker der exakten Wissenschaften* (Leipzig, 1927); and T. O'B. Hubbard and J. H. Ledoboer, *The Flight of Birds*, Royal Aeronautical Society of London, Aeronautical Classics, no. 6 (London, 1911).

II. SECONDARY LITERATURE. The most extensive treatment of Borelli's life is in Angelo Fabroni, *Vitae italorum doctrina excellentium*, II (Pisa, 1778), 222–324. More recently, Gustavo Barbensi, *Borelli* (Trieste, 1947), and Tullio Derenzini, "Giovanni Alfonso Borelli, fisico," in *Celebrazione dell'Accademia del Cimento nel tricentenario della fondazione* (Pisa, 1958), pp. 35–52, offer useful shorter treatments. Luigi Amabile, in his *Fra Tommaso Campanella ne' castelli di Napoli, in Roma ed in Parigi*, 2 vols. (Naples, 1887), published the documents pertaining to Borelli's birth and family and possible connections with Campanella, II, 361–369. Both Max H. Fisch, "The Academy of the Investigators," in E. A. Underwood, ed., *Science, Medicine and History: Essays . . . in Honor of Charles Singer*, I (Oxford, 1953), 521–563; and Nicola Badaloni, *Introduzione a*

G. B. Vico (Milan, 1961), provide much information about the Investiganti and Borelli's relation to it. Howard B. Adelmann's work on Malpighi (cited above) is indispensable for Borelli's life and work after he came to Pisa. For the Fucina and Borelli's connection with the Messina revolt one can begin with Giacomo Nigido-Dionisi, *L'Accademia della Fucina di Messina (1639–1678) ne' suoi rapporti con la storia della cultura in Sicilia* (Catania, 1903), and Giuseppe Olivà, "Abolizione e rinacimento della Università di Messina," in *CCCL Anniversario della Università di Messina* (Messina, 1900), Parte Prima, 209–365.

Borelli's celestial mechanics have been studied in Angus Armitage, "'Borell's Hypothesis' and the Rise of Celestial Mechanics," in *Annals of Science*, 6 (1950), 268–282; Alexandre Koyré, "La mécanique céleste de J. A. Borelli," in *Revue d'histoire des sciences et de leurs applications*, 5 (1952), 101–138; "La gravitation universelle de Kepler à Newton," in *Archives internationales d'histoire des sciences*, 4 (1954), 638–653; "A Documentary History of the Problem of Fall from Kepler to Newton," in *Transactions of the American Philosophical Society*, n.s. 45 (1955), 327–395; and *La révolution astronomique: Copernique, Kepler, Borelli* (Paris, 1961); and Charles Serrus, "La mécanique de J.-A. Borelli et la notion d'attraction," in *Revue d'histoire des sciences et de leur applications*, 1 (1947), 9–25. His physics have been examined in particular in Pierre Varignon, *Projet d'une nouvelle mechanique, avec Un Examen de l'opinion de M. Borelli, sur les propriétez des poids suspendus par des cordes* (Paris, 1687); Giovanni Antonio Amedeo Plana, "Mémoire sur la découverte de la loi du choc direct des corps durs publiée en 1667 par Alphonse Borelli . . .," in *Memorie della Reale Accademia delle scienze di Torino*, 2nd ser., 6 (1844), esp. 1–37; and J. MacLean, "De historische ontwikkeling der stootwetten van Aristoteles tot Huygens," a dissertation (Amsterdam, 1959).

Various particular aspects of Borelli's life and work, as well as additional bibliographical sources, are given in the following: Gustavo Barbensi, "Di una diversa soluzione di un problema di meccanica muscolare da parte di due medici matematici," in *Rivista di storia delle scienze mediche e naturali, Siena*, 29 (1938), 168–180; Pietro Capparoni, "Sulla patria di Giovanni Alfonso Borelli," *ibid.*, 22 (1931), 53–63; Modestino Del Gaizo, *Studii di Giovanni Alfonso Borrelli sulla pressione atmosferica, con note illustrative intorno alla vita ed alle opere di lui* (Naples, 1886); "Di un' antica indagine sul calore animale," in *Atti della R. Accademia medico-chirurgica di Napoli*, 49 (1895), 378–394; "Di un' opera di G. A. Borelli sulla eruzione dell' Etna del 1669 e di Adriano Auzout corrispondente, in Roma, del Borelli," in *Atti della Pontificia Accademia Romana dei Nuovi Lincei*, 60 (1906–1907), 111–117; "Qualche ricordo di Giovanni Alfonso Borelli in Firenze," in *Studium: Rivista universitaria mensile*, 2 (1907), 234–238; "Giovanni Alfonso Borrelli e la sua opera *De motu animalium*, discorso," in *Atti della R. Accademia medico-chirurgica di Napoli*, 62 (1908), 147–169; "Il *De motu animalium* di G. A. Borelli studiato in rapporto del *De motu cordis et sanguinis* di G. Harvey," *ibid.*, 67 (1914), 195–227; and "Ipotesi di antiche fisiologi e specialmente di Giovanni Alfonso Borelli sulla esistenza del succo nervoso," *ibid.,* **69** (1916), 85–108; Giovanni Battista De Toni, "Per la conoscenza delle opinioni sulla ascesa dei liquidi nelle piante," in *Rivista di fisica, matematica e scienze naturali,* **3** (1901), 199–203; Pietro Franceschini, "L'apparato motore nello studio di Borelli e di Stenone," in *Rivista di storia delle scienze mediche e naturali,* **42** (1951), 1–15; Giovanni Giovanozzi, "La patria di Gio. Alfonso Borelli," in *Atti della Pontificia Accademia Romana dei Nuovi Lincei,* **79** (1925–1926), 61–66; Raymond Hierons and Alfred Meyer, "Willis's Place in the History of Muscle Physiology," in *Proceedings of the Royal Society of Medicine,* **57** (1964), 687–692; Michelangelo Macrì, "Lettere d'illustre autori de' secoli XVII e XVIII," in *Nuova Biblioteca Analitica di scienze, lettere ed arti,* **14** (1819), letters 1 and 1 *bis,* 349–353; and Giuseppe Ziino, "G. A. Borelli medico e igienista," in *CCCL Anniversario della Università di Messina* (Messina, 1900), Parte Seconda, 3–40.

THOMAS B. SETTLE

BORGOGNONI OF LUCCA, THEODORIC (*b.* Parma or Lucca, Italy, *ca.* 1205; *d.* Bologna, Italy, 1298), *medicine, surgery.*

It is quite certain that Theodoric's father was Hugh of Lucca, a pioneer of Italian surgery, although this is contested by some. When Theodoric was nine, the family moved to Bologna, the medical capital of medieval Europe, where he became a Dominican friar in 1226. Under his father's tutelage he learned medicine and surgery, and taught these subjects at the University of Bologna for thirty-three years. As a Dominican he first was appointed a papal penitentiary of Pope Innocent IV, then was named bishop of Bitonto (1262), and finally bishop of Cervia (1266). He never took possession of the see of Bitonto, however, and resided but little in Cervia, his usual home being Bologna. His practice of surgery there, unusual for a friar and a bishop, was necessary for his teaching; it provides an apt illustration of the varied occupations of churchmen in the Middle Ages.

Theodoric wrote treatises on mineral salts and on the sublimation of arsenic, both of which have been lost. He wrote also on falconry and on the veterinary science of horses (*Practica equorum*). His most famous work, however, is his *Surgery* (*Chirurgia,* sometimes entitled *Filia principis*), begun while he was a papal penitentiary. He seems to have prepared three redactions before arriving at a definitive version, which he released in 1266 at the urging of a fellow Dominican, Andrew of Abalat, bishop of Valencia, whom he had met in Rome and to whom he dedicated the work. The first printed edition was produced at Venice in 1498, and other editions followed in 1499, 1513, 1519, and 1546. During the medieval period the work was translated into several vernaculars, and in 1955 an English translation was published by two doctors, E. Campbell and J. Colton, whose war service led them to new developments in surgery that they found adumbrated in the work of Theodoric.

The four books of the *Surgery* cover the subject in both its general and its specific aspects. Theodoric recorded, in the main, the surgical knowledge and practices of Hugh of Lucca, appealing over fifty times to the latter's authority. He verified Hugh's work by his own experience, however, and supplemented it where it was incomplete or defective. In his quite modern discussion of fractures and dislocations, for example, he states: "In this book I have not been willing to include anything which I have not tested; nor did I wish my book to seem to contain more of another than of me" (Campbell and Colton, I, 218). He also claimed to be well acquainted with "the accounts of the ancients, especially of Galen. . ." (*ibid.,* I, 4).

Theodoric's methods were progressive, particularly his advocacy of antiseptic surgery at a time when everyone held the theory of "laudable pus." He condemned the use of unguents and poultices to generate pus in a wound, holding that this, far from being necessary for healing, actually impedes nature, prolongs sickness, prevents the uniting and consolidating of the wound, deforms the part, and impedes cicatrization. He described his own revolutionary methods in detail, outlining procedures for cleaning the wound, eliminating dead tissue and foreign matter, accurately reapproximating the wound walls, using stitches where necessary, and adequately protecting the area.

Theodoric also improved techniques for preparing and using soporific sponges to induce sleep before surgery. The sponges were impregnated with a mixture of narcotics, dried out, and stored for use. When needed, they were immersed in hot water, wrung out, and held to the nose of the patient, who was instructed to breathe deeply. Other of his practices include the use of mercurial ointments in the treatment of some skin diseases and the sparing application of cautery.

Unfortunately for the history of medicine, aseptic surgery died with Theodoric's pupil, Henri of Mondeville, the father of French surgery. Despite persecution by his contemporaries, Mondeville applied his master's methods in France and found them most successful. His principal adversary, however, was Guy de Chauliac, whose *Chirurgia magna* (1363) became a standard textbook for centuries. Guy unjustly accused Theodoric of plagiarism and otherwise denigrated him; he particularly rejected Theodoric's aseptic treatment of wounds and thereby perpetuated the older methods. The result was that, with few exceptions (e.g., Mondeville, Ambrose Paré, and Richard Wiseman), one studying the history of surgery encounters "a gulf of 'laudable pus' centuries wide" (*ibid.,* I, xxix).

BIBLIOGRAPHY

I. ORIGINAL WORKS. Theodoric's major work, the *Chirurgia* (Venice, 1498, 1499, 1513, 1519, 1546), was translated by E. Campbell and J. Colton as *The Surgery of Theodoric* (New York: Vol. I, 1955; Vol. II, 1960). The translators' use of modern technical terms occasionally gives a distorted and anachronistic view of Theodoric's contributions. The *Practica equorum* appeared as *El libro de los caballos: Tratado de albeitería del siglo XIII,* G. Sachs, ed. (Madrid, 1936).

II. SECONDARY LITERATURE. Theodoric or his work is discussed in H. F. Garrison, *An Introduction to the History of Medicine,* 4th ed. (Philadelphia, 1929), pp. 153–155; Adalberto Pazzini, "Borgognoni, Teodorico," in *Enciclopedia cattolica* (Rome, 1949–1954), II, cols. 1923–1924, with additional bibliography; Jacques Quétif and Jacques Échard, *Scriptores ordinis praedicatorum,* 2 vols. (Paris, 1719–1721; repr. New York, 1959), I, 354–355, in which the authors confuse Theodoric with Theodoricus Catalanus; and George Sarton, *Introduction to the History of Science,* II, pt. 2 (Baltimore, 1931), 654–656.

WILLIAM A. WALLACE, O.P.

BORN, IGNAZ EDLER VON (*b.* Karlsburg, Transylvania [now Alba Iulia, Rumania], 26 December 1742; *d.* Vienna, Austria, 24 July 1791), *mineralogy.*

Born was descended from a noble German family. At the age of thirteen he began his studies in Vienna with the Jesuits, who induced him to join their order; he remained a member for only about sixteen months, however. Leaving Vienna and the Jesuits behind, Born went to Prague to study jurisprudence. After completing his education there, he traveled in Germany, the Low Countries, and France. Upon his return to Prague, he took up the study of natural history and mining, and in 1770 he joined the department of mines and the mint. In the same year Born visited the principal mines of Hungary and Transylvania. His account of this expedition is preserved in a series of lively and interesting letters addressed to the mineralogist J. J. Ferber. In 1774 Ferber published these letters in a work that later appeared in English, French, and Italian editions. During his visit to a mine at Felso-Banya, Born suffered an accident that nearly cost him his life. He descended into the mine too soon after the fires used to detach the ore had been extinguished, and inhaled a dangerously large quantity of arsenical vapors. This unfortunate occurrence seriously affected Born's health and may well have shortened his life. Upon returning to Prague, he was appointed counselor of mines.

In 1772 Born published *Lithophylacium Bornianum,* a description of his own collection. This work attracted the favorable attention of mineralogists, and Born was soon admitted to various learned societies throughout Europe. In 1776 Empress Maria Theresa, having heard of his reputation, called him to Vienna to arrange and describe the imperial collection. He completed a portion of this task, but after the empress' death in 1780 it was discontinued. In 1779 Born was raised to the office of counselor of the court chamber in the department of mines and the mint.

Born's interests and activities extended into fields other than mineralogy and mining. While in Prague, he had helped to found a literary and philosophical society that was the forerunner of the Bohemian Scientific Society. In Vienna, Born was active in the secret fraternity of Freemasons. After Joseph II's accession to the throne, this brotherhood was allowed to pursue its anticlerical activities with greater freedom. In 1783 Born published *Specimen monachologiae,* a vicious satire against monks in which the various orders were classified according to a system modeled after Linnaeus'.

Besides preparing catalogs of fossil and mineral collections, works of classification, and descriptions of mines and mining equipment, Born invented an amalgamation process for removing gold and silver from various ores. Since the process did not require the usual melting of the ore, its use effected a considerable saving of fuel. A trial of the process in the presence of observers was made at Selmeczbánya (German, Schemnitz), Hungary (now Banská Štiavnica, Czechoslovakia). In 1786 Born published his description of it. The process was adopted in copper mines throughout Hungary, and Born was given a share of the savings occasioned by its use.

BIBLIOGRAPHY

I. ORIGINAL WORKS. Born's writings include *Briefe über mineralogische Gegenstände, auf seiner Reise durch das Temeswarer Bannat, Siebenbürgen, Ober- und Nieder-Hungarn, an den Herausgeber derselben geschrieben,* J. J. Ferber, ed. (Frankfurt–Leipzig, 1774), trans. by R. E. Raspe as *Travels Through the Bannat of Temeswar, Transylvania, and Hungary in the Year 1770, etc.* (London, 1777); *Lithophylacium Bornianum,* 2 vols. (Prague, 1772–1775); *Effigies virorum eruditorum atque artificum Bohemiae et Moraviae, etc.,* 2 vols. (Prague, 1773–1775); *Index rerum naturalium Musei Caesarei Vindobonensis* (Vienna, 1778); *Ueber das*

Anquicken der gold- und silberhältigen Erze, Rohsteine, Schwarzkupfer und Hüttenspeise (Vienna, 1786), trans. by R. E. Raspe as *Baron Inigo Born's New Process of Amalgamation of Gold and Silver Ores, and Other Metallic Mixtures* (London, 1791); and *Bergbaukunde*, 2 vols. (Leipzig, 1789–1790), written with F. W. H. von Trebra. Born edited the *Abhandlungen einer Privatgesellschaft in Böhmen*, 6 vols. (Prague, 1775–1784). He published in L. Crell's *Chemische Annalen* some reports of Matteo Tondi's alleged reduction of the alkaline earths (1790), pt. 2, no. 12, 483–485; (1791), pt. 1, no. 1, 3–10; no. 2, 99–100; no. 5, 387–389.

II. SECONDARY LITERATURE. An excellent biography with numerous and useful citations is Baur's article on Born in *Allgemeine Encyclopädie der Wissenschaften und Künste,* J. G. Ersch and J. G. Gruber, eds., XII (Leipzig, 1824), 38–40. The detailed English biography in Alexander Chalmers' *Biographical Dictionary*, VI (1812), 123–127, is based on an account given in Robert Townson's *Travels in Hungary* (London, 1797). For further biographical sources, see the list in Paul Mayer's article on Born in *Neue deutsche Biographie*, II (1953). In addition, see Robert Keil, *Wiener Freunde, 1784–1808, Beitraege zur Jugendgeschichte der deutsch-oesterreichischen Literatur* (Vienna, 1883), pp. 33–36, which contains three of Born's letters.

J. B. GOUGH

BORODIN, ALEKSANDR PORFIREVICH

BORODIN, ALEKSANDR PORFIREVICH (*b.* St. Petersburg, Russia, 12 November 1833; *d.* St. Petersburg, 27 February 1887), *chemistry.*

Borodin was the illegitimate son of the wife of an army doctor and an Imeretian prince. Between 1850 and 1856 he studied at the St. Petersburg Academy of Medicine and Surgery, where he did his first research in chemistry under the direction of N. N. Zinin. In 1858 he defended his doctoral thesis, "Ob analogy fosfornoy myshyakovoy kislot v khimicheskom i toksikologicheskom otnosheny" ("Analogy of Phosphoric and Arsenic Acids from the Chemical and Toxicological Viewpoints"). From 1859 to 1862, he traveled in Italy, Germany, France, and Switzerland, sometimes in the company of Mendeleev and I. M. Sechonov. As a member of the Russian delegation, Borodin took part in the work of the First International Congress of Chemists in Karlsruhe in 1860. From 1864, Borodin held a professorship at the Academy of Medicine and Surgery, where he helped to found medical courses for women.

Borodin's most important research work was done in organic and physiological chemistry. He was among the first to obtain fluorine benzol, and in 1861 he developed a method for the fluorination of organic compounds. In 1869 he proposed a method for obtaining bromine-producing fatty acids by the action of bromine on the silver salts of acids.

A number of Borodin's studies (1863–1874) were devoted to an investigation of the polymerization and condensation of aldehydes. By the action of metallic sodium on valeric aldehyde ($C_5H_{10}O$), Borodin obtained the condensation products $C_{10}H_{18}O$ and $C_{20}H_{38}O_3$. He also showed that from valeric aldehyde, valeric acid and amyl alcohol are formed:

$$C_4H_9C\!\!\begin{smallmatrix}H\\\\O\end{smallmatrix} \xrightarrow{O_2} C_4H_9\!-\!C\!\!\begin{smallmatrix}OH\\\\O\end{smallmatrix}$$

$$C_4H_9C\!\!\begin{smallmatrix}H\\\\O\end{smallmatrix} \xrightarrow[\text{NaOH}]{H_2} C_4H_9CH_2OH$$

In studying the condensation products of acetaldehyde, Borodin found a substance having two kinds of alcohol aldehydes (aldol), which, dehydrating rapidly, turn into crotonic aldehyde:

$$2CH_3\!-\!C\!\!\begin{smallmatrix}H\\\\O\end{smallmatrix} \longrightarrow CH_3\!-\!CHOH\!-\!CH_2\!-\!C\!\!\begin{smallmatrix}H\\\\O\end{smallmatrix} \longrightarrow$$

$$CH_3\!-\!CH\!=\!CH\!-\!C\!\!\begin{smallmatrix}H\\\\O\end{smallmatrix}$$

This aldol condensation reaction was subsequently employed by I. I. Ostromyslensky to obtain butadiene from alcohol.

In 1876 Borodin developed an azotometric method and apparatus for the quantitative determination of urea by measuring the amount of elementary nitrogen that is extracted from the urea by the action of excess sodium bromate ($Br_2 + NaOH$). The Borodin method was widely adopted in biochemical and clinical laboratories.

Borodin's name is also well-known in music, chiefly as the composer of *Prince Igor,* the first heroic opera on a Russian theme (completed by Rimsky-Korsakov), and of the B-minor symphony and numerous songs.

BIBLIOGRAPHY

I. ORIGINAL WORKS. Borodin's writings include "Über die Einwirkung des Natriums auf Veraldehyd," in *Bulletin de l'Académie imperiale des sciences de St.-Pétersbourg, phys.-math. classe,* **7** (1869), 463–474; "O polucheny produkta uplotnenia obyknovennogo aldegida" ("On Polymerization and Condensation Products of Common Aldehydes"), in *Zhurnal Russkogo khimicheskogo obshchestva,* **6** (1872), 209; "Über einen neuen Abkömmling des Valeraldehyds," in *Berichte der deutschen* chemischen Gesellschaft zu Berlin, **6** (1873), 982–985; Borodin's major work on his methods of azotometric measurement of nitrogen in urea is *Uproshchenni azometrichesky sposob opredelenia azota v primeneny k klinicheskomu opredelenniiu metamorfozy azotistykh veshchestv v organizme s sovremennoy tochki zrenia* (St. Petersburg, 1886).

II. SECONDARY LITERATURE. For biographical information, see N. A. Figurovski and Y. I. Soloviev, *Aleksandr Porfirevich Borodin* (Moscow–Leningrad, 1950).

Y. I. SOLOVIEV

BORREL, JEAN. See **Buteo, Johannes.**

BORRICHIUS (or **BORCH**), **OLAUS** (*b.* Nørre Bork, in Ribe, Denmark, 7 April 1626; *d.* Copenhagen, Denmark, 13 October 1690), *chemistry.*

The son of Oluf Clusen, a rector, Borrichius went to school in Ribe and entered the University of Copenhagen in 1644 to study medicine under Thomas Bartholin, Olaus Worm, and Simon Pauli. He remained a close friend of Bartholin until the latter's death in 1680. Borrichius was a teacher at the chief grammar school in Copenhagen for a time, won fame as a physician during the plague epidemic of 1654, and became tutor to the sons of Joachim Gersdorf, the lord high steward (*Rigshofmester*), in 1655. In 1660 Borrichius was appointed *professor ordinarius* of philology and *professor extraordinarius* of botany and chemistry. The posts were supernumerary until vacancies occurred.

Later in 1660 Borrichius was granted permission by the university to absent himself for two years in order to prepare himself for these posts by study and travel in other countries. He was joined at Hamburg by Gersdorf's sons. Borrichius' diary of the tour, and his correspondence with Bartholin, provide an interesting picture of European intellectual life during the period. He visited Germany, the Netherlands, France, England, and Italy. Among those he met were Sylvius, Swammerdam, Boyle, Petit, Redi, and Gui Patin. Borrichius received the M.D. at Angers in 1664. He gathered much information on the Hermetic sciences during the tour, and was greatly impressed by the Italian alchemist Giuseppe Francesco Borri.

His tour having lasted six years by then, Borrichius was reminded that his university posts could not be kept vacant indefinitely, and he began his journey home from Italy, reaching Copenhagen in 1664. He assumed the posts that he was to hold for nearly thirty years, becoming famous for his polymath erudition and establishing a large and profitable medical practice (he was royal physician to Frederick III and Christian V). He was twice *rector magnificus* at his university, and in 1686 was appointed counselor to the Supreme Court of Justice and in 1689 to the Royal Chancellery. He never married, and before his death bequeathed his house as a *collegium mediceum,* to lodge six students.

Borrichius was famous in his own time as a physician, as a polemicist and defender of Hermeticism, and as a prolific writer on chemical, botanical, and philological topics. His histories of the development of chemistry are among his best-known works. His travels and meetings with other European natural philosophers had not weakened his allegiance to the revived Hermeticism of the sixteenth and seventeenth centuries. Borrichius was prepared to concede that there was no healing virtue in words, seals, and images; astral influences, if they really existed, consisted of balsamic exhalations. At the same time, he believed in the existence of the philosophers' stone. Of all profane sciences, chemistry came closest to the contemplation of divinity in nature, and hence to Scripture. Opposing Athanasius Kircher's views, and especially those of Hermann Conring, Borrichius defended the genuineness and antiquity attributed to the Emerald Table and the Hermetic writings. He also accepted as authentic the alchemical works ascribed to such authors as Democritus, Albert the Great, Arnald of Villanova, Ramón Lull, and Nicolas Flamel. He opposed Conring's views that Paracelsian principles had no use in medicine and that chemistry was better employed in perfecting pharmacy than in presuming to correct physiology and pathology.

BIBLIOGRAPHY

I. ORIGINAL WORKS. Borrichius' chief works are *Docimastice metallica* (Copenhagen, 1660); *De ortu et progressu chemiae dissertatio* (Copenhagen, 1668); *Lingua pharmacopoeorum sive de accurata vocabulorum in pharmacopoliis usitatorum pronunciatione* (Copenhagen, 1670); *Hermetis, Aegyptiorum et chemicorum sapientia, ab Hermanni Conringii animadversionibus vindicata* (Copenhagen, 1674); *De somno et somniferis maxime papevereis* (Copenhagen, 1680); *De usu plantarum indigenarum in medicina* (Copenhagen, 1688); and *Conspectus scriptorum chemicorum illustriorum libellus posthumus, cui prefixa historia vitae auctoris ab ipso conscripta* (Copenhagen, 1697). *De ortu* and *Conspectus* repr. in J. L. Manget, *Bibliotheca chemica curiosa* (Geneva, 1702), I, 1–53. Borrichius also published numerous works on general and Latin philology. His botanical observations in the *Acta Hafniensia* were collected by S. Lyntrup in his *Orationes academicae in duos tomos distributae,* 2 vols. (Copenhagen, 1714). "Nitrum non inflammari" appeared in the *Acta Hafniensia,* **5** (1680), 213–216. Borrichius' autobiographical sketch was ed. by F. Rostgaard in his *Vitae selectae quorundam eruditissimorum ac illustrium virorum* (Bratislava, 1711), pp. 276–294.

II. SECONDARY LITERATURE. Various aspects of Borrichius' life and work are discussed in *Dansk biografisk leksikon* (Copenhagen, 1934), III, 454–462; a fuller treatment is E. F. Koch, *Oluf Borch* (Copenhagen, 1866). Supplementary details are in Lenglet du Fresnoy, *Histoire de la philosophie hermétique* (The Hague, 1742), I, 417–422; C. S. Petersen, *Den danske litteratur* (Copenhagen, 1929), pp. 669–682, 1041; Lynn Thorndike, *A History of Magic and Experimental Science* (New York, 1958), VII, 318–320; VIII, 344–346; and E. Warburg, *Subacute and Chronic Pericardial and Myocardial Lesions* (Copenhagen–London, 1938), esp. pp. 13–14, trans. by H. Anderson and G. Seidelin.

P. M. RATTANSI

BORRIES, BODO VON (*b*. Herford, Westphalia, Germany, 22 May 1905; *d*. Cologne, Germany, 17 July 1956), *electron microscopy.*

The scion of a long line of distinguished civil servants, and on his mother's side related to the Kamps of the pioneering metallurgical firm of Kamp & Harkort, Borries wavered between the law and engineering. He opted for a career in technology and studied electrical engineering in Karlsruhe, Danzig, and Munich. In 1930 he became an assistant to Adolf Wilhelm Matthias at the High-Voltage Institute of the Technische Hochschule in Berlin, where a group of young engineers led by Max Knoll sought to develop the electronic oscilloscope (picture tube) into a technological tool. In 1931, almost simultaneously, G. R. Rüdenberg, research director at the Siemens laboratories in Berlin, applied for the first patent on an electron microscope; Knoll and his group reported their work on it at the Technische Hochschule; and Ernst Brüche described *his* efforts on a similar instrument in the laboratories of the AEG firm in Berlin. Borries was thus involved in electron microscopy from its conception and later contributed significantly to it himself.

In 1937, feeling the need for better facilities than were likely to be made available at an engineering college, Borries and his colleague (and later brother-in-law) Ernst Ruska persuaded Siemens to support their project, thereby giving that firm a lead in the field that persists to the present day. Two years later they put the first transmission electron microscope on the market. Borries not only had a leading part in the design of this instrument and became the outstanding expert in the associated photographic techniques, but also extended its use beyond very thin specimens to metallic surfaces by reflection methods. In 1941 he was awarded the silver Leibniz Medal of the Prussian Academy of Sciences.

After World War II, Borries formed (with joint government and private support) an electron-microscopy institute in Düsseldorf and became its first director, helped to found the German Society for Electron Microscopy, and (after 1953) served as professor of electron optics at the Technische Hochschule in Aachen. Throughout his career he promoted the introduction of electron microscopy into many fields of research, notably in the life sciences. He also took a prominent part in securing public support for science. In 1949 Borries was appointed honorary professor at the Düsseldorf Medical Academy, and in the same year he published a text, *Die Übermikroskopie*. He was the principal organizer of the International Federation of Electron Microscope Societies and served as its president from its foundation in 1954 until his death.

BIBLIOGRAPHY

A list of Borries' publications through 1952 appears in Poggendorff's *Biographisch-literarisches Handwörterbuch*, VIIa. An important text is *Die Übermikroskopie* (Aulendorf, 1949). Partial autobiographies are in *Physikalische Zeitschrift*, **45** (1944), 316, and in *Frequenz*, **2** (1948), 267.

An obituary by Ernst Ruska is in *Zeitschrift der wissenschaftlichen Mikroskopie*, **63** (1956), 129, and in *Electron Microscopy* (the proceedings of the 1956 Stockholm conference on the subject), where it is followed by a further appreciation by V. E. Cosslett. For an account of Borries' place in the development of electron microscopy, see L. Marton, *Early History of the Electron Microscope* (San Francisco, 1968).

CHARLES SÜSSKIND

BORTKIEWICZ (or **Bortkewitsch**), **LADISLAUS** (or **Vladislav**) **JOSEPHOWITSCH** (*b*. St. Petersburg, Russia, 7 August 1868; *d*. Berlin, Germany, 15 July 1931), *mathematics.*

Bortkiewicz's mother was Helene von Rokicka; his father was Joseph Ivanowitsch Bortkewitsch, a member of the gentry from the Kovno [now Kaunas] province of Russia who was a colonel, an instructor in artillery and mathematics, a notary, and an author of several textbooks on elementary mathematics and works in economics and finance.

Bortkiewicz graduated from the Faculty of Law of the University of St. Petersburg in 1890 and took a postgraduate course in political economy and statistics. He also studied at Strasbourg (1891–1892) under G. F. Knapp, at Göttingen (1892) under W. Lexis, and at Vienna and Leipzig. In 1893 he defended his doctoral dissertation in philosophy at Göttingen. Bortkiewicz was a *Privatdozent* in Strasbourg and lectured in actuarial science and theoretical statistics in 1895–1897; in 1897–1901 he was a clerk in the general office of the Railway Pension Committee in St. Petersburg. Simultaneously, from 1899 to December 1900, he taught statistics at the prestigious Alexandrowsky Lyceum. In 1901 he became extraordinary professor of statistics at the University of Berlin, where he spent the rest of his life, becoming ordinary professor of statistics and political economy in 1920. He was a member of the Swedish Academy of Sciences, the Royal Statistical Society, the American Statistical Association, and the International Statistical Institute.

Bortkiewicz's publications concern population and statistical theory; mathematical statistics; and application of the latter and of probabilities to statistics, to actuarial science, and to political economy. Following Lexis' reasoning, Bortkiewicz was a proponent (almost the only one) of connecting statistics with the theory of probabilities and mathematical statistics. This idea was featured in an empirical "law of small numbers" (law of rare events, which formerly, beginning with Jakob I Bernoulli, were considered "morally" impossible and were discarded as such): The small numbers of events in large series of trials are stable in time; oscillations of the numbers of such events are accounted for by the Lexis criterion (Q quotient). The most important feature of this law, contrary to Bortkiewicz's opinion, appeared to be its connection with the Poisson law of large numbers and the popularization of the Poisson distribution. The Q quotient was regularly used by Bortkiewicz (who, moreover, deduced its expectation and standard deviation) in the same way that the x^2 criterion is used now. His other works in the theory of probabilities and mathematical statistics pertain to radioactivity, the theory of runs, and order statistics (he was a pioneer in the latter).

Noting the concrete and social nature of statistical deductions, Bortkiewicz recommended that legislation be based on them. His works are distinguished by independent opinions (dissenting with V. J. Buniakowsky, G. F. Knapp, M. E. L. Walras, and others), rigorous deductions, and voluminous references of international scope. At the same time, being comprehensive and not accompanied by a summary, they make hard reading.

Bortkiewicz was one of the main representatives of the "Continental direction" in mathematical statistics and its application to statistics, but he left no monographs, and the German scientists were only marginally interested in his works. He did not create a school but was closely associated with A. A. Tschuprow.

His last days were marred by a heated argument with Gini, an Italian statistician, who accused Bortkiewicz of plagiarism. Original correspondence on this alleged plagiarism is appended to Andersson's obituary (see bibliography).

BIBLIOGRAPHY

I. ORIGINAL WORKS. The only more or less comprehensive enumeration of approximately 100 of Bortkiewicz's works is in the obituary by T. Andersson (see below). These works include a few books, papers (including rather lengthy ones in various journals), and reviews. Seven of his papers (1889–1910) are in Russian; the other works are almost exclusively in German. Among his writings are *Das Gesetz der kleinen Zahlen* (Leipzig, 1898); *Die radioaktive Strahlung als Gegenstand wahrscheinlichkeitstheoretischer Untersuchungen* (Berlin, 1913); *Die Iterationen* (Berlin, 1917); "Die Variabilitätsbreite beim Gauschen Fehlergesetz," in *Nordisk statistisk tidskrift,* **1** (1922), 11–38, 193–220; and "Variationsbreite und mittlerer Fehler," in *Sitzungsberichte der Berliner mathematischen Gesellschaft,* **21** (1922), 3–11.

Three of his papers are available in English trans. by the W.P.A., published in the early 1940's together with trans. of related works, notably those of W. Lexis: "Kritische Betrachtungen zur theoretischen Statistik" (1894–1896), trans. as "Critical Comments on the Theory of Statistics"; "Homogeneität und Stabilität in der Statistik" (1918), trans. as "Homogeneity and Stability in Statistics"; and "Das Helmertsche Verteilungsgesetz für die Quadratsumme zufälliger Beobachtungsfehler" (1918), trans. as "Helmert's Law of Distribution for the Sum of Squares of Random Errors of Observation." The W.P.A. trans. are accompanied by a short bibliography of Bortkiewicz's works. At least two of his works in economics are also available in English.

Information about the St. Petersburg period of Bortkiewicz's life and about his father is in the U.S.S.R. State Historical Archives, Leningrad. Information about his life in Berlin is in the archives of the Humboldt University, Berlin.

II. SECONDARY LITERATURE. Information on the life and works of Bortkiewicz (with reference to his obituaries) is in *Kürschners deutscher Gelehrten-Kalender* (Berlin–Leipzig, 1931), 274; *Reichshandbuch der deutschen Gesellschaft,* I, *Handbuch der Persönlichkeiten in Wort und Bild* (Berlin, 1930), 188, with portrait; *Neue deutsche Biographie,* II (Berlin, 1955), 478; and Poggendorff, VI, pt. 1. The most comprehensive obituary is T. Andersson, in *Nordisk statistik tidskrift,* **10** (1931), 1–16, published simultaneously in English in *Nordic Statistical Journal,* **3** (1931), 9–26. The latest published biography is E. J. Gumbel, in *International Encyclopedia of the Social Sciences* (New York, 1968).

O. B. SHEYNIN

BORTOLOTTI, ETTORE (*b.* Bologna, Italy, 6 March 1866; *d.* Bologna, 17 February 1947), *mathematics, history of mathematics.*

A disciple of Salvatore Pincherle, Bortolotti received his degree in mathematics *summa cum laude* from the University of Bologna in 1889. He was a university assistant until 1891, when he was appointed professor at the lyceum of Modica, Sicily. After completing postgraduate studies in Paris in 1892–1893, he taught in Rome from 1893 to 1900. In the latter year Bortolotti was appointed professor of infinitesimal calculus at the University of Modena, where he taught analysis and rational mechanics. He was dean of the Faculty of Science from 1913 to 1919, the year in which he assumed the professorship of analytical geometry at the University of Bologna. He retired in 1936.

Bortolotti's early studies were devoted to topology, whereas his later works in pure mathematics dealt largely with analysis: calculus of finite differences, the general theory of distributive operations, the algorithm of continuous fractions and its generalizations, the order of infinity of functions, the convergence of infinite algorithms, summation and asymptotic behavior of series and of improper integrals.

Bortolotti's interest in the history of mathematics was clear in his early works on topology; it increased during his stay in Rome, when he was an associate of the physicist and mathematician Valentino Cerruti; and it was fully developed in Modena, when he made deep studies of Paolo Ruffini's manuscripts. His first published historical work was "Influenza dell'opera matematica di Paolo Ruffini sullo svolgimento delle teorie algebriche" (1902). He later edited Ruffini's *Opere matematiche* (1953–1954). Bortolotti gradually widened the scope of his studies to include more remote times. The period in the seventeenth century during which infinitesimal analysis was developed was the subject of profound studies by Bortolotti, who revealed the importance of Torricelli's infinitesimal results while vindicating Cataldi's claim to the discovery of continuous fractions.

Bortolotti also studied the work of Leonardo Fibonacci and of Scipione Dal Ferro, Nicolò Tartaglia, Girolamo Cardano, Ludovico Ferrari, and Rafael Bombelli. He found and published (1929), with an introduction and notes, the manuscript of books IV and V of Bombelli's *L'algebra*. Among his other contributions is the objective reconstruction of the argumentations of the Sumerian, Assyrian, Babylonian, and Egyptian mathematicians.

BIBLIOGRAPHY

I. ORIGINAL WORKS. Bortolotti's works total more than 220, and lists of them may be found in the appendixes to the articles by Bompiani and Segre (see below). Among his works are "Influenza dell'opera matematica di Paolo Ruffini sullo svolgimento delle teorie algebriche," in *Annuario della R. Università di Modena, 1902–1903*, pp. 21–77; *Lezioni di geometrica analitica*, 2 vols. (Bologna, 1923); *Studi e ricerche sulla storia della matematica in Italia nei secoli XVI e XVII* (Bologna, 1928); *I cartelli di matematica disfida e la personalità psichica e morale di Girolamo Cardano* (Imola, 1933); and *La storia della matematica nella Università di Bologna* (Bologna, 1947). He also edited Books IV and V of *L'algebra, opera di Rafael Bombelli da Bologna* (Bologna, 1929) and Ruffini's *Opere matematiche*, 3 vols. (Rome, 1953–1954).

II. SECONDARY LITERATURE. Works on Bortolotti are E. Bompiani, "In ricordo di Ettore Bortolotti," in *Atti e memorie dell'Accademia di scienze, lettere e arti di Modena,* 5th ser., **7** (1947); E. Carruccio, "Ettore Bortolotti," in *Periodico di matematiche*, 4th ser., **26** (1948), and "Commemorazione di Ettore Bortolotti," in *Atti della Società italiana di scienze fisiche e matematiche "Mathesis"* (1952); and B. Segre, "Ettore Bortolotti—commemorazione," in *Rendiconti dell'Accademia delle scienze dell'Istituto di Bologna, classe di scienze fisiche,* n.s. **52** (1949), 47–86.

ETTORE CARRUCCIO

BORY DE SAINT-VINCENT, JEAN BAPTISTE GEORGES MARIE (*b.* Agen, France, 6 July 1778; *d.* Paris, France, 22 December 1846), *biology.*

As a young boy, Bory de Saint-Vincent wandered about his native Guyenne to escape the persecution by the Jacobins with which his father was threatened. He became interested in plants and insects and, by the age of sixteen, was corresponding with established French naturalists. He was conscripted into the army in 1799 and remained an officer until his retirement in 1840. He was seconded to Baudin's expedition to Australia in 1801 but, officially owing to ill health, spent the year in the Mascarene Islands. After returning to France, Bory de Saint-Vincent saw army service in Germany and Spain. In 1815 he entered politics as deputy for Lot-et-Garonne; this led, at the fall of Napoleon, to his banishment from France between 1816 and 1820. He edited the *Dictionnaire classique de l'histoire naturelle* from 1822 to 1831 and, in 1829, led the scientific section of the French government's expedition to the Peloponnese. He was elected to the Académie des Sciences in 1834 and, in 1840, led an official scientific expedition to Algeria.

Bory de Saint-Vincent is remembered as the leader of successful botanical collecting expeditions and for his contributions to the theory, principles, and knowledge of island faunas; the zoogeography of the seas; and the classification of man.

As a disciple of Buffon and Lamarck, Bory de Saint-Vincent accepted the idea of change in the natural world. He suggested that in earlier times the oceans had covered the globe and that fish were, therefore, the most ancient inhabitants. The continents emerged in their turn and, finally and recently, the volcanic islands. He accepted spontaneous generation but believed that, after initial creations, species changed under the influence of the environment. Developing the ideas of Buffon, he argued that, on continents, species were relatively old and fixed in type but, on recent volcanic islands, such as Réunion, they were still in a state of flux, polymorphic. After many generations the stability of the environment would lead to a stable monomorphic species.

Bory de Saint-Vincent was the first to notice that oceanic islands were without amphibia and speculated on the reasons for flightless birds occurring independently on different islands. While accepting that the Mascarene Islands had emerged from the ocean, he considered the Atlantic islands to be the remains of a continent, the lost Atlantis. He referred to the formation of coral reefs and, many years later, he attempted one of the first biogeographical classifications of the oceans. Further developments along these lines were not made in France, but later devolved upon the English naturalists.

Bory de Saint-Vincent was also prominent in studies on the classification of the races of man by physical characteristics, which had begun with Blumenbach. In 1827 he divided man into fifteen species on the basis of the combined value of all the physical characteristics then known. The fifteen species were grouped into two major types, those with straight hair and those with crinkly hair. Treating man as a creation no different from other animals, Bory de Saint-Vincent unified his biological ideas by suggesting that the species of man were probably created at different times in different parts of the world, some of them on former islands that have become part of Asia.

BIBLIOGRAPHY

Bory de Saint-Vincent's most important writings are *Essais sur les îles fortunées et l'atlantique atlantide* (Paris, 1802); *Voyage dans les quatre principales îles des mers d'Afrique,* 3 vols. (Paris, 1803); *L'homme: Essai zoologique sur le genre humain* (Paris, 1827); *Relation du voyage de la commission scientifique du Morée,* 2 vols. (Paris, 1836–1838); *Exploration scientifique de l'Algérie,* 2 vols. (Paris, 1846–1847); and many contributions to the *Dictionnaire classique de l'histoire naturelle, Encyclopédie moderne,* and *Encyclopédie méthodique.*

There is no biography, but see P. Romieux, *Les carnets de Bory de Saint-Vincent 1813–1815* (Paris, 1934).

WILMA GEORGE

BOSC, LOUIS AUGUSTIN GUILLAUME, known in his youth as **Dantic** (*b.* Paris, France, 29 January 1759; *d.* Paris, 10 July 1828), *natural history, agronomy.*

Bosc belonged to a Protestant family. His father, Paul Bosc d'Antic, the son of a surgeon from the Tarn, was a master glassmaker and a doctor who was acquainted with most of the great naturalists of his time; his mother, Marie d'Hangest, daughter and sister of generals, died when Louis was only two years old. Bosc was interested in nature as early as six or seven, but little is known of what he studied at the Collège de Dijon. At eighteen he became secretary of the Intendance des Postes in Paris. He assiduously followed the courses at the Jardin du Roi, directed by Buffon, where Thouin and Antoine-Laurent de Jussieu taught. A large and varied group, often enamored of and nurtured on Rousseau, met there regularly. He made friends among them, notably with Desfontaines and Mme. Roland, wife of a future member of the National Convention.

The period between 1780 and 1796 was of particular importance for Bosc, who showed equal enthusiasm for science and politics. He took an extremely active part in the Revolution: he became secretary of the Club des Jacobins in 1791 and postmaster general under the Girondist ministry in 1792. After the fall of the Girondins, he took refuge in the ancient priory of Ste. Radegonde, in the forest of Montmorency, from September 1793 to July 1794. Later, an affair of the heart led him into emotional difficulties which he decided to cure by taking a long voyage. He sailed for Charleston, South Carolina, on 8 July 1796.

Bosc's work had already become well known. His first publication was an article in the Abbé Rozier's *Journal de physique* (1784). Bosc was then only twenty-five, but his article was a masterpiece. The insect described was an unusual cochineal, a new genus that was to become the type for the subfamily *Ortheziinae.* In 1792 Bosc named the genus *Ripiphorus,* a coleopteron that was later elevated to the rank of family by Thomson (1864).

Between 1790 and 1792 Bosc published numerous notes on insects, mollusks, birds, and plants. Along with Broussonet, l'Héritier, and a few others, he founded the Société Linnéenne de Paris. Bosc became more and more interested in sciences applicable to agriculture, and in 1796 he agreed to substitute for Thouin and the Abbé Tessier to write on agriculture for the *Encyclopédie de Panckoucke;* thanks to his skill, Volume IV follows the preceding ones without interruption. Again asked to help in 1810, Bosc edited, almost single-handed, the three last volumes of the monumental work (1813–1821). He also collaborated on the *Nouveau dictionnaire d'histoire naturelle* (1803–1804) and on the *Nouveau cours complet d'agriculture théorique et pratique* (1809), and was one of the leading editors of the *Annales de l'agriculture française* from 1811 to 1828.

Little is known of Bosc's stay in America, where he arrived 14 October 1796, except that he made at least two journeys: one to Wilmington, Delaware, where he was named vice-consul, and the other to the border of Tennessee, on which latter trip he gathered material of great scientific value: "500 kinds of seeds; two new quadrupeds, 15 birds, 20 or so reptiles; shells; about 30 fish; 150 zoophytes, worms, or mollusks; 1,200 insects; all these objects described and drawn from life" (Poiret in Lamarck, *Encyclopédie*, VIII [1808], 716–718).

The ocean voyage from Bordeaux to Charleston offered Bosc the opportunity for making several discoveries, notably of two genera: *Tentacularia*, a *Cestoda tetrarhynchus*, which was classed as a family by Poche, and *Oscana*, a mollusk.

In 1797 Bosc was named consul in New York. He never fulfilled his functions as consul, for President John Adams refused the *exaequatur*. His publications indicate that he was scientifically active. In November 1798, Bosc returned to Paris, where he married his cousin, Suzanne Bosc, the following year. He was made inspector of gardens and nurseries in 1803 and a member of the Institute in 1806. He concluded his career by succeeding Thouin as professor at the Muséum d'Histoire Naturelle in 1825.

Bosc's return to France was followed by the publication of a work of considerable importance, *The Natural History of Worms, Shellfish and Crustaceans* (1802), in which new species, and even an annelid genus, *Polydora*, are described.

Bosc never ceased to be interested in worms, and he was responsible for naming the genera *Capsala* (Platyhelminthes), a fish parasite that became the type of a family and even of an order; *Hepatoxylon* (1811), a genus later raised to a family by Dollfus (1940); *Dipodium* (1812), *Thalazia* (1819), and *Nematoda*.

Bosc devoted himself to science without thought of personal gain. The greater part of his collections, often containing descriptions and drawings made from life, were distributed among such specialists as J. C. Fabricius, G. A. Oliver, Latreille, Jean Daudin, Lacépède, and Jean Louis Poiret. It is known, for instance, according to Harper (1940), that he collaborated with Daudin in the latter's research on tree frogs and frogs, and that he discovered, described, drew, and named species from the Carolinas: *Hyla squirella, H. femoralis, H. lateralis, H. ovularis,* and *Rana clamitans.* The same is true of the turtles *Testudo odorata, T. reticularia,* and *T. serrata* and of the lizard *Stellio undulatus.* In arachnology and botany he left some unpublished papers that at the time would have brought to light a great number of new taxa. His arachnology of the Carolinas was published by Walckenaer (1805–1837); but a manuscript on the spiders of the forest of Montmorency (1793), in which eighty-nine species, most of them unknown until then, were described, named, and drawn, remained unpublished.

In botany Bosc discovered, defined, drew, and named numerous species, particularly some *Gramineae,* but most of his names, going unpublished, fell into synonymy. One of the most noteworthy species, published in 1807, is *Hydrocharis spongiosa* Bosc, a type of the American genus *Limnobium* L. C. Richard, which he had discovered in the Carolinas.

An accomplished naturalist who was important in his own time, Bosc was interested in the factual and practical side of science rather than in theories, although perhaps he was the first to point out the idea of "biological competition" in agriculture. He was a typical product of the eighteenth century, and he perhaps became too involved in encyclopedism. A man of good will and truth, Bosc probably will be remembered as a remarkable artisan of natural history and a pioneer in practical natural history.

BIBLIOGRAPHY

I. ORIGINAL WORKS. Bosc's numerous articles and notes appeared in *Transactions of the Linnean Society* (London); *Bulletin de la Société philomatique; Annales du Muséum d'histoire naturelle; Journal des mines; Journal de physique; Mémoires de l'Institut; Annales de chimie; Journal d'histoire naturelle;* and *Annales de l'agriculture française.* His first article was "Description de l'*Orthezia characias*," in *Journal de physique,* **24** (1784), 171–173. The journal he kept while crossing Spain on foot, in the course of his return voyage from America to France, appeared as "Voyage en Espagne, à travers les royaumes de Galice, Léon, Castille vieille et Biscaye," in *Magazin encyclopédique,* **6** (1800), I, 448–493.

Bosc also was largely responsible for the last three volumes of the *Encyclopédie de Panckoucke* (Paris, 1813–1821) and collaborated on the *Nouveau dictionnaire d'histoire naturelle,* 24 vols. (Paris, 1803–1804; 2nd ed., 36 vols., 1816–1819) and the *Nouveau cours complet d'agriculture théorique et pratique,* 13 vols. (Paris, 1809; new ed., 16 vols., 1821–1823). His books include *Histoire naturelle des vers,* 3 vols. (Paris, 1802); *Histoire naturelle des coquilles,* 5 vols. (Paris, 1802); and *Histoire naturelle des crustacés,* 2 vols. (Paris, 1802). Outside science, Bosc published *Appel à l'impartiale postérité* (Paris, 1795), the memoirs of Mme. Roland, with introduction and notes by Bosc and letters from Mme. Roland to Bosc, written between 1782 and 1791.

Work left unpublished by Bosc—at least that signed by him—is represented by a set of MSS preserved in the library of the Muséum National d'Histoire Naturelle in Paris. It consists of the following: a 16-page notebook entitled "Araignées d'Amérique," in which there are descriptions and drawings of 25 species and five plates (MS 841); *Tableau des Aranéides* (Paris, 1805) and *Histoire naturelle des insectes* (Paris, 1837), both published by Walckenaer; a notebook entitled "Araignées de la forêt de Montmorency décrites et dessinées pendant que j'étais caché à Radegonde lors de la Terreur," dated Sept. 1793 (MS 872); a notebook of 100 pages (1788) containing a "Cenaculum insectorum," in the manner of Linnaeus, and descriptions of new species of insects; a mineralogical line drawing, and four-color wash drawing of the *Sphex scutellata* (MS 873); a "Flora Caroliniana," a catalog of the plants observed, with ecological, phenological, and geographical notes, descriptions of new species, principally of the *Gramineae* (these last pages were to be part of his "Agrostographie"), and ten pages dating from 1788, with descriptions of species from various places (MS 874); an "Agrostographie carolinienne," 54 leaves containing the description of *Hydrocharis spongiosa* and that of a plant of the Indies (1791), *Oryza aristata* (MS 875); a notebook of 120 original wash drawings of *Gramineae* and *Cyperaceae*—the illustrations for the "Agrostographie carolinienne" (MS 876); and a list of the seeds of 200 plants of the South China Sea and of Carolina (MS 569), given to the Museum in 1799.

There are also documents on Bosc in the archives of the Académie des Sciences, in particular a heliogravure portrait by Boilly (1821); in the archives of the Institute (Fonds Cuvier 3157); in the Laboratoire de Phanérogamie of the Muséum National (Paris); in the historical library of the city of Paris (MSS 1007, 1008, 1009), an autobiography and a journal of the voyage to the United States; and in the Archives Nationales in Paris (AJ 15, 569).

II. SECONDARY LITERATURE. No critical analysis of Bosc's work has ever been published. The eulogies or notices of Georges Cuvier (*Mémoires du Muséum national d'histoire naturelle,* **18** [1829], 69–92), A. F. de Silvestre (*Mémoires de la Société royale et centrale d'agriculture,* **1** [1829], lxxxi–cvii), and Degérando have no pretensions to being such; they have, however, the value of biographical documents by men who had been Bosc's friends. The memoir of Auguste Rey, "Le naturaliste Bosc. Un Girondin herborisant," in *Revue de l'histoire de Versailles et de Seine et Oise* (1900), 241–277 (1901), 17–42; and C. Perroud, "Le roman d'un Girondin," in *Revue du dix-huitième siècle,* **1** (1916), 57–77, can be read with pleasure and, since they rely on numerous unpublished documents, make an important contribution to our knowledge of Bosc and of his political and private life (his relations with the Rolands, his love for Mme. Roland and then for her daughter, Eudora). Scientific appraisals are in L. Berland, "Voyageurs d'autrefois et insectes historiques," in *Livre du centenaire de la Société entomologique de France* (1932), pp. 157–166; and

especially in Francis Harper, "Some Works of Bartram, Daudin, Latreille and Sonnini and Their Bearing Upon North American Herpetological Nomenclature," in *American Midland Naturalist,* **23,** no. 3 (1940), 692–723. The indications on the arachnological work of Bosc are given by P. Bonnet, in *Bibliographia araneorum,* I (Toulouse, 1945), 278.

JEAN-FRANÇOIS LEROY

BOSCH, CARL (*b.* Cologne, Germany, 27 August 1874; *d.* Heidelberg, Germany, 26 April 1940), *chemistry.*

The Bosch family was of Swabian peasant stock. Two sons had already left the farm by the second half of the nineteenth century, however. The younger of the two founded an electrotechnical firm that later became world-famous. The older of the two, Carl, opened a gas and plumbing equipment business.

The latter gave his name to his son, the eldest of his children. From his very young days, the boy showed a special talent for the natural sciences and technology, which his father ardently encouraged. The younger Bosch was not allowed to study chemistry until he had first completed a few semesters of training in an ironworks and then a few semesters of mechanical engineering. He then turned to chemistry in Leipzig, where, after four years, he obtained his doctorate. He applied for a position at the Badische Anilin- und Sodafabrik in Ludwigshafen and was accepted. Quite by chance, he touched upon the field that would subsequently become his lifework. Wilhelm Ostwald, a winner of the Nobel Prize, claimed to have found a process for obtaining ammonia from nitrogen and hydrogen by conduction over fine wire. Bosch was entrusted with supplementary testing and quickly found the error that Ostwald had made and the reasons for it. Thereupon he was given the task of studying the nitrogen question further. Only the use of atmospheric nitrogen was feasible. Use of the electric arc was not possible because of the high current requirements in Germany. Numerous experiments were carried out. New problems continually arose, but there were so many positive results that a breakthrough appeared near.

In 1909 Fritz Haber of Karlsruhe began work on the synthesis of ammonia, employing unusually high pressures and temperatures. Bosch undertook to transform Haber's laboratory experiments into large-scale technological ones, which in turn developed into a huge industry within five years. Haber's technically unsuitable catalysts had to be replaced. After thousands of experiments, iron with admixed alkaline material proved to be especially suitable. Equipment had to be built that would be capable of withstanding high pressures and temperatures. The furnaces, which were first heated from outside, lasted only a few days; the iron lost its carbon content, and thereby its steel properties, because of the hydrogen, brittle iron carbide being the result. Bosch devised a twin tube that allowed the hydrogen to escape through tiny openings. After numerous experiments, he found a solution to the heat problem whereby he introduced the uncombined gases into the furnace and, accordingly, produced an oxyhydrogen flame, the temperature of which could be regulated according to the quantity of oxygen added. The combination of nitrogen and metals was attempted. The work was conducted at enormous cost. The gases required for synthesis had to be obtained in an exceptionally pure state. The separation of the ammonia that had formed from the untransformed gases was extremely difficult. Bosch's technological know-how proved itself to be the most outstanding aspect of his work, and he was always personally active in all practical testing of his equipment.

Bosch also undertook another experiment in high-pressure engineering, an attempt to obtain urea from ammonium carbamate, and developed the methanol synthesis used in the manufacture of formaldehyde. Finally he tackled the problem of carbon hydrogenation and the production of synthetic rubber.

In 1925 Bosch became president of I. G. Farben, and in 1931 he shared the Nobel Prize with Bergius "for the discovery and development of chemical high-pressure methods."

He died after a long illness.

BIBLIOGRAPHY

I. ORIGINAL WORKS. Bosch's writings include "Verfahren zur Darstellung von Bariumoxyd und von Cyaniden," in *Chemisches Zentralblatt* (1907), 1999; "Verfahren zur Darstellung von Mono- und Dichlorhydrin aus Glycerin und gasförmiger Salzsäure," *ibid.* (1908), 1655; "Verfahren zur Darstellung von Aluminiumstickstoffverbindungen," *ibid.* (1912), 865; "Verfahren zur Herstellung von Ammoniak aus seinen Elementen mit Hilfe von Katalysatoren," *ibid.* (1913), 195; "Stickstoff in Wirtschaft und Technik," in *Naturwissenschaften,* **8** (1920), 867–868; "Entwicklung der chemischen Hochdrucktechnik bei dem Aufbau der neuen Ammoniakindustrie," in *Les prix Nobel en 1931* (Stockholm, 1933); and "Probleme grosstechnischer Hydrierungs-Verfahren," in *Chemische Fabrik,* **7** (1934), 1–10.

II. SECONDARY LITERATURE. For a discussion of Bosch's life and work, see K. Holdermann, "Carl Bosch, 1874–1940," in *Chemische Berichte,* **90** (1957), xix–xxxix; and Carl Krauch, "Carl Bosch zum 60 Gedächtnis," in *Angewandte Chemie,* **53** (1940), 285–288; see also the unsigned tribute "Carl Bosch zum 60 Geburtstag," *ibid.,* **47** (1934), 593–594.

GÜNTHER KERSTEIN

BOSE, GEORG MATTHIAS (*b.* Leipzig, Germany, 22 September 1710; *d.* Magdeburg, Germany, 17 September 1761), *electricity.*

Bose, a merchant's son, was educated at the University of Leipzig, where he concentrated on philosophy, mathematics, and languages. In 1727 he received the M.A. and joined the philosophy faculty as a junior lecturer (*Assessor*) in mathematics and physics. In 1738 he accepted the chair of natural philosophy (*Naturlehre*) at the University of Wittenberg, where he remained until 1760, when the Prussians carried him off to Magdeburg as a hostage of war.

Although at Leipzig Bose had written only on eclipses, sound, and the errors of physicians, he had begun to study electricity, inspired by the weak papers of J. J. Schilling in the *Miscellanea Berolinensa.* Through ignorance of Du Fay's work, however, he had not progressed far by 1738, as is apparent from his inaugural oration, which is interesting chiefly for its attack on action-at-a-distance. Probably at Wittenberg, and independently of C. A. Hausen of Leipzig, he revived Hauksbee's electrical machine, and added a "prime conductor" that greatly enhanced its power.

From 1742 to 1745, after close reading of Du Fay, Bose vigorously and successfully promoted the study of electricity in Germany, where it had never before been cultivated extensively. To this purpose he produced wonderful displays with his electrical machine, a German poem, a French tract, and several high-flown Latin commentaries. This mixture of literary polish and striking demonstration, this "writing sublimely of wonderful things," as a contemporary electrician put it, was Bose's great contribution, for he thereby indirectly brought about the central event in the early history of electricity, the discovery of the condenser (1745–1746). Musschenbroek began the experiments that culminated in the Leyden jar by repeating an impressive Bosean demonstration; and J. G. von Kleist very likely hit on his form of the condenser while attempting to ignite spirits by means of sparks, a recently successful experiment first urged by Bose. In theory Bose followed the Nollet system, much of which he invented independently.

Bose promoted himself as assiduously as he did electricity, urging his work on the royal societies of France and England, the Grand Mufti of Istanbul, and the Pope of Rome. His fulsome praises of Benedict XIV annoyed the Wittenberg theologians, whose rancor culminated, in 1750, in an attempt to expurgate a little tract of Bose's on eclipses (astronomy was his other scientific subject), raising a storm that ultimately involved Frederick the Great and the Royal Society of London.

BIBLIOGRAPHY

I. ORIGINAL WORKS. Bose's chief works on electricity are *Tentamina electrica in academiis regiis Londensi et Parisina primum habita omni studio repetita quae novis aliquot accessionibus locupletavit Georg Matthias Bose* (Wittenberg, 1744), a reprint of his inaugural oration and two other pamphlets, and *Recherches sur la cause et sur la véritable téorie de l'électricité* (Wittenberg, 1745), which contains his Nolletesque theory. Poggendorff, and Jöcher, *Algemeines gelehrten Lexikon,* I (Leipzig, 1784), cols. 2098–2099, give bibliographies of Bose's printed works; his manuscripts apparently were lost in the Thirty Years' War.

II. SECONDARY LITERATURE. For a biography of Bose, see Bose's *Tentamina,* especially pp. 48–53; Jöcher, *loc. cit;* and A. Mercati, "Il fisico tedesco Giorgio Mattia Bose e Benedetto XIV," in *Acta pontificiae academiae scientiarum,* **15** (1952), 57–70. For Bose's works on electricity, see J. L. Heilbron, "G. M. Bose: The Prime Mover in the Invention of the Leyden Jar?," in *Isis,* **57** (1966), 264–267; and Joseph Priestley, *The History and Present State of Electricity,* 3rd ed. (London, 1775), I, 87–88, 93–94.

JOHN L. HEILBRON

BOSE, JAGADIS CHUNDER (*b.* Mymensingh, Bengal, India [now East Pakistan], 30 November 1858; *d.* Giridih, Bengal, India, 23 November 1937), *physics, comparative physiology.*

The son of a deputy magistrate, Bose studied at St. Xavier's, a Jesuit college in Calcutta, and then went to London to study medicine. He transferred to Cambridge University after receiving a scholarship to Christ's College and graduated in natural science in 1884. He was immediately appointed to the professorship of physics at Presidency College, Calcutta, where he remained until his retirement in 1915.

Bose first attracted worldwide attention in 1895 with his meticulous experiments on the quasi-optical properties of very short radio waves, which led him to design and construct some fine generating apparatus. His improvements in the coherer, a tube of iron filings widely used as an early form of radio detector, were of both scientific and technological importance, and led him to formulate a more general theory of the properties of contact-sensitive substances that figures in the history of solid-state physics.

Bose was struck by the way in which the responses of certain inorganic substances to various stimuli resembled biological response. That observation led him to compare the behaviors of animal and plant tissue, a study that occupied him for the rest of his life. His papers and lectures on these subjects fell short of general acceptance, however. In 1901 and again in 1904, his papers were rejected by the Royal Society, partly because of the philosophical terms in which they were couched. Today, when biophysics is a generally recognized discipline and comparative physiology rests on a more scientific basis, the idea that animal and plant tissues exhibit similar responses seems less controversial and may even be taken as foreshadowing Norbert Wiener's cybernetics. Bose aroused general admiration, however, for the extremely sensitive automatic recorders he devised to measure plant growth with great precision and for the way in which he used them to accumulate records of microscopic changes caused by various stimuli.

Bose was knighted in 1917 and was elected a fellow of the Royal Society in 1920, the first Indian physicist so honored. In 1915 he had retired from government service to organize the Bose Research Institute, which he founded in 1917, largely with his own considerable fortune but also with contributions from private well-wishers and from the government of India. He was a great friend of another famous Bengali, the Nobel Prize-winning author Rabindranath Tagore. Bose was happily married for fifty years to Abala Das, daughter of the Calcutta lawyer and political leader Durga Mohan Das.

BIBLIOGRAPHY

I. ORIGINAL WORKS. Bose's books are *Response in the Living and Non-living* (London, 1902); *Plant Response as a Means of Physiological Investigation* (London, 1906); *Electro-physiology: A Physico-physiological Study* (London, 1907); *Researches on Irritability of Plants* (London, 1913); *Life Movements in Plants* (Calcutta, 1918); *The Physiology of the Ascent of Sap* (London, 1923); *The Physiology of Photosynthesis* (London, 1924); *Mechanism of Plants* (London, 1926); *Plant Autographs and Their Revelations* (London, 1927); and *Tropic Movement of Plants* (London, 1929).

His *Collected Physical Papers* (London, 1927) were compiled by Bose himself.

II. SECONDARY LITERATURE. A contemporary biography is Sir Patrick Geddes, *The Life and Work of Sir Jagadis C. Bose* (London, 1920). An obituary by M. N. Saha appears in *Obituary Notices of Fellows of the Royal Society,* **3** (1940), 2–12. An appreciation by S. K. Mitra is in *Journal of the British Institution of Radio Engineers,* **18** (1958), 661; an announcement of an annual award named in Bose's honor appears in an earlier issue of the same journal: **13** (1953), 130.

CHARLES SÜSSKIND

BOŠKOVIĆ, RUDJER J. (*b.* Dubrovnik, Yugoslavia, 18 May 1711; *d.* Milan, Italy, 13 February 1787), *natural philosophy, mathematics, astronomy, physics, geodesy.*

Bošković was perhaps the last polymath to figure in an important way in the history of science, and his career was in consequence something of an anachronism and presents something of an enigma. He stands between the natural philosophy of Newton and Leibniz at one extreme and Faraday and field theory at the other, but too far from both for the connection either forward or backward to appear a coherent one. A somewhat isolated figure, he belonged to no definite eighteenth-century tradition. Croatian by birth, he became a Jesuit; and like many intellectuals from the Dalmatian cities, he was drawn to Italy and lived the first part of his career in Rome. A man of the Enlightenment, he sometimes gives the effect of a Renaissance scholar moving about Europe from place to place for reasons of circumstance and patronage and departing on great journeys at critical junctures. As will appear from consulting his bibliography, he published in the mode of an earlier time. He wrote treatises on whole sciences, and at certain periods in his life composed several such works in the course of a year. Nevertheless, his reputation has been rather that of a forerunner than a survival. His doctrine of atomism which modified the massy corpuscles of Newtonian natural philosophy into immaterial centers of force appeared to foretell, and there are historical reasons to believe that it actually influenced, the basic position of nineteenth-century field physics in regard to the relations between space and matter.

Life. Bošković was the son of Nikola Bošković, a merchant of Dubrovnik, and Paula Bettera, the daughter of Bartolomeo Bettera, a merchant originally from Bergamo, Italy. The family was of average means and was noted for its literary interests and accomplishments. Bošković began his education in the Jesuit college of Dubrovnik and continued it in Rome, first at the novitiate of Sant'Andrea, which he entered in 1725 at the age of fourteen, and later at the Collegium Romanum. He was extraordinarily sharp of mind, comprehensive in intelligence, and tireless in application—in short, an outstanding student. He learned science in a way characteristic of his later career, through independent study of mathematics, physics, astronomy, and geodesy. In 1735 he began studying Newton's *Opticks* and the *Principia* at the Collegium Romanum, where he made himself an enthusiastic propagator of the new natural philosophy. The exact sciences were what always appealed to him—in the first instance mathematics. In 1740,

although he had not yet completed his theological studies, he was appointed professor of mathematics at the Collegium Romanum. That event largely determined the course of his career. Teaching interested him in its methods as well as for its content. In this respect, as in others, his spirit was progressive. He published a textbook of his teaching in 1754—*Elementa universae matheseos*—of which the third and final volume contains an original theory of conic sections.

During this period of his life Bošković undertook, as was customary among qualified clergymen of his time, several practical and diplomatic commissions for lay or ecclesiastical authorities. The cupola of St. Peter's having developed alarming fissures, a commission was appointed consisting of Bošković and two fellow "mathematicians," F. Jacquier and Th. Le Seur, to investigate the causes and make recommendations. Bošković drafted the report which, analyzing the problem in theoretical terms, achieved—despite certain errors—the reputation of a minor classic in architectural statics. Thereafter the papal government entrusted the planning for draining of the Pontine marshes to Bošković. He composed a series of memoirs on the practice of hydraulic engineering, on regulation of the flow of the Tiber and other streams, and on harborworks. He did a plan for the harbor at Rimini in 1764 and for that at Savona in 1771.

Archaeology also interested Bošković. In 1743 he discovered and excavated an ancient Roman villa above Frascati in Tusculum, and in 1746 published a description of a sundial that had been among the finds. In 1750 he also published a critical study of the Augustan obelisk in the Campo Marzio. In 1757 Bošković undertook the most important of his several diplomatic missions, representing the interests of the Republic of Lucca before the Hapsburg court in Vienna in a dispute with Tuscany over water rights. He won the case, and in the intervals of tending to its ramifications, he also while in Vienna completed his major work in the field of natural philosophy, *Philosophiae naturalis theoria,* which appeared in the autumn of 1758.

As the years went by, Bošković fell out of sympathy with certain policies of his ecclesiastical superiors. He resented their rejection of proposals he had advanced looking to the modernization of education both in method and in subject matter. He disliked the Vatican's reaction to the persecution of his order in Portugal. He was disappointed by the negative attitude that a number of Jesuit philosophers—Peripatetics he thought them to be—adopted toward his own system of natural philosophy. It seemed time for a move. The Academy of Sciences in Paris had long since elected him to corresponding membership—he was correspondent of Dortous de Mairan—on the publication in 1738 of his discourse on the aurora borealis. His superiors gave him permission, and in 1759 Bošković set off on his travels, going first to Paris.

There he remained for six months, well received in aristocratic, scientific, and literary circles. He came to know members of the Academy of Sciences at first hand. A diplomatic intervention on behalf of his native city of Dubrovnik took him to the court at Versailles. He decided not to remain in Paris, however, and in 1760 crossed over to London, where again his reputation had preceded him among literary and scientific people. He had discussions with representatives of the Church of England; met Benjamin Franklin, who showed him electrical experiments; and visited Oxford and Cambridge. On 15 January 1761 the Royal Society elected him a fellow, and in recognition of the honor, he dedicated to it a poem on eclipses of the sun and moon. He then lent his weight to efforts to persuade the Society to organize an expedition for the purpose of observing the transit of Venus in June 1761.

Bošković had planned to make such observations himself in Istanbul but, dependent in his plans on a companion, Correr, the new Venetian ambassador to Istanbul, Bošković arrived too late for observation. He made a trip through Flanders, Holland, the court of Stanislas in Nancy, and various centers in Germany. Once in Istanbul, he fell dangerously ill and had to remain there for seven months of recuperation. Partially recovered he set off again, this time in the company of the British ambassador, and traveled through Bulgaria and Moldavia, and went on alone from there to Poland. In Warsaw he was received in ecclesiastical and diplomatic circles. The Czartoryski and the Poniatowski connections took him up. His *Diary* of the trips he made through Bulgaria and Moldavia amounts to a systematic description of the country. It was published in Italian in 1784, having already been translated into French and German. From Poland, finally, he returned to Rome—by way of Silesia, Austria, and Venice—arriving there in November 1763 after an absence of over four years which marked a stage in his life.

Back in Italy, Bošković found a situation in Pavia, where at the end of the year he won election as professor of mathematics at the university, revived under Austrian administration. He organized both his own lectures and his department realistically, with an emphasis upon applied mathematics. At Pavia he concentrated his own efforts mainly in the field of optics and the improvement of telescopic lenses, and

played a leading role in the organization of the Jesuit observatory at Brera near Milan in 1764. Had his program been carried out and the instruments he advocated installed, the observatory would have been one of the most elaborate in Europe. Remembering his interest in the transits of Venus, the Royal Society invited him to lead an expedition to California for the purpose of observing the second of the famous pair of transits, that of 1769. Unfortunately political conditions prevented that trip. In 1770 he moved his work to the department of optics and astronomy at the Scuole Palatine in Milan. As time went on, he provoked opposition among his colleagues at the observatory. In 1772 the court in Vienna yielded to the demands of the majority and relieved Bošković of "concern" for the observatory. In despair he resigned his professorship also. All his world was dissolving: the next year, 1773, the pope suppressed the Jesuit order.

By now Bošković was in his sixty-third year. Influential friends urged him to repair to Paris. There a post was arranged for him as director of optics for the navy, and he even became a subject of the French crown. In Paris during this, the last productive period of his life, he worked mainly on problems of optics and astronomy. It may be that his nature was a little contentious, for there too disputes attended him, one with the young Laplace over Bošković's early method (1746) of determining the path of a comet, another with the Abbé Alexis de Rochon over priorities in the invention of a type of micrometer and megameter consisting of pairs of rotating prisms. The device became important in the design of geodetic telemeters. In search of health and tranquillity, Bošković spent the greater part of each year in the country residing at the estates of one or another of his friends.

In 1782 Bošković received leave to return again to Italy in order to ready his French and Latin manuscripts for the press. He settled in Bassano, and there in 1785 the printing firm of the brothers Remondini brought out his five-volume *Opera*. The preparation of those writings and the strain of proofreading told on Bošković's health. Once again he set out to travel, although only in Italy, in order to visit old friends. He found a cordial welcome in Milan, where former opponents were inclined to let bygones be bygones, and settled down in the Brera observatory, which he had founded, to work on the notes for the third volume of Benedict Stay's poem *Philosophiae recentioris versibus traditae libri X,* on Newtonian natural philosophy. His mental powers were leaving him, however. Forgetfulness, anxiety, fear for his scientific reputation grew upon him, and it was clear that his mind was failing. He mercifully died of a lung ailment before the decline reached an extreme and was buried in the church of Santa Maria Podone in Milan, where, however, all trace of his tomb has been lost.

Bošković's interests were more manifold than was at all normal, even in the eighteenth century, for one who participated deeply in the actual work of science. For purposes of clarity, they may be grouped under the headings of the instrumental sciences of astronomy, optics, and geodesy, and the abstract subjects of mathematics, mechanics, and natural philosophy. It must be appreciated, however, that such a classification is a mere convenience. Bošković's work in the former trio exhibited a consistent penchant for the invention or improvement of instruments of observation as well as for recognition and compensation of procedural errors. In the second, theoretical set of sciences, his writings develop a highly individual point of view. All his work, finally, may be read as physical essays in the working out of an epistemology and metaphysic that styled his career in a way, again, not at all characteristic of his century.

Instrumental Sciences. Bošković's earliest (1736) publication was a description of methods for the determination of the elements of the rotation of the sun on its axis from three observations of a single sunspot. In 1737 there followed an exposition of a graphical method for the resolution on a plane of problems in spherical trigonometry and the treatment of an actual problem in the transit of Mercury. In 1739, two years after the treatise on the aurora borealis, Bošković published an account of the principle of the circular micrometer based on the idea that the circular aperture of the objective may serve for determination of the times at which a celestial body enters and leaves the field of vision of a telescope; these values, when compared with those of a known star, give the relative positions of the two bodies.

From these specific matters, Bošković turned his attention in astronomy to a comprehensive survey of the theoretical foundations and instrumental practice and resources of practical, observational astronomy, and in the years 1742 through 1744 he published a series of works that deal with these matters in a spirit of *severioris critices leges.*

Thereafter, Bošković took up the study of comets. A widely read work of 1746 offered his opinions on a number of questions concerning the nature of comets. In it he proposed his first method—that much later criticized adversely by Laplace—for the determination of parabolic orbits. The procedure was essentially similar to that afterward introduced by J. H. Lambert (1761). Bošković's method, developed in

Volume III of his *Opera pertinenta ad opticam et astronomiam* (1785), comes close to the classic method of H. W. Olbers (1797). An interesting treatise of 1749 concerns the determination of an elliptical orbit by means of a construction previously employed for resolving the reflection of a light ray from a spherical mirror. Bošković employed this method again in 1756, in a treatise discussing the reciprocal perturbations of Jupiter and Saturn, which he entered in a competition on the subject set by the Academy of Sciences in Paris. The winner was Leonhard Euler; Bošković received an honorable mention.

Bošković's interest in optics seems to have developed in the first instance out of his astronomical concerns. As early as 1747 he was discussing the tenuity, or rarity, of sunlight, apparently with the old question in mind of the hypothetical materiality of light, and at the same time attempted to estimate the density of a solar atmosphere, supposing it to reach as far as the earth. Having reflected on the problems of light, Bošković published in 1748 a treatise (in two parts) of a broadly critical nature. The central Newtonian positions in optics did not at all appear to him to be securely established. It is perhaps the most interesting feature of his critical attitude that he regarded rectilinear propagation as an unproved hypothesis, a question on which he dwelt in detail. Some other aspects of optical phenomena he thought hidden or unclear even after Newton's discoveries. Discussing phenomena of parallax, he drew attention to the distance of fixed stars in dimensions of light-years. He formulated, and was the first to do so, a general photometric law of illumination and enounced the law of emission of light known under Lambert's name. He was critical of Newton's account of colors arising from the passage of light through thin plates involving the ether and periodicity, and he provided an alternative interpretation in the spirit of his own theory of natural forces, of which more below.

In his later years at Pavia and at the observatory in Brera, he concentrated his attention on the improvement of lenses and optical devices. A series of five discourses on dioptrics (1767) treats of achromatic lenses and offers an impressive example of Bošković's experimental dexterity and accuracy, most notably in respect of measurements of the reflection and dispersion of light by means of his vitrometer. Having confirmed that two-lens arrangements will recombine only two spectral colors, he recommended a composition involving three or more lenses. He also stressed the importance of the eyepiece in achromatic telescopes. In the actual fabrication of lenses he worked with Stephen Conti of Lucca, who manufactured them according to his specifications and assisted in performing the optical experiments.

At Brera he worked intensively on methods for verifying and rectifying astronomical instruments and improved or invented a number of them, of which accounts later appeared in Volume IV of his *Opera*. Perhaps the most ingenious were a leveler that determined the plane of the edge of a quadrant and a micrometric wedge. To ensure that the border of an astronomical quadrant would be on the same level as the plane passing through the center, Bošković made use of a sort of surveying device. In a canal filled with water leading around the border of the quadrant and along one of its radii floated a small boat with a wire mast hooked at the top. Its point nearly touched the border of the instrument, permitting the measurement of small distances between the point and the water level, thus revealing the true form of the so-called plane of the quadrant. Bošković's micrometric wedge is a metallic wedge truncated on the thin side, which he used to measure the distance between two planes by inserting it into the opening between them and noting the corresponding number on the scale engraved on its side. He also thought that it ought to be possible to decide between Newton's emission theory of light and the wave theory by observations of aberration of light from the fixed stars, first through an ordinary telescope and then through a telescope filled with water. It was his further prediction that observation would detect an aberration of light from terrestrial sources: in these matters research in the nineteenth century failed to confirm his expectations.

Bošković's work in meteorology and geophysics was closely related to astronomical concerns. In 1753 he advanced the idea that the moon was probably enveloped not by an atmosphere like that of the earth, but rather by a concentric layer of some homogeneous, extremely transparent fluid. As to our own atmosphere and its behavior, or misbehavior, he investigated a tornado that devastated Rome in June 1749 and attempted to interpret its effects in terms of Stephen Hales's theory of "fixed air"—it was ever his way to try connecting phenomena in one domain with famous developments in the science of another; his mind ranged over the whole of physical science with more or less cogency, but never without imagination.

It was his idea that mountains had originated from the undulation of rock strata under the influence of subterranean fires, and developing this notion in 1742 led him to the concept of compensation of strata,

which could be taken as basis of the later theory of isostasy. He also conceived the idea of a kind of gravimeter for measuring gravitation even in the ocean. At the same time, he proposed a method for determining the mean density of the earth by measuring the incremental attraction of masses of water at high tide by the deviation of a pendulum situated in the proximity.

Early in his career his interest was drawn to the problem of the size and shape of the earth, an issue intensively discussed in the first half of the eighteenth century, since its resolution was thought to be crucial in an eventual choice between a Cartesian cosmology of vortices, which predicted an earth slightly elongated at the poles, and a Newtonian one of inertial motion under attractive forces, in which case the globe should be slightly flattened. In 1739 Bošković initiated a critical investigation of existing measurements of the length of a degree along the meridian. It appeared to him that in addition to cosmological effects, superficial inequalities and irregularities of structure and density beneath the surface might well affect and distort measurements of distance along a meridian, modify the length of the second pendulum at a given locality, and bias the apparent direction of the vertical.

Bošković always promoted international cooperation in geodesy. On his initiative, meridians were measured in Austria, Piedmont, and Pennsylvania, and he himself readily collaborated with an English colleague, Christopher Maire, rector of the English Jesuit College in Rome, in surveying the length of two degrees of the meridian between Rome and Rimini. The onerous work took three years. Its results confirmed, among other things, the geodetic consequences of unevenness in the earth's strata, the possibility of determining surface irregularities by such measurements, as well as the deviation of meridians and parallels from a properly spherical shape. The report on these measurements came out in Rome at the end of 1755. Bošković employed novel methods for measuring the base line in his surveys, and he developed an exact theory of errors and learned to employ his instruments to the most accurate effect. The earliest device for verifying the points of division on the edge of such an instrument originated with Bošković, who determined from the inequalities of their chords that the circular arcs on the border of the instrument, although theoretically equal, were not in fact so. Having determined errors of division corresponding to 60° by comparing the chord with the radius of the instrument, he proceeded by bisecting to angles of 30°, 15°, and finally 5°. The method of compensating errors being applicable to astronomical as well as geodetic observations, he took an important step toward the newer practical astronomy, which for most astronomers begins with Friedrich Bessel. In the French edition of his report on measurements of the meridian, Bošković included the first theory of the combination of observations based on a minimum principle for determining their most suitable values, making use of absolute values instead of their squares, as Gauss later did in his classical method of least squares.

Abstract Sciences. Science in general took its lead in physics from Newton and in mathematical analysis from Leibniz, and it was at the root of Bošković's idiosyncrasy that, whether deliberately or not, he took the opposite tack in both respects. Mathematics had always attracted him. Instead of the calculus as developed by the great analysts among his own contemporaries—d'Alembert, the Bernoullis, and Euler—he preferred the geometric method of infinitely small magnitudes "which Newton almost always used," as he said, and which embodied the "power of geometry." He particularly applied it to problems of differential geometry, terrestrial and celestial mechanics, and practical astronomy. In 1740 he studied the properties of osculatory circles, and in 1741 devoted an entire treatise to the nature of the infinitely great and small magnitudes employed in that method. He relied upon it also in a few problems of classical mechanics: in 1740 he studied the motion of a material point and in 1743 was the first to solve the problem of the body of greatest attraction.

In mechanics (as in optics), however, his allegiance to Newton was qualified. True, he annotated Stay's elegant Latin verses on Newtonian natural philosophy, the *Philosophiae,* published in Rome in three volumes, the first in 1755. Nevertheless, his heterodoxy in mechanics began to be apparent at least as early as 1745, when he published an important discourse on the subject of living force (*vis viva*). He there put forward the view that the speed of a movement is to be computed from the *actio momentanea* of the force that generates it. Attacking the problem of the generation (*generatio*) of velocity in a new way, by distinguishing between actual and potential velocity and by introducing subtle conceptions in connection with the notion of force, he reduced the famous debate over the true measure of force, whether it be momentum (*mv*) or *vis viva* (*mv*^{2}), to the status of a mere argument "over titles." This discourse contained the first statement of Bošković's universal force law.

That law was inspired partly by Leibniz' law of continuity and partly by the famous thirty-first query

with which Newton concluded the fourth and final edition of his *Opticks.* There Newton raised speculatively the question whether there might not exist both attractive and repulsive forces alternately operative between the particles of matter. From this idea Bošković proceeded by way of an analysis of collision of bodies to the enunciation of a "universal law of forces" between elements of matter, the force being alternately attractive or repulsive, depending upon the distance by which they are separated. As that distance diminishes toward zero, repulsion predominates and grows infinite so as to render direct contact between particles impossible. A fundamental role is played by the points of equilibrium between the attractive and repulsive forces. Bošković called such points "boundaries" (*limes,* the Latin singular). Some of them are points of stable equilibrium for the particles in them and others are points of unstable equilibrium. The behavior of these boundaries and the areas between them enabled Bošković to interpret cohesion, impenetrability, extension, and many physical and chemical properties of matter, including its emission of light.

It was because of its consequences for the constitution of matter that the law of forces was particularly important. In Bošković's natural philosophy the "first elements" of matter became mere points—real, homogeneous, simple, indivisible, without extension, and distinguished from geometric points only by their possession of inertia and their mutual interaction. Extended matter then becomes the dynamic configuration of a finite number of centers of interaction. Many historians have seen in Bošković's derivation of matter from forces an anticipation of the concept of the field, an anticipation still more clearly formulated very much later by Faraday in 1844. Matter, then, is not a continuum, but a discontinuum. Mass is the number of points in the volume, and drops out of consideration as an independent entity. In the special case of high-speed particles, Bošković even envisaged the penetrability of matter.

The principle of inertia itself did not escape his criticism. It was impossible in his view to prove it or indeed to prove any metaphysical principle to be true of physical reality a priori. But neither could it be proved a posteriori as Newtonians were wont to do from "the phenomenon of movement." Bošković emphasized the necessity of defining the space to which the principle relates. Since he held it to be impossible to distinguish absolute from relative motion by direct observation and without invoking "unproven physical hypotheses," he introduced the notion that inertia as it is observed is relative to a space chosen to include all the bodies in the universe that are within range of our senses, i.e., all the subjects of all our experiments and observations. The translation of that space as a whole can have no effect on the motion of a body within it, on its rotation at a given angle, or on its contraction or dilation if there is a simultaneous and equivalent contraction or dilation of the scale of forces. From these considerations Bošković concluded that experiment and observation could never decide whether inertia is relative or absolute.

It must not be supposed, however, that his natural philosophy represents a reversion to a Leibnizian metaphysic. He was in fact as skeptical and critical of the principle of sufficient reason or final causes as of that of inertia. In general Bošković was convinced that we know nothing so far as the absolute is concerned and just as little of what is relative. He often emphasized the impotence of the human mind, and spoke more than once of the imaginability of beings with a geometry different from ours. He had a clear understanding of the hypothetical-deductive nature of geometry, especially of the Euclidean fifth postulate about parallels. In his view our universe is no more than a grain of sand in a horde of other universes. There might well be other spaces quite unconnected to our own and other times that run some different course.

Sharp in thought, bold in spirit, independent in judgment, zealous to be exact, Bošković was a man of eighteenth-century European science in some respects and far ahead of his time in others. Among his works are writings that still repay study, and not only from a historical point of view.

BIBLIOGRAPHY

I. ORIGINAL WORKS. Bošković's more important treatises and works include *De maculis solaribus* (Rome, 1736); *De Mercurii novissimo infra solem transitu* (Rome, 1737); *Trigonometriae sphaericae constructio* (Rome, 1737); *De aurora boreali* (Rome, 1738); *De novo telescopii usu ad objecta caelestia determinanda* (Rome, 1739); *Dissertatio de telluris figura* (Rome, 1739); *De circulis osculatoribus* (Rome, 1740); *De motu corporum projectorum in spatio non resistente* (Rome, 1740); *De inaequalitate gravitatis in diversis terrae locis* (Rome, 1741); *De natura, & usu infinitorum & infinite parvorum* (Rome, 1741); *De annuis fixarum aberrationibus* (Rome, 1742); *De observationibus astronomicis, et quo pertingat earundem certitudo* (Rome, 1742); *Disquisitio in universam astronomiam* (Rome, 1742); *Parere di tre mattematici sopra i danni, che si sono trovati nella cupola di S. Pietro sul fine dell'anno MDCCXLII, dato per ordine di Nostro Signore Papa Benedetto XIV* (Rome, 1742).

Later works are *De motu corporis attracti in centrum immobile viribus decrescentibus in ratione distantiarum reciproca duplicata in spatiis non resistentibus* (Rome, 1743);

"Problema mecanicum de solido maximae attractionis solutum a P. Rogerio Josepho Boscovich," in *Memorie sopra la fisica e istoria naturale di diversi valentuomini*, **1** (Lucca, 1743), 63–88; *Nova methodus adhibendi phasium observationes in eclipsibus lunaribus ad exercendam geometriam, et promovendam astronomiam* (Rome, 1744); *De viribus vivis* (Rome, 1745); *De cometis* (Rome, 1746); *Dissertatio de maris aestu* (Rome, 1747); *Dissertazione della tenuità della luce solare* (Rome, 1747); *Dissertationis de lumine pars prima* (Rome, 1748); *Dissertationis de lumine pars secunda* (Rome, 1748); *De determinanda orbita planetae ope catoptricae ex datis vi, celeritate et directione motus in dato puncto* (Rome, 1749); *Sopra il turbine, che la notte tra gli 11 e 12 di giugno del 1749 daneggiò una gran parte di Roma* (Rome, 1749).

During the 1750's Bošković wrote *De lunae atmosphaera* (Rome, 1753); *De continuitatis lege et ejus consectariis pertinentibus ad prima materiae elementa eorumque vires* (Rome, 1754); *Elementa universae matheseos*, 3 vols. (Rome, 1754); *De lege virium in natura existentium* (Rome, 1755); *De litteraria expeditione per Pontificiam ditionem ad dimetiendos duos meridiani gradus et corrigendam mappam geographicam jussu, et auspiciis Benedicti XIV. Pont. Max. suscepto a Patribus Societ. Jesu Christophoro Maire et Rogerio Josepho Boscovich* (Rome, 1755), trans. into French as *Voyage astronomique et géographique dans l'état de l'Église, entrepris par l'ordre et sous les auspices du Pape Benoît XIV, pour mesurer deux degrés du méridien et corriger la carte dans l'état ecclésiastique par les PP. Maire et Boscovich, traduit du latin* (Paris, 1770); *De inaequalitatibus, quas Saturnus et Jupiter sibi mutuo videntur inducere, praesertim circa tempus conjunctionis* (Rome, 1756); "De materiae divisibilitate, et principiis corporum" (1748), in *Memorie sopra la fisica . . .*, IV (Lucca, 1757); *Philosophiae naturalis theoria redacta ad unicam legem virium in natura existentium* (Vienna, 1758).

Bošković's works in his last quarter-century include *De solis ac lunae defectibus libri V* (London, 1760); *Dissertationes quinque ad dioptricam pertinentes* (Vienna, 1767); *Les éclipses* (Paris, 1779); *Giornale di un viaggio da Constantinopoli in Polonia, dell'Abate R. G. Boscovich* (Bassano, 1784); and *Rogerii Josephi Boscovich Opera pertinentia ad opticam et astronomiam maxima ex parte nova et omnia hucusque inedita in V tomos distributa* (Bassano, 1785).

II. SECONDARY LITERATURE. The earlier works are F. Ricca, *Elogio storico dell'abate Ruggiero Giuseppe Boscovich* (Milan, 1789); M. Oster, *Roger Joseph Boscovich als Naturphilosoph*, dissertation (Cologne, 1909); V. Varićak, "L'oeuvre mathématique de Bošković," in *Rad* (Zagreb), **181, 185, 190, 193** (1910–1912), condensed by Ž. Marković, in *Bulletin des travaux de la classe des sciences mathématiques et naturelles de l'Académie yougoslave de Zagreb*, **1** (1914), 1–24.

See also D. Nedelkovitch, *La philosophie naturelle et relativiste de R. J. Boscovich* (Paris, 1922); *A Theory of Natural Philosophy, Put Forward and Explained by Roger Joseph Boscovich, S. J.*, Lat.-Eng. ed. with trans. by J. M. Child from 1st Venetian ed. (1763), with a short life of Bošković (Chicago-London, 1922); V. Varićak, "Latin-English Edition of Bošković's Work *Theoria philosophiae naturalis*," in

Bulletin des travaux de la classe des sciences mathématiques naturelles de l'Académie de Zagreb, **19-20** (1923–1924), 45–102; L. Čermelj, "Roger Joseph Boscovich als Relativist," in *Archiv für Geschichte der Mathematik, der Naturwissenschaft und der Technik,* **2,** no. 4 (1929), 424–444; and H. V. Gill, *Roger Boscovich, Forerunner in Modern Physical Theories* (Dublin, 1941).

A bibliography of publications on Bošković in English, French, German, and Italian up to 1961 is in L. L. Whyte, ed., *Roger Joseph Boscovich, S.J., F.R.S., 1711–1787, Studies of His Life and Work on the 250th Anniversary of His Birth* (London, 1961), which contains articles on Bošković by E. Hill, L. L. Whyte, Ž. Marković, L. P. Williams, R. E. Schofield, Z. Kopal, J. F. Scott, C. A. Ronan, and Churchill Eisenhart. G. Arrighi has published newly found correspondence between Bošković and G. A. Arnolfini of Lucca in *Quaderni della rivista "La provincia di Lucca,"* **3** (1963), **5** (1965), *Studi scientifici;* and correspondence between Bošković and G. A. Slop, the Pisan astronomer, in *Studi trentini di scienze storiche,* **43,** no. 3 (1964), 209–242; he also published a study on Bošković's good friend Conti, "Scienziati lucchesi del settecento: Giovan Stefano Conti," in *La provincia di Lucca,* **2,** no. 3 (July–Sept. 1962), 31–44. R. Hahn, "The Boscovich Archives at Berkeley," in *Isis,* **56,** no. 183 (Spring 1965), 70–78, reports on the literary legacy of Bošković that has been at the University of California since 1962. Of the recent articles, we should mention P. Costabel's "Le *De viribus vivis* de R. Boscovic ou de la vertu des querelles de mots," in *Archives internationales d'histoire des sciences,* **14,** nos. 54–55 (Jan.–June 1961), 3–12.

The literature on Bošković in Yugoslavia is abundant. On the occasion of the centenary of his death, the Yugoslav Academy of Arts and Sciences in Zagreb issued a collection of works on Bošković in its publication *Rad,* **87, 88,** and **90** (1887–1888), including his correspondence from the archives of the observatory at Brera as transcribed by G. V. Schiaparelli. The latter correspondence was reprinted in *Publicazioni del R. Osservatorio astronomico di Milano–Merate,* n.s. no. 2 (1938). *Gradja za život i rad Rudjera Boškovića* ("Material Concerning the Life and Work of Rudjer Bošković"), 2 vols. (Zagreb, 1950–1957), is a separate publication of the Yugoslav Academy of Arts and Sciences.

Other publications on Bošković in languages other than Serbo-Croatian are in *Actes du symposium international R. J. Bošković 1958* (Belgrade–Zagreb–Ljubljana, 1959); *Actes du symposium international R. J. Bošković 1961* (Belgrade–Zagreb–Ljubljana, 1962); and *Atti del convegno internazionale celebrativo del 250° anniversario della nascita di R. G. Boscovich e del 200° anniversario della fondazione dell' Osservatorio di Brera* (Milan, 1963).

Studies on Bošković have made considerable advances in Yugoslavia, as shown by the works of V. Varićak, in the Yugoslav Academy's *Rad;* B. Truhelka, in various reviews, based on unpublished material on Bošković, especially correspondence with his brothers; S. Hondl, in *Almanah Bošković* ("The Bošković Almanac") of the Croatian Society of Natural Science; J. Majcen; Ž. Marković; Ž. Dadić; D. M. Grmek; and others. Mention should also be made of D. Nedeljković's numerous articles in reviews, as well as in the publications of the Serbian Academy of Arts and Sciences in Belgrade; and of the works of S. Ristić, D. Nikolić, and others. A comprehensive general bibliography up to 1956 can be found in "Bošković," in *Enciklopedija Jugoslavije* ("The Encyclopedia of Yugoslavia"), II (Zagreb, 1956).

ŽELJKO MARKOVIĆ

BOSS, LEWIS (*b.* Providence, Rhode Island, 26 October 1846; *d.* Albany, New York, 5 October 1912), *positional astronomy.*

Boss, who was honored by the Royal Astronomical Society for his "long-term work on the positions and proper motions of fundamental stars," had little, if any, academic training for this work. As a student at Dartmouth College he followed a classical course, but also frequented the observatory, where he learned to handle astronomical instruments and to reduce observations. After graduation he worked as a clerk in various government offices in Washington, D.C., and frequented the U.S. Naval Observatory, from which he borrowed small astronomical instruments.

In 1872 Boss was appointed assistant astronomer for the survey of the 49th parallel, between the United States and Canada; his job during the next four years was to locate, by celestial observations, latitude stations from which the surveyors could work. His observations with a zenith telescope led him to realize that latitude determinations can be no more accurate than the stellar declinations on which they are based. Therefore, while the survey was still in progress, Boss developed a homogeneous system of declinations, as free as possible from systematic errors resulting from faulty observations and methods of reduction. From a comparison of numerous star catalogs he devised tables for the systematic correction of each, as well as a new catalog of the declinations and proper motions of 500 stars, which was adopted by the American Ephemeris in 1883.

In 1876 Boss became director of the Dudley Observatory, a position he held for the rest of his life. His first major project at Albany, New York, was observation and reduction of a zone for Leipzig's Astronomische Gesellschaft. By determining his magnitude equation and investigating the flexure of, and division corrections needed by, each of the two circles of the Pistor and Martins meridian circle, Boss was able to keep his probable errors to less than $\pm 0''.6$ for each observation—well within the limits expected for the society's catalog. Although he had little assistance, and started ten years after the work on many other zones was begun, Boss was the first to finish his zone. A comparison of the zone results with earlier observations led him to realize the need for an extensive analysis and comparison of the many available star catalogs, in order to make a reliable determination of proper motions.

The outcome of this study—financed in large part by the Carnegie Institution, which in 1906 established a department of meridian astrometry under the direction of Boss, and later of his son Benjamin—was published in numerous papers and four great catalogs. The *Preliminary General Catalogue* (1910) included information on 6,188 bright stars. The *San Luis Catalogue* (1928) was based on observations of 15,333 stars made with the great meridian circle of the Dudley Observatory, moved temporarily to Argentina. The *Albany Catalogue* (1931) included 20,811 stars observed with the meridian circle at Albany, and the *General Catalogue of 33,342 Stars* (1937) contains "the standard positions and proper motions of all stars brighter than the seventh magnitude, extending from the north to the south pole, and some thousands of additional fainter stars promising to yield reasonably accurate proper motions."

While at Dudley, Boss undertook several other projects. He computed the orbits of many comets and in 1881, under the pseudonym of Hipparchus III, won the $200 Warner Prize for the best essay on comets. The following year Boss took charge of the U.S. government party sent to Santiago, Chile, to observe and photograph the transit of Venus. From 1883 to 1906 he served as superintendent of weights and measures of the state of New York. In 1893 Boss moved the Dudley Observatory to a more astronomically advantageous location in Albany. With experience gained from editing and managing the daily Albany *Morning Express,* in 1897 Boss became associate editor, and in 1909 editor, of the *Astronomical Journal.*

Among Boss's many honors besides the gold medal of the Royal Astronomical Society (1905), the Lalande Prize of the Paris Académie des Sciences (1911), and membership in the National Academy of Sciences (1889), the Königlich Preussischen Akademie der Wissenschaften (1910), and the Imperial Academy of Sciences of St. Petersburg.

BIBLIOGRAPHY

Among Boss's writings is his prize-winning essay, "Comets: Their Composition, Purpose, and Effect Upon the Earth," in *History and Work of the Warner Observatory, 1883-6* (Rochester, N.Y., 1887), pp. 25-30. The four star catalogs, all prepared at the Dudley Observatory, Albany, N.Y., and published by the Carnegie Institution of Washington, D.C., are the *Preliminary General Catalogue of 6188 Stars* (1910), by Lewis Boss; *San Luis Catalogue of 15,333 Stars* (1928), by Lewis and Benjamin Boss; *Albany Catalogue of 20,811 Stars* (1931), and *General Catalogue of 33,342 Stars* (1936-1937), both the work of Benjamin Boss.

Additional information and a bibliography of his scientific writings is in Benjamin Boss, "Biographical Memoir of Lewis Boss, 1846-1912," in *Biographical Memoirs of the National Academy of Sciences,* IX (Washington, D.C., 1920), 239-260. Also of value is "Address Delivered by the President, H. H. Turner, on Presenting the Gold Medal of the Society to Professor Lewis Boss," in *Monthly Notices of the Royal Astronomical Society,* **65** (1904-1905), 412-425.

DEBORAH JEAN WARNER

BOSSE, ABRAHAM (*b.* Tours, France, 1602; *d.* Paris, France, 14 February 1676), *geometry, graphic techniques.*

The son of Louis Bosse, a tailor, and Marie Martinet, Bosse settled in Paris around 1625 and worked as a draftsman and engraver. In 1632 he married Catherine Sarrabat; four of their children lived to adulthood.

His drafting technique was obviously derived from the *méthode universelle* of perspective, presented by Girard Desargues as early as 1636. Bosse became Desargues's most ardent propagandist, and it was through his efforts that Desargues's methods achieved some success among artists of the seventeenth century and spread to foreign countries.

The art world of the seventeenth century was split into vigorously warring factions. Bosse sided with Desargues, who was conducting violent polemics, and in 1643 published two treatises, *La pratique du trait à preuves de Mr. Desargues . . . pour la coupe des pierres en l'architecture* and *Manière universelle de Mr. Desargues . . . pour poser l'essieu & placer les heures et autres choses aux cadrans au soleil,* which were complex expositions of two essays that Desargues had written in 1640 on the cutting of stone and on gnomonics.

In 1648 Bosse published a third tract, *Manière universelle de Mr. Desargues pour pratiquer la perspective,* which included several texts by Desargues himself, some of which had not been published before. Among them was the famous theorem on perspective triangles. In 1653 the work was amplified by a demonstration of the application of perspective to curvilinear surfaces. Bosse followed this work with several others dealing with particular applications, and became involved in controversies that eventually cost him his membership in the Académie Royale de Peinture et de Sculpture.

Bosse also illustrated books, particularly works on

science. These included such various works as Glaser's *Traité de la chymie,* M. Cureau de La Chambre's *Traité de la lumière,* Moyse Charas's *Pharmacopée royale,* and a series of botanical plates for Dodart's *Mémoires pour servir à l'histoire des plantes.*

BIBLIOGRAPHY

I. ORIGINAL WORKS. Bosse's writings include *La pratique du trait à preuves de Mr. Desargues, Lyonnois, pour la coupe des pierres en l'architecture* (Paris, 1643), also translated into German (Nuremberg, 1699); *La manière universelle de Mr. Desargues, Lyonnois, pour poser l'essieu & placer les heures et autres choses aux cadrans au soleil* (Paris, 1643), also translated into English (London, 1659); *Traité des manières de graver en taille douce sur l'airin par le moyen des eaux fortes et des vernix durs et mols* (Paris, 1645), often reissued and translated; *Manière universelle de Mr. Desargues pour pratiquer la perspective par petit-pied, comme le géometral. Ensemble les places et proportions des fortes et foibles touches, teintes et couleurs* (Paris, 1648), also translated into Dutch (Amsterdam, 1664, 1686); *Moyen universel pour pratiquer la perspective sur les tableaux ou surfaces irrégulières. Ensemble quelques particularitez concernant cet art & celuy de la gravure en taille douce* (Paris, 1653), also translated into Dutch (Amsterdam, 1664, 1686); *Représentations géométrales de plusieurs parties de bastiments faites par les reigles de l'architecture antique* (Paris, 1659); *Traité des manières de dessiner les ordres de l'architecture antique en toutes leurs parties* (Paris, 1664); *Traité des pratiques géométrales et perspectives enseignées dans l'Académie Royale de la Peinture et Sculpture* (Paris, 1665); *Le peintre converty aux précises et universelles regles de son art* (Paris, 1667); *Regle universelle pour décrire toutes sortes d'arcs rampans sur des points donnez de sujetion* (Paris, 1672); *Catalogue des traitez que le Sieur Bosse a mis au jour* (Paris, 1674); and *Recueil des plantes gravées par ordre du roi Louis XIV,* 3 vols. (Paris, n.d.), with N. Robert and L. Chatillon.

A more complete bibliography is in J. C. Brunet (see below) and especially in A. Blum, *Abraham Bosse et la société française du dix-septième siècle,* pp. 217–227, which also reproduces numerous documents relating to the polemic between Bosse and the Académie Royale de Peinture et de Sculpture.

II. SECONDARY LITERATURE. Bosse or his work is discussed in the following (listed chronologically): J. and L. G. Michaud, *Biographie universelle,* new ed., V (Paris, 1843), 124–125; J. M. B. Renouvier, *Des types et des manières des maîtres-graveurs,* XVI–XVII, pt. 2 (Montpellier, 1856), 117–123; P. J. Mariette, *Abecedario,* P. de Chennevières and A. de Montaiglon, eds., II (Paris, 1851–1853), 159–161; G. Duplessis, *Catalogue de l'oeuvre d'A. Bosse* (Paris, 1859); J. C. Brunet, *Manuel du libraire,* I (Paris, 1860), cols. 1126–1129; F. Hoefer, *Nouvelle biographie générale,* IV (1862), cols. 786–787; G. Poudra, *Oeuvres de Desargues,* 2 vols. (Paris, 1864), I, 352–493, II, 1–113, and *Histoire de la perspective* (Paris, 1864); A. Jal,

Dictionnaire critique de biographie et d'histoire, 2nd ed. (Paris, 1872), pp. 348–352; A. de Montaiglon, *Procès-verbaux de l'Académie Royale de Peinture et de Sculpture, 1648–1792,* I (Paris, 1875), *passim;* E. Haag and E. Haag, *La France protestante,* 2nd ed., II (Paris, 1879), cols. 922–928; A. Valabrègue, *Abraham Bosse* (Paris, 1892); G. C. Williamson, *Bryan's Dictionary of Painters and Engravers,* new ed., I (London, 1903), 174; U. Thieme and F. Becker, *Allgemeines Lexikon der bildenden Künstler,* IV (Leipzig, 1910), 402–403; A. Fontaine, *L'art dans l'ancienne France. Académiciens d'autrefois* (Paris, 1914), pp. 67–114; F. Amodeo, "Lo sviluppo della prospettiva in Francia nel secolo XVII," in *Atti dell'Accademia Pontaniana,* **63** (Naples, 1933); A. Blum, *Abraham Bosse et la société française du dix-septième siècle* (Paris, 1924), and *L'oeuvre gravé d'Abraham Bosse* (Paris, 1925); R. Taton, *L'oeuvre mathématique de Desargues* (Paris, 1951), see Index H, and "La première oeuvre géométrique de Philippe de La Hire," in *Revue d'histoire des sciences,* **6** (1953), 93–111; M. L. Blumer, in *Dictionnaire de biographie française,* VI (Paris, 1954), cols. 1146–1147; F. Bénézit, *Dictionnaire des peintres, sculpteurs, dessinateurs et graveurs,* new ed., II (Paris, 1961), 33–34; and A. Kondo, "Abraham Bosse et Poussin devant les problèmes de l'espace et du temps," in *Annales,* 23rd year (1968), 127–135.

A more complete bibliography relating to the artistic aspect of Bosse's work is given by A. Blum in *Abraham Bosse et la société française du dix-septième siècle,* pp. 213–221; more precise references to the geometrical aspect of the problems are in R. Taton, *L'oeuvre mathématique de Desargues,* pp. 70–71.

RENÉ TATON

BOSSUT, CHARLES (*b.* Tartaras, Rhône-et-Loire, France, 11 August 1730; *d.* Paris, France, 14 January 1814), *mathematics, mechanics.*

Bossut was the son of Barthélemy Bossut and Jeanne Thonnerine. His father died when Charles was six months of age, and the boy was raised by a paternal uncle. He entered the Jesuit Collège de Lyon at fourteen and was a student of Père Béraud, a mathematician whose pupils included Jean Étienne Montucla and Joseph Jérome Lalande. Bossut took minor ecclesiastical orders and was an *abbé* until 1792. He was aided in his professional formation by d'Alembert, Clairaut, and the Abbé Charles Étienne Louis Camus. Bossut never married, was without family, and, according to some, lived his last years as a misanthrope.

Bossut's importance for the history of science lies in his role as a major contributor to European scientific education. His career began in 1752, when he was appointed as professor of mathematics at the École du Génie at Mézières. He remained as professor until 1768, then continued as examiner of students until 1794. His other teaching post was from 1775 to 1780, in the chair of hydrodynamics established by Turgot at the Louvre. For a time he was also examiner of students at the École Polytechnique. Bossut wrote a series of textbooks that appeared in several French and foreign-language editions and won wide acceptance from the 1770's until the early years of the Empire. The texts of Bossut and Étienne Bézout best represent the emergence in the eighteenth century of a standardized, rigorous system of engineering physics textbooks. In France, for example, Bossut's course was used at the Benedictine Collège de Sorèze, the Collège de France, the École du Génie, the École des Ponts et Chaussées, and the École des Mines. He also wrote a history of mathematics that achieved popularity, but never the scholarly recognition of Montucla's history. He edited the works of Pascal, contributed to the *Encyclopédie méthodique,* and aided d'Alembert in editing contributions to Diderot's *Encyclopédie.*

Bossut was one of a very few whom d'Alembert took as students, and as such he was admitted as a *correspondant* to the Académie des Sciences on 12 May 1753; subsequently, he rose to *géomètre, mécanicien,* and *mathématicien.* In 1761, 1762, and 1765 he won or shared prizes given by the Academy for memoirs on mechanics applied to the operation of ships and on the resistance of the ether in planetary motions. He won additional prizes for his mechanics memoirs from the academies of Lyons and Toulouse, and was elected to the scientific academies of Bologna, Turin, and St. Petersburg. In 1775 he participated with d'Alembert and Condorcet in a well-known series of experiments on fluid resistance. Never more than a minor mathematician or physicist, Bossut is nevertheless one of the important figures in the history of physics and engineering education.

BIBLIOGRAPHY

I. ORIGINAL WORKS. Most of Bossut's memoirs appeared in the *Mémoires* and publications of the Académie des Sciences, Paris. Some of these were reissued in the collection *Mémoires de mathématiques, concernant la navigation, l'astronomie physique, l'histoire . . . par Charles Bossut* (Paris, 1812). His first textbook, a volume that does not figure in the catalogs of most major libraries, is *Traité élémentaire de méchanique et de dinamique appliqué principalement aux mouvemens des machines* (Charleville, 1763). The various editions of his textbooks (*Cours de mathématiques, Traité élémentaire d'arithmétique,* and others) are cited in the general catalogs of the Bibliothèque Nationale and the British Museum. The first edition of his history of mathematics is *Essai sur l'histoire générale des mathématiques,* 2 vols. (Paris, 1802). For Bossut's edition of Pascal's works see Blaise Pascal, *Oeuvres complètes,* 5 vols. (The Hague, 1779).

II. SECONDARY LITERATURE. For a short biography, see M. E. Doublet, "L'abbé Bossut," in *Bulletin des sciences mathématiques,* 2nd ser., **38** (1914), 93–96, 121–125, 158–160, 186–190, 220–224. See also the *éloge* by J. B. J. Delambre in *Mémoires de l'Académie Royale des Sciences de l'Institut de France—Année 1816,* **1** (1818), xci–cii. For Bossut's career at Mézières and for his general influence on education, see René Taton, ed., *Enseignement et diffusion des sciences en France au XVIIIe siècle* (Paris, 1964); Vol. XI of the series Histoire de la Pensée. Bossut's appointment to the chair of hydrodynamics is discussed in Roger Hahn, "The Chair of Hydrodynamics in Paris, 1775–1791: A Creation of Turgot," in *Acts of the Xth International Congress of the History of Science* (*Ithaca*) (Paris, 1964), pp. 751–754. A convenient summary of Bossut's work in fluid resistance is in René Dugas, *A History of Mechanics,* J. R. Maddox, trans. (Neuchâtel, 1955), pp. 313–316. On the question of whether Bossut was a Jesuit, see Thomas F. Mulcrone, S.J., "A Note on the Mathematician Abbé Charles Bossut," in *Bulletin— American Association of Jesuit Scientists,* **42** (1965), 16–19.

C. STEWART GILLMOR

BOSTOCK, JOHN (*b.* Liverpool, England, 1773; *d.* London, England, 6 August 1846), *medical chemistry.*

The only child of Edinburgh graduate and Liverpool physician John Bostock the elder (*d.* 1774), John grew up amid the town's active and prospering Protestant Dissenter community. Bostock enjoyed a good education, and in 1792 he attended Joseph Priestley's chemical lecture course at Hackney College. Further study with an apothecary and attendance at the Liverpool General Dispensary preceded his move to Edinburgh University in the autumn of 1794. Fellow medical students there included Alexandre Marcet, Thomas Thomson, and Thomas Young; and Bostock was elected a member, then a president, of the Medical Society. Graduating M.D. in 1798 with a thesis on the secretion of bile, he returned to Liverpool as a physician to the General Dispensary. Soon active in the town, Bostock played key roles in the formation of the Botanic Garden, the Fever Hospital, and the Philosophical and Literary Society, and he was also quickly launched on a career of prolific scientific publication.

For several years Bostock wrote nearly all the medical and scientific articles in the *Monthly Review,* as well as publishing a host of original papers in the *Edinburgh Medical and Surgical Journal,* Nicholson's *Journal of Natural Philosophy, Chemistry and the Arts,* and the *Transactions* of the London Medico-Chirurgical Society. An early interest in physiology led to his *Essay on Respiration* (Liverpool, 1804). This was well received, a commission to write many medical articles for David Brewster's *Edinburgh Encyclopaedia* being one result. Bostock's most successful work was his three-volume *Elementary System of Physiology* (1824–1827), which enjoyed wide popularity and reached a fourth edition in 1844. He also wrote critical pamphlets on the new Edinburgh (Liverpool, 1807) and London (London, 1811) pharmacopoeias, a *History . . . of Galvanism* (London, 1818), a *History of Medicine* (London, 1835), and an incomplete translation of Pliny's *Natural History* (London, 1828).

Bostock developed an extensive medical and chemical consulting practice; and in 1817, having made a secure fortune, he abandoned Liverpool medicine for London and the full-time pursuit of science in its social and administrative, as much as its laboratory, context. He soon succeeded his friend Marcet as chemical lecturer at Guy's Hospital, and (with A. Aikin) he for two years edited the *Annals of Philosophy,* following Thomas Thomson's move to Glasgow. His widening scientific activity is reflected in his work as secretary of the Geological Society (president, 1826), council member of the Royal Society (vice-president, 1832), and treasurer of the Medico-Chirurgical Society. He also served on the councils of the Linnean, Zoological, and Horticultural societies, and the Royal Society of Literature.

Bostock's primary research interest was medical chemistry and he made valuable contributions to, *inter alia,* the study of body fluids and urinary components. He also gave the first complete description of hay fever. Equally interesting to the historian is the way that Bostock's career typifies the scientific research and administrative opportunities available to the British medical man of the early nineteenth century. In this respect his life forms an instructive contrast to the activities of such less formally educated and more industrially oriented contemporary chemists as, say, Friedrich Accum and William Nicholson.

BIBLIOGRAPHY

I. ORIGINAL WORKS. Bostock's separately published writings are *Essay on Respiration* (Liverpool, 1804); *Remarks on the Reforms of the Pharmaceutical Nomenclature; and Particularly on That Adopted by the Edinburgh College* (Liverpool, 1807); *Remarks on the Nomenclature of the New London Pharmacopoeia* (London, 1810); *History . . . of Galvanism* (London, 1818); *Elementary System of Physiology,* 3 vols. (London, 1824–1827; 3rd ed., 1 vol., London, 1876); and *History of Medicine* (London, 1835). He also was responsible for a partial translation of Pliny's *Natural History* (London, 1828). An incomplete list of Bostock's multitudinous journal and encyclopedia contributions is in T. J. Pettigrew, *Biographical Memoirs of the Most Celebrated Physicians,* III (London, 1839), sec. 4, 1–20.

II. SECONDARY LITERATURE. Further information on Bostock's life may be gleaned from the obituary notice in *Proceedings of the Royal Society,* 5 (1846), 636–638. His medical chemistry is evaluated in J. R. Partington, *A History of Chemistry,* III (London, 1962), 711–712.

ARNOLD THACKRAY

BOTALLO, LEONARDO (*b.* Asti, Italy, *ca.* 1519; *d.* Chenonceaux or Blois, 1587/1588), *medicine.*

Botallo studied and obtained a degree in medicine at the University of Pavia, after which he continued his studies for a time at the University of Padua under Gabriele Falloppio. He then practiced medicine in Asti. He joined the French forces in Italy, at least by 1544, since he refers to his participation in the battle of Ceresole as a military surgeon. He was already located in Paris as one of the physicians of Charles IX in 1560, the same year in which his surgical treatise *De curandis vulneribus sclopettorum* was published in Lyons. Based partly on earlier, similar treatises and partly on Botallo's own experiences as a military surgeon, the work is notable chiefly for its support of the opinion, first advocated in print by Ambroise Paré in 1545, that gunshot wounds were not envenomed and ought to receive mild rather than harsh treatment. It was also concerned with the neurological effects of cranial injuries and the indications for treatment. The work was frequently and widely reprinted.

Botallo's name appears in the eponymous nomenclature of anatomy through the terms Botallo's duct (*ductus arteriosus*) and Botallo's foramen (*foramen ovale cordis*), actually incorrect attributions of discovery based upon Botallo's brief note "Vena arteriarum nutrix a nullo antea notata" in his *De catarrho commentarius.* Assertions that this note appeared in an earlier form entitled *De foramine ovalis dissertatio* appear to be incorrect. Through accidental discovery of the above structures in the calf's heart and thereafter in various other animals, and in particular through his chance observation of persistence of the *foramen ovale,* Botallo was led to believe that the blood's passage from the right to the left side of the heart was by way of this opening rather than through the imaginary pores of the cardiac septum, as (incorrectly) proposed by Galen, or through the lungs, as (correctly) proposed by Realdo Colombo. Actually, Botallo's "discovery" had been mentioned in the second century by Galen and, more recently, the *ductus arteriosus* by Falloppio, in 1561 and the *ductus arteriosus* and *foramen ovale* by Vesalius, also in 1561. Botallo may therefore be credited merely with independent rediscovery; but, since he did not dissect the fetus, he failed to recognize the true significance of the structures, although it appears to have been known to Galen and was later reemphasized by William Harvey.

A second note in *De catarrho commentarius,* entitled "Addita est in fine monstrorum renum figura, nuper in cadavere repertorum," provides a careful description, accompanied by a detailed illustration, of an instance of fused kidneys with horseshoe configuration. This anomaly, too, had previously been observed and described, although more briefly, by Berengario da Carpi in the *Isagogae* (1522, f. 17v). Nonetheless, Botallo's detailed account indicates his interest in anatomy and his not inconsiderable ability as a dissector and observer.

Botallo's other writings are of lesser significance. The *Luis venereae curandae ratione* was characteristic of its time; but *De incidendae venae, cutis scarificandae et hirudinum applicandarum modo,* through presentation of Botallo's independent, anti-Galenic opinions regarding venesection, gained him the enmity of the conservative Parisian physicians. Botallo believed in the therapeutic value of liberal bloodletting. The *Commentariola duo, alter de medici, alter de aegroti munere,* dealing with medical ethics and the physician-patient relationship in general, reveals Botallo as skeptical of the value of astrology to medicine.

Throughout his years in the French royal medical service, Botallo enjoyed the favor and confidence of the queen mother, Catherine de' Medici, in part perhaps because of their common Italian origin. In any event, she was instrumental in having his services transferred to her favorite son, the duke of Anjou, later Henry III. It was during this latter service, and no doubt as a reflection of his fame as a military surgeon, that Botallo was temporarily disengaged in 1575 to undertake the care and treatment of Henry I of Lorraine, duke of Guise, who had received a gunshot wound of the cheek and ear. Botallo was, at least professionally, inactive during the final years of his life as a result of sickness, most likely the effects of malaria. He died probably at Chenonceaux or Blois, but there is no available information as to where he was buried.

BIBLIOGRAPHY

I. ORIGINAL WORKS. Botallo's works include *De curandis vulneribus sclopettorum* (Lyons, 1560, 1564, 1566, 1575, 1583), translated into German as *Von den Schuss-Wunden, und wie dieselben zu heilen* (Nuremberg, 1676); *De foramine ovalis dissertatio* (Lyons, 1561); *Luis venerae curandae ratione* (Paris, 1563); *De catarrho commentarius* (Paris, 1564); *Commentariola duo, alter de medici, alter de aegroti munere* (Lyons, 1565); and *De incidendae venae, cutis scarificandae et hirudinum applicandarum modo* (Lyons, 1565).

II. SECONDARY LITERATURE. In addition to the few autobiographical remarks in Botallo's writings, there is a biographical study by Leonardo Carerj, *Leonardo Botallo Astese, medico regio* (Asti, 1954). Also see John A. Benjamin and Dorothy M. Schullian, "Observations on Fused Kidneys With Horseshoe Configuration: The Contribution of Leonardo Botallo (1564)," in *Journal of the History of Medicine and Allied Sciences,* **5** (1950), 315–326; Leonardo Carerj, "Leonardo Botallo, il foro ovale e il dotto arterioso," in *Minerva medica,* **2** (1955), varia, 789–795; K. J. Franklin, "A Survey of the Growth of Knowledge About Certain Parts of the Foetal Cardio-vascular Apparatus, and About the Foetal Circulation, in Man and in Some Other Mammals. Part I: Galen to Harvey," in *Annals of Science,* **5** (1941), 57–89; E. J. Gurlt, *Geschichte der Chirurgie und ihrer Ausübung,* II (Berlin, 1898), 403–415; Antonio Nitto, "Considerazioni medico-storiche sulla fossa ovale, il legamento arterioso e la priorità della loro scoperta tra Leonardo Botallo e Giulio Cesare Aranzio," in *Policlinico, sez. med.,* **68** (1961), 299–312; and Mario Truffi, "Leonardo Botallo sifilografo," in *Minerva medica,* **46** (1955), varia, 34–42.

C. D. O'MALLEY

BOTHE, WALTHER WILHELM GEORG (*b.* Oranienburg, Germany, 8 June 1891; *d.* Heidelberg, Germany, 8 February 1957), *physics.*

Bothe's father was Fritz Bothe, a merchant. During the period 1908 to 1912 Walther studied at the University of Berlin, where his training included not only physics and mathematics but also chemistry. In 1914 he obtained his doctorate under Max Planck for a study of the molecular theory of refraction, reflection, dispersion, and extinction, a subject he continued to study from 1915 to 1920 while a prisoner of war in Russia. On his return to Germany, where he married Barbara Below, Bothe accepted Hans Geiger's invitation to work at the radioactivity laboratory of the Physikalische-Technische Reichsanstalt. Much of his early experimental work was done with Geiger, and Bothe later said that it was Geiger who had initiated him into his researches in physics. Bothe taught physics at the University of Berlin from 1920 until he accepted the professorship of physics at Giessen in 1931. In 1934 he became director of the Max Planck Institute at Heidelberg, where he remained until his death. Bothe received the Max Planck Prize, and he shared the Nobel Prize with Max Born in 1954.

From 1921 to 1924 Bothe was active in both theoretical and experimental work on the scattering of alpha and beta rays. He devised a statistical theory for processes involving multiple scattering through small angles, a phenomenon far more complex than large-angle scattering. Bothe studied multiple scattering of electrons experimentally by tracking the trajectories on photographic plates. He also deduced mathematical expressions for the relationships between scattering angle and foil thickness, using a nuclear model of the atom.

Among the topics that Bothe studied in 1924 was the ejection of electrons by X rays, and it was in connection with this phenomenon that he and Geiger performed an important experiment. In an effort to reconcile the particulate and wavelike properties of radiation, Bohr, Kramers, and Slater in 1924 formulated a new quantum theory of radiation. According to their hypothesis, momentum and energy are conserved only statistically in interactions between radiation and matter. Bothe and Geiger suggested that this could be tested experimentally by examining individual Compton collisions. Bothe introduced a modification into the Geiger counter that made it appropriate for use in coincidence experiments (a very novel procedure in 1924). Using two counters, they studied the coincidences between the scattered X ray and the recoiling electron. Correlating photons with electrons, Bothe and Geiger found a coincidence rate of one in eleven; since the chance coincidence rate for the situation was 10^{-5}, the experimental results contradicted the theoretical predictions and indicated small-scale conservation of energy and momentum.

With Werner Kolhörster, Bothe used the coincidence method again in 1929 to demonstrate that cosmic rays might be particles. Ever since their discovery in 1912, physicists had assumed that cosmic rays were high-energy photons, and Millikan's hypothesis that they were released during the elementary synthesis of elements by fusion in the atmosphere was especially popular. In the experiments of Bothe and Kolhörster, two Geiger counters were separated by about 4 cm. of gold; and in order for a photon to produce a pulse in a counter, it would have to undergo a Compton collision and produce an ionizing electron. The known probability of Compton collisions and the average energy of the photons indicated that coincidences between the two counters were highly improbable. The high coincidence rate in the experiment, approximately 75 percent of the original single-counter rate, therefore indicated that the cosmic radiation might well be particulate.

Nuclear transmutation was a third new topic of interest for physicists at this time. In 1919 Rutherford had produced oxygen nuclei and protons by bombarding nitrogen with alpha particles, and during the following decade various laboratories worked on this type of transmutation. Bothe took up the subject in 1926, and in the following years he studied the transmutation, via alpha particles, of boron to carbon. He was among the early users of the electronic counter to detect the protons in this type of reaction. With H. Becker he searched systematically for a gamma radiation accompanying the transmutation; its existence seemed reasonable because there were some light elements, such as beryllium, that did not disintegrate. In these experiments there were problems in finding a suitable source of alpha particles (one that did not produce other radiations as well), and Bothe himself finally prepared one by a process of chemical extraction. In 1930 Bothe and Becker detected a highly penetrative radiation from beryllium bombarded by alpha particles, and they assumed that it was gamma radiation. Bothe estimated the photon energy from the degree of absorption of the secondary electrons. When physicists studied this "beryllium radiation," estimating its energy constituted a problem, for it varied greatly according to the substance used as absorber. Chadwick later suggested that the radiation was particulate and consisted of a new particle, the neutron.

After detecting the new radiation in 1930, Bothe continued studying nuclear transmutation, and made coincidence measurements on the products of the reaction between alpha particles and beryllium. When he became director of the Max Planck Institute, he was involved in the construction of a Van de Graaf accelerator there and in the planning of a cyclotron which was finally completed in 1943. After the outbreak of World War II he did much work on uranium and on neutron transport theory, and he was one of the foremost scientists of Germany's "uranium project" for nuclear energy.

In the early 1950's Bothe again dealt with questions of electron scattering and cosmic rays, and of beta and gamma spectra. Thus, over a period of more than thirty years Bothe studied a broad range of highly relevant problems in a variety of ways.

BIBLIOGRAPHY

I. ORIGINAL WORKS. A few of Bothe's more important papers are "Ein Weg zur experimentellen Nachprüfung der Theorie von Bohr, Kramers, und Slater," in *Zeitschrift für Physik,* **26** (1924), 44 (written with H. Geiger); "Ueber das Wesen des Comptoneffekts; ein experimentellen Beitrag zur Theorie der Strahlung," in *Zeitschrift für Physik,* **32** (1925), 639–663 (written with H. Geiger); "Das Wesen der Hoehenstrahlung," in *Zeitschrift für Physik,* **56** (1929), 75–77 (written with W. Kolhörster); "Kunstliche

Erregung von Kern-γ-Strahlen," in *Zeitschrift für Physik,* **66** (1930), 289–306 (written with H. Becker). Other papers are listed in *Science Abstracts.*

II. SECONDARY LITERATURE. Discussions of Bothe's work on scattering are in E. Rutherford, J. Chadwick, and C. D. Ellis, *Radiations from Radioactive Substances* (Cambridge, 1930), pp. 209–212, 219–220, 237–238. In connection with the work on cosmic rays, see Bruno Rossi, *Cosmic Rays* (New York, 1964), pp. 30–42. The context of the early research on nuclear transformations may be found in M. Korsunsky, *The Atomic Nucleus* (New York, 1965), pp. 137–145. M. Jammer, *The Conceptual Development of Quantum Mechanics* (New York, 1966), pp. 181–188, and B. L. Van der Waerden, ed., *Sources of Quantum Mechanics* (Amsterdam, 1967), pp. 12–14, discuss the significance of the 1925 experiment. There is an account of Bothe's role in the German uranium project in S. A. Goudsmit, *Alsos* (New York, 1947). Obituaries are Lise Meitner, in *Nature,* **179** (1957), 654–655; and R. Fleischmann, in *Die Naturwissenschaften,* **44** (1957), 457–460.

SIGALIA DOSTROVSKY

BOTTAZZI, FILIPPO (*b.* Diso, Apulia, Italy, 23 December 1867; *d.* Diso, 19 September 1941), *physiology.*

Bottazzi received the M.D. in Rome in 1893. Early the following year, he became an assistant in physiology at the Institute of Higher, Practical, and Postgraduate Studies of Florence (now the University of Florence), and in 1896, *Privatdozent* in physiology. In 1902 he was appointed director of the Institute of Physiology of the University of Genoa, and in 1905, director of the Institute of Physiology of the University of Naples. While in Naples he was actively engaged in research at the Zoological Station, and from 1915 to 1923 he was director of its department of physiology.

Through his association with his teacher Giulio Fano, Bottazzi belonged to the physiological school of Luigi Luciani, which, with the school of Angelo Mosso, was at that time the most important in Italy. Bottazzi's work in physiology is distinguished by its close relationship to biological and physical chemistry. This relationship became evident in his *Elementi di chimica fisica* (1906) and his *Trattato di chimica fisiologica* (1898–1899), which for decades were the standard works on the subjects in Italy. Their recognition abroad is attested by H. Boruttau's German translation, *Physiologische Chemie für Studierende und Ärzte* (1901).

In 1894 Bottazzi's earliest investigations demonstrated the diminution of the osmotic resistance experienced by the red corpuscles as they travel through the splenic cycle: this is the hemocatatonistic function of the spleen, which is a part of the wider function of the splenic hemocatheresis and, more generally, of the endothelial reticulum.

A similar chemicophysical basis was demonstrated by his research on the osmotic pressure of the organic liquids, which Bottazzi explored in nearly all classes of animals, from the invertebrates to man (and in the case of man, also in a variety of physiological and pathological conditions). He arrived at the conclusion that homeo-osmosis—that is, the constancy of the osmotic pressure of the *milieu intérieur* (blood and interstitial liquids)—must be considered a relatively late philogenetic acquisition. Homeo-osmosis does not occur in aquatic invertebrates or in cartilaginous fishes, animals whose internal liquids are nearly in osmotic equilibrium with the water of the external environment. In the teleost fishes there is the beginning of a limited or conditioned osmotic independence of the external environment. In all other vertebrates, starting with the amphibians, the osmotic pressure of the blood becomes an absolute physical constant, like the body temperature of birds and mammals. Therefore, Bottazzi distinguished between homeo-osmotic and poikilosmotic animals, in much the same way that one distinguishes between homeothermic and poikilothermic animals.

The same broadly comparative criterion that was adopted in these investigations was also used in those that Bottazzi and his collaborators conducted on the smooth and striated muscles. Thanks to this work, Bottazzi was able to attribute an essentially tonic function to the sarcoplasm, that is, to the part of the muscle cell that is not differentiated into myofibril. According to the theory formulated by Bottazzi, the fibrillar formations serve for the rapid clonic contraction, while the sarcoplasm serves for the slow and sustained tonic contraction. Therefore, the more readily a muscle attains tonus, the more sarcoplasm it contains (following this decreasing scale: smooth muscle, red striated muscle, and pale striated muscle). The sarcoplasm, which is less irritable and slower to contract, carries out the simple function of tone. The fibrillar anisotropic substance, which is more irritable, is capable of rapid movements and usually is more fully developed, depending on how quickly the muscle reacts to stimuli.

In the area of practical studies, special mention must be made of Bottazzi's research on the physiology of nutrition. This work was presented in *Fisiologia dell'alimentazione con speciale riguardo all'alimentazione delle classi povere* (1910), written with G. Jappelli, and *L'alimentazione dell'uomo* (1919).

Bottazzi translated Michael Foster's *Treatise on Physiology* in 1899. He and Foster, who in 1894 invited him to teach a practical course on physiology for advanced students at Cambridge, shared a keen interest in the history of science. The main results of this interest were numerous studies that Bottazzi wrote on Leonardo da Vinci from 1902 to the eve of his death, and the new national edition of the works of Lazzaro Spallanzani (1932–1936).

BIBLIOGRAPHY

I. ORIGINAL WORKS. Bottazzi's writings include *Trattato di chimica fisiologica,* 2 vols. (Milan, 1898–1899), trans. by H. Boruttau as *Physiologische Chemie für Studierende und Ärzte* (Leipzig–Vienna, 1901); *Trattato di fisiologia,* 4 vols. (Milan, 1899), a translation of Michael Foster's *Treatise on Physiology; Elementi di chimica fisica* (Milan, 1906), with G. Jappelli; *Fisiologia dell'alimentazione con speciale riguardo all'alimentazione delle classi povere* (Milan, 1910); and *L'alimentazione dell'uomo* (Naples, 1919). He was also an editor of the new national edition of *Le opere di Lazzaro Spallanzani,* 6 vols. (Milan, 1932–1936).

II. SECONDARY LITERATURE. A fundamental source for this article was Pietro Rondoni's "Filippo Bottazzi," a discerning commemoration of the man and his work, in *Annuario della Reale Accademia d'Italia,* **14** (1941–1942), 156–169. Complete lists of Bottazzi's writings, with brief biographical sketches, are in *Annuario della Reale Accademia d'Italia,* **1,** (1929), 87–102; and in *Annuario della Pontificia Accademia delle scienze,* **1** (1936–1937), 159–185.

LUIGI BELLONI

BÖTTGER, RUDOLPH CHRISTIAN (*b.* Aschersleben, Germany, 28 April 1806; *d.* Frankfurt am Main, Germany, 29 April 1881), *chemistry.*

Böttger entered the University of Halle in 1824 to study theology. Despite the time devoted to theology and philosophy, he regularly attended the chemistry lectures of Johann S. C. Schweigger, thus fulfilling a youthful ambition to study chemistry.

On leaving the university in 1828, he continued his interest in chemistry while employed as a tutor, corresponding with Schweigger and pursuing a program of research in his spare time. By 1835 he had published a dozen papers in the leading German chemical periodicals. In that year, he was called to the Physicalischer Verein at Frankfurt am Main, where he taught physics and chemistry for the rest of his long, active life. In 1837 he received the doctorate from the University of Halle, and in 1841 he married Christiane Harpke.

Böttger's interests in chemistry were far-reaching, and he was particularly interested in practical applications of research. For example, he invented a useful kindling apparatus modified from Schönbein's lamp, and in 1841 he developed an electroforming process for reproducing illustrations which was widely used.

Böttger showed in 1843 that nickel could be plated on other metals by electrodeposition, although the technology of the times was insufficient for commercial use, and in 1845 he produced high-purity iron by electrolytic deposition.

Böttger has been credited with the independent discovery of guncotton, first announced by Schönbein in March 1846. He had collaborated with Heinrich Will at Giessen on styphnic (hydroxypicric) acid and was able to advise Schönbein in July 1846 that the preparation of guncotton could be improved by use of a mixture of sulfuric and nitric acid.

Shortly after Anton Schrötter discovered red phosphorus in 1847, Böttger introduced match heads covered with a mixture of potassium chlorate, red lead, and a gum, to be used on match boxes whose striking surfaces were coated with red phosphorus.

Böttger investigated silver and copper acetylides, chrome alum, chromic oxide, and lampic acid. He devised tests for nitrites and chlorates still used today. He also studied the reduction of palladous chloride, and the chemistry of indium, thallium, and cesium.

Böttger was an able chemist, a "skillful experimenter whose tact in manipulation is well known" (Jerome Nicklès, "Correspondence . . . 1858"). His work, mainly qualitative, was ingenious and accurate. He rarely pursued a particular topic in depth, turning instead to the other aspects of chemistry that intrigued him, nor was he prone to hypothesize or to frame chemical theories, preferring instead the daily routine of laboratory experimentation.

BIBLIOGRAPHY

I. ORIGINAL WORKS. Böttger wrote more than one hundred papers. Convenient but incomplete lists may be found in Poggendorff, *Biographisch-literarisches Handwörterbuch,* I (1963), 150–151; and in the Royal Society's *Catalogue of Scientific Papers,* X (1867), 508–511; VII (1877), 223–224; IX, 303. In 1846 he founded the *Polytechnisches Notizblatt* and edited it for 35 years. One of his major works was the three-volume *Beiträge zur Physik und Chemie* (Frankfurt am Main, 1838–1846).

II. SECONDARY LITERATURE. Theodor Petersen gives a brief description of Böttger's life and work in *Berichte der Chemischen Gesellschaft,* **14** (1881), 2913–2919. Robert Knott's biography in *Allgemeine deutsche Biographie,* XLVII, 143–144, is based on Petersen. J. R. Partington, *A History of Chemistry,* IV (London, 1964), 196, gives a concise summary of Böttger's work. See also Jerome Nicklès, "Correspondence of Jerome Nicklès, Dated Paris, Oct. 26th, 1858," in *American Journal of Science,* **27** (1859), no. 79, 121. There is no detailed study of Böttger's life.

LOUIS I. KUSLAN

BOUCHER DE CRÈVECOEUR DE PERTHES, JACQUES (*b*. Rethel, Ardennes, France, 10 September 1788; *d*. Abbeville, France, 5 August 1868), *archaeology*.

Boucher was the director of the customshouse at Abbeville, where he spent his leisure time in archaeological pursuits. Here he found evidences of Stone Age cultures, which he reported and interpreted in a series of monographs. Although rejected by the scientific society of Abbeville, his work came to the attention of a group of eminent British scientists (including Lyell), who in 1859 visited the sites of his excavations and supported his conclusions. For a complete study of his scientific accomplishments and writings see Supplement.

BOUÉ, AMI (diminutive of **Amédée**) (*b*. Hamburg, Germany, 16 March 1794; *d*. Vöslau, Austria, 21 November 1881), *geology*.

Boué's father, Jean-Henri, was a shipbuilder and shipowner; his mother, Suzanne de Chapeaurouge, was the daughter of an Alsatian merchant who had settled in Hamburg. Orphaned at the age of eleven, he was taken in by relatives in Geneva and later went to Paris, where he was educated by an uncle, Antoine Odier, a banker. He showed no particular interest in either business or bookkeeping, and convinced his relatives that he should not enter the family shipping business. He also had no inclination for the intricacies of the law, and he therefore interrupted his legal studies (which his uncle had urged him to begin) when, at the age of twenty, he came into an inheritance.

Boué decided at the beginning of 1814 to study medicine at the University of Edinburgh and learned English. Through the influence of one of his teachers, the mineralogist Robert Jameson, he became interested in geology and botany, which he studied while traveling throughout Scotland. In 1815 he published in the *Edinburgh Philosophical Journal* an unsigned article on a crystallized hyacinth found in gneiss along the Caledonian Canal. On 15 September 1817, he received the M.D. after having defended a thesis on the botanical geography of Scotland.

Although Boué continued his medical studies in Paris (1818–1819), Berlin (1820), and Vienna (1821), he decided to devote himself exclusively to geology and traveled through the Auvergne, the south of France, and almost all of Germany, Austria-Hungary, and Italy. His *Essai géologique sur l'Écosse*, dedicated to Jameson, appeared in 1820. Two years later he published "Mémoire géologique sur l'Allemagne." His observations on the geology of Germany were completed in *Geognotisches Gemälde von Deutschland* (1829), in which he discussed the ages of the various mountain chains.

In 1830 Boué went to Paris and, with his friends Constant Prevost, Paul Deshayes, and Jules Desnoyers, founded the Société Géologique de France, of which he became president in 1835. In 1830–1831, in collaboration with Jobert and Claude Rozet, he published *Journal de géologie,* followed by *Mémoires géologiques et paléontologiques* in 1832. Boué expressed his views on geological controversies with complete candor, and he did not fail to criticize the authorities whenever he felt they were wrong. Thus, he reproved Cuvier for having refused (1823) to acknowledge the age of the human skeleton he had found among fossil mammal remains at the base of the loess at Lahr (near Strasbourg). He also censured Élie de Beaumont for his daring theory on the pentagonal network.

From 1830 to 1834 Boué published bibliographical notices on geological progress in foreign countries in the *Bulletin de la Société géologique de France.* In 1833, when Paul-Émile Botta published his "Observations sur le Liban et l'Anti-Liban," Boué remarked in a note to the article that, according to the fossils sent back by the author, the three stages distinguished in Lebanon correspond to the Lower Cretaceous, greensand, and Jurassic limestone.

In 1835 Boué left Paris for Vienna, just after the first volume of his *Guide du géologue-voyageur, sur le modèle de l'Agenda geognostica de M. Léonhard* had been published. (Leonhard's work was published in 1829.) Boué expanded the subject considerably, discussing preparations and preliminary instructions for geological trips, physical geography, and various aspects of geology.

In 1836, 1837, and 1838 Boué made three trips to European Turkey to study the resources of the country and its people. *La Turquie d'Europe* was published in 1840.

When he returned to Austria, Boué bought property at Vöslau, where during the summer he worked in his gardens and vineyards. In 1845 his synthesis of geological knowledge, *Essai de carte géologique du globe terrestre,* was published. He was elected a member of the Academy of Sciences of Vienna in 1849.

BIBLIOGRAPHY

Boué's principal publications are *Dissertatio inauguralis de methodo floram cujusdam conducendi, exemplis é flora Scoticâ, etc., ductis, illustrata* (Edinburgh, 1817); *Essai géologique sur l'Écosse* (Paris, n.d. [1820]); "Mémoire géologique sur l'Allemagne," in *Journal de physique, de chimie et d'histoire naturelle,* **94** (1822), 297–312, 345–378; **95** (1822), 31–48, 88–112, 173–200, 275–304; "Allgemeine geologische Beobachtungen über die Entstehung der Gebirge Schottlands," in *Taschenbuch für die gesammte Mineralogie von Karl Cäsar Leonhard* (Frankfurt, 1823), pp. 239–362; *Geognotisches Gemälde von Deutschland mit Rücksicht auf die Gebirgsbeschaffenheit nachbarlicher Staaten* (Frankfurt, 1829); "Des progrès de la géologie," in *Bulletin de la Société géologique de France,* **1** (1831), 71–75, 94–97, 105–124; *Journal de géologie,* 3 vols. (Paris, 1830–1831); "Résumé des progrès de la géologie en 1831," in *Bulletin de la Société géologique de France,* **2** (1832), 133–218; *Mémoires géologiques et paléontologiques* (Paris, 1832); "Résumé des progrès de la géologie, et de quelques unes de ses principales applications, pendant l'année 1832," in *Bulletin de la Société géologique de France,* **3** (1833), ii–clxxxviii; "Résumé des progrès des sciences géologiques pendant l'année 1833," *ibid.,* **5** (1834); *Guide du géologue-voyageur, sur le modèle de l'Agenda geognostica de M. Léonhard,* 2 vols. (Paris, 1835–1836); *La Turquie d'Europe . . .,* 4 vols. (Paris, 1840); *Essai de carte géologique du globe terrestre* (Paris, 1845); *Der ganze Zweck und der hohe Nutzen der Geologie in allgemeiner und in specieller Rücksicht auf die Oesterreichischen Staaten und ihre Völker* (Vienna, 1851); *Sur l'établissement de bonnes routes et surtout de chemins de fer dans la Turquie d'Europe* (Vienna, 1852); and *Ueber die Nothwendigkeit einer Reform des bergmännischen Unterrichtes in Österreich . . .* (Vienna, 1869).

A secondary source is Franz Ritter von Hauer, "Zur Erinnerung an Dr. Ami Boué," in *Jahrbuch der Kaiserlich-Königlichen geologischen Bundesanstalt* (Vienna), **32** (1882), 1–6.

Arthur Birembaut

BOUELLES, CHARLES DE. See **Bouvelles, Charles.**

BOUGAINVILLE, LOUIS ANTOINE DE (*b.* Paris, France, 11 November 1729; *d.* Paris, 31 August 1811), *geography, mathematics.*

Bougainville was the son of a notary, Pierre-Yves de Bougainville. To escape his father's profession he joined the army, saw service with Montcalm in Canada, and, on his own initiative, founded a French colony in the Falkland Islands in 1764. Two years later he was commissioned to sail around the world. On his return he received many honors and was promoted in both the army and the navy. He saw further service in North America. He married into a naval family in 1780 and had four children. Despite his royalist sympathies, he survived the Terror. He escaped the massacre of Paris and lived quietly for the rest of his life. He was an associate of the Académie des Sciences, a member of the Legion of Honor, a count of the empire under Napoleon, and a senator. He was buried with full honors in the Panthéon.

Bougainville's contributions to science were twofold: he began a career in mathematics but achieved his greatest fame as an explorer. At the completion of his schooling he came under the influence of d'Alembert, and as a result he wrote the *Traité du calcul-intégral* during 1752. L'Hospital had written the first textbook on calculus in 1696. Bougainville's contribution was to extend L'Hospital's treatise to cover the integral calculus and to bring the differential calculus up to date. He brought such clarity and order to the subject, as well as incorporating new work, that he achieved immediate recognition. The Académie des Sciences noticed the work in January 1753. It was published the following year, and at the beginning of 1756, it brought Bougainville election to the Royal Society of London. A further volume was published in 1756, and this was the end of his career as a mathematician.

At the end of 1766 Bougainville left Nantes in the frigate *La Boudeuse*. After handing over the Falkland Island colony to Spain in 1767, he called at Rio de Janeiro to meet his supply ship. On board was the botanist Commerson. Among the plants Commerson collected around Rio de Janeiro was a climbing shrub with large purple-red bracts which he named bougainvillea.

The two ships left the Falkland Islands in July 1767 and sailed through the Strait of Magellan. By the end of March 1768, Bougainville was discovering new islands in the Pacific archipelago of Tuamotu. He sailed on to Tahiti, only to find that La Nouvelle Cythère, as he named it, had been discovered eight months earlier by Samuel Wallis. Sailing west, he almost reached the Great Barrier Reef but turned north without exploring further. Bougainville sailed through an archipelago that he named the Louisiade, and discovered two of the Treasury Islands before reaching the Solomons. On 1 July he left the west coast of Choiseul Island and for three days sailed along "a new coast which is of an astonishing height." This is now Bougainville Island, and the strait between it and Choiseul is Bougainville Strait.

Putting into the Moluccas, Bougainville found a "species of wild cat that carries her young in a pocket below her belly," and thus confirmed what Buffon had doubted, that pouched mammals exist in the East Indies. In 1771 Bougainville published the best-selling *Voyage autour du monde.*

It has been said by Frenchmen that, in spite of his mathematical abilities, Bougainville was no great navigator. But he was the first Frenchman to sail around the world. His voyage took three years and, in an age when the death rate for sailors was high, he lost only seven men. He named new islands in the Solomons and the Tuamotu Archipelago; and he was the first to make systematic astronomical observations of longitude, providing valuable charts for future sailors in the Pacific.

Bougainville's attitude toward exploration can be summed up in his own words: "But geography is a science of facts; one cannot speculate from an armchair without the risk of making mistakes which are often corrected only at the expense of the sailors" (*Voyage autour du monde*, p. 210).

BIBLIOGRAPHY

I. ORIGINAL WORKS. Bougainville's works include *Traité du calcul-intégral, pour servir de suite à l'analyse des infiniment-petits du Marquis de l'Hôpital*, 2 vols. (Paris, 1754–1756); *Voyage autour du monde* (Paris, 1771); "Journal de l'expédition d'Amérique . . .," in *Rapport de l'archiviste de la province de Québec* (1923/1924), pp. 204–393, trans. and ed. by E. P. Hamilton as *Adventure in the Wilderness, the American Journals 1756–60* (Norman, Okla., 1964). MSS are in the Archives Nationales, Paris.

II. SECONDARY LITERATURE. Works on Bougainville are J. Dorsenne, *La vie de Bougainville* (Paris, 1930); and J. Lefranc, *Bougainville et ses compagnons* (Paris, 1929).

WILMA GEORGE

BOUGUER, PIERRE (*b.* Croisic, France, 16 February 1698; *d.* Paris, France, 15 August 1758), *geodesy, hydrography, physics.*

The son of Jean Bouguer, royal professor of hydrography, Pierre Bouguer was a prodigy who at the age of fifteen, upon the death of his father, applied for and obtained the professorship. He quickly became the leading French theoretical authority on all things nautical, and by the time he was twenty-nine had won three prizes for essays on subjects set by the Académie Royale des Sciences: on the masts of ships (1727), on the best way of observing the altitudes of stars at sea (1729), and on the observation at sea of the magnetic declination (1731). In 1731 Bouguer was made an associate geometrician of the Académie Royale, and in 1735 he became a full Academician. In the same year he was sent, with Charles Marie de La Condamine, Louis Godin, and Joseph de Jussieu, on the celebrated expedition to Peru that was to measure an arc of the meridian near the equator.

Bouguer's work on this expedition, from which he did not return until 1744, was of high quality. Apart from the main geodetic program, he did an astonishing amount of other scientific work, measuring the dilatation of various solids by making use of the large range of temperatures found in the Cordillera, investigating the phenomena of atmospheric refraction and the measurement of heights with the barometer, devising a new type of ship's log, and undertaking a number of other researches, in spite of the very difficult physical conditions under which the geodetic measurements had to be carried out. The results of these measurements were published formally in 1749 as *La figure de la terre, déterminée par les observations de Messieurs De la Condamine et Bouguer. . . .*

His work on naval architecture and navigation produced *Traité du navire* (1746), *Nouveau traité de navigation* (1753), and *De la manoeuvre des vaisseaux . . .* (1757), as well as several papers in the *Mémoires* of the Academy. These treatises seem to have been very useful to the naval services of the time—for example, his early paper on "lines of pursuit" (1732), one of several that display his considerable mathematical ability. He was also good with instruments, as is shown by his invention of the heliometer in 1748.

Nevertheless, in the twentieth century Pierre Bouguer is probably best known as the father of photometry, in spite of the fact that the subject seems to have been a part-time occupation, a hobby to which he returned in the last years of his life.

His interest in the measurement of light dates from about 1721, when J. J. d'Ortous de Mairan proposed a problem that necessitated a knowledge of the relative amount of light from the sun at two altitudes. Bouguer succeeded in making such a measurement of the light from the full moon on 23 November 1725, by comparing it with that of a candle.

Bouguer's achievement was to see that the eye could be used, not as a meter but as a null indicator, i.e., to establish the equality of brightness of two adjacent surfaces. He then made use of the law of inverse squares, first clearly set forth by Kepler. In his *Essai d'optique sur la gradation de la lumière* (1729), he showed how to compare lights in this way; he then went on to deal with the transmission of light through partly transparent substances. In the latter part of the *Essai*, Bouguer published the second of his great optical discoveries, often called Bouguer's law: In a medium of uniform transparency the light remaining in a collimated beam is an exponential function of the length of its path in the medium. This law was restated by J. H. Lambert in his *Photometria* (1760) and, perhaps because of the great rarity of copies of Bouguer's *Essai*, is sometimes unjustifiably referred to as Lambert's law.

Just before he died, Bouguer completed a much larger book on photometry, the *Traité d'optique sur la gradation de la lumière*, published posthumously

(1760) by his friend the Abbé Nicolas Louis de la Caille. The *Traité* goes far beyond the *Essai,* describing a number of ingenious kinds of photometers, including a method of goniophotometry, and even attempting an elaborate theory of the reflection of light from rough surfaces, although this was not successful. The third and last part of the book, however, gives a valid elementary theory of the horizontal visual range through an obscuring atmosphere, arriving at a law, usually credited to H. Koschmieder, considered to belong to the twentieth century. It is fair to consider Pierre Bouguer not only the inventor of the photometer but also the founder of an important branch of atmospheric optics. The eighteenth century is not an outstanding epoch in the history of optics, but Bouguer's contribution to that science is notable by any standard.

BIBLIOGRAPHY

I. ORIGINAL WORKS. Works by Bouguer are *Essai d'optique sur la gradation de la lumière* (Paris, 1729), reprinted in the series *Les maîtres de la pensée scientifique* (Paris, 1921); "De la méthode d'observer exactement sur mer la hauteur des astres" (1729), in *Recueil des pièces qui ont remporté le prix de l'Académie Royale des Sciences . . . ,* **2,** no. 4 (1732); "De la mâture des vaisseaux" (1727), *ibid.,* **1,** no. 8 (1732); "De la méthode d'observer en mer la déclinaison de la boussole" (1731), *ibid.,* **2,** no. 6 (1732); *Traité du navire, de sa construction, et de ses mouvemens* (Paris, 1746); *La figure de la terre, déterminée par les observations de Messieurs De la Condamine et Bouguer, de l'Académie Royale des Sciences, envoyés par ordre du Roy au Pérou pour observer aux environs de l'équateur . . .* (Paris, 1749); *Nouveau traité de navigation, contenant la théorie et la pratique du pilotage* (Paris, 1753); *De la manoeuvre des vaisseaux . . .* (Paris, 1757); and *Traité d'optique sur la gradation de la lumière: Ouvrage posthume . . . publié par M. l'Abbé de la Caille . . .* (Paris, 1760), Latin translation by Joachim Richtenburg (Vienna, 1762), Russian translation by N. A. Tolstoy and P. P. Feofilov with a commentary by A. A. Gershun (Moscow, 1950), English translation with introduction and notes by W. E. K. Middleton (Toronto, 1961). Bouguer also contributed more than thirty articles to the *Mémoires de l'Académie Royale des Sciences* and the *Journal des Sçavans.*

II. SECONDARY LITERATURE. Works on Bouguer include Jean Paul Grandjean de Fouchy, "Éloge de M. Bouguer," in *Histoire de l'Académie Royale des Sciences, Paris* (1758), 127–136; Roland Lamontagne, *La vie et l'oeuvre de Pierre Bouguer* (Montreal and Paris, 1964), a short memoir dealing mainly with Bouguer's relations with the Americas that contains a brief list of manuscript sources on pp. 95–96; M. Prevost and R. d'Amat, eds., *Dictionnaire de biographie française* (Paris, 1954), VI, 1298; and Vasco Ronchi, *Storia della luce* (Bologna, 1952), Ch. 6.

W. E. KNOWLES MIDDLETON

BOUILLES, CHARLES DE. See **Bouvelles, Charles.**

BOUIN, POL ANDRÉ (*b.* Vendresse, Ardennes, France, 11 June 1870; *d.* Vendresse, 5 February 1962), *biology.*

Pol Bouin, the son and grandson of veterinary surgeons, grew up in the Ardennes, where at that time horse-breeding was a flourishing occupation. He would often tell how his interest in testicular physiology and pathology arose out of his father's method of treating cryptorchism in horses and pigs. While a student at Nancy he was attracted to the study of histology by the example of his teacher, Auguste Prenant. As early as 1895, he fixed his attention on phenomena of degeneration in the testes, to which problem he devoted what became a significant medical thesis in 1897. He began working with Paul Ancel in 1903, a collaboration which, developing through thirty years of close friendship and fruitful cooperation, laid the fundamental groundwork for the rapid development of reproductive endocrinology. Bouin and Ancel performed many types of operations on laboratory animals, and to test their experimental results relied on the morphology of the gonads, the genital tract, and secondary sexual characteristics. They were pioneers in the physiology of reproduction long before the isolation (around 1930) of sex hormones.

It will be useful to summarize here their essential discoveries, which continue to be valid. By employing convergent techniques, Bouin and Ancel elucidated the dual function of the testis: in the first place, gametogenesis (the production of semen) in the interior of the seminiferous tubules; and in the second place, the secretion of hormones in the interstitial gland located between the seminiferous tubules. They demonstrated that the interstitial gland controls the secondary sexual characteristics in the male. What used to be called the interstitial theory attracted few supporters at the outset, a large number of specialists remaining faithful to the old superstition about the importance of the "seed" in male potency. Violent controversies set in, reaching their peak between 1920 and 1925, which is to say on the eve of the discovery of male hormones. Some biologists, for example Champy in Paris and Stieve in Halle, bitterly resisted the demonstration that the interstitial gland is the source of male hormones. On the other side Steinach in Vienna and Lipschütz in Dorpat (currently living in Santiago de Chile) defended the theory ardently. Those extinct disputes are worth recalling as an essential chapter in the history of testicular endocrinology.

The same pattern appears in the work of Bouin

and Ancel on ovarian physiology and especially on the corpus luteum. Among the original techniques they devised was that of using a male rabbit which had been rendered sterile (while remaining potent) by ligaturing of the ductus deferens. During sexual intercourse the rabbit was able to rupture the graafian follicle of the female, inducing ovulation. Between 1909 and 1911 the two colleagues demonstrated irrefutably that in the absence of fertilization the corpus luteum, through an internal secretion, controls the readying of the uterine mucosa for implantation of the ovum as well as the morphogenetic development of the mammary glands. The effect is particularly striking in female rabbits. These results gave rise to intensive discussion until progesterone, the hormone secreted by the corpus luteum, was isolated by the epoch-making work of George Corner and Willard Allen in 1929.

From time to time Bouin worked in the field of cytology, which he enjoyed enormously. His drawings of spermatogenesis in myriopods would in themselves have assured his distinguished reputation among cytologists in the early decades of the century.

Concern for teaching in the university played a great part in Bouin's scientific life. From the outset he collaborated with his own teacher, Prenant, in the preparation of a *Traité d'histologie* (published in two volumes, 1904–1911). A very full work for the time, completely illustrated by the authors themselves, it continues to be valuable as a source of iconography. Bouin's own *Éléments d'histologie* (two volumes, 1929–1932), a sumptuously illustrated work, is now out of print, but the illustrations have been reproduced in more recent standard publications. In his textbooks Bouin laid down the main lines of the lectures in which he attempted to exhibit correlations between structure and function. As a professor he enjoyed enormous prestige. He spoke without notes in a quiet voice and in a manner both familiar and confidential, illustrating his account with drawings of great elegance. His course made an indelible impression on his audience and was the starting point of a significant number of scientific careers.

It was in laboratory work, however, which he always followed closely, that Bouin picked out his future disciples, in the course of conversations back and forth across the microscope. Having no confidence in selecting talent by competitions, he preferred to choose his collaborators directly. He encouraged students with a flair for research to begin work in his laboratory at as youthful an age as possible. There he watched over them, particularly at the outset, with paternal solicitude. Bouin thus trained numerous disciples who have made their mark on

various levels of the university structure. The full list would be excessively long, but a few may be named: Rémy Collin at Nancy, Max Aron at Strasbourg, Robert Courrier (permanent secretary of the Academy of Science in Paris) at the Collège de France, Jacques Benoit of the Collège de France, and the author of the present article at Strasbourg.

Bouin's laboratory was for many years, and particularly during his time at Strasbourg, the starting point of a number of significant discoveries: Courrier's work on folliculin (estrone) in the female and on the physiology of periodic sexual activity in the testicle; the discovery by Stricker and Grüter in 1928 of the lactogenic hormone produced by the anterior pituitary; and the numerous works of Max Aron on comparative endocrinology. From 1925 on, the pace of Bouin's personal work slowed, but he continued to participate with undiminished vigilance in the work of his students, though without adding his signature to theirs except in very rare instances. More and more he effaced himself in the work of his collaborators while continuing to give them the benefit of his illuminating advice almost to the day of his death. His involvement in teaching reached far beyond the institute of which he was director. In consequence of a number of trips abroad he had developed very definite views on the way to recruit talent for scientific research, particularly in biology. The Rockefeller Foundation showed him great confidence through the years, especially in nominating candidates for fellowships. In 1927 the Foundation made him an extremely important grant for the construction of an entirely up-to-date Institute of Histology. Around 1930 Bouin was one of the promoters of the Caisse Nationale des Sciences, forerunner of the present Centre National de la Recherche Scientifique in Paris.

Bouin's gentle nature and surpassing kindness remained alive in the memory of all who knew him. Severe in his judgment of himself and of his collaborators when it came to the publication of scientific results, he liked to converse at length on the progress of an experiment when it was under way and, if need be, to defend its results with his authority. Having done his duty in every respect during the war of 1914–1918 and again throughout the black years from 1939 to 1945, his tolerance in political and religious matters was as complete as it was uncommon. He became a world-famous scientist during his years at Strasbourg, from 1919 to 1939 and then lost all his possessions in the course of World War II. Thereupon, he retired to his native village and devoted himself to forestry, a subject of great interest to him and one in which he had attained considerable reputation.

During the years of his retirement, from 1945 to

1962, Bouin remained continually in touch with the progress of biology, partly by keeping up with the journals and partly by correcting in a manner both kindly and precise the manuscripts that his former students continued to submit to his judgment. The example he gave of a scientist entirely devoted to disinterested research and the compassionate nature that led him to participate in the personal life of all his acquaintanceship remain a vivid memory among the numerous disciples who count themselves among the school of Bouin.

Bouin's academic career was distinguished. He was *préparateur d'histologie* in the Faculty of Medicine in Nancy in 1892 and received the *docteur en médecine* there in 1897 (when he also served as *chef des travaux d'histologie*), becoming *professeur-agrégé* of anatomy (histology) in 1898. He was *professeur titulaire* of histology and pathological anatomy at the medical school of Algiers in 1907, *professeur titulaire* of histology of the Faculty of Medicine in Nancy in 1908, and held the same position at Strasbourg in 1918.

Bouin received many honors. He was a commander of the Legion of Honor; *membre titulaire* of the Academy of Sciences of Paris and of the Académie Nationale de Médecine, Paris; and honorary foreign member of the Royal Belgian Academy of Medicine of Brussels. He won a number of prizes, including the Prince Albert I of Monaco award of the Academy of Medicine (which he shared with Paul Ancel) in 1937, the Prix de la Fondation Singer-Polignac (again with Paul Ancel) in 1951, and the gold medal of the Centre National de la Recherche Scientifique, Paris, in 1961.

BIBLIOGRAPHY

R. Courrier's *Notice sur la vie et les travaux de Pol Bouin* (Paris, 1962) contains a complete list of Bouin's scientific writings, in addition to extensive biographical information, a list of biographical sources, and a portrait.

MARC KLEIN

BOULE, MARCELLIN (*b.* Montsalvy, Cantal, France, 1 January 1861; *d.* Montsalvy, 4 July 1942), *human paleontology, geology.*

Boule was born at the beginning of the decade during which the stratified deposits of the caves of southern France were to support in abundance the long record of man's newly discovered antiquity. It was in Cantal and in its neighboring departments that, one after another, the sites were excavated to help complete the record of ancient man. Time and place set the intellectual scene for the emergence of Boule as the central figure in French prehistoric studies during the half century of his scientific career.

In 1880 Boule enrolled at the Faculty of Sciences of Toulouse, and during the succeeding four years earned the *licence* in natural sciences and then that in physical science. He completed his work toward the coveted teaching certificate in 1887 at the Museum of Natural History in Paris, to which he had received a scholarship the preceding year. The museum was then at its height as a center of research in the natural sciences, particularly geology. The influence of the museum pushed Boule in the direction of research rather than that of teaching, for which he had prepared. Although his initial interests were in the problems of stratigraphy and petrography, it was finally to paleontology that he devoted most of his efforts and to which he made his most significant research contributions. His personal association with Louis Lartet and Albert Gaudry, and particularly the enthusiasm of the latter, were responsible for the final localization of his interests. Returning to Paris in 1890 after a brief teaching assignment at Clermont-Ferrand, Boule received a doctorate in natural sciences in 1892. In the same year he became *préparateur* in the paleontological laboratory of the museum in preference to the offer of a professorship at Montpellier. An assistant to Gaudry, he succeeded him as professor of paleontology at the museum, a position he held until his retirement in 1936.

Although he began as a geologist, with much of his research in descriptive geology and stratigraphy, Boule's importance lies in the role he played in the establishment of prehistory or paleoanthropology in France. Boule himself illustrates the close kinship between geology and prehistory in the period of the latter's emergence, for in its beginnings prehistory was an extension of geology, drawing from it both its methodology and its scientific status and pretensions. No geologist working in the general region of the Auvergne could ignore the importance of the stratified deposits which provided the record of a vastly expanded time period for human existence and which made of man a species to be fitted into a geological context.

As Boule's interests in nonhuman paleontology were shaped by his association with Lartet and Gaudry, so his archaeological and paleoanthropological work was stimulated by his close association and friendship at Toulouse with Émile Cartailhac, already a distinguished prehistoric archaeologist. As early as 1884 Boule described a prehistoric flint mine; and in 1887 he made stratigraphic studies of several newly discovered Mousterian rock shelters and, with

Cartailhac, published a monograph on the Grotte de Reilhac which demonstrated that the transition from the Paleolithic to the Neolithic was such as to cast doubt on the classical thesis of a clear break between the two epochs. These early studies foreshadowed an increasing concern with the earlier phases of human prehistory; and to both the collection and the interpretation of data Boule was able to bring a unique synthetic approach that was the product of his training and competence in stratigraphic geology, paleontology, and prehistoric archaeology. It was this total view of prehistoric man that formed the essential orientation of *Les hommes fossiles: Éléments de paléontologie humaine,* which was first published in 1921 and for a quarter of a century remained, in its several editions, the essential synthesis in paleoanthropology. Here he brought together the archaeological, geological, and zoological data in order to provide the record of human achievement and adaptation through the changing landscapes of the geological past. In this he saw human evolution in the proper sense, not as a series of anatomical stages alone but rather as the continuing process by which the human form adapted to a constantly changing ecology.

Although its extensive approach was adumbrated by his earlier work with Cartailhac, *Les hommes fossiles* was built upon two decades of detailed work in paleoanthropology, of which the central accomplishment was the three-part monograph "L'homme fossile de la Chapelle-aux-Saints" (1911–1913). Its anatomical account of the most complete specimen of Neanderthal man then known set the standard for such detailed descriptions. Now known to be wrong in several particulars, Boule's precise anatomical definition of Neanderthal man and the subsequent reconstruction provided the authority for his view that such specimens represented a distinct species population more primitive or apelike than modern man, one that could not be ancestrally related to him. It was this view that long formed the cornerstone of the theoretical structure of French paleoanthropology.

Apart from his many contributions to the rapidly expanding body of knowledge relating to man's past, Boule was one of the most distinguished statesmen and persuasive representatives of this burgeoning science. One of the founders of *L'anthropologie* in 1890, he was its editor from 1893 to 1920. When Albert I of Monaco, impressed by the remains uncovered in his own principality, founded the Institute for Human Paleontology in Paris in 1914, Boule was appointed its first director, a position he held until his death. The institute, whose opening was delayed until 1920 by World War I, served as the center and instigator of research in human paleontology. Boule founded its *Archives* and was the active agent of its researches. As editor of the two most distinguished journals in the field and as director of the only research establishment devoted solely to its pursuit, Boule set the tone and the tempo for Old World paleoanthropology in the first third of this century.

BIBLIOGRAPHY

I. ORIGINAL WORKS. Works by Boule include "Essai de paléontologie stratigraphique de l'homme," in *Revue de anthropologie* (1888–1889); *Les grottes de Grimaldi: Géologie et paléontologie* (Monaco, 1906–1910); "L'homme fossile de la Chapelle-aux-Saints," in *Annales de paléontologie,* **6-8**; *Les hommes fossiles: Éléments de paléontologie humaine* (Paris, 1921).

II. SECONDARY LITERATURE. See "Jubilé de M. Marcellin Boule," in *L'anthropologie,* **47** (1937), 583–648, which includes a complete bibliography through 1937; and H. V. Vallois, "Marcellin Boule," *ibid.,* **50** (1946), 203–210.

J. GRUBER

BOULLANGER, NICOLAS-ANTOINE (*b*. Paris, France, 11 November 1722; *d*. Paris, 1 September 1759), *geology, philosophy.*

Boullanger received a classical education at Beauvais College in Paris, then studied mathematics and architecture. He later joined the army as an engineer. In 1745 he joined the Département des Ponts et Chaussées as superintendent of works. He was appointed deputy engineer in 1749; two years later he was posted to the generality of Paris and, sometime afterward, to that of Tours.

As early as 1745 Boullanger became interested in the morphology of the Marne Basin and the peculiarities of the sedimentary terrains under its workings. In the freestone quarries he paid special attention to the soft layers, but he mistook the oolites for the eggs or embryos of shellfish. He continued his observations as far as the confluence of the Seine and the Marne, where he mistook oolites for the Miliola fossils of the rough limestone of the Paris region. He published these observations in the *Mercure de France* for June 1753. Although this work was republished several times, no naturalist before d'Archiac (1862) pointed out its errors.

Boullanger collected his observations and comments on the courses of the Loire and the Marne in "Anecdotes de la nature." Having determined that most of the strata involved had been formed from the remains of marine shellfish, he deduced that these deposits had originally constituted continuous layers in the ocean and that, after the sea had retreated, they had been eroded by the currents. He did not, however, study stratigraphic succession or identify the fossils in the various layers. Instead of adhering to observation, he sought to develop a theory on the formation of the earth that involved a universal deluge. Boullanger retained Descartes's hypothesis of a subterranean stratum of water, and attributed the deluge to a vast and sudden eruption of this water through springs. Since he could not assume the age of the earth to be that assigned it by biblical chronology, he read and cited the ancient authors in their original languages.

The modern distribution of the oceans suggested a complementary hypothesis, that of the elasticity of the earth's strata, half of which had, by bending, caused the elevation of the other half. Boullanger presented this hypothesis in his *Mémoire sur une nouvelle mappemonde* (1753) and *Nouvelle mappemonde dédiée au progrès de nos connoissances* (1753). His map showed two hemispheres: the terrestrial, with its center near Paris, comprised most of the continents; the maritime contained practically all the oceans. Boullanger considered the lifting or sinking of the earth's strata to have been the origin of the universal deluge. He expressed this theory in the article "Déluge" in the *Encyclopédie* (1754). Boullanger retired in 1758 with the rank of engineer.

BIBLIOGRAPHY

I. ORIGINAL WORKS. Boullanger's published works are *Mémoire sur une nouvelle mappemonde* (Paris, 1753); *Nouvelle mappemonde dédiée au progrès de nos connoissances* (Paris-Nuremberg, 1753; Paris, 1760); "Déluge," in *L'encyclopédie*, IV (1754); *Recherches sur l'origine du despotisme oriental* (Geneva, 1761; Paris, 1763; Amsterdam, 1766); and *L'antiquité dévoilée par ses usages* . . . (Amsterdam, 1766). An unpublished MS is "Anecdotes de la nature sur l'origine des vallées, des montagnes et des autres irrégularités extérieures et intérieures du globe de la terre . . .," Library of the Muséum d'Histoire Naturelle, MS 869. It was sent to Buffon about 1750, and he borrowed part of the description of the Langres Plateau for *Les époques de la nature* (the borrowing was reported to the *Journal de littérature, science et arts* by Nicolas Gobet). The MS was abstracted by Nicolas Desmarest as part of the article "Géographie physique," in *L'encyclopédie méthodique,* I (Paris, an III), 8–28.

II. SECONDARY LITERATURE. The basic source of information on Boullanger's life is the anonymous introduction to *L'antiquité dévoilée* (Amsterdam, 1766), attributed to Diderot by Grimm (see *Correspondance littéraire, philosophique et critique par Grimm,* Maurice Tourneux, ed., VI [Paris, 1878], 468). Other sources are John Hampton, *Nicolas-Antoine Boulanger et la science de son temps* (Geneva-Lille, 1955); and Jacques Roger, "Un manuscrit inédit perdu et retrouvé: Les *Anecdotes de la Nature* de Nicolas-Antoine Boulanger," in *Revue des sciences humaines* (Lille) (July–Sept. 1953), 231–254.

ARTHUR BIREMBAUT

BOULLIAU, ISMAEL (*b.* Loudun, France, 28 September 1605; *d.* Paris, France, 25 November 1694), *mathematics, astronomy.*

Boulliau was born of Calvinist parents, but he became a Roman Catholic at the age of twenty-one. About four years later, he was ordained a priest. His early studies had been in law and the humanities, but upon settling in Paris in 1633, he resumed an early interest in astronomical observation, a taste he had shared with his father. Thereafter, he pursued a predominantly scientific career, becoming known as Clarissimus Bullialdus. In addition to the usual French and Latin spellings of his name, there were such variants as Bouillaud, Boulliaud, and Bulliald.

The Galilean storm broke during the very year that Boulliau joined the Parisian scientific circle. A recent convert both to Catholicism and to science, he nevertheless joined his friend Gassendi in support of Galileo. Boulliau's publication of the *Philolaus* in 1639 placed him squarely in the Copernican camp, although not yet as a Keplerian. In assuming that the sun stood still, so that he could retain uniform circular motions, Copernicus had been right for the wrong reason. So it was with Boulliau. In the *Philolaus,* Boulliau went further than Copernicus in suggesting the resolution of rectilinear accelerated motion in free fall into two uniform circular components. His law of fall (equivalent to $s = k$ vers t) is in close agreement with the definitive Galilean formulation for small intervals of time only.

In 1645 Boulliau published his most significant scientific work, a more accomplished heliocentric treatise entitled *Astronomia philolaica.* He had now become one of the very few astronomers to accept the ellipticity of orbits, but he categorically rejected all those suggestions of variation in celestial forces which had made Kepler's *Astronomia nova* of 1609 more revolutionary, in a sense, than the work of Copernicus. As against Kepler's astrophysics, Boulliau preferred a geometrical astronomy which saved uniformity of circular motion. He asserted, however, that *if* a planetary moving force did in fact exist, then it should vary inversely as the square of the distance—and not, as Kepler had held, inversely as the first power. The inverse-square hypothesis, which Boulliau published in his *Astronomia philolaica,* evidently had been carried over from his *De natura lucis* of 1638, in which the inverse-square law for intensity of illumination, used earlier by Kepler, had appeared.

Rejecting all dynamic hypotheses, including the inverse-square hypothesis in astronomy, Boulliau proposed instead a kinematic representation of planetary motion in which a planet moved along a linear element of an oblique cone while the element in turn revolved uniformly about the axis of the cone. In this way, he reconciled ellipticity of orbits with uniformity of circular motion. Seth Ward modified the scheme shortly afterward in a hypothesis by which the motion of the planet is uniform as seen from the "blind" focus of the ellipse.

The *Astronomia philolaica* was one of the most important treatises written in the period between Kepler and Newton. In his *Principia,* Newton referred to Boulliau's inverse-square hypothesis and praised the accuracy of his tables (Bk. 3, Phen. 4). Boulliau was also highly regarded as a mathematician. Before he was thirty, he had prepared the first printed edition (1644) of the *Arithmetica* of Theon of Smyrna; in his fifties, he published (besides several minor works) the *De lineis spiralibus* (1657), a work inspired by Archimedes; and when he was more than seventy-five years of age, he published a ponderous *Opus novum ad arithmeticam infinitorum* (1682), purporting to clarify the *Arithmetica infinitorum* of Wallis. The mathematical works of Boulliau had little influence on the development of the subject, however, because they were old-fashioned. He evidently failed to see the significance of the Cartesian contributions, whether to mathematics or to science, and seems pointedly to have avoided mentioning Descartes's name. Boulliau's astronomical observations at Paris covered over half a century, but it has been ungenerously said that Boulliau's only permanent contribution to science is the word "evection" in astronomy. Nevertheless, it was Boulliau who, in his *Ad astronomos monita duo* of 1667, first established the periodicity of a variable star, Mira Ceti. His explanation of the phenomenon as a rotating semiluminous body or "half sun" was incorrect, but his estimate of the period as 333 days was accurate, exceeding by less than two days that determined since then.

Boulliau was one of the last reputable scholars to maintain confidence in astrology. Among the works he edited were the *Astronomicon* of Marcus Manilius (1655) and the *De judicandi facultate* of Ptolemy (1667). Despite all his publications, Boulliau's contribution to science should perhaps be measured less by his treatises and ideas than by his scientific activity. He rivaled Mersenne as a correspondent. He served as librarian, first to the brothers du Puy, then to de Thou, French ambassador in Holland, and ultimately to the Bibliothèque Royale in Paris. There he joined the groups which gave rise to the Académie des Sciences. Although never elected to the Academy, in 1663 he was among the first foreign associates elected to the Royal Society of London. It was to Boulliau that Huygens first entrusted his secret of the rings of Saturn and to him that he sent his earliest pendulum clocks. The distribution in Paris of Huygens' *Systema saturnium* (1658) was entrusted to Boulliau; and it was through Boulliau that Pascal's *Lettres d'Amos Dettonville* (1658–1659) went to English and Dutch mathematicians. Prince Leopold in Italy and Hevelius in Danzig depended upon Boulliau to keep them informed of scientific news from Paris, although at times Boulliau was himself traveling to England or Poland or the Levant, seeking out manuscripts, books, and information.

BIBLIOGRAPHY

I. ORIGINAL WORKS. Thirty-nine volumes containing Boulliau's unedited papers and correspondence are to be found in Paris (Bibliothèque Nationale, fonds franc. 13019–13058). His published works include *De natura lucis* (Paris, 1638); *Philolaus* (Amsterdam, 1639); *Astronomia philolaica* (Paris, 1645); *De lineis spiralibus* (Paris, 1657); *Ad astronomos monita duo* (Paris, 1667); *Opus novum ad arithmeticam infinitorum* (Paris, 1682). He also edited works of Theon of Smyrna (Paris, 1644), Ptolemy, and Marcus Manilius, as noted in the text.

II. SECONDARY LITERATURE. There is no biography of Boulliau. Some information on his life and work may be found in G. Bigourdan, *Histoire de l'astronomie d'observation et des observatoires en France,* pt. 1 (Paris, 1918), and in J. P. Niceron, *Mémoires pour servir à l'histoire des hommes illustres dans la république des lettres* (Paris, 1727–1745), Vols. I, X.

CARL B. BOYER

BOUQUET, JEAN-CLAUDE (*b.* Morteau, Doubs, France, 7 September 1819; *d.* Paris, France, 9 September 1885), *mathematics.*

After entering the École Normale Supérieure in 1839, Bouquet became a professor at the lycée of Marseilles. He received the *doctorat ès sciences* in 1842, presenting a thesis on the variation of double integrals, and was appointed professor at the Faculté des Sciences of Lyons. There he found his school friend Charles Briot, with whom he collaborated throughout his career.

Bouquet taught special mathematics at the Lycée Bonaparte (now the Lycée Condorcet) from 1852 to 1858, then at the Lycée Louis-le-Grand until 1867. After serving as *maître de conférence* at the École Normale Supérieure and *répétiteur* at the École Polytechnique, Bouquet succeeded J. A. Serret in the chair of differential and integral calculus at the Sorbonne (1874–1884). He was elected to the Académie des Sciences in 1875.

After his thesis Bouquet took up differential geometry, writing a memoir on the systems of straight lines of space and one on orthogonal surfaces that was basic to the important research carried on successively by Ossian Bonnet, Gaston Darboux, Maurice Levy, and Arthur Cayley.

From 1853 on, Bouquet's name is generally associated with that of his friend Briot. Their joint scientific work was a profound study and clarification of the analytic work of Augustin Cauchy. In a memoir that has remained famous since 1853, they proposed to establish precisely the conditions that a function must fulfill in order to be developable into an entire series. They also perfected the analysis by which Cauchy had, for the first time, established the existence of the integral of a differential equation. They opened the way to research on singular points and showed their importance for knowledge of the integral. Their works of 1859 and 1875 on elliptic functions finally brought out the great force of Cauchy's analytic methods.

The mathematical activity of Bouquet and Briot was equaled by remarkable teaching activity. Bouquet, who was as fond of teaching as of science, taught Jules Tannery. Collaborating with Briot, he produced several textbooks that went into numerous printings.

BIBLIOGRAPHY

I. ORIGINAL WORKS. Bouquet's works include "Sur la variation des intégrales doubles," doctoral thesis (Faculté des Sciences, Paris, 1842); "Remarques sur les systèmes de droites dans l'espace," in *Journal des mathématiques pures et appliquées,* 1st ser., **11** (1846), 125 ff.; "Note sur les surfaces orthogonales," *ibid.,* 446 ff.; *Mémoire sur les propriétés d'un système de droites* (Lyons, 1848); "Sur la courbure des surfaces," a note in Cournot's *Traité de la théorie des fonctions* (Paris, 1857), along with other, lesser notes by Bouquet and Briot; "Mémoire sur la théorie des intégrales ultra-elliptiques," in a shorter version in *Comptes rendus des séances de l'Académie des sciences* (1868), which led to a report by J. A. Serret on 4 July 1870, in *Recueil des savants étrangers,* pp. 417–470; *Notice sur les travaux mathématiques de M. Bouquet* (Paris, 1870); "Sur l'intégration d'un système d'équations différentielles totales simultanées du Ier ordre," in *Bulletin des sciences mathématiques et astronomiques,* **3** (1872), 265 ff.; "Note sur le calcul des accélérations des divers ordres dans le mouvement d'un point sur une courbe gauche," in *Annales scientifiques de l'École normale supérieure,* 2nd ser., **3** (1874).

Works written in collaboration with Charles Briot are "Note sur le développement des fonctions en séries con-vergentes, ordonnées suivant les puissances croissantes de la variable," in *Comptes rendus des séances de l'Académie des sciences,* **36** (1853), 334; "Recherches sur les séries ordonnées suivant les puissances croissantes d'une variable imaginaire," *ibid.,* 264 ff.; "Recherches sur les propriétés des fonctions définies par des équations différentielles," *ibid.,* **39** (1854), *séance* of 21 August; "Additions au mémoire précédent," *ibid.*—Cauchy's report on this memoir, *ibid.,* **40** (1855), 567 ff.; "Recherches sur les fonctions doublement périodiques," *ibid.,* **40** (1855), 342 ff.; "Mémoire sur l'intégration des équations différentielles au moyen des fonctions elliptiques," *ibid.,* **41** (1855), 1229, with Cauchy's report in **43** (1856), 27, *séance* of 7 July 1856. All these memoirs, divided into three distinct parts, form, "with certain modifications," the *Journal de l'École polytechnique,* **36** (1856).

Other works are *Théorie des fonctions doublement périodiques et en particulier des fonctions elliptiques* (Paris, 1859), also translated into German (Halle, 1862); *Leçons de géométrie analytique* (Paris, 1875); *Leçons nouvelles de trigonométrie* (Paris, 1875); and *Théorie des fonctions elliptiques* (Paris, 1875).

II. SECONDARY LITERATURE. Works on Bouquet are Michel Chasles, *Rapport sur les progrès de la géométrie* (Paris, 1870), pp. 214–215; G. H. Halphen, "Notice nécrologique sur Bouquet," in *Comptes rendus des séances de l'Académie des sciences,* **102**, no. 23 (7 June 1886); and Jules Tannery, "Notice nécrologique sur Bouquet," in *Mémorial de l'Association des anciens élèves de l'École normale* (Paris, 1885).

JEAN ITARD

BOUR, EDMOND (*b.* Gray, Haute-Saône, France, 19 May 1832; *d.* Paris, France, 9 March 1866), *mathematics, analytical mechanics, celestial mechanics.*

Bour, the son of Joseph Bour and Gabrielle Jeunet, came from a rather modest provincial family. After receiving his secondary education in Gray and Dijon, he was admitted in 1850 to the École Polytechnique, from which he graduated first in his class in 1852; he then continued his studies at the École des Mines in Paris. At this time he worked on the paper "Sur l'intégration des équations différentielles de la mécanique analytique," which he read before the Académie des Sciences of Paris on 5 March 1855. He also wrote two theses in celestial mechanics, one on the three-body problem and the other on the theory of attraction, which he set forth brilliantly before the Faculté des Sciences in Paris on 3 December 1855.

In July 1855 Bour became both a mining engineer and professor of mechanics and mining at the École des Mines of Saint-Étienne, but he returned to Paris at the end of 1859 as lecturer in descriptive geometry at the École Polytechnique. The following year he was appointed professor at the École des Mines, and professor of mechanics at the École Polytechnique in 1861. Also in 1861 he received the grand prize in mathematics awarded by the Académie des Sciences for his paper "Théorie de la déformation des surfaces." In April 1862 Bour was a candidate for membership in the Académie des Sciences but was defeated by Ossian Bonnet. Disappointed by this failure, he concentrated entirely on his course in mechanics at the École Polytechnique.

Although Bour died of an incurable disease at the age of thirty-four, he left valuable works in mathematical analysis, algebra, infinitesimal geometry, theoretical and applied mechanics, and celestial mechanics. In mechanics his essential contributions dealt with differential equations in dynamics, the theme of his first memoir and of another published in 1862; the analytical study of the composition of movements (1865); and the reduction of the three-body problem to the plane case. In infinitesimal geometry his memoir on the deformation of surfaces, in line with the analogous studies of Bonnet and Codazzi, contained several theorems on ruled surfaces and minimal surfaces; but in its printed version this work does not include the test for the integration of the problem's equations in the case of surfaces of revolution, which had enabled Bour to surpass the other competitors for the Academy's grand prize.

BIBLIOGRAPHY

I. ORIGINAL WORKS. A nearly complete list of Bour's published works is given in Poggendorff and the *Catalogue of Scientific Papers* (see below). Among his works are "Sur l'intégration des équations différentielles de la mécanique analytique," in *Journal de mathématiques pures et appliquées,* **20** (1855), 185–202; his theses for the *docteur-ès-sciences* were published separately (Paris, 1855) as *Thèses présentées à la Faculté des Sciences à Paris pour obtenir le grade de docteur-ès-sciences. . . .* and reproduced in *Journal de l'École polytechnique,* **21**, cahier 36 (1856), 35–84; "Théorie de la déformation des surfaces," *ibid.,* **22**, cahier 39 (1862), 1–148; *Cours de mathématiques et machines,* 3 vols. (Paris, 1865–1874); and *Lettres choisies,* Joseph Bertin and Charles Godard, eds. (Gray, 1905).

II. SECONDARY LITERATURE. Works on Bour are M. Chasles, *Rapport sur les progrès de la géométrie* (Paris, 1870), pp. 211, 295, 325–327; M. D'Ocagne, *Histoire abrégée des sciences mathématiques* (Paris, 1955), p. 300; A. Franceschini, in *Dictionnaire de biographie française,* VI (1954), col. 1383; A. de Lapparent, in *École Polytechnique. Livre du centenaire,* I (Paris, 1895), 143–145; "Notice biographique sur Edmond Bour," in *Nouvelles annales de mathématiques,* 2nd ser., **6** (1867), 145–157; Poggendorff, III, 172–173; and Royal Society of London, *Catalogue of Scientific Papers, 1800–1863,* I (1867), 532.

RENÉ TATON

BOURBAKI, NICOLAS. Bourbaki is the collective pseudonym of an influential group of mathematicians, almost all French, who since the late 1930's have been engaged in writing what is intended to be a definitive survey of all of mathematics, or at least of all those parts of the subject which Bourbaki considers worthy of the name. The work appears in installments that are usually from 100 to 300 pages long. The first appeared in 1939 and the thirty-third in 1967; many intervening installments have been extensively revised and reissued. The selection of topics is very different from that in a traditional introduction to mathematics. In Bourbaki's arrangement, mathematics begins with set theory, which is followed, in order, by (abstract) algebra, general topology, functions of a real variable (including ordinary calculus), topological vector spaces, and the general theory of integration. To some extent the order is forced by the logical dependence of each topic on its predecessors. Bourbaki has not yet reached the other parts of mathematics. Although the work as a whole is called *Elements of Mathematics,* no one could read it without at least two years of college mathematics as preparation, and further mathematical study would be an advantage.

The exact composition of the Bourbaki group varies from year to year and has been deliberately kept mysterious. The project was begun by a number of brilliant young mathematicians who had made important contributions to mathematics in their own right. At the beginning they made no particular attempt at secrecy. With the passage of time, however, they seem to have become more and more enamored of their joke, and have often tried to persuade people that there is indeed an individual named N. Bourbaki, who writes the books. Indeed, Bourbaki once applied for membership in the American Mathematical Society, but was rejected on the ground that he was not an individual. The original group included H. Cartan, C. Chevalley, J. Dieudonné, and A. Weil (all of whom are among the most eminent mathematicians of their generation). Many younger French mathematicians have joined the group, which is understood to have ten to twenty members at any one time and has included two or three Americans. The founding members are said to have agreed to retire at the age of fifty, and are believed to have done so, although with some reluctance.

The origin of the name Nicolas Bourbaki is obscure. The use of a collective pseudonym was presumably intended to obviate title pages with long and changing lists of names and to provide a simple way of referring to the project. The family name appears to be that of General Charles-Denis-Sauter Bourbaki (1816–

1897), a statue of whom stands in Nancy, where several members of the group once taught. Possibly the Christian name was supposed to suggest St. Nicholas bringing presents to the mathematical world.

In the early days Bourbaki published articles in mathematical journals, as any mathematician would. He soon gave that up, however, and his reputation rests on his books. People who are unsympathetic to the "new mathematics" introduced into the schools since 1960 accuse Bourbaki of having inspired that movement. The accusation is probably unjustified, although aspects of his work bear a superficial resemblance to less attractive aspects of new mathematics. Bourbaki himself does not intend his approach to be used even in college teaching. Rather, it is meant to improve a mathematician's understanding of his subject after he has learned the fundamentals and to serve as a guide to research.

The most obvious aspects of Bourbaki's work are his insistence on a strict adherence to the axiomatic approach to mathematics and his use of an individual and (originally) unconventional terminology (much of which has since become widely accepted). The former is the more important. Any mathematical theory starts, in principle, from a set of axioms and deduces consequences from them (although many subjects, such as elementary algebra, are rarely presented to students in this way). In classical axiomatic theories, such as Euclidean geometry or Peano's theory of the integers, one attempts to find a set of axioms that precisely characterize the theory. Such an axiomatization is valuable in showing the logical arrangement of the subject, but the clarification so achieved is confined to the one subject, and often seems like quibbling.

A good deal of the new mathematics consists of introducing such axiomatizations of elementary parts of mathematics at an early stage of the curriculum, in the hope of facilitating understanding. Bourbaki's axiomatization is in a different spirit. His axioms are for parts of mathematics with the widest possible scope, which he calls structures. A mathematical structure consists, in principle, of a set of objects of unspecified nature, and of certain relationships among them. For example, the structure called a group consists of a set of elements such that any two can be combined to give a third. The way in which this is done must be subject to suitable axioms. The structure called an order consists of a set of elements with a relationship between any two of them, corresponding abstractly to the statement (for numbers) that one is greater than the other.

Having studied a structure, one may add axioms to make it more special (finite group or commutative group, for example). One can combine two structures, assuming that the objects considered satisfy the axioms of both (obtaining, for example, the theory of ordered groups). By proceeding in this way, one obtains more and more complicated structures, and often more and more interesting mathematics. Bourbaki, then, organizes mathematics as an arrangement of structures, the more complex growing out of the simpler.

There are great advantages in dealing with mathematics in this way. A theorem, once proved for an abstract structure, is immediately applicable to any realization of the structure, that is, to any mathematical system that satisfies the axioms. Thus, for example, a theorem about abstract groups will yield results (which superficially may look quite different) about groups of numbers, groups of matrices, or groups of permutations. Again, once it is recognized that the theory of measure and the theory of probability are realizations of a common set of axioms, all results in either theory can be reinterpreted in the other. Historically, in fact, these two theories were developed independently of each other for many years before their equivalence was recognized. Bourbaki tries to make each part of mathematics as general as possible in order to obtain the widest possible domain of applicability. His detractors object that he loses contact with the actual content of the subject, so that students who have studied only his approach are likely to know only general theorems without specific instances. Of course, the choice of an axiom system is never arbitrary. Bourbaki's collaborators are well aware of the concrete theories they are generalizing, and select their axioms accordingly.

Bourbaki has been influential for a number of reasons. For one thing, he gave the first systematic account of some topics that previously had been available only in scattered articles. His orderly and very general approach, his insistence on precision of terminology and of argument, his advocacy of the axiomatic method, all had a strong appeal to pure mathematicians, who in any case were proceeding in the same direction. Since mathematicians had to learn Bourbaki's terminology in order to read his work, that terminology has become widely known and has changed much of the vocabulary of research. The effect of the work in the development of mathematics has been fully commensurate with the great effort that has gone into it.

BIBLIOGRAPHY

I. ORIGINAL WORKS. Works by Bourbaki include "The Architecture of Mathematics," in *American Mathematical*

Monthly, **57** (1950), 221–232; and *Éléments de mathématique,* many numbers in the series Actualités Scientifiques et Industrielles (Paris, 1939–　　　).

II. Secondary Literature. André Delachet, "L'école Bourbaki," in *L'analyse mathématique* (Paris, 1949), pp. 113–116; Paul R. Halmos, "Nicolas Bourbaki," in *Scientific American,* **196,** no. 5 (May 1957), 88–99.

R. P. Boas, Jr.

BOURDELIN, CLAUDE (*b.* at or near Villefranche-sur-Saône, France, *ca.* 1621; *d.* Paris, France, 15 October 1699), *chemistry.*

Bourdelin was a beneficiary of the tradition of iatrochemistry. After having completed his apprenticeship under master apothecaries in Paris, he purchased an apothecary's license from the house of "Monsieur" (the king's younger brother, Gaston of Orléans). For some twenty years he held two offices in the house of Monsieur: that of assistant apothecary to Monsieur and the officers of his household, and that of apothecary to the stable.

Bourdelin's scientific knowledge and his title assured him prominent patients and powerful connections, which helped him become a member of the Royal Academy of Sciences when it was created in 1666. Next to the meeting room of the Academicians he installed the Academy's laboratory, equipped with furnaces and a distilling apparatus. There he began research in chemical analysis in March 1667 and continued until the end of 1686.

Initially, Bourdelin worked with Samuel Cottereau-Duclos, the king's physician, on the analysis of mineral waters. Subsequently, he devoted himself to the chemical analysis of plant, animal, and mineral substances; of normal and pathological organic liquids; and of water, both fresh and salt. His usual technique for plant analysis was distillation, which enabled him to find phlegm, an acid or corrosive spirit, volatile salt, oil, solid salt (sometimes in the form of tartar and sometimes of marine salt), and a residue, the *caput mortuum* of the alchemists.

Bourdelin kept careful records of his expenses, for which the Academy reimbursed him at the beginning of each year, and of the authorized transfers of chemical substances to other chemists or naturalists of the Academy. As of 1 January 1687, he was authorized to work at home, and until his death he continued his experimentation and his record-keeping.

Although Bourdelin's scientific work is of no value today, his importance lies in his having made clear to some of his contemporaries and to his successors that progress in chemical knowledge required use of less antiquated experimental methods and the elaboration of hypotheses as guidelines for research.

BIBLIOGRAPHY

I. Original Works. The archives of the Academy of Sciences contain eleven handwritten records of plant analyses carried out by Bourdelin between 14 June 1672 and 2 September 1699. The Bibliothèque Nationale (MS dept.) has other handwritten records kept by Bourdelin, which had been stolen by Libri: the record of expenses incurred for the laboratory between 1667 and 1699, n.a. fr. 5147; and fourteen records of analyses covering 1667–1668, n.a. fr. 5133, and 1672–1699, n.a. fr. 5134–5146. Some of Bourdelin's findings are published in *Histoire de l'Académie royale des sciences* (Paris, 1733), I, 27–35, 345–346; II, 9–10, 26–27, 68.

II. Secondary Literature. Bourdelin's laboratory at the Academy is illustrated by Sébastien Leclerc in *Mémoires pour servir à l'histoire des plantes dressés par M. Dodart* (Paris, 1676). Valuable articles are A. Birembaut, "Le laboratoire de l'Académie royale des sciences," in *Revue d'histoire des sciences* (1969); and Paul Dorveaux, "Les grands pharmaciens. Apothicaires membres de l'Académie royale des sciences," in *Bulletin de la Société d'histoire de la pharmacie* (Aug. 1929), 290–298.

Arthur Birembaut

BOURDELOT, PIERRE MICHON (*b.* Sens, France, 2 February 1610; *d.* Paris, France, 9 February 1685), *medicine, dissemination of science.*

Bourdelot was the son of Maximilien Michon, a barber-surgeon, and of Anne Bourdelot. About 1629 he began medical studies in Paris, where he had two uncles on his mother's side: Edmé Bourdelot, physician to Louis XIII, and Jean Bourdelot, a jurist and distinguished Hellenist. They adopted young Michon in 1634 and obtained for him the right to bear the name of Bourdelot. They also introduced him into the intellectual life of Paris. François de Noailles made Bourdelot his physician and took him to Rome in 1634.

When he returned to Paris in 1638, Bourdelot entered the service of Prince Henri II de Condé. He accompanied the latter on his campaigns in Spain, taking advantage of stopovers in Paris to pass his medical examinations. Having earned the title of king's physician, he settled in Paris early in 1642 and became the Condé family's physician. Eager for fame, he founded the Académie Bourdelot, the biweekly meetings of which were attended by nobles, men of letters, philosophers, and devotees of new fashions who were more critical than knowledgeable. Men interested in science also came, as did such truly learned men as Roberval, Gassendi, and Étienne and Blaise Pascal. Although Bourdelot often allowed the reading of extravagant theses at the meetings, his academy, along with that of Mersenne, played an important role in spreading scientific ideas in Paris. During the winter of 1647/1648 several new experiments on the vacuum were presented and discussed.

Upon the death of Henri II de Condé in 1646, Bourdelot served his son, Louis II. Political disorders brought on by the Fronde interrupted the academy's activity, and when Condé was arrested in January 1650, Bourdelot followed the dowager duchess into hiding. In October 1651, Bourdelot left the Condé family to go to Sweden as physician to Queen Christina, over whom he gained marked influence. This success aroused widespread animosity, and in June 1653 the queen was persuaded to send Bourdelot back to France.

In Paris, he obtained the living of the abbey of Massay, in Berry, which gave him the right to the title *abbé*. When the Great Condé returned from exile in 1659, Bourdelot again became his physician. His success with a treatment for gout, which he had previously developed, brought him new fame with numerous noted patients, among them Mme. de Sévigné. Early in 1664 he resumed the meetings of his academy. These meetings were attended by future members of the Académie Royale, by foreign scholars passing through, by violent partisans of Descartes or Gassendi, and by all sorts of alchemists and visionaries who espoused ideas of the past. The academy continued to meet more or less regularly until 1684. Although its *Conférences,* published in 1672 by Le Gallois, do not give a good idea of its standards and scientific level, references to some of its meetings in contemporary journals, memoirs, and correspondence indicate that interesting experimental work was often done there and that the academy helped to arouse sympathy for and interest in science. This was possible largely because the secrecy surrounding the work of the Académie Royale prevented it from participating in the dissemination of scientific knowledge.

Bourdelot's writings have little more than anecdotal interest. A possible exception is his history of music, published posthumously by his two nephews, which has recently been studied by historians of music. Nevertheless, Bourdelot played an important role in the scientific life of Paris between 1640 and 1680, providing material assistance and a means of diffusing experimental results. He also created a climate favorable to science in influential circles that participated in foreign intellectual exchanges, particularly with Italy.

BIBLIOGRAPHY

I. ORIGINAL WORKS. Bourdelot's writings are *Recherches et observations sur les vipères . . .* (Paris, 1671); *Ré-*

ponse . . . *à la lettre de Boccone . . . sur l'embrasement du Mont Etna,* n.p., n.d. (Paris, 1671); *Histoire de la musique et de ses effets . . .* (Paris, 1715), written with P. Bonnet-Bourdelot and J. Bonnet; and *Histoire générale de la danse sacrée et profane . . .* (Paris, 1732), written with J. Bonnet.

II. SECONDARY LITERATURE. Works on Bourdelot are Roman d'Amat, in *Dictionnaire de biographie française,* VI (1954), cols. 1439–1440; A. Cabanès, *Dans les coulisses de l'histoire* (Paris, 1923), pp. 93–123; A. Chérest, *Un médecin du grand monde au XVIIe siècle (Pierre Michon, devenu par adoption Pierre Bourdelot),* n.p., n.d. (Auxerre, 1861); Henri Chérot, *Trois éducations princières au dix-septième siècle* (Lille, 1896), pp. 120–132, 248; R. J. Denichou, *Un médecin du grand siècle: L'abbé Bourdelot* (Paris, 1928); F. Halévy, *Souvenirs et portraits* (Paris, 1861), pp. 87–115; H. Brown, *Scientific Organizations in Seventeenth Century France* (Bàltimore, 1933), pp. 111–112, 161, 165, 231–253, 296; P. Le Gallois, ed., *Conversations de l'Académie de Monsieur l'Abbé Bourdelot . . .* (Paris, 1672, 1673), and *Conversations académiques, tirées de l'Académie de M. l'Abbé Bourdelot* (Paris, 1674); Jean Lemoine and André Lichtenberger, *Trois familiers du grand Condé* (Paris, 1908), pp. 1–138; René Pintard, "Autour de Pascal. L'Académie Bourdelot et le problème du vide," in *Mélanges . . . offerts à Daniel Mornet* (Paris, 1951), pp. 73–81; D. Riesman, "Bourdelot, a Physician of Queen Christina of Sweden," in *Annals of Medical History,* **9** (1937), 191; and D. C. Vischer, *Der musikgeschichtliche Traktat des Pierre Bourdelot (1610–1684 [sic])* (Bern, 1947), dissertation (available at Bibliothèque Nationale, Paris, 8⁰ θ *Bern.* ph. 2062).

Numerous references are in *Correspondance du P. Marin Mersenne,* C. de Waard, ed., 10 vols. (Paris, 1932–   ); René Pintard, *Le libertinage érudit en France dans la première partie du XVIIe siècle,* 2 vols. (Paris, 1943); and René Taton, *Les origines de l'Académie Royale des Sciences* (Paris, 1966).

RENÉ TATON

BOURDON, EUGÈNE (*b.* Paris, France, 8 April 1808; *d.* Paris, 29 September 1884), *instrumentation.*

Bourdon was the son of a merchant who, expecting him to enter business, sent him to Nuremberg for two years in order to learn German. After his father's death in 1830, however, Bourdon spent two years in an optician's shop and, in 1832, set up his own instrument and machine shop. He moved in 1835 to 71 Faubourg du Temple, and continued to work there until 1872, when his sons took over its management. After his retirement, Bourdon continued to perform experiments that interested him. He died from a fall that occurred while he was testing an anemometer he had designed, one that employed a venturi tube.

In 1832 Bourdon made and presented to the Société d'Encouragement pour l'Industrie Nationale a model of a steam engine with glass cylinders; subsequently he built perhaps two hundred small steam engines. His major contributions were in instrumentation, however, and the most important single innovation was his "metallic manometer," which in his patent of 18 June 1849 was described as a "pressure gauge without mercury." This gauge is by far the most widely used for indicating pressures in the range of 15 to 100,000 pounds per square inch. The sensing element, or transducer, of the gauge was and is the Bourdon tube, which is a metal tube with an elliptical cross section. This tube, bent into a C, a helix, or a spiral, or simply twisted about its central axis (all except the spiral were used by Bourdon in 1851), tends to straighten out when pressure is applied to a fluid within it. When one end of the tube is fixed, the movement of the other end will indicate variation of pressure. Obituary notices repeat the story that Bourdon was led to the principle of the Bourdon tube by observing the action of a lead cooling coil under internal pressure. Judging from his painstaking attention to detail, this explanation is not unreasonable. Important aspects of the design of Bourdon tubes are still based upon empirical evidence rather than mathematical analysis.

In 1851, as a result of the success of his gauges at the London International Exhibition, Bourdon was awarded the Legion of Honor.

BIBLIOGRAPHY

A paper by Bourdon on his most famous instrument is "Description de manomètres métalliques sans mercure, pour indiquer la pression de la vapeur dans les chaudières," in *Bulletin de la Société d'encouragement pour l'industrie nationale,* **50** (1851), 197–200.

A definitive review of theoretical treatment (17 references) is Robert W. Bradspies, "Bourdon Tubes," in *Giannini Technical Notes* (Jan.-Feb., 1961), pp. 1–10, published by the Giannini Controls Corp., Duarte, Calif.

Obituary notices are "Eugène Bourdon," in *Revue scientifique,* 3rd ser., **21** (1884), 542–543; and "Notice sur M. Eugène Bourdon, par M. Henri Tresca," in *Bulletin de la Société d'encouragement pour l'industrie nationale,* **83** (1884), 515–519.

EUGENE S. FERGUSON

BOURNON, JACQUES-LOUIS, COMTE DE (*b.* Metz, France, 21 January 1751; *d.* Versailles, France, 24 August 1825), *mineralogy.*

Bournon was an early and ardent supporter of the Abbé Haüy's theories of crystal structure. In approximately twenty scientific memoirs he followed Haüy's procedure in identifying the integrant molecules of various mineralogical species, but he did not hesitate to criticize Haüy's judgment when he considered it erroneous. His major work was the handsomely illustrated three-volume *Traité complet de la chaux carbonatée et de l'arragonite* (1808), in which he described minutely all of the currently known crystal variations of calcite and aragonite.

Bournon's father, the owner of the Château de Fabert, near Metz, had formed a large mineralogical collection that stimulated Bournon's early and lasting interest in mineralogy. Bournon pursued a military career, becoming a lieutenant of the marshals of France. In 1791 he emigrated to the Rhineland and fought in the army of the princes in the campaign of 1792, after which he went to England. He was well received in scientific circles there, owing to his *Essai sur la lithographie de St. Étienne-en-Forez et sur l'origine de ses charbons de pierre* (1785).

In England, Bournon lectured frequently on mineralogy and organized the large mineralogical collections of Lord Grenville, Sir Abraham Hume, and Sir John St. Aubyn. He was elected a fellow of the Royal Society in 1802 and helped to found the Geological Society, of which he was the first foreign secretary, from 1811 to 1814. He returned to France after the restoration of the Bourbons and became the director general of the mineralogical cabinet of Louis XVIII. The mineral bournonite, a sulfantimonite of lead and copper characterized by beautifully shaped crystals that are often twinned, was named after Bournon, who first described it completely in 1804.

BIBLIOGRAPHY

Bournon's important works are *Essai sur la lithographie de St. Étienne-en-Forez et sur l'origine de ses charbons de pierre* (Paris, 1785); *Traité complet de la chaux carbonatée et de l'arragonite,* 3 vols. (London, 1808); *Traité de minéralogie,* 3 vols. (London, 1808); *Catalogue de la collection minéralogique du Comte de Bournon* (London, 1813); and *Catalogue de la collection minéralogique particulière du roi,* 2 vols. (Paris, 1817). His mineralogical memoirs were published principally in the *Philosophical Transactions of the Royal Society,* London, the *Journal des mines,* and *Transactions of the Geological Society.*

JOHN G. BURKE

BOUSSINESQ, JOSEPH VALENTIN (*b.* St.-André-de-Sangonis, Hérault, France, 15 March 1842; *d.* Paris, France, 19 February 1929), *mechanics, theoretical physics.*

Boussinesq came from a family of small farmers, and his first lessons were given by the village schoolteacher and by his uncle, a priest. He then attended the small seminary at Montpellier. After receiving the *baccalauréat,* he became an assistant master in a private school but was not responsible for teaching the children. When he obtained his *licence ès sciences* in 1851, Boussinesq went on to teach at the Collège d'Agde, then at Le Vigan, and later at Gap. Self-taught in scientific matters, he nevertheless was able, in 1865, to present a report on capillarity to the Académie des Sciences. In 1867 his thesis on the spreading of heat won him his *docteur ès sciences* as well as the goodwill of the academician and mathematician Barré de Saint-Venant. Boussinesq then became a professor at the Faculté des Sciences in Lille in 1873, and later he was assigned the chair of physical and experimental mechanics in Paris, followed by those of mathematical physics and of the calculus of probabilities. He was elected to the Académie des Sciences in January 1866 and eventually became its dean; at his death he was its oldest member.

Boussinesq led a simple, secluded life dedicated entirely to science and meditation on philosophical and religious problems, particularly on the conciliation of determinism and free will. He humbly admitted "the smallness of the ensemble of our unclouded knowledge lost in an ocean of darkness."

Faithful to mechanistic thought, which seeks kinematic representations, Boussinesq started with the principle of the conservation of energy and the principle that the accelerations of the points in an isolated system depend solely upon its static state and not on the velocities. He combined a great imaginative boldness with submission to experimental results. One of his conclusions was that simplicity is indispensable in scientific organization and that intuition is a valuable guide. Boussinesq loathed the introduction of such monsters as continuous functions without derivatives and of non-Euclidean space. Hostile to relativist innovations, he remained loyal to classical mechanics and sure of the reality of the ether. He did, however, make important contributions to all branches of mathematical physics except that of electromagnetism.

Boussinesq brought the theoretical study of ether closer to the study of experimental hydrodynamics in his researches on light waves and the theory of heat. His work on hydraulics was considerable; and with extraordinary insight he was able to use a method of legitimate approximation that made it possible to carry out intricate calculations concerning the study of whirlpools, liquid waves, the flow of fluids, the mechanics of pulverulent masses, the resistance of a fluid against a solid body, and the cooling effect of a liquid flow.

Although Boussinesq approached mathematics only in order to apply it practically, he was led to some interesting analyses in seeking the solution of particular problems. In the field of elasticity he obtained some intuitive results when considering certain potentials (logarithmic potentials with three variables, spherical potentials with four variables). In 1880 Boussinesq came upon nonanalytic integrals of hydrodynamic equations. He also found some asymptotic solutions of differential equations corresponding to cases of physical indetermination.

Boussinesq left a considerable amount of work. Besides the hundred or more papers he submitted to learned societies, he published several scholarly and abstruse books, full of original ideas but unorganized and often obscure. By virtue of the spirit of his research he can be considered one of the last figures of classical science in the nineteenth century.

BIBLIOGRAPHY

Among Boussinesq's works are *Étude dynamique d'un effet de capillarité* (Paris, 1865); "Propagation de la chaleur (Ellipsoïde des conductibilités linéaires)," his thesis (1867); "Essai sur la théorie des eaux courantes, précédé d'un rapport sur le mémoire, suivi d'additions et d'éclaircissements," in *Mémoires présentés par divers savants à l'Académie des Sciences de l'Institut National de France,* XXIII, no. 7 (1872) and XXIV, no. 2 (1875); *Essai théorique sur l'équilibre des massifs pulverulents comparé à celui des massifs solides et sur la poussée des terres sans cohésion* (Brussels, 1876; 1885); *Leçons synthétiques de mécanique générale, introduction au cours de mécanique physique* (Paris, 1883); "Applications des potentiels à l'étude de l'équilibre et du mouvement des solides élastiques," in *Annales de l'École Normale Supérieure* (1885); and *Cours de physique mathématique,* 4 vols. (Paris, 1901–1929). The correspondence between Boussinesq and Saint-Venant is in the archives of the Academy of Sciences, Paris.

LUCIENNE FÉLIX

BOUSSINGAULT, JEAN BAPTISTE JOSEPH DIEUDONNÉ (*b.* Paris, France, 2 February 1802; *d.* Paris, 11 May 1887), *agricultural chemistry.*

Boussingault's education, although not extensive, was influenced by Thénard, Gay-Lussac, Georges Cuvier, and Haüy; he also studied engineering. His South American geological and meteorological research in 1821–1832, recommended by Alexander von Humboldt, earned him recognition as a scientist and election to the Académie des Sciences in 1839.

From 1834 to 1876, Boussingault applied organic analysis in field and laboratory research on his farm at Bechelbronn, Alsace, to problems of soil fertility, crop rotation, plant and soil fixation of nitrogen, ammonia in rainwater, and nitrification, in order to determine the sources of plant nitrogen. From 1837 to 1854 he studied the proportions of organic materials that pass through plants and animals. In his 1837–1838 fixation experiments, he suggested that legumes may fix nitrogen from atmospheric sources. Between 1838 and 1841 Boussingault showed that legumes, when grown with cereals in initially exhausted soil, will restore to soil far more nitrogen than can be attributed to fertilizers; that both herbivores and carnivores obtain their nitrogen from plants; that the nitrogen of all plants, except in the case of legumes, may be accounted for by organic fertilizer; and that rainwater does not contain enough ammonia to satisfy the nitrogen needs of plants.

Because his 1854 fixation experiments, more strictly controlled, were largely negative, Boussingault turned to soil as the prime source of plant nitrogen. In 1855–1856 he showed that *Helianthus* plants grow to maturity in artificial, organic-free soil when watered with nitrates. In 1859 he demonstrated the spontaneous increase of nitrates in plant-free soil and the soil fixation of nitrogen, suggesting, even though temporarily, the action of microorganisms. From 1860 to 1876 he studied the chemistry of nitrification, identifying fertile soil as a prerequisite.

Boussingault's experiments on nitrogen fixation from 1834 to 1854 and his work on nitrification from 1855 to 1876 brought the problem of plant nitrogen essentially to the threshold of its modern microbiological formulation.

BIBLIOGRAPHY

Among Boussingault's books are *Économie rurale,* 2 vols. (Paris, 1843–1844, 1851), also trans. into English, 1 vol. (New York–Philadelphia, 1845), German, 2 vols. (Halle, 1844–1845; 2nd ed. of Vols. I and II, 1851), and Italian, 2 vols. (Venice, 1850); *Agronomie, chimie agricole et physiologie,* 2nd ed., rev. and enl., 8 vols. (Paris, 1860–1891); and *Mémoires de J.-B. Boussingault,* 5 vols. (Paris, 1892–1903), which deals with his life to 1832, particularly his South American sojourn.

His articles include "Recherches sur la quantité d'azote contenue dans les fourrages, et sur leur équivalens," in *Annales de chimie et de physique,* 2nd ser., **63** (1836), 225–244, and **67** (1838), 408–421; "Recherches chimiques sur la végétation, entreprises dans le but d'examiner si les plantes prennent de l'azote à l'atmosphère," *ibid.,* 1–54, and **69** (1838), 353–367; "Sur la quantité d'ammoniaque contenue dans l'eau de pluie recueillie loin des villes," in *Comptes rendus de l'Académie des sciences,* **37** (1853), 207–208, 798–806; "Mémoire sur le dosage de l'ammoniaque contenue dans les eaux," in *Journal de pharmacie et de chimie,* 3rd ser., **25** (1854), 122–131; "Recherches sur la végétation. De l'action du salpêtre sur le développement des plantes," *ibid.,* **46** (1856), 5–41; "De la terre végétale considérée dans ses effets sur la végétation," in *Annales des sciences naturelles,* Section Botanique, 4th ser., **12** (1859), 354–372; "Observations relatives au développement des mycodermes," in *Annales de chimie et de physique,* 3rd ser., **61** (1861), 363–367; "Sur la nitrification de la terre végétale," *ibid.,* 4th ser., **29** (1873), 186–206; and "Influence de la terre végétale sur la nitrification des matières organiques azotées employées comme engrais," *ibid.,* 5th ser., **8** (1876), 1–24.

Publications about Boussingault are M. Lenglen, *Un aspect peu connu de J.-B. Boussingault à la Société Centrale d'Agriculture, 1842–1887* (Beauvais, 1937); and George R. Cowgill, "Jean Baptiste Boussingault," in *Journal of Nutrition,* **84,** no. 1 (Sept. 1964), 1–9.

RICHARD P. AULIE

BOUTROUX, PIERRE LÉON (*b.* Paris, France, 6 December 1880; *d.* France, August 1922), *mathematics, history, philosophy of science.*

Pierre Boutroux came from a distinguished family. The only son of the celebrated French philosopher Émile Boutroux and Aline Catherine Eugénie Boutroux, he was also the nephew of the statesman Raymond Poincaré and the physicist Lucien Poincaré and a cousin of the noted mathematician Henri Poincaré.

Boutroux's serious academic life began with his studies at the École Normale Supérieure in Paris. In 1900, when he was but nineteen, the University of Paris published his thesis of *licence, L'imagination et les mathématiques selon Descartes.* After lecturing in mathematics at the University of Montpellier, Boutroux served as professor of integral calculus at the University of Poitiers from 1908 until 1920. During this period he traveled widely. In 1909 he was a visiting professor at the University of Nancy. Shortly thereafter he lectured at the Collège de France on mathematical functions defined by first-order differential equations. Then he departed for the United States and Princeton University, where he occupied the chair of higher mathematics from 1913 through 1914. At Princeton he also assumed the chairmanship of the graduate department of mathematics.

With the advent of World War I, Boutroux took a leave of absence from Princeton in order to join the French army. After serving with distinction, he remained in France. In 1920 he returned to the Collège de France, where he accepted the professorial chair of the general history of science, which Auguste Comte had first sought to have created in 1832. Although it was finally established in 1892, Boutroux was the first historian of science to occupy it. Had it not been for his untimely death at the age of forty-one, Boutroux, with his extensive erudition, might have made famous the chair of Comte. After his death in 1922, the chair was discontinued.

The writings of Boutroux reflect a wide-ranging scientific interest. In the area of pure mathematics, his chief contribution was his study of multiform functions and the singularities of differential equations.

In the nineteenth century, Augustin Cauchy, Karl Weierstrass, and Henri Poincaré had made significant advances in the theory of differential equations in the complex domain. Late in the century the French mathematician Paul Painlevé undertook the study of the singularities of analytic functions. After 1887, in a series of brilliant articles, he established a firm foundation for the analytic theory of differential equations and specifically introduced new equations not integrable in terms of elliptic functions or any of their degenerate cases. These equations defined new transcendents. Early in the twentieth century Boutroux not only continued Painlevé's work on these new transcendents, but also helped develop Henri Poincaré's and Charles Picard's study in the complex field, around a zero point, of the differential system

$$\frac{dx^1}{X_1} = \frac{dx^2}{X_2} = \cdots = \frac{dx^n}{X_n}$$

where the X's are all zero in o and holomorphic in its neighborhood.

Boutroux's principal pure mathematical publication is *Leçons sur les fonctions définies par les équations différentielles du premier ordre*. After reading this text and several of his articles, one can see that his main contributions to mathematics arose from the extension and clarification of extant ideas rather than from his formulation of new ones.

Boutroux's contributions to the history and philosophy of science are, however, more original and more extensive. The two-volume *Les principes de l'analyse mathématique* is a transitional work encompassing both pure mathematics and the history and philosophy of mathematics. These volumes contain a comprehensive view of the whole field of mathematics in the second decade of the twentieth century, both as a body of knowledge and as a mode of thought. Boutroux's topics range from rational numbers to an analysis of the notion of function. In light of the historical method used by the author, he might better have entitled this book "An Analysis of the Progress of Mathematical Thought." Some of his historical sections are open to criticism. In one instance, for example, his underrating of the accomplishments of

Isaac Barrow and Gottfried Leibniz detract from his analysis of the development of the infinitesimal calculus.

Boutroux clearly presented his view of the nature of mathematical analysis in *Les principes*. He saw analysis as the combination or reconciliation of two often opposing approaches to explaining the world's phenomena: empiricism and rationalism. His summary of historical developments strikingly shows that modern analysis now envelops these two approaches.

Les principes is a substantial contribution to mathematical literature. Its lucid presentation of some of the most important topics in the field has proved to be a valuable guide for graduate students and teachers of mathematics. In addition, this book is a useful source of information for historians of mathematics.

Probably Boutroux's foremost work is *L'idéal scientifique des mathématiciens dans l'antiquité et dans les temps modernes*. In this volume he asserts that the synthetic conception of Cartesian algebra represents a median period in the evolution of mathematics between the aesthetic, contemplative Greek attitude and the apparently groping and incoherent researches of contemporary mathematicians. Throughout these three different ages runs the unity of a search for progress, the attainment of a higher reality. This progress depends neither solely upon mathematicians nor upon the abstract systems of rational or conventional construction. Progress involves many varied rational and practical advances.

The main purpose of Boutroux in writing this book, however, was not to investigate the constituent elements of progress. He had two didactic goals in mind. After showing that the different sciences do not progress independently, he first asserted that the history of science should be a study of the continuous interactions between the various sciences. He opposed the view of the history of science as consisting only of narrow, technical studies. Second, he told teachers and researchers that no one type of solution exists for all problems. He felt that the nature of the problem best dictated the methods needed for its solution.

Boutroux's contributions to the literature of the history of science extend beyond the general surveys mentioned above. His edition of the works of Blaise Pascal provided the source material needed for the study of seventeenth-century mathematics. He also improved upon some of Pierre Duhem's studies of mechanics and carefully analyzed the writings of the French historian Paul Tannery. Judging from his writings, Boutroux fits into the group of historical thinkers consisting of Auguste Comte, Paul Tannery, Pierre Duhem, and George Sarton.

BIBLIOGRAPHY

I. ORIGINAL WORKS. Books by Boutroux are the following: *L'imagination et les mathématiques selon Descartes* (Paris, 1900); *Leçons sur les fonctions définies par les équations différentielles du premier ordre* (Paris, 1908), with notes by Paul Painlevé; *Oeuvres de Blaise Pascal, pub. suivant l'ordre chronologique avec documents complémentaires* (Paris, 1908– ; 2nd ed., 1929), with introduction and notes by Léon Brunschvicg and Boutroux; *Henri Poincaré: L'oeuvre scientifique, l'oeuvre philosophique* (Paris, 1914), written with Vito Volterra, Jacques Hadamard, and Paul Langevin; *Les principes de l'analyse mathématique. Exposé historique et critique,* 2 vols. (Paris, 1914–1919); and *L'idéal scientifique des mathématiciens dans l'antiquité et dans les temps modernes* (Paris, 1920).

Boutroux's articles include "Les origines du calcul des probabilités," in *Revue du mois,* **5** (1908), 641–654; "Le calcul combinatoire et la science universelle," in *Revue du mois,* **9** (1910), 50–62; "Fonctions analytiques: Exposé d'après l'article allemand de W. F. Osgood," in *Encyclopédie des sciences mathématiques* (Paris, 1904–1913), Tome 2, Vol. II, written with Jean Chazy; "Remarques sur les singularités transcendantes des fonctions de deux variables," in *Comptes rendus de l'Académie royale des sciences,* **39,** nos. 2–3 (1911), 296–304; "L'edifice géométrique et la démonstration," in *L'enseignement mathématique,* **14,** no. 6 (1912), 281–305; "Les étapes de la philosophie mathématique," in *Revue de métaphysique et de morale,* **21,** nos. 3–5 (1913), 307–328; "Recherches sur les transcendantes de M. Painlevé et l'étude asymptotique des équations différentielles du second ordre," in *Annales scientifiques de l'École Normale Supérieure,* 3rd ser., **30,** nos. 6–12 (1914), 255–375, and **31,** nos. 2–6 (1914), 99–159; "L'histoire des sciences et les grands courants de la pensée mathématique," in *Revue du mois,* **20** (1915), 604–621; "Sur une mode de définition d'une classe de fonctions multiformes dans tout le domaine d'existence de ces fonctions," in *Comptes rendus de l'Académie royale des sciences,* **163** (1919), 1150–1152; "Sur une famille de fonctions multiformes définies par des équations différentielles du premier ordre," *ibid.,* **170** (1920), 15–26; "L'enseignement de la mécanique en France au XVIIᵉ siècle," in *Isis,* **4** (1921), 276–295; "L'histoire des principes de la dynamique avant Newton," in *Revue de métaphysique et de morale,* **28** (1921), 656–688; "On Multiform Functions Defined by Differential Equations of the First Order," in *Annals of Mathematics,* **22** (1922), 1–29; "Sur les fonctions associées à un groupe autogène de substitution," in *Comptes rendus de l'Académie royale des sciences,* **173** (1922), 821–832; and "L'oeuvre de Paul Tannery," in *Osiris,* nos. 4–5 (1938), 690–705.

II. SECONDARY LITERATURE. A book containing material on Boutroux is Doyen Roissonnade, *Histoire de l'Université de Poitiers passé et présent (1432–1932)* (Poitiers, 1932). An article dealing with Boutroux is Léon Brunschvicg, "L'oeuvre de Pierre Boutroux," in *Revue de métaphysique et de morale,* **29–30** (1922), 285–289.

RONALD S. CALINGER

BOUVARD, ALEXIS (*b.* Contamines, Haut Faucigny, France, 27 June 1767; *d.* Paris, France, 7 June 1843), *astronomy.*

Alexis Bouvard is known chiefly for his *Tables astronomiques* of Jupiter, Saturn, and Uranus (1821). His aim in drawing up the tables was to provide a basis for reliable predictions of future locations of the three planets: unexpectedly, his Uranus tables agitated astronomers for two decades. Those of Jupiter and Saturn were revisions of tables that he had published in 1808 and that had proved satisfactory. Since the discovery of Uranus in 1781 many accurate observations had been made, notably the fine series at the Paris and Greenwich observatories. Uranus, however, has a very long orbital period of eighty-four years. Eleven prediscovery sightings of the planet as a star (including three by Lemonnier) had been traced, scattered over the previous ninety years, but Bouvard needed more prediscovery observations in order to compute a satisfactory orbit. He therefore searched through fifteen folio volumes of Pierre Lemonnier's observations made between 1736 and 1780. Although they were in great disorder and badly written, and many were inaccurately timed, Bouvard found nine more observations of Uranus, besides the three Lemonnier had himself traced, giving a total of twenty prediscovery observations. Using Laplace's formulas for perturbations, Bouvard formed seventy-seven equations of condition, but he was dismayed that no orbit would fit both prediscovery and postdiscovery observations. He therefore calculated his Uranus tables from the postdiscovery observations alone, rejecting the others.

Within a few years Bouvard's Uranus tables failed, the planet lagging farther and farther behind the tabular predictions. Earlier than most astronomers, he became convinced that the cause was an unknown perturbing body. Until he died, he held to this belief, which was confirmed three years after his death by the discovery of the planet Neptune. Then it became possible to reconcile prediscovery and postdiscovery observations, and also to show that Neptune had accelerated the motion of Uranus for several years before 1821, thereafter retarding its motion. The very failure of Bouvard's tables was what induced J. C. Adams and U. J. J. Leverrier to solve the problem of Uranus' motion, and thus hastened the discovery of Neptune, probably by several decades.

Bouvard's rise to eminence in mathematical astronomy was dramatic. He arrived in Paris in 1785, an Alpine peasant youth unable to afford school fees. He attended free lectures and soon showed a flair for mathematics. In 1793 he became a pupil at the Paris

Observatory and an astronomer there two years later. He taught mathematics, and became a valuable assistant to Laplace, who left to him all the detailed calculations for the *Mécanique céleste*. Through Laplace's support Bouvard became, in 1804, a member of the Bureau des Longitudes, supplying tables to the *Annuaire* (similar to the *Nautical Almanac*) for many years. He was soon elected to the Académie des Sciences. A keen observer, he discovered eight comets and computed their orbits. He annotated Caussin's translation of the work of the medieval Arab astronomer, Ibn-Yūnus.

Brilliant but modest, Bouvard was an indefatigable calculator, and engaged in computation until the eve of his death. It could well be said of him that he ceased calculating only when he ceased living.

BIBLIOGRAPHY

I. ORIGINAL WORKS. Most of Bouvard's work is in the *Annuaire du Bureau des Longitudes* and in Laplace's *Mécanique céleste* (5 vols. and suppl., Paris, 1799–1827). Among works worthy of separate mention are "Nouvelles tables des planètes Jupiter et Saturne," in *Tables astronomiques publiées par le Bureau des Longitudes* (Paris, 1808), his earlier tables of these planets; "Extrait des registres des observations astronomiques faites par Lemonnier . . . ," in *Connaissance des temps* (1819), pp. 339–347, his account of his search of Lemonnier's registers for prediscovery observations of Uranus; and *Tables astronomiques publiées par le Bureau des Longitudes de France, contenant les tables de Jupiter, de Saturne et d'Uranus, construites d'après la théorie de la Mécanique céleste* (Paris, 1821), with an introduction describing the work and problems.

II. SECONDARY LITERATURE. Works on Bouvard are a biography in F. Hoefer, ed., *Nouvelle biographie universelle*, VII (Paris, 1853), cols. 141–142; G. B. Airy, "Circumstances Connected With the Discovery of a Planet Exterior to Uranus," in *Monthly Notices of the Royal Astronomical Society,* **7** (1846), 121–152, which includes Airy's correspondence with Eugène Bouvard, nephew of Alexis, about the latter's attempts to revise the Uranus tables; and A. F. O'D. Alexander, *The Planet Uranus* (London, 1965), which contains many details and references regarding the prediscovery observations, Bouvard's work, and the subsequent studies.

A. F. O'D. ALEXANDER

BOUVELLES, CHARLES (*b.* Saucourt, Picardy, France, *ca.* 1470; *d.* Noyon, France, *ca.* 1553), *philosophy, theology, philology, mathematics.*

The most important mathematical work of Bouvelles, who was also known as Charles de Bouelles, was published in three languages: in Latin as *Geometricae introductionis* (1503); in French as *Livre*

singulier et utile (1542, with several later editions); and in Dutch as *Boeck aenghaende de Conste en de Practycke van Geometrie* (1547). According to H. Bosmans (*Bibliotheca mathematica,* **7** [1906], 384) this translation is a bit abbreviated. The *Geometricae* includes chapters on stellated polygons, which had been discussed in Bradwardine's *De geometria speculativa* (1495). It is very likely that Bouvelles knew this tract, for he refers to Bradwardine in his introduction to the section on the quadrature of the circle, which also was discussed in the *Geometria*. Extending the sides of a regular convex polygon results in a stellated polygon of the first order; in the same way the latter can be transformed into a stellated polygon of the second order, and so on. Bouvelles started with the stellated pentagon, the first stellated polygon of the first order, and showed that the sum of its angles equals two right angles. For this he used the regularity of the polygon and showed that every angle is 36°, so the sum is 180°. After having shown that the sum of the angles of a stellated hexagon equals four right angles, he went on to the first stellated polygon of the second order, the heptagon; and, referring to his proof for the pentagon, he said that the sum of the angles of the heptagon also equals two right angles.

Bouvelles made several attempts to solve the old problem of the quadrature of the circle. In the Middle Ages there had been several treatises on that subject: the *De quadratura circuli* of Franco of Liège (eleventh century), the *De triangulis* of Jordanus de Nemore and the *De quadratura et triangulatura circuli* of Ramón Lull (thirteenth century), the *De geometria speculativa* of Bradwardine (according to Bouvelles, his quadrature is not right), and the *Quaestio de quadratura circuli* of Albert of Saxony (fourteenth century); the *De circuli quadratura* of Nicholas of Cusa (fifteenth century) was refuted by Regiomontanus, but Bouvelles agreed with it, remarking that Nicholas used infinite dimensions unknown to any geometer who would never confess that they were possible.

In the age of Bouvelles, too, there were treatises: Oronce Fine's *De quadratura circuli* (1544), Jean Buteo's *De quadratura circuli* (1559), and Joseph Scaliger's *Cyclometrica elementa* (1594), which was refuted by Vieta in his *Munimen adversus nova Cyclometrica* (1594) and in his *Pseudo-mesolabium* (1595). In the solution given in the *Livre singulier*, Bouvelles considered a circle rolling along a straight line. After a quarter of a revolution, the point on the circle at which the distance from the line is equal to the radius of the circle has touched the line and has described an arc of a circle, the center of which lies 5/4 *r* (radius) beneath the starting point of the center of the given circle. His construction agrees with the Hindu value of $\pi = \sqrt{10}$. Günther has seen in this the first genetic construction of the cycloid, but this is very unlikely.

In his *Liber de XII numeris* (1510) Bouvelles wrote on perfect numbers, i.e., numbers that are equal to the sum of all their possible factors, such as 6, 28, and 496. He asserted, without proof, that a perfect number (except 6) is always a multiple of 9, plus 1, but that the inverse is not true. This rule was given, also without proof, by Tartaglia in his *General trattato di numeri et misure* (1556).

In 1511 Bouvelles published the *Géométrie en françoys,* probably the first geometrical treatise printed in French.

BIBLIOGRAPHY

I. ORIGINAL WORKS. Bouvelles' major work appeared in three versions: in Latin, as *Geometricae introductionis libri sex, breviusculis annotationibus explanati, quibus annectuntur libelli de circuli quadratura, et de cubicatione spherae et introductione in perspectivam* (Paris, 1503); in French, as *Livre singulier et utile touchant l'art et pratique de géométrie, composé nouvellement en françoys, par Maistre Charles de Bouvelles, chanoyne de Noyon* (Paris, 1542); in Dutch, as *Boeck aenghaende de Conste en de Practycke van Geometrie* (Antwerp, 1547). His other works are *Liber de XII numeris* (Paris, 1510) and *Géométrie en françoys* (Paris, 1511).

II. SECONDARY LITERATURE. Works on Bouvelles are Marshall Clagett, *Archimedes in the Middle Ages* (Madison, Wis., 1964), pp. 33–36; J. Dippel, *Versuch einer systematischen Darstellung der Philosophie des Carolus Bovillus* (Würzburg, 1865); J. Fontès, "Sur le *Liber de numeris perfectis* de Charles de Bouëlles," in *Mémoires de l'Académie des Sciences, Inscriptions et Belles-Lettres de Toulouse,* **6** (1894), 155–167; S. Günther, "Lo sviluppo storico della teoria dei poligoni stellati nell' antichità e nel medio evo," in *Bollettino di bibliografia e di storia,* **6** (1873), 313–340; S. Günther, "War die Zykloide bereits im XVI. Jahrhunderte bekannt?," in *Bibliotheca mathematica,* **1** (1887), 8–14; D. Mahnke, *Unendliche Sphäre und Allmittelpunkt* (Halle, 1937), pp. 108–117.

H. L. L. BUSARD

BOVERI, THEODOR (*b.* Bamberg, Germany, 12 October 1862; *d.* Würzburg, Germany, 15 October 1915), *biology.*

The distinguished American cytologist Edmund B. Wilson wrote in a memorial volume to Boveri (1918) that Boveri's work "enriched biological science with some of the most interesting discoveries and fruitful new conceptions of our time."[1] When these words appeared in print, Thomas Hunt Morgan's *The Theory of the Gene* had not yet been published, and evidence for the linear order of genes had not yet been presented. Fifty years later, when the chromosomal basis of heredity had not only been firmly established but had also been successfully elucidated at a molecular level, the fruitfulness of Boveri's discoveries and conceptions became fully apparent. Many were of primary importance in leading to the concepts of the chromosomal theory of heredity and were brilliant feats of intellectual and experimental analysis.

Boveri was the second of four sons of Theodor Boveri, a physician descended from a family of Frankish origin, and Antonie Elssner Boveri. He attended school in Bamberg from 1868 to 1875, and the Realgymnasium in Nuremberg from 1875 to 1881. In that year he entered the University of Munich, where after a single semester of concentration on historical-philosophical studies, he turned to natural science. His first scientific training was in anatomy; he studied with Carl von Kupffer, whom he also assisted, at the Anatomical Institute in Munich, and he received the doctorate *summa cum laude* in 1885. His dissertation, on work performed under Kupffer's guidance, dealt with the structure of nerve fibers.

In 1885 Boveri was awarded a five-year fellowship, the Lamont-Stipendium (later renewed for two years). This enabled him to transfer in 1885 to the Zoological Institute in Munich, the directorship of which had just been assumed by Richard Hertwig. It was Hertwig who drew Boveri's interest toward research in cell biology, the area in which he was to make his most significant contributions. Boveri began his work with Hertwig in May 1885 and remained at the Zoological Institute until 1893. He was habilitated in zoology and comparative anatomy in 1887; from 1891 to 1893 he was Hertwig's assistant.

In 1893, at the age of thirty, Boveri became professor of zoology and comparative anatomy, and director of the Zoological-Zootomical Institute, at the University of Würzburg. He remained there essentially for the rest of his life, although, like many of his contemporaries and successors, he made a number of working visits to the Zoological Station at Naples— the first in 1888, the last in 1914. He received invitations to leave Würzburg for other positions; the most noteworthy was the call, in 1912, to become director of the Kaiser Wilhelm Institute for Biology in Berlin-Dahlem, one of the prototypes of modern biological research laboratories. He declined in 1913. In 1897 Boveri had married an American biologist, Marcella O'Grady, who participated in many of his investigations. They had one daughter, Margret, a well-known writer and journalist.

Boveri had a complicated personality. He is said to have had a somewhat turbulent temperament, yet at least in his later years he succeeded in appearing outwardly cool and objectively self-possessed. His satisfaction with his life in Würzburg, and his enjoyment of the very different style of life at Naples, perhaps reflected two conflicting sides of his character. He had a witty sense of humor, but is known to have been a sharp critic. He also was afflicted at times by strong doubts of his own ability, and was as critical of himself as of others.

Like his parents, Boveri had a lively interest in both art and music. He was an exceptionally fine pianist, and music was an integral part of his daily life. His talent in painting was such that when young he had considered becoming a painter; characteristically, however, he eventually became so dubious of his own ability that he showed his paintings only to his closest friends.

Boveri's uprightness and strength of character, expressed in his daily life and in his high standards of scientific workmanship, profoundly influenced those who worked with him; many of his associates have attested to the fact that he had a particular talent for friendship. Nonetheless, like others with varied talents and demanding standards, Boveri paid a price for his abilities by suffering physical breakdowns. As early as the summer of 1890, troubled by the fact that his father had fallen into debt and that his mother was ill, he himself became ill with what was considered first to be influenza, then neurasthenia. He became so severely depressed that he was unable to work for months. When he recovered, Boveri returned to his laboratory in Munich for the winter semester of 1891. He was frequently ill thereafter, and subject to recurrent depression and to chronic rheumatism. His poor health may have been a primary factor in his decision not to move to the Kaiser Wilhelm Institute; he suffered a serious illness, involving slight paralysis of one side, shortly before giving his final refusal. Deeply troubled by the outbreak of World War I, Boveri suffered a further decline in his already failing health. He was only fifty-three when he died.

Boveri's mind was clearly analytical, and penetrated to the core of problems that were to become central to twentieth-century biological thought; his work lay at the borderlines of the disciplines that by midcentury would be distinguished as cytology, embryology, and genetics. He once wrote that most of his work was devoted "to the investigation of those processes by which a new individual with particular attributes develops from the reproductive material of its parents."[2]

In 1885 Boveri began a brilliant series of studies on the chromosomes. By this time it had been established that the fusion of the nuclei of egg and spermatozoon was an essential feature of fertilization, the fusion nucleus of the fertilized egg giving rise to all the nuclei of the body; hence the nucleus of each body cell contains nuclear substance from both parents. This had led to the conclusion, first expressed clearly in 1884–1885, that the cell nucleus carries the physical basis of heredity. By 1885 it was also known that at nuclear division part of the nuclear substance, the chromatin, forms definite rods, the chromosomes, which are split longitudinally; at cell division, the longitudinal halves of each chromosome had been observed to separate and pass to the two daughter cells. It also had been shown, for some organisms, that the chromosome number is constant for each species; and in 1883–1884 Edouard Van Beneden had made an important discovery in the eggs of *Ascaris megalocephala,* a roundworm: namely, that the chromosomes of the offspring are derived in equal number from the nuclei of egg and spermatozoon, thus equally from the two parents. The egg of *Ascaris* is particularly favorable for cytological studies because it has a small number (two or four) of large chromosomes.

Boveri, inspired by the work of Van Beneden, began to carry out his own studies on the eggs of *Ascaris* in 1885; preliminary reports began to appear in print in 1886 and 1887, and three of his exhaustive cell studies (*Zellenstudien*), dealing with *Ascaris* development, appeared in 1887, 1888, and 1890. The first described some aspects of the maturation of the egg and the formation of its polar bodies. The second, on fertilization and cleavage, demonstrated the individuality of the chromosomes, a discovery fundamental to the whole subsequent development of theories concerning the role of the chromosomes in inheritance.

The chromosomes are visible as such in the nuclei only during periods of nuclear division; at other times they are not discernible as separate entities. Inheritance implies continuity; if the chromosomes were to be construed as being involved in heredity, their seeming disappearance during part of the cell cycle presented a great problem. A few investigations by Van Beneden and others, published in the early 1880's, had suggested that the chromosomes represented continuing elements in the cell, but these were not conclusive. The nuclei of *Ascaris* show finger-shaped lobes at early cleavage stages. By using these lobes as landmarks, Boveri demonstrated the individuality of the chromosomes. His observations were morphological, but his interpretations of them transcended the purely descriptive; he considered the individual chromosomes to be independent entities and emphasized particularly that they were *organized* structures. Several years later (1904), in a theoretical paper on the nature of the chromatic substance, he compared them to "elementary organisms [that] lead an independent existence within the cell."[3] Wilson wrote in 1918 that Boveri's theory of chromosome individuality provided the working basis of nearly all cytological interpretations of genetic phenomena; this evaluation still holds.

The third cell study (1890) confirmed and extended the observations previously made by Van Beneden that at fertilization the egg and spermatozoon contribute equivalent sets of chromosomes to the new individual. This study, integrally related to that of chromosome individuality, completed the shift of emphasis from the nucleus as a whole to the chromosomes as the agents of inheritance. Again, in Wilson's words, it "first pointed the way to a physical explanation of Mendel's law of heredity and of genetic phenomena generally."[4]

Among other outstanding discoveries made by Boveri in his early studies on *Ascaris* was one concerning the role in fertilization of the midpiece of the spermatozoon. In animals, when the nucleus of the fertilized egg divides, a small structure called the centrosome is an integral part of the cytoplasmic apparatus that organizes the separation of the chromosome halves into the two daughter cells. Independently of one another, Boveri and Van Beneden had previously observed the centrosome in cleaving eggs; Boveri, in studies begun on *Ascaris* in 1887, showed that the centrosome introduced into the egg at fertilization by the midpiece of the spermatozoon provides the division centers for the dividing egg cell and all its progeny.

Boveri was later to consider other aspects of the development of *Ascaris,* but in the meantime he turned, under the influence of the Hertwigs, to the study of the sea urchin egg. His early investigations on the eggs of *Ascaris* were largely observational, and it was clear to him that the role of the nucleus as agent of heredity required experimental proof. He could perform experiments on the eggs of the sea urchin that for technical reasons could not be carried out on those of *Ascaris*. Boveri's powers of observation as a microscopist were remarkable, and he was also extremely gifted in devising illuminating experiments.

Of his many experiments on sea urchin eggs, several require special mention here. The Hertwigs had shown in 1887 that unfertilized sea urchin eggs could be broken up, by shaking, into fragments that can

be fertilized. In 1889 Boveri fertilized nucleated and nonnucleated fragments, and found that both types could develop normally; he found also that occasionally nonfertilized fragments, containing only the egg nucleus, developed normally. This established experimentally the equivalence of the maternal and the paternal nucleus.

In spite of this and other demonstrations of the importance of the nucleus and its chromosomes in development, Boveri remained open-minded as to the possibility that the cytoplasm of the egg might play some role in heredity; accordingly, in 1889 he began experiments that he thought might test this possibility. He attempted to fertilize nonnucleated fragments of one species of sea urchin eggs with spermatozoa of another species. He found that some resultant larvae resembled larvae of the maternal species; others, larvae of the paternal species. Boveri concluded that the former had developed from fertilized nucleated fragments and the latter from fertilized nonnucleated fragments, and interpreted the results as confirming the primary role of the nucleus, as opposed to the cytoplasm, in determining hereditary traits. But there were technical sources of error in the experiments, which Boveri tried vainly to overcome, and it was not until sixty-five years later that the experiments were successfully carried out by Ubisch. The later experiments showed that Boveri's results were probably correct, at least for the stages at which he terminated the experiments.

Boveri was eventually to demonstrate that the cytoplasm does play an important role in development, if not in inheritance as such, but before proceeding to this demonstration it is appropriate to summarize one further contribution concerning the role of the chromosomes in development and inheritance. This, the proof of the differential value of the chromosomes, was one of Boveri's most significant contributions. It was not yet known, when Boveri began his work, whether each chromosome contained factors responsible for the totality of development, for all the hereditary qualities of the individual, or whether each chromosome differed from the others in being responsible for only particular hereditary features, the sum of the various hereditary traits being divided among them all. Boveri proved experimentally the validity of the latter alternative.

He had known, as early as 1888, that in *Ascaris* certain eggs form four rather than two cells at the first cleavage, each cell with a different number of chromosomes. It had been shown that in the sea urchin such eggs could be produced experimentally by double fertilization. When two spermatozoa enter a single egg, the egg may divide into three or four cells at the first cleavage. Boveri ascertained that under such conditions, the chromosomes are almost always divided unequally among the cells. By studying the abnormalities of development of dispermic eggs, and by relating them to abnormal chromosome distribution, he proved in a most ingenious manner that it was "not a specific number, but a specific assortment of chromosomes [that] is responsible for normal development, and this can mean only that the individual chromosomes possess different qualities."[5] The preliminary report of this investigation was published in 1902, the very year that Walter Sutton called attention to "the probability that the association of paternal and maternal chromosomes in pairs and their subsequent separation during the reduction division . . . may constitute the physical basis of the Mendelian law of heredity."[6] Although Sutton had begun his work independently of Boveri, he stated that he was publishing a description of it in 1902 because of "the appearance of Boveri's recent remarkable paper on the analysis of the nucleus by means of observations on double-fertilized eggs."[7]

It was said above that Boveri's work on fertilization of egg fragments in the sea urchin reflected his interest in a possible role of the cytoplasm in heredity or development. His observations on *Ascaris* development, begun as early as 1887, later (1904, 1909, 1910) led to an appreciation of the importance of the cytoplasm in nuclear control. The eggs of the roundworm cleave in a unique pattern, and their chromosomes are unusual at early mitoses in that those in the cells at the lower part of the egg, destined to become the germ cells of the larva, exhibit a behavior different from that of those in the remaining cells. In the cells of the germ cell line, the large chromosomes divide typically; when their split halves separate they pass, as they are, to the two daughter cells in several successive mitoses. In the cells at the upper part of the egg, destined to form the body, at the early mitoses each nucleus discards some of the chromatin. This process, called chromatin diminution, was first described in detail for *Ascaris;* it has subsequently been shown to occur in a very few other animal species.

Boveri found that the number of cells exhibiting chromosome diminution may be altered in dispermic eggs separating into several cells at the first cleavage, and he also found that he could alter it by centrifuging the egg to alter the position of the nuclei in the cytoplasm. He concluded that the cells not undergoing diminution are normally located in a particular zone of cytoplasm, and that the behavior of the chromosomes is determined by the cytoplasm in which the nuclei lie. This was for many years the most cogent demonstration available of the influence of the cytoplasm upon the nucleus. At a time when much emphasis was placed on the overwhelming importance of the nucleus in development, Boveri wrote almost prophetically on the significance of reciprocal interaction between nucleus and cytoplasm.

Chromosome diminution in *Ascaris* occurs typically only at the upper part of the egg. It is a polar phenomenon. Boveri also wrote a number of pioneering and important papers on the polarity of the developing sea urchin egg. These led to more exhaustive studies by others, beginning in the 1920's, that demonstrated double gradients in echinoderm embryos. But some of the concepts deriving from Boveri's own interpretations of polarity, particularly with respect to the lower region of the egg, which he envisioned as a "privileged" region where differentiation begins and whence influence spreads, may have influenced the development of the organizer theory for the amphibian egg.

Boveri made a number of other important contributions; among them was his discovery of the segmental excretory organs in *Amphioxus,* believed in his day to be an organism close to the type from which vertebrates evolved. More closely related to his chromosomal studies was his development of a theory, published in 1914, that tumor cells may become malignant as a result of abnormal chromosome numbers; he was early to view the tumor problem as a cell problem. He also tried to explain, on the basis of aberrant chromosome distribution, a condition in bees in which male and female characters are mosaically distributed (1915). Significant as these contributions were, Boveri's primary influence on subsequent biology emanated from his demonstrations of chromosome individuality and his proof of the differential value of the chromosomes, which, again to borrow Wilson's words, "laid the basis for the cytological explanation of Mendel's law of heredity."[8]

NOTES

1. E. B. Wilson, in W. C. Roentgen, ed., *Erinnerungen an Theodor Boveri,* p. 67.
2. T. Boveri, "Die Potenzen der Ascaris-Blastomeren bei abgeänderter Furchung," p. 133.
3. T. Boveri, *Ergebnisse über die Konstitution der chromatischen Substanz des Zellkerns,* p. 90.
4. E. B. Wilson, *op. cit.,* p. 71.
5. T. Boveri, "Ueber mehrpolige Mitosen als Mittel zur Analyse des Zellkerns," p. 75.
6. W. S. Sutton, "On the Morphology of the Chromosome Group in *Brachystola magna,*" in *Biological Bulletin,* **4** (1902), 39.
7. *Ibid.,* p. 24.
8. E. B. Wilson, *op. cit.,* p. 76.

BIBLIOGRAPHY

I. ORIGINAL WORKS. Boveri's writings include "Ueber die Bedeutung der Richtungskörper," in *Sitzungsberichte der Gesellschaft für Morphologie und Physiologie zu München,* **2** (1886), 101–106; "Ueber den Anteil des Spermatozoon an der Teilung des Eies," *ibid.,* **3** (1887), 151–164; "Ueber die Befruchtung der Eier von *Ascaris megalocephala,*" *ibid.,* 71–80; "Ueber Differenzierung der Zellkern während der Furchung des Eies von *Ascaris megalocephala,*" in *Anatomischer Anzeiger,* **2** (1887), 688–693; "Zellenstudien I. Die Bildung der Richtungskörper bei *Ascaris megalocephala* und *Ascaris lumbricoides,*" in *Jenaische Zeitschrift für Naturwissenschaft,* **21** (1887), 423–515; "Zellenstudien II. Die Befruchtung und Teilung des Eies von *Ascaris megalocephala,*" *ibid.,* **22** (1888), 685–882; "Ein geschlechtlich erzeugter Organismus ohne mütterliche Eigenschaften," in *Sitzungsberichte der Gesellschaft für Morphologie und Physiologie zu München,* **5** (1889), 73–80; "Zellenstudien III. Ueber das Verhalten der chromatischen Kernsubstanz bei der Bildung der Richtungskörper und bei der Befruchtung," in *Jenaische Zeitschrift für Naturwissenschaft,* **24** (1890), 314–401; "Die Nierenkanälchen des *Amphioxus,*" in *Zoologische Jahrbücher,* **5** (1892), 429–510; "Ueber die Befruchtungs- und Entwicklungsfähigkeit kernloser Seeigeleier und über die Möglichkeit ihrer Bastardierung," in *Wilhelm Roux' Archiv für Entwicklungsmechanik der Organismen,* **2** (1895), 394–443; "Ueber das Verhalten der Centrosomen bei der Befruchtung des Seeigeleies nebst allgemeinen Bemerkungen über Centrosomen und Verwandtes," in *Verhandlungen der Physikalischen-medizinischen Gesellschaft zu Würzburg,* n.s. **29** (1895), 1–75; "Die Entwicklung von *Ascaris megalocephala* mit besonderer Rücksicht auf die Kernverhältnisse," in *Festschrift für Carl von Kupffer* (Jena, 1899), pp. 383–430; "Die Polarität von Oocyte, Ei und Larve des *Strongylocentrotus lividus,*" in *Zoologische Jahrbücher, Abteilung für Anatomie und Ontogenie der Tiere,* **14** (1901), 630–653; "Ueber die Polarität des Seeigeleies," in *Verhandlungen der Physikalischen-medizinischen Gesellschaft zu Würzburg,* n.s. **34** (1901), 145–176; "Zellenstudien IV. Ueber die Natur der Centrosomen," in *Jenaische Zeitschrift für Naturwissenschaft,* **35** (1901), 1–220; "Ueber mehrpolige Mitosen als Mittel zur Analyse des Zellkerns," in *Verhandlungen der Physikalischen-medizinischen Gesellschaft zu Würzburg,* n.s. **35** (1902), 67–90, trans. by Salome Glücksohn-Waelsch in B. H. Willier and Jane M. Oppenheimer, eds., *Foundations of Experimental Embryology* (Englewood Cliffs, N. J., 1964), pp. 76–97; "Ueber den Einfluss der Samenzelle auf die Larvencharaktere der Echiniden," in *Wilhelm Roux' Archiv für Entwicklungsmechanik der Organismen,* **16** (1903), 340–363; *Ergebnisse über die Konstitution der chromatischen Substanz des Zellkerns* (Jena, 1904); "Noch ein Wort über Seeigelbastarde," in *Wilhelm Roux' Archiv für Entwicklungsmechanik der Organismen,* **17** (1904), 521–525; "Ueber die Entwicklung dispermer Ascariseier," in *Zoologischer Anzeiger,* **27** (1904), 406–417, in collaboration with Nettie Maria Stevens; "Zellenstudien V. Ueber die Abhängigkeit der Kerngrösse und Zellenzahl der Seeigellarven von der Chromosomenzahl der Ausgangszellen," in *Jenaische Zeitschrift für Naturwissenschaft,* **39** (1905), 445–524; *Die Organismen als historische Wesen. Rektoratsrede* (Würzburg, 1906); "Zellenstudien VI. Die Entwicklung dispermer Seeigeleier. Ein Beitrag zur Befruchtungslehre und zur Theorie des Kerns," in *Jenaische Zeitschrift für Naturwissenschaft,* **43** (1907), 1–292; "Die Blastomerenkerne von *Ascaris megalocephala* und die Theorie der Chromosomenindividualität," in *Archiv für Zellforschung,* **3** (1909), 181–268; "Ueber die Möglichkeit, *Ascaris*-Eier zur Teilung in zwei gleichwertige Blastomeren zu veranlassen," in *Sitzungsberichte der Physikalischen-medizinischen Gesellschaft zu Würzburg* (1909), 44–48, in collaboration with Mary Jane Hogue; "Ueber die Teilung centrifugierter Eier von *Ascaris megalocephala,*" in *Wilhelm Roux' Archiv für Entwicklungsmechanik der Organismen,* **30** (1910), 101–125; "Die Potenzen der *Ascaris*-Blastomeren bei abgeänderter Furchung. Zugleich ein Beitrag zur Frage qualitativ ungleicher Chromosomenteilung," in *Festschrift für Richard Hertwig* (Jena, 1910), III, 133–214; "Ueber die Charaktere von Echiniden-Bastardlarven bei verschiedenem Mengenverhältnis mütterlicher und väterlicher Substanzen," in *Verhandlungen der Physikalischen-medizinischen Gesellschaft zu Würzburg,* n.s. **43** (1914), 117–135; *Zur Frage der Entstehung maligner Tumoren* (Jena, 1914), trans. by Marcella Boveri as *The Origin of Malignant Tumors* (Baltimore, 1929); "Ueber die Entstehung der Eugsterschen Zwitterbienen," in *Wilhelm Roux' Archiv für Entwicklungsmechanik der Organismen,* **41** (1915), 264–311; and "Zwei Fehlerquellen bei Merogonieversuchen und die Entwicklungsfähigkeit merogonischer, partiell-merogonischer Seeigelbastarde," *ibid.,* **44** (1918), 417–471.

II. SECONDARY LITERATURE. Writings on Boveri are F. Baltzer, *Theodor Boveri. Leben und Werk eines grossen Biologen 1862–1915* (Stuttgart, 1962), trans. by Dorothea Rudnick as *Theodor Boveri. Life and Work of a Great Biologist 1862–1915* (Berkeley–Los Angeles, 1967); and "Theodor Boveri," trans. by Curt and Evelyn Stern in *Science,* **144** (1964), 809–815; W. C. Roentgen, ed., *Erinnerungen an Theodor Boveri* (Tübingen, 1918); and Leopold von Ubisch, "Theodor Boveri," in H. Freund and A. Berg, eds., *Geschichte der Mikroskopie; Leben und Werk grosser Forscher* (Frankfurt am Main, 1963), I, 121–132.

JANE OPPENHEIMER

BOVILLUS. See **Bouvelles, Charles.**

BOWDITCH, HENRY PICKERING (*b.* Boston, Massachusetts, 9 April 1840; *d.* Boston, 13 March 1911), *physiology.*

Bowditch was the son of Jonathan Ingersoll Bowditch, a Boston merchant, and Lucy Orne Nichols; his paternal grandfather, Nathaniel Bowditch, a self-educated mathematician, was the author of the *New American Practical Navigator* (1802) and the translator of Laplace's *Mécanique céleste*. His mother was the granddaughter of Timothy Pickering, who served as George Washington's secretary of state, and was also related to the astronomers Edward and William Pickering and to the important American mathematician Benjamin Peirce.

Bowditch enjoyed a Boston boyhood, an adolescence on the new family estate at West Roxbury, on the outskirts of Boston, and a preparatory education at the school conducted by Epes S. Dixwell; among his classmates was Oliver Wendell Holmes, Jr. He entered Harvard College in September 1857 and graduated in 1861. Intending ultimately to prepare for a career in medicine, he entered the Lawrence Scientific School in Cambridge and commenced studies in natural history and chemistry. By November 1861 the call to arms interrupted his studies, and he accepted a commission as second lieutenant in the First Massachusetts Cavalry. During the course of the Civil War he saw action on numerous occasions and was wounded in battle at New Hope Church in 1863. Having risen to the rank of major, he resigned his command in June 1865 and reentered the Lawrence Scientific School, where he undertook studies in comparative anatomy with Jeffries Wyman. During this same period he completed the requirements of the Harvard Medical School and received the M.A. in 1866 and M.D. in 1868. His graduation thesis, a study of the physiological action of potassium bromide, which included a review of recent work as well as new data gathered at the Harvard Medical School, was published in the *Boston Medical and Surgical Journal* (1868).

Late in the summer of 1868 Bowditch departed for Europe to continue his medical and scientific studies. He did not return to Boston until September 1871, when he took up a teaching post at the Harvard Medical School at the invitation of the new president of the university, Charles W. Eliot. These few years were critical in determining his future career and the pattern that his research and teaching took. Although the notebook (in the Harvard Medical Archives) of his first months in Paris has many references to the clinicians Jean-Martin Charcot, Paul Broca, and Pierre Louis—suggesting his intention to combine medical practice and scientific investigation—his later letters give clear indication of a greater attraction toward the purely scientific part of the profession; these were written during his period of study with Claude Bernard and Louis-Antoine Ranvier, when he was devoting three days a week to physiology and another three to microscopy. His notebook indicates that he also heard lectures by many other Paris scientists of the day: Étienne-Jules Marey, on the

physics of flight; Jules Gavarret, on the physiology of muscle action; Paul Bert, on the nature of sound and the physiology of its perception; and Edmé-F. A. Vulpian on chemistry of the blood. But his judgment of Parisian medical science was negative: "French physiology has no system."

At the suggestion of the German physiologist Wilhelm Kühne, Bowditch turned to Germany, first, in May 1869, to study microscopic anatomy at Bonn with Max Schultze and Eduard Rindfleisch, and then, in September 1869, to the Leipzig physiological laboratory of Carl Ludwig. Ludwig's prominence as a teacher and research scientist made his laboratory one of the most exciting centers of biological research of the period, and there Bowditch met the new generation of experimental physiologists: Thomas Lauder Brunton of Scotland, Ray Lankester of England, Angelo Mosso of Italy, Hugo Kronecker of Germany, and C. Ustimovitsch of Russia. He quickly caught the spirit of the new laboratory, and in November 1869 he developed an improvement of Ludwig's kymograph, for automatically registering time relations of blood-pressure tracings on the revolving smoked cylinder. He later invented the "Bowditch clock" for marking various periods of elapsed time. An enthusiastic report of German methods and techniques and a description of Ludwig's institute were the basis of a letter published in the *Boston Medical and Surgical Journal* (1870). He was particularly impressed with the apparatus that had been developed for the multitude of tasks in physiological experimentation, and devoted a good deal of time to acquiring many instruments to take back to the Harvard laboratory. The month of November 1870 was spent at Munich, where he attended a course of lectures, on nutrition and metabolism, by Carl Voit. On 9 September 1871, five days before sailing home, Bowditch married Selma Knauth, the daughter of a Leipzig banker.

Several important papers record Bowditch's experimentation carried out under Ludwig's direction. One, dealing with the peculiarities of the irritability of cardiac muscle, has long been considered a classic in physiology. Two fundamental characteristics are demonstrated: the *Treppe,* or steplike increase of contraction of cardiac muscle in response to repeated uniform stimuli, and the "all-or-none law," showing maximum contraction, or no contraction at all, independently of the strength of stimulation (1871). A second paper studied the influence of variations of arterial blood pressure upon the accelerator and inhibitor nerves of the heart.

On returning to Boston, Bowditch took the post of assistant professor of physiology at Harvard Medical School and installed his newly collected apparatus in the only space allotted him, two small attic rooms at the building on North Grove Street. There he established the first teaching laboratory for physiology in the United States. Emulating his own teacher, Bowditch gathered around him as pupils many talented experimenters, including Charles S. Minot, Warren P. Lombard, James J. Putnam, William James, Joseph W. Warren, Isaac Ott, Robert W. Lovett, and G. M. Garland in physiology and pharmacology and G. Stanley Hall and William F. Southard in experimental psychology. The approach of the Leipzig laboratory, a strong reliance on physical concepts and physical apparatus, was carried over to the Boston laboratory; a new form of induction apparatus permitting variation of intensity, a new form of plethysmograph for registering changes in volume of organs, a new device for artificial respiration, a cannula for observing vocal cords, and an arrangement of unpolarizable electrodes were all developed and used in experimentation.

Bowditch's scientific interests moved in several directions: in a paper with Minot he showed that chloroform was more effective than ether in depressing vasomotor reflexes (1874); with Garland he studied the "effect of respiratory movements on the pulmonary circulation," concluding that expansion of the lungs decreases the size of pulmonary vessels, while collapse of the lungs has the opposite effect (1879–1880); with Southard and G. Stanley Hall he investigated the physiology of perception, with particular attention to vision (1880–1882); with Warren he conducted an extensive study of the effect of varying rates and strengths of peripheral stimulation upon contraction and dilation of blood vessels, demonstrating that by varying the stimulation it was possible to cause constriction, constriction followed by dilation, or dilation alone, with rapid stimulation causing constriction and later dilation (1883, 1886). He also conducted another series of experiments with Warren on the effects of voluntary activity and external stimulation on the knee jerk, demonstrating that activity in one part of the nervous system may directly affect activity in another part. The functioning of the nervous system served as a focus for Bowditch's experimentation for some time and led to one of his most important experiments, which brought a controversy to a close and gave final demonstration of the indefatigability of the nerve trunk, a fact of fundamental importance in the physiology of the nervous system (1885).

As early as 1872 Bowditch began a series of studies in anthropometry, examining the rate of growth in Boston schoolchildren. His results indicated that mode of life—nutrition and environment—were prob-

ably more important factors than race in determining the size of growing children. He also called attention to loss of weight in growing children as a warning of the approach of acute or chronic illness (1877, 1881).

Bowditch was one of the principal founders of the American Physiological Society in 1887 and was elected its second president in 1888, succeeding S. Weir Mitchell; he returned to the presidency from 1891–1895. He served as an American editor of Sir Michael Foster's *Journal of Physiology* from its founding in 1877 and published the reports of his Harvard laboratory there until the establishment of the *American Journal of Physiology* in 1898.

Bowditch taught physiology at Harvard for thirty-five years, being appointed full professor in 1876 and serving as first occupant of the George Higginson professorship of physiology from 1903 to his retirement in 1906. He was continually involved in the reforms in medical education, and for the decade 1883–1893 he served as dean of the Harvard Medical Faculty, during which time the four-year medical course was introduced and a new chair of bacteriology established, thus giving recognition to another independent discipline.

Active in Boston civic affairs, Bowditch was a member of the School Committee (1877–1881), president of the Massachusetts Infant Asylum (1886) and the Boston Children's Aid Society, and a trustee of the Boston Public Library. He was elected a fellow of the American Academy of Arts and Sciences in 1872 and to the National Academy of Sciences in 1887; he was also a member of many other learned academies in the United States and Europe. He was honored by degrees from the universities of Cambridge, Edinburgh, Toronto, Pennsylvania, and Harvard.

At the time of his retirement in 1906 Bowditch had become afflicted with paralysis agitans, which made serious inroads upon his health and proved fatal.

BIBLIOGRAPHY

I. ORIGINAL WORKS. Bowditch's graduation thesis is in *Boston Medical and Surgical Journal*, **78** (1868), 177–184; the letter on German methods and techniques, and a description of Ludwig's laboratory, *ibid.*, **82** (1870), 305–307. His work on the irritability of the cardiac muscle is presented in "Über die Eigenthümlichkeiten der Reizbarkeit, welche die Muskelfasern des Herzens zeigen," in *Berichte über die Verhandlungen der Königlichen Sächsischen Gesellschaft der Wissenschaften zu Leipzig*, Math.-phys. Klasse, **23** (1871), 652–689. The paper on the effect of chloroform on vasomotor reflexes, written with

BOWDITCH

Minot, is in *Boston Medical and Surgical Journal,* **91** (1874), 493–498; results of his studies of Boston schoolchildren, in the eighth *Annual Report of the Massachusetts State Board of Health* (Boston, 1877), pp. 275–325, and in *Transactions of the American Medical Association,* **32** (1881), 371–377; the paper on the effect of respiratory movements on the pulmonary circulation, studied with Garland, in *Journal of Physiology,* **2** (1879–1880), 91–109; the study of the effect of peripheral stimulation upon blood vessels, done with Warren, in *Zentralblatt für medizinische Wissenschaften,* no. 29 (1883), 513–514, and *Journal of Physiology,* **7** (1886), 416–460; and his work on the indefatigability of the nerve trunk, *ibid.,* **6** (1885), 133–135.

II. Secondary Literature. Other works on Bowditch are Walter Bradford Cannon, in *Memoirs of the National Academy of Science,* **17** (1922), 183–196; Frederick W. Ellis, "Henry Pickering Bowditch and the Development of the Harvard Laboratory of Physiology," in *New England Journal of Medicine,* **219** (1938), 819–828; and Fielding H. Garrison, in *Dictionary of American Biography.*

Everett Mendelsohn

BOWDITCH, NATHANIEL (*b.* Salem, Massachusetts, 26 March 1773; *d.* Boston, Massachusetts, 16 March 1838), *astronomy.*

Bowditch, a poor boy, is a fine example of the autodidact. Apprenticed to a ship's chandler at an early age, he acquired skill in languages and considerable knowledge of mathematics and other sciences through reading and study. Bowditch's scientific career was largely one of self-education; the United States of his day afforded very little opportunity for original research in astronomy and mathematical physics. As a young boy he went through the not inconsiderable book resources of Salem, including the library of Richard Kirwan, which had been seized by a local privateer. In 1790 he learned Latin in order to read the *Principia;* at the age of forty-five he started to study German in order to read the scientific literature appearing in that language. Between 1795 and 1803 Bowditch participated in five long sea voyages, the last as master of a ship bound for Sumatra; he continued his studies on these long trips. When he retired from the sea in 1804, he entered the business world; at his death, he was an insurance actuary in Boston. Offers from American universities never strongly tempted Bowditch, for they had little to offer a man of his caliber.

Beyond his obviously considerable native ability, Bowditch brought two characteristics to his scientific work. In addition to his erudition in mathematics, astronomy, and physics, he was apparently one of those who delight in mathematical computations. Not surprisingly, his early work often consisted of corrections of errors in the writings of others, apparently

uncovered while working through the literature. Of this nature is the *New American Practical Navigator,* which originated in corrections and extensions of the work of John Hamilton Moore. By the third edition (1802) the work had changed sufficiently to bear Bowditch's name, as it does in successive editions to this day. By 1815 he had contributed pieces on astronomy, mathematics, and physics to both American and European publications. His article in *Nicholson's Journal* (1811) on the 1807 meteor explosion over Weston, Connecticut, was the most spectacular, while his report in the *Memoirs* (1815) of the American Academy of Arts and Sciences on the motion of a pendulum suspended from two points was probably the most significant. Even before the publication of his translation of Laplace's *Mécanique céleste,* his writings had earned Bowditch membership in the Royal Society and other honors.

By 1818 Bowditch had completed his translation of the first four volumes of the *Mécanique céleste.* His purpose was threefold: to supply steps omitted from the original text; to incorporate later results into the translation; and to give credits omitted by Laplace. There is no evidence that Laplace ever responded to any communication from Bowditch, a fact sometimes ascribed to the third purpose. The four volumes appeared in 1829, 1832, 1834, and 1839, the last posthumously. The delay in publication was undoubtedly due in part to financial problems. Bowditch, who would not have people subsidize, out of regard for him or other irrelevant reasons, a book they could not read, printed the work at his own expense. It is also most likely that he continued to work over the volumes between 1818 and their appearance, particularly to bring the subject matter up to date. The fifth volume of the *Mécanique céleste* appeared too late for translation by Bowditch. Probably the only person who aided Bowditch was Benjamin Peirce, who read over part of the text for errors. Printed in a small edition, the work was perhaps more widely admired than read, simply serving to confirm the translator's already high reputation. Nevertheless, outside of France, particularly in English-speaking countries, Bowditch's edition, rather than the original, was often the means of learning about the mechanics of the heavens.

BIBLIOGRAPHY

I. Original Works. By far the best source of information on Bowditch are his papers and his library, in the Boston Public Library. These collections have not yet received the attention they deserve; much of our present knowledge of Bowditch derives from older works, often

368

written with little recourse to original sources of this nature. A few letters from the Bowditch Collection are in N. Reingold, *Science in Nineteenth Century America, a Documentary History* (New York, 1964), pp. 11–28. The manuscript of his journal during his fourth voyage was edited by T. R. McHale and M. C. McHale as *Early American-Philippine Trade: The Journal of Nathaniel Bowditch in Manila, 1796,* Yale University Southeast Asia Studies, Monograph Series, No. 2 (New Haven, 1962). Aside from a few remarks on Chinese numerical notations, the journal does not relate to Bowditch's intellectual interests.

No complete bibliography of Bowditch's writings exists. The best single source of bibliographical information, as well as other data on Bowditch, was published by the Peabody Museum: *A Catalogue of a Special Exhibition of Manuscripts, Books, Portraits and Personal Relics of Nathaniel Bowditch (1773–1838) With a Sketch of the Life of Nathaniel Bowditch by Dr. Harold Bowditch and an Essay on the Scientific Achievements of Nathaniel Bowditch With a Bibliography of his Publications by Professor Raymond Clare Archbald* (Salem, Mass., 1937). This publication is the best individual introduction to Bowditch, his writings, and the collections in the Boston Public Library. The bibliography, while quite adequate on Bowditch's larger works and the publications in the *Memoirs* of the American Academy of Arts and Sciences, does not attempt to specify many of Bowditch's mathematical and astronomical contributions, which often appeared in the form of letters or brief extracts from letters. Solutions to mathematical problems are in Robert Adrain's *The Analyst,* 2 vols. (Philadelphia, 1808–1814); and R. Adrain and J. Ryan, *Mathematical Diary,* 2 vols. (New York, 1825–1828)—thirty-two solutions are in the latter, for example. Other examples of his work appear in Zach's *Monatliche Correspondenz* and the *Correspondence astronomique,* as well as the *Zeitschrift für Astronomie.* The *North American Review,* **20** (April 1825), has an important Bowditch review of several recent works in astronomy.

II. SECONDARY LITERATURE. The best biography of Bowditch remains the one prepared by his son, Henry Ingersoll Bowditch, and published in Volume IV of the translation of the *Mécanique céleste,* and separately in subsequent editions. Despite its understandable filiopietism and a tendency to ramble, the work does convey much information and shows signs of honest attempts to gather information by consulting the Bowditch papers and old friends. Bowditch's descendants are a very distinguished Massachusetts family; and in writings by or about them there is information of indeterminate validity about Nathaniel Bowditch. Of the obituaries published at Bowditch's death, the most useful is John Pickering, *Eulogy on Nathaniel Bowditch, LL.D. . . .* (Boston, 1838). Robert E. Berry, *Yankee Stargazer* (New York, 1941), is a good popular biography but not much of an advance over Henry Ingersoll Bowditch. For indications of Bowditch's reputation in the last century, see I. Todhunter, *A History of Mathematical Theories of Attraction and the Figure of the Earth* (London, 1873), pp. 309–366. Harold L. Burstyn, *At the Sign of the Quadrant,* Publication No. 32 of the Marine

Historical Association (Mystic, Conn., 1957), pp. 11–30, is a good introduction to the hydrographic part of Bowditch's career. Reingold, *op. cit.,* has a brief discussion of Bowditch.

NATHAN REINGOLD

BOWEN, NORMAN LEVI (*b.* Kingston, Ontario, 21 June 1887; *d.* Washington, D.C., 11 September 1956), *geology.*

Norman L. Bowen was the principal investigator and leader, in the twentieth century, of the magmatist school of geology. The son of English immigrants to Canada, he was educated in Kingston's public schools before entering Queen's University in 1903. He took honors courses in chemistry and mineralogy before being granted the M.A. in 1907. He then entered the Faculty of Applied Science. In 1909 he was awarded the B.S. by the School of Mining.

Preparation for his work in experimental petrology continued when Bowen was employed by the Ontario Bureau of Mines before entering the Massachusetts Institute of Technology for doctoral studies in 1909. During the summers of 1910 and 1911, he worked for the Canadian Geological Survey in western Canada, supplementing his investigations at the Geophysical Laboratory of the Carnegie Institution of Washington, D.C. These years of advanced study saw the development of his pattern of research, which combined laboratory experiments with field investigations.

In preparing his doctoral dissertation on a phase-equilibrium study of the nepheline-carnegieite-anorthite system, Bowen followed the work of the Norwegian J. H. L. Vogt, who had made petrological analyses using physical chemistry. He worked under the direction of A. L. Day of the Geophysical Laboratory and was also influenced by early association with R. A. Daly.

Bowen published critical-phase diagrams for the study of the major igneous rocks: the plagioclase system in 1913, the MgO-SiO_2 system and the ternary system diopside-forsterite-silica in 1914, and, with colleagues, another twenty-one phase diagrams; the last appeared almost coincidentally with his death. From the beginning, his principal concern was the differentiation of igneous rocks. In 1927 he wrote: ". . . rock series can not be partitioned off into such divisions as gabbro, diorite, etc., each having a eutectic of its own. All of these belong to a single crystallization series, to a single polycomponent system, which is dominated by reaction series."

Silicate phase-equilibria studies, in particular his own plagioclase diagram, formed the bases on which Bowen published his carefully reasoned theory of the evolution of the igneous rocks (1915). "... The rocks of any area," he stated, "vary among themselves in a systematic manner which indicates derivation from a common stock ... through differentiation." He ruled out assimilation of country rock as a major factor in differentiation and dismissed palingenesis (the refusion of sedimentary terranes), holding that gravitative separation by sinking and floating of early-formed crystals, and the separation of residual liquids, were the "all-important instruments of differentiation." Bowen formulated a simplified reaction series for the subalkaline rocks to illustrate his reaction principle.

olivines
$\searrow$
Mg pyroxenes   (spinels)   calcic plagioclases
$\searrow$ $\swarrow$
calci-alkalic plagioclases
Mg-Ca pyroxenes
$\searrow$ $\swarrow$
alkali-calcic plagioclases
amphiboles
$\searrow$ $\swarrow$
alkalic plagioclases
biotites
$\searrow$ $\swarrow$
potash feldspar
muscovite
quartz

According to Bowen's reaction principle, typical series of igneous rocks are produced from a primary basaltic magma by the continual reaction, during crystallization, of early-formed crystals with liquid, the differentiation being brought about by the separation of crystals from liquid in various proportions and at various stages. The implications of these ideas for the theory of ore formation (through residual volatile fluids), for volcanology, for the basic physics of the earth, as well as for his primary field of petrogenesis, supplied work not only for the remainder of Bowen's life, but also for many of the most distinguished scientists of his time. His reaction principle is now ensconced in elementary textbooks of geology as one of the fundamental concepts of the science.

Bowen's studies were interrupted by work on optical glass projects during World War I. In 1919 he served at Queen's University as a professor of mineralogy, returning to the Geophysical Laboratory in 1920. Between 1937 and 1945 he resumed academic duties as professor of petrology at the University of Chicago. He returned to the Washington laboratory in 1947.

Until his death Bowen examined the physical-chemical bases for geological processes. His major conclusions were brought together in *The Evolution of Igneous Rocks* (1928).

In his work Bowen bridged gaps between the chemist and the geologist. He was among the first to analyze the behavior of inclusions in magma by physical-chemical methods. He influenced thought in petrology by skilled experimentation that supplemented inferences made from field investigations. Through numerous papers in professional journals, he contributed significantly to the mineralogical knowledge of rock-forming minerals.

Active in numerous professional societies, Bowen served as president of the Geological Society of America and of the Mineralogical Society of America. His accomplishments were recognized by medals from various professional societies, including the Penrose Medal of the Geological Society of America (1941).

BIBLIOGRAPHY

I. ORIGINAL WORKS. Among Bowen's writings are "The Later Stages of the Evolution of the Igneous Rocks," in *Journal of Geology,* supp. **23** (1915), and *The Evolution of Igneous Rocks* (Princeton, 1928).

II. SECONDARY LITERATURE. Articles on Bowen are C. Tilley, in *Biographical Memoirs of Fellows of the Royal Society,* III (London, 1957), 7–22; and C. R. Langwill and John Rogers, eds., *Bowen Volume, American Journal of Science* (New Haven, 1952).

CORTLAND P. AUSER

BOWER, FREDERICK ORPEN (*b.* Ripon, England, 4 November 1855; *d.* Ripon, 11 April 1948), *botany.*

Bower came of a prosperous, long-established Yorkshire family and was early introduced to field studies by his naturalist uncle, the Rev. F. A. Morris. In 1868 he went to school at Repton, and although formal instruction in science was lacking, as in most schools of the time, he was much encouraged in natural history by a wise headmaster; he acquired a microscope and even before leaving school for the university in 1874 he had decided to make botany his lifework. Bower entered Trinity College, Cambridge, but it was a matter of deep regret to him that he found only the scantiest teaching in science, save for Michael Foster's course in elementary biology. It was Bower's peculiar lot that he should have commenced his academic career when the teaching of science, in the modern sense, at school and university barely existed. He also witnessed and assisted the spread throughout Britain of the new science teaching, remaining an active, and indeed a dominant, figure in the great expansion of all the experimental sciences in the twentieth century.

All this valuable firsthand experience was recorded by Bower in his *Sixty Years of Botany in Britain (1875–1935),* a book of strongly autobiographical cast that sheds authentic if personal light upon the lives of many distinguished biologists who worked within this period. Bower's disappointment in his earliest year in Cambridge was tempered by the appearance in 1875 of the English edition of Sachs's *Textbook,* which provided a clear prospect of the rejuvenation of botany already apparent in Germany. Soon afterward he began to work with S. H. Vines, who had experience of Huxley's teaching at South Kensington and had studied with Sachs in Würzburg. Bower obtained a first-class degree and in 1877 went to study under Sachs. Two years later, under de Bary at Strasbourg, he did his first original research, work on the fungi and on the development of conceptacles in the Fucaceae. At this time the German universities were the fountainhead of new botanical thought, and Bower was inspired not only by his eminent teachers but also by the brilliant and aspiring students of all nations whom they attracted. Under these influences Bower turned from the prevalent angiosperm taxonomy so successfully pursued by Kew, the British Museum, and Edinburgh, and moved toward those fields of comparative morphology in which he was to make so distinctive a contribution.

In 1880 Bower became assistant to Daniel Oliver at University College, London, and, later, lecturer under T. H. Huxley. Meanwhile, he worked in the Jodrell Laboratory at Kew, where alongside D. H. Scott and W. Gardiner he made anatomical studies of seedling *Welwitschia,* of *Phylloglossum,* and of apospory in *Athyrium.* He had made so great an impression upon the leaders of British botany that in 1885, at the age of only twenty-nine, he was propelled by them into the Regius chair of botany at the University of Glasgow, a post he held until his retirement in 1925. The professorship gave Bower scope not only for his own research but also for his considerable talents for lecturing and for administration, and he became the source of inspiration for many students and collaborators who conferred distinction upon the Glasgow school. The school was housed from 1901 in new buildings designed to meet Bower's requirements for a modern scientific subject. His deep interest in teaching is apparent in his constant reversion to this theme in *Sixty Years of Botany;* in his translation with D. H. Scott of de Bary's *Comparative Anatomy* (1884); his *Practical Botany for Beginners* (1894); the same work, rewritten jointly with D. T. Gwynne Vaughan (1902); and his elementary textbook *Botany of the Living Plant* (1919).

In the wide range of Bower's original research the vascular cryptogams were of particular importance, and while in Glasgow he carried out the extensive investigations that were presented and analyzed in his three-volume book *The Ferns* (1923–1928). This monumental work has been described as "carrying the classification of ferns within the groups arranged on grounds of convenience to the much higher level of coherent evolutionary arrangement" (Lang, 1949). It is noteworthy that the period of Bower's own development was also that of the great expansion of modern paleobotany. Bower was in close touch with the results of this activity, knew all its leaders, and constantly sought to bring their findings into relation with those of his own theoretical morphology. Bower's name is particularly associated with his book *The Origin of a Land Flora* (1908), in which he developed Celakovsky's theory of the origin of alternation of generations by the interpolation of the sporophyte by division and progressive sterilization of the zygote of a primitive sexually reproducing plant.

Bower saw the development of the sporophytic generation as following from the evolutionary advantage accruing to plants newly colonizing dry land, and his book became the accepted exposition of the "Antithetic," as opposed to the "Homologous," theory of alternation of generations. He consciously adopted the view that "A working hypothesis, open like others to refutation, is better than no hypothesis at all": in retrospect its major value probably lay in the manner in which it facilitated the organization and presentation of massive and detailed work on comparative plant morphology and stimulated research in many directions.

Later in life Bower himself reconsidered the views expressed in the *Land Flora,* presenting his more mature judgment in *Primitive Land Plants* (1935), published six years after he had given the Huxley Memorial Lecture entitled "The Origin of a Land Flora, 1908–1929." He retained the primary concept of the interpolation theory but abandoned his earlier theory of the strobilus. He also gave weight to the vastly increased knowledge of fossil plants provided by the intervening years, more especially as regards the primitive earliest land plants of the Devonian age, which appeared with such unfamiliar undifferentiated forms but nevertheless might be reckoned as belonging to the *Pteridophyta.* Lang rightly emphasizes Bower's tendency "always to get further, by the use of his scientific imagination" and adds, "This found its full expression in the two surveys of archegoniate plants in 1908 and 1935, between which a change from a more theoretical to a more inductive method had become evident in his study of the Filicales."

A distinct facet of Bower's morphological studies is expressed in his presidential address to the Royal Society of Edinburgh in 1920, "Size, a Neglected Factor in Stelar Morphology." In this, and in his book

Size and Form (1930), he showed that much morphological evidence pointed to the need in plant tissues to maintain a certain relationship between surface and bulk. Even though the underlying causes, probably physiological and concerned with translocation, might be unknown, the consequence appeared to be that evolutionary increase in bulk of plant organs carried not a mere scaling up in dimensions of the primary conducting elements, but an increase of fluting, lobing, or replication that had the effect of maintaining the original ratio of surface to bulk. This was particularly evident in the steles of ferns, but it seemed that a similar principle might be involved in the vascular tissues of other groups and even in the elaborate flanged chloroplasts of the larger desmids.

Bower was a self-centered although kindly man of brisk and confident bearing, who never married and who derived his greatest pleasures first from his scientific work and second, but scarcely less, from music. He retained his faculties wonderfully well, his *Sixty Years of Botany* being published when he was eighty-three, thirteen years after he had retired to live in his native town of Ripon. His scientific distinction was acknowledged by many honors: he became a fellow of the Royal Society of London in 1891, and received its Royal Medal in 1910 and its Darwin Medal in 1938. He received the Linnean Medal in 1909 and was Hooker Lecturer in 1917 and Huxley Memorial Lecturer in 1929. He presided over the Royal Society of Edinburgh and the British Association, received honorary doctorates from many universities, and was an honorary member of many learned academies and societies outside his own country. Perhaps we may say, however, that Bower's greatest memorial has been the number, devotion, and distinction of his former students.

BIBLIOGRAPHY

I. ORIGINAL WORKS. Bower published numerous articles in learned journals over the period 1850 to 1937, many of great distinction: these are cited in the biography by Lang (see below). The major themes and much of the detail of his investigations are, however, summarized in his books: *The Origin of a Land Flora: A Theory Based Upon the Facts of Alternation* (London, 1908); *Plant-life on Land, Considered in Some of Its Biological Aspects* (Cambridge, 1911); *The Ferns (Filicales),* 3 vols.: I, *Analytical Examination of the Criteria of Comparison* (Cambridge, 1923); II, *The Eusporangiatae and Other Relatively Primitive Ferns* (Cambridge, 1926); III, *The Leptosporangiate Ferns* (Cambridge, 1928); *Size and Form in Plants: With Special Reference to the Primary Conducting Tracts* (London, 1930); *Primitive Land Plants, Also Known as the Arche-*

goniatae (London, 1935). The most important of his textbooks were *The Botany of the Living Plant* (London, 1919); the pioneer book *A Course of Practical Instruction in Botany* (London, 1885), reprinted several times and rewritten with S. H. Vines (London, 1902); and *Practical Botany for Beginners* (London, 1894). His last book was *Sixty Years of Botany in Britain* (*1875–1935*): *Impressions of an Eye-witness* (London, 1938).

II. SECONDARY LITERATURE. A comprehensive and authoritative biography is W. H. Lang, in *Obituary Notices of Fellows of the Royal Society,* VI (1949), 753–755. Shorter obituaries by J. Walton, E. J. Salisbury, and L. F. J. Brimble appeared in *Nature,* **161** (15 May 1948), and a great deal of autobiographical material is in Bower's *Sixty Years of Botany* (see above).

HARRY GODWIN

BOWIE, WILLIAM (*b.* Grassland, Anne Arundel County, Maryland, 6 May 1872; *d.* Washington, D.C., 28 August 1940), *geology.*

Bowie was descended from two old Maryland families. He began his advanced education at St. Johns College, Maryland, and completed his B.S. degree at Trinity College in Connecticut, where in 1907 he earned the M.A. In 1895 his early career preparation was completed when he received a C.E. degree from Lehigh University.

Bowie's lifelong association with the U.S. Coast and Geodetic Survey began in Washington in July 1895. As a junior officer he began fieldwork, acting as party chief for triangulation and base measurement teams in many states, Alaska, Puerto Rico, and the Philippines. In 1909 he was made chief of the Survey's Division of Geodesy.

Bowie completed many projects of national significance in his more than forty years with the Survey. As chief of the Division of Geodesy he established many needed controls over triangulation and leveling surveys, as well as over studies for determining gravity effects at different locations in the United States.

To eliminate inaccuracies in triangulation, Bowie sponsored the improvement of theodolites, including the substitution of silver circles for bronze. In a series of papers and articles, he became an articulate propagandist for the production of more accurate maps, impressing upon both his colleagues and the public the extent of this need.

Bowie also achieved acceptance and use of the North American Datum by the United States, Canada, and Mexico. This geodetic datum consists of the latitude and longitude of one station and the azimuth from this station to another station. The three governments agreed upon the Meades Ranch Triangulation Station in Kansas as the initial point for setting up triangulation surveys.

To avoid costly duplication of map services within the government, Bowie pressed for the establishment of the Federal Board of Surveys and Maps in 1919 and for the creation of a Division of Surveys and Mapping in the American Society of Civil Engineers.

Much of Bowie's importance as a scientist lies in his presentation of theories of isostasy. His research in this area dates from 1912. His early studies had been of the relations between gravity anomalies and geologic formations, and his findings on these unbalanced areas were presented accurately. His investigations in isostasy were the subjects of numerous official Survey publications, culminating in the publication of his book *Isostasy* (1927).

In isostatic investigations, Bowie carried on the work of two British observers, Airy and Pratt, and extended the research of two Americans, Dutton and Hayford, the latter a senior colleague in the Survey. In 1855 Pratt had explained the cause of abnormal plumb-line deflections near mountain ranges by theorizing that such an earth mass was compensated for by a deficiency in the mass of rock below it; that it would be less dense than the mass underlying the plain adjacent to the range. For this balancing phenomenon Dutton later used the term *isostasy*, meaning "equal standing," for the condition was one of equilibrium between the earth's outer material and that below. What was termed the "level of isostatic compensation" was located at the depth at which a balance existed.

Bowie also refined the hypothesis of Pratt and Hayford that mountains had been uplifted from the underlayer like "fermenting dough." He stated that over long periods, erosion and sedimentation had caused the earth's crust to become overloaded. There had followed a compensating action within the crust, light rock being pushed upward. Subcrustal matter then entered the crustal spaces to restore balance.

Again following the lead of Hayford, Bowie also computed reduction tables for the depths of compensation, using data from gravity values and information from deflection readings in many locations. As a result of this detailed study, Bowie was recognized as bringing the study of isostasy into the realm of mathematical computation. The methods of his research on this problem paralleled his efforts within the Survey to secure purely scientific data beyond the agency's function of producing information for practical use alone.

Bowie also supported the idea that the crust of the earth under oceans was in isostatic equilibrium. Familiar with the work of F. A. Vening Meinesz, who had developed a method of accurately determining gravity over ocean areas, and eager to improve measurement methods, he arranged for the U.S. government and interested agencies to work with the Dutch scientist and authorities in 1928 and in 1931–1932 on expeditions recording gravity values at sea. A significant conclusion of the study, which Bowie included in his book *Isostasy,* was that isostatic compensating levels began at the physical earth's surface, and not at sea level.

Before his death Bowie's reputation was international. He was a member of over thirty professional organizations, including the National Academy of Sciences, the American Geographical Society, and the Geological Society of America. He was particularly active in two related organizations that he served as president: the International Association of Geodesy and its larger affiliate, the International Union of Geodesy and Geophysics.

A list of nearly 400 articles and papers written by Bowie during his active career (compiled as part of a memoir by the National Academy of Sciences) attests, in a measure, to the nature and the range of his accomplishments.

BIBLIOGRAPHY

Bowie's major work is *Isostasy* (New York, 1927). A bibliography of his articles and papers is in J. A. Fleming, *Biographical Memoir,* pp. 79–97.

Works on Bowie are J. A. Fleming, *Biographical Memoir of William Bowie, 1872–1940* (Washington, D.C., 1949); N. H. Heck, "Memorial to William Bowie," in *Proceedings of the Geological Society of America,* **40** (June 1941), 163–166; and W. Heiskanen, "William · Bowie as an Isostasist and as a Man," in *Transactions of the American Geophysical Union,* **30** (Oct. 1949), 629–635.

CORTLAND P. AUSER

BOWMAN, ISAIAH (*b.* Waterloo, Ontario, 26 December 1878; *d.* Baltimore, Maryland, 6 January 1950), *geography.*

Bowman was the third of eight children of Samuel Cressman Bowman, a farmer of moderate means, whose father had been a schoolteacher and farmer. The family moved to Michigan eight weeks after Isaiah was born. Bowman began teaching in country schools at the age of seventeen, continuing his own education during the summers. He attended Ferris Institute at Big Rapids, Michigan, and later the State Normal School at Ypsilanti, where he was inspired by Mark Jefferson's approach to general geographical problems through physical geography. With Jefferson's encouragement, Bowman went to Harvard to study under William Morris Davis and was awarded the B.S. in 1905. He served as an instructor in the geology department at Yale until he earned the Ph.D. from that university in 1909 and became an assistant professor. The study of physiography, which Davis did so much to advance, shaped Bowman's interests for many years. His work in this field culminated in *Forest Physiography* (1911). In this large textbook on landforms, Bowman presented the first comprehensive account of the relief, climate, soils, and vegetation of the United States.

Despite the lasting contribution made by *Forest Physiography* and his extensive work on such problems as water supply and oil-well wastes, Bowman displayed his principal geographical accomplishments in South American and frontier studies. He participated in two Yale expeditions to South America in 1907 and 1911, and in 1913 he returned to South America as leader of an expedition sponsored by the American Geographical Society. The results of these journeys are described in *The Andes of Southern Peru* (1916), *Desert Trails of Atacama* (1924), and several papers. After Bowman became director of the American Geographical Society in 1915, he encouraged other studies on South America and initiated the very important project to map Hispanic America on a scale of 1:1,000,000 to meet the standards of the International Millionth Map.

When he took over the leadership of the American Geographical Society, Bowman began to convert an amateur organization into an institution of geographical scholarship. He saw a clear need for intensive yet wide-ranging research for the professionalization of geography. He expanded and remodeled the Society's *Bulletin* into the quarterly *Geographical Review* and initiated publication of monographs. During World War I, the government used the facilities of the Society, and as a member of the American delegation to the peace conference in 1918–1919, Bowman advised on the establishment of postwar boundaries. During the twenty years he directed the Society, he investigated modern frontier areas around the world, demonstrating that the "passing of the American frontier" around 1890, noted by F. J. Turner and others, had been much less rapid and complete than usually presumed. In Bowman's view, historians had overemphasized the Census Bureau's decision in 1890 to abandon mapping a frontier line. The line was discarded because isolated bodies of settlement destroyed its meaning, not because the frontier had been settled or because pioneer conditions had disappeared. He carried out fieldwork in Garfield County, Montana, in 1930, and the following year published *The Pioneer Fringe*, in which he developed his idea that under pioneer conditions man has his most direct confrontation with nature. He pointed out how little scientific study of the pioneer fringe had been undertaken, and suggested that this study in particular could contribute to the development of political and social policies. He recognized that in modern pioneering in an industrial and commercial world, economic law is as vital a factor as any in the natural environment.

In 1931 Bowman was president of the Association of American Geographers; from 1931 to 1934 he served as president of the International Geographical Union. He was chairman of the National Research Council from 1933 to 1935, and when President Franklin D. Roosevelt established the Science Advisory Board in July 1933, it was at Bowman's suggestion. In 1935 Bowman was appointed president of The Johns Hopkins University. His active participation in public affairs increased after this change. A small but significant part of his publications continued to be devoted to geography. During 1943 he served as president of the American Association for the Advancement of Science. In August 1944 he took a prominent part in the World Security Conference at Dumbarton Oaks, and in the spring of 1945 he participated in the implementation of plans creating the United Nations. On his retirement from the presidency of Johns Hopkins University in December 1948, the department of geography was renamed the Isaiah Bowman School of Geography. In 1949 he accepted the position of consultant to the Economic Cooperation Administration.

BIBLIOGRAPHY

I. ORIGINAL WORKS. A complete list of Bowman's published and unpublished books and articles accompanies the memorial by George F. Carter (see below). His most important books are *Forest Physiography* (New York, 1911); *The Andes of Southern Peru* (New York, 1916); *The New World: Problems in Political Geography* (Yonkers, N.Y., 1921), with supplements in 1923 and 1924; *Desert Trails of Atacama*, American Geographical Society spec. pub. no. 5 (New York, 1924); *The Pioneer Fringe, ibid.*, no. 13 (New York, 1931); and *Geography in Relation to the Social Sciences* (New York, 1934). A sample of his late geographical thought appeared as "Settlement by the Modern Pioneer," in Griffith Taylor, ed., *Geography in the Twentieth Century* (New York, 1951), ch. 11. Bowman's records of his important governmental activities, deposited at The Johns Hopkins University, are to remain sealed until 1975.

II. SECONDARY LITERATURE. Works on Bowman are George F. Carter, in *Annals of the Association of American Geographers,* **40** (Dec. 1950), 338–350; and Gladys M. Wrigley, "Isaiah Bowman," in *The Geographical Review,* **41** (Jan. 1951), 7–65, the most complete and informative biography.

BERT HANSEN

BOWMAN, WILLIAM (*b.* Nantwich, England, 20 July 1816; *d.* Dorking, England, 29 March 1892), *medicine.*

William Bowman was the third son and fourth child of John Eddowes Bowman and Elizabeth Eddowes, who were first cousins. The father, a banker by profession and a naturalist by inclination, was a founding member of the Manchester Geological Society, a member of the Linnean and Geological societies, and the author of works on geology and botany. He carried on an active correspondence with many notable scientists, including Louis Agassiz, Thomas Bewick, and Sir Charles Lyell, who noted his observations on certain coal seams.

They were a closely knit family of Dissenter beliefs. The letters of John Bowman to his son at all stages of his career show a kindly yet admonitory attitude that obviously had a great deal of influence on the formation of the young man's character. One is reminded of the similar background and relationship between father and son in the case of Bowman's near contemporary Joseph Lister.

In 1826 Bowman was sent to Hazelwood School in Birmingham, whose headmaster, the eccentric but conscientious Thomas Wright Hill, was a friend of his father. Hill's son Rowland, founder of the penny post, also taught in the school. Bowman was apprenticed in 1832 to W. A. Betts, house surgeon to the Birmingham Infirmary; continuing in the habit of placing himself under distinguished teachers, he worked at the same time under the aegis of a well-known Birmingham surgeon, Joseph Hodgson, who in 1864 was the first provincial surgeon to become president of the Royal College of Surgeons.

In Bowman's day, membership of this college, which was his aim, required a period of attendance at a London teaching hospital. Therefore, in 1837 he went to the recently founded medical department of King's College, London, where the professor of anatomy was Richard Partridge, previously a pupil of Hodgson at Birmingham. An even more important colleague was the professor of physiology, the brilliant teacher Richard Bentley Todd, to whom Bowman became prosector in 1838. In the same year Bowman undertook a European hospital tour, acting as mentor to Francis Galton, later renowned as the founder of eugenics.

Bowman was appointed assistant surgeon to King's College Hospital, London, in 1840, and sixteen years later he became surgeon to the hospital, resigning this position shortly afterward because of the claims of an expanding private practice. In 1842 he married Harriet Paget, daughter of a Leicester surgeon (but not connected with the famous surgeon Sir James Paget).

Professionally, Bowman's work fell into two periods. In the years before his marriage, his histological researches brought him fellowship of the Royal Society in 1841, and its Royal Medal the following year. Subsequently he turned to surgery, and in particular to ophthalmic surgery, to which his contributions were fundamental and lasting. He became a fellow of the Royal College of Surgeons in 1844 and was made a baronet by Queen Victoria in 1884.

Bowman's physiological interest was initiated by Hodgson and was developed by Todd. He assisted the latter with his *Cyclopaedia of Anatomy and Physiology* (1836–1852), for which he wrote the articles "Mucous Membranes," "Muscle," "Muscular Motion," and "Pacinian Bodies." Their *Physiological Anatomy and Physiology of Man* (1843–1856) is an important landmark. The two works provided a new approach to the teaching of medicine and gave Bowman the opportunity, hitherto unknown, to make the most minute investigations into histological anatomy. These researches were necessary because they had not been done before, and were made possible by recent developments in microscope and lens manufacture. Bowman's compound microscope, made by Powell and presented to him before he left Birmingham, may still be seen at King's College Hospital. Although he was still only in his twenties, all Bowman's previous training seems to have combined to fit him for this work, and for several years his accurate eye and descriptive pen (not to mention his artistic pencil) produced masterly accounts of histology. New and detailed descriptions were made of skin, muscle, nerves, sense organs, kidney, bone, and cartilage.

Sir Arthur Keith stated that he knew no parallel to this feat of Bowman's in making so enormous a series of new discoveries while producing material for a book. Henry Power wrote that the *Physiological Anatomy* constituted "... an epoch in physiology. It was the first physiological work in which histology—the accurate description of the structure of the various organs and tissues as displayed by the microscope—was given" (*Collected Papers,* I, xvi). Most of the sections and woodcuts were made by Bowman himself, and Power states that his hand was so steady that many of his drawings were made directly on the wood. His histological studies appear the more remarkable when we consider the primitive techniques of teasing and maceration available to him. In these early days, staining of microscopic sections was unknown, but Bowman made use of new methods of injection, such as that introduced by Doyère a short time before, in which successive injections of potassium bichromate and lead acetate were made into an organ, the resulting precipitate indicating the disposition of the vessels.

On 18 June 1840 the paper "On the Minute Structure and Movement of Voluntary Muscle" was communicated to the Royal Society by Todd. It resulted in Bowman's election to fellowship at the age of twenty-five.

Bowman's meticulous approach is nowhere better shown than in a table giving measurements of the diameters of muscle fasciculi in forty-four animals, including man, both male and female. Among the more important observations in this paper are his minute descriptions of the transverse and longitudinal striae of voluntary muscle and the first complete description of the fascicular tunic, to which he gave the name *sarcolemma* (although he generously yielded priority to Schwann's contemporaneous description). Little was added to Bowman's descriptions of muscle fibrils until the advent of the electron microscope. Even more important to physiology is Bowman's insistence that the form of a structure is subservient to its function. This may be best exemplified in his paper "The Malpighian Corpuscles of the Kidney," read to the Royal Society on 17 February 1842. Using Doyère's injection technique, Bowman demonstrated that the capsule surrounding the Malpighian capillary mass is continuous with the basement membrane of the uriniferous tubule. This capsule now bears his name—Bowman's capsule. Arguing from the minute anatomy of the parts, Bowman proposed his theory of secretion, the main tenet of which was the elimination of water and salts in the glomeruli:

> The peculiar arrangement of the vessels in the Malpighian tufts is clearly designed to produce a retardation in the flow of the blood through them. And the insertion of the tuft into the extremity of the tube, is a plain indication that this delay is subservient in a direct manner to some part of the secretive process [*Collected Papers*, I, 77].

The importance of this paper lies not only in its content but also in the way in which the anatomical features are related to the physiological functions they perform. Such a concept, although not entirely new, had a deep influence on contemporary thinking and teaching.

With the completion of these studies, Bowman passed to the surgical phase of his career. Here his chief interest lay in ophthalmology, and in 1846 he was appointed assistant surgeon at Moorfields Eye Hospital, then known as the Royal London Ophthalmic Hospital. He brought to ophthalmology the same qualities of precision and investigation that had characterized his physiological work; indeed, his many contributions to the anatomy, physiology, and surgery of the eye were often related to his previous studies.

In histology, he described the cornea, including its anterior elastic membrane, Bowman's membrane, and the radial fibers of the ciliary muscle, Bowman's muscle. "Bowman's tubes" is the name given to certain tubular appearances between the corneal lamellae, which he produced artificially by injection of mercury.

In surgery Bowman wrote of a method of operating for artificial pupil in cases of corneal opacity or closure of the pupil due to adhesion of the iris. This is known as "Bowman's operation," and his instruments for probing the obstructed lacrymal ducts are called "Bowman's probes." In May 1857 he was the first in England to perform Albrecht von Graefe's iridectomy for glaucoma, and he was early in recognizing the value of Helmholtz' ophthalmoscope (1851).

Many of Bowman's surgical procedures have now been superseded, although his lacrymal probes are still in daily use; but most of his anatomical observations have been confirmed. More important was the impetus he gave to the study and understanding of eye disease.

Bowman was never elected to high office in the Royal College of Surgeons, but he was a well-liked teacher, lucid and earnest, and was greatly concerned with the well-being of King's College Hospital. He assisted in founding St. John's Sisterhood of Nursing, and corresponded for years with such eminent people as Florence Nightingale, Charles Darwin, Graefe, and Donders, of whom he wrote a biographical obituary note. The universities of Cambridge, Edinburgh, and Dublin conferred honorary degrees upon him, and he was founder-president in 1880 of the Ophthalmological Society. A few years later the Society instituted an annual lecture, the Bowman lecture, which still honors distinguished ophthalmologists. To his patients Bowman was attentive and gentle, and one described his touch as "the lightest and most enquiring."

Few men have contributed so greatly to medicine in general, for Sir William Bowman appears as a towering nineteenth-century figure, as father both of histological anatomy and of ophthalmology in England.

BIBLIOGRAPHY

I. ORIGINAL WORKS. Among Bowman's writings are "Mucous Membranes," "Muscle," "Muscular Motion," and "Pacinian Bodies," in R. B. Todd, ed., *Cyclopaedia of Anatomy and Physiology*, 5 vols. (London, 1836–1852; supp., 1859); *The Physiological Anatomy and Physiology of Man*, 2 vols. in 4 pts. (London, 1843–1856), written with R. B. Todd; and "Frans Cornelius Donders, 1819–1889. In Memoriam," in *Proceedings of the Royal Society,* **49** (1891), vii–xxiv. Many of his works are brought together in *The Collected Papers of Sir William Bowman, Bart., F.R.S. Edited for the Committee of the Bowman Testimonial Fund,* J. Burdon-Sanderson and J. W. Hulke, eds., 2 vols. (London, 1893), including plates, portraits, and references to original sources.

The letters from his father, and many MSS relating to the family, particularly to William Bowman, are in the possession of his great-grandson, Sir John Bowman, Newbury, Berkshire.

II. Secondary Literature. Works on Bowman are K. B. Thomas, "The Manuscripts of Sir William Bowman," in *Medical History,* **10** (1966), 245–256; and an obituary notice in *British Medical Journal* (1892), **1,** 742–745, with portrait and references to original sources.

K. Bryn Thomas

BOYLE, ROBERT (*b.* Lismore, Ireland, 25 January 1627; *d.* London, England, 30 December 1691), *natural philosophy, physics, chemistry.*

The son of Richard Boyle, first earl of Cork and a great Elizabethan adventurer, and his second wife, Katherine Fenton, Robert Boyle was born to considerable affluence and was related, by blood or marriage, to all the great Anglo-Irish families of his day. He was the youngest son in a family of fourteen children. At the age of eight, after private tuition at home, he was sent for several years to Eton, which the sons of gentlemen were just beginning to attend, and then, at the age of twelve, to the Continent with his next older brother, Francis, later Lord Shannon. There a citizen of Geneva tutored him privately in the polite arts, the conventional subjects of a liberal education, and practical mathematics; then, or in the course of his subsequent travels, he was introduced to the new science, including Galileo's *Dialogue on the Two Chief World Systems,* which he read in Florence in 1642.

The outbreak of the Anglo-Irish wars, as well as the Civil War in England, led to his return home. Although his father was a Royalist, Boyle was persuaded by his elder sister, Katherine, Lady Ranelagh, a strong Parliamentarian (as befitted a friend of John Milton), to look favorably on the Parliamentary side. Lady Ranelagh also introduced him to Samuel Hartlib, who seems to have turned his interests to medicine and such practical matters as agriculture. Medicine led him to chemistry, at first for the preparation of drugs; but he soon became not only a skillful chemical experimenter but also an original chemical thinker. He read the chemists who wrote in English, French, or Latin, as well as the most important writers on other sciences. His early interest in astronomy per-

sisted for a time but, under the combined influence of Bacon and Descartes, he soon turned to wider problems. Soon his point of view, except for his belief that chemistry was an important *physical* science (not merely a practical art or a mystic science), coincided with that of the leaders of the English scientific movement (such as John Wilkins, John Wallis, and Seth Ward), whom he joined at Oxford about 1656.

After the Restoration, Boyle was frequently in London, finally settling there in 1668. He was one of the founders of the Royal Society and throughout his life was its most notable and influential fellow. He was active in Irish affairs, was (from 1661) governor of the Society for the Propagation of the Gospel in New England, and had some connection with the Court. His lodgings (in his sister's house) were always open to visitors, and his laboratory became a center for research. In spite of frequent ill health he was continuously active in scientific endeavors, and with the aid of assistants (many of whom later became famous scientists) he experimented until his final illness. He was a prolific author, writing on science, philosophy, and theology.

Although Boyle's first scientific interest was chemistry, his first published scientific book, the one that established his fame, was on pneumatics: *New Experiments Physico-Mechanicall, Touching the Spring of the Air and its Effects* (1660). Three years earlier he had learned of Guericke's invention of an air pump and, immediately perceiving the scientific potentialities of the instrument, set his laboratory assistants to work designing one that had a glass receiver and was so constructed that objects could be easily inserted. Robert Hooke's successful design permitted Boyle to devise and carry out a brilliant series of experiments upon the physical nature of air: he proved that the phenomena of Torricelli's experiment were indeed caused by the air, that sound was impossible in a vacuum, that air was truly necessary for life and flame, and that air was permanently elastic. In an appendix to the second edition of *New Experiments* (1662), he developed this last discovery into a quantitative relationship (that volume varies inversely with pressure), rightly called Boyle's law; here he also endeavored to refute several critics (including Hobbes and the English Jesuit Francis Linus) who tried to defend and uphold the old Scholastic view that there was no such thing as a vacuum and that some mysterious force, rather than atmospheric pressure, was responsible for the phenomena associated with suction pumps and syphoning.

At intervals throughout his life, Boyle published further accounts of the experiments *in vacuo* that he never tired of devising and that he alone, among the scientists of his day, was capable of devising without cessation. Perhaps the most influential of these experiments were those showing that many fruits and vegetables contain air (actually carbon dioxide), which they give off during fermentation—the eighteenth-century chemist's "fixed air." Although Boyle's reputation in experimental physics rests on his pneumatic experiments, he also worked in the related field of hydrostatics. His *Hydrostatical Paradoxes* (1666) is both a penetrating critique of Pascal's work on hydrostatics, full of acute observations upon Pascal's experimental method, and a presentation of a series of important and ingenious experiments upon fluid pressure.

The air pump experiments showed Boyle to be a confirmed opponent of Aristotelian and Scholastic physics, as well as an able and original experimental physicist. His scientific associates knew him better as a profound believer in the need to establish an empirically based, mechanistic theory of matter and in the possibility of establishing a scientific, rational, theoretical chemistry by means of just such a theory of matter. In 1660 he had already partially prepared a series of treatises upon both subjects, and he occupied himself for the rest of his life with experiments and arguments furthering these beliefs. His first published declaration of his positions appeared in 1661 in *Certain Physiological Essays,* a work whose arguments were somewhat obscurely supported by the now better known *Sceptical Chymist,* which was published later in the same year; both had circulated among scientists in earlier, manuscript versions.

Certain Physiological Essays made plain Boyle's decided support for the particulate theories of matter then slowly displacing the Aristotelian view of the joint role of matter and form. Boyle was long remembered as "the restorer of the mechanical philosophy" in England, and he regarded his corpuscularian philosophy as an original and useful theory of matter. He had been familiar with Epicurean atomism since boyhood, when he read Diogenes Laertius' *Lives of the Philosophers;* he now read the extant writings of his contemporaries, like Gassendi's brief *Epicuri philosophiae Syntagma* (1649) and Walter Charleton's *Physiologia Epicuro-Gassendo-Charletoniana* (1654). He was, however, too devout to be a true Epicurean and too aware of the developments of contemporary science—to which he was, moreover, contributing fully—to accept any attempt to apply literal Epicureanism to the current scientific scene. Like all his contemporaries, he was familiar with Democritean atomism as confuted by Aristotle, but it had the same disadvantages as Epicureanism.

What really influenced him first were Bacon's suggestive outlines of the possibilities of an empirically based particulate theory of matter (principally in *Novum organum,* 1620), and Descartes's ambitious outline of a completely mechanistic and logical particulate view of the universe (in *Principia philosophiae,* 1644). From Bacon, he learned to regard heat as a mode of motion of the least particles of matter; he also learned to believe that experiment could lead one to demonstrate, and possibly to prove, the existence of such particles, and that it could further aid in the deduction of how the shape and motion of the particles could provide an explanation of the observed properties of bodies.

Similarly, Boyle took many specific explanations of the properties of matter from Descartes—for example, the view that solidity and fluidity depend upon the amount of relative motion of the constituent particles, the particles of solids being relatively quiescent—although he rejected Descartes's detailed structure of particles, particularly the omnipresent Cartesian ether, for which he could find no experimental justification. He was also enormously influenced by the commanding scope of Descartes's great system of the world, built logically from a few definitions of matter and laws of motion.

Boyle was an eclectic; what mattered most to him was destroying all Aristotelian forms and qualities—semantic explanations at best, such as the "form of heat" or "the dormitive virtue of opium"—and substituting for them rational, mechanical explanations in terms of what he called "those two grand and most catholic principles, matter and motion."

"Mechanical," to Boyle and his contemporaries, was always in opposition to both "Aristotelian" and "mystical"; mechanical explanations were rational and also, inasmuch as they dealt with particles of matter and their motion, consonant with the newly formulated laws of mechanics. It was, Boyle insisted, no derogation of God's majesty to compare His creative power to that of a watchmaker, the creator of the most elaborate mechanism known to the seventeenth century. Boyle's first aim in *Certain Physiological Essays;* in the more elaborate *Origine of Formes and Qualities (According to the Corpuscular Philosophy),* published in 1666; in the detailed and specific *Experiments, Notes &c. About the Mechanical Origine or Production of Divers Particular Qualities,* published in 1675; and in numerous other minor treatises was to refute the older Scholastic or Aristotelian view and establish the mechanical one in its place. His second aim was to show that this was best done by the use of experiment, and he devoted great care and ingenuity to devising (and conducting) experiments that should demonstrate the nonexistence of the supposed "substantial forms" and "real qualities" and the positive existence of particles whose size, shape, and motion could easily and rationally account for the observed behavior and properties of matter. The many experiments with which his works are filled made them useful even to those who did not accept his conclusions, and such experiments as those demonstrating the mechanical production of heat and magnetism can still command admiration. Since Boyle rejected both the atoms of the Epicureans and the complex hierarchy of particles of Descartes, preferring the neutral word "corpuscle," his discussions were, as he hoped, acceptable and convincing to all mechanical philosophers, whatever theory of matter they chose to espouse.

No one except a dedicated Aristotelian could fail to find Boyle's arguments powerful and convincing; the only question was whether the immense labor of the experimental approach was worthwhile or not. Such rationalists as Huygens and Leibniz were inclined to doubt the value of demonstrating by experiment what they (and all "rational" thinkers) knew to be true by logical reasoning. In 1662 and 1663 Boyle conducted (through Henry Oldenburg, who often acted as his editor and literary agent) a long dispute with Spinoza on the question of whether experiment could provide *proof:* to Spinoza, only logical thought could provide the conviction that Descartes had taught the philosophical world to regard as proof, while experiment could only confirm or (possibly) refute; to Boyle, experiment was an essential ingredient of proof, and logical argument merely meant the employment of a priori hypotheses. This was an important difference in scientific method in the seventeenth century; although Boyle at first had few disciples, his eventual influence in this respect was very great—one of his firmest followers was Isaac Newton, a careful and impressionable student of Boyle's works.

Boyle's recognition of the complexities of the experimental approach was very rare in his day. Few before him had realized that empiricism required technique and the working out of methodical procedure. One reason for the now tedious length of most of his treatises was his desire to describe his experiments faithfully and in such a way that others could follow. He also was always careful to describe experiments that did not succeed, a procedure he defended in two of *Certain Physiological Essays* as essential to progress in experimental philosophy. Nonempiricists might very reasonably find all this tiresomely prolix,

but heuristically it was important and influential. Through his writing on his experiments, Boyle helped establish the experimental method in many branches of physics and chemistry.

Successful though Boyle's empirically based corpuscular philosophy was, it was not without its weaknesses and failures. He was always reluctant to antagonize those with fixed convictions, and therefore was often inclined to avoid committing himself to a definite and limiting view. Thus, he never satisfactorily described his own explanation of the cause of air's elasticity, although he wrote about the problem on many occasions; indeed, he went so far in his first book on the air pump as to cite the analogy, originated by the anatomist Jean Pecquet, between air particles and coils of raw wool, an analogy that he almost certainly did not accept as an explanation. Yet readers of only this book cannot know of his later doubts, hesitations, and tentative suggestions for a more satisfactory explanation. (In fact, he seems to have held that the elasticity was caused by a combination of the shape of the particles and their motion.)

Again, although he made it very clear that he regarded the cause of heat as nothing more than the vibratory motion of particles, he never clearly defined cold as mere absence of motion, even in the special treatise he wrote on the subject, *New Experiments and Observations Touching Cold* (1665), which has very valuable discussions of thermometry and of freezing mixtures. He also spoke ambiguously on the nature of light and fire; and his conviction that all properties must ultimately reside in the properties of particles gave him curiously mixed results when, in his *Experiments and Considerations Touching Colours* (1664) he tried to understand what made matter appear colored. Whiteness and blackness (the nearly total reflection and nearly total absorption of light, respectively) he understood thoroughly and illustrated brilliantly with what came to be considered classic experiments, such as noting the effects of white and black cloths laid on snow on a sunny day. He also observed the colors on soap bubbles and thin glass surfaces ("Newton's rings"). But he did not understand the relation of light and color, nor did he try to explain this relation or the prismatic colors in terms of modification of light; rather, he thought of light as having a physical constancy and color as being the result of an action by the material particles of bodies. In fairness, however, it must be noted that Boyle appreciated the treatment accorded light by Hooke in his *Micrographia* (1665) and by Newton in his papers on light and colors (1672, 1675), and recognized their superiority to him in optics.

It was not surprising that Boyle regarded extraordinary effects such as optical phenomena as the result of the configuration of particles, for he was, after all, a chemist as well as a physicist; and chemistry had been the first science he thoroughly mastered. He was a practiced and devoted technical chemist in his twenties, whereas he came to experimental physics (in the form of pneumatics) only at the age of thirty. It is true that many of his ideas on the nature and structure of matter were formulated before he began work on the air pump, but it becomes apparent, if one studies his work chronologically, that his first approaches to this subject were chemical. Indeed, his first specific publication on the corpuscular theory of matter, *Certain Physiological Essays,* also contains his first published account of chemical experiments. This is the complexly titled third essay: "Some Specimens of an Attempt to Make Chymical Experiment Usefull to Illustrate the Notions of the Corpuscular Philosophy," with the subtitle "A Physico-chemical Essay, Containing an Experiment Touching the Differing Parts and Redintegration of Salt-Petre"; the body of the essay was subsequently referred to by Boyle as "The Essay on Nitre." This, as he indicated, was an attempt to use a purely *chemical* experiment (the conversion of niter—KNO_3—to its seemingly component parts by means of a glowing lump of charcoal and its subsequent reconstitution from the fixed and volatile parts) to demonstrate the strong probability of the existence of particles that could persist through physical and chemical changes. Boyle recognized this as a novel approach, and also saw it as an attempt to show chemists that the physicist's approach, the employment of the mechanical philosophy, might be useful to chemistry; for he considered that it contributed much to an understanding of the reaction involved if one thought in terms of particles (whether simple or complex). He expressly stated in the preliminary discussion that he hoped "to beget a good understanding 'twixt the chymists and the natural philosophers," a lifelong desire only partially achieved.

It is difficult to realize how confused and confusing chemical reactions appeared before chemists thought in corpuscular terms. Chemistry in Boyle's day still applied a sort of Aristotelian plenum: the only possibility of breaking down such a substance as niter was to resolve it into its component elements. Seventeenth-century elements, like the Greek elements but unlike nineteenth-century elements, were not merely the simplest bodies into which chemical substances could be analyzed or resolved; they were also the necessary ingredients of all bodies, the substances into which all bodies were analyzable. Thus, if salt was

taken to be an element, then salt was present in all bodies and would appear as a product of rigorous analysis. Boyle not only thought that corpuscles were the only things universally present in all bodies; but he also suspected that none of the then accepted elements—whether the earth, air, fire, and water of the Aristotelians; the salt, sulfur, and mercury of the Paracelsans; the phlegm, oil, spirit, acid, and alkali of later chemists—was truly elementary, as the term was then understood. He tried to explain all this in the *Sceptical Chymist,* a curiously literary piece of polemic that is much misunderstood in modern times. Here, in spite of what is commonly said, Boyle did *not* give a modern definition of an element, but (specifically and intentionally) a clear definition of an element as it was understood in his day. The work is cast in a decidedly turgid dialogue form, perhaps in imitation of Galileo, perhaps merely as a relic of Boyle's youthful literary proclivities; its chief value in its day, aside from its main message, was the wealth of chemical experiment that, like the "Essay on Nitre," showed the chemist how to employ corpuscular terms in chemical explanation and also presented new chemical facts. For, prolific experimenter that he was, Boyle almost always found new chemical combinations and reactions, as well as a few new chemical substances; the best-known of these is hydrogen, which he prepared from steel filings and strong mineral acid, but there were also various copper and mercury compounds. Unlike other chemists of his day, he never stressed the novelty of such preparations, for it was the reactions and their interpretation that interested him.

Convinced as he was that the term *element,* as used in his day, was an erroneous and misleading concept, Boyle never approached the modern definition, which emerged during the eighteenth century as the influence of his teaching helped to weaken the older view. He seems not to have felt the need of any elements other than corpuscles; in this he was perhaps, as some of his contemporaries complained, too much a physicist and too little a chemist in his mode of thought. But this skepticism did not prevent him from recognizing at least some classes of substances by a method and in a fashion far more useful to chemistry than the old notion of element had been. Characteristically, he arrived at this classification empirically and as an outgrowth of a combination of physical and chemical investigations.

The color changes observed in the course of chemical reactions had always interested Boyle, especially since he thought they showed how evanescent and unreal Aristotelian forms really were; in the *Sceptical Chymist* he described many reactions involving color changes. He went further in *Experiments and Considerations Touching Colours,* for here he not only described various ways of producing color changes, such as the conversion of a blue vegetable solution to red or green, but he also emphatically indicated a *use* for these color changes: chemical classification and identification. It had long been known that some acids turned the blue syrup of violets red; Boyle claimed to be the first to realize that all acids did so and that those substances that did not do so were not acids—a bold but useful distinction. Similarly, he claimed to be the first to note that alkalies—all alkalies—turned syrup of violets green. This left him with three classes of salts: acid, alkali, and those that were neither. He reinforced this empirically derived classification by observing that the blue opalescence of the yellow solution of *lignum nephriticum* (a South American wood with supposed medical virtues and of considerable optical interest) was destroyed when the solution was acidified and could be restored by the addition of alkali; he also used this reaction to determine the relative strength of acidic and alkaline solutions.

These tests also allowed Boyle to determine the purity of chemicals bought from apothecary shops. He discovered a further useful color change when he demonstrated (what he claimed to have deduced) that different alkalies give differently colored precipitates with mercury sublimate (mercuric chloride): "vegetable alkalis" (potassium carbonate and possibly sodium carbonate) give an orange precipitate (a form of mercuric oxide), while "animal alkalis" (ammonia compounds) give a white precipitate (ammonium-mercury chloride). Since limewater was already known to turn cloudy when a solution of niter was added, Boyle now had the ability to distinguish among all the common alkalies.

The importance of these tests, upon which Boyle placed absolute reliance, was very great, for in the late seventeenth century there was still great confusion over the identity, not to mention the composition, of various simple substances. He found it necessary on the one hand to insist that all salts were not common salt, but on the other that salt of tartar, hartshorn, and vegetable alkali were all one salt—a point not always appreciated by his contemporaries. Many chemists of his day insisted upon sweeping generalizations like that of the acid-alkali hypothesis (which claimed that all substances were either acids or alkalies, and all reactions therefore were neutralizations), or carelessly confused end products with starting materials.

Boyle was unique in realizing the continual need for meticulous care in examining purity, testing composition, and searching for chemical differences and

similarities. How methodical he could be is amply demonstrated in his two investigations into the nature of phosphorus, *The Aerial Noctiluca* (1680) and *New Experiments and Observations Made Upon the Icy Noctiluca* (1682), in the course of which he discovered the chief chemical and physical properties of phosphorus and phosphoric acid, and in *Short Memoirs for the Natural Experimental History of Mineral Waters* (1685), an admirable set of analytical directions. Few other chemists of his day seem to have been sufficiently patient to elaborate an analytical procedure, although it became commonplace in the next century.

To his work on acids and alkalies Boyle added a host of other specific tests: for copper by the blue color of its solutions; for silver by its ability to form silver chloride, with its characteristic blackening over time; for sulfur and various mineral acids by their characteristic reactions. Some of these were new, others had been known for years or even centuries. These tests enabled him to discuss the composition of substances in what can only be called positivistic terms—that is, in terms of empirically determined components rather than in terms of metaphysical, a priori "elements." This was perhaps Boyle's greatest contribution to chemistry, for while few chemists followed him in altogether dispensing with elements, most chemists saw the utility of distinguishing in analysis between empirically verifiable components and a priori elements. When this occurred generally, the way lay open for the immense strides to be made in analytical chemistry in the eighteenth century. And although it was quite possible to practice this sort of chemistry without paying more than lip service to the corpuscular philosophy (a physicist's theory, after all), there is no doubt that Boyle was helped by his adherence to the corpuscular philosophy, and perhaps would never have formulated his new chemical method without his habit of thinking in corpuscular terms. And it is not without significance that this more physical way of approaching chemistry was introduced into France by William Homberg, who worked for some time in Boyle's laboratory.

In his lifetime Boyle was honored not only as an original chemist and physicist, a great exponent of English experimental philosophy, and a pillar of the Royal Society, but also as a prolific writer on natural theology, the point where religion and science met. He was a truly devout man and scrupulous to the point of having a tender conscience where oaths were concerned, as he explained in declining to serve as president of the Royal Society in 1680—presumably because he thought he might be subject to the provisions of the Test Act, as a public officer. Yet he was not dogmatic, and he was a devoted scientific investigator. Fortunately, he experienced no conflicts of conscience; for him a God who could create a mechanical universe—who could create matter in motion, obeying certain laws out of which the universe as we know it could come into being in an orderly fashion—was far more to be admired and worshiped than a God who created a universe without scientific law.

Boyle's God stands in the same relation to the watchmaker as the watchmaker might to an untutored savage who thinks a watch is a living creature because its hands move. Boyle never tired of writing on this subject, finding his thoughts becoming more devout the more he studied the wonders of nature. Not all his numerous books on religious subjects were an offshoot of his scientific endeavors, but many were, and it was these that were influential. At his death Boyle left a sum of money to found the Boyle lectures (really sermons), intended for the confutation of atheism; and his contemporaries immediately concluded that he meant the arguments against atheism to be drawn from the scientific advances of his day. Hence the first and most famous series of Boyle lectures, by Robert Bentley, was filled with arguments and illustrations drawn from Bentley's discussions with Newton. Subsequent Boyle lectures (by Clarke, Whiston, Woodward, Derham, and others) followed this pattern to produce what is thought of as a characteristically eighteenth-century form of "natural" religion, much less formal and theological than anything usual in Boyle's day.

In this, as in so much else, Boyle set the tone and inspired the methods of thought widely accepted by the next two generations. In large part this was so because eighteenth-century Newtonians found that Boyle's opinions, discoveries, and scientific method usefully supplemented those of Newton. Modern historians see this as a sign of Boyle's very real influence upon Newton; Newtonians saw it as a proof that the "new science" was a product of the English methods proclaimed in the charter of the Royal Society.

BIBLIOGRAPHY

The standard edition of Boyle's works is Thomas Birch, ed., *The Works of the Honourable Robert Boyle,* 5 vols. (London, 1744), 2nd ed., 6 vols. (London, 1772); available in a facs. repr. Separate works are *The Sceptical Chymist* (London–New York, 1911, and later eds.) and *Experiments and Considerations Touching Colours* (repr. New York, 1964). John Fulton, *A Bibliography of the Honourable Robert Boyle,* 2nd ed. (Oxford, 1961), is a complete bibliography of works by Boyle and of secondary sources to 1960. M. B. Hall, ed., *Robert Boyle on Natural Philosophy* (Bloomington, Ind., 1965), contains an introductory discussion of his work and long illustrative excerpts from his writings. Boyle's manuscripts are preserved chiefly in the archives of the Royal Society. Many letters to Boyle are published in Birch's edition cited above; his letters to Oldenburg are published in A. R. and M. B. Hall, eds., *The Correspondence of Henry Oldenburg* (Madison, Wis., 1965–   ).

Marie Boas Hall

BRACE, DE WITT BRISTOL (*b.* Wilson, New York, 5 January 1859; *d.* Lincoln, Nebraska, 2 October 1905), *optics.*

De Witt Bristol Brace, professor of physics and specialist in optics at the University of Nebraska, is best remembered for his experimental test of the Lorentz-Fitzgerald contraction hypothesis in 1904. He received his bachelor's degree from Boston University in 1881 and went on to graduate study at the Massachusetts Institute of Technology and Johns Hopkins University. In 1883 his admiration for Kirchhoff and Helmholtz took him to Berlin, where he wrote a doctoral dissertation on magneto-optical effects. In 1888, shortly after his return to the United States, Brace became professor of physics at the University of Nebraska, where he remained until his death. He was survived by his wife of four years, Elizabeth Russell Wing of Massachusetts. Brace was a member of the American and British Associations for the Advancement of Science.

For eight years Brace was the entire physics department at Nebraska and had little opportunity for research until the faculty was expanded in 1896; then, however, he began a series of experiments on the effect of various external factors, such as magnetism (the "Faraday effect"), pressure, and strain on light passing through a transparent medium. In the course of this research he invented several new instruments, including a spectropolariscope and a spectrophotometer which today bear his name.

In 1904 the opportunity arose for Brace to apply the extremely sensitive optical techniques he had developed to one of the crucial problems of his day. Two years earlier, Lord Rayleigh had proposed that the Lorentz-Fitzgerald contraction, if it existed, might produce an observable double refraction in a moving transparent medium. Rayleigh made experiments in which he failed to find the predicted effect, but his work was not quite accurate enough to be conclusive. Brace pointed this out and reconducted the investigation in his own laboratory, establishing beyond a doubt the absence of double refraction caused by movement of the refracting medium through the ether. This did not disprove the contraction hypothesis, but Brace at first believed that it did. Joseph Larmor showed that double refraction need not result from Lorentz contraction if matter is composed of electrically charged particles that contract in the same proportion as large bodies; he thus saved the Lorentz hypothesis and gave the electron its status as a fundamental particle of matter.

Brace remained interested in the problems of contraction, and in 1905 performed experiments to detect higher-order effects that might clear up the issue. Death kept him from seeing its final resolution in Einstein's theory of special relativity.

BIBLIOGRAPHY

I. ORIGINAL WORKS. Articles by Brace include "Observations on Light Propagated in a Dielectric Normal to the 1 Lines of Force," in *Philosophical Magazine,* **44** (1897), 342–349; "Description of a New Spectrophotometer . . .," *ibid.,* **48** (1899), 420–430; "Observation on the Circular Components in the 'Faraday Effect,'" in *Nature,* **62** (1900), 368–369; "A Sensitive-strip Spectropolariscope," in *Philosophical Magazine,* n.s. **5** (1903), 9; "Double Refraction in Matter Moving Through the Ether," *ibid.,* n.s. **7** (1904), 317–328; and three articles on tests for the "ether drift," *ibid.,* n.s. **10** (1905).

II. SECONDARY LITERATURE. Articles relating to Brace's work are Joseph Larmor, "On the Ascertained Absence of Effects of Motion Through the Aether . . .," in *Philosophical Magazine,* n.s. **7** (1904), 621; and Lord Rayleigh, "Does Motion Through the Aether Cause Double Refraction?," *ibid.* (1902).

The only substantial biographical material about Brace is found in the *Dictionary of American Biography,* II, 540, and *Who's Who in America, 1903–1905.* His role in the Lorentz contraction controversy is discussed in Florian Cajori, *A History of Physics* (repr. New York, 1962), p. 378. For bibliography, see the *Royal Society Catalogue of Scientific Papers,* XIII, 757, and Poggendorff, V, 157.

EUGENE FRANKEL

BRACHET, ALBERT (*b.* Liège, Belgium, 1 January 1869; *d.* Brussels, Belgium, 27 December 1930), *embryology.*

Brachet was the only son of Auguste Brachet, an industrialist, and Louise Despae. A shy, sensitive, and self-contained child, he was a mediocre student in elementary school, and later said that his last years in secondary school reduced him to intellectual torpor. Having decided to study medicine, he entered the University of Liège and at once came under the influence of its celebrated professor of zoology,

Edouard Van Beneden, whose lectures awoke young Brachet's enthusiastic interest in the form and embryonic development of animals and man. At Van Beneden's invitation, Brachet worked in the zoology laboratory in 1887–1888, learning the techniques of biological research. Thereafter, while still a medical student, he became histological preparator in the laboratory of Auguste Swaen, professor of anatomy. There Brachet began research on the development of the long bones of birds, which resulted in his first scientific publication, a monograph that appeared in 1893. In 1894 he was granted the M.D. by the University of Liège. About this time, at Swaen's suggestion Brachet, in spite of his youth, boldly attacked some of the most difficult problems in vertebrate embryology—the earliest development of the liver and pancreas, and of the diaphragm and the pleuroperitoneal cavity. He published these studies in various French and German scientific periodicals from 1895 to 1897.

When Brachet received his medical degree at the age of twenty-five, his parents wished him to practice medicine and even furnished an office for him, but by this time he had become thoroughly committed to morphological research. Winning a government traveling fellowship, he went to the University of Edinburgh, a famous center of human anatomy and the art of dissection; then to the laboratory of Ernst Gaupp at Freiburg im Breisgau to study the embryology of the head; and finally to Gustav Born at Breslau, where he learned the important new method of constructing enlarged models of embryos and their internal structures by the wax-plate method devised by Born. In Born's laboratory he also observed newly introduced procedures of experimental embryology, by which Born and other embryologists were beginning to analyze embryonic development by excising parts of early embryos (chiefly of frogs and salamanders), transplanting limb buds, and producing local damage in the ovum and in early embryos.

After Brachet's return to Liège in 1895, as assistant in anatomy, he collaborated with Swaen in studies involving the whole vertebrate group, seeking to compare the early development of the heart, blood vessels, and urinary organs in mammals with that in the lower vertebrates (fishes and amphibians), where the pattern often is simpler and more comprehensible.

This broadened experience in comparative morphology turned Brachet's attention to the earliest stages of development—the first cleavage of the fertilized ovum, the early differentiation of the embryonic area, and the beginnings of the head and trunk. These phenomena, complex and obscure in the higher animals, are susceptible of analysis by comparison with simpler processes of the same nature in lower vertebrates and in the invertebrates. For example, there is a well-known stage when the embryo has the form of a hollow ball so deeply indented at one point that the indented region coats the inside of the outer wall and the embryo is thus a two-layer sphere with an opening to the outside, the blastopore. The region of the blastopore becomes the active center of development of the embryonic body. In the vertebrates, however, the gastrula stage is so modified that it is recognizable only with difficulty. Brachet made notable contributions to the solution of this problem.

Another and even more recondite set of problems includes such questions as the extent to which embryonic structures are laid down in the undivided ovum, and the relation of the first planes of its cleavage to the axis of symmetry of the embryo. Such problems as these are to be solved partly by descriptive studies, partly by experiment. Brachet devoted himself to them for the rest of his life, by his own researches and those of the numerous advanced students who came to work with him. To the elucidation of these problems he brought the great variety of insights and methods he had gained at several centers of biological research. Among his most important studies at this time was an analysis of gastrulation in amphibians, in which he pointed out the similarity of this process to that of more primitive animals.

In 1900 Brachet was promoted to the post of *chef des travaux pratiques,* i.e., director of the students' laboratory work, from which the next step would be to a professorial chair. No such vacancy was likely to occur soon in Liège, however, and when the chair of anatomy at Brussels became vacant in 1904 Brachet, with Van Beneden's warm support, was appointed professor of anatomy and embryology, and director of the Institute of Anatomy of the University of Brussels.

Soon after he settled at Brussels, Brachet married Marguerite Guchez, a gifted student whose devotion and talents freed him from domestic concerns and allowed him to attack with undivided attention the tasks of building up the anatomy department, conducting his own intricate investigations, and guiding the numerous research students who came to his laboratory. The Brachets had two children, one of them the distinguished biochemist Jean Brachet.

At this time Brachet's experimental work was directed chiefly to analyzing the inherent capacities of the egg cell and the way in which these potentialities of future development become localized in the embryo. For example, by pricking one of the two cells into which the fertilized ovum first divides, or similarly damaging one or another region of an embryo a few days old, he could discover the rate at which the embryonic cells differentiate into organ-forming areas. Brachet also devoted much time to the study of ova, chiefly of the frog, into which, by experimental treatment, he caused more than one sperm cell to enter, with resulting abnormalities of development that threw light on the normal process. He was one of the first to confirm the possibility of causing unfertilized ova to develop parthenogenetically by mechanical stimulation, and he pioneered in experimental attempts to cultivate the mammalian embryo (rabbit) *in vitro.*

The results of his varied and persistent investigations have become integral to today's biological thought. It is to Brachet, perhaps more than to any other biologist of his time, that we owe our understanding that the fertilized egg cell, of whatever animal species, is neither a diminutive model that has only to unfold and enlarge in order to become an adult (preformation) nor an undifferentiated mass to be transformed by some mysterious force into adult tissues and organs (epigenesis) but, rather, a packet of living materials endowed with potentialities of growth and differentiation under inherent physical and chemical influences.

When World War I broke out, Brachet was in France, at a seaside laboratory in Roscoff, Brittany, and was not able to return to Brussels. He was invited to join the Medical Faculty of the University of Paris as adjunct professor of anatomy and embryology. On frequent trips to the Belgian front he gave anatomical instruction to the hospital surgeons. A highly successful series of special lectures at the Collège de France led to publication of an important book embodying Brachet's findings of the previous decade, *L'oeuf et les facteurs de l'ontogénèse* (1917).

After the war Brachet returned to Brussels, bearing with him the high regard of French colleagues, a regard soon expressed by corresponding membership in the Institut de France and an honorary doctorate from the University of Paris. Resuming his chair at Brussels, he published a valuable textbook, *Traité d'embryologie des vertèbres* (1921). After the death of Van Beneden he assumed the editorship of the influential journal *Archives de biologie.* Always working on the fundamental problems of the organization of the ovum, the nature of fertilization, and the pattern of segmentation and early embryonic differentiation, he had at his side a succession of young biologists who, inspired by his enthusiasm and intellectual force, went on to become professors of anatomy, embryology, or zoology in universities of Belgium, France, and Portugal. From 1923 to 1926, Brachet was rector of the University of Brussels. In the winter of 1928/1929 he made a successful lecture tour of the United States.

BIBLIOGRAPHY

I. ORIGINAL WORKS. Among Brachet's writings are *L'oeuf et les facteurs de l'ontogénèse* (Paris, 1917) and *Traité d'embryologie des vertèbres* (Paris, 1921).

II. SECONDARY LITERATURE. Works on Brachet are A. Celestino da Costa, "L'oeuvre embryologique d'Albert Brachet," in *Bulletin de la Société Portugaise des Sciences Naturelles,* **11** (1932), 179–220, with a list of Brachet's publications; A. M. Dalcq, "Albert Brachet, 1869–1930," in *Florilège des sciences en Belgique* (Brussels, 1968), pp. 991–1013, with a portrait; Giuseppe Levi, "Commemorazione del socio straniero, Albert Brachet," in *Rendiconti della Reale Accademia dei Lincei,* **14** (1931), 382–393, with a list of Brachet's publications; and H. de Winiwarter, *Notice d'Albert Brachet* (Brussels, 1932), with a portrait and list of publications.

GEORGE W. CORNER

BRACONNOT, HENRI (*b.* Commercy, France, 29 May 1780; *d.* Nancy, France, 13 January 1855), *chemistry.*

Braconnot, a pioneer in the study of plant and animal chemistry, was the son of Gabriel Braconnot, a lawyer. His father died in 1787, leaving to his widow's care not only Henri but also a younger brother, André. His mother enrolled Henri in the Collège de Commercy, a Benedictine school, but he rebelled against its strict discipline and she was forced to remove him and find private means of education. Meanwhile, Mme. Braconnot remarried. This compounded Henri's unhappiness, for his stepfather, a physician named Huvet, disliked him from the start and did all he could to come between the boy and his mother.

Braconnot was apprenticed to an apothecary in Nancy at the age of thirteen; two years later he went to Strasbourg as a pharmacist in a military hospital. He remained in Strasbourg until 1801, studying scientific and medical subjects at a number of institutions, the most important being the École Centrale du Département du Bas-Rhin. In 1801 he went to Paris to complete his scientific education, attending courses in chemistry, biology, and geology given by such luminaries as Fourcroy and Étienne Geoffroy Saint-Hilaire. He made a good impression on his teachers, and reinforced it by his first major paper, "Recherches sur la force assimilatrice dans les végétaux" (1807). Through the influence of Fourcroy, Braconnot secured the directorship of the Jardin Botanique de

Nancy, a position he held for the rest of his career. In 1823 he was elected a corresponding member of the Institut de France. After the death of his stepfather, Braconnot lived with his mother, to whom he was very much attached, until her death in 1843. He was highly skeptical of physicians and suffered greatly from an untreated cancer of the stomach, which caused his death.

Braconnot lived a life of great simplicity; his only amusements were literature and the theater. In adult life, in contrast to his childhood, he was retiring and painfully shy. He never married.

Braconnot's research was conditioned by his double interest in botany and chemistry. What made it original and fruitful was not any novelty of theory or experimental method but, rather, the scope and detail of his investigations, carried out over thirty years. Added to this were his experimental facility and his sensitivity to the presence of previously unknown substances. A guiding theme, exhibited in his first major paper in bizarre, romantic chemical terms and in a number of subsequent important papers, was the attempt to elucidate the steps by which the complex organic constituents of plants were synthesized from simple inorganic substances.

Braconnot's methods of analysis remained conservative—similar, for example, to those outlined by Fourcroy in 1801 for organic substances. Although he made careful gravimetric determinations of the initial and final products collectively, he almost never attempted quantitative analysis of the individual products that he had discovered. He was generally content to describe such substances as new "vegetable acids" or "animal substances" and to give some idea of their chemical properties.

From 1807 to 1819, Braconnot analyzed a variety of plant and animal substances. One of his first discoveries was a cellulose substance in mushrooms, which he named fungine. He began a study of fatty substances, which he analyzed physically into combinations of a solid tallow and a liquid oil, but his work was superseded by that of Chevreul. In 1817 he published a paper in which he disproved the idea, enunciated by Fourcroy and held by Berzelius, among others, that there existed a unitary "extractive principle" in vegetable substances. The following year, he published his discovery of ellagic acid in nutgalls.

Beginning in 1819, Braconnot embarked upon a series of researches on the effects of sulfuric acid on wood and ligneous fibers. He discovered that sawdust, when treated with concentrated sulfuric acid, was converted into a gum that, in turn, was convertible into sugar and what he called a "vegeto-sulfuric" ulmin—a substance discovered by Vauquelin in 1797.

He went on to study the effects of sulfuric acid on animal substances: gelatin, muscle fibers, and wool. In the case of gelatin, he discovered a sugar-like substance which he called *sucre de gélatine,* later named glycocoll (glycine). Sulfuric acid converted wool and muscle fiber to a white substance he called leucine.

In the 1820's and 1830's Braconnot's discoveries included pectic acid; legumin, a substance discovered in beans that he thought was analogous to albumin; populin (benzoylsalicin), discovered in the bark of the aspen; pyrogallic acid, produced from the heating of gallic acid; and xyloïdine (nitrocellulose), produced by the action of concentrated nitric acid on potato starch or wood. Various substances he thought he had discovered turned out subsequently to be identical with known ones; these included *aposépédine,* a product obtained from the distillation of the liquid of petrified cheese, later shown to be leucine, and equisetic acid, shown to be maleic acid.

BIBLIOGRAPHY

I. Original Works. For a listing of Braconnot's many articles, see the Royal Society of London's *Catalogue of Scientific Papers,* I (1867), 557–561. The biography by M. J. Nicklès (see below) contains a bibliography taken from Braconnot's own catalog of his works. He published no large monographs or textbooks. His papers include: "Recherche sur la force assimilatrice dans les végétaux," in *Annales de chimie,* 1st ser., **61** (1807), 187–246; "Mémoire sur le principe extractif et sur les extraits en général," in *Journal de physique, de chimie, d'histoire naturelle et des arts,* **84** (1817), 267–296, 325–349; "Observations sur la préparation et la purification de l'acide gallique, et sur l'existence d'un acide nouveau dans la noix de galle," in *Annales de chimie et de physique,* 2nd ser., **9** (1818), 181–189; "Mémoire sur la conversion du corps ligneux en gomme, en sucre, et en un acide d'une nature particulière, par le moyen de l'acide sulfurique; conversion de la même substance ligneuse en ulmine par la potasse," *ibid.,* **12** (1819), 172–195; "Mémoire sur la conversion des matières animales en nouvelles substances par le moyen de l'acide sulfurique," *ibid.,* **13** (1820), 113–125; "Recherches sur un nouvel acide universellement répandu dans tous les végétaux," *ibid.,* **28** (1825), 173–178; "Nouvelles observations sur l'acide pectique," *ibid.,* **30** (1825), 96–102.

II. Secondary Literature. M. J. Nicklès, "Braconnot sa vie et ses travaux," in *Mémoires de l'Académie Stanislaus* (1855), xxiii–cxlix, is the only extensive biography of Braconnot. Although a bit melodramatic about his personal life, it is very thorough in its account of his scientific career. See also E. Frémy, *Encyclopédie chimique,* I (Paris, 1882), fasc. 1, 101–103; M. J. Nicklès, "Correspondence of J. Nicklès," in *American Journal of Science,* 2nd ser., **21** (1856), 118–119; and J. R. Partington, *A History of Chemistry,* IV (London, 1964), 251.

Seymour H. Mauskopf

BRADFORD, JOSHUA TAYLOR (*b.* Bracken County, Kentucky, 9 December 1818; *d.* Augusta, Kentucky, 31 October 1871), *medicine, surgery.*

The son of early Kentucky settlers, William and Elizabeth Johnson Bradford, Joshua attended Augusta College and began the study of medicine in the Augusta surgery of his brother Jonathan. He was graduated M.D. in 1839 from the medical school of the University of Transylvania in Lexington, Kentucky. After establishing a practice in Augusta, Bradford spent most of his professional life there and in the nearby Kentucky and Ohio counties. On 4 February 1845 he married Sarah Emily Armstrong of Augusta; their children were William and Emily.

A believer that boiled water was the best surgical dressing, Bradford became the most successful early ovariotomist of record, on either side of the Atlantic. In the early 1840's, when the newly developed operation for the removal of ovarian tumor was being abandoned because of its danger, Bradford operated on thirty patients, with only three deaths. No other surgeon of his time approached Bradford's accomplishment of keeping deaths at no more than 10 percent of all patients operated on.

During the Civil War, Bradford served as a brigade surgeon with the Union Army. In this period, especially in 1861–1862, he developed improved techniques of camp sanitation and battlefield surgery.

Ironically, in the later years of his practice Bradford devised and prescribed an ointment effective against skin cancer—but died at fifty-two of cancer of the liver.

BIBLIOGRAPHY

I. Original Works. Among Bradford's writings are "Selections From a Report on Ovariotomy," presented to the annual meeting of the Kentucky State Medical Society, Louisville, Ky. (Apr. 1857), printed in *Kentucky Medical Journal,* **15** (1917), 142–165; "Report of Cases of Ovariotomy Occurring in Kentucky in 1857," in *Medical News* (Aug. 1859); and "Complete Rupture of the Perineum of Ten Years' Standing, Successfully Operated on," in *Lancet and Obstetrics* (Feb. 1869).

An unpublished diary covering 1862 is on deposit in the Division of Manuscripts, Library of Congress. Unpublished letters and notes are in the possession of Helen Yoder Johnson (Mrs. Howard Johnson), Mrs. Charles Bradford, and the writer.

II. Secondary Literature. Works on Bradford include W. W. Anderson, "Dr. Joshua Taylor Bradford," in *Kentucky Medical Journal,* **15** (1917), 140–142; Charles Clay, *Results of the Operation for Extirpation of Diseased Ovaria* (Manchester, 1848); E. R. Peaslee, *Ovarian Tumors, Their Pathology, Diagnosis and Treatment* (New York, 1872); and "Early History of Ovariotomy in Kentucky," in J. N. McCormack, ed., *Some of the Medical Pioneers of Kentucky* (Bowling Green, Ky., 1917), pp. 105–107.

See also *Cyclopedia of American Medical Biography; Dictionary of National Biography;* and *Biographical Encyclopedia of Kentucky* (Cincinnati, 1876).

Charles O'Neill

BRADLEY, JAMES (*b.* Sherbourne, Gloucestershire, England, March 1693; *d.* Chalford, Gloucestershire, England, 13 July 1762), *astronomy.*

The Bradley family has been traced as far back as the fourteenth century at Bradley Castle, near Wolsingham, Durham, but a branch to which James Bradley's father belonged had moved south to Gloucestershire. James, the third son of William Bradley and his wife Jane Pound, was intended for the Church. His father's income was limited, however, and his education was helped financially by his uncle, the Reverend James Pound, rector of Wanstead, Essex, who was then one of the ablest amateur astronomers in England and who fostered his nephew's fondness for astronomy. Bradley was educated at Northleach Grammar School and at Balliol College, Oxford, which he entered in 1711 and from which he received his B.A. in 1714 and his M.A. in 1717; upon his appointment as astronomer royal in 1742, Oxford awarded him an honorary D.D.

Bradley was ordained in 1719 and installed as vicar of Bridstow, near Ross, Monmouthshire, by the bishop of Hereford, who also presented him with an additional sinecure living and soon after made him his chaplain. A distinguished career in the Church seemed in prospect for the clever young scholar; but Bradley, whose parochial duties were very light, was able to continue his visits to Wanstead and to take part in his uncle's astronomical observations.

Pound had introduced his nephew to a friend of his, the eminent astronomer Edmund Halley, and in 1716 Bradley had made accurate and prompt observations of Mars and certain nebulae at Halley's request. A year later Halley drew the special attention of the Royal Society to Bradley's erudition, ability, and industry, predicting that he would advance astronomical studies. In 1718 Bradley was elected a fellow of the Royal Society. Three years later he was appointed to the Savilian professorship of astronomy at Oxford and resigned his livings and gave up his

prospects in the Church, since he did not believe he could do full justice to two different employments; his Oxford appointment made astronomy no longer a spare-time hobby. Many years later, for the same reason, he refused the living of Greenwich as a means of supplementing his meager salary of £100 per year as astronomer royal.

When Halley died in 1742, Bradley was appointed—as Halley had wished—to succeed him as astronomer royal; and he held that office with great distinction for twenty years until his death. In 1744 Bradley married Susannah Peach of Chalford, Gloucestershire. There was one daughter of the marriage, born in 1745. Bradley's wife died in 1757. Bradley was humane, benevolent, and kind; a good son and an affectionate husband and father. He was very abstemious. Apart from an attack of smallpox in 1717, he seems to have enjoyed excellent health for most of his life. A hard worker, he was able to endure long hours of observing and intensive calculating with no apparent ill effects. In the last few years of his life, partly through overwork, Bradley's health gradually deteriorated, and he began to suffer from severe headaches. By 1761 he became unfit for regular work, and was obsessed by the unfounded fear that his brain was giving way. He was cared for by his deceased wife's family until he died of an abdominal inflammation.

Bradley was a fellow of the Royal Society for over forty years, and by 1748 his brilliant discoveries and work at the Royal Observatory brought him preeminence among both English and foreign astronomers. He was elected a member of the Académie Royale des Sciences and of the academies of Berlin, Bologna, and St. Petersburg.

Bradley's celebrated discovery of the aberration of light is a good example of the way in which his accuracy, industry, and clarity of perception could extract an unforeseen success from an apparent failure. Since the stars should appear to be very slightly displaced in direction because of the earth's annual motion round the sun, these parallactic displacements would, if measurable, reveal the distances of the stars. Robert Hooke had unsuccessfully attempted this in 1669, and in 1725 Samuel Molyneux, a wealthy amateur astronomer, tried to better Hooke's effort to measure the parallax of the star Gamma Draconis by means of an improved twenty-four-foot zenith sector, made by George Graham and erected at Molyneux's house at Kew. He invited his friend Bradley to join in the observations. Gamma Draconis, passing almost through the zenith, was chosen to avoid refraction and to have the telescope fixed vertically, so that it could easily be checked. Within a few days Molyneux and Bradley detected a small but increasing deviation of the star, a displacement too large and in the wrong direction to be due to its parallax. Having verified the accuracy of the instrument, they carefully measured the deviations of Gamma Draconis, finding that they went through a cycle in the course of a year and that a similar effect occurred with other stars.

Molyneux gave up the observations but Bradley continued, using a smaller and more convenient sector made by Graham that would take in a greater number of stars; this was erected at Wanstead in 1727. Bradley tested numerous hypotheses to explain the effect, but none of them would fit. One story tells that he obtained the clue when on a pleasure trip on the Thames by noticing that every time the boat put about, the vane at the masthead shifted slightly; the sailors assured him that the wind direction had not changed—the shift of the vane was due to the boat's change of direction. Bradley concluded that the phenomenon he had observed in the stars was due to the combined effect of the velocity of light and the orbital motion of the earth. He verified this by calculation, and presented an account of the work and his discovery of the aberration of light to the Royal Society in 1729, in the form of a long letter to Halley, then astronomer royal. In this paper Bradley stated that if the parallax of any of the stars he observed had been as great as one second of arc, he would have detected it, and concluded that their parallaxes were much smaller than had been hitherto supposed. He was quite correct: there are only twenty-one stars with parallaxes exceeding $0''.25$, and that of Gamma Draconis is approximately $0''.017$. The discovery not only provided an essential correction for star positions but was also the first direct observational proof of the Copernican theory that the earth moves round the sun.

In 1727 Bradley had noticed a small "annual change of declination in some of the fixed stars" for which neither precession nor aberration completely accounted, so he continued to observe the stars involved with his zenith sector. He found that stars of the right ascension near 0 hours and 12 hours were affected differently than were those near right ascension 6 hours and 18 hours. By 1732 he had guessed the real cause, suspecting "that the Moon's action upon the equatorial parts of the earth might produce these effects. . . ." He felt confident that a complete cycle of these displacements of the stars due to the moon's action would correspond to the period (nineteen years) of the revolution of the nodes of the moon's orbit, so he continued the observations for

twenty years, finding at the end of nineteen "that the stars returned into the same positions again, as if there had been no alteration at all in the inclination of the earth's axis. . . ."

Since this effect on star positions arose from a slow nodding of the earth's axis due to the moon's attraction, Bradley called it "nutation." In 1748 he announced the results to the Royal Society in a very long letter to his patron and friend the Earl of Macclesfield, himself a keen amateur astronomer. The paper contained much geometrical discussion and tables of precession, aberration, and nutation for several stars for the years 1727–1747. (At current values, aberration ranges from zero to $20''.4958$, nutation from zero to $9''.210$.) Bradley further improved the exact determination of star positions by deriving practical rules for refraction from elaborate calculations, introducing corrections for air temperature and barometric pressure.

On becoming astronomer royal, Bradley tested, adjusted, and had repairs made on the astronomical equipment at Greenwich Royal Observatory. Then, with one assistant, he embarked on an intensive program of star observations. He found, however, that Halley's instruments had developed defects that caused observational errors. He managed to obtain a grant of £1,000 from the Admiralty, and by 1750 had thoroughly reequipped the observatory; the chief additions were two mural quadrants and a transit instrument, all made by John Bird, a pupil of Graham's. As a result, the massive program of observations (at least 60,000) made at Greenwich from 1750 to 1762 attained a very high standard of accuracy, sufficient to make them useful to modern astronomers.

Throughout his adult life Bradley made many observations of bodies in the solar system as well as of stars. With his uncle, in 1719 he had derived an improved value for the solar parallax from observations of Mars. He observed and calculated the elements of several comets, and published short papers on three. In one paper (1726) Bradley derived the longitudes of Lisbon and New York from differences in the observed times of eclipses of one of Jupiter's bright satellites. He was the only astronomer to record the reappearance of Saturn's ring in 1730 from the edgewise phase. He made laudable attempts at the very difficult feat of measuring the diameters of Venus, Mars, Jupiter, and of Saturn and its ring system, a task that taxed the resources of astronomers with much larger and better telescopes a century and a half later.

As befitted an astronomer royal, Bradley was

keenly interested in the accurate measurement of time. In the early 1730's Graham experimented in London with a clock whose pendulum beat sidereal seconds, and gave Bradley the results. The clock was then sent to Jamaica and tested on the transits of certain stars, with the times and temperatures recorded. From these data Bradley worked out a correction for the higher temperatures in Jamaica and deduced a slowing of the clock by 1 minute, 58 seconds per day due to lower gravity near the equator. From Newton's theory of the relation between latitude and gravity, Bradley derived the same slowing. He then worked out a table, for each five degrees of latitude, of the lengths required for pendulums that would keep the same time as one 39.126 inches long in London, and reported the results of the investigation to the Royal Society in 1734. One use Bradley made of his new quadrants at the observatory after 1750 was to determine accurately the latitude of Greenwich. His value, $+51° 28' 38 1/2''$, exceeds the current one by only $1''.3$, and is closer than those derived by two of his successors.

The Royal Observatory had been founded to assist navigation—to increase the safety of ships on ocean voyages by prescribing better methods of finding longitude at sea. Bradley recognized the importance for navigation of magnetic observations, so he included magnetic instruments among his new equipment. In 1755 the Admiralty asked Bradley to examine and report on the usefulness of Tobias Mayer's new lunar tables for finding longitude at sea. After comparing them with more than 230 Greenwich observations, and doing many calculations, Bradley reported in 1756 that, subject to trials on shipboard, the tables should give the longitude to within $1/2°$. Observations made at sea proved less encouraging, however, so in 1759 and 1760 Bradley compared Mayer's tables with many more observations and worked out detailed corrections for them by laborious and intricate calculations. In 1760 he reported that the difficulty of finding longitude by this method was not insuperable, and that the corrected tables should give it with an error of less than $1°$.

Bradley was a brilliant original thinker, a very skillful observer, and a thoroughly practical astronomer who exercised unremitting care in examining the errors of his instruments and in insuring their accurate adjustment. The value of his star observations increases with time, for they provide a firm starting point for long-term investigations of stellar motions. Without his two great discoveries and his work on refraction, it is difficult to see how later progress by others in the determination of star positions, distances, and motions would have been possible.

BIBLIOGRAPHY

I. ORIGINAL WORKS. Bradley's writings are collected in *Miscellaneous Works and Correspondence of the Rev. James Bradley, D.D., F.R.S., Astronomer Royal . . .*, S. P. Rigaud, ed. (Oxford, 1832), and *Supplement to Dr. Bradley's Miscellaneous Works . . .*, S. P. Rigaud, ed. (Oxford, 1833). The 1832 volume includes all Bradley's papers and memoranda; his zenith star observations of 1725–1747; a selection of his observations of sun, moon, planets, and comets of 1715–1742 and some observations of them made at Greenwich between 1743 and 1748 and in 1759; the best of his astronomical correspondence; and a detailed biography by Rigaud. The 1833 supplement includes a discussion of Bradley's refraction calculations. (A reprint of this valuable collection is in preparation.)

Bradley's papers are printed in the *Philosophical Transactions of the Royal Society* as follows: "Comet of 1723," **33**, No. 382 (1723), 41; "Longitudes by Eclipses of a Jupiter Satellite," **34**, No. 394 (1726), 85; "Aberration," **35**, No. 406 (1729), 637; "Pendulum Experiments in London and Jamaica," **38**, No. 432 (1734), 302; "Comet of 1737," **40**, No. 446 (1737) 111; "Nutation," **45**, No. 485 (1748), 1; and "Comet of 1757," **50** (1757), 408.

Much of Bradley's work was recorded in *Astronomical Observations Made at the Royal Observatory at Greenwich From the Year 1750 to the Year 1762 by the Rev. James Bradley D.D., Astronomer Royal . . .*, 2 vols. (Oxford, 1798–1805), the second volume of which includes observations by Bradley's successor, Nathaniel Bliss.

II. SECONDARY LITERATURE. Writings on Bradley or his work are G. F. A. Auwers, *Neue Reduktion der Bradley'schen Beobachtungen aus den Jahren 1750 bis 1762*, 3 vols. (St. Petersburg, 1882–1903), a reduction of all the Greenwich observations of 1750–1762 that shows which of the observations were made by the four men who were, in succession, Bradley's assistant; an earlier reduction is F. W. Bessel, *Fundamenta astronomiae pro anno MDCCLV deducta ex observationibus viri incomparabilis, James Bradley, in specula astronomica Grenovicensi per annos 1750–1762 institutis* (Königsberg, 1818), which contains a catalogue of more than 3,000 stars, based on Bradley's observations.

See also the article on Bradley in *Dictionary of National Biography*; G. Abetti, *The History of Astronomy* (London, 1954); A. F. O'D. Alexander, *The Planet Saturn* (London, 1962), and *The Planet Uranus* (London, 1965); and H. Spencer Jones, *The Royal Observatory, Greenwich* (London, 1948), which contains an excellent short account on pp. 10–13, by a recent astronomer royal, of Bradley's outstanding achievements.

A. F. O'D. ALEXANDER

BRADLEY, RICHARD (*d.* Cambridge, England, 5 November 1732), *botany.*

Bradley's main scientific contributions were his studies on the movement of sap and on the sexual reproduction of plants. His experiments, particularly on trees, led him to consider sap as circulating in some way; from his work on tulips and hazel he drew analogies with animal reproduction, and emphasized the significance of pollination and the importance of insects in fertilization. He then went on to discuss the novel idea of cross-fertilization and the production of different strains. This work was published in his *New Improvements of Planting and Gardening* (1717) and *A General Treatise on Husbandry and Gardening* (1724).

Bradley was a prolific science writer, producing more than twenty botanical works, as well as writing on the plague at Marseilles in 1720, advocating cleanliness and a "wholesome diet" as prophylactics. His style was clear and readable, and his reputation immense; indeed, his publications did much to encourage a scientific approach to gardening and husbandry. Bradley claimed to have invented the kaleidoscope, which he used for preparing symmetrical designs for formal gardens, thus anticipating the claims of Sir David Brewster by some ninety years. He also strongly advocated the use of steam to power the irrigation of gardens and farmland.

On 1 December 1712 Bradley was elected a fellow of the Royal Society of London, and on 10 November 1724 was appointed to the chair of botany at Cambridge University. It is said he obtained the latter by claiming a verbal recommendation from the botanist William Sherard (1659–1728) and promising to provide a botanic garden at his own expense. He provided no garden and was unfamiliar with Latin and Greek, and, because of some supposed scandal, there was a petition to remove him. It proved of no avail, and he died in office. Sir Joseph Banks and other botanists named genera to commemorate him.

BIBLIOGRAPHY

Bradley's books include *The Gentleman and Farmer's Kalendar, Directing What Is Necessary to Be Done Every Month* (London, 1718); *New Improvements of Planting and Gardening, Both Philosophical and Practical; Explaining the Motion of the Sap and Generation of Plants* (London, 1718); *The Plague at Marseilles Consider'd: With Remarks Upon the Plague in General* (London, 1721); *Precautions Against Infection: Containing Many Observations Necessary to Be Considered, at This Time, on Account of the Dreadful Plague in France* (London, 1722); *A General Treatise on Husbandry and Gardening,* 2 vols. (London, 1724); *Philo-* *sophical Account of the Works of Nature* (London, 1725); *A Survey of Ancient Husbandry and Gardening* (London, 1725); *The Country Gentleman and Farmer's Monthly Director* (London, 1726); *A Complete Body of Husbandry* (London-Dublin, 1727); *Dictionarium botanicum,* 2 vols. (London, 1728); *The Riches of a Hop-Garden Explain'd* (London, 1729); *A Course of Lectures Upon the Materia Medica* (London, 1730); and *Collected Writings on Succulent Plants,* with an introduction by G. D. Rowley, a facsimile ed. (London, 1946).

His scientific papers include "Motion of Sap in Vegetables," in *Philosophical Transactions of the Royal Society,* **29** (1716), 486–490; and "Some Microscopical Observations and Curious Remarks on the Vegetation and Exceeding Quick Propagation of Moldiness of the Substance of a Melon," *ibid.,* 490–492.

A work containing information on Bradley is Richard Pulteney, *Historical and Biographical Sketches of the Progress of Botany in England,* II (London, 1790), 129–133.

COLIN A. RONAN

BRADWARDINE, THOMAS (*b.* England, *ca.* 1290–1300; *d.* Lambeth, England, 26 August 1349), *mathematics, natural philosophy, theology.*

Both the date and place of Bradwardine's birth are uncertain, although record of his early connection with Hartfield, Sussex, has often been taken as suggestive. His own reference (*De causa Dei,* p. 559) to his father's present residence in Chichester is too late to be relevant.

Our knowledge of Bradwardine's academic career begins with the notice of his inscription as fellow of Balliol College in August 1321. Two years later we find him as fellow of Merton College, a position he presumably held until 1335. We also have evidence of a number of other university positions during this period. The succession of his Oxford degrees would seem to be the following: B.A. by August 1321; M.A. by about 1323; B.Th. by 1333; D.Th. by 1348.

Bradwardine's ecclesiastical involvement appears to have begun with his papal appointment as canon of Lincoln in September 1333, although his less official entry about 1335 into the coterie of Richard de Bury, then bishop of Durham, was probably of greater importance in determining the remainder of his career. For not only did this latter move place Bradwardine in more intimate contact with some of the more engaging theologians in England, but it also may well have proved to be of some effect in introducing him to the court of Edward III. Indeed, shortly after his appointment as chancellor of St. Paul's, London (19 September 1337), we find him as chaplain, and perhaps confessor, to the king (about 1338/1339). We know that he accompanied Edward's retinue, perhaps to Flanders, but certainly to France during the campaign of 1346. In point of fact, it was late in that year, in France, that Bradwardine delivered his (still extant) *Sermo epinicius* in the presence of the king, the occasion being the commemoration of the battles of Crécy and Neville's Cross. The closeness of his ties with Edward might also be inferred from the fact that the king annulled Bradwardine's first election to the archbishopric of Canterbury (31 August 1348). He was, however, elected a second time (4 June 1349), apparently without Edward's opposition, and consecrated at Avignon approximately a month later (10 July 1349). Bradwardine immediately returned to England, where, after scarcely more than a month as archbishop, he fell before the then raging plague and died at the residence of the bishop of Rochester in Lambeth, 26 August 1349.

Although our evidence is not absolutely conclusive, it seems highly probable that Bradwardine composed all of his philosophical and mathematical works between the onset of his regency in arts at Oxford and approximately 1335.

Early Logical Works. In spite of the lack of any direct testimony, it is nevertheless a reasonable assumption that the early logical works were the result of a youthful Bradwardine first trying his hand at a kind of activity common, even expected, among recent arts graduates in the earlier fourteenth century. A number of these logical treatises ascribed to Bradwardine are undoubtedly spurious, but at least two seem, to judge in terms of present evidence, to be most probably genuine: *De insolubilibus* and *De incipit et desinit.* Neither of these works has been edited or studied, yet the likelihood is not great that they will eventually reveal themselves to be much more than expositions of the *opinio communis* concerning their subjects. Both treatises are of course relevant to the history of medieval logic, but the *De incipit et desinit,* like the many other fourteenth-century tracts dealing with the same topic, had a direct bearing upon current problems in natural philosophy as well. For the medieval works grouped under this title (or under the alternative *De primo et ultimo instanti*) address themselves to the problem of ascribing what we would call intrinsic or extrinsic boundaries to physical changes or processes occurring within the continuum of time. Thus, to cite the fundamental assumption of Bradwardine's *De incipit* (an assumption shared by almost all his contemporaries), the duration of the existence of a permanent entity (*res permanens*) that lasts through some temporal interval is marked by the fact that it possesses a first instant of being (*primum instans in esse*) but no last instant of being (*ultimum instans in esse*); its termination is signified, rather, by an extrinsic boundary, a first instant of nonbeing (*primum instans in non esse*).

Tractatus de proportionibus velocitatum in motibus. It is this work, composed in 1328, that has firmly established Bradwardine's position within the history of science. As its title indicates, it treats of the "ratios of speeds in motions," a description of the contents of the *Tractatus* that becomes more properly revealing once one identifies the basic problem Bradwardine set out to resolve: How can one correctly relate a variation in the speeds of a mobile (expressed, as in the work's title, as a "ratio of speeds") to a variation in the causes, which is to say the forces and resistances, determining these speeds? The proper answer to this question is, without doubt, the fundamental concern of the *Tractatus de proportionibus.* In Bradwardine's own words, to find the correct solution is to come upon the *vera sententia de proportione velocitatum in motibus, in comparatione ad moventium et motorum potentias* (Crosby ed., p. 64).

Answers to this question were, Bradwardine points out, already at hand. Yet they failed, he argues, to resolve the problem satisfactorily. Basically, their failure lay in that they would generate results which were inconsistent with the "postulate" of Scholastic-Aristotelian natural philosophy which stipulated that motion could ensue only when the motive power exceeded the power of resistance: when, to use modern symbols, $F > R$. Thus, for example, one unsatisfactory answer was that implied by Aristotle. For, although Aristotle was certainly not conscious of Bradwardine's problem as such and, it can be argued, never had as a goal the firm establishment of any mathematical relation as obtaining for the variables involved, the medieval natural philosopher took much of what he had to say in the *De caelo* and the *Physics* (especially in bk. VII, ch. 5) to entail what is now most frequently represented by $V \propto F/R$. But this will not do. For, if one begins with a given $F_1 > R_1$, and if one continually doubles the resistance (i.e., $R_2 = 2R_1$, $R_3 = 2R_2$, etc.), then F_1 as a randomly given mover will be of infinite capacity (*quelibet potentia motiva localiter esset infinita* [*ibid.,* p. 98]). In our terms, what Bradwardine intends by his argument is that, under the continual doubling of the resistance, if we hold F_1 constant, then at some point one will reach $R_n > F_1$, which, on grounds of the suggested resolution represented by $V \propto F/R$, implies that some "value" would still obtain for V; this in turn violates the "motion only when $F > R$" postulate. Therefore, $V \propto F/R$ is an unacceptable answer to his problem. Bradwardine also sets forth related arguments against other possible answers, which are usually symbolized by $V \propto F - R$ and $V \propto (F - R)/R$.

The correct solution, in Bradwardine's estimation, is that "the ratio of the speeds of motions follows the ratio of the motive powers to the resistive powers and vice versa, or, to put the same thing in other words: the ratios of the moving powers to the resistive powers are respectively proportional to the speeds of the motions, and vice versa. And," he concludes, "geometric proportionality is that meant here" (*Proportio velocitatum in motibus sequitur proportionem potentiarum moventium ad potentias resistivas, et etiam econtrario. Vel sic sub aliis verbis, eadem sententia remanente: Proportiones potentiarum moventium ad potentias resistivas, et velocitates in motibus, eodem ordine proportionales existunt, et similiter econtrario. Et hoc de geometrica proportionalitate intelligas* [*ibid.*, p. 112]).

Given just this much, it is not at all immediately clear what Bradwardine had in mind. His intentions reveal themselves only when one begins to examine his succeeding conclusions and, especially, the examples he uses to support them. If we generalize what we then discover, we can, in modern terms, say that his solution to his problem of the corresponding "ratios" of speeds, forces, and resistances is that speeds vary arithmetically while the ratios of forces to resistances determining these speeds vary geometrically. That is, to use symbols, for the series $V/n, \cdots V/3, V/2, V, 2V, 3V, \cdots nV$, we have the corresponding series $(F/R)^{1/n}, \cdots (F/R)^{1/3}, (F/R)^{1/2}, F/R, (F/R)^2, (F/R)^3, \cdots (F/R)^n$. Or, straying an even greater distance from Bradwardine himself, we can arrive at the now fairly traditional formulations of his so-called "dynamical law":

$$(F_1/R_1)^{V_2/V_1} = F_2/R_2 \text{ or } V = \log_a F/R,$$
$$\text{where } a = F_1/R_1.$$

Furthermore, if we continue our modern way of putting Bradwardine's solution to his problem, we can more easily express the advantage it had over the medieval alternatives cited above. In essence, this advantage lay in the fact that Bradwardine's "function" allowed one to continue deriving "values" for V, since such values—the repeated halving of V, for example—never correspond to a case of $R > F$ (as was the case with $V \propto F/R$); they correspond, rather, to the repeated taking of roots of F/R, and if the initial $F_1 > R_1$ (as is always assumed), then for any such root $F_n/R_n = (F_1/R_1)^{1/n}$, F_n is always greater than R_n. With this in view, it would seem that Bradwardine's most notable accomplishment lay in discovering a mathematical relation governing speeds, forces, and resistances that fit more adequately than others the Aristotelian-Scholastic postulates of motion involved in the problem he set out to resolve.

It is of the utmost importance to note, however, that almost all we have said in expounding Bradwardine's function goes well beyond what one finds in the text of the *Tractatus de proportionibus* itself. Notions of arithmetic versus geometric increase or of the exponential character of his "function" may well translate his intentions into our way of thinking, but they also simultaneously tend to mislead. Thus, to speak of exponents at once implies or suggests a mathematical sophistication that is not in Bradwardine, and also obscures the relative simplicity of his manner of expressing (by example, to be sure) his "function." This simplicity derives from the symmetrical use of the relevant terminology: If one *doubles* a speed, he would say, then one *doubles* the ratio of force to resistance, and if one *halves* the speed, then one *halves* the ratio. Although we feel constrained to note that doubling or halving a *ratio* amounts, in our terms, to squaring or taking a square root, such an addendum was unnecessary for Bradwardine, since for him the effect of applying such operations as doubling or halving to ratios was unambiguous. To double A/B always gave—again in our terms—$(A/B)^2$, and never $2(A/B)$. What is more, the examples Bradwardine utilizes to express his function deal *merely* with doubling and halving, a factor which makes it evident that he was still at a considerable remove from the general exponential function so often invoked in explaining the crux of the *Tractatus de proportionibus*.

This limitation not only derived from the fact that the relevant material in Aristotle so often spoke of doubles and halves, but may also be related to the possible origin of Bradwardine's function itself. The locale of this origin is medieval pharmacology, where we find discussion of a problem similar to Bradwardine's; in place of investigating the corresponding variations between the variables of motion, we have instead to do with an inquiry into the connection of variables within a compound medicine and its effects. Given any such medicine, how is a variation in the strength (*gradus*) of its effect related to the variation of the relative strengths (*virtutes*) of the opposing qualities (such as hot-cold or bittersweet) within the medicine which determine that effect? As early as the ninth century, the Arab philosopher al-Kindī replied to this question by stipulating that while the *gradus* of the effect increases arithmetically, the ratio of the opposing *virtutes* increases geometrically (where this geometric increase follows the progression of successive "doubling," that is, squaring). Now, not only was the pertinent text of al-Kindī translated into Latin, but the essence of his answer to this pharmacological puzzle was analyzed, developed, and, in a way, even popularized by the late thirteenth-century physician and alchemist Arnald of Villanova. From Arnald's work al-Kindī's "function" found its way into early fourteenth-century pharmacological works, even into the *Trifolium* of Simon Bredon, fellow Mertonian of Bradwardine in the 1330's.

Now it is certainly possible, indeed even probable, that Bradwardine may have appropriated his function from the al-Kindian tradition (a borrowing that may also have occurred in the case of the use of "exponential" relations within certain fourteenth-century alchemical tracts as well). But even admitting this, Bradwardine did a good deal more than simply transfer the function from the realm of compound medicines to the context of his problem of motion. For, quite unlike his pharmacological forerunners, he developed the mathematics behind his function by axiomatically connecting it with the whole medieval mathematics of ratios as he knew it. Thus, the entire first chapter (there are but four) of his *Tractatus* is devoted to setting forth the mathematical framework required for his function. A beginning exposition of the standard Boethian division of particular numerical ratios (e.g., *sesquialtera, superpartiens,* etc.) furnishes him with the terminology with which he was to operate. Second, and of far greater insight and importance, he axiomatically tabulated the substance of the medieval notion of composed ratios. That is, to use our terms, A/C is composed of (*componitur ex*) $A/B \cdot B/C$. Furthermore (and here lies the specific connection with Bradwardine's function), when $A/B = B/C$, then $A/C = (A/B)^2$. Or, as Bradwardine stated in general, if $a_1/a_2 = a_2/a_3 = \cdots a_{n-1}/a_n$, then $a_1/a_n = a_1/a_2 \cdot a_2/a_3 \cdots a_{n-1}/a_n$ and $a_1/a_n = (a_1/a_2)^{n-1}$. In point of fact, the insertion of geometric means and the addition of continuous proportionals that are here manipulated were Bradwardine's, and the standard medieval, way of dealing with what are (for us), respectively, the roots and powers involved in his function.

The fact that Bradwardine was thus able to state in its general form the medieval mathematics behind his function suggests that, although his expression of the function itself in mathematical terms was never general, this was due to his inability to formulate such a general mathematical statement. The best he could do was, perhaps, to give his function in the rather opaque, and certainly mathematically ambiguous, form we have quoted *in extenso* above, and then merely to express the mathematics of it all by way of example.

Proper generalization of Bradwardine's function had to await, it seems, his successors. Hence, John

Dumbleton, like Bradwardine a Mertonian, gave a more general interpretation of the function through a more systematic investigation of its connections with the composition of ratios (see his *Summa de logicis et naturalibus,* pt. III, chs. 6–7). He also extended Bradwardine by translating him, as it were, into the then current language of the latitude of forms (that is, equal latitudes of motion [V] always correspond to equal latitudes of ratio [F/R], where the corresponding "scales" of such latitudes are, respectively, what we would term arithmetic and geometric).

A further development of Bradwardine, in many ways the most brilliant, occurred in the *Liber calculationum* of Richard Swineshead, yet another Mertonian successor. In *Tractatus* XIV (entitled *De motu locali*) of this work, Swineshead elaborates his predecessor's function by setting forth some fifty-odd rules that, assuming Bradwardine to be correct, specify which different *kinds* of change (uniform, difform, uniformly difform, and so on) in F/R obtain relative to corresponding variations in V. Swineshead also extended Bradwardine in *Tractatus* XI (*De loco elementi*) of his *Liber calculationum,* where, in what is something of a fourteenth-century mathematical tour de force, he applies his function to the problem of the motion of a long, thin, heavy body (*corpus columare*) near the center of the universe.

Another significant medieval development of Bradwardine's function was effected by Nicole Oresme in his *De proportionibus proportionum.* Here one observes an extension of the mathematics implicit in the function into a whole new "calculus of ratios" in which rules are prescribed for dealing with what are, for us, rational and irrational exponents. Moreover, Oresme then applies this calculus to the problem of the possible incommensurability of heavenly motions and the consequences of such a possibility for astrological prediction.

Many other Scholastic legatees of the Bradwardinian tradition could be cited as well, but, unlike the three we have mentioned above, most appear to have concerned themselves chiefly with rather belabored expositions of what Bradwardine meant, although a few, such as Blasius of Parma and Giovanni Marliani, produced somewhat unimpressive dissents from his opinion.

One should not close an account of the *Tractatus de proportionibus* without some mention of its final chapter. Here, in effect, Bradwardine attacks the question of the appropriate measure of a body in uniform motion, a matter that becomes problematic when rotational movement is considered. Again investigating, and rejecting, proposed alternative solutions to his question, he argues that the proper measure must be determined by the fastest-moving point of the mobile at issue. Once more his decision bore fruit, especially in his English successors. The resulting "fastest moving point rule" gave birth to an extensive literature treating of the sophisms that arise when one attempts to apply the rule to bodies undergoing condensation and rarefaction or generation and corruption. (The work of the Mertonian William Heytesbury furnishes the best example of this literature.)

Tractatus de continuo. In book VI of the *Physics,* Aristotle had formulated a battery of arguments designed to refute, once and for all, the possible composition of any continuum out of indivisibles. Like all Aristotelian positions, this received ample confirmation and elaboration in the works of his Scholastic commentators. Yet two features of the medieval involvement with this particular segment of *Physics* VI are especially important as background to Bradwardine's entry, with his *Tractatus de continuo,* into what was soon to become a heated controversy among natural philosophers. To begin with, from the end of the thirteenth century on, Scholastic support and refortification of Aristotle's anti-indivisibilist position almost always included a series of mathematical arguments that did not appear in the *Physics* itself or in the standard commentary on it afforded by Averroës. Considerable impetus and authority were given to the inclusion of such arguments by the fact that Duns Scotus had seen fit to feature them, as it were, in his own pro-Aristotelian treatment of the "continuum composition" problem in book II of his *Commentary on the Sentences.* The second important medieval move in the history of this problem occurred in the early years of the fourteenth century, when we witness the eruption of anti-Aristotelian, proindivisibilist sentiments. These two factors alone do much to explain the nature and purpose of Bradwardine's treatise, for he wrote it (sometime after 1328, since it refers to his *Tractatus de proportionibus*) to combat the rising tide of atomism, or indivisibilism, as personified by its two earliest adherents: Henry of Harclay (chancellor of Oxford in 1312) and Walter Chatton (an English Franciscan, *fl. ca.* 1323). Furthermore, in attacking the atomistic views of his two adversaries, Bradwardine used as his most lethal ammunition the appeal to mathematical arguments that, as we have noted, were by now standard Scholastic fare. But he developed this application of mathematics to the problem at issue far beyond that of his predecessors.

The *Tractatus de continuo* was, first of all, mathematical in form as well as content, for it was modeled on the axiomatic pattern of Euclid's *Elements,* begin-ning with twenty-four "Definitions" and ten "Suppositions," and continuing with 151 "Conclusions" or "Propositions," each of them directly critical of the atomist position. These "Conclusions" purport to reveal the absurdity of atomism in all branches of knowledge (to wit: arithmetic, geometry, music, astronomy, optics, medicine, natural philosophy, metaphysics, logic, grammar, rhetoric, and ethics), but the nucleus of it all lies in the geometrical arguments Bradwardine brought to bear upon his opponents.

To understand, even in outline, the substance and success of what Bradwardine here accomplished, one should note at the outset that the atomism he was combating was, at bottom, mathematical. The position of the fourteenth-century atomistic thinker consisted in maintaining that extended continua were composed of nonextended indivisibles, of points. Given this, Bradwardine astutely saw fit to expand the mathematical arguments that were already popular weapons in opposing those of atomist persuasion. Such arguments can be characterized as attempts to reveal contradictions between geometry and atomism, in which the revelation takes place when assorted techniques of radial and parallel projection are applied to the most rudimentary of geometrical figures. For example, parallels drawn between all the "point-atoms" in opposite sides of a square will destroy the incommensurability of the diagonal, while the construction of all the radii of two concentric circles will, if both are composed of extensionless indivisibles, entail the absurdity that they have equal circumferences. In applying these and related arguments, Bradwardine effectively demolished the atomist contentions of his opponents, at least when they maintained that the atoms composing geometrical lines, surfaces, and solids were finite in number or, if not that, were in immediate contact with one another. His success (and that of others who employed similar arguments against atomism) was not as notable, however, in the case of an opponent who held that continua were composed of an infinity of indivisibles between any two of which there is always another. Here the argument by geometrical projection faltered due to a failure—which Bradwardine shared—to comprehend the one-to-one correspondence among infinite sets and their proper subsets (although this property was properly appreciated, it seems, by Gregory of Rimini in the 1340's).

The major accomplishment of Bradwardine's *Tractatus de continuo* lay, however, in yet another mathematical refutation of his atomist antagonist. To realize the substance of what he here intended, we should initially note that Aristotle's own arguments in *Physics* VI against indivisibilism made it abundantly clear that the major problem for any prospective mathematical atomist was to account for the connection or contact of the indivisibles he maintained could compose continua. As if to grant his opponent all benefit of the doubt, Bradwardine suggests that this problematic contact of point-atoms might appropriately be interpreted in terms of the eminently respectable geometrical notion of superposition (*superpositio*), a respectability guaranteed for the medieval geometer in the application of this notion within Euclid's proof of his fundamental theorems of congruence (*Elements* I, 4 and 8; III, 24). However, immediately after this concession to the opposing view, Bradwardine strikes back and, in a sequence of propositions, conclusively reveals that the superposition of any two geometrical entities systematically excludes their forming a single continuum. Consequently, the urgently needed contact of atoms is geometrically inadmissible.

Finally, as if to reveal his awareness of the mathematical basis of his whole *Tractatus*, toward its conclusion Bradwardine puts himself the question of whether, in using geometry as the base of his refutation of atomism, he had perhaps not begged the very question at issue; does not geometry *assume* the denial of atomism from the outset? He replies by carefully pointing out that while some kinds of atomism are, by assumption, denied in geometry, others are not. And he explains why and how. In our terms, he has attempted to point out just which continuity assumptions are independent of the axioms and postulates, both expressed and tacit, of Euclid's *Elements* and which are not. That he realized the pertinence of such an issue to the substance of the medieval continuum controversy is certainly much to his credit.

Geometria speculativa and *Arithmetica speculativa.* These two mathematical works, about which we lack information concerning the date of composition, are both elementary compendia of their subjects and were intended, it seems plausible to claim, for arts students who may have wished to learn something of the quadrivium, but with a minimal exposure to mathematical niceties. The *Arithmetica* is the briefer of the two and appears to be little more than the extraction of the barest essentials of Boethian arithmetic. More interesting, both to us and to the medievals themselves, to judge from the far greater number of extant manuscripts, is the *Geometria speculativa*. From the mathematical point of view, it contains little of startling interest, although it does include elementary materials not developed in Euclid's *Elements* (e.g., stellar polygons, isoperimetry, the filling of space by touching polyhedra [*impletio loci*], and so on). Of

greater significance would seem to be Bradwardine's concern with relating the mathematics being expounded to philosophy, even to selecting his mathematical material on the basis of its potential philosophical relevance. Such a guiding principle was surely in Bradwardine's mind when he saw fit to have his compendium treat of such philosophically pregnant matters as the horn angle, the incommensurability of the diagonal of a square, and the puzzle of the possible inequality of infinites. Indeed, it is precisely to passages of the *Geometria* dealing with such questions that we find reference in numerous later authors, such as Luis Coronel and John Major. Such authors were fundamentally philosophers—philosophers, moreover, with little mathematical expertise—and it would seem fair to conclude that Bradwardine had just this type of audience in view when he composed his *Geometria.*

Theological Works. Bradwardine's earliest venture into theology is perhaps represented by his treatment of the problem of predestination, extant in a *questio* entitled *De futuris contingentibus.* His major theological work, indeed the *magnum opus* of his whole career, is the massive *De causa Dei contra Pelagium et de virtute causarum ad suos Mertonenses,* completed about 1344. Its primary burden was to overturn the contemporary emphasis upon free will, found in the writings of those with marked nominalist tendencies (the "Pelagians" of the title), and to reestablish the primacy of the Divine Will. Although this reaffirmation of a determinist solution to the problem of free will is not of much direct concern to the history of science, brief excursions into sections of the *De causa Dei* have revealed that it is not without interest for the development of late medieval natural philosophy. Thus, to cite but two instances, Bradwardine discusses the problem of an extramundane void space and, within the context of rejecting the possible eternity of the world, again struggles with the issue of unequal infinites. One is tempted to suggest that closer study of the *De causa Dei* will reveal that Bradwardine's theological efforts contain yet other matters of importance for the history of science.

BIBLIOGRAPHY

I. LIFE. The fundamental point of departure is A. B. Emden, *A Bibliographical Register of the University of Oxford to A.D. 1500,* I (Oxford, 1957), 244–246. One may also profitably consult H. A. Obermann, *Archbishop Thomas Bradwardine, a Fourteenth Century Augustinian* (Utrecht, 1958), pp. 10–22. The *Sermo epinicius* has been edited with a brief introduction by H. A. Obermann and J. A. Weisheipl, in *Archives d'histoire doctrinale et littéraire du moyen age,* **25** (1958), 295–329.

II. WRITINGS AND DOCTRINE. The most complete bibliography of the editions and MSS of Bradwardine's works is to be found in the unpublished thesis of J. A. Weisheipl, "Early Fourteenth-Century Physics and the Merton 'School'" (Oxford, 1957), Bodl. Libr. MS D. Phil. d.1776.

Logical Works. The unedited *De insolubilibus* is extant in at least twelve MSS, including Erfurt, Amplon. 8° 76, 6r–21v and Vat. lat. 2154, 13r–24r. For the equally unedited *De incipit et desinit:* Vat. lat. 3066, 49v–52r and Vat. lat. 2154, 24r–29v. Although Bradwardine's treatises are not considered, the kinds of problems they bear upon are dealt with (for the *De insolubilibus*) in I. M. Bochenski, *A History of Formal Logic* (Notre Dame, Ind., 1961), pp. 237–251; and (for the *De incipit*) in Curtis Wilson, *William Heytesbury. Medieval Logic and the Rise of Mathematical Physics* (Madison, Wis., 1956), pp. 29–56. A variety of other logical writings, although often ascribed to Bradwardine in MSS, are most likely spurious; they are too numerous to mention here.

Tractatus de proportionibus velocitatum in motibus. This has been edited and translated, together with an introduction, by H. Lamar Crosby as *Thomas of Bradwardine. His Tractatus de Proportionibus. Its Significance for the Development of Mathematical Physics* (Madison, Wis., 1955). Corrections to some of Crosby's views can be found in Edward Grant, ed., *Nicole Oresme. De proportionibus proportionum and Ad pauca respicientes* (Madison, Wis., 1966), pp. 14–24, a volume that also contains a text, translation, and analysis of Oresme's extension of the mathematics of Bradwardine's "function." For the problem and doctrine of Bradwardine's *Tractatus* one should also note Marshall Clagett, *The Science of Mechanics in the Middle Ages* (Madison, Wis., 1959), pp. 215–216, 220–222, 421–503; and Anneliese Maier, *Die Vorläufer Galileis im 14. Jahrhundert,* 2nd ed. (Rome, 1966), pp. 81–110. Discussion of some of the factors of the above-cited application of Bradwardine's function in the *Liber calculationum* of Richard Swineshead can be found in John E. Murdoch, *"Mathesis in philosophiam scholasticam introducta:* The Rise and Development of the Application of Mathematics in Fourteenth Century Philosophy and Theology," in *Acts of the IVth International Congress of Medieval Philosophy, Montreal, 1967* (in press); and M. A. Hoskin and A. G. Molland, "Swineshead on Falling Bodies: An Example of Fourteenth Century Physics," in *British Journal for the History of Science,* 3 (1966), 150–182, which contains an edition of the text of Swineshead's *De loco elementi* (*Tractatus* XI of his *Liber calculationum*). For a new interpretation of how Bradwardine's function should be understood, see A. G. Molland, "The Geometrical Background to the 'Merton School': An Exploration Into the Application of Mathematics to Natural Philosophy in the Fourteenth Century," in *British Journal for the History of Science,* 4 (1968), 108–125. A brief discussion and citation of the relevant texts in Dumbleton that treat of Bradwardine will appear in an article by John Murdoch in a forthcoming volume of the *Boston University Studies in the Philosophy of Science.* Finally, the issue of the probable pharmacological origin of Bradwardine's function is treated in Michael McVaugh,

"Arnald of Villanova and Bradwardine's Law," in *Isis,* 58 (1967), 56–64.

Tractatus de continuo. The as yet unpublished text of this treatise was first indicated, and extracts given, in Maximilian Curtze, "Über die Handschrift R. 4° 2: Problematum Euclidis Explicatio, des Königl. Gymnasial Bibliothek zu Thorn," in *Zeitschrift für Mathematik und Physik,* 13 (1868), Hist.-lit. Abt., 85–91. A second article giving a partial analysis of the contents of the *Tractatus* is Edward Stamm, "Tractatus de Continuo von Thomas Bradwardina," in *Isis,* 26 (1936), 13–32, while V. P. Zoubov gives a transcription of the enunciations of the definitions, suppositions, and propositions of the *Tractatus,* with an accompanying analysis of the whole, in "Traktat Bradvardina 'O Kontinuume,'" in *Istoriko-matematicheskiie Issledovaniia,* 13 (1960), 385–440. A critical edition of the text has been made from the two extant MSS (Torun, Gymn. Bibl. R. 4° 2, pp. 153–192; Erfurt, Amplon. 4° 385, 17r–48r) by John Murdoch and will appear in a forthcoming volume on mathematics and the continuum problem in the later Middle Ages. Some indication of the issues dealt with in the *De continuo* can be found in Anneliese Maier, *Die Vorläufer Galileis im 14. Jahrhundert,* 2nd ed. (Rome, 1966), pp. 155–179; and John Murdoch, *"Rationes mathematice." Un aspect du rapport des mathématiques et de la philosophie au moyen age,* Conférence, Palais de la Découverte (Paris, 1961), pp. 22–35; "Superposition, Congruence and Continuity in the Middle Ages," in *Mélanges Koyré,* I (Paris, 1964), 416–441; and "Two Questions on the Continuum: Walter Chatton (?), O.F.M. and Adam Wodeham, O.F.M.," in *Franciscan Studies,* 26 (1966), 212–288, written with E. A. Synan.

Mathematical Compendia. The *Arithmetica speculativa* was first printed in Paris, 1495, and reprinted many times during the fifteenth and sixteenth centuries. The *Geometria speculativa* (Paris, 1495) was also republished, and has recently been edited by A. G. Molland in his unpublished doctoral thesis, "Geometria speculativa of Thomas Bradwardine: Text with Critical Discussion" (Cambridge, 1967); cf. Molland's "The Geometrical Background to the 'Merton School,'" cited above. Brief consideration of the *Geometria* can also be found in Moritz Cantor, *Vorlesungen über Geschichte der Mathematik,* 2nd ed., II (Leipzig, 1913), 114–118. One might note that a good deal of Bradwardine's *Geometria* was repeated in a fifteenth-century *Geometria* by one Wigandus Durnheimer (MS Vienna, Nat. Bib. 5257, 1r–89v). The *Rithmomachia* ascribed to Bradwardine (MSS Erfurt, Amplon. 4° 2, 38r–63r; Vat. Pal. lat. 1380, 189r–230v) is most probably spurious.

The *Questio de futuris contingentibus* was edited by B. Xiberta as "Fragments d'una qüestió inèdita de Tomas Bradwardine," in *Beiträge zur Geschichte der Philosophie des Mittelalters,* Supp. 3, 1169–1180. The *editio princeps* of the *De causa Dei* at the hand of Henry Savile (London, 1618) has recently been reprinted (Frankfurt, 1964). The basic works dealing with Bradwardine's theology are Gordon Leff, *Bradwardine and the Pelagians* (Cambridge, 1957), and H. A. Obermann, *Archbishop Thomas Bradwardine. A Fourteenth Century Augustinian* (Utrecht,

1958), whose bibliographies give almost all other relevant literature. For the discussion of void space and infinity in the *De causa Dei*, see Alexandre Koyré, "Le vide et l'espace infini au XIVe siècle," in *Archives d'histoire doctrinale et littéraire du moyen age,* **17** (1949), 45–91; and John Murdoch, *"Rationes mathematice"* (see above), pp. 15–22. Also of value are A. Combes and F. Ruello, "Jean de Ripa I Sent. Dist. XXXVII: De modo inexistendi divine essentie in omnibus creaturis," in *Traditio,* **23** (1967), 191–267; and Edward Grant, "Medieval and Seventeenth-Century Conceptions of an Infinite Void Space Beyond the Cosmos," in *Isis* (in press).

If one disregards the various epitomes of the *De causa Dei*, it would appear that the only remaining work which may well be genuine is a *Tractatus de meditatione* ascribed to Bradwardine (MSS Vienna, Nat. Bibl. 4487, 305r–315r; Vienna, Schottenkloster 321, 122r–131v). Of the numerous other works that are in all probability spurious, it will suffice to mention the *Sentence Commentary* in MS Troyes 505 and the *Questiones physice* in MS Vat. Pal. lat. 1049, which is not by Bradwardine but, apparently, by one Thomas of Prague.

JOHN E. MURDOCH

BRAGG, WILLIAM HENRY (*b.* Westward, Cumberland, England, 2 July 1862; *d.* London, England, 12 March 1942), *physics.*

Born on his father's farm near Wigton, Bragg was the eldest child of Robert John Bragg, former officer in the merchant marine, and Mary Wood, daughter of the vicar of the parish of Westward. His mother died when he was seven. A bachelor uncle, William Bragg, a pharmacist and the dominant member of the family, then took his namesake to live with him. After six years Bragg's father removed his son from the uncle's house in Market Harborough (50 miles northeast of Cambridge) and sent him to King William's College, a public school on the Isle of Man. Bragg continued, however, to return to Market Harborough during vacations even after he had gone up to Cambridge, and to look forward to his uncle's pride in his accomplishments.

Bragg was always at the top of his school class, quiet and rather unsocial but tall, strong, and good at competitive sports. Having outstripped his schoolmates, he made little progress in his final year, 1880–1881. "But a much more effective cause for my stagnation was the wave of religious experience that swept over the upper classes of the school during that year. . . . we were terribly frightened and absorbed; we could think of little else."[1] The mature Bragg preserved his composure by refusing to take literally the biblical threat of eternal damnation, although he retained his faith and his abhorrence of atheism.

Bragg entered Trinity College on a minor scholarship, obtaining a major scholarship the following year. Beginning his work at Cambridge in the long vacation, July and August 1881, he went up every "long" afterward. Under Routh's coaching he read mathematics, and only mathematics, "all the morning, from about five to seven in the afternoon, and an hour or so every evening" for three years, coming out third wrangler in Part I of the mathematical tripos in 1884. "I never expected anything so high. . . . I was fairly lifted into a new world. I had new confidence: I was extraordinarily happy."[2] Bragg obtained first-class honors in Part III of the mathematical tripos in 1885, and left Cambridge at the end of that year upon being appointed to succeed Horace Lamb as professor of mathematics and physics at the University of Adelaide. Although in his last year at Cambridge Bragg attended lectures by J. J. Thomson at the Cavendish Laboratory, at the time of his appointment his physical studies had not included any electricity; he subsequently attempted Maxwell's *Treatise* only after reading more elementary texts.

At Cambridge, Bragg published nothing; in his first eighteen years at Adelaide (1886–1904) he published three minor papers on electrostatics and the energy of the electromagnetic field. Rather, his efforts were invested in the development of a marvelously, indeed beguilingly, simple and comprehensible style of public and classroom exposition, in the affairs of his university, and in those of the Australasian Association for the Advancement of Science. One of the Australian notables by virtue of his office, in 1889 he married the daughter of the postmaster and government astronomer, Charles Todd, and fell in with the extensive but relaxed social life and out-of-doors recreations. His elder son, William Lawrence, caddied for his father, a fine golfer; his daughter was a devoted companion.

This is not the sort of life that brings election to the Royal Society of London (1907), the Bakerian lectureship (1915), the Nobel Prize in physics (1915), the Rumford Medal of the Royal Society (1916), sixteen honorary doctorates (1914–1939), presidency of the Royal Society (1935–1940), and membership in numerous foreign academies, including those of Paris, Washington, Copenhagen, and Amsterdam. The new life began, at age forty-one, in 1903–1904.

In 1903 Bragg was once again president of Section A (astronomy, mathematics, and physics) of the Australasian Association for the Advancement of Science. His presidential address, delivered at Dunedin, New Zealand, on 7 January 1904, was entitled "On Some Recent Advances in the Theory of the Ionization of Gases."[3] Conscious that he was addressing Rutherford's "friends and kindred," and possibly stimulated by the unavoidable comparison between his own accomplishments and those of the younger man, Bragg gave a highly critical review of the field, finding fault with much of the work that had been done and with many of the assumptions upon which it rested. The most damaging criticism was directed toward the work on the scattering and absorption of the ionizing radiations (α, β, and γ rays) by matter—the atoms of which Bragg, following the most modern views, supposed to consist of "thousands of electrons." The absorption of the particulate β and α rays had, unjustifiably, been assumed analogous to the exponential decrease in intensity of a wave traversing an absorbing medium; moreover, the analogy confounded energy flux and particle flux. "The exponential law is not applicable to this kind of radiation. . . . 'Amount of radiation' is not a term with definite meaning."[4] If an exponential law seemed to hold, that was only because of the superposition of a variety of factors—principally the broad spectrum of initial velocities of the particles and the scattering of the particles by the absorber.

In the spring of 1904, "through the generosity of a constant friend of the University of Adelaide"[5] and with the assistance of R. D. Kleeman, Bragg began experiments on the absorption of α particles emitted by a radium bromide source. Early in September, Bragg and Kleeman reported the results of a rather thorough investigation that combined simple experiments and highly ingenious analysis.[6] The α particles fell into a few groups, each of which had a definite range, and thus a definite initial velocity. Each group corresponded to a different radioactive species in the source, so that the measurement of α particle ranges soon became an invaluable tool in identifying radioactive substances.

For the next two and a half years, until the spring of 1907, Bragg followed up this line of investigation very vigorously, publishing a paper every few months. Then, as in 1903–1904, a highly critical review paper ("On the Properties and Natures of Various Electric Radiations")[7] heralded a reorientation of his interest. Again the title was a misnomer, for the main point of the paper was to present arguments supporting "the possibility that the γ and X rays may be of a material nature," specifically neutral pairs consisting of an electron and an α particle. (This was a full year before Rutherford and Geiger found the α particle to be doubly charged.)

As early as January 1904, Bragg had expressed doubts about the identity of γ rays and X rays—the latter just then being rather convincingly shown to have many properties of transverse ether pulses.[8] Now, considering γ and X rays to be of the same

nature, he declared the evidence in favor of the ether pulse theory to be "overrated," and emphasized that the theory was unable to account for the large quantity of energy and momentum that remained in the ray regardless of the distance from its source, and that could all be delivered to a single electron. During the following five years Bragg backed off somewhat from this concrete model of the γ ray, emphasizing its "corpuscular" rather than its "material" nature,[9] but did not abandon the general concept of an electron-with-its-charge-neutralized until after the discovery of X-ray diffraction in 1912. Thus, initially without being aware of the views of Einstein and Stark, Bragg became the first, and remained the foremost, English-language advocate of a view of X rays that stressed their "quantal" properties.[10]

Barkla answered Bragg's challenge,[11] and their exchange of body blows over the distribution of scattered X rays initiated a continuing feud. Thereafter, Bragg's experiments, and the controversy, focused upon a remarkable inference that Bragg drew from his neutral-pair theory: the ionization accompanying the passage of X rays and γ rays through matter is not produced by the direct action of these rays, but is entirely a secondary effect occurring only after the ray has been converted into a high-speed electron (through removal of the neutralizing positive charge).

Until the spring of 1911 the available data were ambiguous, and the opponents numerous.[12] However, the first result to come out of C. T. R. Wilson's cloud chamber was a clear demonstration that the exposure of a gas to a beam of X rays did not produce a diffuse homogeneous fogging, but a large number of short wiggly lines; ionization occurred only along the path of the photoelectron.[13] Bragg's inference became—and has remained—the accepted view of the interaction of high-frequency radiation with matter. And yet, just as Bragg's contention was receiving striking experimental support, the theory from which he derived it seemed to be decisively refuted by the discovery of an interference phenomenon accompanying the passage of an X-ray beam through a crystal.

But to pick up the biographical thread: Bragg's star rose rapidly after his first publications. In 1907, nominated by Horace Lamb and supported by Rutherford, he was elected to the Royal Society of London; in 1908 he was appointed Cavendish professor of physics at the University of Leeds, returning to England in March 1909. The first year or two at Leeds were not happy ones; the removal from Australia, the lack of solid scientific results, and the sniping criticism of his work by Barkla undermined Bragg's self-esteem. Things brightened in 1911–1912 with the vindication of his views on ionization by X rays, and of his views on the scattering of β and α particles (in this latter question he was closely allied with Rutherford against J. J. Thomson).[14] After completing a detailed account of his researches and views, *Studies in Radioactivity* (1912), Bragg was on the lookout for a new problem.[15]

During the summer and fall of 1912 the Laue-Friedrich-Knipping phenomenon was, naturally, *the* subject of discussion. After some initial success in construing the photographs on the corpuscular hypothesis,[16] Bragg and his son convinced themselves that a wave interpretation was unavoidable. This transition was smoothed by the instrumentalist epistemology that Bragg had adopted in the course of his corpuscular hypothesis campaign: "Theories were no more . . . than familiar and useful tools."[17] Early in November, William Lawrence, working at the Cavendish, showed how the Laue phenomenon might be regarded as a *reflection* of electromagnetic radiation in the incident beam from those planes in the crystal that were especially densely studded with atoms, and he derived the famous Bragg relation, $n\lambda = 2d \sin \theta$, connecting the wavelength of the X ray with the glancing angle at which such a reflection could occur.[18]

The younger Bragg's paper was entitled "The Diffraction of Short Electromagnetic Waves"—not "X rays"—for he wished to hold open the possibility that X rays (as known especially by their ionizing properties) were nevertheless his father's corpuscles, the diffracted-reflected entity affecting the photographic plates being merely the *Bremsstrahlung* necessarily accompanying the stopping of cathode rays in the X-ray tube. Despite the uncertainty whether the reflected rays could ionize—and even despite some counter evidence—Bragg's epistemology did not allow him to see the issue any longer as either/or: "The problem then becomes, it seems to me, not to decide between two theories of X-rays, but to find, as I have said elsewhere, one theory which possesses the capacities of both."[19]

In January 1913 Bragg succeeded in detecting the reflected rays with an ionization chamber,[20] and by March he had constructed the first X-ray spectrometer. Initially Bragg used it to investigate the spectral distribution of the X rays, relations between wavelength and Planck's constant, the atomic weight of emitter and absorber, and so on.[21] But very quickly he adopted his son's interest in the inversion of the Bragg relation: using a known wavelength in order to determine d, the distances between the atomic planes, and thus the structure, of the crystal mounted in the spectrometer. Apart from specifying general

symmetry conditions, before June 1912 it had not been possible to give the actual arrangement of the constituent atoms of any crystal. Laue's assignment of a simple cubic lattice to zinc sulfide had been corrected by William Lawrence to face-centered cubic, and he went on to analyze the crystal structure of the alkali halides on the basis of "Laue diagrams" that he had made at Cambridge. The spectrometer first served to confirm these structures and to determine the absolute values of the lattice spacings, and then was applied to more difficult cases.[22] By the end of 1913 the Braggs had reduced the problem of crystal structure analysis to a standard procedure.

In 1915 Bragg moved to London as Quain professor of physics at University College, and throughout the war he continued to direct some crystal analyses. He had, however, already become involved in war work, and it soon took almost all of his time. Bragg was a member of the panel of scientific experts attached to the Central Committee of the Board of Invention and Research, an institution created by Lord Fisher in July 1915 to aid the navy by screening inventions and sponsoring research. In April 1916, with the title of resident director of research and a staff of two physicists and a mechanic, Bragg was installed at the Naval Experiment Station at Hawkcraig to work on submarine detection. No satisfactory cooperation could be obtained here because of intraservice rivalry between Fisherites and anti-Fisherites, and at the end of 1916 the work was transferred to Harwich, with much loss of time and momentum.[23] "It was," Andrade opined, "probably in acknowledgment of his war work, as well as of his scientific eminence, that Bragg was made a C.B.E. in 1917 and was knighted as a K.B.E. in 1920."[24]

"The outbreak of war," Bragg asserted in 1920, "practically put a stop to the work with the spectroscope [i.e., X-ray spectrometer], which had been commenced in England, and we have fallen behind other countries which have been able to push on with it."[25] Of the two sorts of work—measuring λ (or, more generally, the properties of X rays and the X-ray spectra emitted by atoms) and measuring d (or, more generally, the structure of various crystals)—the first and more fundamental task, although pioneered by Barkla, Bragg, and Moseley, was largely abandoned in Britain after the war. Bragg assumed his duties at the University of London and began gathering a research school about himself. In 1923, when Bragg became head of the Royal Institution, this young and energetic group was installed in the previously moribund Davy-Faraday Research Laboratory. Their work, following a tacit agreement between Bragg and his son, was confined to the analysis of organic crystals. And in this field, which has now become so fundamental to molecular biology, Bragg put Britain way out in front.[26]

Bragg was president of the Royal Society at a very difficult time (1935–1940). He was one of the three Britons who had been members of the Deutsche Physikalische Gesellschaft since before World War I, and he now welcomed "certain ambiguous advances from learned bodies in Nazi Germany, and he did his best to further ostensible plans for an understanding between the two countries which, in his goodness of heart, he took at their face value."[27] Then the Royal Society was caught in the cross currents of agitation over the study of the social relations of science and the assertion of the social responsibility of science. Finally, there was the war, with its innumerable committees and councils—and air raids. Bragg's mind remained keen, even for scientific questions, but his energy began to fail. On 10 March 1942 he "had to take to his bed: two days later he was dead."[28]

NOTES

1. Autobiographical note quoted by Bragg and Caroe, pp. 171–172.
2. *Ibid.,* p. 173.
3. *Report of the Australasian A.A.S.* (Dunedin), **10** (1904), 47–77.
4. *Ibid.,* p. 69. Bragg's critique, contrary to the usual account, was not limited to (and thus not derived from the peculiar constitution of) the α particle.
5. Bragg, *Studies in Radioactivity* (London, 1912), p. 5.
6. Bragg, "On the Absorption of X-rays, and on the Classification of the X-rays of Radium," in *Philosophical Magazine,* 6th ser., **8** (Dec. 1904), 719–725; Bragg and Kleeman, "On the Ionization Curves of Radium," *ibid.,* 726–738. Dated 8 September 1904.
7. *Philosophical Magazine,* 6th ser., **14** (Oct. 1907), 429–449. Read before the Royal Society of South Australia, 7 May and 4 June 1907.
8. See the article on Barkla in *D.S.B.*
9. Bragg, "The Consequences of the Corpuscular Hypothesis of γ and X-rays, and the Range of β Rays," in *Philosophical Magazine,* 6th ser., **20** (Sept. 1910), 385–416; *Studies in Radioactivity.*
10. Not everyone shut his mind to this new gospel: "Personally, I have long been a convert to Professor Bragg's views on the nature of X-rays. . . ." H. L. Callendar, "Presidential Address, Section A," in *Report of the British A.A.S.* (Dundee, 1912), p. 396. Cf. Russell McCormmach, "J. J. Thomson and the Structure of Light," in *British Journal for the History of Science,* **3** (1967), 362–387.
11. See the article on Barkla in *D.S.B.*
12. Bragg, in *Philosophical Magazine,* 6th ser., **20** (Sept. 1910), 385–416; **22** (July 1911), 222–223; and **23** (Apr. 1912), 647–650.
13. C. T. R. Wilson, "On a Method of Making Visible the Paths of Ionising Particles Through a Gas," in *Proceedings of the Royal Society of London,* **85A** (9 June 1911), 285–288. Received 19 April 1911.
14. J. L. Heilbron, "The Scattering of α and β Particles and Rutherford's Atom," in *Archive for History of Exact Sciences,* **4** (1968), 247–307.

15. R. A. Millikan, *Autobiography* (London, 1951), pp. 95, 99.
16. Bragg, "X-rays and Crystals," in *Nature,* **90** (24 Oct. 1912), 219; dated 18 October. P. P. Ewald, "William Henry Bragg and the New Crystallography," in *Nature,* **195** (28 July 1962), 320–325. P. Forman, "On the Discovery of the Diffraction of X-rays by Crystals: Why Munich, Which X-rays?," in *Acts du XIIe Congrès International d'Histoire des Sciences, Paris, 1968.*
17. Bragg, "Radiations Old and New," in *Report of the British A.A.S.* (Dundee, 1912), pp. 750–753.
18. W. L. Bragg, "The Diffraction of Short Electromagnetic Waves by a Crystal," in *Proceedings of the Cambridge Philosophical Society,* **17** (14 Feb. 1913), 43–57. Read 11 November 1912.
19. Bragg, "X-rays and Crystals," in *Nature,* **90** (28 Nov. 1912), 360–361. The "elsewhere" may refer to *Studies in Radioactivity,* p. 192.
20. Bragg, "X-rays and Crystals," in *Nature,* **90** (23 Jan. 1913), 572. Dated 17 January.
21. W. H. Bragg and W. L. Bragg, "The Reflection of X-rays by Crystals," in *Proceedings of the Royal Society of London,* **88A** (1 July 1913), 428–438, received 7 April 1913; W. H. Bragg, "The Reflection of X-rays by Crystals (II)," *ibid.,* **89A** (22 Sept. 1913), 246–248, received 21 June 1913.
22. W. H. Bragg and W. L. Bragg, "The Structure of Diamond," *ibid.* (22 Sept. 1913), 277–291, received 30 July.
23. J. J. Thomson, *Recollections and Reflections* (New York, 1937), pp. 207–210.
24. Andrade, "William Henry Bragg 1869–1942," p. 284.
25. Bragg, as president of the Physical Society of London, opening a discussion on X-ray spectra, in *Proceedings of the Physical Society of London,* **33** (1920), 1.
26. Articles by J. M. Robertson, J. D. Bernal, and K. Lonsdale, in P. P. Ewald, ed., *Fifty Years of X-Ray Diffraction* (Utrecht, 1962).
27. Andrade, *op. cit.,* p. 290.
28. *Ibid.*

BIBLIOGRAPHY

I. ORIGINAL WORKS. An excellent chronological bibliography prepared by K. Lonsdale is appended to the article by Andrade (see below). Bragg's papers at the Royal Institution, London, include a collection of offprints, research notebooks covering 1903–1913, summaries of some literature read, a few MS drafts (notably that of *Studies in Radioactivity*), miscellaneous scientific correspondence after 1920, a very little scientific correspondence before 1920, autobiographical notes on his youth, and family correspondence. Bragg's correspondence with Rutherford, some fifty letters written between 1904 and 1915, is in the Rutherford papers at the Cambridge University Library; copies are available at the Royal Institution and at McGill University, Montreal. The locations of thirty-one letters from Bragg to other correspondents are given in T. S. Kuhn *et al., Sources for History of Quantum Physics* (Philadelphia, 1967), p. 26.

II. SECONDARY LITERATURE. Works on Bragg are E. N. da C. Andrade, "William Henry Bragg 1869–1942," in *Obituary Notices of Fellows of the Royal Society of London,* **4** (1943), 277–300; Sir Lawrence Bragg and Mrs. G. M. Caroe (Gwendolen Bragg), "Sir William Bragg, F.R.S.," in *Notes and Records of the Royal Society of London,* **16** (1961), 169–182; and *Who Was Who 1941–1950* (London, 1952), p. 134.

PAUL FORMAN

BRAHE, TYCHO (*b*. Skåne, Denmark [now in Sweden], 14 December 1546; *d*. Prague, Czechoslovakia, 24 October 1601), *astronomy*.

The second child and eldest son of Otto Brahe and his wife, Beate Bille, Tycho (Danish, Tyge) was born at the family seat, Knudstrup. He had five sisters and five brothers, including his still-born twin. Otto Brahe was a privy councillor and later became governor of Helsingborg Castle. Probably Tycho and Christine, whose last name is unknown and who was not of noble family, were never formally married, but they lived together from about 1573 to the end of his life. They had five daughters and three sons; their daughter Elizabeth married Tycho's assistant, Franz Gansneb Tengnagel von Camp. Tycho's best observing was done on the island of Hven from 1576 to 1597. His observations of the nova of 1572 and several comets forced abandonment of the traditional celestial spheres, and his observations of Mars enabled Kepler to discover the laws of planetary motion. Information about his observatory and observational techniques was widely disseminated, and his geoheliocentric system gained numerous supporters.

Tycho was brought up by his paternal uncle, Jörgen Brahe, and from the age of seven was taught Latin and the preparatory subjects by a tutor. From April 1559 to February 1562 he attended the Lutheran University of Copenhagen, where the theologians and faculty were under the influence of Melanchthon as well as Aristotle and the Scholastics. Tycho must have begun his studies in the Faculty of Philosophy by applying himself first to the *trivium;* his study of the arts probably began under the lecturers in pedagogy, who emphasized the writing and speaking of Latin. No doubt he received instruction in the articles of faith from the Lutheran catechism on Sunday mornings. He must have studied Greek grammar and Greek and Latin literature, and probably also dialectic, attending lectures in Greek on Aristotle's *Dialectics* and lectures on the Latin rhetorical works and on Roman epistolary authors.

Since his family was a noble one, Tycho did not need a university degree to establish himself in a profession. Therefore, he must have entered on the study of the *quadrivium* as soon as he was able, without waiting to earn a degree. Ethics and singing were included in the university *quadrivium;* and at the chapter house of the cathedral, students practiced and heard lectures on singing. Also available were lectures on harmonic theory, a mathematical discipline since the time of Pythagoras. From the lectures on the natural sciences and philosophy that Tycho may also have heard, he would have emerged as a convinced Aristotelian. By 1560 he was, no doubt,

studying arithmetic, then Sacrobosco's *Sphaera* and Peter Apian's *Cosmographia.* His copies of the *Sphaera,* a medical handbook, an herbal, Gemma Frisius' edition of Apian's *Cosmographia,* and Regiomontanus' *Tabulae directionum* are preserved.

In 1561 and 1562 Tycho was probably attending lectures on Aristotle's *Physics,* Euclid's *Elements,* Ptolemy's theory of the planets, and on astrology, which united astronomy with medicine. Tycho made friends with, and later wrote an epitaph for, Hans Fransden, from Ribe in Jutland (Johannes Franciscus Ripensis), who lectured on Hippocrates and Galen as well as on mathematics, acted as physician to the king, and prepared an annual astrological almanac. Tycho also made friends with Johannes Pratensis, who later became professor of medicine and whose copy of Ptolemy's *Almagest* Tycho probably inherited in 1576. On 21 August 1560 the occurrence at the predicted time of a solar eclipse, although only partial in Copenhagen, turned Tycho toward observational astronomy, which was not part of the university curriculum. He immediately obtained a copy of Stadius' *Ephemerides,* which is based on the *Prutenic Tables* and, consequently, on the Copernican system.

So that he would be parted from friends interested in science and would study law, a necessary part of the education of a member of the nobility, Tycho's uncle sent him to the University of Leipzig, where he arrived in March 1562. With him, as tutor, went Anders Sörensen Vedel, only four years his senior. Vedel had spent less than a year attending lectures on divinity and studying history at the university, but he was later to distinguish himself as a historian. Except for two short visits, Tycho remained away from his homeland until 1570.

At Leipzig, although Vedel tried to keep his charge busy with the study of law, Tycho's interest in astronomy was not to be thwarted; and as late as May 1564 he was pursuing it secretly, while Vedel slept. During the daytime he attended to the studies prescribed by his uncle. He used what money he could save for the purchase of astronomical books, tables, and instruments. Not content with Stadius' *Ephemerides,* he also obtained the *Alphonsine Tables* and *Prutenic Tables,* and used the *Ephemerides* of Giovanni Battista Carellus (1557). To learn the constellations, he secretly used a globe no bigger than a fist.

A conjunction of Saturn and Jupiter in August 1563 was later regarded by Tycho as the turning point in his career. Although equipped with only a pair of compasses, he recorded his observations relative to it. The discrepancy between the time of the observed closest approach of the two planets and that computed from the tables, about a month using the *Al-*

phonsine Tables and a few days by the *Prutenic Tables,* greatly impressed Tycho. On 1 May 1564 he began observing with a radius, or cross staff, consisting of a three-foot arm along which could slide the center of an arm of half that length. Both arms were graduated. Bartholomaeus Scultetus subdivided the instrument for him by means of transversals. There was a fixed sight at the end of the longer arm that he held near his eye. To measure the angular distance between two objects, Tycho set the shorter arm at any graduation of the longer arm and moved a sight along the shorter arm until he saw the two objects through it and a sight at the center of the transversal arm. The required angle was then obtained from the graduations and a table of tangents. This instrument was not very accurate, but, since he could not get money from Vedel for a new one, he made a table of corrections to apply to it.

Tycho left Leipzig 17 May 1565 and traveled to Copenhagen via Wittenberg and Rostock. Of his family, only his mother's brother, Steen Bille, showed any sympathy for his scientific interests. When his Uncle Jörgen died, 21 June 1565, there was no longer any reason for him to remain at home. He reached Wittenberg 15 April 1566 and began studies under Caspar Peucer. He left after five months, however, arriving in Rostock 24 September and matriculating at the university soon thereafter.

On 29 December 1566, in an unfortunate duel with another Danish nobleman, part of Tycho's nose was cut off. This he replaced by what was long thought to be a composition of gold and silver, but probably had considerable copper content. When his tomb was opened 24 June 1901, a bright green stain was found on the skull at the upper end of the nasal opening.

At Rostock, Tycho met several men devoted to astrology and alchemy as well as to medicine and mathematics. He observed a lunar eclipse 28 October 1566 and a partial solar eclipse 9 April 1567. That summer he visited home, but was back in Rostock by 1 January 1568. He immediately began observations, although without an instrument until he used the cross staff 19 January. His last recorded observation in Rostock was 9 February. On 14 May 1568, King Frederick II of Denmark formally promised Tycho the first vacant canonry in the cathedral chapter at Roskilde, Zealand. He matriculated at the University of Basel in 1568. and, probably early in 1569, went to Augsburg via Lauingen in Swabia, where he met the astronomer Cyprian Leowitz. He entered into the intellectual life of Augsburg, where he made his first observation 14 April.

Among Tycho's friends in Augsburg were Johann Baptist Hainzel, an alderman, and his brother, Paul,

the burgomaster,[1] who helped Tycho arrange for the manufacture of a wooden quadrant, suspended at the center, with a radius of about nineteen feet. The divisions marked on the arc and a plumb line gave altitude measures. Tycho does not seem to have used it himself, and it was destroyed in a storm in December 1574. Tycho also designed a portable sextant, which he used and gave to Paul Hainzel, and ordered a five-foot globe. His last recorded observation in Augsburg was made in Hainzel's presence 16 May 1570. At Augsburg he argued with Ramus, who advocated constructing a new astronomy based entirely on logic and mathematics, without recourse to any hypothesis. They agreed on the need for new and accurate observations before attempting to explain the celestial motions, and it is obvious that Tycho was aware of the need for good instruments to obtain those observations. He returned home in 1570, probably because of his father's poor health. On the way, in Ingolstadt, he met Philip Apian, son of Peter.

Although at his father's death, 9 May 1571, he and his brother Steen inherited Knudstrup, Tycho soon moved to Heridsvad Abbey, the home of his uncle, Steen Bille, where he devoted himself to chemical experiments until 11 November 1572. After sunset on that day, almost directly overhead, in the constellation Cassiopeia he noticed a star shining more brightly than all the others and immediately realized it had not been there before.

To measure the star's angular distances from the neighboring stars in Cassiopeia, Tycho used a sextant similar to the one he had left with Hainzel. The two arms of seasoned walnut, less influenced by climate than other woods and lighter than metal, were joined by a bronze hinge. A 30° arc, graduated by individual minutes, without transversals, was fixed to one arm; the other arm could slide along the arc. Square metal sights with holes through the centers were attached at the ends of the arms. Tycho later described this instrument in the *Mechanica* and in the *Progymnasmata,* by itself and, as used for the nova observations, in the plane of the meridian, pointing out a window with the end of the arm where the arc was fixed (this time a 60° arc) resting on the sill while the end of that arm, near the joining of the two arms, rested on a post some five feet inside the window. To make sure that this arm was horizontal, it was moved until a plumb line, hanging from the end of the arc, touched a mark in the middle of the arm. The plumb line would show any change in position of the instrument, thus indicating the correction to be made to the observation.

To make sure that observations made the same night were made under the same conditions, Tycho left the instrument clamped in position between such observations. He measured the angular distance of the new star, at both upper and lower culmination, from the star Schedar (α Cassiopeia), which crossed the meridian at nearly the same time, and found no parallax. He measured the distance of the nova from nine stars in Cassiopeia and found no variation between observations. Had the new star been as close to the earth as the moon, a parallax of 58'30'' would have been found. Tycho observed the star until the end of March 1574, when it ceased to be visible. His records of its variations in color and magnitude identify it as a supernova. At first clear white, with the magnitude of Venus at its brightest, it grew yellowish and diminished in brightness to that of Jupiter. By February and March it was of the first magnitude and reddish, in April and May of the second magnitude and lead-colored. Thereafter its color did not change. By August it was a third-magnitude star, fourth-magnitude by October, hardly more than fifth-magnitude at the turn of the year, and sixth-magnitude or less in February 1574.

Tycho concluded that the phenomenon was not an atmospheric exhalation and was not attached to the sphere of a planet, since it did not move contrary to the direction of the diurnal rotation, but that it was situated in the region of the fixed stars. He called it a star, not a comet, because, as the ancients asserted, comets are generated in the upper regions of the air, not in the heavens. He noted that it twinkled like a star and did not have a tail like a comet. It could not be a comet with its tail turned away from the earth because Peter Apian and Gemma Frisius had shown that the tail of a comet is turned away from the sun. Tycho thought it not impossible that the star would again cease to be visible, as he wrote in a brief tract published in 1573, while the star was still visible. This tract, dedicated to Johannes Pratensis, at whose urging it had been printed, included an exchange of letters between the latter and Tycho, a section on the astrological significations of the star, the introduction to an astrological calendar, and that part of the calendar dealing with the lunar eclipse of December 1573.

All over Europe scholars observed the star. Some, using crude observational procedures, such as holding a thread before their eyes, assured themselves that the newcomer did not move relative to certain known fixed stars. Such observations, showing the star to be supralunar, were widely appreciated as necessitating an alteration in cosmological theories.

Tycho's scholarly treatise concerning the star, the *Progymnasmata* (1602), was the first volume of a proposed trilogy. The second chapter on planets

having been printed and paged first, there was space in chapter 1 to describe the lunar theory, the complexity of which delayed publication of the volume. The work reprinted most of Tycho's 1573 tract and gave his carefully compiled observations of the nova, discussing its position in space and its expected annual parallax if the Copernican system were true. Tycho attempted to calculate the real diameters of the sun, moon, planets, and the nova from his measurements of their apparent diameters. He estimated the maximum distance of Saturn as 12,300 semidiameters of the earth, the distance of the fixed stars as 14,000—not all at the same distance—and that of the new star as 13,000. His estimate of the real diameter of the new star at its first appearance was 7-1/8 times that of the earth. He assigned the diminution in light to actual decrease in size. Galileo pointed out[2] the impossibly enormous sizes of the stars if Tycho's estimates of their diameters were correct. The *Progymnasmata* also reprinted, summarized, or criticized the works on the nova by others. Tycho deplored Hagecius' use of clocks because of their inaccuracy. Because he was unable to observe the star with his sextant at upper culmination, Tycho used Hainzel's observations made at Augsburg with the big quadrant.

Tycho's observations of the nova were separately recorded. His journal of observations skips from one made at Helsingborg 30 December 1570 to his entries of three distance measurements between the nova and known fixed stars made with a parallax instrument 10 May 1573. There are entries for 14 August and for a lunar eclipse observed at Knudstrup 8 December, for observations at Heridsvad in March and April 1574, and at Copenhagen at the end of April and May. None appear for 1575.

In September 1574, in the first lecture of his course for young noblemen at the University of Copenhagen, Tycho spoke of the skill of Copernicus, whose system, although not in accord with physical principles, was mathematically admirable and did not make the absurd assumptions of the ancients, who let certain bodies move irregularly in respect to the centers of the epicycles and eccentrics. Doubtless, Tycho had Copernicus' rejection of Ptolemy's equant in mind. The influence of the stars on nature—seasons, tides, weather—seemed obvious. If forewarned, thanks to astrology, men could conquer the influence of the stars on themselves, but Tycho had reservations concerning public calamities.

Soon after completing these lectures, early in 1575, and wondering where to settle permanently, Tycho went first to Kassel, where he visited Landgrave William IV. The two men, convinced of the need for systematic observations, observed together for more than a week, Tycho with some of his own portable instruments and the landgrave with his quadrants and torqueta. They made an accurate determination of the position of Spica. Their discussion of the retardation of the sun near sunset spurred Tycho later to study refraction at low altitudes. The landgrave was so impressed by Tycho's ability that he suggested to the Danish monarch that something be done to enable Tycho to pursue his astronomical studies in his native land.

Tycho's next stop was Frankfurt am Main. There, at the book fair, he purchased many pamphlets on the recent nova. He next journeyed to Venice via Basel, where he contemplated settling, and then returned to Augsburg, inquiring about instruments he had ordered during his previous visit. Wherever he went, he met the leading astronomers and, whenever possible, inspected their astronomical instruments.

At Regensburg, where the future emperor, Rudolph II, was crowned King of the Romans, 1 November 1575, Tycho met Rudolph's physician, Hagecius, who had written an excellent book on the nova of 1572. From him Tycho obtained a copy of Copernicus' *Commentariolus* and a copy of a letter from Hieronymo Mugnoz to Hagecius about the new star. It is probable that at the same time Tycho presented Hagecius with a copy of his tract on that star. At Saalfeld, on the return journey, Tycho saw the manuscripts of Erasmus Rheinhold, who had prepared the *Prutenic Tables.* In Wittenberg, Tycho examined the wooden parallactic instrument, or triquetrum, with which Wolfgang Schuler had observed the nova after his earlier observations with Johannes Praetorius, made with an old wooden quadrant, had resulted in the finding of a large parallax that was inconsonant with the results obtained by the landgrave.

Tycho reached home near the end of 1575. In February 1576, possibly because of the landgrave's recommendation, King Frederick II offered him the island of Hven in the Danish Sound and asked him to erect suitable buildings and construct instruments there. Tycho accepted, feeling that he could thus obtain in his native land the desired quiet and convenience. He immediately visited the island, and on 23 May a document was signed by the king conferring and granting in fee the island and its tenants and servants, with the rent therefrom; there was also the obligation to govern it in accordance with the law and to attend to the welfare of the inhabitants. Tycho was also given sufficient funds to augment his own, in order to erect a suitable residence and other buildings necessary to his work, and certain landholdings, the income from which, together with his own fortune,

made it possible for him to lead an almost regal existence. From time to time additional sources of income were made available.

The island is roughly 2,000 acres in area. The inhabitants lived in a village near the northern coast and tilled about forty farms in common. Near the center of the island, at the highest point, about 160 feet above sea level, Tycho began construction of Uraniborg (heavenly castle), the edifice that was to be his home and observatory for more than twenty years. He made one observation of Mars in October 1576 and began observations of the sun 14 December. Although he probably moved into the building that winter, it was not completed until 1580, and even thereafter additions and alterations were made. On the island were the workshops of the artisans who constructed his instruments, a windmill, a paper mill begun in 1590 and completed in 1592, which could also be used to grind corn and prepare hides, and nearly sixty fishponds, one of which, for the use of the mill, was secured by a large dam.

The main building was erected exactly in the center of a square enclosure the walls of which were about 255 feet long, eighteen and one-half feet high, and seventeen feet wide at the base. At the center of each wall was a semicircular bend about seventy-six feet in diameter that enclosed a pavilion. There were gates at the eastern and western corners, and above the gates were kennels in which two English watchdogs were kept to warn of arrivals. At the northern corner was a small house for servants in the same Gothic-Renaissance style as the main house. A similar house at the southern corner housed a printing office. The press was installed in 1584. Four roads directed exactly to the cardinal points led from the main house to the gates and houses. Within the enclosure were herbaries and flower gardens and about 300 trees of various species.

The main house, too, was exactly square, its four walls, about fifty-one feet long and thirty-eight feet high, facing the four points of the sky. The rounded towers added on the south and north were eighteen and one-half feet in diameter, with eight and one-half-foot galleries encircling them. From the ground to the Pegasus weathervane, the house measured about sixty-four feet. Beneath the entire house was a cellar more than ten feet deep, divided into many rooms, and beneath the towers were the well and arrangements for storing food. The original four corridors on the ground floor, which met at right angles, were later reduced to three so as to make possible the establishment, behind the furnace, of a small chemical laboratory, thereby lessening the need to go down to the large subterranean one. There were a fountain that could turn, sending water in all directions, and pipes and pumping apparatus to distribute water to rooms on both floors. On the ground floor there were also a library, a kitchen, a table for collaborators in each corner of the building, and spare bedrooms. The observatories were on the upper level, the larger southern and northern ones containing several of the important, large instruments—such as the azimuthal semicircle, Ptolemaic rulers, brass sextant and azimuthal quadrant, and parallactic rulers that also showed azimuths. An octagonal gallery contained one of the globes on which an instrument could be placed and turned in all directions. At the very top of the house were eight bedrooms for assistants.

About a hundred feet south and slightly east of Uraniborg a separate observatory, Stjerneborg (castle of the stars), constructed about 1584, housed additional instruments in five subterranean rooms. Stone columns outside could be used to support Ptolemaic rulers or the portable armillae. There were also places for globes on which instruments could be placed and turned. In this building was a study with only the vaulted roof and the top of the walls above ground. On the ceiling was depicted the Tychonic system, and on the walls were the portraits of Timocharis, Hipparchus, Ptolemy, al-Battānī, King Alfonso X of Castile, Copernicus, Tycho, and the still unborn but hoped-for descendant, Tychonides, each with a legend beneath it—that for Tychonides expressing the wish that he would be worthy of his great ancestor.

The accuracy of the observations depended on the instruments and the care with which they were used. Although Tycho's were without magnification, error was minimized by their huge size and by the graduations carefully marked on them to facilitate angular measurements on the celestial sphere, altitudes, and azimuths. Tycho checked instruments against each other and corrected for instrumental errors. Unfortunately, he considered refraction negligible at altitudes above 70°. He observed regularly and achieved an accuracy within a fraction of a minute of arc, an accuracy unsurpassed from the time of Hipparchus to the invention of the telescope.

In the library was the globe, almost five feet in diameter, ordered from Augsburg. Tycho filled the cracks, restored the spherical shape with pieces of parchment, tested it for two years to see whether it would retain its shape and whether it would withstand the seasonal temperature changes, then covered it with brass sheets and again had it smoothed. On it he engraved the zodiac and the equator with their poles and, using transversal points, divided each degree of these circles into sixty minutes. The globe could be turned on an axis through its poles inside the meridian and horizon circles that were mounted on it and that were divided into degrees and minutes. A vertical brass quadrant marked in degrees and minutes indicated altitudes as well as azimuths along the horizon. On this globe, over the years, Tycho marked the exact positions, referred to the year 1600, of the fixed stars that he observed. He also investigated the planet motions with reference to this globe.

In the southwest room on the ground floor at Uraniborg, affixed to a wall in the plane of the meridian, was Tycho's most famous instrument, the mural quadrant with a radius of about six feet. The degrees marked off on its arc were so far apart that each minute was divided by transversal points into six subdivisions of ten seconds each, making it possible to read off measurements of five seconds. In a wall pointing exactly east and west, and over the center of the quadrant, was a square hole that could be opened and closed and that contained a brass cylinder along both sides of which the observer could sight, using one of two pinnules on the quadrant. Each pinnule had a square plane the width of which was exactly equal to the diameter of the cylinder. Each side of the plane had a slit for use in determining a star's altitude and meridian transit at the same time. To determine the altitude alone, which was done to the sixth of a minute, an observer looked through the upper and lower slits and the corresponding sides

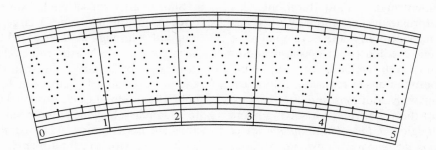

FIGURE 1. Method of dividing an arc by transversal points, proof of the applicability of the method to curved lines and pinnules for use in sighting.

of the cylinder, and an assistant entered the reading on the record. A third person watched two clocks when the observer at the pinnule signaled, and the time was noted in the ledger. Two clocks that gave seconds as accurately as possible and could be checked against each other were necessary. Tycho had four. Elsewhere he expressed his distrust of clocks, preferring to check the time by observation. Despite his faith in this quadrant, he also consulted other large instruments.

Inside the quadrant's arc, for ornamental purposes, was painted a life-size portrait of Tycho seated at a table, with arm outstretched as though pointing to the cylinder. In a niche in the wall, above and near the head, was a brass globe fitted with interior wheels. It could turn to imitate diurnal rotation and to show the paths of the sun and moon and the lunar phases.

The smaller southern observatory housed a brass armillary instrument with four armillae, or rings; the smaller northern observatory, another with three armillae. In the northern tower were the sextant with which one observer could measure distances, the bipartite arc for measuring small angular distances, and the sextant with which Tycho had observed the nova. Among his other instruments were several smaller quadrants and sextants of various designs for various purposes, an astronomical radius, an astronomical ring, a small astrolabe, an azimuth semicircle, and some parallactic or ruler instruments, one of which had belonged to Copernicus.

In these fantastically ornate but exceedingly useful observatories, Tycho watched the skies and trained his assistants. Some of the larger instruments could not have been used without their aid. Among these assistants were Peter Jacobsøn Flemløs, Longomontanus, Elias Olsen, Gellius Sascerides (who stayed six years), Otto Islandus (Oddur Einarsson, who was bishop in Iceland), and Willem Blaeu (who later made excellent maps and globes). Paul Wittich, who was an assistant at Uraniborg in 1580 and who, at Kassel in 1584, described Tycho's instruments, including the transversal divisions, so impressed the landgrave that he had his instrument maker, Joost Bürgi, alter his instruments to conform to the description. Wittich was probably largely responsible for the development of the prosthaphaeretic method (from πρόσθεσις [addition] and ἀφαίρεσις [subtraction]) for simplifying trigonometrical computations by replacing multiplications and divisions with additions and subtractions. This is the basis of the set of rules for solving plane and spherical triangles, *Triangulorum planorum et sphaericorum praxis arithmetica,* drawn up, without proof, by Tycho and made available in numerous

manuscript copies for the use of his assistants. Wittich also revealed this method at Kassel, to the annoyance of Tycho; he was even more annoyed, however, by the inclusion of the first two rules in a book by Nicolai Reymers Bär (Ursus), printed at Strasbourg in 1588. Afterward the method was further developed by other mathematicians. Ursus had visited Hven in 1584. Tycho was also visited by members of the nobility, possibly including Frederick II and certainly Frederick's son, the future Christian IV (1592), as well as James VI of Scotland, the future James I of England (1590). Christoph Rothmann, Landgrave William IV's mathematician, was there from 1 August to 1 September 1590.

Although Tycho saw no objection to the adoption of the Gregorian calendar by the Protestant world, since questions of theology were not involved, he does not seem to have used it until early 1599, when, on the Continent, he began to date his letters in the new style. His first observation so dated was made 22 July of that year.

From Hven, Tycho carried on a vast correspondence that kept alive the personal contacts made in his student days, apprised the scholarly world of his work, and provided him with the observations of others for comparison with his own. Although Tycho and William IV never met again after Tycho's 1575 visit to Kassel, in later years they exchanged letters, sending each other records of their observations. The correspondence, including letters between Tycho and Rothmann, was printed at Uraniborg in 1596. It begins with data concerning the comet of 1585 and largely concerns the techniques of observation, the instruments used, and their divisions. Appended is a description of Hven, with its observatories and instruments. The majority of Tycho's other letters, written between 14 January 1568 and 30 April 1601, first appeared in print in the *Opera omnia*. They provide a survey of observational astronomy in the last three decades of the sixteenth century, having achieved that dissemination of ideas which is now the province of learned journals.

Shortly after sunset on 13 November 1577, Tycho noticed, for the first time, a large comet with a very long tail. Although he later heard that the comet had been seen in the Northwendic Sea on 9 November, in his opinion it had begun with the new moon that had occurred shortly before, on 10 November at one hour after midnight.[3] He observed from 13 November to 26 January, by which time it was barely distinguishable. He used a radius and a sextant, and occasionally a quadrant with an azimuth circle—the larger instruments were not yet all installed. He fixed the quadrant in the meridian. Shortly after the comet ceased to be visible, he described it in a short German tract, first published in 1922.[4]

Five hours after noon on 13 November, Tycho found the comet 26°50′ from the bright star in Aquila and 21°40′ from the lowest star in the horn of Capricorn, toward which the tail was stretched. Using trigonometry, he computed the comet's position as 7°15′ in Capricorn, with a declination of 8°20′ north of the ecliptic. In the next twenty-four hours it moved 3°30′ in its circle. Having found it moved more rapidly in the beginning, Tycho decided it had moved 4° in its circle each of the days before he saw it, at new moon having been near the ecliptic beneath the twenty-fifth degree of Sagittarius in the line of the Milky Way, which he considered the place whence comets usually come. He traced the comet's path from west to east. It had described a quarter of a great circle from the twenty-fifth degree of Sagittarius in the ecliptic, intersecting the equator at an angle of 34° at a point 300°40′ from the vernal equinox. Its rate of motion gradually decreased, so that in the end it moved only 20′ in a day, or 4°20′ from 13 January to 26 January. Its tail, 22° long in the beginning, gradually became smaller and shorter, and could scarcely be seen in January. Tycho used the direction of comets' tails as evidence that the tails are merely solar rays transmitted through the head of the comet, an argument against Aristotle's theory of the formation of the tail out of "dry fatness."

In the first chapter of the untitled German tract, Tycho described Aristotle's theory of comets and objected to it on the grounds that the star in Cassiopeia four years before had been supralunar, having had no parallax and having remained stationary like the fixed stars, for which reasons many had abandoned the Aristotelian theory in favor of the belief that something new can be born in the heavens. Tycho suggested that other comets could be born there, and are not composed of dryness and fatness pulled up from the earth. He said that Aristotle's proof had been based on meditation, not mathematical observation or demonstration, whereas comets *are* generated in the heavens.

Tycho referred frequently to his still incomplete Latin work on the same phenomenon, considering the two works as serving different purposes. The German one was intended for a wider audience than could be reached by a work in Danish, but it was meant for a less skilled audience than the one for whom the Latin work was written. Because it could reach only the literate, the German work would have an intelligent audience, but not one expected to be trained in mathematics. Repeatedly Tycho referred to the mathematical explanations in the Latin work, which the "masters" could read and understand. Indeed, the numerical values, such an important part of the Latin work, are almost entirely absent from the German. Tycho's main objective was to determine the comet's distance from the earth as a means of refuting Aristotle. He was also concerned with the comet's physical appearance—color, magnitude, and the direction of the tail.

As clearly as anything he wrote, this tract shows Tycho as a product of his times. Breaking with established tradition, he knew exactly where he stood in the historical development of astronomy. Moreover, the tract demonstrates how early and how fully he understood the implications of his break and stresses his insistence on putting observation above deduction by reasoning. Emphasis is placed on the comet's lack of parallax and the resultant untenability of the so-called Aristotelian doctrine of solid spheres in an unchanging heaven. It hints at Tycho's own system of the universe, on which he was already working. It deals at length with the astrological implications of this fiery sign, but secondarily to the observational revelations.

De mundi aetherei recentioribus phaenomenis (1588), on the comet of 1577, the second volume of Tycho's proposed trilogy, was printed on his own press and is profusely illustrated with useful diagrams. Chapter 1 records in detail, day by day, each of Tycho's observations of the comet. The next chapter gives his positional data, computed from his observations, for the comparison stars used in observing the comet. In chapter 3 the comet's latitude and longitude for each day are derived by means of spherical trigonometry, using observed angular distances of the comet from certain fixed stars. The diagrams, but not the mathematical steps, are reproduced. Chapter 4 treats the comet's right ascension and declination with respect to the equator, and chapter 5 deals with the portion of a circle described by the comet, ending with a table of its daily motion, latitude, longitude, right ascension, and declination (first southern, then northern) for 9 November 1577 to 26 January 1578. Chapter 6 treats the comet's parallax as a measure of its distance from the earth and states that the comet was in the etherial rather than the elementary region and moved in a great circle. Tycho's observations of the comet's angular distance from certain fixed stars are compared with those of other observers in other localities. Chapter 7 deals with past writings about the direction of comet tails and with the 1577 comet's tail, which was directed away from Venus. In chapter

9, however, Tycho states his opinion that this was an illusion, since it would seem more likely that the tail be directed away from the sun. Chapter 8 discusses the comet's position in regard to the planetary spheres.

Since his observations of the nova of 1572 and the comet of 1577 had made him discard the reality of the spheres, Tycho included a description of his own geoheliocentric system of the universe. The comet, whose greatest elongation from the sun was 60°, moved about that body in a circle outside that of Venus, that part of the circle where Tycho observed the comet being closer to the earth than Venus was. Moreover, the comet's orbit, inclined to the ecliptic

at an angle of 29°15′, was not a true circle, but an oval. Chapter 9 is concerned with the actual size of the comet and its tail, the diameter of the head being 3/14 of the diameter of the earth, and the length of the tail in November being ninety-six semidiameters if turned from Venus. The tenth and last chapter summarizes in detail the observations of others, both of those who found the comet supralunar and those who thought they found it sublunar.

At least six later comets were visible to the naked eye before Tycho left his island. The comets of 1580, 1582, 1585, and 1590 were supposed to be treated in the third volume of the trilogy, but that volume was never written. Tycho observed the comet of 1580

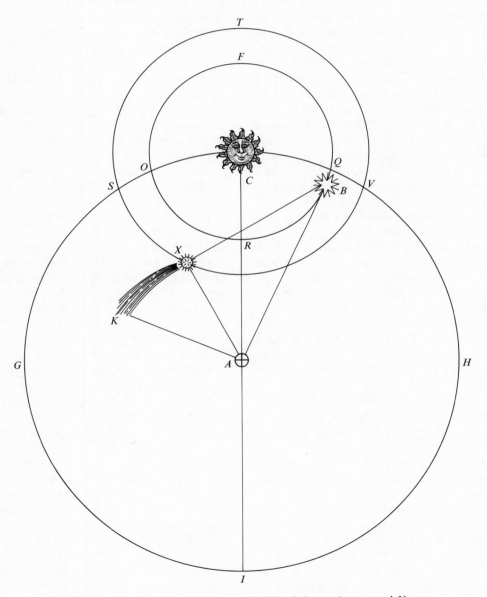

FIGURE 2. The position of the comet of 1577 relative to the sun and Venus.

from 10 October to 25 November and again on 13 December, after it had passed perihelion. On 12, 17, and 18 May 1582 he observed another comet. By 1585 his major astronomical instruments, including a large armillary instrument at Stjerneborg, had been installed. His excellent observations of the tailless comet visible in October and November of that year appeared in 1586 in the first book printed on the island, the *Diarium astrologicum et metheorologicum* of his assistant Elias Olsen. They were more fully preserved in manuscript and studied in detail in the nineteenth century. The comet of 1590 was observed at Hven the end of February and the beginning of March, whereas that of 1593 was not observed at Hven but at Zerbst in Anhalt (Seruesta Anhaldinorum) by one of Tycho's former students, Christiernus Johannis Ripensis. Tycho saw the comet of 1596 in Copenhagen

on 14, 15, and 16 July. More complete observations were made at Uraniborg on 18, 21, 24, and 27 July.

Hinted at in the German tract on the comet of 1577, probably first worked out by 1583, and first described in print in the 1588 Latin work on the comet of 1577, the Tychonic system was never presented in detail. In it the earth is at rest in the center of the universe, and there is still need for a sphere of fixed stars revolving in twenty-four hours. The planets circle the sun while the sun circles the earth. The orbits of Mercury and Venus intersect the orbit of the sun in two places but do not encompass the earth. The orbit of Mars also twice intersects that of the sun, but encloses the earth and its orbiting moon. The orbits of Jupiter and Saturn enclose the entire path of the sun.

Tycho prized parts of the Copernican doctrine or

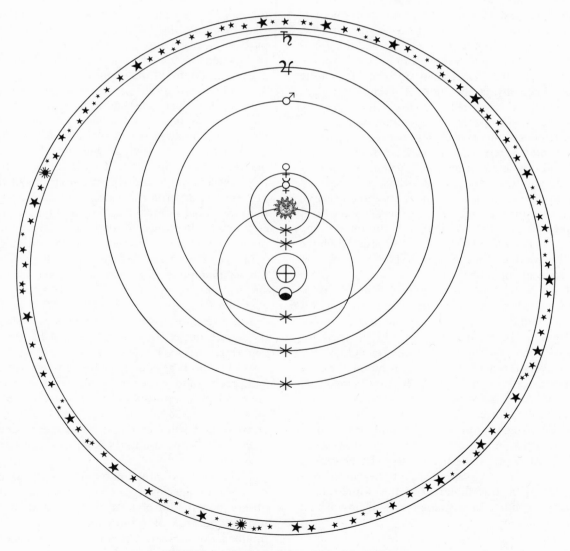

FIGURE 3.   Tycho Brahe's system of the universe.

at least acknowledged the abilities of its originator, but could not bring himself to accept a sun-centered universe. His reluctance to do so can be ascribed partly to his respect for Scripture and partly to his feeling of common sense, but largely to his inability to conceive of a universe so immense that an observer as accurate as he knew himself to be could not detect any stellar parallax, the necessary consequence of the earth's motion around the sun. The Tychonic system was timely and gained acceptance in many quarters. It did not bring its author into conflict with the theologians, yet it cared for observed phenomena, including the motion of comets through space, which had necessitated Tycho's rejection of the Aristotelian spheres. It could account for the phases of Venus, first observed by Galileo and not explicable by the Aristotelian and Ptolemaic schemes.

Just as Tycho was only one of a number of observers who stressed the supralunar position of comets and novae, so his compromise theory of the universe was only one of a number that accentuated the abandonment of Aristotelian tradition and helped prepare men to accept the Copernican doctrine. It is only natural, especially in the light of Tycho's arrogant ways, that there was some feeling of rivalry, especially toward Ursus, who described a similar system.

In Aristotelian theory the planets were attached to spheres and rotated with them. The destruction of these solid orbs made it necessary to find a cause for the motion of the planets, and this cause was provided by the next generations of astronomers and physicists, the sun assuming an importance not accorded to it by either Copernicus or Tycho. Undoubtedly the traditional crystalline spheres would eventually have been discarded without the aid of Tycho's work, but he speeded up the change.

Tycho presented his cosmologic views in his introduction to a pamphlet[5] on weather forecasting by his assistant Flemløs. To explain how the heavens influenced matters on earth and so could be used for prognostication, Tycho described his cosmology, but focused not so much on the system as on the way the heavens affect the earth. He maintained the concept of "free will" while conceding celestial influence. Accepting three elements—earth, water, and air—he theorized that air is the instrument by which the celestial region influences the terrestrial, with the animals and plants therein and, to a lesser extent, men (some more than others). Thus he voiced disagreement with traditional concepts while maintaining the validity of astrology and distinguishing it from astronomy.

Elsewhere Tycho criticized astrologers who drew improper conclusions based on superstition and error rather than astrology itself, which he considered a science for which both accurate knowledge of the course of the stars and experience gained from signs seen in the elementary world were needed. From the lunar eclipse observed during his stay in Leipzig, he predicted the wet weather that followed. Also while in Leipzig, he calculated Caspar Peucer's horoscope, predicting the misfortunes that befell him, as well as his reestablishment. In Rostock, from the lunar eclipse of 28 October 1566, Tycho predicted the death of the aged Sultan Suleiman the Magnificent, but later learned that Suleiman had died before the eclipse. Tycho calculated horoscopes for the three sons of Frederick II; but, although he continued to prepare annual prognostications for his ruler, by 1588, if not earlier, he held them of little importance, preferring to devote himself to the restoration of astronomy.

The German tract on the comet of 1577 stressed the comet's astrological significance, whereas the Latin work did not. In the *Progymnasmata,* the main part of the 1573 nova tract was reprinted, but not the section on the star's signification. These differences can, no doubt, be explained by the differences in the intended audience and a change in Tycho's point of view. Yet as late as 1598, in the autobiography included in the *Mechanica,* he said that both natural and judicial astrology are more reliable than one would think, provided the times are correctly determined and the paths of the celestial bodies and their entrances into the separate divisions of the sky are used in accordance with the observed sky, and their directions of motion and revolution are properly computed. He indicated that he had developed a method for this that he did not care to divulge.

In the *Astrologia,* Flemløs gave 399 short rules for weather prediction from the appearance of the sky, sun, moon, and stars, or animal behavior. However, the daily weather record kept at Hven from 1 October 1582 to 22 April 1597 was not published until the nineteenth century. It recorded the arrivals and departures of Tycho, his visitors, and students or assistants; and, although no instruments were used and precise times were not entered, it provided useful meteorological information for the area—frequency of wind, rain, snow, fog, hail, thunder, halos, and aurorae, and whether the sky was clear, semiclear, or covered. Some estimates were made of the force of winds.

Tycho's main occupation on Hven was the redetermination of the positions of the fixed stars and the observation of the planets, the sun, and the moon for the purpose of improving the theory of their motions. For six years, beginning in 1582, the distance between Venus and the sun was measured with the triangular sextant, which required two observers. Simultaneously the altitudes, and occasionally the azimuths, of Venus and the sun were measured. The distance of Venus from selected bright stars near the zodiac was measured with the same sextant after sunset, altitudes and declinations also being noted. The motions of Venus and the sun between daytime and nighttime observations were considered in calculating the positions of the observed stars. A star's declination was measured directly, but the difference in right ascension between the sun and a star was obtained by trigonometry. Using the right ascension of the sun as given in the tables, the right ascension of the star could be found. The stars were connected with α Arietis by distance measures. By suitable selection of observations, minimizing the effects of parallax and refraction, he determined the right ascension of α Arietis, and with this as reference, he determined the right ascensions of eight standard stars. Later he added three stars near the zodiac.

In determining the position of another star, a meridian quadrant or armillary was used to measure the declination, and a sextant was used to measure the distance from a known star. For the complete determination, two or three standard stars were used as reference. Included in the *Progymnasmata* (1602), before the section on the nova, are revisions of the solar and lunar theories and a catalog giving the positions of 777 fixed stars. Having indicated familiarity with the work of his predecessors, Tycho, using diagrams, described his observational methods and depicted the instruments used. In his later years he brought the list of stars to 1,000 by the less careful determination of the positions of 223 additional ones. The *Tabulae Rudolphinae,* prepared by Kepler in accordance with his modification of the Copernican system but on the basis of Tycho's observations, did not appear until 1627. Included were logarithm and other tables, the most significant of which were those of the positions of the sun and moon and five planets, and of 1,000 fixed stars calculated for the year 1600.

When he had more instruments, Tycho used several quadrants simultaneously for repeated observations of the sun's meridian altitude, begun 14 December 1576. From March 1582 he mostly used the great mural quadrant. He determined the equinoxes for the years 1584–1588, using the time when the sun was 45° from the equinoxes to determine the position of the apogee and the eccentricity of the orbit instead of using the solstice, the exact moment of which was difficult to find. He believed that the sun moved uniformly in an eccentric circle, but by 1591 he might have noted, from the motion of Mars, another inequality due to that eccentricity. He considered his

tables of the sun's motion to be accurate within 10″ or at most 20″. His values were 95°30′ for the longitude of the apogee with an annual motion of 45″ and .03584 for the eccentricity of the orbit, the greatest equation of center being 2°3′15″.

The difference in the colatitude as determined from his solar observations and his observations of the polestar led Tycho to investigate the effects of refraction, using the armillae at Stjerneborg, and to compose a refraction table. Unfortunately, he assumed the value of 3′ for the sun's horizontal parallax. He also composed a refraction table for the stars. He erred in believing refraction negligible at 45° and over, but made a step forward in determining the refraction for an observation and in correcting the instruments.

Tycho's handling of the lunar theory illustrates not only the accuracy of his observations and his awareness of the need to observe over long periods of time and over the whole course of the moon's orbit, but also his computational prowess and talent for theory construction. His discoveries of new inequalities in both longitude and latitude stem from his efforts at accurate determination of eclipses and his interest in parallax. Making approximately 300 observations of the moon in different parts of its orbit from 1582 to 1595, he noted its position relative to known fixed stars, observing in such a way as to minimize the effects of parallax. In the *Progymnasmata* he recorded twenty-one lunar and nine solar eclipses.[6] At his death all the important lunar perturbations, with the exception of the secular variation of the mean motion, were known.

Tycho made his first discovery regarding the moon's motion in 1587, when preparing his observations of the comet of 1577 for publication. The comet's position obtained from observations of its stellar distances differed by 21′ from the position computed from the lunar distance, suggesting some error in his theoretical position of the moon. Four lunar observations in August 1587 confirmed his suspicion that the inclination of the lunar orbit was 5°15′ instead of the previously accepted 5° of Ptolemy. When Tycho announced this finding in his book on the comet of 1577,[7] he expressly interpreted it as due to a long-term change rather than as a correction of Ptolemy. But in 1595 he discovered that the inclination varied in the short term—that he had, by chance, observed the moon's latitude in quadrature, whereas previous interest in the moon's latitude had been focused on syzygy, where eclipses occur. To account for the semimonthly fluctuations of the inclination, Tycho let the pole of the lunar orbit describe a circle twice a month to bring the pole 5° from the ecliptic when the moon was in syzygy and 5°15′ from it in quadrature, and also to provide a smooth variation in between. Since this device implied an oscillation of the nodes along the ecliptic, Tycho sought and found empirical evidence that such an oscillation did occur, thus making what has been described as "a true deductive discovery." From his determinations of the extreme values for the inclination of the orbit (4°58′30″ to 5°17′30″), Tycho deduced a value of 1°46′ for this nodal oscillation.

Tycho's discovery of the third inequality in longitude began with his observation of the lunar eclipse of 1590, in which the moon reached opposition about an hour before the time he had computed. By 1595 he had isolated the cause of his difficulty and had determined the approximate value of the "variation," the discovery of which he announced in his *Mechanica*.[8] During the winter of 1598–1599 another refractory eclipse led him to a fourth inequality—the so-called annual equation with a period of a solar year.

Tycho's theory was put into its finished form by Longomontanus in 1601 and was published in the *Progymnasmata*. In it the first inequality (4°58′27″) was represented by a double epicycle, while the second appeared in the form of a hypocycle by means of which the center of the deferent was made to pass through the earth twice a month at syzygies and to reach its greatest distance from the earth at quadratures. The third inequality (40′30″) was accounted for by letting the center of the large epicycle librate on the deferent in the period of half a synodic revolution. Since these mechanisms left no room for the fourth inequality, Longomontanus introduced it—only partially, and to Tycho's expressed displeasure—by dispensing with the anomalistic component of the equation of time.

After the death of Frederick II, 4 April 1588, Tycho gradually lost the favor he had enjoyed at court. His own personality had much to do with this. He was arrogant, haughty with members of the royal family, neglectful of the welfare of the tenants on Hven, and careless in the maintenance of the public buildings on his fiefs. Although Hven had been conferred on him for life and he had some inherited wealth, the maintenance of his buildings and instruments required additional funds. Young King Christian IV, after gaining majority, did not seem to find that the astronomical work warranted the large expenditures. A quarrel with his former pupil Gellius Sascerides, who was engaged to his daughter Magdalene, put Tycho in an unpleasant light and may have contributed to his desire to leave Denmark. Besides, he may have wanted more opportunity for intellectual inter-

course than he had on his island; and he may have hoped for patronage from Emperor Rudolph II, of whose interest in alchemy and astronomy he must have been aware through his correspondence with Hagecius and with Vice-Chancellor Curtius, who had written describing Clavius' method of dividing instruments, which was similar to Vernier's later, more practical one.

After 15 March 1597, the date of the last observation at Hven, Tycho's instruments, printing press, chemical apparatus, and portable possessions were transported to his house in Copenhagen; the mural quadrant and three other large instruments were left behind. Little is known of Tycho's activities in Copenhagen. Early in June he sailed for Rostock with his instruments, press, and other belongings, as well as his family and entourage, including Tengnagel, who had come to Hven in 1595.

On 10 June 1597 the Roskilde prebend was conferred on another. Tycho made an unsuccessful attempt at reconciliation with Christian IV and in October, at the invitation of Heinrich Rantzov, took up residence in the castle at Wandsbeck, near Hamburg. There he continued his efforts to have the king permanently endow Uraniborg. Tycho began observing again 21 October, using only a radius until February 1598, when he got some of his better instruments together. He observed the solar eclipse of 25 February 1598, and later he received records of observations by others and information that it had been observed from beginning to end at Hven. He observed two lunar eclipses and some meridian altitudes but concentrated on the planets. He was assisted by the mathematician Johannes Müller, from Brandenburg, who had visited Hven in 1596 and whom the electress of Brandenburg had asked Tycho to train in chemistry and the preparation of medicines. Among visitors at Wandsbeck was the astronomer David Fabricius.

Tycho now completed the *Mechanica* and dedicated it to Emperor Rudolph II. Excellent woodcuts accompany Tycho's descriptions of his globe and of each of his instruments and its use. Also included are descriptions of Hven and its buildings, the instrument sights and the method of dividing by transversals, and a brief autobiography. From Wandsbeck he distributed a large number of manuscript copies of his star catalog, also dedicated to Rudolph.

Tycho's eldest son brought the emperor the catalog, the *Mechanica,* and a letter expressing the hope that the astronomer could complete his work under the emperor. At the same time Tycho sent bound copies of the catalog to scholars and influential people, including Christian IV, to whom he also addressed a respectful letter. On 24 March 1598 Tycho wrote to Longomontanus, inquiring about Wittich's books and manuscripts, and asked if Longomontanus had seen a recent publication by Ursus that Tycho did not consider deserving of refutation. He requested Longomontanus to join him at Wandsbeck, perhaps to continue work on the lunar theory.

Rantzov asked the elector of Cologne to use influence with the emperor and to try to interest Barwitz, the Austrian privy councillor, in Tycho's cause. Tycho himself wrote to Hagecius, hoping he would influence the emperor and the vice-chancellor. He also investigated the possibilities for settling in the Netherlands. Shortly after the middle of September 1598, having been assured that he would be welcome in Prague, Tycho left Wandsbeck with his sons, his students, and a few instruments. Longomontanus reached Wandsbeck after Tycho's departure but accompanied Tycho's ladies as far as Magdeburg. He returned to Denmark, however, and did not rejoin Tycho until January 1600. An epidemic of pestilence and dysentery in Prague caused Tycho to remain in Dresden. The first week in December, he moved to Wittenberg.

On Tycho's arrival in Prague in June 1599, he was escorted to the home of the late Vice-Chancellor Curtius and was soon granted an audience by the emperor, who arranged for him to receive financial support. Tycho had only a few instruments with him, but tried to display them in the same splendid setting they had had at Uraniborg. He never again got his instruments properly set up, nor did he make any important observations. He observed the end of a partial solar eclipse 22 July. He did not want to remain in the city of Prague and soon took up residence in the castle of Benatky, one of those offered him by the emperor. On a hill above the Iser about twenty-two miles northeast of Prague, Benatky had unobstructed views of the skies. It was small, but he altered it to fit his needs, building a laboratory and an observatory and planning to set up the instruments in separate rooms. He had difficulty, however, in obtaining the necessary funds. His family arrived, and he sent his eldest son for the four large instruments left at Hven. These, as well as the instruments and books that Tycho had brought with him as far as Magdeburg, were delayed in transit, the latter not arriving in Prague until November 1600.

Tycho's assistants in Bohemia included Longomontanus (January 1600–4 August 1601), David Fabricius (June 1601), Johannes Müller (March 1600–Spring 1601), and Melchior Joestelius, a mathematician from Wittenberg, who returned there before June 1600 but who was probably responsible for completing the solution of triangles by the prosthaphaeretic method that Tycho said he and Joestelius had done together. The assistant most important for the future of astronomy, Johannes Kepler, a firm believer in the heliocentric system, arrived at Benatky 3 February 1600. Longomontanus was working on Mars, but that planet was eventually turned over to Kepler. The relations between Tycho and Kepler were frequently strained.

In the summer of 1600 Tycho moved to Prague and set up his instruments in the Belvedere, a villa belonging to the emperor and close to the castle. Kepler, who had returned to Graz to settle his affairs and call for his family, arrived in Prague in October. Until April 1601 he was mostly engaged, at Tycho's behest, in a refutation of Ursus, although the latter had died in August 1600. Because of Tycho's death, the refutation remained unpublished until the nineteenth century. The emperor bought Curtius' house, and Tycho took possession of it in February 1601. The Kepler family moved there, too, although Kepler returned to Graz on business from April to August 1601. Kepler worked on the theories of Mercury, Venus, and Mars, and tried to persuade Tycho of the impossibility of describing the motion of the sun (or of the earth) as uniform in an eccentric circle.

Tycho died after an illness of eleven days, probably caused by prostate difficulties. He was buried with pomp on 4 November in the Tyn Church in the city's main square, his tomb marked by an upright slab bearing a life-size raised image of him with an inscription. On his deathbed, Tycho begged Kepler to complete the *Rudolphine Tables* as quickly as possible and expressed the wish that their theory be demonstrated in accordance with the Tychonic system.

Kepler did not obtain Tycho's instruments. They were stored beneath the Curtius house, and their subsequent fate is uncertain. The great globe was placed in the Round Tower in Copenhagen in the middle of the seventeenth century, having first been in Silesia, at Rosenborg Castle in Denmark, and at the University of Denmark. Some instruments must have been carried off during the Thirty Years' War, for they were discovered in a castle in Sweden in the twentieth century. Kepler had difficulties with Tengnagel and Tycho's other heirs over the records and publications. Giving him due credit, Kepler used the records of Tycho's observations, especially of Mars, to derive the laws of planetary motion, announcing the first two in his *Astronomia nova* (1609) and the third in the *Harmonices mundi libri V* (1619). He published Tycho's *Progymnasmata* (1602), already partly printed at Uraniborg, and the *Tabulae Rudolphinae* (1627), in conformity with a heliocentric system.

Thus Tycho's accurate observations of the positions of the sun, moon, stars, and planets provided the basis for refinements of the Copernican doctrine. Had the observations been as accurate as Tycho considered them, or less accurate than they actually were, the history of astronomy would have been different. But they provided the suitable degree of accuracy at the critical time. A discrepancy of 8' of arc between theory and observation led Kepler to his reformation of astronomy.

NOTES

1. *Opera omnia,* II, 342–343; V, 81. Dreyer (1890), p. 30, erred in describing the Hainzels.
2. *Dialogue Concerning the Two Chief World Systems,* Stillman Drake, trans. (Los Angeles, 1962), pp. 358 ff.
3. Pingré, *Cométographie,* I (1783), 511, says the comet was seen in Peru as early as 1 November.
4. *Opera omnia,* IV^2.
5. *En Elementisch oc Jordisch ASTROLOGIA,* 1591.
6. *Opera omnia,* II, 98.
7. *Ibid.,* IV, 42.
8. *Ibid.,* V, 111.
9. A broadside, item 3026 in Zinner, *Geschichte und Bibliographie* (Leipzig, 1941), is not included.

BIBLIOGRAPHY

There is no complete bibliography of the vast literature dealing with Tycho Brahe's life or work. Neither is there a printed list of his writings. Also lacking is a bibliography of works with references to him. Nevertheless, the following bibliography is selective.

The impact of Tycho's work must be studied in the writings, both printed and MS, of his contemporaries and immediate followers. Works by and about Kepler, including the recent ones, are of particular importance, but the writings of less important seventeenth-century men also give evidence of the influence of Tycho in Europe and the East. In honor of the 300th anniversary of Tycho's death (1901) and the 400th anniversary of his birth (1946) much was written, both scholarly and popular.

I. ORIGINAL WORKS. Tycho's writings were collected as *Tychonis Brahe Dani Opera omnia,* J. L. E. Dreyer, ed., 15 vols. (Copenhagen, 1913–1929), which includes charts, diagrams, facsimiles, maps, portraits, and tables, and is copiously annotated.[9]

His books on the nova of 1572 are *De nova et nullius aevi memoria prius visa stella* . . . (Copenhagen, 1573; facs. ed., 1901), trans. into Danish by Otto Gelsted as *Tyge Brahe: Den ny stjerne (1572)* . . . (Lemvig, 1923), and partially trans. into English by John H. Walden in Harlow Shapley and Helen E. Howarth, eds., *A Source Book in Astronomy* (New York–London, 1929), pp. 13–19; and *Astronomiae instauratae progymnasmata* . . . (Prague, 1602; Frankfurt, 1610). A number of seventeenth-century tracts summarized or translated excerpts from the *Progymnasmata,* the most important work on the 1572 nova.

Tycho's book on the comet of 1577 is *De mundi aetherei recentioribus phaenomenis* . . . (Uraniborg, 1588; Prague, 1603; Frankfurt, 1610). Part of ch. 8 is trans. in Marie Boas and A. Rupert Hall, "Tycho Brahe's System of the World," in *Occasional Notes of the Royal Astronomical Society,* **3,** no. 21 (1959), 252–263 (trans. on pp. 257–263).

His letters have been brought together by Dreyer in the *Opera omnia* and in *Tychonis Brahe Dani Epistolarum astronomicarum* . . . (Uraniborg, 1596; Nuremberg, 1601; Frankfurt, 1610); *Tychonis Brahei et ad eum doctorum virorum epistolae* . . ., F. R. Friis, ed., 2 vols. (Copenhagen, 1876–1909); and Wilhelm Norlind, *Ur Tycho Brahes brevväxling, från Latinet* (Lund, 1926); 23 letters trans. into Swedish, with notes, and "Några Anteckningar till Tycho Brahes brevväxling," in *Nordisk astronomisk tidsskrift* (1956), no. 2, 51–55.

Tycho's book on his instruments is *Astronomiae instauratae mechanica* (Wandsbeck, 1598; Nuremberg, 1602), also in facsimile of 1598 ed., B. Hasselberg, ed. (Stockholm, 1901); the 1598 ed. was printed in Rantzov's castle near Hamburg on Tycho's press by Philip de Ohr. For trans., see Hans Raeder, Elis Strömgren, and Bengt Strömgren, eds. and trans., *Tycho Brahe's Description of His Instruments and Scientific Work* . . . (Copenhagen, 1946).

His tables are in *Historia coelestis* . . ., Lucius Barrettus (pseud. of Albert Curtz), ed. (Augsburg, 1666). Kepler's *Tabulae Rudolphinae* . . . (Ulm, 1627) are based on Tycho's observations and the Copernican–Keplerian system of the universe.

The MS material has been thoroughly used by Dreyer in his biography and in the *Opera omnia,* and MSS for which he gives bibliographical details will not be described here. For his biography Norlind has examined MS sources; see also his "On Some Manuscripts Concerning Tycho Brahe," in *The Observatory,* **78,** no. 903 (1958), 73–75. It is impossible to list here MSS in which Tycho is discussed, e.g., Gregoriana (Rome) 530, ff. 208–211, a letter dated 26 January 1601 from Magini in Mantua to Clavius in Rome, which speaks of Tycho's book on the star of 1572; or Ambrosiana (Milan) D 246 inf. 83r, the fragment of a letter from Padua in 1592 that speaks of Tycho and Galileo, who had just begun his lectures there. Nor need the location and description of the presentation copies of the *Mechanica* and the MS copies of the catalog of stars be listed.

Letter no. 102 (*Opera omnia,* XIV, 68) is at The Historical Society of Pennsylvania, Philadelphia, as are an undated autograph and an autograph dated 10 August 1594. Presumably the letter from Tycho to T. Saville (1 December 1590) cited in the British Museum's Sloane Collection catalog of 1782 is the same as the museum's Harleian 6995, 40 used by Dreyer (*Opera omnia,* VII, 283–285). The same catalog of the Sloane Collection lists an MS of the *De mundi aetherei* . . . . Two letters in the hand of a sixteenth-century scribe are in the possession of the author: Tycho to Caspar Peucer, 13 September 1588, 23 leaves (*Opera omnia,* VII, 127–141), and Caspar Peucer to Tycho, 10 May 1589, 9 leaves (*Opera omnia,* VII, 184–191).

An interesting summary (from Padua) of Tycho's work, *Epitome de restitutione motuum solis ac lunae, et de nova stella anni 1572,* is preserved in Venice (Marciana lat. Cl. VIII, Cod. XXXVII, 3493). In Milan (Ambrosiana D 246 inf. 84r–87v) there are part of the *Mechanica* and epigrams to Scaliger.

II. SECONDARY LITERATURE. The best single treatment of Tycho's life and work is J. L. E. Dreyer, *Tycho Brahe, a Picture of Scientific Life and Work in the Sixteenth Century* (Edinburgh, 1890; repr. New York, 1963). This is based on and cites the sources available in 1890, and forms the basis for this article. Except for Tycho's major publications, works cited by Dreyer are not in this bibliography, although they include much material to which the reader may want to refer, such as Gassendi's biography of Tycho (1654) and Tycho's *Opera omnia* (1648), which presents the *Progymnasmata* and *De mundi aetherei* rather than the complete works. More recent biographies are John Allyne Gade, *The Life and Times of Tycho Brahe* (Princeton, 1947), with a bibliography that, while not selective, includes some useful items that appeared after Dreyer's work; and Wilhelm Norlind, *Tycho Brahe. Mannen och verket. Efter Gassendi overs. med kommentar* (Lund, 1951); *Tycho Brahe* (Stockholm, 1963); and *Tycho Brahe. En biografi. Med nya bidrag belysande hans liv och verk* (Lund, in press), with a summary in German.

The island of Hven is discussed in the anonymous "Stjerneborg," in *Nordisk astronomisk tidsskrift,* n.s. **20,** no. 3 (1939), 79–99; Francis Beckett and Charles Christensen, *Uraniborg og Stjaerneborg* (Copenhagen–London, 1921), text in Danish, summary and explanation of plates in English, title also given in English: *Tycho Brahe's Uraniborg and Stjerneborg on the Island of Hveen;* C. L. V. Charlier, *Utgräfningarna af Tycho Brahes observatorier på ön Hven sommaren 1901,* which is *Acta universitatis Lundensis. Lunds universitets årsskrift,* **37,** afdeln. 2, no. 8 (Lund, 1901); John Christianson, "The Celestial Palace of Tycho Brahe," in *Scientific American,* **204,** no. 2 (1961), 118–128; Charles D. Humberd, "Tycho Brahe's Island," in *Popular Astronomy,* **45** (1937), 118–125, which reproduces the Cologne map of 1586 and translates the Latin explanations inserted on the map and its back; William Lengert, *Tycho Brahe-tryck* (Malmö, 1940); N. A. Møller Nicolaisen, "Et Tycho Brahe-minde paa Hven," in *Nordisk astronomisk tidsskrift,* n.s. **11,** no. 3 (1930), 122–128; "Tycho Brahes mølledaemning paa Hven," *ibid.,* no. 4, 173–175; "Tycho Brahes papirmølle," *ibid.,* n.s. **14,** no. 3 (1933), 85–95; and *Tycho Brahes papirmølle paa Hven. Udgravningen 1933–34 og forsøg til rekonstruktion . . .* (Copenhagen, 1946); Harald Mortensen, "Johannes Mejers kort over øen Hven," in *Skåne årsbok* (1925), pp. 9–16; and "Et Tycho Brahe-minde paa Hven," in *Nordisk astronomisk tidsskrift,* n.s. **11,** no. 4 (1930), 172–173; and Lauritz Nielsen, *Tycho Brahes bogtrykkeri. En bibliografisk-boghistorisk undersøgelse* (Copenhagen, 1946).

Works treating other subjects are Joseph Ashbrook, "Tycho Brahe's Nose," in the column "Astronomical Scrapbook," in *Sky and Telescope,* **29,** no. 6 (1965), 353, 358; F. Burckhardt, *Zur Erinnerung an Tycho Brahe 1546–1601 . . .* (Basel, 1901); John Christianson, "Tycho Brahe at the University of Copenhagen, 1559–1562," in *Isis,* **58**

(1967), 198–203; and "Tycho Brahe's Cosmology From the 'Astrologia' of 1591," *ibid.,* **59** (1968), 312–318; J. L. E. Dreyer, "Note on Tycho Brahe's Opinion About the Solar Parallax," in *Monthly Notices of the Royal Astronomical Society,* **71,** no. 1 (1910), 74–76; "The Place of Tycho Brahe in the History of Astronomy," in *Scientia,* **25,** no. 83–3 (Mar. 1919), 177–185; and "On Tycho Brahe's Manual of Trigonometry," in *The Observatory,* no. 498 (Mar. 1916), 127–131; Antonio Favaro, "Ticone Brahe e la corte di Toscana," in *Archivio storico italiano,* 5th series, **3** (1889); Edvard Gotfredsen, "Tycho Brahes sidste sygdom og død" ("Tycho Brahe's Last Disease and Death"), in *Københavns Universitets medicinsk-historiske museum: Årsberetning 1955–1956;* Poul Hauberg, "Tycho Brahes opskrifter paa Laegemidler," in *Dansk tidsskrift for farmaci,* **1,** no. 7, 205–212; C. Doris Hellman, "Was Tycho Brahe as Influential as He Thought?," in *British Journal for the History of Science,* **1,** pt. 4, no. 4 (Dec. 1963), 295–324; Flora Kleinschnitzová, "Ex Bibliotheca Tychoniana Collegii Soc. Jesu Pragae ad S. Clementem," in *Nordisk tidskrift för bok- och biblioteksväsen,* **20** (1933), 73–97; Wilhelm Krebs, "Facsimile einer eigenhändigen Zeichnung Tycho's de Brahe von dem grossen Kometen 1577," in *Das Weltall. Illustrierte Zeitschrift für Astronomie und verwandte Gebiete,* **12** (1911), 52–53; Martha List, *Des handschriftliche Nachlass der Astronomen Johannes Kepler und Tycho Brahe* (Munich, 1961); Knud Lundmark, "Tycho Brahe och astrofysiken," in *Nordisk astronomisk tidsskrift,* n.s. **11,** no. 3 (1930), 89–112; and "Om Tycho Brahes liv och gärning," in *Cassiopeia* (1945), 14–47; N. A. Møller Nicolaisen, "Nicholai Raimarus Ursus contra Tycho Brahe," *ibid.* (1942), 81–91; Harald Mortensen, "Portraeter af Tycho Brahe," *ibid.* (1946), 52–77; "Tycho Brahe i Wandsbek," in *Astronomiska sällskapet Tycho Brahe ärsbok* (1945), pp. 94–98; and "Tychoniana," in *Cassiopeia* (1948), 21–27; Wilhelm Norlind, "Tycho Brahe och Thaddaeus Hagecius: Ur en brevväxling," *ibid.* (1939), 122–130; "A Hitherto Unpublished Letter From Tycho Brahe to Christopher Clavius," in *Observatory,* **74** (1954), 20–23; and "Tycho-Brahé et ses rapports avec l'Italie," C. Cardot, trans., in *Scientia,* **49** (1955), 47–61; Eiler Nystrøm, "Tyge Brahes Brud med Faedrelandet," in *Festskrift til Kristian Erslev, dem 28. Decbr. 1927 . . . ,* pp. 291–320; and *Epistolae et acta ad vitam Tychonis Brahe pertinentia* (Copenhagen, 1928); Wilhelm Prandtl, "Die Bibliothek des Tycho Brahe," in *Philobiblon; eine Zeitschrift für Bücherliebhaber,* **5,** no. 8 (1932), 291–300, no. 9, 321–330; Hans Raeder, "Tycho Brahe og hans korrespondenter," in *Edda,* **27** (1927), 250–264; Edward Rosen, "Kepler's Defense of Tycho Brahe Against Ursus," in *Popular Astronomy,* **54,** no. 8 (1946), 1–8; Henrik Sandblad, "En Tycho Brahenotis," in *Lychnos* (1937), 366–368, concerning the duel in which Tycho lost part of his nose; Aydin Sayili, "Islam and the Rise of Seventeenth Century Science," in *Belleten* (Ankara), **22,** no. 87 (July 1958), 353–368; and "Tycho Brahe Sistemi Hakkinda XVII. Asir Başlarina ait Farça Bir Yazma. An Early Seventeenth Century Persian Manuscript on the Tychonic System," in *Anatolia revue annuelle de l'Institut d'Archéologie de l'Université d'Ankara,* **3** (1958),

79-87; Ottomar Schiller, "Tycho Brahe à Prague," in *Archeion,* **22,** no. 4 (12 Feb. 1941), 372-375; H. C. F. G. Schjellerup, "Tycho Brahes Original-Observationer, benyttede til Banebestemmelse af Cometen 1580," in *Det Kongelige Danske Videnskabernes selskab. Skrifter. 5 Raekke, Naturvidenskabelig og Matematisk Afdeling.* IV (1856-1859), pp. 1-39; Christine Schofield, "The Geo-heliocentric Mathematical Hypothesis in Sixteenth Century Planetary Theory," in *British Journal for the History of Science,* **2** (1965), 291-296; Harold Spencer Jones, "Tycho Brahe (1546-1601)," in *Nature,* **158** (1946), 856-861; E. S., "Tycho Brahes Immatrikulation ved Universitetet i Leipzig vinterhalvaaret 1561-62," in *Nordisk astronomisk tidsskrift,* n.s. **9,** no. 2 (1928), 41-42; Elis Strömgren, "Tycho Brahes sekstanter," *ibid.,* n.s. **14,** no. 2 (1933), 69-75; F. J. Studnička, ed., *Prager Tychoniana* (Prague, 1901); and, as author, *Bericht über die astrologischen Studien des Reformators der beobachtenden Astronomie Tycho Brahe. . . .* (Prague, 1901); Sevim Tekeli, "Nasirüddin, Takiyüddin ve sesi" ("The Comparison Instruments of Taqi al Din and Tycho Brahe"), in *Ankara Üniversitesi, Coğrafya Fakültesi Dergisi,* **16** (1958), 301-393; and "Solar Parameters and Certain Observational Methods of Taqî al Dîn and Tycho Brahe," in *Proceedings of the 10th International Congress of the History of Science,* I (Paris, 1964), 623-626; and Victor E. Thoren, "Tycho Brahe on the Lunar Theory," doctoral dissertation (Indiana Univ., 1965); "Tycho and Kepler on the Lunar Theory," in *Publications of the Astronomical Society of the Pacific,* **79,** no. 470 (Oct. 1967), 482-489; "An Early Instance of Deductive Discovery: Tycho Brahe's Lunar Theory," in *Isis,* **58** (1967), 19-36; and "Tycho Brahe's Discovery of the Variation," in *Centaurus,* **12,** no. 3 (1967), 151-166.

Dr. Thoren kindly advised on the description of Tycho's lunar theory and helped in the final draft of that section.

C. DORIS HELLMAN

BRAHMADEVA (*fl. ca.* 1092), *astronomy.*

Brahmadeva was the son of Candrabudha (or Śrīcandra, or Candrabhaṭṭa), a Brāhmaṇa of Mathurā (or Madhurā). The epoch date of his only work, the *Karaṇaprakāśa,* is Thursday, 11 March 1092. The work contains nine chapters:

1. On the mean longitudes of the planets.
2. On *tithis* and so on.
3. On the true longitudes of the star-planets.
4. On the three problems relating to diurnal motion.
5. On lunar eclipses.
6. On solar eclipses.
7. On heliacal risings and settings.
8. On the lunar crescent.
9. On planetary conjunctions and latitudes.

The work is based on the *Āryabhaṭīya* of Āryabhaṭa I, with modifications proposed by Lalla (see Essay V).

It was particularly popular in Madras, Mysore, and Mahārāṣṭra.

There are commentaries on the *Karaṇaprakāśa* by Amareśa in the Kannada language (*Karṇāṭabhāṣā-vyākhyāna*); by Brahmaśarman (*Vyākhyā*); by Dāmodara, the pupil of Padmanābha (*fl. ca.* 1575) (*Vṛtti*); by Govinda, the son of Viśvanātha Tāmbe (*Vivṛtti*); by Sampatkumāra (*Vyākhyā*); and by Śrīnivāsa Yajvan (*Prabhā, ca.* 1275). There also exist an *Udāharaṇa,* once (probably erroneously) ascribed to Viśvanātha of Benares (*fl.* 1612-1630), and a *Sadvāsanā* by Sudhākara Dvivedin, who published the *Karaṇaprakāśa* along with this commentary as the twenty-third work in the Chowkhambā Sanskrit Series (Benares, 1899).

BIBLIOGRAPHY

Additional works concerning Brahmadeva are Ś. B. Dīkṣita, *Bhāratīya Jyotiḥśāstra* (Poona, 1896; repr. Poona, 1931), pp. 240-243; and Sudhākara Dvivedin, *Gaṇaka-taraṅgiṇī* (Benares, 1933; repr. from *The Pandit,* n.s. **14** [1892]), pp. 31-33.

DAVID PINGREE

BRAHMAGUPTA (*b.* 598; *d.* after 665), *astronomy.*

Brahmagupta was the son of Jiṣṇugupta; the names compounded with *-gupta* may indicate membership in the Vaiśya caste. At the age of thirty, he composed the *Brāhmasphuṭasiddhānta;* the reigning king was Vyāghramukha of the Cāpavaṃśa of the Gurjaras, and we know from the account of the Chinese pilgrim Hiuan-tsang (641) that the capital of the Gurjaras was Bhillamāla (modern Bhinmal, near Mt. Abu in Rajasthan). In the colophon of chapter 24 of the *Brāhmasphuṭasiddhānta* and in Pṛthūdakasvāmin's commentary on the *Khaṇḍakhādyaka,* Brahmagupta's second work, he is called Bhillamālācārya—the teacher from Bhillamāla. The *Khaṇḍakhādyaka* uses as its epoch Sunday, 15 March 665. Both of these treatises were studied primarily in Rajasthan, Gujarat, Madhya Pradesh, Uttar Pradesh, Bihar, Nepal, Panjab, and Kashmir.

The *Brāhmasphuṭasiddhānta,* whose planetary parameters are mainly derived from the *Paitāma-hasiddhānta* of the *Viṣṇudharmottarapurāṇa* (see Essays IV and XII), contains twenty-four chapters, with the twenty-fifth appended in some manuscripts.

1. On the mean longitudes of the planets.
2. On the true longitudes of the planets.
3. On the three problems relating to diurnal motion.
4. On lunar eclipses.
5. On solar eclipses.
6. On heliacal risings and settings.

7. On the lunar crescent.
8. On the lunar "shadow."
9. On planetary conjunctions.
10. On conjunctions of the planets with stars. (These ten chapters form the *Daśādhyāyī*, which sometimes is found independently in manuscripts.)
11. Examination of previous treatises on astronomy.
12. On mathematics.
13. Additions to chapter 1.
14. Additions to chapter 2.
15. Additions to chapter 3.
16. Additions to chapters 4 and 5.
17. Additions to chapter 7.
18. On algebra.
19. On the gnomon.
20. On meters.
21. On the sphere.
22. On instruments.
23. On measurements.
24. Summary of contents.
25. Versified tables.

A commentary (*Vāsanābhāṣya*) on the *Brāhmasphuṭasiddhānta* was written by Pṛthūdakasvāmin of Kurukṣetra (*fl.* 864); unfortunately, it is but imperfectly preserved in the few surviving manuscripts. There are also an anonymous commentary (*Ṭīkā*) on the *Daśādhyāyī* in Vishveshvarananda Vedic Research Institute 2363, and another (*Ṭīkā*) on chapter 18 in two manuscripts (one in Calcutta, one in London). A translation of chapters 12 and 18 was presented by H. T. Colebrooke in *Algebra, With Arithmetic and Mensuration: From the Sanscrit of Brahmegupta and Bháscara* (London, 1817); the preface is reprinted in Colebrooke's *Miscellaneous Essays,* II (Madras, 1872), 417–531. The whole text, with his own Sanskrit commentary, was edited by Sudhākara Dvivedin (Benares, 1902; reprinted from *The Pandit,* n.s. **23** [1901] and **24** [1902]). It was published again by Ram Swarup Sharma in four volumes (New Delhi, 1966): Volume I contains a sometimes useful introduction by Satya Prakash (pp. 1–344) and the text based on five of some fifteen known manuscripts; Volume II, chapters 1–9 with fragments of Pṛthūdakasvāmin's commentary on chapters 1–3, excerpts from Sudhākara Dvivedin's commentary, a new Sanskrit commentary (*Vijñānabhāṣya*), and a Hindi explanation; Volume III, chapters 10–16 with the same commentaries, save that, in this volume, the available portions of Pṛthūdakasvāmin's *Vāsanābhāṣya* are strangely missing; and Volume IV, chapters 17–25 as in Volume III, but with Pṛthūdakasvāmin's commentary on chapter 21 added as an appendix.

The *Khaṇḍakhādyaka* is the best-known treatise on

the *ārddharātrika* system (see Essay VI). It contains eight chapters:
1. On computing the *tithis* and *nakṣatras.*
2. On the longitudes of the planets.
3. On the three problems relating to diurnal motion.
4. On lunar eclipses.
5. On solar eclipses.
6. On heliacal risings and settings.
7. On the lunar crescent.
8. On planetary conjunctions.

There also exists an appendix (*Uttarakhaṇḍakhādyaka*). If one follows Utpala (*fl.* 966), it contained three chapters:
1. On the conjunctions of the planets with the stars.
2. On the *pātas* of the sun and moon.
3. On the projection of eclipses.

But the (incomplete) manuscript tradition of Pṛthūdakasvāmin's version provides only one chapter in the *Uttarakhaṇḍakhādyaka*—one in which new methods of approximation are presented; and Āmarāja (*fl.* 1180) cites various verses from the *Uttara* which are found in neither Pṛthūdakasvāmin nor Utpala. The whole problem of the extent and authorship of the *Uttarakhaṇḍakhādyaka* needs to be extensively investigated.

Commentaries have been written on the *Khaṇḍakhādyaka* by the following scholars: Lalla; Pṛthūdakasvāmin (*Vivaraṇa,* 864); Utpala (*Vivṛti,* 966); Someśvara (1040); Āmarāja (*Vāsanābhāṣya,* 1180); Śrīdatta, the son of Nageśvara Miśra Mahopādhyāya (*Ṭīkā*); and Yāmaṭa (*Ṭīkā*); as well as a number of anonymous *ṭīkās* and *udāharaṇas.* No manuscripts of the commentaries of Lalla and of Someśvara have yet been identified. Dīkṣita also refers to a *ṭīkā* by one Varuṇa. The version and commentary of Āmarāja was edited by Babua Miśra (Calcutta, 1925). The recension and commentary of Pṛthūdakasvāmin were edited by P. C. Sengupta (Calcutta, 1941); an appendix contains additional verses from the version of Utpala. Sengupta has also translated Pṛthūdakasvāmin's version into English (Calcutta, 1934).

BIBLIOGRAPHY

Virtually every paper on every aspect of Indian astronomy discusses Brahmagupta. Listed here are only those which deal especially with his works. For the others, the reader is referred to David Pingree, *A Census of the Exact Sciences in Sanskrit* (Philadelphia, 1969). It should also be noted that the early 'Abbāsid *Zīj al-Arkand* and *Zīj al-Sindhind* have been said to be versions, respectively, of the *Khaṇḍakhādyaka* and of the *Brāhmasphuṭasiddhānta;*

but in neither case is a direct influence discernible. See David Pingree, "The Fragments of the Works of Yaʿqūb ibn Ṭāriq," in *Journal of Near Eastern Studies,* **27** (1968), 97–125; and E. S. Kennedy and David Pingree, *The Kitab ʿilal al-zījāt of al-Hāshimī.* Both of Brahmagupta's works were known in Sanskrit to al-Bīrūnī; he cites them extensively, especially in *India* and in *Al-Qānūn al-Masʿūdī.* In his catalog of his own works, D. J. Boilot, ed., in *Mélanges de l'Institut Dominicain d'études Orientales du Caire,* **2** (1955), 161–256, al-Bīrūnī includes *Translation of What Is in the Brahmasiddhānta of the Method of Calculation* (*RG* 40).

Additional literature on Brahmagupta includes B. Datta, "On the Supposed Indebtedness of Brahmagupta to *Chiu-chang Suan-shu,*" in *Bulletin of the Calcutta Mathematical Society,* **22** (1930), 39–51; Ś. B. Dīkṣita, *Bhāratīya Jyotiḥśāstra* (Poona, 1931; repr. of Poona, 1896), pp. 216–227; Sudhākara Dvivedin, *Gaṇakataraṅgiṇī* (Benares, 1933; repr. from *The Pandit,* n.s. **14** [1892]), pp. 18–19; P. C. Sengupta, "Brahmagupta on Interpolation," in *Bulletin of the Calcutta Mathematical Society,* **23** (1931), 125–128; M. Simon, "Zu Brahmegupta diophantischen Gleichungen zweiten Grades," in *Archiv der Mathematik und Physik,* **20** (1913), 280–281; G. Thibaut, *Astronomie, Astrologie und Mathematik, Grundriss der indo-arischen Philologie und Altertumskunde,* III, pt. 9 (Strasbourg, 1899), 58–59; and H. Weissenborn, "Das Trapez bei Euclid, Heron und Brahmagupta," in *Abhandlungen zur Geschichte der Mathematik,* **12** (1879), 167–184.

Reference should also be made to the solar and lunar tables based on the *Brāhmasphuṭasiddhānta* that were published by R. Sewell in *Epigraphia Indica,* **17** (1923–1924), 123–187, 205–290.

DAVID PINGREE

BRAIKENRIDGE (BRAKENRIDGE), WILLIAM (*b.* ca. 1700; *d.* 30 July 1762), *mathematics.*

The precise date and the place of Braikenridge's birth are not known. He lived in a period of intense mathematical activity, one that abounded in illustrious mathematicians: the Bernoullis, Maclaurin, and Brook Taylor, to name but a few. Newton was still in his prime, but his interest in mathematics had begun to wane (no doubt as a result of his important duties as master of the Mint).

The main lines of development in mathematics at this time were the extension and systematization of the calculus, the further study of the theory of equations, and a revival of interest in geometry. It was in the last of these that Braikenridge excelled, and it is upon his *Exercitatio geometrica de descriptione linearum curvarum* (1733) that his reputation mainly rests.

This work is divided into three parts, and its scope is indicated by their titles: "De descriptione curvarum primi generis seu linearum ordinis secundi," "De descriptione linearum cujuscunque ordinis ope linearum ordinis inferioris," and "Ubi describuntur sectiones conicae ope plurium rectarum circa polos moventium."

The study of the properties of curves has always been an inexhaustible subject of speculation and research among geometers. Colin Maclaurin had already published his *Geometria organica* (1720), which contained an elegant investigation of curves of the second order by regarding them as generated by the intersection of lines and angles turning about fixed points, or poles. Many of Maclaurin's theorems were discovered independently by Braikenridge, notably the Braikenridge-Maclaurin theorem: If the sides of a polygon are restricted so that they pass through fixed points while all the vertices except one lie on fixed straight lines, the free vertex will describe a conic or a straight line. A general statement of this appeared in 1735 in the *Philosophical Transactions* (no. 436), and a dispute at once arose regarding priority. Braikenridge, in the Preface to the *Exercitatio,* maintained that as early as 1726, when he was living in Edinburgh, he had discovered many of the propositions contained in that work and had actually discussed some of them with his contemporaries, including Maclaurin. There followed a lively correspondence between the two men which, however, it would be profitless to discuss here.

About the middle of the century, interest in the geometry of curves began to languish. It was revived, however, when a group of French mathematicians—Monge, Carnot, Poncelet—by employing projective methods, gave the study a fresh impetus.

Braikenridge was a noted theologian, and for many years he was rector of St. Michael's, Bassishaw, London. On 6 February 1752 he was elected fellow of the Royal Society of Antiquaries, and on 9 November of the same year he became a fellow of the Royal Society.

Braikenridge contributed a number of papers to the *Philosophical Transactions.* Their titles reflect the wide range of his interests: "A General Method of Describing Curves, by the Intersection of Right Lines, Moving About Points in a Given Plane"; "A Letter . . . Concerning the Number of Inhabitants Within the London Bills of Mortality"; "A Letter . . . Concerning the Method of Constructing a Table for the Probabilities of Life in London"; "A Letter . . . Concerning the Number of People in England"; "A Letter . . . Concerning the Present Increase of the People in Britain and Ireland"; "A Letter . . . Containing an Answer to the Account of the Numbers and Increase of the People of England by the Rev. Mr. Forster"; "A Letter Containing the Sections of a Solid, Hitherto not Considered by Geometers."

BIBLIOGRAPHY

Works concerning Braikenridge are Moritz Cantor, *Vorlesungen über Geschichte der Mathematik,* III (Leipzig, 1894–1898), 761–766, 773; and J. F. Montucla, *Histoire des mathématiques,* III (Paris, 1799–1802), 87.

J. F. SCOTT

BRAMER, BENJAMIN (*b.* Felsberg, Germany, *ca.* February 1588; *d.* Ziegenhain, Germany, 17 March 1652), *mathematics.*

After the death of his father in 1591, Bramer was taken as a foster son into the home of his sister and her husband, the court clockmaker Joost Bürgi, in Kassel. His brother-in-law tutored Bramer and awakened his passion for mathematics, which was later combined with his architectural abilities. When Bürgi left Kassel in 1604, Bramer accompanied him to the imperial court at Prague; he returned to Kassel in 1609. In 1612 Landgrave Moritz of Hesse-Kassel appointed Bramer the master builder of the court in Marburg, and he was naturalized there on 16 February 1625. (Since 1620 he had been directing the construction of fortifications at the castle and in the town.) In the same year he was consultant to the count of Solms at the fortress of Rheinfels. From 1630 to 1634, Bramer was in charge of the fortifications in Kassel, and in November 1635 he was appointed princely master builder and treasurer of the important Hessian fortress of Ziegenhain.

In his first publication on the calculation of sines (1614), Bramer's talents are evident. In a work on the vacuum (1617), we can see his wide-ranging interests, but no particular field of concentration. The problem of empty space, which had been under active investigation since classical times, was of special topical interest in the seventeenth century. On this matter Bramer held the views of Tommaso Campanella, the contemporary and follower of Galileo.

The problem of central perspective obtained by means of instruments, which had been taken up by Leone Battista Alberti in 1435 and for which instruments had been designed by Albrecht Dürer in 1525 and by Bürgi in 1604, was further developed by Bramer in 1630 by means of a device that enabled one to draw accurate geometrical perspectives true to nature. He described his method in his *Trigonometria planorum* (1617). In 1651 Bramer contributed to the completion of the instruments for triangulation with the semicirculus: he used an inclined ruler, in order to determine simultaneously the sighted point and its inclination; the instrument, however, differed little from a similar one described by Leonhard Zubler in 1607. Another form of this instrument was mounted on a calibrated plate to determine angulation; Bramer used this for the solution of planar triangles.

We know very little of Bramer's architectural achievements. From advice he gave in 1618 to Count Christian von Waldeck, we know of a plan for construction of a new church for the city of Wildungen. Although the project was not undertaken because of the Thirty Years' War, it is of special importance because it is one of the earliest plans to introduce central church construction into Protestant German church architecture.

BIBLIOGRAPHY

I. ORIGINAL WORKS. *Problema, wie aus bekannt gegebenem sinu eines Grades, Minuten oder Sekunden alle folgenden sinus aufs leichteste zu finden und der canon sinuum zu absolviren sei* (Marburg, 1614); *Beschreibung und Unterricht, wie allerlei Teilungen zu den mathematischen Instrumenten zu verfertigen, neben dem Gebrauch eines neuen Proportional-Instrumentes* (Marburg, 1615); *Bericht und Gebrauch eines Proportional-Lineals, neben kurzem Unterricht eines Parallel-Instrumentes* (Marburg, 1617); *Kurze Meldung vom Vacuo oder leerem Orte, neben anderen wunderbaren und subtilen Quaestionen, desgleichen Nic. Cusani Dialogus von Waag und Gewicht* (Marburg, 1617); *Trigonometria planorum mechanica oder Unterricht und Beschreibung eines neuen und sehr bequemen geometrischen Instrumentes zu allerhand Abmessung* (Marburg, 1617); *Etliche geometrische Quaestiones, so mehrerteils bisher nicht üblich gewesen. Solviert und beschrieben* (Marburg, 1618); *Beschreibung eines sehr leichten Perspektiv- und Grundreissenden Instrumentes auf einem Stande: auf Joh. Faulhabers, Ingenieurs zu Ulm, weitere Continuation seines mathematischen Kunstspiegels geordnet* (Kassel, 1630); *Appollonius Cattus oder Kern der ganzen Geometrie,* 3 vols. (Kassel, 1634–1684); *Benjamin Brameri Bericht zu Meister Jobsten seligen geometrischen Triangularinstrument* (Kassel, 1648); *Kurzer Bericht zu einem Semicirculo, damit in allen Triangeln in einer Observation nicht allein die drei latera, sondern auch die drei Winkel eines Triangels zu finden* (Augsburg, 1651); *Von Wasserwerken* (unpub. MS Math. 4°27), National Library, Kassel.

II. SECONDARY LITERATURE. Johann Heinrich Zedler, *Universal-Lexikon,* IV (Halle-Leipzig, 1733), 997; Christian Gottlieb Jöcher, *Allgemeines Gelehrten-Lexikon,* I (Leipzig, 1750), 1328; Friedrich Wilhelm Strieder, *Grundlage zu einer hessischen Gelehrten- und Schriftstellergeschichte,* I (Göttingen, 1781), 521 ff.; *Nouvelles annales de mathématiques (Bulletin de bibliographie)* (Paris, 1858), 75 ff.; Wolfgang Medding, "Das Projekt einer Zentralkirche des hessischen Hofbaumeisters Benjamin Bramer", in *Hessenland, Heimatzeitschrift für Kurhessen,* **49** (Marburg, 1938), 82 ff.; Karl Justi, "Das Marburger Schloss," *Veröffentlichungen der Historischen Kommission für Hessen und Waldeck,* XXI (Marburg, 1942), 94, 98, 105.

PAUL A. KIRCHVOGEL

BRANDE, WILLIAM THOMAS (*b*. London, England, 11 January 1788; *d*. London, 11 February 1866), *chemistry*.

Brande's father was proprietor of the Brande Pharmacy in Arlington Street, London (Friedrich Accum, one of the pioneers of coal-gas lighting, became his assistant in 1793). The Brandes were apothecaries to George III, and operated shops in both London and Hannover. His family moved to Chiswick when he was about fourteen, and Brande became acquainted with Charles Hatchett, who was keenly interested in chemistry and mineralogy. Hatchett allowed him to help in his laboratory and encouraged him to study the classification of rocks and ores. The mineralogical series with which Brande later illustrated his lectures at the Royal Institution originated in specimens given to him by Hatchett.

Brande was a pupil at the Anatomical School in Windmill Street and began to study chemistry at St. George's Hospital (*ca*. 1804). At about this time he seems to have been befriended by Sir Everard Home, who, as one of the trustees of the Hunterian collection at the Royal College of Surgeons, later entrusted Brande with the analysis of calculi selected from the collection. Brande submitted the report, with observations by Home, to the Royal Society (*Philosophical Transactions*, **98** [1808], 223–243) and was elected a fellow in 1809.

It appears that quite early in life Brande became acquainted with Davy and attended his lectures at the Royal Institution. In 1808 he himself began lecturing on chemistry and pharmacy at London medical schools. In 1812 he became superintendent of chemical operations at Apothecaries' Hall, and the following year succeeded Davy as professor of chemistry at the Royal Institution, in which post he remained until 1852. When Faraday returned from Europe in 1815, he began to assist Brande in the laboratory and, from 1824, as a lecturer. Thus the two men were associated for many years, both in teaching and chemical investigations and in editing the *Quarterly Journal of Science, Literature and the Arts,* published at the Royal Institution, to which they both made many contributions. In 1823 Brande was consulted by the government with a view to obtaining a more coherent metal for dies; his report, which led to improvements and economy at the Mint, led also to his appointment as superintendent of the dies department and, later, as chief officer of the coinage department.

Brande was an indefatigable lecturer and prolific writer, and published many papers on his investigations, but it is difficult to point to any that led to significant progress in chemistry. He was awarded the Copley Medal in 1813 for papers in which he showed, contrary to the prevailing belief, that alcohol was present in fermented liquors as such and not produced as a result of distillation; he also ascertained the alcohol content of many wines. In 1819 Brande examined a substance thought to be benzoic acid, but almost certainly naphthalene, then unknown, and carried out experiments which indicated that it contained no oxygen. He suggested that it was a binary compound of carbon and hydrogen, but carried out no analysis to confirm this or to determine the proportions. In the same year, in a paper read to the Royal Society on the inflammable gases from coal and oil, he inferred that there existed "no definite compound of carbon and hydrogen except that called olefiant gas" (*Philosophical Transactions*, **110** [1820], 11–28), although Dalton and William Henry had clearly distinguished methane and olefiant gas some fifteen years before.

BIBLIOGRAPHY

Brande wrote textbooks based on his courses of lectures on geology, chemistry, and pharmacy: *Outlines of Geology* (London, 1817, 1829); *A Manual of Chemistry: Containing the Principal Facts of the Science Arranged in the Order in Which They Are Discussed and Illustrated in the Lectures at the Royal Institution* (London, 1819; 6th ed., 1848; American ed., New York[?], 1829); *A Manual of Pharmacy* (London, 1825, 1833). He also wrote *Chemistry* (London, 1863), with A. S. Taylor, terming it "especially adapted for students." Among his other reference works should be noted *A Dictionary of Materia Medica and Practical Pharmacy, Including a Translation of the Formulae of the London Pharmacopoeia* (London, 1839), said to have been invaluable to medical students of his day. His catholic interests are evidenced by his editorship of *A Dictionary of Science, Literature and Art* (London, 1842, 1852, 1853; New York, 1847; rev. ed., 3 vols., 1865–1867, 1875). Most of his papers are listed in *The Royal Society Catalogue of Scientific Papers,* I (1867), 564–566. Those omitted are of little importance, and most are in the *Quarterly Journal,* in the period 1816–1830.

No adequate biography exists; the best biographical sketch is the obituary notice in *Proceedings of the Royal Society,* **16** (1868), ii–viii.

E. L. SCOTT

BRANDES, HEINRICH WILHELM (*b*. Groden, near Cuxhafen, Germany, 22 July 1777; *d*. Leipzig, Germany, 17 May 1834), *astronomy, physics*.

The son of a Protestant preacher, Albert Georg Brandes, Heinrich attended the grammar school in Ottendorf and studied natural sciences in Göttingen under A. G. Kästner and G. C. Lichtenberg. From

1801 to 1811 he was a dike official in Eckwarden near Jadebusen, duchy of Oldenburg, and in 1811 he was appointed professor of mathematics at Breslau. He became professor of physics at Leipzig in 1826.

As a student Brandes, with J. F. Benzenberg, developed the method of the corresponding observations of shooting stars. With its aid they determined the planetary velocity and the height, at the border of the atmosphere, of shooting stars. He also discovered the periodicity of the August meteorites. Later, Brandes occupied himself with practical and theoretical problems of the refractions of rays and other problems of atmospheric optics, as well as with the theory of comet tails. His books were widely read and contributed much to the popularization of astronomy.

BIBLIOGRAPHY

I. ORIGINAL WORKS. Among Brandes' more technical writings are *Versuche die Entfernung, die Geschwindigkeit und die Bahnen der Sternschnuppen zu bestimmen* (Hamburg, 1800), written with J. F. Benzenberg; *Beobachtungen und theoretische Untersuchungen über die Strahlenbrechung* (Oldenburg, 1807); *Beitrag zur Theorie der Cometenschweife* (1812); *Lehrbuch der Gesetze des Gleichgewichts und der Bewegung fester und flüssiger Körper* (Leipzig, 1817–1818); and *Beiträge zur Witterungskunde* (Leipzig, 1820).

His popular works include *Die vornehmsten Lehren der Astronomie deutlich dargestellt in Briefen an eine Freundin,* 4 vols. (Leipzig, 1811–1816); and *Unterhaltungen für Freunde der Physik und Astronomie,* 3 vols. (1825–1829).

II. SECONDARY LITERATURE. Additional works on Brandes are Poggendorff, I, 277–278; and H. Schröder, *Lexikon der hamburgischen Schriftsteller,* I (1851), 368, with a list of works.

BERNHARD STICKER

BRANDT, GEORG (*b.* Riddarhyttan, Sweden, 21 July 1694; *d.* Stockholm, Sweden, 29 April 1768), *chemistry, mineralogy.*

A son of Jurgen Brandt, a mineowner and former pharmacist, and Katarina Ysing, Brandt inherited his father's interest in chemistry and metallurgy, and as a child was allowed to participate in his father's experiments in these fields. He continued his studies at Uppsala University and worked for the Council of Mines. Convinced that he needed a more extensive background in the natural sciences, he decided to go abroad. Brandt arrived in Leiden in 1721 and became a pupil of Boerhaave. During three years of intensive study he acquired an extensive knowledge of chemistry, and his medical studies led to the M.D. from

Rheims in 1726. On his way back to Sweden he stopped in the Harz Mountains, where he studied mining and smelting, and when he arrived home, he was made director of the chemical laboratory of the Council of Mines. He was named warden of the Royal Mint in 1730. In 1747 he became associate member of the Council of Mines and in 1757 was named a member.

The Laboratorium Chymium Holmiense, where Urban Hiärne had produced his great lifework, had gradually declined because of Hiärne's advanced age and a lack of funds. When its work was resumed in new offices at the Royal Mint, Brandt's original contributions and his leadership, as well as the work of his collaborators, Henrik Scheffer and Axel Cronstedt, laid the groundwork for the eminence that Swedish chemistry achieved under such scientists as Bergman, Scheele, and Berzelius. Brandt's reputation as a chemical experimenter and as a teacher led to an offer of the chair of chemistry (which he refused) when it was established at the University of Uppsala in 1750.

Besides being an able administrator and chief of the laboratory, and making valuable contributions as a chemist, Brandt did outstanding research on arsenic. His findings, published in 1733, constitute the first detailed treatise on various arsenic compounds, their composition, and their solubility in various media. Henckel had begun to analyze the little that was known about arsenic, but Brandt's research clearly established its metallic nature and proved that white arsenic (arsenious oxide) was an oxide of this metal.

Brandt continued his metallurgical investigations, the results of which he published in a dissertation on semimetals (1735); in addition to mercury, antimony, bismuth, arsenic, and zinc, he dealt with cobalt, which he here showed to be a distinct metal. It is mainly for the discovery of this element that Brandt is known in the history of chemistry. In 1748 he published more findings on cobalt, describing his production of it as a regulus by reducing cobalt pyrite with charcoal, and declaring that it was magnetic.

Brandt also published findings on the difference between soda and potash (1746) and the methods of producing sulfuric acid, nitric acid, and hydrochloric acid (1741, 1743), and the ability of aqua fortis to dissolve gold, provided the gold was alloyed with a certain quantity of silver. In an article on the metallurgy of iron (1751), he proved that thermal brittleness was due to the sulfur content of the iron. However, he stated erroneously that arsenic was the cause of cold brittleness. Before Bergman, Brandt observed that the carbon content of steel was greater than that of cast iron.

BIBLIOGRAPHY

I. ORIGINAL WORKS. Brandt's writings are "De arsenico observationes," in *Acta literaria et scientiarum Sveciae,* **3** (1733), 39–43; "Dissertatio de semimetallis," *ibid.,* **4** (1735), 1–10; "De vitriolo albo," *ibid.,* 10–12; "Acta laboratorii chymici," in *Kongliga Svenska vetenskapsakademiens handlingar,* **2** (1741), 49–63; "Continuation," *ibid.,* **4** (1743), 89–105: "Rön och anmärkningar angående en synnerlig färg-cobolt," *ibid.,* **7** (1746), 119–130; "Rön och anmärkningar angående åtskilnaden emellan soda och pottaska," *ibid.,* 289–290; "Rön och anmärkningar angående det flyktige alcaliske saltet," *ibid.,* **8** (1747), 301–308; "Nytt rön angående gulds uplösning uti skedvatten," *ibid.,* **9** (1748), 45–54; "Cobalti nova species examinata et descripta," in *Acta Regiae Societatis Scientiarum Upsaliensis,* 1st ser., **3** (1748), 33–41; "Rön och försök angåendejärn, des förhållande mot andra kroppar, samt rödbräckt och kallbräckt järns egenskaper och förbättring," in *Kongliga Svenska vetenskapsakademiens handlingar,* **12** (1751), 205–214; "Några rön och anmärkningar angående köks-salt och dess syra," *ibid.,* **14** (1753), 295–312 and **15** (1754), 53–68; and *Tal om färg-cobolter, hållit för Kongliga vetenskaps academien vid praesidii nedläggande den 30 juli 1760* (Stockholm, 1760).

Some of Brandt's writings are in *Abhandlungen der Königlichen Schwedischen Akademie der Wissenschaften* (Hamburg, 1749–1753), and in *Recueil des mémoires les plus intéressants de chymie et d'histoire naturelle, contenus dans les Actes de l'Académie d'Upsal, et dans les Mémoires de l'Académie royale des sciences de Stockholm; publiés depuis 1720 jusqu'en 1760,* trans. by Augustin Roux and Paul-Henri, baron d'Holbach, 2 vols. (Paris, 1764).

There are bibliographies of Brandt's work in *Svenskt Biografiskt Lexikon,* V (Stockholm, 1925), 788–789; in J. R. Partington, *A History of Chemistry,* III (London–New York, 1962), 168–169; and Poggendorff, I, 280.

II. SECONDARY LITERATURE. Works on Brandt are Johan Axel Almquist, *Bergskollegium* (Stockholm, 1909); and Torbern Bergman, *Åminnelsetal öfver Georg Brandt* (Stockholm, 1769).

UNO BOKLUND

BRANDT, JOHANN FRIEDRICH (*b.* Jüterbog, Germany, 25 May 1802; *d.* Baths of Merreküll, Finland, 15 July 1879), *zoology, paleontology, botany.*

Brandt was carefully educated by his parents at Jüterbog, in the Prussian province of Brandenburg, where his father was a successful surgeon. From his great-uncle Hensius he early acquired a liking for botany, which captivated his attention for more than twenty years.

After graduating from the Gymnasium at Jüterbog, Brandt attended the Lyceum of Wittenberg, studying classics, and in 1821 entered the University of Berlin to study medicine. Although he had such famous teachers as Karl A. Rudolphi, Karl A. F. Kluge, and Albrecht von Gräfe, he still preferred botany, zoology, and even mineralogy. During his first vacation he visited the Harz Mountains with his fellow student Julius T. C. Ratzeburg; having won the prize for an essay on respiration, he was able to continue his travels the following year through the Riesengebirge.

The lectures of Martin H. K. Lichtenstein stimulated Brandt's interest in zoology and prompted him to visit many museums of anatomy. At that time he became a protégé of Rudolphi, to whom he was secretary for a short time. In 1825 he published *Flora Berolinensis,* based on his previous field trips. On 24 June 1826, having defended his thesis, "Observationes anatomicae de mammalium quorundam vocis instrumento," he obtained the M.D. During the same summer he passed his state examinations and became a licensed surgeon.

After having been assistant to the famous surgeon Ernst L. Heim for a short time, Brandt became assistant at the Anatomical Institute of the University of Berlin in 1827. He at once began, in collaboration with his friend Ratzeburg, to work on the first volume of their *Medizinische Zoologie* (1829–1833). This work, considered one of the major achievements of his career, was an enumeration and description of the animals used in the preparation of medical drugs.

Brandt was accepted as *Privatdozent* at the University of Berlin in 1828 and lectured on several subjects, among which medical botany and pharmacology were his favorites. Although he wrote many articles for the *Encyklopädische Lexikon,* his research continued to be more in botany than in zoology, as shown by *Deutschlands phanerogamische Giftgewächse* (1828) and *Tabellar Uebersicht d. offizin. Gewächse nach d. Linn. Sexualsystem u. d. natürl. System* (1829), each the first part of a major work. In 1830 he began writing monographs on the myriopods and *Oniscidae,* as well as a memoir on mammals based on Friedrich Bürde's *Abbildungen merkwürdiger Säugethiere.*

However, in spite of his achievements Brandt was unable to find any permanent position in Germany, and like many other German scientists of that time he emigrated to Russia. He left Berlin in 1831, and through the influence of Humboldt and Rudolphi he was appointed an associate member of the Academy of Sciences of St. Petersburg, as well as an assistant in its zoological museum, of which he later became director. In that position he succeeded another German scientist, K. E. von Baer, who a few years earlier had left his position in Königsberg to join the Academy of St. Petersburg, but found life in that town not to his liking and returned home.

Brandt was elected an ordinary member of the

Academy in 1833, a position he held until his death. Besides his activity in the Academy, he taught at the Central Pedagogical Institute, a teacher's college, and for eighteen years (1851–1869) was professor of zoology at the Military-Medical Academy, where army surgeons were trained.

Many honors were bestowed upon Brandt: he became an Imperial Russian Councillor, received the title of "Excellency," was invested with several distinguished orders, and was elected honorary member of many academies and scientific societies of Europe.

The fiftieth anniversary of his doctoral degree was celebrated in January 1876 with great pomp and with the participation of many of his students and friends. A special medal was struck for the occasion, and the Brandt Prize was established to reward outstanding zoological works. At this time Brandt's published scientific writings numbered 318, and their distribution among different scientific disciplines illustrates the extent of his knowledge: 176 publications are zoological, twenty-four relate to comparative anatomy, thirty-five are paleontological, eleven deal with geographical zoology, and the remainder pertain to archaeological zoology, botany, and various other subjects.

Russia presented Brandt with unusual opportunities for original studies. His activity followed two major lines: research and collecting specimens. He had found the zoological collection of the Academy very incomplete, and he undertook its development by means of many scientific expeditions financed by the Academy. He went to the Crimea, to Bessarabia, and to Nicolayev in search of the mammoth, and to the Caucasus to study its fish. For comparative purposes, and also to keep in touch with the progress of science in the West, he visited and studied in the museums of many European countries. Brandt collected not only animals during his travels but also books, making the zoological division of the Academy's library outstanding.

Although Brandt's zoological publications are remarkable, his fame is based essentially on his paleontological writings, which relate to the fossil Mammalia. The most important of these, *Untersuchungen über die fossilen und subfossilen Cetaceen Europa's,* gives a complete account of all the European Cetacea known until 1873. This work includes descriptions of species of *Cetotherium, Pachyacanthus, Cetotheriopsis, Cetotheriomorphus, Delphinapterus, Heterodelphis, Schizodelphis, Champsodelphis, Squalodon, Zeuglodon,* and other remarkable types. Several important memoirs relate to *Elasmotherium, Dinotherium, Rhytina,* the elk, and the mammoth. Another monograph is devoted to the characters of the Sirenia,

and their relations to different orders. Brandt also made important contributions to the knowledge of the osteology and structure of many other groups of mammals.

As a paleontologist, Brandt ranks among the best. His exhaustive and lucid monographs were written with a full understanding of their philosophical implications, an attitude very close to the final aim of scientific research.

BIBLIOGRAPHY

Among Brandt's writings are *Flora Berolinensis, sive descriptio plantarum phanerogamarum circa Berolinum sponte crescentium vel in agris cultarum additis filicibus et charis* (Berlin, 1824); *Deutschlands phanerogamische Giftgewächse* (Berlin, 1828); *Tabellar Uebersicht d. offizin. Gewächse nach d. Linn. Sexualsystem u. d. natürl. System* (Berlin, 1829); *Medizinische Zoologie oder getreue Darstellung und Beschreibung der · Thiere die in der Arzneimittellehre in Betracht kommen,* 2 vols. (Berlin, 1829–1833), written with J. T. C. Ratzeburg; *Uebersicht d. Charactere d. Familien d. offizin. Gewächse nach R. Brown, De Candolle, Jussieu, . . .* (Berlin, 1830); *Deutschlands kryptogamische Giftgewächse* (Berlin, 1838), published together with *Deutschlands phanerogamische Giftgewächse* as *Abbildung und Beschreibung der in Deutschland wild wachsenden und in Gärten in freien ausdauernden Giftgewächse, nach natürlichen Familien erläutert, mit Beiträgen von P. Phoebus und J. T. C. Ratzeburg* (Berlin, 1838); *Symbolae Sirenologicae quibus praecipue Rhytinae historia naturalis illustratur* (St. Petersburg, 1846); *Symbolae Sirenologicae . . .,* fasc. 2 and 3 (St. Petersburg, 1861–1868), also *Mémoires de l'Académie impériale des sciences, St. Pétersbourg,* 7th ser., **12,** no. 1; *Untersuchungen über die fossilen und subfossilen Cetaceen Europa's mit Beiträgen von Van Beneden, Cornalia, Gastaldi, Quenstedt, und Paulson, nebst einem geologischen Anhange von Barbot de Marny, G. von Helmersen, A. Goebel und Th. Fuchs, ibid.,* **20,** no. 1 (1873); *Ergänzungen, ibid.,* **21,** no. 6 (1874); and *Bericht über die Fortschritte, welche die zoologischen Wissenschaften den von der kaiserlichen Akademie der Wissenschaften zu St. Petersburg von 1831 bis 1879 herausgegeben Schriften verdanken* (St. Petersburg, 1879).

An index to Brandt's works is *J. F. Brandtii index operum omnium* (St. Petersburg, 1876), issued as a *Festschrift.*

ALBERT V. CAROZZI

BRASHEAR, JOHN ALFRED (*b.* Brownsville, Pennsylvania, 24 November 1840; *d.* Pittsburgh, Pennsylvania, 8 April 1920), *astrophysical instruments.*

Until 1881 John Brashear was a mechanic in a Pittsburgh steel mill by day and an amateur telescope maker by night; then, through the encouragement of Samuel Pierpont Langley and with the financial support of William Thaw, he was able to establish a workshop for making astronomical and physical instruments. During the next half century the John A. Brashear Company produced many of the major instruments used throughout the world for astrophysical research. In 1926 the Brashear concern was bought by J. W. Fecker of Cleveland, Ohio.

Besides a dozen or so workmen and "Uncle John," as he was widely and affectionately known, the Brashear Company employed two notable "associates": Charles Sheldon Hastings, an optical physicist at Yale University, and James McDowell, Brashear's son-in-law. Hastings computed the curves of most of the objective lenses figured in the Brashear shops, and McDowell did most of the actual optical work.

The Brashear Company began at an opportune time: establishing large and well-equipped astronomical observatories had recently become an acceptable philanthropy; and astronomers, beginning to study the quality and quantity, as well as the position, of starlight, needed new types of instruments. Since most other astronomical instrument makers concentrated on equatorial refracting and reflecting telescopes or apparatus for terrestrial and celestial surveying, Brashear, who was adept at producing special-purpose instruments, had few competitors.

Among Brashear's astronomical contributions were an improved and soon widely used process for silvering glass mirrors; the concave metal mirrors on which Henry A. Rowland ruled diffraction gratings; spectroscopes for use with the large refractors at the Allegheny, Lick, Princeton, and Yerkes observatories; George Ellery Hale's first spectroheliograph for photographing solar prominences; the optical parts of the interferometer with which Albert A. Michelson measured the standard meter; a 16-inch-aperture, double-photographic doublet for Max Wolf at Heidelberg; and numerous telescope objectives—both lenses and mirrors—culminating in the 72-inch-aperture primary mirror for the Dominion Observatory in Canada.

BIBLIOGRAPHY

The best original sources for an instrument maker are the instruments themselves; and the best secondary sources are the articles about the instruments and the work done with them published in scientific journals and in observatory annals.

I. ORIGINAL WORKS. Brashear wrote many short articles, frequently describing his techniques and work in progress, which were published in most of the contemporary astronomical journals; the first, "Hints on Silvering Specula, Periscopic Eyepieces, & c.," appeared in *English Mechanic,* **31** (1880), 327. Also of value is his *The Autobiography of a Man Who Loved the Stars* (Boston, 1925).

II. SECONDARY LITERATURE. Among the numerous published accounts of Brashear's life that stress his many educational and philanthropic activities, mention may be made of J. S. Plaskett, "James B. McDowell, an Appreciation," in *Journal, Royal Astronomical Society, Canada,* **18** (1924), 185–193; and Frank Schlesinger, "John Alfred Brashear, 1840–1920," in *Popular Astronomy,* **28** (1926), 373–379.

DEBORAH JEAN WARNER

BRASHMAN, NIKOLAI DMITRIEVICH (*b.* Rassnova, near Brno, Czechoslovakia, 14 June 1796; *d.* Moscow, Russia, 13 May 1866), *mathematics, mechanics.*

Although Brashman's family was of limited means, he was able to study at the University of Vienna and the Vienna Polytechnical Institute by working as a tutor. In 1824 he went to Russia, and after a short stay in St. Petersburg he obtained the post of assistant professor of physicomathematical sciences at the University of Kazan, where he taught mathematics and mechanics.

In 1834 Brashman accepted a professorship of applied mathematics (mechanics) at the University of Moscow. Here he became known as a gifted scientist and teacher, and laid the foundations of instruction in both theoretical and practical mechanics.

In his lectures on mechanics and in his articles Brashman not only tried to show the achievements of this science, but also worked out its most difficult sections. He also prepared textbooks for Russian institutions of higher education. His texts on mathematics and mechanics reflect the state of science at that time, and his proofs of important theorems show originality, clarity, and comprehensiveness. Brashman wrote one of the best analytical geometry texts of his time, for which the Academy of Sciences awarded him the entire Demidov Prize in 1836.

In 1837 Brashman published the textbook on mechanics, *Teoria ravnovesia tel tverdykh i zhidkikh,* which contains an original presentation of problems of statics and hydrostatics. Upon the recommendation of Ostrogradski, this work also brought Brashman the full Demidov Prize.

In 1859 Brashman published a textbook, *Teoreticheskaya mekhanika* ("Theoretical Mechanics"), dealing with the theories of equilibrium and the motion of a point and of a system of points.

In addition to texts, Brashman wrote articles on various problems in mathematics and mechanics. Brashman's memoirs on mathematics were intended for those interested in the progress of the mathematical sciences, and dealt with the latest results of Russian and foreign scientists.

More important are Brashman's memoranda on mechanics. "O prilozhenii printsipa naimenshego deystvia k opredeleniu obema vody na Vodoslive" ("On the Application of the Principle of Minimum Action to the Determination of Water Volume in a Spillway," 1861), which was published in both Russian and foreign periodicals, drew much favorable attention.

Also in 1861 Brashman published "Note concernant la pression des wagons sur les rails droits et des courants d'eau sur la rive droite du mouvement en vertu de la rotation de la terre" (*Comptes rendus de l'Académie des sciences,* **53,** [1861], 370–376). With the aid of general equations, he tried to prove in this article that the rotation of the earth invariably imposes a pressure on the right rail of a railroad track as a train travels over it and on the right bank of a river as the current moves along it, no matter in what direction the train is moving or the river is flowing, provided this force is a single one (i.e., the motion must be rectilinear and uniform).

Another article of considerable interest is his "Printsip naimenshego deystvia" ("Principle of Minimum Action") that appeared in *Mélanges mathématiques et astronomiques* (**1** [1859], 26–31).

Brashman was not only an important scientist but also an excellent teacher. His students included such prominent scientists as P. L. Chebyshev, I. I. Somov, and other talented specialists in mathematics and mechanics. He founded the Moscow Mathematical Society and its journal, *Matematicheskiy sbornik* ("Mathematical Symposium"), the first issue of which appeared in the year of his death. This journal was equal to the best European publications in its scientific value and wide range of contents.

For his distinguished services to science, Brashman was elected a corresponding member of the Petersburg Academy of Sciences in 1855.

BIBLIOGRAPHY

I. ORIGINAL WORKS. Brashman's writings include *Kurs analiticheskoy geometrii* ("Course in Analytical Geometry"; Moscow, 1836); *Teoria ravnovesia tel tverdykh i zhidkikh. Statika i gidrostatika* ("Theory of Equilibrium of Solid and Liquid Bodies. Statics and Hydrostatics"; Moscow, 1837); and *Teoreticheskaya mekhanika* ("Theoretical Mechanics"; Moscow, 1859).

II. SECONDARY LITERATURE. Works on Brashman are A. Davidov, *Biograficheskiy slovar professorov i prepodovateley Moskvskogo Universiteta* ("Biographical Dictionary of Professors and Teachers at Moscow University"), I (Moscow, 1855), 206; *Matematicheskiy sbornik,* **1** (1866); A. T. Grigorian, *Ocherki istorii mekaniki v Rossii* ("Essays on the History of Mechanics in Russia"; Moscow, 1961), pp. 96–107; I. I. Liholetov and S. H. Yanovskaja, "Iz istorii prepodavaniya mehaniki v Moskovskom Universitete" ("From History of Teaching Mechanics at Moscow University"), in *Istoriko-matematicheskie issledovaniya,* **8,** 294–368; M. Viyodski, "Matematika i eyo deyateli v Moskovskom Universitete vo vtoroy polovine XIX V." ("Mathematics and Its Representatives at Moscow University in the Second Half of the Nineteenth Century"), *ibid.,* **1,** 141–149.

A. T. GRIGORIAN

BRAUN, ALEXANDER CARL HEINRICH (*b.* Regensburg, Germany, 10 May 1805; *d.* Berlin, Germany, 29 March 1877), *botany, philosophy.*

For more than twenty-five years Braun was professor of botany and director of the botanical gardens at the University of Berlin, and during his lifetime was the most highly regarded botanist of the *Naturphilosoph* school. His father, also named Alexander, was a civil servant with scientific interests ranging over mineralogy, physics, and astronomy; his mother, Henriette Mayer, was the daughter of a mathematics professor and former priest. Braun himself married twice. In 1835 he married Mathilde Zimmer, who died in 1843 after the birth of their sixth child. Five children survived to adulthood; two of the daughters from this marriage married the German botanists Robert Caspary and Georg Mettenius. In 1844 Braun married Adele Messmer, who bore him five more children, four surviving to adulthood. She died just a few months after her husband.

Braun grew up in Karlsruhe in Baden, surrounded by the natural beauty of the Schwarzwald area, and his interest in natural history and botany developed at a very early age. After private tutoring, in 1816 he entered the Karlsruhe Lyceum, where he was still a student when he published his first paper at the age of sixteen. While still a youth Braun also discovered several new species of cryptogams that now bear his name: *Chara braunii, Orthotrichum braunii,* and *Aspidium braunii.* In 1824 he enrolled at the University of Heidelberg, and in compliance with his father's wishes, neglected the liberal arts in order to take up the study of medicine. Medicine was soon pushed into the background, however, as his abiding interest in botany took pride of place. At Heidelberg he became intimate friends with Carl Friedrich Schimper and Louis Agassiz. Braun and Agassiz became inseparable friends, and Agassiz eventually married Braun's sister, Silly. In 1827 Braun and Agassiz went to the University of Munich, attracted especially by the fame of the *Naturphilosophen* Oken and Schelling, and in 1829 both went on to

Tübingen, where they received their doctorates in that same year.

After four more years of study and travel, including an eventful stay in Paris, Braun accepted a position as teacher of botany and zoology at the newly instituted polytechnic school in Karlsruhe. He remained there until 1846, when he accepted the chair of botany at Freiburg im Breisgau. In 1849 he was elected prorector of the Freiburg *Hochschule,* and his diplomatic leadership during the Baden revolution did much to keep the school free from political strife. In 1850 Justus von Liebig persuaded Braun to move to Giessen, but he had hardly established residence there before he was offered a position at the prestigious University of Berlin. After some hesitation, Braun accepted the call to the big city in 1851, and he remained there the rest of his life.

Braun made his early reputation in botanical circles by his work on the arrangement of leaves. With his old Heidelberg friend Carl Schimper, Braun established the doctrine of spiral phyllotaxis, according to which growth in a stem has an upward direction in a spiral line such that the leaves are arranged on the stem according to fixed geometrical rules. Most anomalies were accounted for by a formula expressed as a simple continuous fraction. Between 1830 and 1835, Braun and Schimper each published articles introducing and explicating the doctrine, and their friendship was interrupted by Schimper's rather bellicose claim that he deserved full credit for the theory. Years later, a reconciliation was achieved. Braun, in particular, extended the theory between 1840 and 1860.

The Schimper-Braun theory focused attention on the important question of the relative positions of plant organs and inspired much of the detailed work of the opposing school of "genetic morphologists," such as Wilhelm Hofmeister, who claimed that the developmental history of plants proved the theory erroneous. Numerous exceptions to the rule certainly did exist, but it served as a roughly valid description of the arrangement of leaves on adult plants, and under its influence the morphological examination and comparison of plants, inflorescences, and vegetative shoots reached unprecedented completeness.

Braun's most important single work was *Betrachtungen über die Erscheinung der Verjüngung in der Natur*, written while he was at Freiburg and originally delivered as the prorectorial address for 1849; its publication was delayed until 1851 by Braun's call to Giessen and by the Baden revolution. Braun's chief object in this volume is to show that the phenomenon of "rejuvenescence" distinguishes the organic realm from the inorganic. His diffuse concept of rejuvenescence was an extension of

Goethe's doctrine of metamorphosis and included a consideration of developmental history, reproduction, and the dissolution of formed structures. More significant than his particular object, however, were Braun's contributions to the morphology of plants, to the biology of freshwater algae, and especially to a reconstruction of the cell theory. In this last area, his investigation of algae swarm-spores led him to oppose Schleiden and Schwann's emphasis on the cell wall, and to insist instead that the cell contents were the site of all the physiological activities of the cell. In passages remarkable for the beauty of their language, Braun suggested dramatically that the cell wall was in fact the structure that *entombed* the true life of the cell, and that could eventually destroy that life by interfering with "rejuvenescence."

It is clear from Braun's other important general work, "Das Individuum der Pflanze in seinem Verhältnisse zur Species" (1853), that he believed in the transmutation of species, but he insisted that the process was teleological. He objected strongly to Darwin's principle of natural selection and to any "mechanistic" explanations that substituted blind external forces for inner direction and purpose. Braun's general interpretations were always colored by his *Naturphilosophie*, and his work may have exerted less influence than it deserved because he was so obviously and genuinely a *Naturphilosoph* at a time when that mode of looking at nature was becoming unfashionable.

While at Berlin, Braun had among his pupils Anton De Bary and A. W. Eichler, his successor, who extended the natural system of classification developed by Braun for the ordering of the university's botanical gardens. In 1879 a bust of Braun was unveiled and placed in the botanical gardens.

BIBLIOGRAPHY

I. Original Works. The Schimper-Braun theory of phyllotaxis was developed primarily in the following series of papers: Carl Schimper, "Beschreibung des Symphytum Zeyheri und seiner zwei deutschen Verwandten . . .," in *Magazin für Pharmacie von Geiger,* **3** (1830); Braun, "Vergleichende Untersuchung über die Ordnung der Schuppen an den Tannenzapfen, als Einleitung zur Untersuchung der Blattstellung überhaupt," in *Nova acta Academiae Caeserae Leopoldino Carolinae Germanicae naturae curiosorum,* **15** (1831), 195–402; and Braun, "Dr. Carl Schimper's Vorträge über die *Moglichkeit eines wissenschaftlichen Verständniss der Blattstellung,"* in *Flora, oder allgemeine botanische Zeitung* (Regensburg), **18** (1835), 145–192. See also report of the meeting of 20 Sept. 1834, *ibid.,* 7–8. For Braun's reasonableness on the question of priority, see his "Nachträgliche Erläuterungen zu meinem

Aufsatz in Nr. 10, 11, und 12 der 'Flora' laufenden Jahres über Dr. Schimper's Vorträge," *ibid.*, 737–746; Schimper's intemperate reply is *ibid.*, 748–758.

Braun's most important general works were *Betrachtungen über die Erscheinung der Verjüngung in der Natur, insbesondere in der Lebens- und Bildungsgeschichte der Pflanze* . . . (Leipzig, 1851), translated by Arthur Henfrey, in *Ray Society Botanical and Physiological Memoirs* (1853), vii–xxvi, 1–341; and "Das Individuum der Pflanze in seiner Verhältnisse zur Species, Generationsfolge, Generationswechsel und Generationstheilung der Pflanze," in *Abhandlungen der Königlichen Akademie der Wissenschaften Berlin* (Physikalische Klasse) (1853), 19–122, translated by Charles Francis Stone, in *The American Journal of Science and Arts* (*Silliman's Journal*), 2nd ser., **19** (1855), 297–318; **20** (1855), 181–200; and **21** (1856), 58–79.

For Braun's contributions in the area of systematics, see Paul F. A. Ascherson, *Flora der Provinz Brandenburg* . . . (*Nebst einer Übersicht des natürlichen Pflanzensystems nach A. Braun*) (Berlin, 1864); and A. W. Eichler, *Blüthendiagramme*, 2 vols. (Leipzig, 1875–1878), *passim* (esp. I, 3, 9, 11, 14–30). Most of Braun's scientific papers are listed in the *Royal Society Catalogue of Scientific Papers* (I, 582–585; VII, 248; IX, 333–334). Braun left behind an extensive manuscript collection that the Berlin Royal Academy of Sciences acquired in 1879 and turned over to the Royal Herbarium for safekeeping.

II. SECONDARY LITERATURE. Of the existing sketches of Braun's life and work, those written by his daughter Cecilie, though uncritical, are the most interesting because they are illuminated by Braun's personal letters. See Cecilie Mettenius, "Alexander Braun," in *Leopoldina*, **13** (1877), 50–60, 66–72; and *Alexander Braun's Leben nach seinem handschriftlichen Nachlass dargestellt* . . . (Berlin, 1882). The best source for estimating Braun's place in the history of botany is Ferdinand G. Julius von Sachs, *Geschichte der Botanik vom 16. Jahrhundert bis 1860* (Munich, 1875), pp. 185–195. It should be pointed out, however, that Sachs is unsympathetic toward Braun's general mode of viewing nature. For other sketches of Braun's life and work, see Robert Caspary, in *Flora*, n.s. **25** (1877), 433–442, 449–457, 465–471, 497–507, 513–519; A. W. Eichler, in *Leopoldina*, **15** (1879), 163–165; *Allgemeine deutsche Biographie*, XLVII (1903), 186–193; and *Neue deutsche Biographie*, II (1953), 548.

GERALD L. GEISON

BRAUN, FERDINAND (*b.* Fulda, Germany, 6 June 1850; *d.* Brooklyn, New York, 20 June 1918), *physics.*

Braun studied at the University of Marburg and received his doctorate from the University of Berlin in 1872 with a dissertation on the vibrations of elastic rods and strings. He later did work in thermodynamics, but his major accomplishments were in electricity. Braun began his career as assistant to Quincke at Würzburg and later held positions at

Leipzig, Marburg, Karlsruhe, and Tübingen; during the short period that he spent at Tübingen he founded the Physical Institute. From 1880 to 1883 Braun was at Strasbourg, and he returned there permanently in 1895 to become professor of physics and director of the Physical Institute. He was called to the United States to testify in litigation involving radio broadcasting and then was detained when the United States entered World War I. He died in a Brooklyn hospital on 20 June 1918.

Although his contributions were all in the realm of pure science, in 1909 Braun shared the Nobel Prize in physics with Marconi for his practical contributions to wireless telegraphy. The work recognized by the Nobel committee was his fundamental modification of Marconi's transmitting system. Braun was first drawn to the study of wireless transmission by the puzzle of why it was so difficult to increase the range of the transmitter over 15 kilometers. It seemed to Braun that the range should easily be increased by increasing the power of the transmitter. His study of Hertz oscillators indicated that the attempt to increase the power output by increasing the length of the spark gap eventually reached a limit at which the spark caused a decrease in output. The solution, Braun thought, was to produce a sparkless antenna circuit. The power from the transmitter was coupled magnetically to the antenna circuit by a transformer effect instead of having the antenna directly in the power circuit. The principle has been applied to all such transmissions, including radio, radar, and television. A patent was granted on this circuit in 1899. Braun also developed an antenna that directed the transmission of electric waves in one direction.

In 1874 Braun published the results of his research on mineral metal sulfides. He found that these crystals conducted electric currents in only one direction. This information was important in electrical research and in measuring another property of substances, the electrical conductivity, but Braun's discovery did not have immediate practical application. In the early twentieth century the principle that Braun had discovered was employed in crystal radio receivers.

The first oscilloscope, or Braun tube, was introduced in 1897. In order to study high-frequency alternating currents Braun used the alternating voltage to move the electron beam within the cathode tube. The trace on the face of the cathode tube represented the amplitude and frequency of the alternating-current voltage. He then produced a graph of this trace by use of a rotating mirror. The Braun tube was a valuable laboratory instrument, and modifications of it are a basic device in electronic testing and research. The principle of the Braun tube, moving an electron beam by means of alternating voltage, is the principle on which all television tubes operate.

BIBLIOGRAPHY

I. ORIGINAL WORKS. Among Braun's writings are "On the Conduction of Current Through Sulpho-Metals," in *Poggendorff's Annalen*, **102** (1874), 550, and *Drahtlose Telegraphie durch Wasser und Luft* (Leipzig, 1901). His papers are listed in the Royal Society's *Catalogue of Scientific Papers, 1884–1900* (1914), pp. 773–774, and in the *International Catalogue of Scientific Literature* (1902), p. 65; (1904) p. 74; (1907) pp. 83–84; (1908) p. 85; (1912) pp. 74–75; (1917) pp. 73–74.

II. SECONDARY LITERATURE. There are no full-length biographies of Braun. He is best remembered by biographers for his Nobel Prize, although his most important work was in pure science. Some information is given in N. de V. Heathcote, *Nobel Prize Winners in Physics 1901–1950* (New York, 1953), pp. 81–86; and *The Nobel Prize-Winners and the Nobel Foundation 1901–1937* (Zurich, 1938), pp. 52–53.

HAROLD I. SHARLIN

BRAUNER, BOHUSLAV (*b.* Prague, Czechoslovakia, 8 May 1855; *d.* Prague, 15 February 1935), *chemistry.*

Brauner's family was one of comfortable means, extensive education, and wide-ranging scientific and political interests. His father, Dr. Francis Brauner, was a lawyer and Czech political leader. His mother, Augusta, was the daughter of Karl August Neumann, professor of chemistry at the Prague Technical College. As a boy, Brauner came into contact with the many scientific, intellectual, and political personalities who frequented his parents' home. He showed an early interest in science and studied at the Czech Polytechnical High School. In 1873 he entered the University of Prague, where he attended courses in chemistry and performed research in metal analysis and organic preparations. Preferring inorganic chemistry, Brauner went to Heidelberg in 1878 to train under Robert Bunsen. He returned to Prague in 1880 to take his doctorate and, still widening his experience, he went to England in that year to work under the direction of Sir Henry Roscoe at Owen's College, Manchester.

In 1882 Brauner was appointed lecturer in chemistry in the Czech branch of the Charles University, Prague, where gradually his influence made English the language of the laboratory. He rose to docent in 1885, assistant professor in 1890, and full professor in 1897. Brauner played a large part in the construction of a chemical institute, completed in 1904, at the university. He retired from academic life in 1925.

Brauner led an active and athletic life, playing soccer, bicycling, skiing, and hiking. He suffered a thrombosis in 1922, but his health was good and he was not incapacitated. In 1886 Brauner married Ludmilla, the adopted daughter of Professor Safarik, his predecessor in Prague. The couple had two sons and one daughter.

Brauner's scientific work consisted largely in the exemplification and perfection in the laboratory of Mendeleev's periodic law and system of classifying the chemical elements, published in 1869. Since the system had many problems—gaps, too many elements for one position, atomic weight anomalies—it was not immediately popular. It was supported in 1875, however, by the discovery of "eka-aluminum" (now called gallium), which Mendeleev had predicted. This finding, by Boisbaudran, convinced Brauner of the validity of Mendeleev's system. Brauner, who was to become a correspondent and friend of Mendeleev's, chose as his life's work the "experimental examination of the problems connected with Mendeleev's system. . . ."

Brauner began this work by trying to ascertain the atomic weight of beryllium. Its accepted value, 13, was not in agreement with its position in Mendeleev's periodic table. Working with John I. Watts, Brauner showed that previous measurements were faulty and that the correct value was 9, thus confirming beryllium's place at the head of Group II, as Mendeleev had insisted. Thereafter, Brauner devoted most of his attention to determining the proper positions of the rare earth elements. While working on cerium, he produced $CeF_4 \cdot H_2O$ and was thus the first to prepare a salt of quadrivalent cerium. From this compound, he computed cerium's atomic weight to be 141.1, placing it in Group IV. Later he revised this value to 140.22. From crude ceria, Brauner isolated compounds of other elements and determined their atomic weights: lanthanum, 138.92; praseodymium, 140.9; neodymium, 144.3; samarium, 150.4. This time-consuming, exacting analysis enabled Brauner to conclude that the rare earths are a group of closely related elements which occupy a single place in the periodic table—that between number 57 (lanthanum) and number 72 (hafnium). Brauner also studied the atomic weight of tellurium, an anomaly because it was thought to be 128, higher than that of iodine (127), although it was supposed to precede iodine in Mendeleev's system. Brauner's value of 127.61 for tellurium, although still an inversion, remains the accepted value today. In the decades following 1900, Brauner revised his earlier atomic weight results and also investigated the weights of tin and thorium.

In other areas, Brauner discussed the position of hydrogen in the periodic table, supporting Mendeleev's assignment of this element to the place above Group I. During his experiments with cerium he became the first to prepare elemental fluorine by a chemical method. When a fluorine-oxygen compound was produced in 1927, he speculated on its composition. When inert gases were discovered in the atmosphere, Brauner was reluctant to recognize them as new elements: he suggested that helium might be an allotrope of hydrogen and that argon might be triatomic nitrogen. He was also interested in astronomy and physiology, and made small contributions in both fields.

In 1888 Brauner advocated the adoption of oxygen ($=16$) instead of hydrogen ($=1$) as the standard for calculating atomic weights. Reviving an argument previously put forth by Marignac, Brauner claimed that the change would be advantageous, since most of the elements would then have atomic weights closer to a whole number. An international commission for atomic weights formed, at Brauner's suggestion, to consider the problem decided to use the oxygen standard, starting in 1904. Brauner was a member of the International Committee on Chemical Elements from 1921 to 1930. In 1921 he made a number of proposals regarding the naming of terms—atomic weight, for example—which had become clouded as a result of the discovery of isotopes. Brauner called for the formation of a subcommittee for atomic weights and served as its first president.

Brauner was invited to contribute sections on atomic weights for Abegg's *Handbuch der anorganischen Chemie,* and he spent the years between 1904 and 1913 preparing and translating the necessary materials. In 1906 he wrote a section on rare earth elements for a revised edition of Mendeleev's *Principles of Chemistry.* He collaborated with his assistant, H. Krepelka, on a textbook of qualitative analysis (in Czech) published in 1919. Additionally, he supported a journal, *Collection of Czechoslovak Chemical Communications,* which was founded in 1929 and was edited by E. Votocek and J. Heyrovsky. As a cultural "neo-Slavist," Brauner popularized Mendeleev's ideas and wrote for English journals on the contributions of other Russian scientists.

Brauner received numerous honors in his lifetime. He was a prominent member of the Czech Academy of Science and of Czechslovakia's National Research Council. He was recognized by scientific societies in England, the United States, France, Poland, Russia, and Austria; and he was honored and decorated by the governments of Austria, Yugoslavia, and France.

BIBLIOGRAPHY

I. ORIGINAL WORKS. An autobiographical source is "D. I. Mendeleef," in *Pokrokova revue* (1907). It was translated into English in *Collection of Czechoslovak Chemical Communications,* **2** (1930), 219–243; a bibliography of Brauner's scientific papers precedes it on pp. 212–218.

A selected list of Brauner's scientific papers includes the following: "On the Atomic Weight of Beryllium," in *Philosophical Magazine,* **11** (1881), 65–72; "On the Specific Volumes of Oxides," *ibid.,* 60–65, written with John I. Watts; "Contributions to the Chemistry of Rare Earth-Metals," in *Journal of the Chemical Society,* **41** (1882), 68–79; **43** (1883), 278–289; **47** (1885), 879–897; "The Atomic Weight of Tellurium," in *Journal of the Russian Physical-Chemical Society* (1883); "The Standard of Atomic Weights, I," in *Chemical News,* **58** (1888), 307–308; "Experimental Researches on the Periodic Law. I. Tellurium," in *Journal of the Chemical Society,* **55** (1889), 382–411; "Experimental Studies on the Periodic Law," in *Chemicke listy,* **14** (1889), 1–30; "The Standard of Atomic Weights, II," in *Chemische Berichte,* **22** (1889), 1186–1192; "Fluoplumbates and Free Fluorine," in *Journal of the Chemical Society,* **65** (1894), 393–402, and in Czech Academy, *Bulletin,* **18** (1894), 1–9; "Atomic Weight of Tellurium," in *Journal of the Chemical Society,* **67** (1895), 549–551; "Note on the Gases of the Helium and Argon Type," in *Chemical News,* **71** (1895), 271; "On the Compound Nature of Cerium," in Czech Academy, *Bulletin,* **2** (1895), 1–6; "Contributions to the Chemistry of Thorium; The Atomic Weight of Thorium; On the Compound Nature of Cerium; On Praseodymium and Neodymium," in *Proceedings of the Chemical Society,* **14** (1898), 67–72; "Contributions to the Chemistry of Thorium. Comparative Researches on the Oxalates of the Rare Earths," in *Journal of the Chemical Society,* **73** (1898), 951–985.

Also see "On the Atomic Weight of Lanthanum and the Error of the Sulphate Method for the Determination of the 'Equivalent' of the Rare Earths [written with F. Pavlicek]; On the Atomic Weight of Praseodymium; On Praseodymium Tetroxide and Peroxide; Note on Neodymium; Contribution to the Chemistry of Thorium," in *Proceedings of the Chemical Society,* **17** (1901), 63–68; "On the Position of Hydrogen in the Periodic System," in *Chemical News,* **84** (1901), 233–234, and in Czech Academy, *Bulletin,* **34** (1901), 1–4; "Revision of the Atomic Weight of Tin," in *Journal of the American Chemical Society,* **42** (1920), 917–925, written with H. Krepelka; "The New International Commission on Chemical Elements," in *Chemical News,* **123** (1921), 230–232; "Atomic Weight of Silver," in *Nature,* **119** (1927), 348, 526; "Oxide of Fluorine or Fluoride of Oxygen?," *ibid.,* **120** (1927), 842;

"Some Physiologico-optical Experiments," in Czech Academy, *Bulletin*, **38** (1929).

II. SECONDARY LITERATURE. Two biographical sources are Gerald Druce, *Two Czech Chemists, Bohuslav Brauner and Frantisek Wald* (London, 1944), pp. 4–44, bibliography pp. 62–65; and "Obituary of Bohuslav Brauner," in *Nature*, **135** (30 Mar. 1935), 497–498.

SUSAN G. SCHACHER

BRAUNMÜHL, ANTON VON (*b*. Tiflis, Russia, 12 December 1853; *d*. Munich, Germany, 7 March 1908), *history of mathematics*.

Braunmühl, descended from the old Bavarian nobility, was the son of the famous architect Anton von Braunmühl (1820–1858), who had studied with Fr. Gärtner, and Anna Maria Schlenz (1823–1892). In 1879 he married Franziska Stölzl (1853–1917), who bore him two daughters.

After the sudden death of his father, Braunmühl grew up in Munich and enrolled in its university in 1873. There he attended lectures on astronomy by Johann Lamont, on physics by Philipp Jolly, on the history of literature by Michael Bernays, and on cultural history by Wilhelm Riehl; he also studied mathematics under Ludwig Seidel, Gustav Bauer, and Friedrich Narr. At the Munich Technical University, Braunmühl studied further under Alexander Brill, Felix Klein, and Johann Bischoff. In 1888 he was appointed extraordinary professor of mathematics at the Technical University and was promoted to ordinary professor of mathematics in 1892. He was recognized as a scientist and was held in extraordinary esteem as a teacher. Braunmühl's lectures on the history of mathematics, given regularly after 1893, were unique in that they were offered without credit, as were the seminars on the history of mathematics that were given right after the lectures. These lectures and seminars stimulated Wilhelm Kutta, Axel Bjoernbo, and Carl Wallner, among others, to undertake independent work in the history of mathematics.

At the turn of the century Braunmühl, Moritz Cantor, Maximilian Curtze, and Sigmund Günther were leading authorities on the history of mathematics in Germany. Braunmühl's contributions, pertaining especially to the history of trigonometry, surpass those of many of his contemporaries in thorough study of sources, complete reflection of previous literature, and precise presentation of specific details, as well as in their critical evaluation.

BIBLIOGRAPHY

I. ORIGINAL WORKS. Braunmühl's writings include *Chr. Scheiner als Mathematiker, Physiker und Astronom*

(Bamberg, 1891); "Beiträge zur Geschichte der Trigonometrie," in *Nova acta Leopoldina*, **71** (1897), 1–30; and *Vorlesungen über Geschichte der Trigonometrie*, 2 vols. (Leipzig, 1900–1903).

Preliminary studies by Braunmühl were utilized after his death by H. Wieleitner in *Geschichte der Mathematik*, II, pt. 1 (Leipzig, 1911).

II. SECONDARY LITERATURE. Works on Braunmühl are S. Günther, "Anton von Braunmühl," in *Mitteilungen zur Geschichte der Medizin und der Naturwissenschaften*, **7** (1908), 362–367; J. E. Hofmann, "Anton von Braunmühl," in *Neue deutsche Biographie*, II (1955), 560; and H. Wieleitner, "Zum Gedächtnis Anton von Braunmühls," in *Bibliotheca mathematica*, 3rd ser., **11** (1910), 316–330, with a portrait and a bibliography.

JOSEPH E. HOFMANN

BRAVAIS, AUGUSTE (*b*. Annonay, France, 23 August 1811; *d*. Le Chesnay, France, 30 March 1863), *botany, physics, astronomy, crystallography*.

The ninth of ten children born to François-Victor Bravais, a physician, and Aurélie-Adelaïde Thomé, Auguste completed his classical education at the Collège Stanislas, Paris, in 1827, winning honorable mention in mathematics in the general competitive examination. He returned to Annonay and failed the polytechnical examination in 1828; after a year of special mathematics at the Collège St.-Louis, he won first prize in mathematics in the general competitive examination and was accepted at the École Polytechnique. He led his class at the end of his first year, and his academic record the next year made him eligible for any technical corps except mining. Since he wanted to participate in exploration, he chose to enter the navy. Bravais became a first-class cadet in 1831 and was sent to the Toulon naval district. He shipped out in January 1832, sailed the Mediterranean, and that April was assigned to map the coast of Algeria.

During his leaves in Annonay (November 1833–June 1835) Bravais studied plant organography with his brother Louis and his friend Charles Martins. The brothers' publications on this subject won them membership in the Société Philomathique de Paris. Auguste's work on shipboard led him to consider various methods of nautical surveying and the stability of ships; these were the subjects of his doctoral thesis, which he presented at Lyons in 1837. Shortly afterward he and Martins were assigned to the Commission Scientifique du Nord and sailed in June 1838 with the expedition that landed near North Cape.

While in Norwegian Lapland (August 1838 to September 1839), Bravais and the other physicists from the commission made numerous observations in astronomy, meteorology, and terrestrial magnetism. He noticed that a certain alga, *Fucus vesiculosus*, formed a yellowish area whose upper limit always occurred at the same height above sea level; this served as a point of reference for surveying ancient shorelines. Accompanied by Martins, Bravais returned overland to Paris, arriving in January 1840. Immediately afterward the navy assigned him to publish an account of the expedition; the volumes dealing with meteorology, terrestrial magnetism, the northern lights, botanical geography, astronomy, and hydrography are largely his own work.

The navy authorized Bravais to teach astronomy at the Faculté des Sciences at Lyons in 1841. Shortly after his arrival, he and J. Fournet founded the Commission Hydrométrique, des Orages et Météorologique de Lyon. Bravais climbed the Faulhorn in 1841 and 1842 with his brother Louis and Martins, in order to make observations. He was elected a member of the Académie Royale des Sciences, Belles-Lettres et Arts de Lyon in 1844, and later that year the minister of public education entrusted him with a scientific mission in the Alps: accompanied by Martins, he climbed Mont Blanc and, once again, the Faulhorn. During his stay in Lyons he wrote the segment of *Patria* that contains a survey of verified falls of meteorites in France from 1198 until 1842.

Bravais was appointed professor of physics at the École Polytechnique in 1845. Among the many communications he sent to the Académie des Sciences, the ones that drew the most attention were those of 1848 and 1849. They concerned reticular groupings and were based on speculations arising from a paper by Delafosse on the meaning of hemihedrism in crystals. The Academy admitted Bravais to its geography and navigation section in 1854.

The relationship between the external forms of crystals and an internal periodic corpuscular structure had been discussed by Kepler, Descartes, Hooke, and Huygens but was neglected in the eighteenth century for studies of the external forms alone, in the manner of Steno's *Prodromus*. After Romé de l'Isle and Haüy, attention was again directed to internal structure seen as the repetition of fundamental polyhedral nuclei. In an exhaustive study of the properties of lattices (1848), Bravais derived the fourteen possible arrangements of points in space. The Bravais lattices effectively combined earlier concepts of periodicity with Haüy's law of rational intercepts. (A. J. Shaler's English translation of this fundamental paper was published in 1949 as Memoir no. 1 of the Crystallographic Society of America.)

In the *Études cristallographiques* (1866), Bravais concentrated on the relationships between the ideal lattice and the material crystal. He proposed to locate his lattice points at the centers of gravity of congruent molecular polyhedra (p. 196). His analysis of the symmetry of the molecular polyhedra (the thirty-two point groups had been derived by Hessel in 1830) led to the later derivation of the space groups by Barlow, Schönflies, and Fedorow. The Bravais molecular polyhedra, repeated in parallel orientation in the same way as the points of the Bravais lattice, constituted the modern representation of the atomic structure of crystals. Each peak of the polyhedron was "a center or pole of force" (*ibid.*), which Cauchy, in a remarkable report introducing the paper, understood as an atom of a particular species. The Bravais rule that referred the most prominent planes of the crystal and the planes of cleavage to the nets of the Bravais lattice with the greatest reticular density (concentration of points) afforded a method by which mineralogists could determine lattice types and, in the simplest cases, structures. Bravais himself applied the rule to most mineral species with excellent but not perfect results.

Only constant work allowed Bravais to carry on extensive studies of the many different subjects that aroused his curiosity. He was, however, not able to bear such a strain indefinitely. He became seriously ill in 1856, resigned from his post at the École Polytechnique, and retired from the navy in 1857. His wife tried to nurse him back to health; on his death she withdrew to the Convent des Clarisses, in Versailles, of which she was founder.

Bravais's work, continued by Friedel, Tammann, Barlow, and others, provided the mathematical and conceptual basis for the determination of crystal structures after Laue's discovery of X-ray diffraction in 1911. The intensive development of solid-state physics in recent times has publicized Bravais's role in the origin of the application of the mathematics of symmetry and groups to the theory of solids.

BIBLIOGRAPHY

I. ORIGINAL WORKS. A complete bibliography is in Poggendorff, I, 283–284; III, 184–185; IV, 177. Bravais's books include *Thèse d'astronomie sur les méthodes employées dans les levés sous voiles* . . . (Paris, 1837); *Über die geometrische Anordnung der Blätter und der Blüthenstände* . . . (Breslau, 1839); *Sur l'équilibre des corps flottants* . . . (Paris, 1840); *Le Mont Blanc* (Paris, n.d. [1854]); and *Études cristallographiques* (Paris, 1866). He also contributed to many works or was a coauthor: "Étoiles," in P. Leroux and J. Reynaud, eds., *Encyclopédie nouvelle* . . ., V (Paris, 1839), 100–109, also published separately as *Les étoiles ou résumé d'astronomie stellaire* (Paris, 1844); the notes for L. F. Kaemtz's *Cours complet de météorologie* . . ., trans. and annotated by Charles Martins (Paris, 1843); the following volumes (as coauthor) of *Voyages de la*

Commission scientifique du Nord . . .: *Météorologie,* 3 vols. (1844–1855); *Magnétisme terrestre,* 3 vols. (1843–1850); *Aurores boréales* (1845); *Géographie physique, géographie botanique, botanique et physiologie,* 2 vols. (1844–1846); and *Astronomie et hydrographie* (n.d.); three letters in A. Quételet, *Lettres à S. A. R. le duc régnant de Saxe-Cobourg et Gotha, sur la théorie des probabilités* . . . (Brussels, 1846), pp. 412–424; and two chapters in *Patria. La France ancienne et moderne* . . ., 2 vols. (Paris, 1847), I, 1–142, 143–176.

Bravais's papers appeared in many journals: the *Annales des sciences naturelles,* from 2nd ser., Botanique, **7** (1837) to 3rd ser., Botanique, **3** (1845); *Comptes rendus hebdomadaires* . . . *de l'Académie des sciences,* from **4** (1837) to **42** (1856); *Mémoires présentés par divers savants* . . ., **9** (1846); *Nouveaux mémoires de l'Académie royale des sciences et belles-lettres de Bruxelles,* **14** (1841); *Mémoires couronnés* . . . *par l'Académie royale* . . . *de Bruxelles,* **15,** pt. 2 (1843); *Annales de chimie et de physique,* from 3rd ser., **5** (1842) to 3rd ser., **46** (1856); *Journal de mathématiques pures ou appliquées* . . ., from **8** (1843) to 2nd ser., **1** (1856); *Journal de l'École polytechnique,* from 30th cahier, **18** (1845) to 34th cahier, **20** (1851); the reports of the 6th and 9th sessions of the Congrès scientifique de France (1839, 1842); the *Bibliothèque universelle de Genève* (1845); *Le moniteur universel* (18 Sept. 1844); *Revue scientifique et industrielle,* 2nd ser., **4** (Jan. 1845); and *Annuaire météorologique de la France* for the years 1849–1853.

His communications to the Société Philomathique are condensed in *L'Institut; 1re section, Sciences mathématiques, physiques et naturelles* between 15 Feb. 1837 and 29 Nov. 1854; they are reproduced, after correction of misprints, in *Extraits des procès-verbaux* . . . of the Society for the years 1837–1854.

Lithographed copies of Bravais's courses are École Polytechnique, 2nd div., "Cours de physique, 1re année d'étude 1847–1848"; École Polytechnique, 1st div., "Cours de physique, 2e année 1848–1849"; École Impériale Polytechnique, 2nd div., "Sommaire du cours de physique, 1re année" (1853–1854); École Impériale Polytechnique, 1st div., "Sommaire du cours de physique, 2e année" (1853–1854); and École Impériale Polytechnique, 1st div., "Sommaire du cours de physique, 2e année" (1854–1855).

II. Secondary Literature. Writings on Bravais or his work are J.-M.-J. Bouillat, "Auguste Bravais, voyageur et savant (1811–1863)," in *Les contemporains,* no. 588 (Paris, 1904); Élie de Beaumont, *Éloge historique d'Auguste Bravais* (Paris, 1865), trans. in the *Smithsonian Report* for 1869, pp. 145–168; J. Fournet, "Rapport sur trois mémoires de Bravais," in *Annales des sciences physiques et naturelles* . . ., **9** (1846), lxxi–lxxv; and Jean Messié, "Auguste Bravais, savant annonéen," in *Revue du Vivarais,* **67** (Jan.–Mar. 1963), 7–11.

Charles Martins wrote several works concerning his work with Bravais: "Lettre sur le voyage aux terres arctiques," in *Revue médicale française et étrangère* (1838), **4,** 433–438; "Observations sur les migrations et les moeurs des Lemmings," in *Revue zoologique* . . . (July 1840), 193–206; "Une ascension au Faulhorn," in *Revue médicale française*

et étrangère (1841), **4,** 209–214; "Un hivernage scientifique en Laponie," in *Revue indépendante* (25 Dec. 1843), 483–511; "Ascension au Mont Blanc par MM. Martins, Bravais et Lepileur," in *L'illustration, journal universel* (5 Oct. 1844), 68–74; "Deux ascensions scientifiques au Mont-Blanc. . .," in *Revue des deux mondes* (15 Mar. 1865), 377–411; and *Du Spitzberg au Sahara* (Paris, 1866).

Archival materials are Bravais's dossiers in the Service Historique de la Marine and in the Archives de l'Académie des Sciences; the *Registre de matricule des élèves,* V (1820–1830), 353, at the École Polytechnique, Secrétariat de la bibliothèque; and the archives of the Société Philomathique, cartons 123–134, at the Bibliothèque de la Sorbonne.

Also used in preparing this article were *Distribution générale des prix aux élèves des collèges royaux de Paris et de Versailles* for 1827 (p. 23) and for 1829 (p. 10); Auguste Bérard, *Description nautique des côtes de l'Algérie* . . . (Paris, 1837); "Instructions pour l'expédition scientifique qui se rend dans le Nord de l'Europe," in *Comptes rendus de l'Académie des sciences,* **6** (23 Apr. 1838), 526–571; (30 Apr. 1838), 585; (13 May 1838), 673; (21 May 1838), 704; Gabriel Delafosse, "Recherches sur la cristallisation, considérée sous les rapports physiques et mathématiques," in *Mémoires présentés par divers savants* . . ., **8** (1843), 641–690, first presented in the *Comptes rendus,* **11** (31 Aug. 1840), 394–400, and reported by Beudant, *ibid.,* **12** (25 Jan. 1841), 205–210; Abbé Filhol, *Histoire religieuse et civile d'Annonay,* IV (Annonay, 1882); *Mémoires de l'Académie royale des sciences, belles-lettres et arts de Lyon. Section des lettres et arts,* **1** (1845), 111; and *Notice des travaux scientifiques de M. A. Bravais* (Paris, 1851, 1854).

Arthur Birembaut

BREDIKHIN, FEDOR ALEKSANDROVICH (*b.* Nikolaev, Russia, 8 December 1831; *d.* St. Petersburg, Russia, 14 May 1904), *astronomy.*

Bredikhin was born into an old aristocratic family. His father, Aleksandr Fedorovich, served with the Black Sea fleet; his mother, Antonida Ivanovna Rogulya, was the sister of an admiral. Since all of his uncles were naval officers, it was expected that Bredikhin would join the navy, but science attracted him instead. Until 1845 he studied at home; at Solonikha, his father's estate near Kherson; and at the Lycée Richelieu in Odessa. In 1851 he enrolled in the Physics and Mathematics Faculty of Moscow University, where he became interested in physics and, in his final year, astronomy.

After graduation in 1855 Bredikhin stayed at the university in order to prepare for a teaching career. He also worked at the Moscow observatory, which was directed by the famous "discoverer of comets," K. G. Schweizer. In 1858–1859 Bredikhin began teaching a lecture course at the university.

He married Anna Dmitrievna Bogolovskaya in

1860; their son, Aleksandr, died tragically in 1888. Bredikhin was a man of great general learning. He knew several European languages, possessed undoubted literary ability, loved music, and played the violin.

In 1861 he published his first scientific paper, "Quelques mots sur les queues des comètes" (on the bright comet Donati of 1858, which, in addition to its primary tail, had several weaker, more distorted ones). At this time he began his series of remarkable investigations of the nature of comets, which was the major work of his life. In 1862 Bredikhin defended his master's thesis, *O khvostakh komet* ("On the Tails of Comets"), and in 1863 was designated deputy extraordinary professor in the astronomy department. He defended his doctoral dissertation, "Vozmushchenia komet, nezavisyashchie ot planetnykh prityazheny" ("Comet Perturbations Which Are Not Caused by Attractions by the Planets") in 1865 and became an ordinary professor. In 1867–1868 Bredikhin visited Italy, where the first classification of star spectra had been developed and where, generally speaking, astrophysics was rapidly being developed. There he studied the technique of spectroscopic observation with Secchi, Tacchini, and other astrophysicists.

After Schweizer's death in 1873, Bredikhin became director of the Moscow observatory, where his fundamental works on the study of comets were written. In 1890, following Struve's retirement, he was elected an academician and director of the Pulkovo observatory. He left this post in 1895 for reasons of health and settled in St. Petersburg, where he worked on his investigations of comets for the rest of his life.

Notwithstanding the great significance that Bredikhin ascribed to theoretical investigations, he was a tireless observer. His observations encompassed all major aspects of contemporary astronomy, including even gravimetry—which was then inextricably associated with astronomy. He observed comets with astronomical instruments and studied them, systematically drawing their heads and tails and the contours of solar protuberances and chromosphere; he also observed comets and gaseous nebulae with the aid of a spectroscope, as well as meteor showers and zodiacal light. In addition, he observed the surfaces of Jupiter (especially the famous red spot) and Mars and conducted gravimetric measurements at various locations in Russia.

Although the fundamental peculiarities of changes in the apparent shape of comets as they approach the sun had been noted before Bredikhin, he was the one who developed the so-called mechanical theory of a comet's form. This theory's basic premise, which

dates as far back as Kepler and, ultimately, to Olbers, consists in the fact that particles of matter, which fly off from the core of the comet at a certain initial velocity, are repelled by the sun and, under the influence of that repulsion, move along hyperbolic trajectories. Bredikhin developed a method for determining the value of the repulsive accelerations (which are designated by $1 + \mu$) in the tails of comets and classified the tails according to these values: tails of type I are formed by forces of repulsion eleven to eighteen times greater than the sun's gravity and are inclined directly away from the sun, although they bend slightly in the direction opposite to the motion of the comet; the tails of type II are wider and strongly bent, their repulsive accelerations encompassing all values from 0.7 to 2.2 times the force of the sun's gravity; all tails of type III are even more inclined in the direction opposite that of the comet's motion, with an acceleration from 0.1 to 0.3. The fourth (anomalous) type of tail, which is directed straight toward the sun, is seen very rarely and always with a tail of one of the first three types. Some comets have tails of two or three different types.

Bredikhin's theory, which was based on an analysis of observations of about forty comets taken by himself and by others, explains several details of the structure of comets: the transverse bands in type II tails (synchrons), the motion of individual clumps in tails, and the form of a comet's head. The physical ideas on which the theory of comet forms was based included the supposition of an interaction between the sun's electric charge and the like charge of the gaseous molecules emanating from the comet's core. The values of the repulsive accelerations of these molecules are inversely proportional to their molecular weights. From this, Bredikhin proposed that hydrogen molecules predominate in type I tails; that hydrocarbons and light metals, such as sodium, predominate in type II tails; and that type III tails might contain molecules of iron. Observations by Bredikhin and his contemporaries seemingly confirmed such an explanation. It has since been proved that type I tails contain ionized molecules of carbon monoxide and nitrogen, while tails of type II and type III consist of neutral gases and dust particles that reflect the rays of the sun.

Through the detailed study of spectra of the heads and tails of comets, the mechanical theory of comet forms has to a large degree been retained. The classification of comet tails proposed by Bredikhin and developed by S. V. Orlov has also retained its significance. Certain peculiarities of comets that follow Bredikhin's theory, such as the parabolic shape of a comet's head, rotation of the core, and the complex movements of clumps of matter in comets' tails, have received exhaustive explanations in contemporary investigations. Bredikhin foresaw in the physical theory of comets the possibility of the influence of electrical forces, which also takes place in the interaction of solar corpuscular streams (so-called solar wind) and particles of matter in a comet.

He also devoted much attention to the study of meteor showers, which he believed occurred as the result of the earth's intersection of a swarm of particles from the tails of comets, these particles having been gradually scattered along the comets' orbits.

Bredikhin directed special attention to astrophysical investigations. In connection with his systematic observations of the sun, he developed a theory of the movement of matter in sunspots and in the rays of the solar corona. He proposed descending and ascending gaseous streams as the explanation of the formation of faculae and spots. On the basis of measurements made from photographs of eight total solar eclipses, taken between 1870 and 1896 by various astronomers, Bredikhin correctly noted the intimate connection between coronal eruptions and chromospheric protuberances and the absence of a direct connection between coronal eruptions and sunspots. Having determined that coronal eruptions are not radial, but somewhat curved, Bredikhin sought a similarity between them and the form of comet tails, proposing that a certain repulsive force also acts on coronal eruptions. He also applied his mechanical theory of comet forms to the analysis of coronal rays. Only in recent times has the physics of the corona received solid substantiation in the theory of the interaction between magnetic fields and a plasma, which is what the solar corona actually is.

Bredikhin's activity as director of the Pulkovo observatory greatly influenced the development of astronomy in Russia. Having replaced Struve, who strictly limited his contacts with other Russian university observatories and who preferred to have Germans and Swedes on the observatory staff, Bredikhin undertook a tour of all Russian observatories in order to familiarize himself with their activities, to help them obtain necessary instruments, to determine the most urgent scientific problems, and to attract the most talented young Russian astronomers to Pulkovo. In his first director's report (for 1889–1891) he wrote: "To the alumni of all Russian universities . . . must be afforded, within the limits of possibility, free access [to the observatory] . . . the recruitment abroad of scientists for its staff must and can be stopped forever." This greatly encouraged Russian astronomers, who now became frequent guests at Pulkovo, learned how to observe, and sometimes remained permanently. Before Bredikhin, there were only two Russians (A. A. Belopolsky and M. N. Morin) on the fifteen-man staff at Pulkovo; soon after he assumed the directorship, the number rose to nine.

Bredikhin was a charter member of the Mathematical Society in Moscow and an active member of the Moscow Society of Natural Scientists. In 1890 he was chairman of the Russian Astronomical Society, which had just been founded in St. Petersburg. He also belonged to many foreign organizations: the Astronomische Gesellschaft, Deutsche Akademie der Naturforscher Leopoldina, the Royal Astronomical Society, the Italian Society of Spectroscopists, and the Bureau des Longitudes in Paris. In 1892 he was awarded an honorary doctorate by the University of Padua.

BIBLIOGRAPHY

I. ORIGINAL WORKS. Bredikhin's complete bibliography of published works contains over 200 titles. Among them are *O khvostakh komet* ("On the Tails of Comets"; Moscow, 1862; 2nd ed., K. D. Pokrovsky, ed., Moscow, 1934), 2nd ed. includes a biographical essay and a bibliography; "Protsess Galileya po novym dokumentam" ("The Trials of Galileo According to New Documents"), in *Russkii vestnik,* **92,** no. 4 (1871), 405–414; "O solnechnoy korone" ("On the Solar Corona"), in *Izvestiya Imperatorskoi akademii nauk,* 5th ser., **9,** no. 3 (1898), 179–207; *Prof. Th. Bredikhin's mechanische Untersuchungen über Cometenformen in systematischer Darstellung,* R. Jaegermann, compil. (Leipzig, 1903), a systematic survey of all of Bredikhin's papers on the mechanical theory of comet forms, compiled under his supervision; *Études sur l'origine des météores cosmiques et la formation de leurs courants* (St. Petersburg, 1903), Bredikhin's survey monograph on meteor showers; and *Etyudy o meteorakh* ("Studies on Meteors"), S. V. Orlov, ed. (Moscow, 1954), with an article and commentary by A. D. Dubyago. His correspondence is in the archives, Academy of Sciences, Leningrad.

II. SECONDARY LITERATURE. Works on Bredikhin include A. A. Belopolsky, "Fedor Aleksandrovich Bredikhin," in *Izvestiya Imperatorskoi akademii nauk,* 5th ser., **21,** no. 2 (1904), i–iv, and "Fizicheskoe stroenie kometnykh khvostov" ("The Physical Structure of Comet Tails"), in *Russkii astronomicheskii kalendar na 1927 god* ("Russian Astronomical Calendar for 1927"; Nizhni Novgorod, 1926), pp. 137–161; S. K. Kostinsky, "Fedor Aleksandrovich Bredikhin," in *Russkii astronomicheskii kalendar na 1905 god* ("Russian Astronomical Calendar for 1905"; Nizhni Novgorod, 1904), pp. 2–29; B. Y. Levin, "F. A. Bredikhin," in *Lyudi russkoy nauki* ("People of Russian Science"; Moscow, 1961), pp. 141–151; O. A. Melnikov, "Fedor Aleksandrovich Bredikhin (k 125-letiyu so dnya rozhdenia)" ("Fedor Aleksandrovich Bredikhin: On the 125th Anniversary of the Day of His Birth"), in

Izvestiya GAO v Pulkove, **20**, pt. 6, no. 159 (1958), 1–27; N. I. Nevskaya, *Fedor Aleksandrovich Bredikhin (1831–1904)* (Moscow–Leningrad, 1964), the most complete biography, with a bibliography of all his works and of 252 secondary sources; S. V. Orlov, *Fedor Aleksandrovich Bredikhin (1831–1904)* (Moscow, 1948), a biographical essay with a bibliography of both original and secondary works; and K. D. Pokrovsky, "Teoria kometnykh form" ("The Theory of Comet Forms"), in *Russkii astronomicheskii kalendar na 1905 god* ("Russian Astronomical Calendar for 1905"; Nizhni Novgorod, 1904), pp. 35–51.

P. G. KULIKOVSKY

BREDON, SIMON (*b.* Winchcomb, England, *ca.* 1300; *d. ca.* 1372), *mathematics, astronomy, medicine.*

Originally a fellow of Balliol College, Oxford, Bredon moved to Merton College and was a fellow there in 1330, becoming junior proctor of the university in 1337 and keeper of the Langton chest about 1339. In 1348 he left Merton to become vicar of Rustington, Sussex, and thereafter held a succession of church appointments. His will, probated in 1372, listed the contents of his library, which covered theology, law, medicine, mathematics, and astronomy, as well as grammar and dialectic.

Bredon's earliest writings were concerned with philosophy, but he soon turned to mathematics and produced an explanation of Boethius' *Arithmetic.* This he split up into two parts, the first dealing with numbers, including multiplication, the second concerned with geometrical figures—triangles, squares, pentagons, hexagons, etc. In his copy of William Rede's astronomical tables for 1341–1344 he jotted down five conclusions on square numbers, which he considered useful for the squaring of the circle. These were followed by two criticisms of statements made by Vitello in his book on perspective, which Bredon dubbed "marvellous but false." His possession of Richard of Wallingford's book on sines and John Maudith's table of chords shows him to have taken an interest in trigonometry, but his own writings on these subjects have not survived except for a few brief notes; therefore it is not possible to assess his contribution in this field.

Bredon's works on astronomy are better attested. He wrote a treatise on the use of the astrolabe, giving detailed instructions how to find the altitude, degree, and declination of the sun; the latitude of any region; the degree of eclipse; and so on. The opening paragraph, entitled "Nomina instrumentorum," is not his work, but a borrowing from Messehallach. His *Theorica planetarum,* sometimes attributed to Walter Brytte, a contemporary at Merton, sometimes to Gerardo da Sabbionetta, is largely a paraphrase of the latter's treatise, although it lacks the two final sections on the latitude of the planets and the invection of the aspects of the planets. The text *De equationibus planetarum* formerly ascribed to Bredon has been shown to belong to Chaucer.

Bredon wrote a commentary on the first three books of Ptolemy's *Almagest.* No complete copy survives, but the work can be reconstructed from two incomplete manuscripts, both of which were annotated by Thomas Allen and John Dee. According to a marginal note in MS Digby 179, Bredon also made a new translation of Ptolemy's *Quadrepartitum,* probably to be identified with the *Astronomia judiciaria* mentioned in John Bale's *Index Britanniae scriptorum.* This translation is inserted into the lower margins of the version done by Egidius de Thebaldis of Parma, a copy of which was in Bredon's library. He drew up tables for the declination of the sun and the ascension of the signs and gave the longitude of Oxford as 14°56′. Bale ascribes three other works to him—*Super introductorio Alcabitii, Astronomia calculatoria,* and *Astronomia judiciaria*—without giving incipits.

Bredon's most ambitious work was the *Trifolium,* a medical compilation modeled on Avicenna's *Canon.* Only one-twelfth of it survives, dealing with the prognostication of disease from feces and urine, and with the composition of medicines. He was physician to Richard, Earl of Arundel, in 1355 and treated Joanna, Queen of Scots, in 1358.

BIBLIOGRAPHY

I. ORIGINAL WORKS. Bredon's writings are *Questiones in X libros Ethicorum Aristotelis:* Vienna, Bibl. Monast. B.V.M. ad Scotos MS 278.

De arithmetica: Oxford, Digby MS 98, fols. 109–117; Digby MS 147, fols. 92–103; Corpus Christi Coll. MS 118, fols. 101–118; Cambridge, Univ. Lib. MS Ee.iii, 61, fols. 92–101; Univ. of Alabama, MS 1, fols. 1–16; Boston Public Lib. MS 1531. On the last, see Margaret Munsterberg, "An Unpublished Mathematical Treatise by Simon Bredon," in *More Books, The Bulletin of the Boston Public Library,* **19** (1944), 411.

Conclusiones quinque de numero quadrato: Digby MS 178, fols. 11v–14.

Massa compoti (of Alexandre de Ville Dieu, not of Grosseteste, as ascribed by Bale): Digby MS 98, fols. 11–21, "bene correctus secundum sententiam Bredone."

Theorica planetarum: London, British Museum Egerton MS 847, fols. 104–122; Egerton MS 889; Oxford, Digby MS 48; Digby MS 93; Digby MS 98. The following MSS listed by Lynn Thorndike do not contain Bredon's work, but the treatise by Gerardo da Sabbionetta: London, B.M. Royal 12 C.ix; Royal 12 C.xvii; Royal 12 E.xxv; Oxford, Digby MS 47; Digby MS 168; Digby MS 207.

Commentum . . . Almagesti: Oxford, Digby MS 168, fols. 21–39; Digby MS 178, fols. 42–87; Cambridge, Univ. Lib. Ee.iii, 61, art. 8.

Astrolabii usus et declaracio: London, B.M. Harl. 321, fols. 24v–28.

Liber Quadrepartiti Ptolemei: Digby MS 179. See Axel Anthon Björnbo, "Die Mittelalterlichen lateinischen Übersetzungen aus dem Griechischen auf dem Gebiete der mathematischen Wissenschaften," in *Archiv für Geschichte der Naturwissenschaften und der Technik,* **1** (1909), 391 ff.

Trifolium: Oxford, Digby MS 160, fols. 102–223.

Bredon is quoted in Thomas Werkworth, *Tractatus de motu octavae spherae* (1396): Digby MS 97, fol. 143.

Two letters addressed to him are in London, B.M. Royal 12 D.xi, fols. 25r, 35r. His longitude for Oxford is in Royal 12 D.v, fol. 50r.

II. SECONDARY LITERATURE. Full biographical details are in A. B. Emden, *A Biographical Register of the University of Oxford to A.D. 1500,* I (Oxford, 1957), 257–258; R. T. Gunther, *Early Science in Oxford,* II (Oxford, 1923), 52–55; and Lynn Thorndike, *A History of Magic and Experimental Science,* III (New York, 1934), 521–522. See also C. H. Talbot, "Simon Bredon (*c.* 1300–1372), Physician, Mathematician and Astronomer," in *British Journal of the History of Science,* **1** (1962–1963), 19–30; and J. A. Weisheipl, "Early 14th Century Physics and the Merton School," Bodl. Lib. MS D.Phil. d.1776. A list of the contents of Bredon's library is in F. M. Powicke, *The Mediaeval Books of Merton College* (Oxford, 1931), pp. 82–86, 138–142.

C. H. TALBOT

BREFELD, JULIUS OSCAR (*b.* Telgte, Germany, 19 August 1839; *d.* Schlachtensee, near Berlin, Germany, 7 January 1925), *mycology.*

Oscar Brefeld, a founder of modern mycology, developed pure culture techniques and a comparative morphological approach in the study and classification of fungi, pioneered in researches on the cereal smuts, and published, over a period of forty years, a monumental fifteen-part treatise on his observations.

He was born in a small town near Münster in Westphalia, the third of four children (two sons and two daughters) of Wilhelm Brefeld, a prosperous pharmacist, and his wife Franziska Povel. Since the elder son, Ludwig, had studied law (in due course he became Prussian minister of trade and commerce), the other son was expected to follow his father's profession. Accordingly, having attended school in Telgte and completed his year of military service, Oscar studied pharmacy at Breslau for a year and a half. After a similar period at Berlin, he passed his state examination in pharmacy in 1863; but preferring chemistry and botany, he went to Heidelberg to work

under Bunsen and Hofmeister. There he obtained his Ph.D. in June 1864, for a thesis entitled "Chlor- und Bromgehalt des Meerwassers."

Soon afterward, a severe attack of pneumonia forced Brefeld to give up chemistry. During convalescence in Italy he studied art. On his return, he managed the family pharmacy for a short period, meanwhile beginning private researches on fungi. In 1868, financially assisted by his father, he went to the Botanical Institute at Halle to work with Anton de Bary. Two years later the Franco-Prussian war intervened, and Brefeld was drafted as an army pharmacist. During the siege of Paris he contracted typhoid fever, which proved nearly fatal. He was invalided home early in 1871 after devoted nursing by a French pharmacist. When fully recovered, he returned briefly to Halle. Thence, after short periods in Munich and at the Botanical Institute at Würzburg, he went in 1873 to Berlin, where he became *Privatdozent* in botany in 1875.

In 1878, shortly after becoming professor of botany at the Forest Academy of Eberswalde, near Berlin, Brefeld suffered a grave mishap. While examining a forestry class in chilly rain, he caught a severe cold, accompanied by ocular inflammation. This culminated in retinal detachment, glaucoma, and surgical removal of the left eye. He spent two years in Italy recuperating, again studying art. In the autumn of 1881 he resumed his researches, having appealed in vain to the Agriculture Ministry for an assistant because of his damaged eyesight.

In 1884 Brefeld became professor of botany at the Royal Botanical Institute and director of the botanical garden at Münster, where he spent fourteen very productive years. His work attracted international attention, and various foreign academies elected him to membership. He traveled in England, France, and Spain, meeting many scientists, including Pasteur, with whom he later corresponded. In 1896 he was appointed *Geheimer Regierungsrat* and in 1897 was made a corresponding member of the Berlin Academy of Sciences.

Brefeld married Elizabeth Godendahl, daughter of a Münster merchant, in 1896. Two years later he succeeded Ferdinand Cohn at Breslau as professor of botany and director of the Institute of Plant Physiology. In 1902, when Brefeld was sixty-three, his wife died shortly after the birth of their only child, Walter. His remaining eye now developed glaucoma, and in 1905 Brefeld became unable to teach; but with his assistant, R. Falck, he continued to work until increasingly defective vision forced his resignation in 1907.

Brefeld moved with his young son and housekeeper to Berlin, where he became completely blind in 1910, following an unsuccessful eye operation. Thereupon he withdrew to a property he owned in Berlin-Lichterfelde. In 1918, wartime malnutrition compelled him to enter a Rhineland sanatorium until 1924, when he moved to a nursing home at Schlachtensee, near Berlin. He remained completely alert mentally until his death from a colonic disorder.

Brefeld's blunt individuality and caustic wit were effective when used in defense of freedom of speech or for prescient warnings against the political philosophy that led Germany into World War I. His scientific reports, however, were sometimes needlessly polemic—a fault that his personal misfortunes, his single-minded attachment to mycology, and the lasting loyalty of his assistants helped to mitigate.

Brefeld's first publication concerned a new species of Myxomycetes, *Dictyostelium mucoroides* (1869). After the war, he began those detailed investigations into the developmental history and systematic relationships of fungi that became his lifework. Part I of his *Botanische Untersuchungen über Schimmelpilze* (1872), respectfully dedicated to his teacher de Bary, described three fungal species of Zygomycetes, a subclass characterized by Brefeld himself. The preface states a fundamental tenet that was to govern all his work: "The developmental history of a mold is deduced completely from the culture of the individual spore."

A report on *Penicillium,* completed while Brefeld was at Würzburg, appeared in 1874. In Berlin he published his first monograph on the Basidiomycetes (1877). These works, which constituted Parts II and III of his *Untersuchungen,* reflect his changing views on the sexuality of fungal fruit bodies. Part IV (1881) included observations on various species of Zygomycetes and Ascomycetes, and on *Bacillus subtilis,* preceded by a section expounding methods he had developed since 1869 for microscopic observations of pure fungal cultures. The same volume reveals an open feud with de Bary, whose claim—eventually verified—that the higher fungi exhibit sexuality Brefeld henceforth denied. Thirty years later, he intransigently wrote: "It is a basic error to correlate fungal pleomorphy with sexuality in the higher fungi, which has been construed after the pattern of the algae, but in reality does not exist." Meanwhile, he reacted unduly whenever criticisms of his work appeared in de Bary's journal, the *Botanische Zeitung.*

Brefeld's cultural methods (first outlined in 1874) stressed the heat sterilization of culture media, glassware, utensils, and instruments; precautions to exclude dust-borne contaminants; and use of sufficiently diluted inocula to permit single-spore transfers. He invented or adapted such useful devices as "capillary

culture chambers" and the "hanging drop" (generally known as the Van Tieghem cell). As basal nutrient medium, he favored decoctions of fresh manure from a herbivore; but solid sterile dung, or bread soaked in dung decoction, prevented dispersal and facilitated study of growing cultures. Addition of gelatin to the fluid medium permitted freer manipulation of preparations under the microscope and reduced evaporation of the medium without altering its transparency or nutritive qualities.

On returning to work after losing his eye, Brefeld made thousands of cultures, employing the foregoing techniques, to demonstrate that parasitic fungi, such as the cereal smuts, might be grown saprophytically. He cultivated over twenty species of *Ustilago,* as well as the potato blight fungus and other usually parasitic species. His observations led him to conclude that the yeasts, hitherto classified as "sprouting fungi," were conidial forms of higher fungal genera. These findings were reported in Part V of the *Untersuchungen* (1883), Part VI, on certain Myxomycetes and Entomophthorales, followed (1884), under the final version of the main title, *Untersuchungen aus dem Gesammtgebiete der Mykologie.*

At Münster, Brefeld had two young assistants, G. Istvánffy and O. J. Olsen (later known as O. Sopp), for Parts VII (1888) and VIII (1889), which reported further studies on over 200 species of Basidiomycetes. De Bary was again attacked in Part VII. He had suggested that Brefeld's views on the "sprouting fungi" were too sweeping and that yeasts were rudimentary forms of Ascomycetes.

F. von Tavel, and to a lesser extent G. Lindau, assisted Brefeld with Parts IX and X, on the Ascomycetes (1891), of which more than 400 species were studied. Work was resumed on the cereal smuts, over sixty species being cultivated on laboratory media. Growing "inexhaustible quantities" of specific fungi saprophytically, Brefeld investigated the mechanisms of infection, and the temporal and nidal variations in host susceptibility, in several smut diseases. These climactic efforts were reported in Parts XI and XII (1895).

Despite the many difficulties, domestic and administrative, that beset Brefeld in Breslau, Part XIII appeared in 1905, with Falck as co-author, describing the mechanisms of blossom infection by smut fungi and their natural modes of dissemination. In retirement, the totally blind mycologist dictated a recapitulation of his cultural methods and also reported miscellaneous earlier observations, published in Part XIV (1908). In Part XV (1912), he reverted mainly to smuts and smut diseases. A sixteenth part in manuscript was never published. Falck, in his obituary tribute, summarizes the contents of each part of the *Untersuchungen.*

Brefeld's manifold contributions to microbiology included a cultural methodology that was far more precise than Pasteur's and stimulated Koch to improve upon the gelatinized nutrient medium he is wrongly credited with having initiated. The indirect practical benefits to North America of Brefeld's work on smuts, especially of wheat, are inestimable. His *Untersuchungen,* often termed the "Bible of mycology," contains some errors of observation and interpretation, as well as unduly repetitive and vituperative passages; but the work is replete with classic observations, novel findings, and prophetic conjectures, recorded in colorful style. The accurate artistry of innumerable drawings on over 100 folio plates ensures the continuing reproduction of samples in mycology texts. Unfortunately, only fragments of his writings are available in English. Brefeld's extraordinary experimental skill, combined with rare patience and complete dedication, inspired A. H. R. Buller to call him "one of the ablest botanists of the nineteenth century."

BIBLIOGRAPHY

I. ORIGINAL WORKS. The first seven pts. of Brefeld's chief work, *Botanische Untersuchungen . . .,* were published between 1872 and 1888 in Leipzig, and the last eight pts. between 1889 and 1912 in Münster. The dates and titles are, under the general title *Botanische Untersuchungen über Schimmelpilze,* I, *Zygomyceten* (1872); II, *Penicillium* (1874); III, *Basidiomyceten I* (1877); IV, *Culturmethoden . . .* (1881); as *Botanische Untersuchungen über Hefenpilze,* V, *Die Brandpilze I* (1883); and, under the comprehensive title *Untersuchungen aus dem Gesammtgebiete der Mykologie,* VI, *Myxomyceten I. Entomophthoreen II* (1884); VII, *Basidiomyceten II* (1888), written with G. Istvánffy and O. J. Olsen; VIII, *Basidiomyceten III* (1889); IX, *Die Hemiasci und die Ascomyceten* (1891), written with F. von Tavel and G. Lindau; X, *Ascomyceten* (1891), written with F. von Tavel; XI, *Die Brandpilze II* (1895), written with G. Istvanffi; XII, *Hemibasidii. Brandpilze III* (1895); XIII, *Brandpilze (Hemibasidii) IV* (1905), written with Richard Falck; XIV, *Die Kultur der Pilze* (1908); and XV, *Die Brandpilze und die Brandkrankheiten V* (1912). Falck, in his obituary on Brefeld, lists twenty-six additional publications in various German scientific journals, the earliest being "Dictyostelium mucoroides, ein neuer Organismus aus der Verwandtschaft der Myxomyceten," in *Abhandlungen herausgegeben von der Senckenbergischen naturforschenden Gesellschaft,* 7 (1869), 85–107.

Translations of works by Brefeld are "Recent Investigations of Smut Fungi and Smut Diseases," trans. from *Nachrichten aus dem Klub der Landwirthe zu Berlin,* nos. 220–222 (1888) by Erwin F. Smith in *Journal of Mycology,*

6 (1890), 1–9, 59–71, 153–164; and *Investigations in the General Field of Mycology, Blossom Infection by Smuts and Natural Distribution of Smut Diseases,* pt. 13, written with R. Falck, trans. by Frances Dorrance (n.p., 1912).

II. SECONDARY LITERATURE. Obituaries are W. Brefeld, "Oscar Brefeld, 'Ein Leben für die Mykologie,' " an unpub. memoir by his son (personal communication, Sept. 1967); R. Falck, "Oskar Brefeld," in *Botanisches Archiv,* 11 (1925), 1–25; M. Kienitz, "Zum Gedächtnis. Dr. Oskar Brefeld, Professor der Botanik an der Forstakademie Eberswalde in den Jahren 1.10.1878–1884," in *Zeitschrift für Forst- und Jagdwesen,* 57 (1925), 709–711; F. Rosen, "Das pflanzenphysiologische Institut," in *Festschrift zur Feier des hundertjährigen Bestehens der Universität Breslau* (Breslau, 1911), see pp. 496–498; and O. Sopp, "Minnetale over prof. dr. Oscar Brefeld," in *Norske Videnskaps-Akademi i Oslo Årbok* (1925), pp. 83–86.

Important references to Brefeld's work are A. H. R. Buller, *Researches on Fungi,* 7 vols. (I–VI, London, 1909–1934; VII, Toronto, 1950; all repr. New York, 1958); A. De Bary, *Comparative Morphology and Biology of the Fungi. Mycetozoa and Bacteria,* Henry E. F. Garnsey, trans. (Oxford, 1887; repr. New York, 1966), pp. 256–257, 272, 295–297; M. Möbius, *Geschichte der Botanik. Von der ersten Anfängen bis zur Gegenwart* (Jena, 1937), pp. 74, 102–106; and J. Ramsbottom, "The Expanding Knowledge of Mycology Since Linnaeus," in *Proceedings of the Linnean Society of London,* 151 (1939), 280–367.

CLAUDE E. DOLMAN

BREGUET, LOUIS FRANÇOIS CLÉMENT (*b.* Paris, France, 22 December 1804; *d.* Paris, 27 October 1883), *instrumentation.*

Breguet's career can be understood only with a knowledge of the milieu in which he lived. His grandfather, Abraham, from Neuchâtel, was one of the best-known clockmakers of Paris; his shop was established as early as 1775. Louis's father, Antoine, became Abraham's partner in 1807. After spending some time in Neuchâtel with his godfather when he was about eight, Louis was apprenticed to Perrelet, in Versailles, for two years, and then joined his father and grandfather. From 1824 to 1827 he worked with Barral in Geneva in order to improve his craft, and upon his return to Paris worked on naval chronometers. His father, having little interest in business, withdrew more and more to the country. Finally, in 1833, the enterprise was organized into a company and turned over to Louis and two other partners, one of whom was a cousin.

After 1830 Breguet turned to making electrical instruments, particularly precision apparatus. His first electric clocks date from 1839. In 1840 he devised a thermometer that registered temperature electrically, and recorded a temperature of −42° at Kazan, Russia. Work on induced currents with Antoine

Masson in 1842 led to the creation of a genuine induction coil, a feat later ascribed to Heinrich Ruhmkorff in 1851. In 1843 Breguet created, for François Arago, an apparatus with a revolving mirror, which could attain a speed of 9,000 rps, for measuring the speed of light. It was used in Fizeau's experiments.

Breguet was then named designer-manufacturer to the Bureau des Longitudes. He gave a definitive form to the Wheatstone dial plate adopted by French railroads and constructed the Foy-Breguet instrument used in the French telegraphic system. In 1856 Breguet's firm made the first clocks to transmit time electrically.

In 1873 his son, Antoine, became his partner, and the Breguets turned to electrotechnics, then in its infancy: the company produced Daniell and Leclanché batteries, arc lamps, and Gramme dynamos. Metal thermometers, barometers, and manometers were made, as were very small, experimental aluminum helicopters for Antoine Pénaud, a pioneer in aeronautics. In 1876 Cornelius Roosevelt, representing Bell in Paris, put the Breguet firm in charge of setting up the French telephone system. The first Exposition Internationale d'Électricité was opened in Paris in 1881, and Antoine Breguet was the director of the installation services. Before his death Antoine collaborated with Charles Richet in founding the *Revue scientifique* (1881), an important journal during the next forty years. (It was the famous "Revue rose.") On 1 January 1882, Louis Breguet retired, leaving his son in charge, but within two years both had died.

BIBLIOGRAPHY

I. ORIGINAL WORKS. Breguet's most important works are *Mémoire sur l'induction* . . . (*. . . présenté à l'Académie des Sciences le 23 août 1841*) (Paris, 1842), written with Antoine Masson; *Télégraphie électrique, son avenir. Poste aux lettres électriques. Journaux électriques; suivi d'un aperçu théorique de télégraphie* (Paris, 1849), written with Victor de Seré; *Manuel de la télégraphie électrique à l'usage des employés des chemins de fer* (Paris, 1851; 2nd ed., 1853; 3rd ed., 1856; 4th ed., 1862); *Notice sur les appareils magnéto-électriques brevetés de Breguet et sur leur application à l'explosion des torpilles et des mines en général* (Paris, 1869); and *Catalogue illustré. Appareils et matériaux pour la télégraphie électrique, instruments divers, électricité, physique, mécanique, météorologie, physiologie, etc.* (Paris, 1873). For lists of his publications, see *Tables générales des comptes-rendus des séances de l'Académie des sciences . . . 1835–1850* (Paris, 1853), pp. 99–100; *1851–1865* (Paris, 1870), p. 74; *1866–1880* (Paris, 1888), p. 88; *1881–1895* (Paris, 1900), p. 96; and *Catalogue général des livres imprimés . . . de la Bibliothèque nationale*, XIX (Paris, 1904), cols. 165–167.

II. SECONDARY LITERATURE. Works on Breguet are Claude Breguet, "La maison Breguet," in *Annuaire de la Société historique du quatorzième arrondissement de Paris* (1962), pp. 65–92; E. Ferret, *Les Breguet* (Paris, n.d. [*ca.* 1890]); and E. de Jonquières, "Notice sur la vie et les travaux de Louis Breguet," in *Comptes-rendus de l'Académie des sciences*, **103** (5 July 1886), 5–14, repr. in Ferret, pp. 60–79.

JACQUES PAYEN

BREISLAK, SCIPIONE (*b.* Rome, Italy, 17 August 1750; *d.* Milan, Italy, 15 February 1826), *geology, natural history.*

Breislak, of German extraction, was a priest who devoted much of his life to the teaching of the natural sciences. He had become interested in them during his early youth, which he spent in Sicily; and when he returned to Rome, he improved his scientific knowledge under Giovanni Fortis and Pietro Petrini. He later published reports on the natural resources of Latium: the Tolfa, Allumiere, Oriolo Romano, Latera, and Civitavecchia mines; underground water; and agriculture.

Subsequently, Breislak moved to Naples, where he taught at the military academy. In 1794 he witnessed the eruption of Vesuvius and made direct observations at the Campi Flegrei and Pozzuoli sulfur mines. *Topografia fisica della Campania* (1798), which discusses his studies on volcanoes, includes his opinion that the volcanic systems of Latium and Campania were connected at the ancient Roccamonfina volcano, whose eruptive apparatus and lava he had discovered. An adherent of Plutonist theory, Breislak believed that metamorphic rocks originated during consolidation of the earth's crust.

Considered one of the founders of volcanology in Italy, Breislak was the first to determine that basaltic rocks were of extrusive origin; he also emphasized that the tufaceous deposits of Campania originated under water, and he reconstructed the evolution of Vesuvius. He concluded that for a long time Monte Somma, the second summit of Vesuvius, had been the sole volcanic apparatus; that it had been active until A.D. 79; that it had been eroded; and that the cone of Vesuvius had been set upon it within historical time.

Breislak's final move was to Milan, where he was inspector of the niter factory and cooperated with the Biblioteca Italiana. He also investigated the mineral resources of most of Lombardy, particularly the building-stone and clay quarries of Brianza and the gold placers of the Tessin, Adda, and Serio rivers. In addition, he studied the igneous rocks on the western shore of Lake Maggiore, between Intra (Verbania) and Arona.

BIBLIOGRAPHY

Breislak's writings are *Topografia fisica della Campania* (1798); *Voyages physiques et lithologiques dans la Campanie, suivis d'une mémoire sur la constitution physique de Rome* (1801), also trans. into German (Leipzig, 1802); *Descrizione geologica della provincia di Milano* (1822); and *Traité sur la structure interne du globe* (1822).

VINCENZO FRANCANI

BREITHAUPT, JOHANN FRIEDRICH AUGUST (*b.* Probstzella, Germany, 18 May 1791; *d.* Freiberg, Germany, 22 September 1873), *mineralogy.*

The son of a local official in Probstzella, Breithaupt received his early education in the schools and Gymnasium of Saalfeld, to which his father was transferred. He was influenced by the mining activity that still thrived near Saalfeld, and decided to prepare for a career in this field. After a year and a half of study at the University of Jena, he went to the Bergakademie at Freiberg, Saxony, in the spring of 1811. There he came under the influence of Abraham Gottlob Werner, who had been a dominant figure at the Bergakademie for nearly forty years.

In 1813 Breithaupt was appointed to the post of assistant teacher (*Hülfslehrer*) in the Mining Academy and also to the post of gem inspector (*Edelstein-Inspektor*); he was the last to hold the latter office. Werner died in 1817 and was succeeded as professor of mineralogy by Friedrich Mohs. When Mohs left for Vienna in 1826, Breithaupt became his successor; he held the post until his retirement in 1866. He became blind soon after he retired, and this put an end to his mineralogical activity, which had been intensive until then.

Breithaupt was married in 1816 to Agnes Ulrike Winkler, the daughter of an official of a *Blaufarbenwerk* (a plant for producing cobalt blue) in the Erzgebirge near Freiberg. They had three daughters and one son, Hermann, who studied at the Bergakademie, was imprisoned for his political activities in 1848, and later became a mining official in Spain.

Breithaupt's first major publication was the completion of C. A. S. Hoffmann's four-volume *Handbuch der Mineralogie* (1816–1818), which was the only authorized publication of Werner's mineral system. Systematic mineralogy—the recognition and classification of minerals and the discovery of new species—was Breithaupt's chief interest. The so-called natural classifications, derived ultimately from Linnaeus, were still much in vogue, and for Breithaupt the elaboration of such a classification was a principal objective for many decades. The result appeared in his *Vollständiges Handbuch der Mineralogie* of which only three of a planned four volumes appeared (1836, 1841, and 1847). Although the work remained incomplete, the taxonomy of minerals into classes, orders, genera, and species and the associated nomenclature show that Breithaupt resisted the introduction of the chemical and crystal-chemical classifications which have since been generally adopted. In contrast, J. D. Dana, who in the first two editions of his *System of Mineralogy* (1837, 1844) had also attempted a "natural classification" with binomial nomenclature, wrote in the preface to the third edition (1850): "To change is always seeming fickleness. But not to change with the advance of science, is worse, it is persistence in error. . . ." Succeeding editions of his work developed into the standard in the field.

Breithaupt was a great observer and named many minerals. His successor and author of a necrology, Albin Weissbach, listed forty-seven, but the true number is even greater. Of the more than eighty mineral names devised by Breithaupt, about half—including such important ones as monazite, phlogopite, and orthoclase—are still regarded as referring to valid species. The naming of new minerals may, however, be regarded as merely a phase of Breithaupt's interest in systematics. Of more fundamental importance was his early work *Über die Echtheit der Krystalle* (1815), on pseudomorphs, which, although they had been recognized as such by Werner, had not received the attention they deserved. Breithaupt also was the first to distinguish amorphous minerals, which he referred to as "porodine," a term long since obsolete.

Breithaupt's greatest contribution by far to mineralogy and to the study of ore deposits was his little book *Die Paragenesis der Mineralien* (1849). Although others had noticed that there is some regularity in the association of different minerals, he was the first to make a comprehensive study of such regularities and to emphasize the importance of age relations among associated minerals. In the year following the publication of the *Paragenesis,* but only occasionally thereafter, Breithaupt gave a formal course of lectures on paragenesis. The importance of his work in this field was immediately recognized. For instance, in the first volume of the English edition of his *Textbook of Chemical and Physical Geology* (1859), Gustav Bischoff based his discussion of mineral associations largely on Breithaupt's work and referred extensively to the *Paragenesis* and related publications. The term "paragenesis" has been generally adopted, and the importance of the relations to which it applies is now recognized by all mineralogists and geologists. The Breithaupt Colloquium held at Freiberg in 1966 to commemorate the one hundred seventy-fifth anniversary of his birth (and, incidentally, just a century after his retirement) was entitled "Problems of Paragenesis in Mineralogy, Geochemistry, Petrology, and Ore Geology."

Breithaupt was a great teacher, and during his last years his students included many Americans: Eugene Hilgard, George Brush, Arnold Hague, and Raphael Pumpelly, among others. In 1865 twenty-four of the fifty-one newly admitted students at the Bergakademie were from the United States, and it is probable that most of them studied under Breithaupt. Pumpelly gave a warm and amusing account of his years at Freiberg (1856–1859), with several references to Breithaupt, of whom he wrote: "Breithaupt was already old; he was, however, one of the fathers of Mineralogy, and an inspiring lecturer. He taught crystallography without mathematics. . . . He created in his students an interest in crystal forms and systems, that I did not find later in the mathematical treatment under Alvin Weissbach" (*My Reminiscences*, 1918).

Breithaupt summarized his views at the end of his career in a contribution to the *Festschrift* published for the centennial of the Bergakademie (1866). From this it is clear that mineral classification was still his chief interest. He had failed to follow the progress of crystallography and had persisted in recognizing only four crystal systems and in attempting to develop the forms of hexagonal and tetragonal crystals from those of the isometric system by means of his *Progressions-Theorie*. He appears to have been unaware of Johann F. C. Hessel's work (1830) on the derivation of the crystallographic symmetry classes and of Bravais's (1850) on translation lattices. Although he knew of the work of William Whewell and William H. Miller (1839), he did not favor their approach. Breithaupt apparently failed to recognize his own most valuable contribution: in summarizing his career, he did not so much as mention the paragenesis of minerals.

BIBLIOGRAPHY

I. ORIGINAL WORKS. A complete bibliography of Breithaupt's publications is in Poggendorff's *Biographisch-litterarisches Handwörterbuch,* I (1863), 290, and III (1898), 187.

His elaboration of "natural classifications" was *Vollständiges Handbuch der Mineralogie,* 3 vols. (Dresden-Leipzig, 1836–1847). The first volume is a textbook of mineralogy and also contains an extended statement of Breithaupt's views on mineral classification; Vols. II and III comprise systematic description of species, arranged by classes, orders, and genera. A planned fourth volume was never published. *Die Paragenesis der Mine-*

ralien (Freiberg, 1849) carries the subtitle *Mineralogisch, geognostisch und chemisch beleuchtet, mit besonderer Rücksicht auf Bergbau.* This little book of 274 pages is by far Breithaupt's most important and lasting contribution.

II. SECONDARY LITERATURE. Franz von Kobell, *Geschichte der Mineralogie, von 1650–1860* (Munich, 1864), is the most comprehensive history of mineralogy by a slightly younger (1803–1882) contemporary of Breithaupt's. It contains many critical comments but only incidental reference to paragenesis.

See also H. J. Rösler, "August Breithaupt—sein Leben und Werk," in *Freiberger Forschungshefte,* **C-230** (Leipzig, 1968), 9–19.

B. Voland, "Über die Entwicklung der Mineralsystematik in der ersten Hälfte des 19. Jahrhunderts durch die Schüler Werners," in *Abraham Gottlob Werner Gedenkschrift, Freiberger Forschungshefte,* **C-223** (Leipzig, 1967), 179–190, is a discussion of the development of mineral systematics that considers Breithaupt's contributions in the light of the advances made by his contemporaries.

Also of value are Raphael Pumpelly, *My Reminiscences,* I (New York, 1918); and *Festschrift zum hundertjärigen Jubiläum der Königl. Sächs. Bergakademie zu Freiberg am 30. Juli 1866* (Dresden, 1866).

ADOLF PABST

BREMIKER, CARL (*b.* Hagen, Germany, 23 February 1804; *d.* Berlin, Germany, 26 March 1877), *astronomy, geodesy.*

After a long period as a geometer with the Rhine-Westphalian Land Survey, Bremiker went to the royal observatory in Berlin, where he served as a mathematician, an observer, and an editor of widely used astronomical and mathematical tables. At the suggestion of Friedrich Bessel, several observatories jointly published the *Berliner academischen Sternkarten*; and from 1841 to 1859 Bremiker observed and calculated the hours 6, 9, 13, 17, and 21 for these atlases. He also took part in the calculations for the *Berliner astronomische Jahrbuch*; and from 1850 to 1877 he edited the *Nautische Jahrbuch.*

In 1868 Bremiker was appointed *Sektionschef* in the Prussian Geodetic Institute. He became well known for his *Logarithmisch-trigonometrische Handbuch* (1856), which, by the advent of the calculating machine, had gone through forty editions. Easy to use and offering an accuracy never before attained, it served as an indispensable tool for generations of calculators. Bremiker's tables, however, with centesimal arguments, were less popular.

BIBLIOGRAPHY

I. ORIGINAL WORKS. Bremiker's publications include *Logarithmisch-trigonometrische Handbuch mit 7 Dezimal-*

stellen (Berlin, 1856); *Logarithmisch-trigonometrische Tafeln mit 6 Dezimalstellen* (Berlin, 1862); *Logarithmisch-trigonometrische Tafeln mit 5 Dezimalstellen* (Berlin, 1872); and *Tafel vierstelliger Logarithmen* (Berlin, 1874). Bremiker was also editor of the second edition of Crelle's *Rechentafeln* (Berlin, 1864) and of the tenth and eleventh editions of Bode's *Anleitung zur Kenntnis des gestirnten Himmels* (Berlin, 1844, 1858).

II. SECONDARY LITERATURE. Further information can be found under Bremiker's name in *Neue deutsche Biographie*, I, 582; Poggendorff, I and III; an obituary notice is L. A. Winnecke, in *Monthly Notices of the Royal Astronomical Society,* London, **38** (1878), 151.

BERNHARD STICKER

BRENDEL, OTTO RUDOLF MARTIN (*b.* Niederschönhausen, near Berlin, Germany, 12 August 1862; *d.* Freiburg, Germany, 6 September 1939), *astronomy.*

After extensive study of astronomy and mathematics from 1883 to 1889 in Berlin, Munich, London, Paris, and primarily in Stockholm, Brendel received his doctorate for "Anwendung der Gyldenschen absoluten Störungstheorie auf die Breitenstörungen" (1890); all his life Brendel considered himself a disciple of Gyldén, the Swedish expert on celestial mechanics. This aspect of celestial mechanics—the development of mathematical methods to consider the influence of perturbations upon the computation of orbits—remained his chief concern.

Whereas the problem of the computation of the orbits of the major planets had been nearly solved by the great works of Laplace, Lagrange, Olbers, and Gauss in the eighteenth and nineteenth centuries, the great number of hard-to-observe minor planets presented the theoreticians with entirely new tasks. A complete consideration of the perturbations to which the minor planets are subjected by Jupiter and Saturn would require considerable time. The methods developed by Brendel are based on consideration of only the largest perturbations and their tabulation, so that the minor planets will not again be lost; this way, at least over a certain period (say about one hundred years) they can again be looked for and identified with certainty during their opposition.

After his habilitation in Greifswald in 1892, Brendel devoted himself to this work. He became extraordinary professor of theoretical astronomy at Göttingen in 1898, also undertaking the teaching of insurance mathematics and geodesy in 1902. In 1907 he went to the Academy of Commerce, Frankfurt-am-Main, where he was lecturer in mathematics and insurance mathematics, and the next year he became director of the newly founded observatory of the Physikalische Verein there. With the support of various foreign academies, he established the Internationales Planeteninstitut, which was to develop his ideas. In 1914 he was appointed ordinary professor at the University of Frankfurt and director of the university's observatory. In 1927 he retired.

Brendel's book on the minor planets was awarded the Prix Damoiseau by the Paris Academy. He participated in the publication of Gauss's works (Volumes VII–XII, 1898–1929).

BIBLIOGRAPHY

I. ORIGINAL WORKS. Brendel's writings include *Theorie der kleinen Planeten,* 4 vols. (Göttingen, 1897–1911); *Theorie des Mondes* (Göttingen, 1905); and *Theorie der grossen Planeten,* 2 vols. (Kiel, 1930–1933).

II. SECONDARY LITERATURE. Obituaries of Brendel are *Astronomische Nachrichten,* **270** (1940), 248; *Neue deutsche Biographie,* II, 584; and Poggendorff, IV (1904), 180; V (1926), 164–165; VI (1936), 322.

BERNHARD STICKER

BRESCHET, GILBERT (*b.* Clermont-Ferrand, France, 7 July 1783; *d.* Paris, France, 10 May 1845), *anatomy.*

Breschet became a nonresident medical student in the Paris hospitals in 1808, a resident student in 1809, and a doctor in 1812. Seven years later he was appointed surgeon and head of anatomical studies at the Hôtel Dieu, and he was *agrégé* in 1825. In 1832 he was elected to the Académie de Médicine, and in 1835 to the Académie des Sciences; the next year he became professor of anatomy at the Faculty of Medicine. Breschet attained this chair after a three-month competitive examination (14 April–9 July 1836) that was decided by a jury composed of professors from the Faculty and members of the Institute and was passionately followed by hundreds of students. He was elected on the third ballot, defeating Pierre-Paul Broc, a mere professor at the École Pratique who was far less learned than he but was an idol of the students. Infuriated by the outcome, the students attempted to sack the Faculty of Medicine. The damage was estimated at 5,000 francs, and the disturbance ended in court, where the journalist Fabre, a supporter of Broc, was fined 500 francs. (Fabre was fined for having published a newspaper, between 1835 and 1836, without having put up the security demanded by law and for having moved the paper's printing plant without having informed the authorities.) He took his revenge by writing *Orfilaïade,* a verse pamphlet illustrated by Daumier that was directed against Mathéo Orfila, the dean of the Faculty of Medicine.

Although Breschet studied under the renowned surgeon Guillaume Dupuytren, whose chair he filled at the Faculty of Medicine, he was never a first-rate surgeon and left no special mark on the history of that discipline. His great and methodical capacity for work was particularly applied to the study of human anatomy, comparative anatomy, and the natural sciences. This work was carried on in collaboration with an excellent team: Milne-Edwards, Vavasseur, Villermé, Roussel de Vauzème, Rayer, Bogros, and Raspail. Breschet was the only doctor-naturalist at the Faculty of Medicine, which was essentially oriented to clinical and practical medicine and to human anatomy. Because of this, at the time of Breschet's death, the Faculty rejected an offer made by the minister of education to create a chair of comparative anatomy.

Breschet became known through his work on the veins of the spine and the human skull, his contributions to knowledge of the auditory system in vertebrates, and his knowledge of the arterial plexuses of the Cetacea, showing their adaptation for diving. With Roussel de Vauzème he discovered the sweat glands, and in 1818 he coined the word *phlebitis* to designate an inflammation that soon dominated medico-surgical pathology. Breschet also studied the human ovum and that of other vertebrates.

Having a genuine gift for languages and being keenly aware of what was being done in foreign countries, Breschet translated into French the classic works of Meckel, Heusinger, Hodgson, Kaltenbrunner, Gimbernait, von Baer, Gottfried Treviranus, Rathke, Pander, Jacobson, and Joseph Arnold. His fame was much greater elsewhere in Europe than in France. At the Stuttgart Congress, for instance, the whole assembly gave him a standing ovation. Breschet was a member of the Académie des Curieux de la Nature, as well as academies and learned societies throughout Europe.

The death of his parents (1842, 1845) deeply grieved Breschet and brought on a slight stroke whose effects progressively became so severe that he died.

BIBLIOGRAPHY

I. ORIGINAL WORKS. A complete bibliography of Breschet's works is in Huard (see below). His principal works are "Recherches sur les hydropisies actives en général et sur l'hydropisie du tissu cellulaire en particulier," *Thèse de Paris,* no. 173 (1812); *Essai sur les veines du rachis* (Paris, 1819); *Recherches historiques et expérimentales sur la formation du cal* (Paris, 1819); *Traité des maladies des artères et des veines par J. Hogdon,* which Breschet translated, adding notes, 2 vols. (Paris, 1819), the work in which he uses *phlébite* for the first time; *Mémoire sur une nouvelle espèce de grossesse extra-utérine* (Paris, 1826); *Recherches anatomiques, physiologiques et pathologiques sur le système veineux,* 30 parts (Paris, 1828); four papers on the structure of the hearing organ in fish, read to the Académie Royale des Sciences, 13 August 1832; "De la structure de l'organe de l'ouïe et particulièrement de celle du labyrinthe chez l'homme et les mammifères," presented to the Académie Royale des Sciences in 1832; *Traité des maladies des enfants,* 2 vols. (Paris, 1832); and *Études anatomiques, physiologiques et pathologiques de l'oeuf dans l'espèce humaine et dans quelques unes des principales familles des animaux vertébrés* (Paris, 1833).

II. SECONDARY LITERATURE. Breschet was the subject of a eulogy by Royer-Collard: "Éloge du 3 novembre 1845 à la Faculté de médecine de Paris," in *Moniteur universel* (14–15 May 1845). Other memorial notices are in *Archives générales de médecine,* **2** (1845), 257–342; *Bulletin de l'Académie de médecine,* **10** (1844–1845), 680–685; *Gazette médicale de Paris,* **2** (1845), 301–316; and *Journal des connaissances médicales pratiques et de pharmacologie,* **12** (1844–1845), 305–306.

See also P. Balme and G. Dastugue, "Gilbert Breschet," in *Clermont médical,* no. 44 (1961), 89–115; A. Corlieu, *Centenaire de la Faculté de médecine de Paris, 1794–1894* (Paris, 1896), pp. 250–256; L. Delhoume, *Dupuytren* (Paris, 1935), pp. 243–260; P. Huard, "Gilbert Breschet," in *Comptes rendus du Congrès des Sociétés savantes Clermont-Ferrand,* **3** (1963), 117–128, which contains Breschet's complete bibliography; and A. Thierry, "Gilbert Breschet," in *Le temps* (6 Dec. 1928).

PIERRE HUARD

BRET, JEAN JACQUES (*b.* Mercuriol, Drôme, France, 25 September 1781; *d.* Grenoble, France, 29 January 1819), *mathematics.*

He was the son of Jacques Bret, a notary. After passing the entrance examinations given at Lyons, Bret entered the École Polytechnique on 22 November 1800 and was admitted to the course of preparation for civil engineering (Service des Ponts et Chaussées). Unfortunately, because of poor health, he did not complete his studies, but was forced to take a leave of absence from October 1802 to November 1803. The school administration offered to let him stay a fourth year on condition that he take the examinations. He was definitely removed from the rolls in December 1803.

In 1804 Bret became professor of transcendental mathematics at the lycée in Grenoble, and from 8 October 1811 until his death, he was professor at the Faculté des Sciences in the same city, having became *docteur ès sciences* on 10 March 1812.

There are some twenty publications by Bret in the

Annales de mathématiques de Gergonne, a note in the *Correspondance* of the École Polytechnique, and a memoir in the latter's journal. Most of his articles deal with analytical geometry on plane surfaces and in space, notably with the theory of conics and quadrics. He sets forth, for example, the third-degree equation that determines the length of the axes of a central quadric.

In this research the cumbersome techniques of the time are unpleasantly obvious. By way of exception, a study on the squares of the distance between a point in space and fixed points is remarkable for its simplicity, elegance, and generality.

Other works have a bearing on the theory of algebraic equations, particularly upon the limitation of real roots, a subject in style at the time. Bret also worked on the theory of elimination, where he used the greatest common divisor of polynomials in order to establish Bézout's theorem on the degree of the polynomial resultant.

Bret became involved in a long polemic with J. B. E. Dubourguet in the *Annales de Gergonne.* This had to do with the demonstration of the fundamental theorem that an algebraic equation admits a number of roots equal to its degree.

BIBLIOGRAPHY

Among Bret's works are "Sur la méthode du plus grand commun diviseur appliquée à l'élimination," in *Journal de l'École polytechnique,* **15** (1809), 162–197; and "Sur les équations du quatrième degré," in *Correspondance de l'École polytechnique,* **2** (1811), 217–219.

Of particular note, all in *Annales de mathématiques,* are "Recherche des longueurs des axes principaux dans les surfaces du second ordre qui ont un centre," **2** (1812), 33–38; "Recherche de la position des axes principaux dans les surfaces du second ordre," *ibid.,* 144–152; "Discussion de l'équation du second degré entre deux variables," *ibid.,* 218–223; "Démonstration de quelques théorèmes relatifs au quadrilatère," *ibid.,* 310–318; "Théorie de l'élimination entre deux équations de degrés quelconques, fondée sur la théorie du plus grand commun diviseur," **3** (1812), 13–18; "Démonstration du principe qui sert de fondement au calcul des fonctions symétriques et de la formule binomiale de Newton," **4** (1813), 25–28; "Théorèmes nouveaux sur les limites des racines des équations numériques," **6** (1815), 112–122; and "Théorie générale des fractions continues," **11** (1818), 37–51.

An article on Bret is Niels Nielsen, "Bret," in *Géomètres français sous la Révolution* (Copenhagen, 1929), pp. 31–37.

JEAN ITARD

BRETHREN OF PURITY. See **Ikhwān al-Ṣafā'.**

BRETONNEAU, PIERRE (*b.* St.-Georges-sur-Cher, France, 3 April 1778; *d.* Passy, France, 18 February 1862), *medicine.*

Bretonneau's father, Pierre, a master surgeon, and his mother, Elisabeth Lecomte, came from the old bourgeois class. Almost completely uneducated during his childhood (at nine he was not yet able to read), he was sent to the École de Santé in Paris in 1795. There he attended the clinical lectures of Corvisart. He abandoned his studies, however, after being unjustifiably failed on an examination (1801) and became a public health officer in Chenonceaux. His skill gained Bretonneau reputation, and he was made chief physician at the Tours hospital; to qualify for this position he took his final examinations and completed his doctoral thesis in 1815. In 1838 he left this post and the directorship of the École de Santé in Tours, to dedicate himself to practicing medicine among the poor. After a first marriage to a woman twenty-five years his senior he married at the age of seventy-eight a girl of eighteen.

A man of many interests, Bretonneau constructed hydraulic hammers, barometers, and thermometers; sculpted and drew; and studied the habits of bees and ants. He was a first-rate botanist and horticulturist, and wrote a treatise on plant grafting; his garden in Palluau was famous throughout Europe. Independent, proud yet modest, and disdainful of honors, Bretonneau was a dedicated physician and an able therapist. His lectures, which were in the Hippocratic tradition, made a profound impression upon his students.

Bretonneau's outlook made him a member of the school of Paris, which considered the lesion to be the trace that makes possible the definition, classification, and comprehension of an illness. Physical signs, as direct mediators of the lesion, were preferred to epiphenomenal symptoms. G. L. Bayle introduced the concept of a definite development of a lesion that defines its specificity instead of altering it. Laennec illustrated this idea by showing that the various lesions of "phthisis" were in fact the gross signs of a specific disease, tuberculosis. In 1801 Bayle defended the unicity of smallpox (either discrete or confluent) in his M.D. thesis, arguing for the existence of cross-contagiousness. This thesis, which described two kinds of smallpox, had many repercussions.

The concepts of specificity and contagiousness, as well as the previous work on smallpox, later gave Bretonneau a model for introducing those concepts into his work on two diseases of the mucous membranes of the digestive and respiratory tracts. He demonstrated that, just as the skin could show a great many reactions, the mucous membranes did not have only one response to all pathogens. Against an excessively narrow concept of tissue pathology, inherited from Bichat, he proposed the concept of specific inflammation.

As early as 1819 Bretonneau individualized typhoid fever (called *dothinentérie*). He demonstrated the localization of the lesion on Peyer's patches in the ileum, the cyclic development of the lesion (each phase had formerly been described as a separate disease), and the uniqueness of the various fevers, and defended the concept of a specific transmissible agent. In his memoir of 1829, Bretonneau described the course of a typhoid epidemic at Chenonceaux and showed the role of contact in its propagation. He observed that the disease was endemic to Paris because the chains of transmission were frequently broken by the immunity of those who had already had the disease. He suspected that besides typhoid there was a petechial pyrexia with a more rapid course (exanthematic typhus) that was often mistaken for typhoid.

From 1818 to 1820 a diphtheria epidemic raged in Tours. In 1821 Bretonneau published his observations. He individualized the disease through analysis of the characteristics of the false membrane, showing its primary tonsillar localization and its possible nasopharyngeal, auricular, and laryngeal ("croup") extensions, which lead to asphyxia. He showed that certain (toxic) symptoms exist regardless of localization, and deduced that the specificity of the inflammation—much more than the type of tissue in which it occurs—is responsible for the disturbance of functions that every inflammatory lesion produces: duration, severity, and danger of most fevers depend on the specificity of the inflammation.

Concerned with preventing fatal asphyxia, Bretonneau, after two experiments that failed in man but succeeded in a dog, performed a successful tracheotomy on a four-year-old girl in July 1825. The operation, the first to be performed on a croup patient, was made possible by his manual dexterity and his ingenuity (he invented the double cannula). He was convinced that diphtheria was contagious and that it was transmitted by drinking glasses. He tried, in vain, to infect animals with the disease. He defended the idea of specific therapy, but his experimental work in that area proved fruitless.

BIBLIOGRAPHY

I. ORIGINAL WORKS. Bretonneau published his works sparingly, some time after they had been written, and at the insistence of his students: *De l'utilité de la compression et, en particulier, de l'efficacité du bandage de Theden dans les inflammations idiopathiques de la peau* (Paris, 1815), his M.D. thesis; *Des inflammations spéciales du tissu muqueux et en particulier de la diphthérite ou inflammation pelliculaire* (Paris, 1826), which consists of two papers read to the Académie Royale de Médecine on 26 June and 6 August 1821; "Notice sur la contagion de la dothinentérie, lue à l'Académie royale de médecine le 7 juillet 1829," in *Archives générales de médecine,* **21** (1829), 57–78; and *Traités de la dothinentérie et de la spécificité,* L. Dubreuil-Chambardel, ed. (Paris, 1922), which contains a biography and an analysis of the work.

II. SECONDARY LITERATURE. Works on Bretonneau are E. Apert, "Bretonneau," in *Biographies médicales,* no. 6 (1938); J. D. Rolleston, "Bretonneau: His Life and Work," in *Proceedings of the Royal Society of Medicine, Section of the History of Medicine,* **18** (1924); and P. Triaire, *Bretonneau et ses correspondants* (Paris, 1892). Useful explanations of Bretonneau's ideas may be found in Trousseau's complete works.

ALAIN ROUSSEAU

BREUER, JOSEF (*b.* Vienna, Austria, 15 January 1842; *d.* Vienna, 20 June 1925), *medicine, physiology, psychoanalysis.*

Breuer's father, Leopold (1791–1872), was a teacher of religion employed by the Jewish community of Vienna, and Breuer described him as belonging to "that generation of [Eastern European] Jews which was the first to step out of the intellectual ghetto into the air of the Western world." Breuer's mother died when he was about four, and he was raised by her mother. His father tutored him until he was eight, and he then entered the Akademisches Gymnasium of Vienna, from which he graduated in 1858. After a year of general university studies, Breuer entered the medical school of the University of Vienna in 1859 and completed his medical studies in 1867. In the same year, immediately after passing his doctoral examination, he became assistant to the internist Johann Oppolzer. When Oppolzer died in 1871, Breuer relinquished his assistantship and entered private practice.

In 1875 Breuer qualified as *Privatdozent* in internal medicine. He resigned the position on 7 July 1885, however, apparently because he felt he had been improperly denied access to patients for teaching purposes; he also refused to let the surgeon C. A. T. Billroth nominate him for the title of professor extraordinarius. His formal relationship to the medical faculty was thus tenuous and strained; yet he was considered one of the best physicians and scientists in Vienna. His practice was his chief interest, and although he once referred to himself as a "general practitioner," he was what today would be called an internist. Some idea of his reputation can be gathered from the fact that among his patients were many of the professors on the medical faculty, as well as Sigmund Freud and the prime minister of Hungary. He was elected to the Viennese Academy of Science in 1894 upon the nomination of three of its most distinguished members: the physicist Ernst Mach and the physiologists Ewald Hering and Sigmund Exner.

Breuer married Matilda Altmann on 20 May 1868, and she bore him five children: Robert, Bertha Hammerschlag, Margaret Schiff, Hans, and Dora. When faced with deportation by the Nazis, Dora committed suicide; she did not kill herself in the United States as stated by Ernest Jones. Breuer's granddaughter Hanna Schiff was killed by the Nazis. The remainder of his descendants live in England, Canada, and the United States.

Breuer was a skeptic in matters of religion. In espousing the views of Fechner and Goethe, he referred to himself as one of "the many intellectuals who have religious needs and find themselves utterly unable to satisfy them within the faith of popular religion." In his will he expressed the wish (which was followed) that he be cremated, a wish inconsistent with conventional Jewish religious practices.

Breuer was one of the great physiologists of the nineteenth century. He had no pupils and no permanent affiliation with a university or institute, which may explain why his fame today is not in proportion to his achievements. His first major scientific study led to the discovery of the reflex regulation of respiration. The work was conducted at the military medical school of Vienna (the Josephinum) in collaboration with its professor of physiology, Ewald Hering, and the results were published in 1868. By the very simple device of occluding the trachea at the end of an inspiration or expiration, Breuer and Hering were able to show that the lung contains receptors that detect the degree to which it is stretched. When the lung is distended by inspiration, nerve impulses arise in the lung and are transmitted to the brain via the vagus nerve; these impulses reflexly initiate expiration. When the lung is deflated, other receptors are stimulated and their impulses, also arriving in the brain via the vagus nerve, reflexly initiate the next inspiration. The whole mechanism, called by Hering and Breuer the "self-regulation" of respiration, was one of the first "feedback" mechanisms to be demonstrated in the mammal. Writing thirty years later, E. H. Starling said that these experiments caused "a complete revolution in our idea of the relationship of the vagus to the respiratory movements." At the time Starling wrote, doubt had been cast on the existence of the receptors that respond to deflation of the lung, but the existence of such receptors was demonstrated

by A. S. Paintal in the 1950's. The picture of the reflex regulation of respiration drawn by Hering and Breuer remains in all essentials the view held today, and the underlying reflex is still known as the Hering-Breuer reflex.

After completing his work with Hering, Breuer began his long series of investigations of the function of the labyrinth, remarkable for their importance and even more remarkable because he conducted them privately, working in his own home and supported only by fees from his medical practice. We now know that the inner ear is a double organ, part of which is the organ of hearing and part of which detects movement of the head and its position in space. The structures of the inner ear are small and delicate, and are placed deep within the skull, which makes them inaccessible to easy experimental investigation. Breuer's first studies of the labyrinth were concerned with the semicircular canals. These canals, three on each side of the head, are filled with fluid (endolymph). The angular position of the canals suggests that they might have something to do with the detection of movement; crude experiments carried out in the 1820's by M. J. P. Flourens showed that injury to them produced disturbances of motor function in animals. In 1870 Friedrich Goltz suggested that the semicircular canals were the sense organs that detect the position of the head relative to the gravitational field; he believed that the lowest part of each canal would, as the result of the weight of the endolymph, be stimulated by pressure.

Our understanding of the function of the semicircular canals dates from the insight that it is not pressure but a tendency of the endolymph to flow within the canals during motion of the head that stimulates the receptors in the ampullae at the end of the canals. This insight was based on Goltz's suggestion of 1870 and was reached essentially simultaneously by Breuer, Mach, and by the Edinburgh chemist A. Crum Brown. (Their initial communications were made on 14 November 1873, 6 November 1873, and 19 January 1874, respectively.) During movement of the head, the endolymph of the canals moves, but its angular rotation lags slightly behind that of the head and results in stimulation of the receptors at the ends of the canals. Thus, the semicircular canals respond to angular acceleration.

Breuer's first article (printed in 1874) concerned mainly the explanation and interpretation of previous observation on animals and humans (thereby resembling Mach's article); his second article, which appeared a year later, reported the results of many experiments, carried out chiefly on pigeons. In those experiments Breuer developed evidence for his theory, which has stood virtually unchallenged since that time. In addition he called attention to the importance of another receptor system connected with posture (also located in the inner ear), the otolith system. The otolith is a minute solid body whose movement stimulates receptors in the utricle, another part of the inner ear. Breuer suggested, and accumulated evidence to show, that the otoliths and the hair cells of the utricle are static position receptors that provide information about the orientation of the head in the gravitational field as well as information about linear acceleration. We are indebted to Breuer for the clear-cut analysis of the differing functions of the semicircular canals and the otoliths, as well as a clear-cut depiction of the relationship of the labyrinthine reflexes to optical nystagmus. His results were by no means immediately accepted and, in particular, his work on the otoliths was not generally known or accepted as late as 1900. Yet it was correct, and today is recognized as the foundation of our knowledge of the sensory receptors for sensations of posture and movement.

Thus, Breuer deserves the credit for two fundamental and far-reaching advances in mammalian physiology: the Hering-Breuer reflex and the elucidation of the function of the labyrinth. His scientific techniques included mastery of physiological experiment and of delicate surgery, as well as the use of histological techniques. Above all, he was a remarkably patient and accurate observer. It must not be supposed that this means he was a passive recorder of events, for observation always implies full awareness of the relation of the facts observed to their meaning for theory and interpretation, as well as the ability to suspend judgment and retain a multitude of observations pending an intellectual survey and rearrangement of them. It has been suggested that Breuer was in some ways less scientific in his psychoanalytic reporting than in his physiological research, but the same sort of active observation, active accumulation of facts, and active suspension of final judgment until the facts arranged themselves into meaningful patterns is entirely characteristic of his investigations of psychopathology.

The general impression that Breuer published little and infrequently is true in the sense that he published relatively few major scientific articles at relatively long intervals; but quite apart from the importance of these articles, it should be noted that some of them were very long and detailed. His purely physiological articles, published over a forty-year period, numbered about twenty and comprised more than five hundred pages.

In the summer of 1880, while attending a man who was seriously ill with a peripleuritic abscess, Breuer observed the onset of a serious psychological disturbance in the man's daughter, "Anna O.," who was also his patient. Her symptoms were later summarized by Freud as follows:

> Her illness lasted for over two years, and in the course of it she developed a series of physical and psychological disturbances which decidedly deserved to be taken seriously. She suffered from a rigid paralysis, accompanied by loss of sensation, of both extremities on the right side of her body; and the same trouble from time to time affected her left side. Her eye movements were disturbed and her power of vision was subject to numerous restrictions. She had difficulties over the posture of her head; she had a severe nervous cough. She had an aversion to taking nourishment, and on one occasion she was several weeks unable to drink in spite of a tormenting thirst. Her powers of speech were reduced, even to the point of her being unable to speak or understand her native language. Finally, she was subject to conditions of *"absence,"* of confusion, of delirium and of alterations of her whole personality ... [*The Complete Psychological Works of Sigmund Freud,* XI, 10].

Breuer noted that Anna O. showed two markedly different states of consciousness each day: during one she seemed relatively normal, during the other she was "clouded." He also found that if, during her normal state, she could be induced to tell him the fantasies that occupied her during her clouded state her restlessness was greatly reduced. To facilitate this "catharsis," he began to hypnotize her. Far more importantly, he eventually noted that under special circumstances of recall she would trace a series of memories back over time until she reached the memory of a "traumatic" episode that had been transformed into a symptom. After seeing several of her symptoms vanish as the result of this sort of recall, Breuer began to visit her twice a day in order to have time for more intensive and frequent hypnosis. He gradually succeeded in relieving all of her symptoms by this process of catharsis.

From his treatment of Anna O., Breuer arrived at two conclusions of fundamental importance: (1) that the symptoms of his patient were the result of "affective ideas, deprived of the normal reaction" which remained embedded in the unconscious, and (2) that the symptoms vanished when the unconscious causes of them became conscious through being verbalized. These two observations form the cornerstone upon which psychoanalysis was later built.

Breuer did not publish or publicize the results of his treatment of Anna O. He did, however, discuss them with Freud, and the cathartic treatment resumed when Freud began to use it under Breuer's guidance. For several years Breuer and Freud jointly explored this form of psychotherapy. Only Freud treated patients, but he and Breuer continually discussed the results and implications of the treatment. Freud first used the cathartic method in either 1888 or 1889. The practical and theoretical conclusions they reached through their collaboration were published in an article in 1893 and as a book (*Studien über Hysterie*) in 1895. The publication of the book very nearly coincided with the end of their collaboration—and of their friendship. The contribution of Breuer and Freud to the development of psychoanalysis may be stated as follows: (*a*) Breuer discovered that neurotic symptoms arise from unconscious processes. (*b*) Breuer discovered that neurotic symptoms disappear when the unconscious processes become conscious. (*c*) These major discoveries were communicated by Breuer to Freud. (*d*) The first serious attempt to explore the implications of these discoveries was made by Freud and Breuer working in close collaboration. (*e*) Breuer was not anxious to pursue these studies, and the major development must be attributed to Freud after he separated from Breuer, during a period when Breuer apparently did not seek another collaborator but dropped the subject. (*f*) If by psychoanalysis we mean a discipline relying on the technique of free association, psychoanalysis was solely Freud's discovery.

Breuer, in writing the theoretical chapter of the *Studien über Hysterie,* advanced a number of very important concepts, among them one rejected by Freud but now regarded as very important: that the hypnoid state and varying levels of consciousness are of great importance in normal and abnormal mental functioning. Other theoretical concepts usually attributed to Breuer include the distinction between the primary and secondary processes, the concept of hallucination as a regression from imagery to perception, and the suggestion that perception and memory cannot be performed by the same psychic apparatus. The "principle of constancy" was first mentioned by Breuer, but he attributed it to Freud. This concept is fundamental to the development of psychoanalytic theory, and one cannot but wonder whether Breuer did not in fact play an important role in formulating it. Breuer after all, formulated the notion of "feedback" in the respiratory cycle and studied the sense organ that plays a key role in postural balance in animals; and the homeostatic devices involved in those systems are very reminiscent of the "principle of constancy."

In his obituary of Breuer, Freud spoke with regret of the fact that Breuer's brilliance had been directed toward the problems of psychopathology for only a brief time. Although Breuer actually dealt with that subject during a period of nearly fifteen years, he did so in a way that deserves special examination. In the first place, Breuer's mastery of hypnosis and his readiness to use it in treating Anna O. may, as Professor E. H. Ackerknecht has suggested to me, indicate that Breuer had more interest in psychopathology than the average internist even before the case of Anna O.; this supposition receives confirmation from the time Breuer spent on that case and from the care with which he recorded it. In the opinion of Freud it was the case of Anna O. that also caused Breuer to draw back from psychotherapy for a time, since the case had, near its end, an unexpected and disturbing result: Anna O. formed a strong attachment to Breuer, an attachment that had a definitely sexual quality. Freud believed that this upset Breuer and prevented him from again practicing "deep" psychotherapy. Breuer himself stated that after the case of Anna O. he gave up treating patients in this manner since such treatment could not be carried out by a physician subject to the demands of a busy general practice. The resumption of that sort of psychotherapy, which was to evolve into psychoanalysis, was undertaken jointly by Breuer and Freud about five years after the case of Anna O., but the treatment of patients was solely in the hands of Freud, with Breuer taking part only in discussion of the techniques and the results of treatment.

There were for a time a few "Breuerians," i.e., physicians who used Breuer's original cathartic therapy without Freud's amplifications. Breuer does not seem to have been a "Breuerian" in this sense, although letters by him in the Medizinhistorisches Institut der Universität Zürich indicate that his handling of psychiatric patients remained very sophisticated. On the whole it is probably correct to say that while Breuer was persuaded intellectually of the validity and importance of the new concepts and techniques that developed from his own work and from the work he did jointly with Freud, he was equally dismayed by the recurrent intrusion of sexuality into the subject. In a sense, therefore, Breuer's anxiety over Anna O.'s reaction to him may be taken as a symbol of the reasons for his ambivalence toward the subject, but only as a symbol, since he returned, via collaboration with Freud, to the very same subject, and did not finally split with Freud until thirteen years after the Anna O. episode. Whatever the nature of Breuer's interest in the subject and whatever the reasons for his ambivalence, nothing can minimize the fact that his treatment of Anna O. can convincingly be regarded as the first modern example of "deep psychotherapy" carried out over a prolonged period of time.

Although they had been very close for many years, Freud and Breuer separated in 1896 and never spoke again. Whatever the roots of this break were in the character of the Breuer and Freud relationship, the quarrels that led up to it grew out of their work on psychotherapy. It was a difficult period for Freud, who felt, among other things, that Breuer was ambivalent about the value of their work, ambivalent about publishing it, and ambivalent about publicly supporting him. Interestingly enough, their final quarrel seems to have concerned a matter in which Breuer was right and Freud only later found himself to be wrong, the question of the reality of the memories of having been seduced in early childhood, which had occurred in many patients. Breuer did refuse to back Freud in his belief that nearly all their patients had experienced such seductions; when Freud finally realized that such memories were memories not of real events but of childhood fantasies, he made one of his most important discoveries.

There is no possibility of meaningfully exploring the dynamics of their relationship at this date. It may be simplest to say that for a long time Freud needed Breuer and depended upon him; he then came to need him less and to depend on him less; and eventually he had a positive need to break with him, which he did thoroughly and in a way that left bad feelings. We cannot say even that much about Breuer; all we can say is that he was very fond of Freud for a long time and deeply wounded by the break. That a relationship between an older and a younger man, first full of warm and close friendship and then of turmoil, should have accompanied the birth of psychoanalysis may have been inevitable. That relationship should not be allowed to obscure the brilliant intellectual and observational contributions each made to the founding of modern psychoanalysis, psychiatry, and psychotherapy, nor should it obscure the fact that their long and close collaboration was an integral part of the creation of psychoanalysis.

Breuer was friendly with many of the most brilliant intellects of his time. He sustained a long correspondence with Franz Brentano, was a close friend of the poet Maria von Ebner-Eschenbach, and was on friendly terms with Mach, whom he had met at the time of their simultaneous work on the labyrinth. His opinion on literary and philosophical questions seems to have been widely respected and often sought. His correspondence with Maria von Ebner-Eschenbach has been preserved as has part of the Brentano-Breuer correspondence. Breuer had a considerable command of languages, and it is interesting to note that his treatment of Anna O. was for a long period conducted in English. The eulogies published after his death all emphasize that the range and depth of his cultural interests were as unusual and important as his medical and scientific accomplishments.

BIBLIOGRAPHY

I. Original Works. No detailed bibliography of Breuer's publications has ever been assembled. His scientific articles can easily be traced through the usual guides to the medical literature and, in particular, in the *Cumulative Author Index to Psychological Index* . . . (Boston, 1960). The Hering-Breuer reflex is described in "Die Selbststeuerung der Athmung durch den *Nervus vagus*," in *Sitzungsb. d. k. Akad. d. Wissensch., Math.-naturwissensch. Klasse,* Abteilung II, **58** (1868), 909–937. Breuer's first major articles on the labyrinth were "Ueber die Funktion der Bogengänge des Ohrlabyrinths," in *Medizinische Jahrbücher,* 2nd series, **4** (1874), 72–124, and "Beiträge zur Lehre vom statischen Sinne (Gleichgewichtsorgan, Vestibularapparat des Ohrlabyrinths)," *ibid.,* **5** (1875), 87–156. Breuer's other articles on the labyrinth may be found with the aid of the bibliographic sources mentioned above or in the bibliographies to the article by Roth and the book by Camis cited below.

Breuer's publications in the sphere of psychopathology, both written with Freud, were "Ueber den psychischen Mechanismus hysterischer Phänomene (Vorläufige Mittheilung)," in *Neurologisches Centralblatt,* **12** (1893), 4–10, 43–47; and *Studien über Hysterie* (Leipzig-Vienna, 1895). The preliminary communication and the book are readily available in English translation as Vol. II of *The Standard Edition of the Complete Psychological Works of Sigmund Freud,* James Strachey, ed. (London, 1955).

Breuer's brief autobiography, entitled simply *Curriculum vitae,* presumably was published in Vienna in 1925 (the actual publication bears no place, date, or publisher's name). There is a photographic copy of this rare pamphlet in the library of the New York Academy of Medicine.

II. Secondary Literature. Apart from the brief autobiography mentioned above, the most detailed sketch of Breuer's life is found in Hans Horst Meyer, "Josef Breuer," in Anton Bettelheim, ed., *Neue Österreichische Biographie* (Zurich-Leipzig-Vienna, 1928), V, 30–47. Additional useful information is found in obituaries: Sigmund Freud, in *Internationale Zeitschrift für Psychoanalysis,* **11** (1925), 255–256, translated in *The Complete Psychological Works of Sigmund Freud,* XIX, 279–280; A. de Kleyn, in *Acta Otolaryngologica,* **10** (1927), 167–171; and A. Kreidl, in *Wiener medizinische Wochenschrift* (1925), 1616–1618. The function of the labyrinth is a difficult and obscure topic. A good survey of it, as well as a clear idea of how pervasive and enduring Breuer's contributions to the subject were, can be gained from Mario Camis, *The Physiology of the Vestibular Apparatus* (Oxford, 1930).

Freud's many comments on Breuer's role in the history of psychoanalysis may easily be located in *The Complete Psychological Works of Sigmund Freud.* The evaluation of the contributions of Breuer and Freud to the founding of psychoanalysis follows that in P. F. Cranefield, "Josef Breuer's Evaluation of His Contributions to Psychoanalysis," in *International Journal of Psychoanalysis,* **39** (1958), 319–322; the same article contains an important letter from Breuer discussing his contributions to psychoanalysis. A good deal of information about Breuer and Freud is found in Ernest Jones, *The Life and Work of Sigmund Freud* (Vol. I, New York, 1953). Jones's book must be used with care, however, since its impressive quantity of information is not always matched by accuracy either of fact or of interpretation.

The most recent detailed biographical article on Breuer is E. H. Ackerknecht, "Josef Breuer," in *Neue Österreichische Biographie ab 1815* (Vienna-Munich-Zurich, 1963), XV, 126–130. Other recent articles include J. E. Gedo et al., "Studies on Hysteria; a Methodological Evaluation," in *Journal of the American Psychoanalytic Association,* **12** (1964), 734–751; N. Roth, "The Place of Josef Breuer in Medical History," in *Comprehensive Psychiatry,* **5** (1964), 322–326; N. Schlessinger et al., "The Scientific Style of Breuer and Freud in the Origins of Psychoanalysis," in *Journal of the American Psychoanalytic Association,* **15** (1967), 404–422; and J. Sullivan, "From Breuer to Freud," in *Psychoanalysis and the Psychoanalytic Review,* **46** (1959), 69–90. The Gedo and Schlessinger articles attempt to evaluate Breuer's scientific and "cognitive" style via a consideration of what little is known of his life and via an analysis of a few of his publications. In these articles one finds a rather mechanical analysis of psychological propositions in terms of their "remoteness from concrete clinical data." The authors' remark that Breuer's work was "limited by deficient scientific reality testing" suffices to show the dangers of the use of unsophisticated ideas about the nature of scientific reasoning and creativity.

For help in obtaining previously unpublished information contained in the above biography of Breuer, I am deeply indebted to the late Dr. Walter Federn, to Professor Erwin H. Ackerknecht, to Professor Erna Lesky, to Dr. Kurt Eissler and to Breuer's granddaughter, Mrs. Felix Ungar.

PAUL F. CRANEFIELD

BREUIL, HENRI ÉDOUARD PROSPER (*b.* Mortain, Manche, France, 28 February 1877; *d.* L'Isle-Adam, Seine-et-Oise, France, 14 August 1961), *prehistory.*

Breuil, the son of farmers, entered the Séminaire St.-Sulpice, Paris, in 1897 and was ordained a priest in 1900. From an early age he displayed a great interest in natural history, particularly geology and human paleontology. He was lecturer in prehistory and ethnography at the University of Fribourg from 1905 to 1910; professor of prehistoric ethnography at the Institut de Paléontologie Humaine, Paris, from 1910; and professor of prehistory at the Collège de France from 1929 to 1947. He was elected a member of the Institut de France in 1938, was a gold medalist of the American Academy of Science and of the Society of Antiquaries of London, and was awarded the Huxley Memorial Medal and the Prestwich Medal for Geology. He was a member of nineteen foreign societies and academies and received honorary degrees from Oxford, Cambridge, Edinburgh, Cape Town, Lisbon, and Fribourg.

Breuil did original research on the Paleolithic period in Europe, China, and South Africa, and was for years the doyen of Paleolithic studies. His first contact with this field was through Émile Cartailhac, professor of prehistoric archaeology at Toulouse, and he was present at the field meetings in the Dordogne in 1901 when Les Combarelles and Font de Gaume were discovered. He was also at La Mouthe when the authenticity of Paleolithic cave art was accepted. He journeyed to Altamira with Cartailhac the following year. From then on, one of his main contributions to the development of archaeology was his painstaking recording and analysis of Paleolithic cave art. He was closely associated with the discovery of Tuc d'Audoubert in 1912 and Les Trois-Frères in 1916, and was the first archaeologist to visit and describe Lascaux in 1940.

Breuil's other main contribution to prehistoric archaeology was his reclassification of Paleolithic industries, which began with his classic paper "Les subdivisions du paléolithique supérieur et leur signification," given at the Geneva Congress of Prehistoric and Protohistoric Sciences in 1912. He was not so successful when he strayed away from his Paleolithic studies to write about the art of the megalith builders of France and Iberia, and toward the end of his life he became involved in controversies about the interpretation of paintings in South Africa and the authenticity of those found at Rouffignac, France, in 1956.

BIBLIOGRAPHY

I. ORIGINAL WORKS. Breuil's writings include *La caverne d'Altamira, à Santillane près Santander,* written with Émile Cartailhac (Monaco, 1906); *La caverne de Font-de-Gaume aux Eyzies (Dordogne),* written with L. Capitan and D. Peyrony (Monaco, 1910); *Les Combarelles aux Eyzies (Dordogne),* written with L. Capitan and D. Peyrony (Paris, 1924); *Rock Paintings of Southern Andalusia,* written with M. C. Burkitt and Montagu Pollock (Oxford, 1929); *Les peintures rupestres schématiques de la péninsule ibérique,* 4 vols. (Paris, 1933–1935); *Beyond the Bounds of History* (London, 1949); *Les hommes de la pierre ancienne,* written with R. Lantier (Paris, 1951); *Quatre cents siècles d'art pariétal; les cavernes ornées de l'âge du renne* (Montignac,

1952); and *The White Lady of Brandberg*, written with Mary Boyle and E. R. Scherz (London, 1955).

II. SECONDARY LITERATURE. *Hommage à l'abbé Henri Breuil pour son quatre-vingtième anniversaire* (Paris, 1957) includes a complete bibliography of Breuil's writings. See also Mary Boyle et al., "Recollections of the Abbé Breuil," in *Antiquity,* **12** (1963); A. H. Brodrick, *The Abbé Breuil, Prehistorian* (London, 1963); and N. Skrotzky, *L'Abbé Breuil* (Paris, 1964).

GLYN DANIEL

BREWSTER, DAVID (*b.* Jedburgh, Scotland, 11 December 1781; *d.* Allerly, Melrose, Scotland, 10 February 1868), *optics.*

The son of Margaret Key and James Brewster, rector of the Jedburgh grammar school, David entered the University of Edinburgh in 1794. Although he completed the prescribed courses, like other students of the time, he did not take a bachelor's degree. Continuing at the university as a divinity student, he was awarded an honorary M.A. in 1800, and in 1804 he was licensed to preach in the Church of Scotland, although he was never ordained a minister. As an evangelical, Brewster became an adviser to the leaders of the Disruption; was long a friend of its leader, Thomas Chalmers; and became a member of the Free Church of Scotland in 1843.

His formal training, however, was but one part of his education. As amanuensis to Dr. Thomas Somerville, scholar, author, and minister of Jedburgh, Brewster acquired in his youth the writing and editing skills that later were his principal source of income. More important, as a child Brewster began to learn about physical science from his father's manuscript notes from the University of Aberdeen. Encouraged and assisted by the "peasant astronomer" James Veitch, Brewster built sundials, microscopes, and telescopes. While studying at the university, he continued to build instruments and to exchange astronomical observations with Veitch. Stimulated by his classmate Henry Brougham, Brewster began his experimental researches on light about 1798. While he believed that he had disproved part of Newton's explanation of the "inflexion" of light, Brewster did not then, or ever, abandon the emission theory of light.

Brewster's income depended on his literary, rather than his scientific, efforts. He was a private tutor from 1799 to 1807; he edited the *Edinburgh Magazine* and *Scots Magazine* from 1802 to 1806, the *Edinburgh Encyclopaedia* from 1807 to 1830, and various scientific journals from 1819 to the end of his life; and he was author of numerous popular books and articles. Throughout his life he lost no opportunity to deplore the lack of paid careers for British scientists, and his repeated failure to obtain a professorship only increased his calls for reform. Moreover, he aggressively promoted scientific education for all groups in society, in the hope that wider knowledge of science would lead to its increased prestige. A leader in the establishment of the Edinburgh School of Arts (1821), the Royal Scottish Society of Arts (1821), and the British Association for the Advancement of Science (1831), Brewster attempted to create organizations, as well as opinions, that would diffuse and promote science and education. Yet with all his effort, he failed in his great plan to establish a national institute patterned on the ideas of Bacon and Newton and on the practice of France.

Brewster was a reform Whig. His political friends, including Brougham, Charles Grant (Lord Glenelg), and the earl of Buchan (who recommended Brewster for the LL.D. at Aberdeen), were sources of influence and honor. Not only did Brougham, as lord chancellor, assist in founding the British Association, but he also obtained pensions and knighthoods for Brewster (1832) and other scientists. Through political influence, two of Brewster's sons became East Indian officials, and in 1838 Brewster was relieved of financial worries by the government's gift of the principalship of the United Colleges of St. Salvator and St. Leonard, St. Andrews. In 1859 Brewster was elected principal of the University of Edinburgh by the town council. Shortly thereafter he also became vice-chancellor.

Brewster received numerous honors, including the LL.D. from Aberdeen (1807) and the D.C.L. from Oxford (1832), fellowships of the Royal Societies of Edinburgh and of London, and a foreign associateship in the French Institute (1848). His awards included the Copley, Rumford, and Royal medals of the Royal Society of London and the Keith Prize of the Royal Society of Edinburgh.

Brewster's interest in astronomy and instruments is evident in his first major scientific publication, *A Treatise on New Philosophical Instruments* (1813). In the latter sections of the book, he reported his determinations of the refractive and dispersive powers of nearly two hundred substances that he had made in a quest for improvement of achromatic telescopes. Not until much of this work was completed did he learn, in 1811 or 1812, that in 1808 Malus had discovered that reflected light acquired the same polarization as one of the doubly refracted beams in Iceland spar. This information, combined with his discoveries that doubly refracting bodies have two dispersive powers, that the single beam transmitted by agate is polarized, and that noncrystallized bodies such as mica "depolarise" light, shifted Brewster's concern from instruments back to optical theory. In exploring the consequences of these experiments, Brewster followed four separate but related lines of research.

Since Brewster had found that light was partially polarized by oblique refraction in mica, he attempted to determine the law of this polarization in the simpler case of successive refractions by a pile of thin glass plates. By the end of 1813 he had concluded that "the number of plates in any parcel, multiplied by the tangent of the angle, at which it [completely] polarises light, is a constant quantity." More important, since "the pencil of light polarised by transmission [comports] itself, in every respect like one of the pencils formed by double refraction," study of the physical optics of transparent bodies ought to enable philosophers "to unfold the secrets of double refraction, to explain the forms and structure of crystallised bodies, and to develope the nature and properties of that etherial matter, which . . . performs . . . a capital part in the operations of the material world." Nothing less was at stake than understanding of the structure of organized matter and the nature of light. In conceiving of his results in this way, Brewster defined much of his optical career for the next twenty years.

Brewster's second line of study was a search for the law of polarization by reflection. While Malus had concluded that the "polarising angle neither follows the order of the refractive powers nor that of the dispersive forces," Brewster was not convinced. His own "measures for *water* and the *precious stones* afforded a surprising coincidence between the indices of refraction and the polarising angles; but the results for glass formed an exception, and resisted every method of classification." Persisting, however, he concluded that chemical changes on the surface of the glass had obscured the general law that "the index of refraction is the tangent of the angle of polarisation."

Moreover, analogously to polarization by successive refractions, successive reflections at any angle continuously increased the quantity of polarized light in the beam. Now making explicit his adoption of an emission theory of light, Brewster explained his results in terms of "polarising forces" that acted on light particles "in every state of POSITIVE and NEGATIVE polarisation from particles completely polarised to particles not polarised at all." Each successive reflection brought the particles nearer to complete polarization. By late 1829 he was convinced not only that his particulate theory was the simplest possible, but also that it was fully adequate to account quantitatively for the intensities and resultant angles of polarization of reflected and refracted light. He regarded "all the various phenomena of polarisation of light by reflexion and refraction as brought under the

dominion of laws as well determined as those which regulate the motions of the planets." In 1816 he received the Copley Medal, in 1819 two Rumford Medals, and in 1831 a Royal Medal for the papers in which he announced these discoveries. On the popular level, Brewster's reputation was established in 1816 by the fad for his kaleidoscope. Its invention was a direct result of his studies of the theory of polarization by multiple reflections.

Study of metallic reflection was a third line of Brewster's research. Using successive reflections to increase the degree of polarization, he concluded that light reflected by metals was neither plane nor circularly—but elliptically—polarized. Moreover, from his results he deduced laws that not only accurately predicted the quantities and angles of polarization of light, but also were the foundation for theoretical researches on metallic reflection by MacCullagh and Cauchy.

Pursuing his fourth line of research, Brewster created the new fields of optical mineralogy and photoelasticity. In 1813, while studying the "depolarising" action of topaz, he observed two sets of elliptical rings (interference patterns) centered on axes in the topaz that were apparently inclined at 65°. He interpreted this to mean that topaz must have two axes, not one, of double refraction, an entirely unexpected result. After many laborious experiments he was able in 1819 to group all but a few of hundreds of minerals and crystals into mutually consistent optical and mineralogical categories: the primitive form determined the number of axes of double refraction.

During these investigations, Brewster quite unexpectedly observed that heat and pressure could produce or change a doubly refracting structure in uncrystallized, crystallized, or organic bodies. Moreover, from the geometry of the interference patterns he deduced equations that permitted him to predict the shapes, numbers, and colors of patterns that would be produced by changes in configuration, temperature, pressure, and method of observation.

In an attempt to improve colored eyeglasses and microscopy, in 1821 Brewster began an intensive study of absorption spectroscopy. Ironically, these researches led Newton's biographer to a profound dissent from Newton's doctrine of colors and to a strong reaffirmation of a "Newtonian" emission theory of light.

In examining a blue eyeglass spectroscopically, he concluded that it caused extreme eye fatigue by transmitting only red and blue rays. Their differing refrangibilities prevented the eye from accommodating to one focal distance. Less than a year later, in utilizing his new monochromatic microscope illuminator in studies of other absorption spectra, Brewster entered the debate over the number of colors in the spectrum: was it seven, as Newton had held, or four, as Wollaston believed, or some other number? Since Wollaston had asserted that yellow was merely a combination of green and red, Brewster first examined the solar spectrum with red- and green-absorbing glasses. Rather than the reds and greens vanishing, "the space from which the colours were absorbed was in both cases occupied by *yellow* light. . . ." While this established, for Brewster, the separate existence of yellow, it invalidated Newton's identification of color and refrangibility, for "*Yellow* light . . . has its *most* refrangible rays mixed with *green* light of equal refrangibility, and its *least* refrangible rays mixed with *red* light of equal refrangibility." Further experiments in which he examined a salted candle flame with these filters led Brewster to the startling conclusion that, while yellow light had an independent existence, "the prism is incapable of decomposing that part of the spectrum which [yellow] occupies." By 1831 he had extended this interpretation to the entire spectrum. However formed, it "consists of *three* spectra of *equal length, beginning and terminating at the same points,* viz. a *red* spectrum, a *yellow* spectrum, and a *blue* spectrum." Moreover, a certain amount of undecomposable white light exists at every point in the spectrum.

This line of research led to Brewster's most effective defense of an emission theory of light. In an attempt to establish techniques for optical chemical analysis, he turned to a detailed examination of the action on the spectrum of plant juices, gases, and the earth's atmosphere. Not only did he succeed in identifying bodies by their characteristic dark lines, but he also added some 1,600 dark lines to Fraunhofer's 354. Impressed by the extremely selective absorption of light by "nitrous acid gas," he concluded that he could "form no conception of a simple elastic medium so modified by the particles of the body which contains it, as to make such an extraordinary selection of the undulations which it stops or transmits."

After the 1830's Brewster directed his attention to such subjects as photography, stereoscopy, and the physiology of vision. At the same time he began to emphasize his writing rather than his editing. His biographies of Newton, Galileo, Tycho Brahe, and Kepler; his numerous articles for the *Encyclopaedia Britannica*; and his hundred or more major essay reviews were, for the most part, written after 1830. His time for research was limited, and he had largely achieved his original research goals. Also, optics was increasingly dominated by an unwelcome theory, the undulatory theory of light.

Brewster never wholeheartedly accepted the undulatory theory. His most honored papers had either been based on the emission theory or had been directed to its defense. Using that theory, he had derived mathematical laws that successfully explained and predicted phenomena. At the same time he frankly admitted his admiration for the "singular power of [the undulatory theory] to explain some of the most perplexing phaenomena of optics. . . ." However, "the power of a theory . . . to explain and predict facts is by no means a test of its truth. . . ." But more important for Brewster, the undulatory theory, based on a hypothetical ether that he could not conceive of in physical terms, and that in principle never could be observed, was fatally "defective as a *physical* representation of the phaenomena of light. . . ."

While Brewster repeatedly asserted the value of theory and was a competent, if not brilliant, mathematician, he was above all an experimenter. And the experimenter, not the theoretician, could achieve "true" knowledge. Most important, however, Brewster believed that the undulatory theory, a mere speculation, had been raised to the level of an assumed Truth. As a devout evangelical Presbyterian who believed in the unity of truth, he felt that such unbridled speculation in physics had profoundly serious implications for religion. To him, "Speculation engenders doubt, and doubt is frequently the parent either of apathy or impiety." To accept the undulatory theory of light would have required Brewster to abandon his deepest convictions about man's ability to know the world and man's duty to serve God.

BIBLIOGRAPHY

I. ORIGINAL WORKS. There is no collected edition of Brewster's works, nor is there a bibliography. An appendix in the *Home Life* (see below) reproduces the bibliography of his articles given in the Royal Society's *Catalogue of Scientific Papers.* It is very incomplete and has some inaccuracies. Many other articles by him of varying importance are printed in the various periodicals that he edited, especially the *Edinburgh Philosophical Journal* and the *Edinburgh Journal of Science.* Most of his anonymous, and very revealing, essay reviews are listed in Walter E. Houghton, ed., *The Wellesley Index to Victorian Periodicals, 1824–1900,* Vol. I (Toronto, 1966). Brewster's own collection of papers was accidentally burned early in the twentieth century, but important manuscript collections of his letters exist at the British Museum (Charles Babbage and MacVey Napier papers), University College, London (Henry, Lord Brougham papers), the National Library of Scotland, and the Royal Society, London.

Information in this article is based upon the following of Brewster's own books and articles: *A Treatise on New Philosophical Instruments, for Various Purposes in the Arts and Sciences. With Experiments on Light and Colours* (Edinburgh-London, 1813); "On some properties of Light," in *Philosophical Transactions of the Royal Society,* **103** (1813), 101–109; "On the affections of Light transmitted through crystallized bodies," *ibid.,* **104** (1814), 187–218; "On the Polarisation of Light by oblique transmission through all Bodies, whether crystallized or uncrystallized," *ibid.,* 219–230; "Results of some recent experiments on the properties impressed upon Light by the action of Glass raised to different temperatures, and cooled under different circumstances," *ibid.,* 436–439; "Experiments on the depolarisation of light as exhibited by various mineral, animal, and vegetable bodies, with a reference of the phenomena to the general principles of polarisation," *ibid.,* **105** (1815), 29–53; "On the effects of simple pressure in producing that species of crystallization which forms two oppositely polarised images, and exhibits the complementary colours by polarised light," *ibid.,* 60–64; "On the laws which regulate the polarisation of Light by reflexion from transparent bodies," *ibid.,* 125–159; "On new properties of heat as exhibited in its propagation along glass plates," *ibid.,* **106** (1816), 46–114; "On the communication of the structure of doubly-refracting crystals to glass, muriate of soda, fluor spar, and other substances by mechanical compression and dilation," *ibid.,* 156–178; "On the Effects of Compression and Dilation in altering the Polarising Structure of Doubly Refracting Crystals," in *Transactions of the Royal Society of Edinburgh,* **8** (1818), 281–286; "On the Laws which regulate the Distribution of the Polarising Force in Plates, Tubes, and Cylinders of Glass that have received the Polarising Structure," *ibid.,* 353–372; "On the laws of Polarisation and double refraction in regularly crystallised bodies," in *Philosophical Transactions of the Royal Society,* **108** (1818), 199–273; "On the connection between the primitive forms of Crystals, and the number of their Axes of double refraction," in *Memoirs* of the Edinburgh Wernerian Society, **3** (1817–1820), 50–74; *A Treatise on the Kaleidoscope* (Edinburgh, 1819); "Observations on Vision through Coloured Glasses, and on their application to Telescopes and Microscopes of great magnitude," in *Edinburgh Philosophical Journal,* **6** (1822), 102–107; "Description of a Monochromatic Lamp for Microscopical purposes, &c. with Remarks of the Absorption of the Prismatic Rays by coloured Media," in *Transactions of the Royal Society of Edinburgh,* **9** (1823), 433–444; "On the production of regular double refraction in the molecules of bodies by simple pressure; with observations on the origin of the doubly refracting structure," in *Philosophical Transactions of the Royal Society,* **120** (1830), 87–96; "On the law of the partial polarisation of light by reflexion," *ibid.,* 69–84; "On the laws of the polarisation of light by refraction," *ibid.,* 133–144; "On the Phenomena and Laws of Elliptic Polarisation, as exhibited in the Action of Metals upon Light," *ibid.,* 287–326; "Decline of Science in England and Patent laws," in *Quarterly Review,* **43** (Oct. 1830), 305–342; "Observations on the Decline of Science in England," in *Edinburgh Journal of Science,* **5** (July 1831), 1–16; "On a New Analysis of Solar Light, indicating three Primary Colours, forming Coincident Spectra of equal length," in *Transactions of the Royal Society of Edinburgh,* **12** (1834), 123–136; "Report on the recent Progress of

Optics," in *Report of the British Association for the Advancement of Science* (1831–1832), pp. 308–322; "Observations of the Absorption of Specific Rays, in reference to the Undulatory Theory of Light," in *London, Edinburgh, and Dublin Philosophical Magazine and Journal of Science,* **2** (1833), 360–363; "Life and Correspondence of Sir James Edward Smith," in *Edinburgh Review,* **57** (April 1833), 39–69 (the quotation on "Speculation" is on p. 41); "Observations on the Lines of the Solar Spectrum, and on those produced by the Earth's Atmosphere, and by the action of Nitrous Acid Gas," in *Transactions of the Royal Society of Edinburgh,* **12** (1834), 519–530; "On the Colours of Natural Bodies," *ibid.,* 538–545; "Arago *Éloge historique de Baron Fourier,*" in *North British Review,* **4** (Feb. 1846), 380–412 (contains his plan for a national institute, particularly pp. 410–412); and *Memoirs of the Life, Writings, and Discoveries of Sir Isaac Newton,* 2 vols. (Edinburgh, 1855). The *Memoirs . . . of Sir Isaac Newton* has been reprinted in 2 volumes (New York, 1965) with a useful introduction by Richard S. Westfall that discusses both Brewster's life and his interpretation of Newton.

II. SECONDARY LITERATURE. Very little contemporary secondary material on Brewster exists, nor is he adequately treated in the standard histories of optics. The only biography that exists is Margaret Maria Gordon (Brewster), *The Home Life of Sir David Brewster,* 2nd ed., rev. (Edinburgh, 1870). While it is generally reliable, it is frankly directed to the "unscientific" reader. It is the source for most of his obituaries. Brewster himself particularly recommended, as very full and complete, the article "Brewster, David," in the *Biographie universelle et portative des contemporaines,* V (Paris, 1836), 77–81. It has biographical information not included in the *Home Life.*

The standard, although very one-sided, histories of the emission-undulation controversy are Ernst Mach, *The Principles of Physical Optics, an Historical and Philosophical Treatment* (New York, 1953); Vasco Ronchi, *Histoire de la lumière,* translated by Juliette Taton (Paris, 1956); and Sir Edmund Whittaker, *A History of the Theories of Aether and Electricity,* Vol. I, *The Classical Theories* (New York, 1960). Brewster's work in optical mineralogy is briefly treated in John G. Burke, *Origins of the Science of Crystals* (Berkeley, 1965). A very useful discussion of Brewster's optical theories is contained in Henry Steffens, "The Development of Newtonian Optics in England, 1738–1831" (unpublished Master's dissertation, Cornell University, 1965).

EDGAR W. MORSE

BRIANCHON, CHARLES-JULIEN (*b.* Sèvres, France, 19 December 1783; *d.* Versailles, France, 29 April 1864), *mathematics.*

There appears to be no record of Brianchon's early years. He entered the École Polytechnique in 1804 and was a pupil of the noted geometer Gaspard Monge. While a student there, he published his first paper, "Sur les surfaces courbes du second degré"

(1806), which contained the famous theorem named after him.

Brianchon graduated first in his class in 1808 and became a lieutenant in artillery in the armies of Napoleon. He took part in the Peninsular campaigns, serving in Spain and Portugal, and is said to have distinguished himself both in bravery and ability. The rigors of his army service affected his health, and after the cessation of hostilities in 1813, Brianchon applied for a teaching position. He was finally appointed professor at the Artillery School of the Royal Guard in 1818.

By this time he had published several works in geometry, including "Sur les surfaces courbes du second degré" (1816), *Mémoire sur les lignes du second ordre* (1817), *Application de la théorie des transversales* (1818), and "Solution de plusieurs problèmes de géométrie" (1818).

Brianchon's teaching duties apparently affected both his output and his interests. In 1820 there appeared "Recherches sur la détermination d'une hyperbole équilatère, au moyen de quatres conditions données," written with Poncelet. It is notable for containing the nine-point circle theorem and is an instance of the many times this theorem has been rediscovered by independent investigators. At any rate, this paper contains the first complete proof of the theorem and the first use of the term "nine-point circle."

Brianchon's next publication, "Description du laboratoire de chimie de l'École d'Artillerie de la Garde Royale" (1822), indicates his change of interests. Two works appeared in 1823: "Des courbes de raccordement" and *Mémoire sur la poudre à tirer*. His last known work, *Essai chimique sur les réactions foudroyantes,* appeared in 1825. Brianchon ceased writing after 1825 and devoted all his time to teaching. Details of his personal life are singularly scarce.

Brianchon's fame rests ultimately on one theorem. In 1639 Pascal had proved that "If all the vertices of a hexagon lie on a circle, and if the opposite sides intersect, then the points of intersection lie on a line." He then boldly extended this result to a hexagon inscribed in any conic, since he recognized that his theorem was projective in nature. Oddly enough, it took 167 years before someone else—Brianchon—realized that since the theorem is projective in nature, its dual should also be true. Simply stated, Brianchon's theorem is "If all the sides of a hexagon are tangent to a conic, then the diagonals joining opposite vertices are concurrent." The theorem is useful in the study of the properties of conics and—if the hexagon is specialized in various ways—for the

study of properties of pentagons, quadrilaterals, and triangles.

BIBLIOGRAPHY

Brianchon's writings are "Sur les surfaces courbes du second degré," in *Journal de l'École Polytechnique* (1806); "Sur les surfaces courbes du second degré," *ibid.* (1816); *Mémoire sur les lignes du second ordre* (Paris, 1817); *Application de la théorie des transversales* (Paris, 1818); "Solutions de plusieurs problèmes de géométrie," in *Journal de l'École Polytechnique,* **4** (1818); "Recherches sur la détermination d'une hyperbole équilatère, au moyen de quatres conditions données," *ibid.* (1820); "Description du laboratoire de chimie de l'École d'Artillerie de la Garde Royale," in *Annales de l'industrie nationale* (1822); "Des courbes de raccordement," in *Journal de l'École Polytechnique,* **12** (1823); *Mémoire sur la poudre à tirer* (Paris, 1823); and *Essai chimique sur les réactions foudroyantes* (Paris, 1825).

S. L. GREITZER

BRIDGES, CALVIN BLACKMAN (*b.* Schuyler Falls, New York, 11 January 1889; *d.* Los Angeles, California, 27 December 1938), *genetics.*

Calvin Blackman Bridges was the only child of Leonard Victor Bridges and Charlotte Amelia Blackman. His mother died when Calvin was two years old and his father a year later, so the boy was brought up by his paternal grandmother. When he was fourteen, he was sent to Plattsburg to attend high school. Because of his deficient primary school training and because he worked to help support himself, he did not graduate from high school until he was twenty. His record was good enough, however, for him to be offered scholarships at both Cornell and Columbia. He chose the latter and entered as a freshman in 1909. His record at Columbia was outstanding, and he graduated in three years in spite of largely supporting himself by outside work and, in the last half of the period, spending much of his time and energy on research with *Drosophila.* In 1912 he married Gertrude Ives. The couple had four children.

In his freshman year Bridges and the writer (then a sophomore) took the beginning course in zoology, which was given (for the only time during his twenty-four years at Columbia) by T. H. Morgan. This was the beginning of a very close association, among the three of us, which lasted until Bridges' death.

Morgan's work on the genetics of *Drosophila* began in earnest in the summer of 1910; and in the academic year 1910-1911 Bridges and I were given desks in his laboratory, a room 16 by 23 feet, which came to be known as "the fly room." Here the three of us reared *Drosophila* for the next seventeen years. A steady succession of American and foreign doctoral and postdoctoral students also had desks there. From 1915 Bridges was a research associate of the Carnegie Institution of Washington, and in 1928 he moved from Columbia to the California Institute of Technology, where he spent the rest of his life.

At the beginning of this period the techniques were unsatisfactory, and Bridges was largely responsible for their improvement. He introduced the use of binocular microscopes instead of hand lenses, he developed dependable temperature controls, and he played the largest part in the improvement and standardization of the culture bottles and media.

The working material for the group was the series of mutant types, and their detection and isolation was one of the major concerns of all of us—but Bridges was so good at this that he contributed many more mutants than did the rest of us. He also had the skill and patience required to organize this material into a coherent body of detailed information and to produce a series of carefully planned and useful stocks of combinations of mutant types. This information and many of these stocks are still basic and are in constant use by students of *Drosophila.*

In the early work there were often found a few exceptions to the usual rules for the inheritance of sex-linked genes, and Bridges undertook a study of them. He published an account in 1913, giving the phenomenon the name "nondisjunction." No satisfactory scheme emerged, until he made a microscopical study of the chromosomes (1914). Here, and especially in his doctoral thesis (1916), he produced a brilliant and characteristically detailed and convincing account that constituted a proof of the correctness of the chromosome theory of heredity.

Bridges followed this with a study of nondisjunction of the small fourth chromosome, and this led to his development of the idea of genic balance, which has played a large part in all later interpretations of the way in which genes influence development. The classic work in this field is Bridges' study of the determination of sex in *Drosophila,* which he based on his combined genetical and cytological study of the offspring of triploid females—again a brilliantly conceived and convincingly thorough piece of work.

Bridges had made himself the outstanding authority on the cytology of *Drosophila,* but the chromosomes were very small and so lacking in structural detail that they could be used effectively in the analysis of only a few of the many chromosome rearrangements that were discovered by genetic means—most of them by Bridges.

In 1933 the work of Heitz and Bauer, and of Painter, showed that the chromosomes of the salivary glands of *Drosophila* and of some other flies had a wealth of structural detail far greater than that known in the chromosomes of any other organism. Bridges threw himself into the study of these chromosomes, and produced a series of drawings of them that are still the standards of reference. This, like much of his work, required great patience, accurate observation, technical skill and ingenuity, and an understanding of what was important. In 1936 he was elected to the National Academy of Sciences.

Bridges was a friendly and generous person. Politically he was rather far to the left—a circumstance related to his visit to Russia in 1931–1932. In his personal and social relations he was a nonconformist, largely as a matter of principle.

BIBLIOGRAPHY

I. ORIGINAL WORKS. Bridges wrote about 125 scientific papers, not counting numerous notes in *Drosophila Information Service,* which he and M. Demerec compiled and edited from 1934 to 1939. The list that follows is a selection of the more important contributions. A fuller listing may be found in Morgan's biography (1941; see below).

Bridges' works include "Dilution Effects and Bicolorism in Certain Eye Colors of *Drosophila,*" in *Journal of Experimental Zoology,* **15** (1913), 429–466, written with T. H. Morgan; "Non-disjunction of the Sex Chromosomes of *Drosophila,*" in *Science,* **37** (1913), 112–113; "Direct Proof Through Non-disjunction That the Sex-linked Genes of *Drosophila* Are Borne by the X-Chromosomes," in *Science,* **40** (1914), 107–109; "A Linkage Variation in *Drosophila,*" in *Journal of Experimental Zoology,* **19** (1915), 1–21; *The Mechanism of Mendelian Heredity* (New York, 1915), written with T. H. Morgan, A. H. Sturtevant, and H. J. Muller; "Non-disjunction as Proof of the Chromosome Theory of Heredity," in *Genetics,* **1** (1916), 1–52, 107–163; *Sex-linked Inheritance in Drosophila,* Carnegie Institution of Washington publication 237 (Washington, 1916); "Deficiency," in *Genetics,* **2** (1917), 445–465; "The Constitution of the Germinal Material in Relation to Heredity," in *Carnegie Institution of Washington Year Book,* XV–XXXVIII (Washington, 1917–1939)—written with T. H. Morgan and A. H. Sturtevant through 1929 and with T. H. Morgan and J. Schultz from 1930, these annual reports give a picture of the work in progress and are often the only published accounts of ideas and experiments.

Also see "The Second-chromosome Group of Mutant Characters" and "The Origin of Gynandromorphs," Carnegie Institution of Washington publication 278 (Washington, 1919), pp. 1–304; "Specific Modifiers of Eosin Eye Color in *Drosophila melanogaster,*" in *Journal of Experimental Zoology,* **28** (1919), 337–384; "Proof of Non-disjunction of the Fourth Chromosome of *Drosophila melanogaster,*" in *Science,* **53** (1921), 308; "Triploid Intersexes in *Drosophila melanogaster,*" in *Science,* **54** (1921), 252–254; *The Third-*

chromosome Group of Mutant Characters of Drosophila melanogaster, Carnegie Institution of Washington publication 327 (Washington, 1923), written with T. H. Morgan; "The Translocation of a Section of Chromosome II on Chromosome III," in *Anatomical Record,* **24** (1923), 426–427; "Crossing Over in the X-Chromosomes of Triploid Females of *Drosophila melanogaster,*" in *Genetics,* **10** (1925), 418–441, written with E. G. Anderson; "The Genetics of *Drosophila,*" in *Bibliographia genetica,* **2** (1925), 1–262, written with T. H. Morgan and A. H. Sturtevant; "Sex in Relation to Chromosomes and Genes," in *American Naturalist,* **59** (1925), 127–137; "Some Physicochemical Aspects of Life, Mutation, and Evolution," in *Colloid Chemistry,* **2** (1928), 9–58, written with J. Alexander; "The Genetic Conception of Life," an address given before the Academy of Science, Leningrad (1931); "Specific Suppressors in *Drosophila,*" in *Proceedings of the 6th International Congress on Genetics,* II (1932), 12–14; "The Mutants and Linkage Data of Chromosome Four of *Drosophila melanogaster,*" in *Biologicheskii zhurnal* (Moscow), **4** (1935), 401–420; "Salivary Chromosome Maps—With a Key to the Banding of the Chromosomes of *Drosophila melanogaster,*" in *Journal of Heredity,* **26** (1935), 60–64; "The Bar 'Gene' a Duplication," in *Science,* **83** (1936), 210–211; "A Revised Map of the Salivary Gland X-Chromosome of *Drosophila melanogaster,*" in *Journal of Heredity,* **29** (1938), 11–13; "A New Map of the Second Chromosome. A Revised Map of the Right Limb of the Second Chromosome of *Drosophila melanogaster,*" *ibid.,* **30** (1939), 475–476, written with P. N. Bridges; *The Mutants of Drosophila melanogaster,* Carnegie Institution of Washington publication 552 (Washington, 1944), completed and edited by K. S. Brehme.

II. SECONDARY LITERATURE. T. H. Morgan wrote four biographical accounts of Bridges: in *Science,* **89** (1939), 118–119; in *Journal of Heredity,* **30** (1939), 355–358; in *Genetics,* **25** (1940), i–v; and in *Biographical Memoirs. National Academy of Sciences,* **22** (1941), 31–48. The last three have two different photographs of Bridges, and the last has a full bibliography.

Additional biographical works are H. J. Muller, in *Nature,* **143** (1939), 191–192; J. Schultz, an unsigned article in *National Cyclopedia of American Biography,* **30** (1943), 374; A. H. Sturtevant, in *Biological Bulletin,* **79** (1940), 24. There are also numerous references in A. H. Sturtevant, *A History of Genetics* (New York, 1965).

A. H. STURTEVANT

BRIDGMAN, PERCY WILLIAMS (*b.* Cambridge, Massachusetts, 21 April 1882; *d.* Randolph, New Hampshire, 20 August 1961), *physics, philosophy of science.*

Bridgman was the only son of Raymond Landon Bridgman, a newspaper correspondent and the author of a number of books on public affairs, and Ann Maria Williams Bridgman. The family moved to Newton, Massachusetts, where Percy attended the public schools until he entered Harvard College in 1900. He graduated with a B.A., *summa cum laude,* in 1904, with rigorous training in physics and mathematics. He remained at Harvard for his M.A. (1905) and Ph.D. (1908) in physics, whereupon he was immediately appointed research fellow in the department of physics, then instructor in 1910. In 1912 Bridgman married Olive Ware. The couple had two children. Bridgman was appointed assistant professor in 1913, professor in 1919, Hollis professor of mathematics and natural philosophy in 1926, Higgins university professor in 1950, and professor emeritus in 1954.

Percy Bridgman's penetrating analytical thought and physical intuition, fertile imagination for mechanical detail, and exceptional dexterity in manipulating equipment defined a clear channel of activity into which he threw himself with untiring energy and singleness of purpose. He was an individualist of the most determined stamp, and refused to be diverted by faculty business, by the demands of society, or by any personal weakness from his main interest: his scholarly activity as experimenter, teacher, and critic of the basic concepts of physical science.

While avoiding almost all university committees, Bridgman was an active member of the American Academy of Arts and Sciences, and served on the board of editors of its journal, *Daedalus.* He was fond of music, and also pursued a number of other avocations—all with concentration and perfectionism, whether it was chess, handball, gardening, mountain climbing, or photography. But play was never allowed to interfere with the main business of his life; his unremitting activity was reflected in the high and steady output of papers on physics and philosophy of science. Bridgman wrote about six papers a year, many with such titles as "The Resistance of 72 Elements, Alloys, and Compounds to 100,000 kg/cm²." His lifetime total was over 260 papers, in addition to thirteen books that were largely the products of his summers at Randolph, New Hampshire. All of his writing is remarkably personal and often in the first person singular; whether the subject is the polymorphism of bismuth or the duties of intelligent individuals in an unintelligent society, the characteristic Bridgman tone and quality are immediately evident.

Bridgman, a man of generosity and integrity, was regarded with affection and admiration by his associates. His honors included the Rumford Medal of the American Academy of Arts and Sciences, the Cresson Medal of the Franklin Institute, the Roozeboom Medal of the Royal Academy of Sciences of Amsterdam, the Bingham Medal of the Society of Rheology, the Comstock Prize of the National Academy of Sciences, the New York Award of the Research Corporation of America, and, "for the invention of an apparatus to produce extremely high pressures, and for the discoveries he made therewith in the field of high-pressure physics," the Nobel Prize in physics for 1946. He was president of the American Physical Society in 1942, a member of the National Academy of Sciences, a fellow of the American Academy of Arts and Sciences, a foreign member of academies of science in England, Mexico, and India, and the holder of honorary degrees from six universities.

Bridgman's early papers give no explanation of the origins of his interest in high pressures. He may have been influenced by Theodore Richards, who had measured the compressibility of elements, or by Wallace Sabine, with whom he took a research course in heat and light for four years.

His first three papers, published in the *Proceedings of the American Academy of Arts and Sciences* (Vol. **44**, 1908–1909), laid the foundation for most of his later work. The maximum pressure attained—6,500 atmospheres—was not much higher than was currently used by other investigators, and was inefficiently produced with a screw compressor turned with a six-foot wrench. Bridgman's first concern appears to have been the establishment of an adequate pressure scale rather than the production of drastically higher pressures. He developed the free-piston gauge, or pressure balance, used earlier by Amagat, and introduced a more convenient secondary gauge based on the effect of pressure upon the electrical resistance of mercury (the subject of his Ph.D. thesis).

The new design of a leakproof pressure seal or "packing"—later called the "unsupported area seal," and the key to so much subsequent achievement—appears in the discussion of the free-piston gauge, with scarcely a suggestion of its importance. Indeed, Bridgman later explained (*American Scientist,* Vol. **31**, 1943) that the self-sealing feature of his first high-pressure packing was incidental to the design of a closure for the pressure vessel that could be rapidly assembled or taken apart; the basic advantages of the scheme were realized only afterward. In his brief autobiographical remarks in a questionnaire filed with the National Academy of Sciences, under the heading "Discoveries Which You Regard as Most Important," Bridgman wrote: "Doubtless the most influential single discovery was that of a method of producing high hydrostatic pressure without leak. The discovery of the method had a strong element of accident."

In principle, the construction insures that the sealing gasket, of rubber or soft metal, is restrained on the upper, or low-pressure, side of the vessel by a

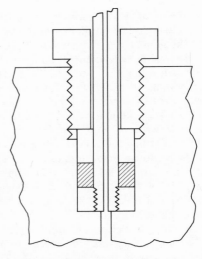

FIGURE 1. The general scheme of the packing, by which pressure in the soft packing materials is automatically maintained at a fixed percentage higher than in the liquid.

fixed surface the area of which is somewhat smaller than that acting on the other side of the packing. Hence, the latter is always compressed to a pressure higher than that to be confined inside the vessel (Fig. 1); the high pressure itself is used to tighten the packing; and the ultimate limitation becomes the strength of the metal parts. It was mainly this advance that allowed Bridgman to open up a virgin field for experimental exploration.

The third paper of the early series gives new measurements of the compressibility of steel, mercury, and glass. We recognize already the characteristic Bridgman style: the evident pleasure in the manipulations of shop and laboratory; the meticulous pursuit of the numerous corrections; the experiments with homely mixtures of mercury, molasses, glycerine, and marine glue. None of these early measurements proved to be definitive; the absolute gauge was soon improved, the mercury gauge was discarded in favor of a manganin wire gauge, and the compressibilities were revised. But his rapid succession of publications quickly transformed the field of high-pressure research.

By 1910 the equipment had been completely redesigned. The screw compressor was replaced by a hydraulic ram, and the new packing was systematically exploited. For the first time, pressures of the order of 20,000 atmospheres and more are reported. Bridgman remarks: "The magnitude of the fluid pressure mentioned here requires brief comment, because without a word of explanation it may seem so large as to cast discredit on the accuracy of all the data." The techniques to be used for the next twenty years had been substantially perfected and were described more fully in the paper "The Technique of High Pressure Experimenting" (1914).

Bridgman had the good fortune to begin his experiments at a time when metallurgical advances were providing steels of unprecedentedly high strength; his achievement of still higher pressures in the 1930's was made possible by the development of the cobalt-bonded tungsten carbides. The leakproof packing would have been of little value with Amagat's steel, but the new alloys permitted spectacular increases of the useful pressure range. Bridgman settled on an electric-furnace chrome-vanadium steel (equivalent to the present AISI 6150) for most of his pressure vessels and connecting tubes. It is not a deep-hardening steel, and in pressure vessels the size of Bridgman's, four or five inches in diameter, the interior remains relatively soft. This condition is advantageous in pressure vessels because the elastic limit is reached first in the ductile material near the bore, which can be stretched appreciably without rupture; at the same time, the expansion of the inner part transmits the load to the strong outer parts, which are inefficiently stressed so long as the whole cylinder remains in the elastic range. Thus Bridgman found that pressures far in excess of predictions based on simple elastic criteria could be contained.

The maximum fluid pressure for routine measurements of the mechanical, electrical, and thermal properties of matter was gradually raised to 30,000 atmospheres. Still higher pressures, to an estimated 400,000 atmospheres, were finally obtained in quasi-fluid systems.

At pressures above 3,000 atmospheres, Bridgman was in a realm of physical conditions new to the physicist; the instruments for measuring pressure had to be devised and calibrated, and novel methods developed for making other kinds of physical measurements. Bridgman's fifty years of concentrated effort, characterized both by the magnitude of the pressures employed and by the range of phenomena investigated, have provided a large part of all the measurements now used in this field and form the basis for most of the recent advances in high-pressure technology. His *The Physics of High Pressure* (1931) has remained the basic work in this field.

Much of Bridgman's work was done while the theory of the solid state was still in its infancy, and the interpretation of many of his measurements has become possible only in recent years. The massive treasure of data that he left has proved invaluable for the development of solid state physics. Also among Bridgman's achievements were an early method of refining by zone melting, the discovery of polymorphism of many materials at high pressures (including

ice at high temperature), and a new electrical effect (internal Peltier heat) in metal crystals. His investigations had great geophysical significance, for they proved that drastic alterations in the physical properties and crystal structure of rock material must take place under the high pressures that prevail in the earth's interior. He lived to see the artificial production of many natural high-pressure mineral forms, such as diamond, coesite, and jadeite, by techniques based on his discoveries.

From the beginning, Bridgman, working alone or with his long-time machinist Charles Chase and research assistant Leonard Abbott, made much of his own apparatus. In almost any weather, he would arrive on his bicycle as soon as the workshop opened at 8:00 A.M. His papers contain many useful bits of shop lore and throw light on the amount of labor and persistence underlying his studies: "It is easy, if all precautions are observed, to drill a hole . . . seventeen inches long in from seven to eight hours." They also helped greatly in the adaptation of his techniques all over the world when, after 1945, there was a great rise of interest in experimental high-pressure work.

One may surmise that Bridgman thoroughly enjoyed the complete personal control he exercised over his equipment. The manipulations took him from pumps to measuring apparatus—usually a set of direct current electrical bridges or potentiometers requiring telescopic observation of galvanometer deflections—to the notebook in which notations were made in his private shorthand, and back to the pumps for a new cycle. All of this was performed as fast as the various thermal and pressure lags would permit, sometimes on a fixed schedule that covered several hours. Much philosophical debate has taken place over the meaning of his term *operational,* but his original meaning must have been closely related to the manifold physical activities of his laboratory, with every adjustment and every measurement dictated by his own mind and controlled by his own muscles.

This desire for full personal involvement in the experiment probably also accounted for Bridgman's reluctance to do joint research or to take on thesis students. He rarely had more than two at one time; the record shows fourteen doctoral theses on high-pressure topics, in addition to several on other subjects that he supervised. He was usually most pleased when least consulted, but was always willing to listen to interesting findings or to put his mind to real difficulties.

Bridgman's mechanical genius was reflected in the essential simplicity of his apparatus and his mastery of manipulative techniques. Whether machining a miniature mechanical part, blowing glass, preparing samples of intractable materials, drawing wires, sealing off volatile liquids, purifying chemicals, or growing simple crystals of unprecedented size, he accomplished his purpose with rapidity, a minimum of equipment, and a remarkably low budget.

During World War I, Bridgman moved with his family to New London, Connecticut, where he engaged in the development of sound-detection systems for antisubmarine warfare. He also developed an application of his high-pressure laboratory technique for the prestraining of one-piece gun barrels. Just before World War II, Bridgman's libertarian outlook and his fear of "the misuse of scientific information" caused him to close his laboratory to "citizens of any totalitarian state." After the war broke out, he undertook a series of studies for the Watertown Arsenal on the plastic flow of steel under high pressure, a consideration related to the problem of the strength of armor plate. For the Manhattan Project he measured the compressibility of uranium and plutonium.

Bridgman's lectures were at first baffling to many students. He spoke quickly, and in spurts, with little regard for clear enunciation. Nevertheless, his basic lucidity of thought and his way of coming to grips with the subject forced students to think deeply for themselves. This was reinforced by problem sets of legendary brevity and difficulty.

One of Bridgman's early teaching assignments—giving two advanced courses in electrodynamics, suddenly thrust upon him in 1914 by the death of B. O. Peirce—turned out to be the genesis of his active interest in philosophy of science. Years later he commented on the obscurity of the underlying conceptual situation that he found in electrodynamics, and the intellectual distress that it caused him. His efforts to meet the logical problems in this area led to a critical examination of the logical structure of physics, until he could say, "I was able to think the situation through to my own satisfaction."

Bridgman's first publication in this area (1916) dealt with dimensional analysis, and he returned to this subject in his first book, *Dimensional Analysis* (1922). It was the first systematic and critical exposition of the principles involved and was characterized by a rigorous analysis of the mental operations involved in dimensional reasoning; the analysis was based on his demand that the equations of physics be given unambiguous meanings by interpreting the letter symbols for the different physical quantities as placeholders for the numbers that form the measure-values of the physical quantities, rather than as place-holders for "physical quantities" formed by multiplying each measure-value by the corresponding physical unit.

Bridgman's success in thinking his way through the confusions of dimensional analysis encouraged him to turn his attention to the larger task of eliminating similar confusions in the broader field of physics proper. He was deeply impressed by Einstein's demonstration of the meaninglessness of the conception of absolute simultaneity between events at different places, noting that the proof involved an analysis of the operations of synchronization of clocks at different locations. That the basic concepts of time and space had been seriously misconceived, that sloppy thinking and uncritical usage of language were revealed at the core of physics, seemed to Bridgman to call for a critical reexamination of the conceptual structure of physics as a whole. In order to circumvent the word traps of ordinary speech, he proposed to use physical and mental operations as the measure of meaning.

The resulting "operational" point of view was brilliantly argued, in simple but stark statements, in *The Logic of Modern Physics* (1927): "In general, we mean by any concept nothing more than a set of operations; the concept is synonymous with the corresponding set of operations. . . . If a specific question has meaning, it must be possible to find operations by which answers may be given to it. It will be found in many cases that the operations cannot exist, and the question therefore has no meaning."

This volume was of immense value to a generation of scientists then facing the apparent paradoxes of a new world of atoms and quanta that flatly refused to follow the rules of common sense. In due course *The Logic of Modern Physics* was followed by other books and papers extending and deepening Bridgman's critical examination of the concepts and theories of physics. His Princeton University lectures were published as *The Nature of Physical Theory* (1936). *The Nature of Thermodynamics* followed (1941), and *A Sophisticate's Primer of Relativity* appeared posthumously (1962). In these studies Bridgman drew attention away from the apparent precision of the mathematical equations of physics and the seemingly rigorous logic of axiomatically constructed theories, and turned it to the matrix of crude observations and approximate verbal explanations from which the symbols and equations derive their significance. His relentless probing exposed a surprising penumbra of uncertainty regarding the interpretation of the symbols in thermodynamics (for example, in different physical situations) and the limits of applicability of its concepts. Through these books, and through papers on the application of his ideas to other areas of science and even to the social sciences, Bridgman's influence spread far beyond the field of physics.

His philosophic point of view is usually classified with the positivism of Stallo, Mach, Charles Peirce, William James, and the Vienna Circle; but it derived from his own experience and maintained its individual line.

Bridgman's influence was strongest among scientists, who found his point of view congenial; and much of what he had to say is commonly accepted among them today. His philosophic·writing was, to be sure, always iconoclastic and stimulated a good deal of controversy, especially among some philosophers of science. Operational analysis, he had to explain, was proposed as an aid to clear thinking, and not as a solution for all the problems of philosophy. Again and again he expressed his dislike of the word "operationalism," with its implication of an associated dogma. Similarly, he gave repeated evidence in operational terms of the seriousness with which he advocated almost ruthless intellectual integrity. One case in point was the publication in 1959 of his own appraisal of *The Logic of Modern Physics.*

A final affirmation of this ideal is to be found in the circumstances of his death. In the essay "The Struggle for Intellectual Integrity" (1933), he had dealt with the choice of death if one's probable future is irreversibly and predominantly painful. This choice came to him with suddenness in his eightieth year, and he was not a man to think one thing and do another. After careful diagnosis by undoubted authorities, he found that, in his own words,

> . . . the disease [Paget's disease] has run its normal course, and has now turned into a well-developed cancer for which apparently nothing can be done. . . . In the meantime there is considerable pain, and the doctors here do not offer much prospect that it can be made better. . . . I would like to take advantage of the situation in which I find myself to establish a general principle, namely, that when the ultimate end is as inevitable as it now appears to be, the individual has a right to ask his doctor to end it for him.

Unable to make such arrangements, and finding that his limbs were rapidly losing mobility, Bridgman felt obliged to take action himself. He left behind a two-sentence note:

> It isn't decent for Society to make a man do this thing himself. Probably this is the last day I will be able to do it myself. P.W.B.

A day after his death, Harvard University Press received one of the last things Bridgman must have written, the index for the collection of his complete scientific papers. His ashes were buried in the garden of his beloved summer home.

BIBLIOGRAPHY

I. ORIGINAL WORKS. Among Bridgman's writings are *Dimensional Analysis* (New Haven, 1922; rev. ed., 1931); *A Condensed Collection of Thermodynamic Formulas* (Cambridge, Mass., 1925); *The Logic of Modern Physics* (New York, 1927); *The Physics of High Pressure* (New York, 1931; new impression with suppl., London, 1949); *The Thermodynamics of Electrical Phenomena in Metals* (New York, 1934); *The Nature of Physical Theory* (Princeton, 1936); *The Intelligent Individual and Society* (New York, 1938); *The Nature of Thermodynamics* (Cambridge, Mass., 1941); *Reflections of a Physicist* (New York, 1950, 1955); *The Nature of Some of Our Physical Concepts* (New York, 1952); *Studies in Large Plastic Flow and Fracture, With Special Emphasis on the Effects of Hydrostatic Pressure* (New York, 1952); *The Way Things Are* (Cambridge, Mass., 1959); *The Thermodynamics of Electrical Phenomena in Metals and a Condensed Collection of Thermodynamic Formulas,* rev. ed. (New York, 1961); *A Sophisticate's Primer of Relativity* (Middletown, Conn., 1962); and *Collected Experimental Papers of P. W. Bridgman,* 7 vols. (Cambridge, Mass., 1964).

Bridgman's books on philosophy of science and his *Collected Experimental Papers* contain reprints of almost all his published papers. A fairly complete listing of individual titles is also contained in the obituary note of the Royal Society of London (1962). Further biographical details are in a booklet of essays presented at the memorial meeting at Harvard University, 24 October 1961, and in an obituary volume of the National Academy of Sciences (in press). Much of the material in this article was drawn from these sources and Birch et al. Bridgman's documentary *Nachlass* is largely at the Harvard University Archives; some materials (e.g., scientific data and laboratory books) are kept in Lyman Laboratory, Harvard University, and at the Center for History and Philosophy of Science, American Institute of Physics, New York City. Much of his equipment is still in use in research laboratories at Harvard, but some items are at the Smithsonian Institution, Washington, D.C.

II. SECONDARY LITERATURE. Among the works on Bridgman are Francis Birch, Roger Hickman, Gerald Holton, and Edwin C. Kemble, "Percy Williams Bridgman," in Faculty of Arts and Sciences, *Harvard University Gazette* (31 March 1962); and Philipp Frank, *The Validation of Scientific Theories* (Boston, 1956), ch. 2.

EDWIN C. KEMBLE
FRANCIS BIRCH
GERALD HOLTON

BRIGGS, HENRY (*b.* Warleywood, Yorkshire, England, February 1561; *d.* Oxford, England, 26 January 1630), *mathematics.*

Although J. Mede of Christ's College, Cambridge, wrote on 6 February 1630, "Mr. Henry Briggs of Oxford, the great mathematician, is lately dead, at

74 years of age," implying thereby that Briggs was born about 1556, it seems that he was in error. The Halifax parish register gives the 1561 date.

After a local grammar schooling in Greek and Latin, Briggs went to St. John's College, Cambridge, about 1577, and was admitted as a scholar on 5 November 1579. He received the B.A. in 1581 and the M.A. in 1585, became examiner and lecturer in mathematics in 1592, and soon afterward was appointed Dr. Linacre's reader of the physic (medicine) lecture. He had been elected fellow of his college in 1589.

Early in 1596 Briggs became the first professor of geometry at the newly founded Gresham College in London. He first worked on navigation and composed a table for the finding of the height of the pole, the magnetic declination being given. By 1609 he was in correspondence with James Ussher, later the famous archbishop of Armagh; from one of Briggs's letters we learn that he was studying eclipses in 1610. By 10 March 1615, however, he was entirely engaged in the study of logarithms, the subject for which he is renowned: "Neper, lord of Markinston, hath set my head and hands a work with his new and admirable logarithms. I hope to see him this summer, if it please God, for I never saw book, which pleased me better, and made me more wonder."

Briggs at once applied his energies to the advancement of logarithms and to lecturing on them at Gresham College. He soon proposed a modification of the scale of logarithms from Napier's hyperbolic form, a change that Napier discussed with Briggs, who went to Edinburgh for a month's visit after completing his lectures in the summer of 1616. One result of these exchanges was that Briggs saw E. Wright's translation of Napier's *Canon mirificus* through the press, Wright having died. To the work Briggs added a preface and some material of his own—"A description of an instrument table to find the part proportional, devised by Mr. Edward Wright" (1616).

Briggs's *Logarithmorum chilias prima* is dated 1617; in the preface, which mentions the recent death of Napier, the change from the hyperbolic form of logarithms is justified and the publication of Napier's *Rhabdologia* foretold. That work duly appeared in 1619, with comments by Briggs himself on the new form of logarithms and on the solution of spherical triangles.

The parts taken by Napier and Briggs in developing logarithms were described by the latter in his *Arithmetica logarithmica* (1624). The proposals there recorded do not yield common logarithms: for if R is the radius, Briggs suggested that $\log R = 0$ and $\log R/10 = 10^{10}$. Napier, having abandoned the hyper-

bolic form in which

$$\text{Nap. } \log y = 10^7 \log_e \frac{10^7}{y},$$

proposed an improvement whereby $\log 1 = 0$ and $\log R = 10^{10}$. Later, Briggs replaced $\log R = 10^{10}$ with $\log 10 = 1$. Brigg's key words are:

> I myself, when expounding this doctrine publicly in London to my auditors in Gresham College, remarked that it would be much more convenient that 0 should be kept for the logarithm of the whole sine (as in the *Canon Mirificus*), but that the logarithm of the tenth part of the same whole sine, that is to say 5 degrees 44 minutes and 21 seconds should be 10,000,000,000. And concerning that matter I wrote immediately to the author himself.

Later, however, in Edinburgh, Napier suggested to Briggs "that 0 should be the logarithm of unity and 10,000,000,000 that of the whole sine; which I could not but admit," says Briggs, "was by far the most convenient."

Briggs's edition of Euclid's *Elements* (Books I–VI), printed without the editor's name, was published in London in 1620. In the previous year Sir Henry Saville had invited Briggs to become professor of geometry at Oxford, where he took up his duties at Merton College in January 1620. In his last lecture, Saville introduced Briggs with the words, "Trado lampadem successori meo, doctissimo viro, qui vos ad intima geometriae mysteria perducet." Tactfully Briggs began his lecture course where Saville had left off, at the ninth proposition of Euclid.

His next achievement was the *Arithmetica logarithmica,* which included thirty thousand logarithms, those from 1 to 20,000 and those from 90,000 to 100,000. The work contains a dissertation on the nature and use of logarithms and proposes a scheme for dividing among several hands the calculation of the intermediate numbers from 20,000 to 90,000. Briggs even offered to supply paper specially divided into columns for the purpose. Chapters 12 and 13 of the introduction explain the principles of the method of constructing logarithms by interpolation from differences, an interesting forerunner of the *Canonotechnia* of Roger Cotes. A second edition of the *Arithmetica,* completed by Adrian Vlacq (or Flack), contained the intermediate seventy chiliads and appeared in 1628.

Vlacq also printed Briggs's tables of logarithmic sines and tangents. The responsibility for seeing this work through the press was entrusted by Briggs, when dying, to his friend Henry Gellibrand, then professor of astronomy at Gresham College, who added a preface explaining the application of logarithms to plane and spherical trigonometry. The work was published in 1633 as *Trigonometria Britannica sive de doctrina triangulorum.*

Briggs was an amiable man, much liked by his contemporaries. Unlike Napier, he scorned astrology, thinking it to be "a system of groundless conceits." His last years were spent at Merton College, Oxford, where he died. Some Greek elegiacs were written for him by his Merton colleague Henry Jacob; they end with the statement that not even death has put a stop to his skill, for his soul still astronomizes while his body measures the earth. Oughtred called him "the mirrour of the age for excellent skill in geometry," and Isaac Barrow expressed in his inaugural lecture at Gresham College the sincere gratitude of mathematical contemporaries to Briggs for his outstanding work on logarithms. The interest of this brilliant man extended to the problem of a northwest passage to the South Seas, on which he wrote a treatise (1622), and to the relative merits of the ancients and moderns.

BIBLIOGRAPHY

I. ORIGINAL WORKS. Briggs's contributions, and the rest of Napier's *Canon mirificus,* were published at London in 1616 and reprinted in 1618; his own *Logarithmorum chilias prima* soon followed the original edition of the *Canon* (London, 1617). Briggs also added comments to Napier's *Rhabdologia* (Edinburgh, 1619) and edited a version of Euclid's *Elements,* Books I–VI (London, 1620), although his name did not appear as editor. His interest in a northwest passage to the South Seas was expressed in a treatise on the subject (London, 1622). A major work by Briggs was *Arithmetica logarithmica* (London, 1624); a second edition, completed by Adrian Vlacq (Gouda, 1628), contained the intermediate seventy chiliads. The relative merits of the ancients and moderns were discussed in *Mathematica ab antiquis minus cognita,* published in the second edition of G. Hakewill's *Apologie* (1630). Briggs's last work was *Trigonometria Britannica sive de doctrina triangulorum* (Gouda, 1633).

II. SECONDARY LITERATURE. Works concerning Briggs are D. M. Hallowes, "Henry Briggs, Mathematician," in *Transactions of the Halifax Antiquarian Society* (1962), 79–92; Christopher Hill, *Intellectual Origins of the English Revolution* (Oxford, 1965), p. 38, where it is claimed that "significant though Briggs was as a mathematician in his own right, his greatest importance was as a contact and public relations man"; C. Hutton, *Mathematical Tables,* 5th ed. (London, 1811), pp. 33–37, and *A Philosophical and Mathematical Dictionary,* I (London, 1815), 254–255; F. Maseres, ed., *Scriptores logarithmici,* I (London, 1791), lxxvi ff. (on Briggs's abacus ΠΑΓΧΡΗΣΤΟΣ and binomials, see especially p. lxviii); Thomas Smith, biography of Briggs, in his *Vitae quorundam eruditissimorum et illustrium*

virorum (1707), translated into English by J. T. Foxell in A. J. Thompson, *Logarithmetica Britannica,* I (Cambridge, 1952), lxvii–lxxvii; H. W. Turnbull, a study of Briggs's work on finite differences, in *Proceedings of the Edinburgh Mathematical Society,* 2nd ser., **3** (1933), 164–170; J. Ward, biography of Briggs, in *The Lives of the Professors of Gresham College* (London, 1740), pp. 120–129, which includes a list of Briggs's writings, both published and unpublished; D. T. Whiteside, "Patterns of Mathematical Thought in the Later Seventeenth Century," in *Archive for the History of the Exact Sciences,* **1** (1961), 232–236.

G. HUXLEY

BRIGHT, RICHARD (*b.* Bristol, England, 28 September 1789; *d.* London, England, 16 December 1858), *medicine.*

The first third of the nineteenth century brought forth an extraordinary flowering of medical talent, among whom Bright was a truly outstanding figure. Born to a well-to-do banking family and always in comfortable circumstances, he could devote himself wholly to medical and scientific pursuits without the financial cares of the less fortunate. He began the study of medicine at the University of Edinburgh in 1808. In his second year he interrupted his studies for a few months to serve as a naturalist accompanying Sir George Mackenzie on an expedition to Iceland. Bright contributed notes on botany and zoology. In 1810 he transferred his medical studies to Guy's Hospital in London, where he spent two years. During this first association with Guy's, he became deeply interested in pathology and postmortem examinations. In 1812 Bright returned to Edinburgh for a year, receiving his degree on 13 September 1813. He then spent two terms at Cambridge, but he left quite dissatisfied and embarked on a period of foreign study and travel, particularly in Berlin, Vienna, and Hungary. He described his travels in *Travels From Vienna Through Lower Hungary,* one of the outstanding travel books of the nineteenth century. Of particular interest are his descriptions of Hungary and the Congress of Vienna in 1814.

Returning to England, he became a licentiate of the London College of Physicians in 1816, but he was not elected a fellow until 1832. In 1820 he was appointed assistant physician at Guy's Hospital, and in 1824 was promoted to physician. For approximately twenty years, besides teaching medicine, he engaged in extensive clinical research and clinico-pathological correlations, always of the highest quality. After 1843 he no longer published papers, and from about 1840 until his death, he was absorbed in practice rather than in research.

We associate Bright's name particularly with kidney

disease, but we must not ignore his broad interest in the entire field of internal medicine. He had an intense concern with diseases of the nervous system, and he also contributed to the knowledge of visceral disease, especially of the pancreas, duodenum, and liver. He wrote extensively on abdominal tumors; and in his textbook, written with Thomas Addison, he provided the first accurate account of appendicitis. In all his investigations he combined meticulous clinical observation and careful postmortem studies.

Bright was, in essence, a "naturalist" who had unrivaled powers of observation. He noted the clinical phenomena of disease. Then, in the tradition of Morgagni, Gaspard Bayle, and Laënnec, he tried to correlate these clinical findings with the postmortem observations, but always on an empirical level. Remote causes or occult properties interested him not at all. Instead, he dealt with facts of observation. Gathering his observations not only at the bedside but also at the autopsy table and in the rudimentary clinical laboratory, he tried to correlate the data so that meaningful patterns might emerge. Constantly he tried to bring together, as he expressed it, "such facts as seem to throw light upon each other." As a scientist he could select, from the total profusion of facts, those which somehow belonged together.

In 1827 Bright published his first great contribution to kidney disease. He had clearly perceived that some relationships existed between three separate features. Each of them was familiar, but he was the first to connect them; and then he provided overwhelming evidence that the association was valid. He pointed out that of all patients with edema, some showed albumin in their urine, and this albumin was coagulable by heat; futhermore, these patients showed structural changes in their kidneys. Bright, with convincing clinico-pathological studies, thus identified a new disease pattern that tied together pathologic changes, chemical alterations, and clinical signs. Later research showed that this pattern was not a simple disease entity but, rather, a congeries of enormous complexity. But this does not detract from the brilliance of Bright's initial correlation.

Bright, one of the great men of Guy's, helped the hospital attain its enviable position among British medical educational institutions. He helped found the journal *Guy's Hospital Reports,* which, as a ready medium of publication, proved important in encouraging research, and he did much to popularize the then-new concept of bedside teaching. A neglected part of medical education, he realized, was meaningful contact between the students and the patients. He helped reform the educational methods so that, in 1837, *Guy's Hospital Reports* (**2,** v-vi) could proudly declare that "each student who has passed three months in the clinical wards is ready to admit that that period has proved the most profitable portion of his medical education. . . . Under the guidance of the experienced physicians, the student is instructed how to make observations upon the sick, and to interpret the signs of disease. . . ." Then, because of his efforts, the hospital set aside special wards for clinical research.

Bright, standing at a crossroads in medical history, exemplified the transition between old and new—the tradition, on the one hand, that emphasized observation with virtually unaided senses and, on the other hand, the tradition that emphasized laboratory and other technical aids to knowledge. Bright used the most rudimentary technique to identify albumin in the urine, heating a sample in a teaspoon held over a candle flame. But even at that very time analytic tools of considerable precision were being forged for chemistry, physiology, anatomy, and pathology. These new tools, and the theories to which they gave rise, became increasingly significant in medicine. Bright ceased active research just at the threshold of a new era.

His link with the past is clearly visible in the textbook written with Addison, which looks backward rather than forward. But his spirit of inquiry, respect for evidence, careful observation, critical acumen, and restrained conclusions, all were forward-looking.

BIBLIOGRAPHY

I. ORIGINAL WORKS. A complete bibliography of Bright's work, compiled by William Hill, is in *Guy's Hospital Gazette,* **64** (1950), 456 ff.; repr. in *Guy's Hospital Reports,* **107** (1958), 531 ff. This includes books, journal articles, and critical and biographical studies.

Among the books by Bright are *Travels From Vienna Through Lower Hungary; With Some Remarks on the State of Vienna During the Congress in the Year 1814* (Edinburgh, 1818); and *Reports of Medical Cases Selected With a View of Illustrating the Symptoms and Cure of Diseases With a Reference to Morbid Anatomy,* 2 vols. (London, 1827–1831). With Thomas Addison he wrote *Elements of the Practice of Medicine* (London, 1839). A collection of his papers on renal disease is the reprint *Original Papers of Richard Bright on Renal Disease,* A. A. Osman, ed. (London, 1937). His numerous periodical publications are listed in Hill's bibliography.

II. SECONDARY LITERATURE. A vast amount of secondary material deals with Bright. Worthy of special mention are B. Chance, "Richard Bright, Traveler and Artist," in *Bulletin of the History of Medicine,* **8** (1940), 909 ff.; F. H. Garrison, "Richard Bright's Travels in Lower Hungary, a Physician's Holiday," in *Johns Hopkins Hospital Bulletin,* **23** (1914), 173 ff.; Sir William Hale-White, "Bright's Observations Other Than Those on Renal Disease," in *Guy's Hospital Reports,* **71** (1921), 143 ff., repr. *ibid.,* **107** (1958), 308 ff.; and "Richard Bright and His Discovery of the Disease Bearing His Name," *ibid.,* **71** (1921), 1 ff., repr. *ibid.,* **107** (1958), 294 ff.; R. M. Kark, "A Prospect of Richard Bright on the Centenary of His Death, December 16, 1958," in *American Journal of Medicine,* **25** (1958), 819 ff.; Samuel Wilks and G. T. Bettany, *Biographical History of Guy's Hospital* (London, 1892).

LESTER S. KING

BRILL, ALEXANDER WILHELM VON (*b.* Darmstadt, Germany, 20 September 1842; *d.* Tübingen, Germany, 8 June 1935), *mathematics.*

Brill, the nephew of the geometer Christian Wiener, was a student of Alfred Clebsch at both the Politechnikum in Karlsruhe and at the University of Giessen. He graduated in 1864 and passed his *Habilitation* in 1867. From then until 1869 he was a *Dozent* at Giessen; from 1869 to 1875, a professor at the Politechnikum in Darmstadt; and from 1875 to 1884, a professor at the Politechnikum in Munich, where he worked with Felix Klein and was influenced by him. From 1884 to 1918, when he retired, Brill was a professor at the University of Tübingen. He worked primarily on the theory of algebraic functions and algebraic geometry, characteristically using algebraic methods, striving to avoid transcendental methods and aiming at "Weierstrassian strictness" of exposition. The systematic study of those properties of algebraic functions which are invariant under birational transformations is contained in his fundamental work, written with Max Noether (1874). In it many of the results obtained by Riemann and by Clebsch and Gordan, using transcendental means, are substantiated by algebraic-geometrical methods. Also noteworthy are his papers on three-dimensional algebraic curves (1907) and on pseudospherical three-dimensional space (1885), where the impossibility of putting such a space into a Euclidean four-dimensional space and the possibility of its being placed in a Euclidean five-dimensional space are proved.

At the end of the last century, Brill published a series of articles on methodology of mathematics, participated—following Klein—in the movement to reform its teaching, and was an initiator of the use of models of geometrical figures in teaching; many such models were prepared under his guidance.

Brill also wrote on the theory of determinants, on the theory of elimination, on the theory of elliptic functions, on some special curves and surfaces, and on the singularities of planar and spatial algebraic curves. He was also concerned with theoretical mechanics. In *Vorlesungen über allgemeine Mechanik*

(1928) and *Vorlesungen über algebraische Kurven und algebraische Functionen* (1925) Brill, who was then retired, summed up his scientific and pedagogical career.

Brill's survey of the development of the theory of algebraic functions ("Die Entwicklung der Theorie der algebraischen Functionen in älterer und neurer Zeit," 1894), which was written with Noether, has significance for the history of mathematics. His last work, published when he was eighty-seven, dealt with Kepler's *New Astronomy.*

BIBLIOGRAPHY

I. ORIGINAL WORKS. Among Brill's writings are "Ueber die algebraische Functionen und ihre Anwendung in der Geometrie," in *Mathematische Annalen,* **7** (1874), 269–370, written with Max Noether; "Bemerkungen ueber pseudophärischen Mannigfaltigkeiten," *ibid.,* **26** (1885), 300–303; "Die Entwicklung der Theorie der algebraischen Functionen in älterer und neurer Zeit," in *Jahresbericht der Deutschen Mathematiker-Vereinigung,* **3** (1894), 107–566, written with Max Noether; "Ueber algebraische Raumkurven," in *Mathematische Annalen,* **64** (1907), 289–324; *Vorlesungen über algebraische Kurven und algebraische Functionen* (Brunswick, 1925); and *Vorlesungen über allgemeine Mechanik* (Munich–Berlin, 1928). For a more complete list see Poggendorff.

II. SECONDARY LITERATURE. See S. Finsterwalder, "Alexander von Brill. Ein Lebensbild," in *Mathematische Annalen,* **112** (1936), 653–663; and F. Severi, "Alexander von Brill," in *Jahresbericht der Deutschen Mathematiker-Vereinigung,* **31** (1922), 89–96

J. B. POGREBYSSKY

BRILLOUIN, MARCEL LOUIS (*b.* Melle, Deux-Sèvres, France, 19 December 1854; *d.* Paris, France, 16 June 1948), *mathematics, physics.*

Brillouin came from a middle-class family. His father was a painter, and the family lived in Paris, where Marcel studied at the Lycée Condorcet. They moved back to Melle during the Franco-Prussian War, and he spent the years 1870 and 1871 reading all the books on philosophy he could find in his grandfather's big library. Back in Paris in 1872, he brilliantly passed his baccalaureate the following year and became a student at the École Normale Supérieure (1874–1878). He then was an assistant, at the Collège de France, to the well-known physicist Mascart, whose daughter he later married. In 1881 Brillouin obtained doctorates in both mathematics and physics. He spent the next several years, as assistant professor of physics, at the universities of Nancy, Dijon, and Toulouse. Brillouin returned to the

École Normale Supérieure in 1888, when he married Charlotte Mascart. From 1900 on, he was professor of mathematical physics at the Collège de France until his retirement in 1931. He became a member of the Académie des Sciences de Paris in 1921.

Brillouin was a prominent theoretical physicist, but he was also a very skillful experimenter. He always had a laboratory and a large library nearby. In his teaching he always outlined the history of the subject and organized a seminar on the history and philosophy of physics for all his students. He had a great influence on the formation and careers of such students as Perrin, Langevin, Villat, Pérès, A. Foch, his son Léon, and J. Coulomb. He also maintained friendly personal relations with many foreign scientists, including Kelvin, Lorentz, Planck, and Sommerfeld.

In his long career Brillouin published more than 200 papers and books. He was a great admirer of Kelvin's lectures and wrote a preface and notes for their translation (1893); he also provided notes for a book of translations of original papers on meteorology (1900), a subject in which he was always highly interested. His interest in the kinetic theory of gases, liquids, and solids is reflected in his contribution of a preface and many notes to the French translation of Boltzmann's book (1902). This was followed by a book on viscosity (1906–1907) and a number of papers on kinetic theory and thermodynamics of liquids (isotropic or anisotropic) and solids, plasticity, and melting conditions. A book on the propagation of electricity (1904) included a complete calculation of proper vibrations for a metallic ellipsoid, a problem that became later of great importance for ultrashort wavelengths.

About 1900 Brillouin spent considerable time building a new model of the Eötvös balance and testing it in the Simplon Tunnel, which was opened in 1906. This is described in a long paper published by the Académie des Sciences in 1908. The Brillouin balance was later used for oil prospecting.

There followed a series of important papers on Helmholtz' flow and surfaces of discontinuity, with applications to hydrodynamics and hydraulic problems, and a long paper on the stability of airplanes.

From 1918 to 1922, and later, Brillouin tried to find an explanation of Bohr's condition of stable atom trajectories and their n, l, m quantum numbers. He attempted to use retarded actions of unknown nature (rather similar to de Broglie waves) and obtained stability conditions containing some sort of quantum numbers. Similar conditions were used later by de Broglie and modified by Schrödinger.

A few papers on the problem of an electromagnetic source in uniaxial or biaxial crystals are of interest for crystal optics. From 1925 on, most of Brillouin's research centered on physics of the earth, especially tides, and was published in the Academy's *Comptes rendus*. He also lectured on these subjects at the Collège de France and the Institut Poincaré (1930). His lectures on tides were edited by J. Coulomb, but most of them remained unpublished. Brillouin discussed a variety of mathematical problems in connection with tides, especially problems of varying boundary conditions, and transformations of spherical harmonics from one polar axis to another, the idea being to use, for tides, an axis of coordinates running through continental regions.

The interests of this wide-ranging, open-minded scientist extended from the history of science to the physics of the earth and the atom.

BIBLIOGRAPHY

I. ORIGINAL WORKS. Books that Brillouin wrote or contributed to are *Conférences de Lord Kelvin,* Lugol, trans. (Paris, 1893), ed., preface, and notes by Brillouin; *Mémoires originaux sur la théorie de la circulation de l'atmosphere* (Paris, 1900), notes by Brillouin; *Théorie cinétique des gaz de Boltzmann* (Paris, 1902), notes and preface by Brillouin; pt. 2, *Sur la condition de l'état permanent. Sur la tendance apparente à l'irréversibilité d'après Gibbs* (Paris, 1905); *Propagation de l'électricité, histoire et théorie* (Paris, 1904); and *Leçons sur la viscosité des liquides et des gaz,* 2 vols. (Paris, 1906–1907).

Papers of special importance are "Vents contigus et nuages," in *Mémoires du Bureau central météorologique* (1897), also in *Annales de chimie et physique,* **12** (1897), 145 ff.; "L'ellipticité du geoïde dans le tunnel du Simplon," in *Mémoires présentés par divers savants à l'Académie des sciences de l'Institut de France,* **23** (1908); "Stabilité des aéroplanes, surface métacentrique, planeurs, etc.," in *Revue de mécanique* (1909–1910); "Surfaces de glissement d'Helmholtz et resistance des fluides," in *Annales de chimie et physique,* **23** (1911); "Structure des cristaux et anisotropie des molécules," Solvay Congress, 1913; "Milieux biaxes," in *Comptes rendus de l'Académie des sciences,* **165** (1917) and **166** (1918); "Sources électromagnétiques dans les milieux uniaxes," in *Bulletin des sciences mathématiques,* **42** (1918); "Actions mécaniques à hérédité discontinue, essai de l'atome à quanta," in *Comptes rendus de l'Académie des sciences,* **168** (1919), **171** (1920), **173** (1921), and **174** (1922); and "Atome de Bohr, fonction de Lagrange circumnucléaire," in *Journal de physique,* **3** (1922).

II. SECONDARY LITERATURE. Works on Brillouin are H. Villat, ed., *Jubilé de M. Brillouin pour son 80ème anniversaire,* 2 vols. (Paris, 1935); and H. Villat, *Titres et travaux scientifiques* (Paris, 1930), pp. 8, 10, 19–21, 25–26, and "Notice nécrologique sur Marcel Brillouin," in *Comptes rendus de l'Académie des sciences,* **226,** no. 25 (1948), 2029.

L. BRILLOUIN

BRINELL, JOHAN AUGUST (*b.* Bringetofta, Sweden, 21 June 1849; *d.* Stockholm, Sweden, 17 November 1925), *metallurgy, materials testing.*

While he is best known as the originator of a standard procedure for determining the hardness of a metal, Brinell also did significant work on the metallurgy of steel.

The son of Johannes Månsson, a farmer, and Katarina Jonasdotter, Brinell graduated in 1871 from the technical school in Borås and was employed in the Swedish iron industry for some fifty years. From 1882 to 1903 he was chief engineer of the Fagersta Ironworks, where his most original scientific work was done. He was chief engineer of Jernkontoret, an iron industry association, from 1903 to 1914, and chairman of the board of Fagersta from 1915 to 1923. He was a member of the Swedish Academy of Science and the (British) Iron and Steel Institute; and he received the Polhem Medal in 1900, the Bessemer Medal in 1907, and an honorary Ph.D. from Uppsala in 1907, as well as many other awards. He was married in 1880 to Selma Nilsson.

Brinell's first studies at Fagersta, which were concerned with changes of the internal structure of steel as it was heated or cooled, compared the appearance of steel fracture surfaces in a very large number of experiments. His first major paper (1885) was, in the opinion of Cyril Stanley Smith, ". . . a monument of imaginative and careful work and shows how much can be learned about steel without knowledge of its microstructure." However, the work of Floris Osmond, in which microstructure was identified through microscopic examination of etched surfaces, published also in 1885, overshadowed Brinell's work. Nevertheless, Osmond's conclusions probably were accepted more readily by the iron industry because they were reinforced by Brinell's, which were based upon an observational procedure well known in the shop.

Brinell's apparatus for testing the hardness of a material was first displayed in 1900 at the Paris Exposition. A hardened steel ball, 10 millimeters in diameter, is pressed into the test surface under a heavy load (up to 3,000 kilograms). The Brinell hardness number (Bhn) in kg/mm^2 is calculated by dividing the load by the area of indentation. This procedure, not essentially modified, is still one of the most widely used tests of hardness.

BIBLIOGRAPHY

I. ORIGINAL WORKS. Brinell's works include "Om ståls texturförändringar under uppvärmning och afkylning," in *Jern-kontorets annaler,* n.s., **40** (1885), 9–38, published in German in *Stahl und Eisen,* **5**·(1885), 611–620, and abstracted in English as "Changes in the Texture of Steel on Heating and Cooling," in *Journal of the Iron and Steel Institute* (1885), no. 1, 365–367; and "Sätt att bestämma kroppars hårdhet jämte några tillämpningar af detsamma," in *Teknisk tidskrift,* **30** (1900) [section on mechanics], 69–87; English version prepared by Axel Wahlberg as "Brinell's Method of Determining Hardness and Other Properties of Iron and Steel," in *Journal of the Iron and Steel Institute* (1901), no. 1, 243–298, and no. 2, 234–271.

II. SECONDARY LITERATURE. The best biographical sketch is in *Svenskt biografiskt lexicon,* VI (Stockholm, 1926), 236–241, which includes a list of Brinell's works. An obituary notice is in *Journal of the Iron and Steel Institute* (1926), no. 1, 482–483. A critical analysis of Brinell's 1885 paper is in Henry M. Howe, *The Metallurgy of Steel* (New York, 1890), pp. 170–175. See also Cyril Stanley Smith, *History of Metallography* (Chicago, 1960), esp. pp. 119–121.

EUGENE S. FERGUSON

BRING, ERLAND SAMUEL (*b.* Ausås, Kristianstad, Sweden, 19 August 1736; *d.* Lund, Sweden, 20 May 1798), *mathematics.*

The son of Iöns Bring, a clergyman, and Christina Elisabeth Lagerlöf, Erland Bring studied jurisprudence at Lund University from 1750 to 1757. Beginning in 1762 he was a reader at Lund and from 1779 a professor. He taught history at the university, although his favorite field was mathematics. In the university library are preserved eight volumes of his manuscript compositions on various questions of algebra, geometry, mathematical analysis, and astronomy, and commentaries on the work of L'Hospital, Christian von Wolf, Leonhard Euler, and other scholars.

In 1786 Bring's *Meletemata* was published. Like many eighteenth-century mathematicians, he attempted to solve equations of higher than fourth degree in radicals by means of reduction into binomial form, employing the transformation of the unknown quantity first proposed by Tschirnhaus (1683). Bring succeeded in reducing a general fifth-degree equation to the trinomial form $x^5 + px + q = 0$, using a transformation whose coefficients are defined by equations of not higher than the third degree. This remarkable result received practically no attention at the time and was obtained independently by George Birch Jerrard in his *Mathematical Researches* (1832–1835). Shortly thereafter, Sir William R. Hamilton demonstrated (1836) that with the aid of this operation a general fifth-degree equation reduces to any of four trinomial forms. It is not known whether Bring hoped to solve the fifth-degree equation in radicals with the aid of his transformation; Jerrard retained this hope, even though Niels Abel proved (1824–1826) that such a solution is impossible for a general fifth-degree equation.

In 1837 Bring's nephew, the historian Ebbe Samuel Bring, tried unsuccessfully to attract the attention of mathematicians to the algebraic investigations of his uncle. The deep significance of the Bring-Jerrard transformation was ascertained only after Charles Hermite (1858) used the above-mentioned trinomial form for the solution of fifth-degree equations with the aid of elliptic modular functions, thereby laying the foundations for new methods of studying and solving equations of higher degrees with the aid of transcendental functions.

Hermite cited only Jerrard, calling his result the most important event in the theory of fifth-degree equations since Abel. Shortly thereafter, in 1861, the scholarly world also recognized Bring's merits, mainly through the efforts of Carl J. D. Hill, professor of mathematics at Lund University.

BIBLIOGRAPHY

Bring's major work is *Meletemata quaedam mathematica circa transformationem aequationum algebraicarum* (Lund, 1786).

Writings on Bring include Moritz Cantor, *Vorlesungen über Geschichte der Matematik,* IV (Leipzig, 1908), 130–132; C. J. D. Hill, "Nagra ord om Erland Sam. Brings reduktion af 5te gradens equation," in *Öfversigt af Kongelige vetenskapsakademiens förhandlingar* (1861), pp. 317–355; Felix Klein, *Vorlesungen über die Ikosaeder* (Leipzig, 1884), pp. 143–144, 207–209, 244; and *Svenska män och kvinnor biografisk uppslagsbok,* I (Stockholm, 1942), 466.

A. P. YOUSCHKEVITCH

BRINKLEY, JOHN (*b.* Woodbridge, England, 1763; *d.* Dublin, Ireland, 14 September 1835), *astronomy, mathematics.*

Brinkley, whose greatest contribution was his researches into stellar parallaxes, received his early education at Woodbridge Grammar School and with a Mr. Tilney of Harleston. He went on to Caius College, Cambridge, and received his B.A. as senior wrangler and first Smith's Prizeman in 1788. During his senior year he was assistant to N. Maskelyne at Greenwich and was fellow of his college from 1788 to 1792. Upon Maskelyne's personal recommendation he was appointed Andrews professor of astronomy at Dublin University, 11 December 1790. The following year Brinkley was ordained a priest at Lincoln and received his M.A. at Cambridge. In 1792 he was incorporated at Dublin and elected first astronomer royal for Ireland. He proceeded D.D. (Dublin) 1806.

Between 1790 and 1808 he prepared the excellent textbook *Elements of Plane Astronomy,* published in 1808, and ten mathematical papers, some with direct application to celestial astronomy.

Upon acquiring a splendid eight-foot meridian circle in 1808, Brinkley attempted to determine the long-sought parallax of the fixed stars, with a view to determining their distances. Two years later he announced the detection of an annual (double) parallax for α Lyrae of $2''.52$, and in 1814 similarly large values of $2''.0$, $5''.5$, $2''.2$, and $2''.1$ for the stars α Lyrae, α Aquilae, Arcturus, and α Cygni, respectively. The validity of these measurements was disputed in the literature for fourteen years by Pond, who was unable to deduce analogous results with Greenwich instruments. This controversy, by necessitating repeated tests of the observations, was of great value in stimulating the study of previously unappreciated factors affecting the measurements. Brinkley's results, although now themselves discredited, thus led to the later successful detection of stellar parallaxes.

Among Brinkley's other major work was the publication of a new theory of astronomical refractions (1815), estimation of the obliquity of the ecliptic (1819), determination of north polar distances of the principal fixed stars (1815, 1824), and determination of the precession of the equinoxes (1828). He also used the south polar distances of certain fixed stars observed by Sir Thomas Brisbane at Paramatta, New South Wales, to investigate the accuracy of separate determinations by himself and by Bessel of their north polar distances (1826). His astronomical career ended with his elevation, after numerous ecclesiastical preferments, as bishop of Cloyne, 28 September 1826.

Brinkley's honors were many. Fellowship of the Royal Society (1803) was followed by the Conyngham Medal of the Royal Irish Academy, for his essay on investigations relating to the mean motion of the lunar perigee (1817). He was also awarded the Copley Medal of the Royal Society (1824) for his scientific achievements and his approximations to the solution of the parallax problem. He was president of the Royal Irish Academy from 1822 to 1835, vice-president of the Astronomical Society from 1825 to 1827, and its president from 1831 to 1833.

BIBLIOGRAPHY

I. ORIGINAL WORKS. Brinkley's various observations at Greenwich (1787–1788) are distributed through Maskelyne's *Astronomical Observations Made at the Royal Observatory, Greenwich,* **3** (1799), starting with an entry for 23 Sept. 1787. Maskelyne appends the letters *JB* to

Brinkley's observations; those by Brinkley's contemporary John Bumpstead appear under Bumpstead's full name.

His elementary astronomical textbook was compiled from lectures given between 1799 and 1808 to undergraduates at Dublin University. The earliest record of the course is *Synopsis of Astronomical Lectures to Commence October 29, 1799 at Philosophical School, Trinity College, Dublin* (Dublin, 1799). The finished book, *Elements of Plane Astronomy* (Dublin, 1808), was prepared at the request of the board of the college when the acquisition of a meridian circle diverted Brinkley's efforts to practical astronomy. The book went through five editions subject to his revision during his lifetime; a sixth edition was edited and revised by Thomas Luby (Dublin, 1845), and two further editions were revised and partly rewritten by J. W. Stubbs and F. Brünnow (London, 1874, 1886).

Ten mathematical papers of considerable elegance were published between 1800 and 1818, nine in the *Transactions of the Royal Irish Academy* (see its Index) and one in *Philosophical Transactions of the Royal Society*, **97** (1807), 114–132.

Eighteen significant astronomical papers on various subjects appeared between 1810 and 1828, eight in *Transactions of the Royal Irish Academy*, eight in *Philosophical Transactions of the Royal Society*, and two in *Memoirs of the Astronomical Society* (see Royal Society's *Catalogue of Scientific Papers*, I [1867], 627–629). Those relating to the parallax question include the following: Brinkley's original announcement of his detection of the annual (double) parallax of α Lyrae, communicated to the Royal Society by Maskelyne, in *Philosophical Transactions*, **100** (1810), 204. The 1814 report of similar and even larger results for other stars, in *Transactions of the Royal Irish Academy*, **12** (1815), 33–75. Discordance with Pond's results suggested to be due to uncertainty of elements used in reduction of Greenwich observations, in *Philosophical Transactions*, **108** (1818), 275–302. Results of further observations introducing a determination of the constant of aberration and of that of lunar nutation, *ibid.*, **109** (1819), 241–248, and **111** (1821), 327–360. An instrumental investigation of the effect of solar nutation cited to exhibit the competence of his equipment to detect the larger quantity of parallax, first reported to the Royal Irish Academy in 1822, in *Transactions of the Royal Irish Academy*, **14** (1825), 3–37. Disengagement from Greenwich results of a parallax for α Lyrae not differing sensibly from that measured at Dublin, in *Memoirs of the Royal Astronomical Society*, **1**, pt. 2 (1822), 329–340. Reassertion of parallax of α Lyrae and attempt to form a correct estimate of the absolute and relative degrees of accuracy of the Dublin and Greenwich instruments, in *Philosophical Transactions*, **114** (1824), 471–498.

Among the ten remaining catalogued papers, see *Transactions of the Royal Irish Academy*, **13** (1818), 25–51, containing an essay on investigations relative to the mean motion of the lunar perigee, which was awarded the Conyngham Medal of the Academy; and *Memoirs of the Astronomical Society*, **2**, pt. 1 (1826), 105–123, containing Brisbane's Paramatta observations. There are several minor

references in the *Quarterly Journal of Science, Literature and the Arts*, **9** (1820), 164–167; **11** (1821), 364–370, 370–372; and **12** (1822), 151–154; and in *Astronomische Nachrichten*, **3** (1825), cols. 105–106; **4** (1826), cols. 101–104; and **5** (1827), cols. 131–138.

II. SECONDARY LITERATURE. An excellent discussion of Brinkley's life and work is contained in *Dictionary of National Biography*, VI (1886); a more general account is in Sir Robert Ball, *Great Astronomers* (London, 1895), pp. 233–246. A synopsis of the contents of his Royal Society papers is in *Proceedings of the Royal Society*, **3** (1835), 354–355. An account of the oration by Sir Humphry Davy upon the award to Brinkley of the Copley Medal may be found in *Philosophical Magazine*, **64** (1824), 459–462.

Obituaries are Henry Cotton, *Fasti ecclesiae Hibernicae*, I (Dublin, 1851), 307–309; *Gentlemen's Magazine*, **11** (1835), 547; Rev. J. B. Leslie, *Clogher Clergy and Parishes* (Enniskillen, 1929), p. 47; and *Memoirs of the Royal Astronomical Society*, **9** (1836), 281–282.

SUSAN M. P. MCKENNA

BRIOSCHI, FRANCESCO (*b.* Milan, Italy, 22 December 1824; *d.* Milan, 14 December 1897), *mathematics, hydraulics.*

Brioschi graduated in 1845 from the University of Pavia, where he was a student of Antonio Bordoni. From 1852 to 1861 he was a professor of applied mathematics there, teaching theoretical mechanics, civil architecture, and hydraulics. He was the general secretary of the Ministry of Education in 1861–1862, a senator from 1865, and, from 1870 until 1882, a member of the Executive Council of the Ministry of Education. In 1863 Brioschi organized the Istituto Tecnico Superiore in Milan, serving as director and professor of mathematics and hydraulics until his death. From 1884 he was president of the Accademia Nazionale dei Lincei.

From the beginning of his career, Brioschi strove to overcome the backwardness of Italian mathematics, to popularize new scientific trends, and to raise the quality of the teaching of mathematics in secondary schools and universities. He published many essays and reviews, and participated in the organization of the journal *Annali di matematica pura ed applicata*, heading its editorial staff from 1867 until his death (until 1877 in conjunction with Cremona). He also helped to organize the journal *Politecnico*.

In his original papers Brioschi appears as a virtuoso in computation, as an analyst, and as an algebraist. In the works of his most fruitful decade (1851–1860) he widely applied and developed the still new theory of determinants. His *Teoria dei determinanti* (1854) was the first nonelementary statement of the theory and its basic applications. Brioschi devoted several important papers, following Caley, Sylvester, and

Hermite, to the then developing theory of forms of two or more variables, which Hermite termed ". . . one of the major mathematical achievements of our time." He applied exclusively algebraic means of solution to such questions as the deduction of equations in partial derivatives for the discriminant of a binary form and for the resultant of two such forms. A significant part of his results in this area was included in a monograph published in the first four volumes of *Annali di matematica*.

In these same years Brioschi added new results to the theory of the transformation of elliptic and Abelian functions. In his greatest achievement, following Hermite and simultaneously with Kronecker, he applied elliptical modular functions to the solution of fifth-degree equations. At the same time, Brioschi popularized Gauss's theory of surfaces in Italy and brought forth, in connection with this, geometric papers.

During the 1860's and 1870's Brioschi continued his work in algebra and analysis in traditional directions, using the Weierstrass theory of elliptic functions. From these viewpoints, he addressed himself to the theory of differential equations and, in the 1880's, to the theory of hyperelliptic functions. His second great achievement relates to this latter period: the solution of sixth-degree equations with the aid of hyperelliptic functions.

Brioschi did not propound any strikingly new ideas in mathematics, nor did he discover any new fields. "I am only a calculator," he humbly characterized himself. However, he was a brilliant analyst with algebraic propensities and possessed a rare mobility of thought that responded to new ideas from their very inception. This enabled him to enrich science with new results for half a century.

Along with Betti, Brioschi began a new epoch in the history of Italian mathematics, leading it out of its provincial backwardness. He was the teacher of its most outstanding representatives in the next generation, among them Casorati, Cremona, and Beltrami.

In mechanics Brioschi dealt with problems of statics, proving Moebius' results by analytic means; with the integration of equations in dynamics, according to Jacobi's method; with hydrostatics; and with hydrodynamics. His work as a hydraulic engineer was significant, although it is reflected comparatively little in his publications. Brioschi used the findings of a series of major projects or participated in the projects' development—for example, in the regulation of the Po and Tiber (which goals remained unaccomplished). Two more of Brioschi's works should be mentioned: with Betti he brought out a treatment of the first six

books of Euclid's *Elements* for secondary schools, and he edited Leonardo da Vinci's *Codice Atlantico,* an important source for the history of science and technology.

An adherent of pure mathematics, Brioschi highly valued its significance in application and allotted to it a significant place in technical education, emphasizing the great role of the latter in the development of national industry. At the same time he insisted on the value of the humanities and, simultaneously with his founding of the Politechnicum, he organized the Accademia Scientifica-Litteraria in Milan.

In addition to the publication of the *Codice Atlantico,* Brioschi produced several important articles on contemporary mathematicians.

BIBLIOGRAPHY

I. Original Works. Many of Brioschi's writings have been brought together in Ascoli *et al.,* eds., *Opere,* 5 vols. (Milan, 1901–1908). Among individual works of note are *Teoria dei determinanti* (Pavia, 1854) and "La teoria dei covarianti e degli invarianti delle forme binarie, e le sue principali applicazioni," in *Annali di matematica,* **1** (1858), 269–309, 549–561; **2** (1859), 82–85, 265–277; **3** (1860), 160–168; **4** (1861), 186–194.

II. Secondary Literature. The fullest characterization of Brioschi's scientific work is in M. Noether, "Francesco Brioschi," in *Mathematische Annalen,* **50** (1898), 477–491. On Brioschi as an engineer, see E. Paladini, "Commemorazione di F. Brioschi," in *Atti del Collegio degli ingegneri ed architetti* (Milan), **30** (1898). See also E. Beltrami's obituary notice of Brioschi in *Annali di matematica,* 2nd ser., **26** (1897), 340–342; Charles Hermite, "Notice sur M. F. Brioschi," in *Comptes rendus de l'Académie des sciences,* **125** (1897), 1139–1141; and the speeches given at Brioschi's funeral, in *Reale Istituto tecnico superiore, programma 1891–1898* (Milan, 1898).

Joseph Pogrebyssky

BRIOT, CHARLES AUGUSTE (*b.* St.-Hippolyte, France, 19 July 1817; *d.* Bourg-d'Ault, France, 20 September 1882), *mathematics, physics.*

Briot's father, Auguste, a merchant at St.-Hippolyte, had a considerable reputation in the tanning trade. Charles, the eldest of a large family, became a teacher after an accident that left him with a stiff arm. He was sent to Paris and in only five years attained a remarkable level of scholarship. When he entered the École Normale Supérieure in 1838, he was ranked second. Three years later he completed the course and received his *agrégation* in mathematics with the highest rank. In March 1842 he received his doctorate of science, having presented his thesis on the movement of a solid body round a fixed point. This brilliant success lit the way for a group of young men from his native Franche-Comté: Claude Bouquet, L. E. Bertin, and Louis Pasteur.

Briot devoted himself to teaching, first as a professor at the Orléans Lycée and afterward at the University of Lyons, where he reencountered his friend Claude Bouquet. In 1851 he moved to Paris, where he taught the course in *mathématiques speciales* (preparation for the École Normale Supérieure and the École Polytechnique) at the Lycée Bonaparte and later at the Lycée Saint-Louis, as well as acting as substitute at both the École Polytechnique and the Faculté des Sciences for the courses in mechanical engineering and surveying (1850), calculus (1853), and mechanics and astronomy (1855). From 1864 on, he was a professor at the Sorbonne and at the École Normale Supérieure. In his courses he particularly stressed the relation between thermodynamics and rational mechanics.

Briot's studies on heat, light, and electricity were based on the hypothesis of the existence in the ether of imponderable molecules acting upon each other, as well as upon the ponderable molecules of matter. Particularly in his study of the crystalline medium, he linked his findings to Pasteur's experimental work on the dissymmetry of crystals. These studies, which were conducted from a mathematical point of view, led to the simplification of methods for integral calculus and the advance of the theories of elliptic and Abelian functions. To honor him for this work, the Göttingen Academy named him a corresponding member.

A large part of Briot's activity was devoted to the writing of textbooks for students, so that he and Bouquet could provide them with a library of basic books on arithmetic, algebra, calculus, geometry, analytical geometry, and mechanics. These books were published in numerous editions and for many years contributed to establishing the level of mathematics teaching in France. Briot also published, with Bouquet, an important work on elliptic functions (1875) and, alone, a treatise on Abelian functions (1879). The Académie des Sciences awarded Briot the Poncelet Prize in 1882 for his work in mathematics.

BIBLIOGRAPHY

Briot's works include "Recherches sur la théorie des fonctions," in *Journal de l'École Polytechnique* (1859), also published as an independent work (Paris, 1859); *Théorie des fonctions doublement périodiques,* written with Bouquet, 2 vols. (Paris, 1859; 2nd ed., 1875); *Essai sur la théorie mathématique de la lumière* (Paris, 1864); *Théorie mécanique de la chaleur* (Paris, 1869); *Théorie des fonctions elliptiques,* written with Bouquet (Paris, 1875); and *Théorie des fonctions abéliennes* (Paris, 1879).

LUCIENNE FÉLIX

BRISBANE, THOMAS (*b.* Brisbane House, Ayrshire, Scotland, 23 July 1773; *d.* Brisbane House, 27 January 1860), *astronomy.*

Although himself an able practical astronomer, Brisbane is better remembered as a munificent patron of science through his founding and equipping of Paramatta (astronomical) and Makerstoun (magnetic) observatories, the personal remuneration of their observers, and the provision of support for the publication of their findings.

Brisbane was descended from the distinguished Brisbane family of Bishopton. His early education was under tutors at home; he then studied at Edinburgh University and at Kensington Academy, where he attended lectures on astronomy and mathematics. Brisbane was gazetted an ensign in 1789 and progressively advanced to the rank of general (1841). He saw active service in Europe, the West Indies, and Canada. He was elected a fellow of the Royal Society in 1810, corresponding member of the Paris Institute in 1816 (for protecting its premises from military attack earlier that year), vice-president of the Astronomical Society in 1827, president of the Royal Society of Edinburgh in 1833, and honorary member of the Royal Irish Academy in 1836. He received honorary degrees from Edinburgh (1824), Oxford (1832), and Cambridge (1833); was created baronet in 1836; and was made G.C.B. in 1837.

Brisbane's decision to master practical astronomy came on his first voyage to the West Indies (1795), when an error of the ship's commander in taking the longitude resulted in their being almost wrecked. Retired on half pay for health reasons from 1805 to 1810, he built an observatory at Brisbane House in 1808 and became skilled in the use of astronomical instruments. This was the second of two observatories then in Scotland and the foremost in equipment, having a four-and-a-half-foot transit and an altitude and azimuth instrument (both by Troughton), a mural circle, and an equatorial. During the Peninsular campaigns (1812–1813) Brisbane took regular observations with a pocket sextant and, while serving in France (1815–1818), computed a set of tables for determining apparent time with a sextant from the altitudes of the sun and stars. These tables, commissioned by the Duke of Wellington and published privately by the army in 1818, also formed the subject of his first scientific contribution to the Royal Society of Edinburgh.

Appointed governor of New South Wales in 1821, Brisbane decided to establish, at his own expense, an observatory at Paramatta, in order to promote knowledge of the then little-known stars of the Southern Hemisphere. The observatory, equipped with a five-and-a-half-foot transit and a two-foot mural circle by Troughton and other instruments, opened on 2 May 1822 under his personal direction, with Charles Rümker and James Dunlop as observers. The importance of this station was underlined a month later by Dunlop's rediscovery, in its predicted place (invisible from Europe), of Encke's comet, thus establishing the existence of comets of short period and providing information on their spatial motions. Besides standard astronomical observations, the greatest effort at Paramatta was the cataloging of 7,385 stars between 1822 and 1826 ("Brisbane Catalogue," 1835). Unfortunately, the inherent unsteadiness of the transit instrument used in this program has since caused the catalog to prove largely useless. Brisbane's provision of an observatory in the Southern Hemisphere was honored by the award of the gold medal of the Astronomical Society in 1828.

When he returned to Scotland, Brisbane built and equipped another observatory at Makerstoun in 1826, making astronomical observations there until about 1847. It is noteworthy, since he later supported a worldwide effort—instigated by Humboldt in 1837 and undertaken by the British and other national governments, the East India Company, and private enterprise in 1839—to elucidate the problems of terrestrial magnetism, that a personal letter from him to the Royal Society of Edinburgh dated as early as 15 March 1830 regrets that the taking of magnetic measurements should be neglected in Britain. His support of the international cooperation took the form of personally founding and equipping a magnetic observatory at Makerstoun in 1841, thus filling the need, in view of its extreme northwesterly position in Europe, of taking magnetic measurements in Scotland. The results obtained at this station under the director John Allan Broun now constitute the most valuable fruits of Brisbane's patronage of science. His philanthropy in its establishment and maintenance, and in the dissemination of its results, was honored by the award of the Keith Medal of the Royal Society of Edinburgh in 1848.

Other benefactions included the founding of two medals for reward of scientific merit—one to be awarded by the Royal Society of Edinburgh, the other by the Scottish Society of Arts—and the endowment of Brisbane Academy, Ayrshire.

BIBLIOGRAPHY

I. ORIGINAL WORKS. Brisbane's writings include *Tables for Determining the Apparent Time From the Altitudes of the Sun and Stars* (France, 1818); "A Method for Determining the Time . . .," in *Transactions of the Royal Society of Edinburgh,* **8,** pt. 2 (1818), 497–506; and papers on the repeating reflecting circle and on a method of determining the latitude by a sextant or circle, *ibid.,* **9** (1823), 97–102 and 227–234, respectively. *Memoirs of General Sir T. M. Brisbane* (Edinburgh, 1860) contains personally compiled accounts of his military campaigns.

A great variety of observations made at Paramatta between 1822 and 1826 by Brisbane and/or his assistants were forwarded by Brisbane for publication in the journals of the Royal Society of London and the Royal Society of Edinburgh, and in Schumacher's *Astronomical Notices* (see *Royal Society Catalogue of Scientific Papers,* I, 632–633). A large collection of assorted Paramatta observations, compiled by Charles Rümker, appeared in *Philosophical Transactions of the Royal Society,* **119,** pt. 3 (1829), 1–152. The bulk of Brisbane's personal observations are contained in *A Catalogue of 7385 Stars Chiefly in the Southern Hemisphere . . .* ("The Brisbane Catalogue"), compiled by William Richardson (London, 1835).

A variety of observations, mainly planetary, made at Makerstoun astronomical observatory by Brisbane and/or his assistants, appeared in *Monthly Notices of the Royal Astronomical Society,* vols. **1, 2, 4, 7, 8** and in *Memoirs of the Royal Astronomical Society,* vols. **4, 5, 9, 10.**

A personal letter from Brisbane to the Royal Society of Edinburgh concerning the taking of magnetic measurements in Britain is published in *Transactions of the Royal Society of Edinburgh,* **12** (1834), 1–2. Significant results obtained at Makerstoun magnetic observatory by John A. Broun and his staff, published at the joint expense of Brisbane and the Royal Society of Edinburgh, appear in *Transactions of the Royal Society of Edinburgh,* **17** (1845)–**19** (1850) and in a supplement to **22** (1861) published after Brisbane's death.

II. SECONDARY LITERATURE. Writings on Brisbane include A. Bryson, "Memoir of General Sir Thomas Makdougall Brisbane, GCB . . .," in *Transactions of the Royal Society of Edinburgh,* **22** (1861), 589–605, which contains many anecdotes of his military campaigns and a complete quotation of Herschel's presentation address (see below); Fraser, *Genealogical Table of Sir T. M. Brisbane* (Edinburgh, 1840); and the original address by Sir John Herschel upon the presentation of the gold medal of the Astronomical Society to Brisbane, in *Memoirs of the Astronomical Society,* **3** (1829), 399–407.

A general account of his life and work appear in the *Dictionary of National Biography,* VI (1886). Obituaries are in *Gentlemen's Magazine,* pt. 1 (1860), 298–302; *Monthly Notices of the Royal Astronomical Society,* **21** (1861), 98–100; and *Proceedings of the Royal Society,* **11** (1862), iii–vii.

SUSAN M. P. MCKENNA

BRISSON, BARNABÉ (*b*. Lyons, France, 11 October 1777; *d*. Nevers, France, 25 September 1828), *hydraulic engineering, mathematics.*

The son of Antoine-François Brisson, inspector of commerce and manufacture for the financial district of Lyons, Brisson studied at the Collège Oratorien de Juilly and was admitted to the École des Ponts et Chaussées in December 1793. A year later, at the newly founded École Centrale des Travaux Publics (the future École Polytechnique), he became one of the brilliant team of aspiring instructors and was highly thought of by Gaspard Monge. In December 1796, upon graduation from this school, he was admitted to the Corps des Ponts et Chaussées, where he remained for the rest of his career.

After completing his professional training at the École des Ponts et Chaussées in May 1798, Brisson specialized in the design and construction of ship canals. In 1802 he and his colleague Pierre-Louis Dupuis-Torcy presented a brilliant memoir based on applying methods of descriptive geometry to the determination of crest lines and of thalwegs, as well as establishing the course of the canals. After having been the civil engineer for the department of Doubs, he collaborated from 1802 to 1809 in the construction of the Canal de St.-Quentin, and then in the extension of the dikes and canals of the department of l'Escaut (until 1814). Appointed professor of stereometry and construction at the École des Ponts et Chaussées in 1820, he later assumed the additional duties of inspector for the school (from 1821) and secretary of the Conseil Royal des Ponts et Chaussées (from 1824).

Brisson remained one of Monge's favorite disciples, and his marriage in 1808 to Anne-Constance Huart, the latter's niece, strengthened his admiration and affection for the famous geometer. In 1820 he edited the fourth edition of Monge's *Géométrie descriptive* and finished off the work with two previously unpublished chapters on the theory of shadows and on perspective, which he revised with great care. But his favorite field of study was the theory of partial differential equations. Brisson drew up two important reports on this subject. One was read before the Académie des Sciences by Biot, his fellow student at the École Polytechnique and his brother-in-law. This paper was published in 1808. The other was read in 1823 and was not published. The main idea in these reports was the application of functional calculus, through symbols, to the solution of certain kinds of linear differential equations and of linear equations with finite differences.

The 1823 report was the object of lively discussion in 1825 before the Academy and was approved of by Cauchy, who, although he had some reservations about the validity of some of the symbols used and the equations obtained, emphasized the elegance of the method and the importance of the objects to which they were applied. Cauchy followed the way opened by Brisson, who thus became one of those who developed the methods of functional calculus.

BIBLIOGRAPHY

I. ORIGINAL WORKS. Brisson's writings include "Essai sur l'art de projeter les canaux de navigation," in *Journal de l'École polytechnique*, **7**, no. 14 (Apr. 1808), 262–288; "Mémoire sur l'intégration des équations différentielles partielles," *ibid.*, 191–261; *Notice historique sur Gaspard Monge* (Paris, 1818); *Nouvelle collection de 530 dessins ou feuilles de textes relatifs à l'art de l'ingénieur et lithographiés . . . sous la direction de M. Brisson*, 2 vols. (Paris, 1821–1825); and *Essai sur le système général de navigation intérieure de la France* (Paris, 1829).

II. SECONDARY LITERATURE. Biographical sketches of Brisson are A. Debauve, *Les travaux publics et les ingénieurs des ponts et chaussées depuis le XVIIe siècle* (Paris, 1893), pp. 381–382; *École polytechnique—Livre du centenaire*, III (Paris, 1895), 62–64, *passim*.; F. Hoefer, in *Nouvelle biographie générale*, VII (1863), cols. 436–437; H. Massiani, in *Dictionnaire de biographie française*, VII (1956), col. 364; J. and L. G. Michaud, *Biographie universelle*, new ed., V (1843), 565–567; *Le moniteur* (19 Oct. 1828); N. Nielsen, *Géomètres français sous la Révolution* (Paris, 1937), pp. 37–38, 83–84; J. Petot, *Histoire de l'Administration des ponts et chaussées (1599–1815)* (Paris, 1955); S. Pincherle, "Opérations fonctionnelles," in *Encyclopédie des sciences mathématiques*, II, fasc. 26, 10; Poggendorff, III (1898), col. 196; and *Procès verbaux de l'Académie des sciences*, VIII (Hendaye, 1918), 223–226.

RENÉ TATON

BRISSON, MATHURIN-JACQUES (*b*. Fontenay-le-Comte, Vendée, France, 30 April 1723; *d*. Brouessy, Commune of Magny-les-Hameaux, near Versailles, France, 23 June 1806), *physics, natural history.*

Brisson was the eldest son of Mathurin Brisson, who was named *président des traites* at Fontenay in 1726, and of Louise-Gabrielle Jourdain. He belonged to one of the most famous families of the legal nobility of the Poitou, particularly known for the jurist Barnabé Brisson, *président à mortier* of the Parliament of Paris who was executed in 1591 by the Holy League. Brisson was also related to the illustrious naturalist Réaumur; Catherine Brisson, his father's sister, had married Réaumur's younger brother.

After completing his early studies at the Collège de Fontenay in 1737–1738, Brisson finished a year of philosophy at the Collège de Poitiers and then turned to theology. He passed his baccalaureate in theology in 1744, and after taking minor orders he was allowed to continue his studies at the St.-Sulpice Seminary in Paris in 1745. But in 1747, just when he was to be elevated to the subdiaconate, he renounced that vocation and soon returned to his family.

Brisson then resumed the study of natural history, which he had begun with Réaumur when the latter spent his vacation on his country estate in the Poitou. In October 1749 Réaumur engaged him as caretaker and demonstrator of his own collection of natural history, as a successor to the Abbé Menou, who had recently died. This position, paying 600 livres a year, was underwritten by the Académie des Sciences, to which Réaumur had donated his collection. This post was a responsible one, for the attendant not only had to classify and care for Réaumur's collections, but also to help him during his observations and experiments and to be his main collaborator and confidant. Brisson's first research was thus set in the line of fire of the great rivalry between Réaumur and Buffon.

Buffon had attempted in his *Histoire naturelle* to give a general description of the animal world based upon the collections in the Cabinet du Roi, and Réaumur desired to launch a similar enterprise in extending the six volumes of his *Mémoires pour servir à l'histoire des insectes* by using the innumerable observations he had made or gathered from his correspondents, as well as the numerous specimens in his collection. Brisson was to play the principal role in this project. After having translated J. T. Klein's *Système du règne animal* (1754), he published the *Règne animal* (1756), a bilingual work with Latin and French texts printed side by side. In it he announced the project, presented the classification, and dealt with the study of the first two classes: quadrupeds and cetaceans. He then went on to the study of ornithology, in which specialty Réaumur's collection was extremely rich. But after Réaumur's death in October 1757, Brisson had to give up the care of his collection, which the Academy had transferred to the Cabinet du Roi, under the supervision of Buffon and Daubenton. Allowed for a time to continue his research, Brisson soon found himself denied access to the collections, but in spite of this he managed to publish the six volumes of his *Ornithologie* (1760).

This work, also in Latin and French, contained the descriptions of 1,500 species of birds, grouped into 115 genera, twenty-six orders, and two classes (distinguished by the presence or absence of webbed feet). There were 220 plates by F.-N. Martinet of 500 birds, many of which had never been illustrated before. In spite of its insufficient classification, this work, essentially didactic and written without style or pictorial research, was one of the most complete treatises in ornithology before the *Histoire des oiseaux* of Buffon, Guéneau de Montbeillard, and Gabriel Bexon.

Brisson, who had continued to receive the payment previously allocated to him as caretaker of Réaumur's collection, was elected an adjoint fellow in botany of the Academy in 1759 and royal censor in 1760. But forever deprived of any access to direct documentation and being the target of Buffon and his colleagues' hostility, he understood that it was useless to continue his work as a naturalist. On the advice of the Abbé Nollet he then turned to experimental physics, to which he devoted all his time.

In 1768 Nollet, who had been appointed to the Collège de La Fère, had Brisson named his deputy professor and successor to the chair of experimental physics that had been created for him at the Collège de Navarre in 1753. In 1770, a few months before his death, Nollet also arranged that Brisson be named his successor as "master of physics and natural history to the children of France," which position put him in touch with the royal family and assured him a comfortable living. In 1771 Brisson translated Priestley's *History of Electricity* and took this occasion to defend passionately Nollet's point of view against that of Franklin. The few memoirs he presented before the Academy concerned physics: the measurement of density, refraction, burning mirrors, barometers, magnetism, and atmospheric electricity.

But it was as a botanist that Brisson was made an associate member of the Academy in 1779 and a supernumerary pensioner in 1782, and it was only upon the reorganization of 1785 that he became a pensioner of the new section of general physics. In the meantime he had published the *Dictionnaire raisonné de physique* (1781), which was a fair presentation of various aspects of physics at that time but was soon out of date in spite of some additions in 1784, at the time of the first aerostatic experiments. His *Pesanteur spécifique des corps* (1787) was of more lasting interest, for many rather precise experimental data were included. In 1789 Brisson published in his *Traité élémentaire ou Principes de physique* the essentials of his courses given both privately and at the Collège de Navarre. The success of these courses is borne out by the testimony of a Russian traveler, P. I. Strakhov, who attended them from 1785 to 1787 and was enthusiastic over the presentation of Brisson's new discoveries on gases. On his return to Russia, Strakhov organized a course in experimental physics at the University of Moscow and published a Russian translation of the *Traité élémentaire*.

Brisson married Marie-Denise Foliot de Foucherolles in 1775. Their son, Louis-Antoine, who had the king and queen as godparents, died when he was only ten. There also were two daughters. Brisson was financially comfortable until the Revolution. In 1792 he became a member of the Academy commission entrusted with preparations for setting up the metric system, but was removed in 1793. He was reinstated after Thermidor and also was on the first list of professors for the new *écoles centrales*. In December 1795 he was appointed resident member of the experimental physics section, first class, of the Institut National. From 1796 on, Brisson taught experimental physics and chemistry at the Collège des Quatre Nations and published well-conceived, up-to-date manuals. He also published, but prematurely, several lessons on the comparison between the new and old units of measure, a subject he had studied when on the Commission of Weights and Measures. In 1801 Chaptal saw to it that his salary as professor was continued, but his appointment to the professorship at the Lycée Bonaparte in 1805 was purely honorific. He died only a short time later, following a stroke that made his last months very painful.

Having undergone an involuntary adjustment in his activities, Brisson carried on two successive careers, a short one as a naturalist and Réaumur's collaborator, and a longer one as Nollet's disciple and the disseminator of the ideas of experimental physics. His rather considerable influence was due to his teaching and his works, which, although not containing any original or important discoveries, were nevertheless an excellent means of spreading the scientific knowledge of the time. Probably his creative contribution would have been more important had not Buffon opposed the pursuit of his work as a naturalist.

BIBLIOGRAPHY

I. ORIGINAL WORKS. Brisson's writings include *Regnum animale in classes IX distributum... Le règne animal divisé en IX classes...* (Paris, 1756; Leiden, 1780); *Ornithologia, sive Synopsis methodica sistens avium divisionem in ordines ... Ornithologie ou Méthode contenant la division des oiseaux en ordres ...,* 6 vols. (Paris, 1760; Latin part reissued, 2 vols., Leiden, 1763, and 1 vol., Paris, 1788); *Dictionnaire raisonné de physique,* 3 vols. (Paris, 1781; 2nd ed., Paris, 1800); *Observations sur les nouvelles découvertes aérostatiques ...* (Paris, 1784); *Pesanteur spécifique des corps* (Paris, 1787); *Traité élémentaire ou Principes de physique...,* 3 vols. (Paris, 1789; 3rd ed., 1800), translated into Russian by P. I. Strakhov, 3 vols. (Moscow, 1801–1802; 2nd ed., incomplete, 2 vols., 1812), also translated into Georgian (Tiflis, 1812); *Rapport sur la vérification du mètre*

qui doit servir d'étalon (Paris, 1795), with Borda; *Instruction sur les nouveaux poids et mesures* (Paris, 1795); *Réduction des mesures et poids nouveaux* (Paris, 1799), new ed. entitled *Instruction sur les mesures et poids nouveaux* (1800); *Principes élémentaires de l'histoire naturelle et chymique des substances minérales* (Paris, 1797); and *Élémens ou principes physico-chymiques, destinés à servir de suite aux principes de physique à l'usage des écoles centrales* (Paris, 1800, 1803).

Manuscripts are "Dossier Brisson, Mathurin Jacques," in Archives de l'Académie des Sciences, Paris; and Library of the Institut National, Paris, MS 2041, no. 90: "Principales étapes de la vie de M. Brisson écrites par lui-même," among the papers of J. M. Delambre, transmitted by J. Bertrand.

II. SECONDARY LITERATURE. Works on Brisson are Roman d'Amat, in *Dictionnaire de biographie française,* VII (1956), cols. 366–367; H. Beauchet-Filleau and Paul Beauchet-Filleau, in *Dictionnaire historique et généalogique des familles du Poitou,* 2nd ed., II (Poitiers, 1895), 6, and III (1905), 389; A. Birembaut, "Les liens de famille entre Réaumur et Brisson, son dernier élève," in *Revue d'histoire des sciences,* **9** (1958), 167–169, and in the collection *La vie et l'oeuvre de Réaumur* (Paris, 1962), pp. 168–170; J. B. Delambre, in *Mémoires de la classe des sciences mathématiques et physiques de l'Institut National de France* (2nd semester 1806), pp. 184–205; Constant Merland, "Mathurin-Jacques Brisson," in *Biographies vendéennes,* II (Nantes, 1883), 1–47, partially repr. in *Revue de la Société Littéraire Historique et Généalogique de la Vendée* (1st trimester 1883), pp. 145–161, and (2nd trimester 1883), pp. 37–46; Poggendorff, I (1863), col. 301; J. Quérard, *La France littéraire,* I (Paris, 1827), 518–519, in which two notices on B. Brisson are wrongly attributed to M. J. Brisson; R. Taton, ed., *L'enseignement et la diffusion des sciences en France au XVIIIe siècle* (Paris, 1964), esp. pp. 158, 630–632, 640, 648; J. Torlais, *L'abbé Nollet* (Paris, 1954), esp. pp. 234–236, and *Réaumur,* rev. ed. (Paris, 1961), esp. pp. 343–345; and M. G. Th. Villenave, in F. Hoefer, *Nouvelle biographie générale,* VII (1863), cols. 437–438.

RENÉ TATON

BRITTEN, JAMES (*b.* London, England, 3 May 1846; *d.* Brentford, Middlesex, England, 8 October 1924), *botany.*

Britten was very clearly interested in botany as a child, and for many years he continued to be a keen field botanist, contributing notes on various flora of English counties. He has acknowledged the pleasures he derived from Anne Pratt's *Flowering Plants, Grasses, Sedges and Ferns of Great Britain* (1855). He was educated privately and for five years, until he reached the age of twenty-three, he resided with a doctor at High Wycombe, Buckinghamshire, as a preliminary to entering the medical profession. During that period he was secretary to the local natural history society and editor of its magazine. But he abandoned his medical studies when, in 1869, he was appointed assistant in the herbarium of the Royal Botanic Gardens, Kew. The following year he attended a course of lectures at University College, London, given by Daniel Oliver, who at the time was also keeper of the herbarium at Kew. Oliver befriended Britten and greatly encouraged him in botanical field pursuits, which they often shared. On Oliver's advice, Britten applied for a post in the department of botany in the British Museum, then still part of the main establishment at Bloomsbury. Much to the resentment of Sir Joseph Hooker, he left Kew, after only two years, to begin what was to be an industrious and somewhat tempestuous career at the museum, where his irascible, controversial temperament was often an embarrassment to his colleagues.

Britten's most important contributions to botany concerned historical, literary, and biographical aspects of the subject; and his long obituary notices, notes, and anecdotal comments, occasionally caustic and vituperative, are most valuable reference sources. With G. S. Boulger he produced in 1893 the invaluable *Biographical Index of British and Irish Botanists,* to which three supplements were published before his death and of which a second edition, revised by Dr. A. R. Rendle, appeared in 1931. His interest in old English dialects and folklore was manifest in many of his writings, especially in two works published by the English Dialect Society: the important *Dictionary of English Plant Names* (1878–1886), compiled in cooperation with Robert Holland, and his reprint, with notes, of William Turner's *The Names of Herbes* (1881). He also published a number of articles of ephemeral importance in the popular scientific press of the day.

The herbarium of Sir Hans Sloane, probably the most extensive collection of plants in existence in the seventeenth or eighteenth century, was purchased when the British Museum was founded in 1753. Britten's historical bent led him, throughout his service in the museum, to accumulate a mass of data, written on slips of paper, that until recently were the only commentary to the contents of Sloane's 265 bound volumes of *exsiccatae.* They formed the basis of *The Sloane Herbarium,* an annotated list of the *horti sicci* composing the herbarium, with biographical accounts of the principal contributors revised and edited by J. E. Dandy; it was published by the trustees of the British Museum in 1958.

Britten's first published work was a short note on locations of rare plants, mostly in the Thames Valley in Irvine's *The Phytologist* (November 1862). In the following year he contributed the paper "Rare and Exotic Plants at Kew Bridge, Surrey" to the first volume of the *Journal of Botany,* which he later edited for almost forty-five years. He used his editorial prerogative in a highly individualistic manner, and never missed an opportunity to express his candid criticism, deserved or not. This attitude caused resentment, and he was quick to pounce on any apparent shortcomings of the authorities and publications of Kew, which became a constant target for his pungent comments. Relations between his department and Kew were severely strained after an official committee recommended in 1901 that the herbarium collections at the museum should be transferred to Kew. Britten did not conceal his malice toward Kew, particularly criticizing the administration and making personal attacks on members of the staff. His indiscretions led to legal action, and he was obliged in the same year to make a public apology to the Kew authorities and to pay a donation to an agreed charity. His wit was always evident and perhaps one of his best efforts concerned the supposed demise of the regular numbers of the Kew *Bulletin* in a period when four appendices appeared and he surmised that the main publication had developed appendicitis!

Britten was elected a fellow of the Linnean Society in 1870. He was admitted to the Roman Catholic Church when he was twenty-one, and with his characteristic energy threw himself with zest into the propaganda activities of his adopted church. He was particularly prominent in the work of the Catholic Truth Society, and for this and other religious causes he was made a Knight of the Order of St. Gregory in 1897 by Pope Leo XIII and promoted to Knight Commander in 1917.

BIBLIOGRAPHY

Among Britten's writings are "Rare and Exotic Plants at Kew Bridge, Surrey," in *Journal of Botany,* **1** (1863), 375–376; *Dictionary of English Plant Names* (London, 1878–1886), compiled with Robert Holland; editing and notes for a reprint of William Turner's *The Names of Herbes* (London, 1881); *Biographical Index of British and Irish Botanists* (London, 1893), written with G. S. Boulger, 2nd ed., rev. by A. R. Rendle (London, 1931); and "The History of Aiton's 'Hortus Kewensis,'" in *Journal of Botany,* **50** (1912), supp. 3. A bibliography accompanies the obituary notice by A. B. Rendle, in *Journal of Botany,* **62,** 337.

GEORGE TAYLOR

BRITTON, NATHANIEL LORD (*b.* Staten Island, New York, 15 January 1859; *d.* New York, N. Y., 25 June 1934), *botany.*

Britton was educated at the School of Mines of Columbia College, from which he graduated as Engineer of Mines in 1879. He then became assistant in geology at Columbia and later served as botanist and assistant geologist for the Geological Survey of New Jersey for five years. Although his early training was in geology and mining, botanical interests dominated his career. Thus, in 1887 he returned to Columbia as instructor in botany and geology, in 1890 became adjunct professor of botany, and in 1891 was made professor of botany.

He was married in 1885 to Elizabeth Gertrude Knight (1858–1934), herself a botanist of distinction. Best known in her own specialty of bryology, she also was a constant helper in her husband's work.

Britton is best known for his role in the establishment and development of the New York Botanical Garden, a process set in motion in 1888, on a visit to the Royal Botanic Gardens at Kew, England, when his wife asked, "Why couldn't we have something like this in New York?" This question led to the formation of a committee by the Torrey Botanical Club to consider the establishment of a botanical garden in New York City. It appealed for funds in 1889, and in 1891 the New York Legislature chartered the New York Botanical Garden Corporation, which by July 1895 had persuaded the city to set aside 250 acres in Bronx Park for the development of the garden. In 1896 Britton was formally appointed director in chief, and during the next thirty-three years, thanks to his enthusiasm, initiative, drive, and organizing ability, this undeveloped area without buildings or roads became a garden with greenhouses, laboratories, library, and herbarium that make it one of the world's great botanical institutions.

Britton's own interests were primarily taxonomic and concerned mainly with the plants of eastern North America and the West Indies. His adherence to the American Code of Nomenclature and his extremely narrow generic concept have made much of the nomenclature of his works obsolete, but their value as comprehensive descriptive surveys remains. Britton founded the *Bulletin of the New York Botanical Garden* in 1896, the garden's *Journal* and *Memoirs* in 1900, and *Addisonia* in 1916, as well as the *North American Flora* in 1905. The periodical *Brittonia* (founded in 1931) is named for him, as are the plant genera *Brittonamra*, *Brittonastrom*, and *Brittonella*. *Bryobrittonia* commemorates Mrs. Britton.

BIBLIOGRAPHY

I. ORIGINAL WORKS. The most important of Britton's publications are *Illustrated Flora of the Northern United States, Canada and the British Possessions,* 3 vols. (New York, 1896–1898; 2nd ed., 1913), written with Addison Brown; *Manual of the Flora of the Northern States and Canada* (New York, 1901; 2nd ed., 1905); accounts of various families in *North American Flora* (1905–1930); *North American Trees* (New York, 1908), written with J. A. Shafer; *Flora of Bermuda* (New York, 1918); *The Cactaceae,* 4 vols. (Washington, D.C., 1919–1923), written with J. N. Rose; *The Bahama Flora* (New York, 1920), written with C. F. Millspaugh; and *Botany of Porto Rico and the Virgin Islands,* 2 vols. (New York, 1923–1930), written with P. Wilson.

II. SECONDARY LITERATURE. Writings on Britton are H. A. Gleason, "The Scientific Work of Nathaniel Lord Britton," in *Proceedings of the American Philosophical Society,* **104** (1960), 205–226; M. A. Howe, "Nathaniel Lord Britton," in *Journal of the New York Botanical Garden,* **35** (1934), 169–180; E. D. Merrill, "Biographical Memoir of Nathaniel Lord Britton," in *Biographical Memoirs of the National Academy of Sciences of the United States of America,* **295** (1934), 147–202; and T. A. Sprague, "Nathaniel Lord Britton," in *Kew Bulletin* (1934), 275–279.

WILLIAM T. STEARN

BROCA, PIERRE PAUL (*b.* Sainte Foy-la-Grande, near Bordeaux, France, 28 June 1824; *d.* Paris, France, 8 July 1880), *medicine, anthropology.*

Broca was the son of a Huguenot doctor, Benjamin Broca; his mother was the daughter of a Protestant preacher. At the local college he received a *bachelier ès lettres* and diplomas in mathematics and physical sciences. He entered the University of Paris medical school in 1841, and in an unusually short time became *externe* (1843), *interne* (1844), and prosector of anatomy (1848); he received the M.D. degree in 1849.

Broca's graduate studies were in pathology, anatomy, and surgery, and in 1853 he became assistant professor at the Faculty of Medicine and surgeon of the Central Bureau. He was an active figure in the Anatomical Society of Paris and in the Society of Surgery. His interests later turned to anthropology, and he was one of the most outstanding pioneers of the new discipline. During this period he held important posts in the hospitals of Paris, finally serving as surgeon to the Necker Hospital. In 1867 Broca was elected to the chair of *pathologie externe* at the Faculty of Medicine, and the following year he became professor of clinical surgery. He was elected a life member of the French Senate, representing science, six months before he died. He also received many honors in the medical and scientific world, and at his death was vice-president of the French Academy of Medicine.

Broca's versatility was noteworthy and his knowledge wide; his bibliography reveals the breadth of his scientific and clinical work. He made important contributions to anatomy, pathology, surgery, cerebral function, and other areas of medicine, and to anthropology. He showed deep interest in all his work and approached each problem with enthusiasm and thoroughness. He married the daughter of a Paris physician named Lugol.

Broca published several minor papers on anatomy, as well as *La splanchnologie,* a volume of the *Atlas d'anatomie descriptive.* During the twenty years or so after his graduation, he wrote extensively on pathology, including a two-volume work on tumors, *Traité des tumeurs.* These studies were closely associated with his contributions to surgery, which also appeared in his publications of this period; a book on strangulated hernia (1853) and one on aneurysm (1856) demonstrated his theoretical and practical knowledge of surgery.

Broca is, however, better known for his role in the discovery of cortical localization in the brain. This concept had begun with the phrenologists earlier in the century; but the majority of physicians, following Pierre Flourens, denied it. In a famous discussion in Paris in 1861, Broca was able to provide the essential link in the argument favoring the localization of speech function in the left inferior frontal gyrus (since known as Broca's convolution); an aphasic patient was found to have a lesion there. Much later it was shown that the lesion was not so precisely located as Broca had claimed, but his evidence was nevertheless a significant step toward proving that the cerebral hemisphere has localized areas of function, although precise parcelation is no longer accepted. He published extensively on cerebral localization and on normal, comparative, and pathological anatomy of the brain.

Broca's equally important labors were in anthropology, which field he helped to create. In 1847 he served on a commission to report on excavations in the cemetery of the Celestins, and this led him to study craniology and ethnology. These subjects suited him best, for they allowed him to use his anatomical and mathematical skills as well as his diversified knowledge; and his synthetic abilities were necessary to coordinate the wide range of data presented. He was mainly responsible for the formation of the Société d'Anthropologie de Paris in 1859, of the *Revue d'anthropologie* in 1872, and of the École d'Anthropologie in 1876. At this time anthropology was considered by both church and government to be sinister and subversive, but Broca surmounted all opposition and eventually established it securely. He invented at least twenty-seven instruments for the more accurate study of craniology, and he helped to standardize methods. Between 1850 and his death he published 223 papers and monographs on general anthropology, ethnology, physical anthropology, and other aspects of the field.

BIBLIOGRAPHY

I. ORIGINAL WORKS. S. Pozzi compiled a bibliography of Broca's writings according to subject (see below); this has been reprinted by Huard (see below). In addition, *Mémoires sur le cerveau de l'homme et des primates,* S. Pozzi, ed. (Paris, 1888), contains a wide selection of his papers. Broca's books are *La splanchnologie* (Paris, 1850–1866), Vol. III of Broca, C. Bonamy, E. Beau, *Atlas d'anatomie descriptive du corps humain* (Paris, 1844–1866); *De l'étranglement dans les hernies abdominales et des affections qui peuvent le simuler* (Paris, 1853; 2nd ed., 1856); *Des anévrismes et de leur traitement* (Paris, 1856); and *Traité des tumeurs,* 2 vols. (Paris, 1866–1869).

II. SECONDARY LITERATURE. There is an obituary of Broca in *The Lancet* (1880), **2**, 153–154. Articles on Broca (listed chronologically) include J. R. C., "Paul Broca of Paris," in *Edinburgh Medical Journal,* **26** (1880), 186–192; "Paul Broca, Honorary Member," in *Journal of the Anthropological Institute* (London), **10** (1880–1881), 242–261; S. Pozzi, "Biographie-bibliographie," in *Revue scientifique,* 3rd ser., **2** (1881), 2–12; *Popular Science Monthly,* **20** (1881–1882), 261–266; R. Fletcher, "Paul Broca and the French School of Anthropology," 15 April 1882, in *Saturday Lectures No. 6* (Washington, D.C., 1882), and in Fletcher's *Miscellaneous Papers 1882–1913* (Washington, D.C.); S. Zaborowski, "La psychologie et les travaux de M. Broca," in *Revue internationale des sciences biologiques,* **10** (1882), 141–159; M. Genty, "Broca (Paul) (1824–1880)," in *Les biographies médicales,* **9** (1935), 209–224, with portraits and references to iconography; K. Goldstein, "Pierre Paul Broca (1824–1880)," in W. Haymaker, ed., *Founders of Neurology* (Springfield, Ill., 1953), pp. 259–263; and P. Huard, "Paul Broca (1824–1880)," in *Revue d'histoire des sciences,* **14** (1961), 47–86, which contains references to most of the secondary material on Broca and the Pozzi bibliography of 1881.

EDWIN CLARKE

BROCARD, PIERRE RENÉ JEAN-BAPTISTE HENRI (*b.* Vignot, France, 12 May 1845; *d.* Bar-le-Duc, France, 16 January 1922), *mathematics, meteorology.*

Henri Brocard, born in a small, unpretentious town in northeastern France, was the son of Jean Sebastien and Elizabeth Auguste Liouville Brocard. No record has been found of brothers, sisters, or other close relatives, and Brocard never married. He is now known chiefly for his work in the geometry of the triangle, but he is also remembered as a French army officer and a meteorologist.

For some time, knowledge of Brocard's life fell far short of knowledge about the Brocard configuration, on which his renown rests. This was remedied by an autobiographical account published in 1894 at Bar-le-Duc. It covers the first fifty years of Brocard's life and tells of his mathematical and scientific publications and activities. He sent a copy of this pamphlet to the Smithsonian Institution shortly after its publication.

Brocard received his early education at the *lycée* of Marseilles, and the *lycée* and academy of Strasbourg. He attended the École Polytechnique from 1865 to 1867, and then joined the Corps of Engineers of the French army. It is known that he was a prisoner of war at Sedan in 1870, but for the most part his army career was devoted to teaching and research rather than to active combat. He became a life member of the newly organized Société Mathématique de France in 1873, and in 1875 he was made a life member of the Association Française pour l'Avancement des Sciences and of the Société Météorologique de France. For several years after 1874 he was assigned to service in north Africa, chiefly in Algiers and Oran. He was a co-founder of the Meteorological Institute at Algiers.

As a member of the local committee for the tenth session of the Association Française pour l'Avancement des Sciences, which met in Algiers in 1881, he presented a paper entitled "Étude d'un nouveau cercle du plan du triangle." It was in this paper that he announced the discovery of the circle that is now known by his name. In 1884 he returned to Montpellier, where he had taught for a short time after his graduation from the École Polytechnique.

There followed appointments to many government commissions and many scientific honors. Brocard served with the Meteorological Commission at Montpellier, Grenoble, and Bar-le-Duc. In 1894 he became a member of the Society of Letters, Sciences, and Arts of Bar-le-Duc; and it is through the publications of this society that one can follow the activities of the last twenty-six years of his life. His scientific and mathematical publications began when he was about twenty-three, and over the years showed him to be an indefatigable correspondent with the editors of mathematical and scientific journals. Brocard contributed to *Nouvelles annales de mathématiques, Bulletin de la Société mathématique de France, Mathesis, Zeitschrift für mathematischen und naturwissenschaftlichen Unterricht, Educational Times, El progreso matemático, L'intermédiaire des mathématiciens,* and many others. In his autobiography, a brief descriptive paragraph of about three or four lines is devoted to each journal, giving the names of the editors, the dates of publication, etc. These paragraphs provide a succinct and handy source of information, particularly for journals that later ceased publication.

Brocard's most extensive publication was a large, two-part work entitled *Notes de bibliographie des courbes géométriques,* followed by *Courbes géométriques remarquables,* which appeared under the joint authorship of Brocard and T. Lemoyne. The first part of the earlier work appeared in 1897, and the second in 1899. Probably no more than about fifty copies of this work were prepared, lithographed in the printscript of the author, and privately distributed. The *Notes* may be regarded as a source book of geometric curves, with a painstakingly prepared index containing more than a thousand named curves. The text consists of brief descriptive paragraphs, with diagrams and equations of these curves. About twenty years later, Volume I of the projected three-volume work *Courbes géométriques remarquables* was published in Paris. In 1967 both Volume II and a new edition of Volume I were published in Paris. *Courbes géométriques remarquables* is described as an outgrowth of *Notes de bibliographie des courbes géométriques.*

During the latter part of his life, Brocard made his home in Bar-le-Duc. He lived completely alone and rarely had visitors. He obviously enjoyed his membership in, and his work as librarian of, the Society of Letters, Sciences, and Arts of Bar-le-Duc, although he had declined the honor of becoming president. Largely through his efforts, one of the streets of Bar-le-Duc was named for Louis Joblot, a native Barisian who was an acknowledged but almost forgotten pioneer in the field of microscopy. When he retired from the army in 1910, Brocard was a lieutenant colonel and an officer in the Legion of Honor. In his retirement he spent much of his time making astronomical observations with a small telescope in the garden behind his house. Every fourth year he took a long trip to the meetings of the International Congress of Mathematicians.

The unit of mathematical theory identified as the Brocard configuration is founded upon two points, O and O', in a triangle ABC such that the angles OAB, OBC, and OCA, and the angles $O'BA$, $O'CB$, and $O'AC$ are equal. Brocard readily admitted that he had no claim to priority in the discovery of the existence of these points. Yet his influence upon his contemporaries was so great that the points O and O' are now universally recognized as the Brocard points of a triangle.

Of the several solutions available for the construction of the Brocard points of a triangle, the most striking and familiar is one in which circles are drawn as follows: A circle tangent to side *AB* of triangle *ABC* at *A* and passing through *C;* a second circle tangent to *BC* at *B* and passing through *A;* and a third circle tangent to *CA* at *C* and passing through *B.* It is easily proved that these three circles are concurrent at a point *O* which satisfies the above conditions (see Figure 1). Point *O'* is obtained in a similar manner, after a slight modification in procedure. The angle *OAB* (angle *W*) is called the Brocard angle of triangle *ABC,* and it is a simple matter to prove that

$$\cot W = \cot A + \cot B + \cot C.$$

Obviously a similar relation holds for angle *O'BA* (angle *W'*). Brocard's truly original contribution to the theory of the geometry of the triangle was his discovery of the circle drawn on the line segment *PK* as diameter, where *P* is the circumcenter of the triangle and *K* is its symmedian point. This circle, called the Brocard circle of a triangle, passes through the points *O* and *O'* and has many additional interesting geometric properties.

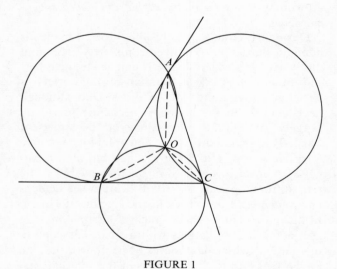

FIGURE 1

During the last decade of the nineteenth century several books were published about the Brocard configuration. The subject, which stirred the imagination and aroused the enthusiasm of many mathematicians in different parts of the world, has remained a pleasant and fruitful topic for discussion.

On 16 January 1922, Brocard was found dead at his desk. In accordance with his specific request, he was buried in the small cemetery at Vignot, next to his father and mother.

BIBLIOGRAPHY

I. ORIGINAL WORKS. Brocard's works are *Notice sur les titres et travaux scientifiques* (Bar-le-Duc, 1895); *Notes de bibliographie des courbes géométriques,* 2 vols. (Bar-le-Duc, 1897–1899); and *Courbes géométriques remarquables,* 2 vols. (I, Paris, 1920; new ed., 1967; II, Paris, 1967), written with T. Lemoyne.

II. SECONDARY LITERATURE. Works dealing with Brocard are Lucien Braye, "De New York à Bar-le-Duc sur les traces d'un théorème," in *L'est républicain,* Bar-le-Duc sec. (16 Sept. 1951); A. Emmerich, *Die Brocard'schen Gebilde* (Berlin, 1891); Laura Guggenbuhl, *Concerning Notes de bibliographie des courbes géométriques* (New York, 1951), and "Henri Brocard and the Geometry of the Triangle," in *Mathematical Gazette,* **32,** no. 322 (Dec. 1953), 241–243, also in *Proceedings of the International Congress of Mathematicians,* II (Amsterdam, 1954), 420–421; and Roger A. Johnson, *Modern Geometry* (Boston, 1929), chs. 12, 16, 17, 18; repr. in paperback as *Advanced Euclidean Geometry* (New York, 1960). Illustration courtesy of *Mathematical Gazette.*

LAURA GUGGENBUHL

BROCCHI, GIOVANNI BATTISTA (*b.* Bassano, Italy, 18 February 1772; *d.* Khartoum, Sudan, 23 September 1826), *geology.*[1]

The son of Cornelio Brocchi and Lucrezia Verci, Brocchi was brought up in a cultured and well-to-do family, educated in the classics and literature, but also brought into contact with the outdoors by his father's enthusiasm for hunting. He early developed strong interests in antiquities and natural history despite parental discouragement. Sent to Padua to study law, he preferred the botanical garden and the lectures in botany by Bonato. Upon the death of his father, Brocchi went to Rome, where he studied the art and monuments of antiquity intensively for six months. Returning to Bassano, he devoted himself to literature, especially the works of Dante, for two years.

In 1802 Brocchi became an instructor in natural history at the Gymnasium in Brescia. Appointment in 1808 as inspector of mines at Milan gave him the opportunity to travel widely through Italy, making extensive notes and collecting numerous specimens. The return of Lombardy to Austria in 1814 deprived Brocchi of this position but did not lessen his activity, which henceforth was centered in Rome. In 1821 he was restored to his position, but meanwhile he had accepted the invitation of the viceroy of Egypt to conduct a survey of the mineral resources of that country and to organize its mining industry. In the fall of 1822 he sailed from Trieste to Egypt, whence he made excursions up the Nile, and into Syria and Palestine. In 1826, as he was preparing to return to

Italy, he contracted bubonic plague,[2] of which he died. His last journals and collections are preserved in the Museo Civico, Bassano.

Brocchi published five major books and contributed about seventy articles to various journals. He wrote upon an amazing range of subjects from antiquities to zoology in carefully documented papers replete with classical references. While at Brescia he published zoological and mineralogical articles; these include observations on the anatomy of insect eyes and on infusoria. In 1818 he conducted experiments on "night air" at Rome, in the hope of finding the cause of malaria; the results were negative but duly reported.[3] He also published several articles on recent shells.

Brocchi's most significant contributions, however, were in the field of geology. Early papers such as the memoir on the Val di Fassa consist largely of mineralogical descriptions. The geognostical introduction to this report shows no appreciation of the stratigraphic significance of fossils beyond the uncertain importance of their presence or absence as criteria for "secondary" or "transition" rocks. The origin of basalts interbedded with limestones is discussed in terms of the Neptunist-Vulcanist controversy.

Brocchi's masterpiece is the *Conchiologia fossile subappennina* (1814). It opens with an eighty-page survey of paleontological studies in Italy—a mine of historical data that has been freely used by Lyell, Zittel, and other writers. The nature of the fossiliferous deposits at various localities is described in detail.[4] He noted the contrast between the Subapennine fossils, most of which could be identified with the living Mediterranean fauna, and those described by Lamarck from the Paris Basin, most of which were extinct. The possibility that deposits of greater antiquity have fewer living species is mentioned, but not examined in detail.[5] A chapter is devoted to the problem of extinction.

This work was completed before William Smith had published on the stratigraphic significance of fossils, and probably before Brocchi had read Cuvier and Brongniart's *Essai sur la géographie minéralogique des environs de Paris* (1811).[6] It is doubtful whether knowledge of the chronological value of fossil shells would have enabled Brocchi to reach more fundamental conclusions concerning these deposits; nearly all his collections were from Pliocene deposits—indeed, they constitute much of the "type" Pliocene of Lyell.[7]

Brocchi made his first extensive exploration of central Italy in 1811–1812. In the course of this he witnessed an eruption of Vesuvius and was thus able to compare the state of its crater before and after an eruption. From 1814 until 1820 his work was largely on volcanic rocks, especially tuffs. Impressed by the wide distribution of certain ash beds around Rome and Naples, he argued for the submarine deposition of these even in the face of included freshwater fossils, which he insisted were transported. His descriptions of these deposits are thorough and accurate, and his *De stato fisico del suolo de Roma* (1820) still contains valuable data on the geology of the Imperial City.[8] The *Catologo ragionato* (1817) likewise is a useful compendium of original observations on the geology of central and southern Italy.

Brocchi's scientific contribution lay in the accurate observation, recording, and incorporation into the current body of scientific knowledge of a vast amount of new data from very diverse fields, especially the earth sciences.

NOTES

1. Or natural history. Brocchi's journals cover many phases of natural history and archaeology.
2. Malaria, according to Sacchi.
3. It is interesting to note that at this date Brocchi believed that the agent responsible for malarial infection entered the body through the skin rather than by respiration, and he concluded (without, however, suspecting the mosquito) that the draining of swamps would reduce the incidence of the disease.
4. Most of the collection is preserved in the Museo Civico di Storia Naturale di Milano. Its recent history has been summarized by Carla Rossi Ronchetti.
5. Lyell refers repeatedly to Brocchi's work in the *Principles of Geology*. He criticizes him (III, 18–19) for correlating the Subapennine formations with those of the Paris Basin despite the faunal dissimilarity. To what extent Brocchi's suggestive but incomplete analysis of this matter influenced Lyell in formulating his subdivision of the Tertiary into epochs is unknown; it certainly was noted and accorded a place in the exposition of this principle.
6. Brocchi in 1817 alludes to Cuvier's work and to Tertiary fossils "buried at the time of the great revolutions of the earth."
7. Lyell, *Principles of Geology,* 2nd ed. (1833), III, 157, refers various Subapennine beds of Brocchi to the Miocene, Older Pliocene, and Newer Pliocene. Ronchetti, p. 7, considers all but one of the localities of the Brocchi collection to be Pliocene.
8. *Cf.* Clerici, p. xciii.

BIBLIOGRAPHY

I. ORIGINAL WORKS. Lists of Brocchi's writings are in *Biographie universelle ancienne et moderne, deuxième edition, par MM Michaud,* V (Paris, 1880), 580–584; and Giuseppi Roberti, in G. I. Ferrazzi, ed., *Atti della festa commemorativa il primo centenario della nascita di Giambattista Brocchi celebratosi in Bassano il xv ottobre MDCCCLXXII* . . . (Bassano, 1873; repr. Milan, 1874, 1881), pp. 37–42 (the pagination is different in each edition). Meli (see below) cites several other, less extensive lists and adds a number of previously unnoticed titles.

Brocchi's major works are *Memoria mineralogica sulla*

valle di Fassa in Tirolo (Milan, 1811); *Conchiologia fossile subappennina, con osservazioni geologiche sugli Appennini e sul suolo adiacente di G. Brocchi . . .,* 2 vols. (Milan, 1814); *Catologo ragionato di una raccolta di rocca deposto con ordine geografico per servire alla geognosia dell'Italia* (Milan, 1817); *Dello stato fisico del suolo di Roma . . .* (Rome, 1820); and *Giornale delle osservazioni fatte ne viaggi in Egitto, nella Siria e nella Nubia di G. B. Brocchi,* 5 vols. (Bassano, 1841–1843).

II. SECONDARY LITERATURE. Works on Brocchi are Giambattista Baseggio, "Della vita e degli studii di Giambattista Brocchi," in G. I. Ferrazzi, ed., *Di Bassano e dei Bassanesi illustri . . .* (Bassano, 1847), pp. 325–358, with portrait; Enrico Clerici, "In occasione del centenario dell'opera di Giovanni Battista Brocchi *Dello stato fisico del suolo di Roma,*" in *Bollettino della Società geologica italiana,* **38** (1919), lxxxiii–xciii; Giovanni Larber, *Elogio storico di Gio. Batt. Brocchi bassanese compilato dal suo concittadino Giovanni Larber* (Padua, 1828), with portrait, the most detailed source; Romolo Meli, "Una lettera inedita dell'insigne naturalista Giambattista Brocchi," in *Bollettino della Società zoologica italiana,* 2nd ser., **7** (1906), 303–323, which contains references to numerous other biographies; Carla Rossi Ronchetti, "I tipi della *Conchiologia fossile subappennina* di G. Brocchi," in *Rivista italiana di paleontologia e stratigrafia,* supp. **57–62** (1951–1956); Defendente Sacchi, "Elogio biografico," in *Annali universali di statistica,* no. 144 (Feb. 1828), 132 ff.; and Antonio Stoppani, "Elogio di Giambattista Brocchi letto in occasione del primo centenario celebratosi in Bassano al di 15 ottobre 1872," in G. I. Ferrazzi, ed., *Atti di festa commemorativa il primo centenario della nascità di Giambattista Brocchi celebratosi in Bassano il xv ottobre MDCCCLXXII . . .* (Bassano, 1873; repr. Milan, 1874, 1881), pp. 42 ff. (pagination is different in each edition).

JOSEPH T. GREGORY

BROCHANT DE VILLIERS, ANDRÉ-JEAN-FRANÇOIS-MARIE (*b.* Villiers, near Mantes, France, 6 August 1772; *d.* Paris, France, 16 May 1840), *geology, mineralogy.*

Brochant warmly supported Haüy's theories of crystal structure, although his writings also aided in the diffusion in France of A. G. Werner's mineral classification and nomenclature, as well as the early crystallographic ideas of C. S. Weiss. Wernerian principles influenced his geological memoirs, which were concerned exclusively with the geology of the Alps. He devoted the last two decades of his life primarily to the preparation of a geological map of France.

Brochant studied mineralogy under Werner at Freiberg from 1791 to 1793 and entered the newly organized École des Mines in 1794. He became an engineer in the Agence des Mines in 1800 and an editor of the *Journal des mines* in 1801. In 1804 Brochant was named professor of geology and min-

eralogy at the École des Mines, at that time located at Pesey in Tarentaise (Savoy), and he retained this post when the school was moved to Paris in 1815. He then became a member of the Académie des Sciences, a director of the glass factory at St. Gobain, and later inspector general of mines.

Stimulated by the publication of Greenough's geological map of England in 1822, Brochant pleaded successfully for the preparation of a similar map for France. After a preliminary journey to England with his collaborators, Armand Dufrénoy and Élie de Beaumont, to establish procedures, Brochant began the survey in 1825. During the next ten years, Élie and Dufrénoy made summer field trips, the former in eastern France and the latter in western France, while Brochant supervised the work and compiled the results. He published a report on the project, "Notice sur la carte géologique générale de la France," in the *Comptes rendus* (**1** [1835], 423–429). The completed map was published in 1841, after his death.

BIBLIOGRAPHY

I. ORIGINAL WORKS. Brochant published two works in mineralogy: *Traité élémentaire de minéralogie, suivant les principes du professeur Werner,* 2 vols. (Paris, 1801–1802; 1808); and *De la cristallisation considérée géométriquement et physiquement, ou traité abrégée de cristallographie* (Strasbourg, 1819). In geology he compiled a four-volume *Mémoires pour servir à une description géologique de la France* (Paris, 1830–1838); published posthumously was his *Explication de la carte géologique de la France, rédigée sous la direction de M. Brochant de Villiers . . . par M. M. Dufrénoy et Élie de Beaumont* (Paris, 1841). Brochant's most important geological memoirs were "Observations géologiques sur les terrains de transition qui se trouvent dans la Tarentaise et autres parties des Alpes," in *Journal des mines,* **23** (1808), 321–380; "Observations sur les terrains de gypse ancien qui se trouvent dans les Alpes," in *Annales des mines,* **2** (1817), 256–300; and "Considérations sur la place qui doivent occuper les roches granitoides du Mont Blanc et d'autres cimes centrales des Alpes dans l'ordre d'antériorité des terrains primitif," *ibid.,* **4** (1819), 283–300.

II. SECONDARY WORKS. Brochant is discussed in Alfred Lacroix, "Notice historique sur le troisième fauteuil de la section de minéralogie," in *Académie des sciences—séance publique annuelle du lundi 17 décembre 1928* (Paris, 1928), pp. 18–26.

JOHN G. BURKE

BRODIE, BENJAMIN COLLINS (*b.* Winterslow, Wiltshire, England, 8 June 1783; *d.* Broome Park, Betchworth, Surrey, England, 21 October 1862), *physiology, surgery.*

Benjamin Collins Brodie was the third son of Rev. Peter Brodie, the rector of the parish of Winterslow, and Sarah Collins, the daughter of a banker from Salisbury. He received his early education at home, being taught—along with his elder sister and brothers—by his father. At eighteen he went to London to study medicine and began attending the anatomy lectures of John Abernethy, pupil and "disciple" of John Hunter, at St. Bartholomew's Hospital. He entered the Windmill Street School of Anatomy in 1802 and in 1803 became surgical pupil of Everard Home, enrolling in St. George's Hospital in June 1804. His father had died in March of that year, leaving the family in difficult circumstances. Fortunately, through his uncle, Thomas Denman, a distinguished obstetrician, Brodie became known to, and was helped by, many of the prominent medical men in London at that time. In May 1805, he was appointed house surgeon at St. George's, and on 18 October of that year was admitted as a member of the Royal College of Surgeons. He became assistant surgeon at St. George's in March 1808, and began lecturing on surgery at the Windmill Street School of Anatomy. He continued this course until 1830. In 1816 he married Anne Sellon; they had four children, one of whom, Benjamin, Jr., became a famous chemist.

Brodie's scientific career has three aspects: he was a researcher, a surgeon and general practitioner, and a member of the medical establishment. He contributed six papers to the *Philosophical Transactions* of the Royal Society between 1809 and 1814. These papers, whose significance is further discussed below, were not so much concerned with physiological theory as with factual experimental reporting. They were widely recognized, however, and their impact on the Royal Society gave Brodie considerable professional prominence. He was elected a member of the Royal Society, at the age of twenty-six, in February 1810, and in 1811 was awarded the Copley Medal, the youngest member ever to receive it. He was the Croonian Lecturer in 1810 and 1813, and in 1858 was elected president. He was the first surgeon to hold this post.

Around 1811, however, Brodie realized that he would, in effect, have to choose between research and teaching on the one hand, and surgery and private practice on the other. Thus, from that time on, his written publications consisted mainly of reports to the clinical journals. He had kept scrupulous case notes from the very beginning of his career, and sixteen volumes of these were given to St. George's Hospital by his grandson. His book *Diseases of the Joints* was extremely influential and ran to five editions, the first

appearing in 1818 and the last in 1850. It is based on an analysis of case histories, and Brodie clearly preferred to retain limbs rather than amputate them. In an age when women were cosseted indoors, he was a pioneer advocate of fresh air and exercise, and was able to demonstrate how many joint afflictions probably had hysterical origins.

Brodie was an excellent diagnostician and built up a flourishing practice as the leading surgical consultant. He became personal surgeon to King George IV in 1828, and president of the Royal College of Surgeons in 1844, having been an active and reforming member of its council for a number of years. He was knighted in 1834, and three years later, as he felt befitted his new station in life, bought a landed estate in Surrey.

In retrospect, Brodie's six papers in the *Philosophical Transactions* seem to have had an impact out of all proportion to their theoretical importance, for the positive contributions were slight. In trying to assess why this was so, we find important clues to the prevailing state of physiological thought at the time. With the exception of the first paper, which was communicated to the Society by Everard Home, all the papers were communicated by, or first read to, the Society for Promoting Knowledge of Animal Chemistry, which had been founded *ca.* 1802 and of which Humphry Davy was a member. Physiology in England had received a great stimulus from the work of Joseph Black, Joseph Priestley, and Adair Crawford, and was also influenced—to a lesser extent—by the researches of Lavoisier and Laplace on respiration and animal heat. In particular Adair Crawford's theory of animal heat production, based both on the chemical theory of respiration and on Black's theory of specific heats, apparently tied up in a neat theoretical form one of the most perplexing problems of animal physiology. The importance of the new chemistry for physiology was recognized by the founding of the society mentioned above and by active research by many medical men.

Brodie's papers made their impact almost solely because the empirical results they presented challenged the whole chemical theory of animal heat, with respiration (and, by implication, combustion) as the actual source of heat production. The results were indisputable. He destroyed the animal's brain by pithing, decapitation, or poisoning, yet maintained respiration and heartbeat artificially—managing to do this for periods up to two and a half hours, getting the appropriate changes of color in the blood. If respiratory changes were the immediate cause of the heat in animals, then the temperature of the animals should be maintained. This did not occur. Moreover, if Brodie inactivated the higher cerebral centers by poisoning, then gradually allowed the animal to recover, as the "sensibility" was recovered, the animal also recovered the power of generating heat, until it could counteract the loss of heat due to the cold of the surrounding atmosphere. Brodie concluded, rightly, (1) that the presence of the brain was not *directly* necessary to the action of the heart, but only indirectly, by maintaining the "life" of the organs; (2) that if the brain is destroyed, the secretory functions and heat production are totally impaired; (3) that respiratory changes could not, *of themselves,* be responsible for animal heat production, because in his experimental situation, with the respiration artificially maintained, if the air inspired was cooler than the natural temperature of the animal, the effect of the artificial respiration was to diminish the heat of the animal, not increase it; (4) that the phenomena of animal heat production were very complicated indeed, and it was relevant to question whether, in view of the multifarious processes going on in the animal body, one was justified in attributing only one of them to animal heat production.

In later years Brodie was often represented as producing a "nervous" theory of animal heat (e.g., by Claude Bernard, in his *La chaleur animale,* 1876, p. 290). This is wrong: there is little trace of any theory in these papers. Brodie said, at the end of the 1812 paper, that he did not wish to advance some opinions, but simply to state facts. In certain aspects his empirical findings needed to be explained, and his doubts were genuine ones. Animal heat production and maintenance are controlled by nervous centers. It was recognition of this fact that led Bernard so many years later to quote Brodie. But it was the direct conflict between Brodie's results and the contemporary chemical ideas that made Brodie's papers the sensation they were.

BIBLIOGRAPHY

The Works of Sir B. C. Brodie, collected by C. Hawkins, includes an autobiographical sketch in the first volume, pp. 1–116.

Biographies of Brodie are T. Holmes, *Sir Benjamin Brodie* (1898); and William R. LeFanu, "Sir Benjamin Brodie, F.R.S. (1783–1862)," in *Notes and Records of the Royal Society of London,* **19**, no. 1 (1964), 42–52. See also G. J. Goodfield, *The Growth of Scientific Physiology* (1960), especially ch. 4, pp. 76–99.

G. J. GOODFIELD

BRODIE, BENJAMIN COLLINS, JR. (*b.* London, England, 5 February 1817; *d.* Torquay, England, 24 November 1880), *chemistry.*

Brodie was the son of a prominent surgeon who was also a president of the Royal Society. He attended Harrow and then entered Balliol College, Oxford. After graduating, he left England for the famous chemical laboratory at Giessen, where, in the summer of 1845, he worked under Liebig on the analysis of beeswax. He returned home about 1847 and continued his chemical studies in a private laboratory in London. He was elected a fellow of the Royal Society in 1849. In 1855 he became Waynflete professor of chemistry at Oxford, a position he held until 1873.

Brodie pursued the investigation of waxes that he had begun in Germany, and soon discovered and named cerotic acid, cerotin, and melissic acid. A few years later he examined graphite and discovered graphitic acid. Brodie discussed his findings in this early work in terms of the accepted language of the atomic theory, representing the new substances by conventional formulas. He soon abandoned this treatment, however.

Brodie is interesting as a historical figure on account of his drastic proposals for an alternative approach to chemistry, which he first put before the Royal Society in 1866. By this time a skeptical attitude toward Dalton's atomic theory had arisen. Chemists welcomed the convenience of the theory as a summary of known facts and employed its language, but they were not prepared to discuss the question of the ultimate divisibility of matter. It was sufficient to know that certain masses were undivided by the powers of chemistry. Gerhardt's statement that chemical formulas did not represent actual atomic arrangements, but merely the relations between substances in chemical change, was quoted with approval by Brodie, who placed it at the head of his 1866 paper.

This was not enough for Brodie, however. The advertisement in a chemical journal of a set of balls and wires as an aid to the study of chemical combination was evidence enough for him that the science of chemistry had gone "off the rails of philosophy." Only an accumulation of errors could have produced such a "bathos." He therefore proposed to substitute an exact language, free from any association with Dalton's theory. He said that this would be independent of any hypothesis on the nature of matter. Its symbols would simply express the facts.

The new symbols represented chemical operations performed on space. Brodie regarded the method as an applied algebra and stated that he had been guided by algebraic procedures in geometry and logic. He made several references to George Boole. Just as in geometry a symbol could indicate the operation on a unit of length by which a line was generated, so in chemistry a symbol could represent an operation on space which produced a weight. All substances were considered to be perfect gases. The chemical unit of ponderable matter was that which occupied 1,000 cc., the "unit of space," at standard temperature and pressure. The symbol α represented the operation on the unit of space from which a unit of hydrogen resulted. The compound that resulted from the successive operations α and χ had the symbol $\alpha\chi$. The logarithmic relation $\alpha + \chi = \alpha\chi$ was one of the fundamental equations of the calculus.

In Brodie's scheme only weight would be considered; the form, color, and other properties of matter would be neglected. He would investigate the distribution of weights in chemical change by the appropriate symbols, which were derived with the aid of experimental data on gases. For example, the decomposition of water vapor, in which two volumes of water produce two volumes of hydrogen and one of oxygen, was represented as $2\phi = 2\phi_1 + \phi_2$, where ϕ, ϕ_1, ϕ_2 are the symbols of units of water, hydrogen, and oxygen, respectively.

Let $\phi = \alpha^m \xi^n$, $\phi_1 = \alpha$, $\phi_2 = \alpha^p \xi^q$, where α and ξ symbolize uncompounded component weights (prime factors) and m, n, p, and q are positive integers. By the fundamental logarithmic relationship $2\phi = 2\phi_1\phi_2$, or $(\alpha^m \xi^n)^2 = \alpha^2 \alpha^p \xi^q$, so that $2m = 2 + p$ and $2n = q$. Density data were brought into the calculation and the equations were finally solved, subject to the condition of a minimum number of prime factors. The unique solution is then $m = 1$, $n = 1$, $p = 0$, $q = 2$. The symbol for the unit of oxygen is therefore ξ^2 and that for water is $\alpha\xi$.

Symbols of other substances, obtained by similar reasoning, formed three distinct classes. One group of substances, typified by hydrogen, was represented by a single letter, that is, only one operation on space was needed for their production. The group of double-lettered symbols indicated that two successive operations were needed to form the substances concerned. This was the case with oxygen, ξ^2 or $\xi\xi$. The third group included chlorine, $\alpha\chi^2$; nitrogen, αv^2; and hydrogen peroxide, $\alpha\xi^2$. These substances could not be formed by fewer than three operations on the unit of space.

Brodie discussed the exciting implications of his symbols. Substances regarded as elements were of the same symbolic form as substances known to be compounds. The ξ^2 component of hydrogen peroxide indicated the presence of oxygen. But how were χ^2, v^2, and ξ to be interpreted? They could not be dismissed as imaginary units, since, Brodie argued, they had been discovered in the course of analysis. Nor would he positively claim that v, ξ, and χ represented real pieces of matter. He preferred to call such symbols "ideal."

He could not exclude the possibility that chlorine, for example, might really consist of α and χ. This view that the elements might be compounded had earlier been favored by Davy and Prout. Brodie speculated that at some remote age, when the earth was very hot, the simple forms of matter—α, χ, ξ, and so forth—might have existed. As the earth's temperature fell, these formed combinations, like chlorine, which were so stable that they never decomposed again. The primitive materials might still exist, however, on the sun and in distant nebulae. The independent existence of χ and v might be detected by a spectroscopic examination of heavenly bodies. Indeed, a recent investigation of a nebula had shown its spectrum to be like that of nitrogen, but less complex. Later, he also seized on some erroneous experiments on chlorine as evidence of its compound nature.

Brodie failed to convince chemists to abandon their association with atoms. The weakness of the calculus of operations was indicated by Naquet, who translated Brodie's work into French. He pointed out that there was no way to distinguish isomers, compounds such as acetaldehyde and ethylene oxide, which have identical compositions by weight but exhibit completely different properties. This anomaly was readily explained on the atomic theory by assuming different arrangements of particles in space. Brodie had restricted his treatment to weights, and without additional suppositions his calculus could not explain the different qualitative changes resulting from identical gravimetric redistributions. The spatial properties of matter assumed particular importance in the stereochemistry of Van't Hoff and Le Bel, which appeared in 1874. The excess explanatory capacity of the atomic theory won the confidence of chemists, and Brodie's calculus was never adopted. It was left as a curious relic of the positivistic tendencies of nineteenth-century chemistry.

BIBLIOGRAPHY

I. ORIGINAL WORKS. Some of Brodie's scientific papers include "An Investigation on the Chemical Nature of Wax," in *Philosophical Transactions,* **138** (1848), 147–158, 159–170, and **139** (1849), 91–108; "On the Atomic Weight of Graphite," *ibid.,* **149** (1859), 249–259; "On the Decomposition of the Simple Weight X Effected by Victor Meyer," in *Journal of the Chemical Society,* **35** (1879), 673–682. A list of Brodie's other scientific papers is given in the *Royal Society Catalogue of Scientific Papers.*

Brodie presented his calculus in "The Calculus of Chemical Operations," in *Philosophical Transactions,* **156** (1866), 781–859, and **167** (1877), 35–116. A less formal exposition, together with some reactions to the calculus, can be found in Brodie's "On the Mode of Representation

Afforded by the Chemical Calculus, as Contrasted With the Atomic Theory," in *Chemical News,* **15** (1867), 295–305. A corrected version of this was later published as *Ideal Chemistry* (London, 1880).

II. SECONDARY LITERATURE. Brodie's work has been discussed in W. H. Brock and D. M. Knight's "The Atomic Debates: Memorable and Interesting Evenings in the Life of the Chemical Society," in *Isis,* **56** (1965), 5–25; and in W. V. Farrar's "Sir B. C. Brodie and his Calculus of Chemical Operations," in *Chymia,* **9** (1964), 169–179. A. Naquet's critique of Brodie's calculus may be found in "Considerations on the Two Memoirs of Sir B. C. Brodie on the Calculus of Chemical Operations," in *Philosophical Magazine,* **7** (1879), 418–432. Some additional information on Brodie can be found in J. R. Partington, *A History of Chemistry,* IV (London, 1961–   ), 425–427.

D. C. GOODMAN

BRØGGER, WALDEMAR CHRISTOPHER (*b.* Christiania [now Oslo], Norway, 10 November 1851; *d.* Oslo, 17 February 1940), *geology.*

Brøgger was the son of Anton Wilhelm Brøgger, a well-known book publisher, and Oline Marie Bjerring. In 1878 he married Antonie Siewers; their home fostered musical and other cultural interests. After receiving his baccalaureate in 1869, Brøgger took the *examen philosophicum* (a year's study of various subjects, before specialization) at the University of Oslo in 1870 and then began to study zoology. In 1872 he published a paper on the mollusks of the Oslo Fjord. Attracted by Theodor Kjerulf, professor of mineralogy and geology, he transferred to that department and in 1876 received an appointment as assistant at the mineralogical institute of the university. At the same time he served as assistant at the Geological Survey of Norway. During this period he was president of the Norwegian Students' Union several times.

During the next few years, Brøgger engaged in rich and varied scientific activity, and in 1881 he was appointed professor at the newly established Stockholms Høgskola (now the University of Stockholm). There he founded a first-class mineralogical institute, as well as teaching and conducting research that dealt mainly with the geology and mineralogy of Norway.

In 1890 Brøgger succeeded Kjerulf as professor at the University of Oslo, remaining in this post until 1917. His main contribution was in the study of the Permian eruptive rocks of the Oslo district; and he was one of the pioneers in the theory of magmatic differentiation. Besides his writings, Brøgger published, alone or in collaboration with his colleague and successor J. Schetelig, numerous geological maps. Among other important petrographical works is that

on carbonatite-containing rocks at Fen, in the Precambrian just outside the Oslo district, published when he was nearly seventy; this type of rock was one of his main concerns. Outstanding among Brøgger's many mineralogical contributions is his long treatise on pegmatite minerals from Langesund Fjord, in the southernmost part of the Oslo district (1890).

Other scientific achievements are Brøgger's important studies on tectonic geology, Cambro-Silurian stratigraphy and paleontology, and Quaternary geology. At the presentation of the Wollaston Medal to Brøgger in 1911, the president of the Geological Society of London said: "In an age of specialization he is a specialist, but a specialist in almost every branch of science. That it should have fallen to one man to do so much and so well almost passes belief."

With his forceful personality and his administrative ability, Brøgger became a leader in Norwegian scientific circles at an early stage in his career. For a time he was rector of the University of Oslo, and for many years served as president of the Norwegian Academy of Science in Oslo. By establishing a number of scientific endowments, largely through private and institutional subscriptions, and through his untiring efforts to achieve recognition for scientific research, he had a strong and lasting effect on the history of his country. Between 1900 and 1906 he was a member of the Storting (parliament), where he championed the cause of science.

BIBLIOGRAPHY

I. ORIGINAL WORKS. Brøgger's writings include "Bidrag til Kristianiafjordens molluskfauna," in *Nyt magazin for naturvidenskaberne,* **19** (1872), 103–145; "Om paradoxidesskifrene ved krekling," *ibid.,* **24** (1878), 18–88; "Die silurischen Etagen 2 und 3 im Kristianiagebiet und auf Eker, ihre Gliederung, Fossilien, Schichtenstörungen und Contactmetamorphosen," in *Universitätsprogramm,* 2nd sem. 1882, no. 8; "Spaltenverwerfungen in der Gegend Langesund-Skien," in *Nyt magazin for naturvidenskaberne,* **28** (1884), 253–419; "Ueber die Bildungsgeschichte des Kristianiafjords. Ein Beitrag zum Verständnis der Fjord- und Seebildung in Skandinavien," *ibid.,* **30** (1886), 99–231; "Die Mineralien der Syenitpegmatitgänge der südnorwegischen Augit- und Nephelinsyenite. Mit zahlreichen chemisch-analytischen Beiträgen von P. T. Cleve," in *Zeitschrift für Krystallographie und Mineralogie,* **16** (1890); "Die Eruptivgesteine des Kristianiagebietes. I. Die Gesteine der Grorudit-Tinguait-Serie," in *Videnskaps-selskapets skrifter, mathematisk-naturvidenskapelig klasse* (1894), no. 4; "Die Eruptivgesteine des Kristianiagebietes. II. Die Eruptionsfolge der triadischen Eruptivgesteine bei Predazzo in Südtyrol," *ibid.* (1895), no. 7; "Die Eruptivgesteine des Kristianiagebietes. III. Das Ganggefolge des Laurdalits," *ibid.* (1897), no. 6; "Om de senglaciale og postglaciale nivåforandringer i Kristianiafeltet (molluskfaunan). . .," in *Norges geologiske undersøgelse,* no. 31 (1900); "Strandliniens beliggenhed under stenalderen i det sydøstlige Norge," *ibid.,* no. 41 (1905); "Die Eruptivgesteine des Kristianiagebietes. IV. Das Fengebiet in Telemark, Norwegen. . .," in *Videnskaps-selskapets skrifter, mathematisk-naturvidenskapelig klasse* (1920), no. 9; *Geologisk oversiktskart over Kristianiafeltet. 1:250,000* . . . (Christiania, 1923); "Die Explosionsbreccie bei Sevaldrud zwischen Randsfjord und Sperillen," in *Norsk geologisk tidsskrift,* **11** (1930), 281–346; "Die Eruptivgesteine des Oslogebietes. V. Der grosse Hurumvulkan," in *Norske Videnskaps-Akademi i Oslo, matematisk-naturvidenskapelig klasse* (1930), no. 6; "Die Eruptivgesteine des Oslogebietes. VI. Über verschiedene Ganggesteine des Oslogebietes," *ibid.* (1931), no. 7; "Essexitrekkens erupsjoner. Den elste vulkanske virksomhet i Oslofeltet," in *Norges geologiske undersøkelse,* no. 138 (1933); "Die Eruptivgesteine des Oslogebietes. VII. Die chemische Zusammensetzung der Eruptivgesteine des Oslogebietes. . .," in *Norske Videnskaps-Akademi i Oslo, matematisk-naturvidenskapelig klasse* (1933), no. 1; "On Several Archäan Rocks From the South Coast of Norway. I. Nodular Granites From the Environs of Kragerø," *ibid.,* no. 8; and "On Several Archäan Rocks From the South Coast of Norway. II. The South Norwegian Hyperites and Their Metamorphism," *ibid.* (1934), no. 1.

II. SECONDARY LITERATURE. A special publication, *Ved W. C. Brøggers bortgang* (Oslo, 1940), was printed and distributed by Norske Videnskaps-Akademi soon after Brøgger's death. It contains, besides biographical data, speeches delivered at the memorial held in the university auditorium on the day of his funeral and at a special meeting of the Academy of Science and Letters in Oslo on 8 March 1940. The scientific achievements of Brøgger are discussed by V. M. Goldschmidt and Olaf Holtedahl in that publication, which also contains a complete bibliography by W. P. Sommerfeldt on pp. 57–105.

OLAF HOLTEDAHL

BROGLIE,   LOUIS-CÉSAR-VICTOR-MAURICE DE (*b.* Paris, France, 27 April 1875; *d.* Neuilly-sur-Seine, France, 14 July 1960), *physics.*

The ancient family of de Broglie has long supplied France with soldiers, diplomats, and politicians of the highest rank. Maurice, the second of the family's five children and the eldest son, was virtually required by tradition to follow a diplomatic or a military career. After some discussion, his grandfather, the head of the family, allowed him to enter the navy, the most technically demanding of the services, which Maurice preferred partly from a taste for the sea and partly from a youthful but sincere interest in the physical sciences. After a brilliant career at the École Navale (1893–1895), he was assigned to the Mediterranean Squadron, which he improved by installing the first

French shipboard wireless. Simultaneously he continued his education in the schools of Toulon and Marseilles University, from which he emerged with the *licence ès science* in 1900.

As Maurice de Broglie's experience of science and technology grew, he thought to resign his commission and to follow a career in physics. In 1898 he broached the possibility to his family. His grandfather was scandalized. "Science," said the old duke, "an old lady content with the attractions of old men," was no career for a de Broglie. A compromise was effected: Maurice fitted out a room of the family mansion as a laboratory and returned to the navy. There he so distinguished himself in wireless work that it appeared that he might add lustre to the family name by following his bent; and so he was able, after the death of his grandfather, to convert the furlough he obtained for his marriage in 1904 into an indefinite leave, which lasted until he formally resigned his commission in 1908. During those years he prepared for his new career, first at the observatory at Meudon, where he studied spectroscopy with Deslandres, and then at the Collège de France, where, in 1908, he successfully defended a thesis on ionic mobilities which he had prepared under the direction of Paul Langevin.

The "ions" of de Broglie's thesis were charged particles of smoke and dust floating about in a gas. His research involved two central problems in the physics of the time, the mechanism of ionization and the measurement of Brownian motion. He accordingly had occasion to work with and to improve upon some of the most advanced techniques then employed in studying and producing ionization; in particular, he tried to improve the capricious apparatus used to generate X rays. The research was done in his own home, in his unusually well-equipped private laboratory, in which he was to work for the rest of his long career.

For a time de Broglie pursued themes suggested by his thesis, either alone or in collaboration with his old teacher from Toulon, L. Brizard. These investigations, which were gradually moving him out of the mainstream of physics, ended in 1912, when Laue and the Braggs showed that X rays could yield diffraction patterns. De Broglie immediately took up the study of X-ray spectra, which became the chief field of his researches and the subject of his most notable discoveries. His earliest important contribution was the "method of the rotating crystal," an application, and perhaps an independent discovery, of the "focusing effect" first described by the Braggs. With this technique, which eliminates spurious spectral lines arising from local imperfections in the face of the diffracting crystal, de Broglie explored the X-ray emission spectra at the same time that Moseley was preparing his classic papers (1913–1914); but whereas the latter breathlessly mapped a few high-frequency lines from many elements, and so arrived at his well-known formulas, the former, proceeding more cautiously, investigated a wider spectrum in only a few metals and found no regularities. World War I interrupted the work of both men. Moseley enlisted in the army and was killed at Gallipoli; de Broglie rejoined the navy and labored on submarine communications, for which he received a medal. Meanwhile the neutral Swedes, particularly Manne Siegbahn, advanced the study of X-ray spectra by extending Moseley's mapping with the aid of de Broglie's technique.

After the war de Broglie returned to his laboratory and the X rays, attending primarily to their absorption spectra, which he had briefly examined during a period of leave in 1916. Then he had made the capital discovery of the third L absorption edge, a matter of great theoretical interest; now he began (partly with the aid of A. Dauvillier) a careful study of the fine structure of the various edges. This investigation led naturally to the exploration of "corpuscular spectra," i.e., of the velocities of photoelectrons released by X rays of a given frequency ν. These "spectra" can reveal the various absorption edges of an atom, as the difference between $h\nu$ and the kinetic energy of a liberated electron gives the energy of the absorption edge with which that electron was associated before its release. De Broglie was joined in these researches, which date from 1921–1922, by his brother Louis, still undecided about whether to settle on physics for his own career; and their cooperation proved very helpful in refining Bohr's specification of the substructure of the various atomic shells. Subsequently (1924) the brothers briefly studied an analogous phenomenon together, the Compton effect.

In the mid-1920's de Broglie began to direct more of his energy toward the leadership of his laboratory. Although he continued to work on diverse problems involving X rays, he began increasingly to look for other aspects of the interaction between radiation and matter. His private laboratory, kept up to date, began to attract students, some of whom were to become leaders of French science. The first group included (besides Dauvillier and L. de Broglie) J. Thibaud, J. Trillat, F. Dupré la Tour, and L. Leprince-Ringuet. After their initiation they tended to follow their own interests, and so de Broglie's private laboratory became the scene of pioneering studies in nuclear physics and cosmic radiation. He followed this work closely, initially (1930–1932) as a collaborator, and subsequently as an influential, inspirational master. In this last role, for which his informed, independent, natural —we might even say aristocratic—authority admirably prepared him, he made what are perhaps his most lasting contributions to French physics.

Many honors came to de Broglie, among which we may single out election to the Académie des Sciences (1924), the Académie Française (1934), the French Atomic Energy Commission, the Académie de Marine, and the Institut Océanographique. He also played a part in international science—for example, through his participation in the Solvay Congresses and his successful early texts on X rays, one of which was translated into English. He was also, perhaps, the last representative of a type that has contributed mightily to the advancement of science—the wealthy independent experimentalist who could follow what he pleased as far as his energies and ability might carry him.

BIBLIOGRAPHY

I. ORIGINAL WORKS. Adequate although not exhaustive bibliographies of de Broglie's writings will be found in W. Wilson, "Maurice, Le Duc de Broglie," in *Biographical Memoirs of Fellows of the Royal Society* (1961), pp. 31–36, and in P. Lépine, *Notice sur la vie et les travaux de Maurice de Broglie* (Paris, 1962). Among the most important of his papers are "Sur un nouveau procédé permettant d'obtenir la photographie des spectres de raies des rayons de Röntgen," in *Comptes rendus de l'Académie des sciences,* **157** (1913), 924–926 (the rotating crystal); "Sur un système de bandes d'absorption correspondant aux rayons L . . .," *ibid.,* **162** (1916), 352–354 (the third L edge); "Les spectres corpusculaires . . ." (several articles alone and in collaboration with L. de Broglie), *ibid.,* **172** (1921), 274–275, 527–529, 746–748, 806–808; **173** (1921), 939–941, 1157–1160; **174** (1922), 939–941; **175** (1922), 1139–1141; and "La relation $h\nu = E$ dans les phénomènes photo-électriques . . .," in *Atomes et électrons* (Paris, 1923), pp. 80–130 (de Broglie's report to the Solvay Congress of 1921). Among the most important of his books are *La théorie du rayonnement et les quanta* (Paris, 1912), M. de Broglie and P. Langevin, eds. (the proceedings of the first Solvay Congress); *Les rayons X* (Paris, 1922); and, with L. de Broglie, *Introduction à la physique des rayons X et gamma* (Paris, 1928).

II. SECONDARY LITERATURE. For biographical material, see Lépine's *Notice;* the obituaries by Wilson (*op. cit.*); L. Leprince-Ringuet, *Comptes rendus de l'Académie des sciences,* **251,** pt. 3 (1961), 297–303; and R. Sudre, *Revue de deux mondes* (July–Aug. 1960), 577–582; family reminiscences by the Comtesse de Pange (Pauline de Broglie), "Comment j'ai vu 1900," *ibid.* (Apr. 1962), pp. 548–557; and L. de Broglie, *Savants et découvertes* (Paris, 1951), pp. 298–305; and the romantic dynastic history by La Varende, *Les Broglie* (Paris, 1950), pp. 265–320. For some assessment of de Broglie's work on X rays and its background, see

J. L. Heilbron, "The Kossel-Sommerfeld Theory and the Ring Atom," in *Isis*, **58** (1967), 451–485, and works there cited.

ADRIENNE R. WEILL-BRUNSCHVICG
JOHN L. HEILBRON

BROILI, FERDINAND (*b.* Mühlbach, Germany, 11 April 1874; *d.* Mühlbach, 30 April 1946), *paleontology, geology.*

Ferdinand was the son of J. B. Broili, squire of the castle of Mühlbach, near Karlstadt. The family was of Italian origin; an ancestor had emigrated in 1741 from Treviso to Würzburg. At first Broili attended the village school in Mühlbach, then the Gymnasium in Würzburg. While still a child he collected his first fossils from a shell limestone quarry on the estate and thus became interested in geology. In 1894 Broili began his study of the natural sciences at the University of Würzburg. The following year he transferred to Munich, where he was the favorite student of the internationally renowned paleontologist Karl von Zittel, under whose guidance he received the Ph.D. in 1898 with a thesis on paleontology.

In 1899, after one year as assistant in the geology department of the Technische Hochschule of Munich, Broili became Zittel's assistant at the State Paleontological Collection in Munich, which at that time was probably the most significant of its kind. In 1901 Zittel sent him to Texas, where he and the American Charles Sternberg successfully collected and investigated amphibian and reptile fossils of the Permian era. For nearly a decade he occupied himself extensively with the Permian fauna in Texas, and between 1904 and 1913 he published several works on his investigations, especially on saurians.

In 1903 Broili qualified as academic lecturer under Zittel, again with a paleontological work. When Zittel died in 1904, Broili was appointed the custodian of the State Paleontological Collection; in 1909 he became curator, and after 1908 he had the title of professor. In 1919 he was appointed director of the Institute for Paleontology and Historical Geology of the University of Munich, as well as director of the State Paleontological Collection. In 1904 he had married Emma Morneburg of Passau; they had one son and one daughter.

Broili's main concern was paleontology, but he also participated in the geological investigations in the Bavarian Alps.

In paleontology, Broili was very active in many areas. In 1919 he began extensive investigations of the many fossils of the laminated lime formations of the upper Malm at Sonthofen and in Eichstätt, in Upper Franconia, most of them unique surviving fossils. He was especially successful in his investigations of winged reptiles, demonstrating that they had hairy coverings, and thus were warm-blooded, as well as that they had webbed skin and a pecten on the crown of the head. Broili did not allow his duties as director of the State Paleontological Collection to restrict his scientific work, but conducted many-faceted investigations of the Paleozoic and Mesozoic eras. At the beginning of his career he had been active outside central Europe, and he continued foreign investigations in the 1920's and the 1930's, stimulating and organizing several expeditions to the Karroo formation in South Africa and also taking a leading part in the evaluation of the findings. In his investigations of fossils Broili did not stop at description and systematic explanation, but also attempted to depict the main life habits of the animals involved and succeeded in working out several excellent descriptions.

Broili also worked on the methodology of paleontology and developed fundamental methods for the evaluation of fossil deposits. As director of the State Paleontological Collection he continued Zittel's pioneer work and greatly enlarged the collection, both in general scope and in number of local Bavarian specimens.

In 1930 he became editor-in-chief of the journal *Paleontographica,* and was coeditor of several other journals. He resigned from his various positions in 1939 and gave his full time to his private investigations, especially to devising a unified description of the amphibia, which remained unfinished. In 1943 Broili left Munich, where he had been active for so long, and spent the rest of his life in Mühlbach.

BIBLIOGRAPHY

I. ORIGINAL WORKS. Although Broili's writings have been only partially published, more than 100 scientific works, predominantly in paleontology, are in print. These are dispersed in many different journals and cover the years 1899–1942. Among his published works should be mentioned *Die permischen Brachiopoden von Timor* (Stuttgart, 1916); *Paläozoologie* (*Systematik*) (Berlin–Leipzig 1921); "Ein neuer Fund von Plesiosaurus aus dem Malm Frankens," in *Abhandlungen der Bayerischen Akademie der Wissenschaften,* Math.-nat. Abt., **30** (1926), Abh. 8; "Über Gemündina Stürtzi Traquair," *ibid.,* n.s. (1930), Abh. 6. The majority of Broili's publications are found in *Sitzungsberichte der Bayerischen Akademie der Wissenschaften.* Math.-nat. Abt. For bibliography, see Dehm and Schroeder (below).

II. SECONDARY LITERATURE. Broili's life and works were

discussed during his lifetime by W. D. Matthew, "Notes on the Scientific Museums of Europe," in *Natural History,* **21** (1921), 184–190. Obituary notices include R. Dehm and J. Schroeder, "Ferdinand Broili 1874–1946," in *Neues Jahrbuch für Mineralogie, Geologie und Paläontologie,* Sec. B (1945–1948), pp. 257–271, with complete bibliography; B. Peyer, "Ferdinand Broili 1874–1946," in *Verhandlungen der Schweizerischen naturforschenden Gesellschaft* (1946), 358–360; and D. M. S. Watson, "Ferdinand Broili," in *Nature,* **158** (1946).

HANS BAUMGÄRTEL

BROMELL, MAGNUS VON, known as **Bromelius** before being raised to the nobility in 1726 (*b.* Stockholm, Sweden, 26 March 1679; *d.* Stockholm, 26 March 1731), *geology.*

Bromell was the son of Olof Bromelius, a prominent physician and botanist in Göteborg. During his studies in Holland, England, and France from 1697 to 1704, he acquired a thorough knowledge of medicine, anatomy, chemistry, and botany; in 1703 he became a doctor of medicine in Rheims. Returning to Sweden, Bromell practiced as a physician in Stockholm, where he periodically gave lectures as a professor of anatomy and in 1724 was elected head of the Collegium Medicum; about 1715 he lectured, as a medical professor, in natural history at the University of Uppsala. An accomplished chemist and mineralogist, he became associated with the Board of Mines, where, in 1720, he was named assessor and, in 1724, head of the chemical laboratory.

Bromell earned his scientific renown as a geologist and mineralogist. He was a passionate collector whose great natural history cabinet—some of it inherited from his father—contained a beautiful collection of ore, mineral, and fossil specimens that he described and partly illustrated. In his small *Mineralogia* (1730), which was also translated into German and which had considerable influence, Bromell classified, to a degree, minerals according to their chemical characteristics and thus became a forerunner of A. F. Cronstedt and later eighteenth-century mineralogists. His "Litographiae Svecanae specimen secundum" (1727–1730) is a pioneer paleontological work that describes a multitude of Swedish animal and plant fossils, including trilobites, ammonites, and corals from Gotland limestone.

BIBLIOGRAPHY

I. ORIGINAL WORKS. Bromell's writings are "Litographiae Svecanae specimen primum et secundum," in *Acta literaria Sveciae,* II (1725–1729) and III (1730–1734); and *Mineralogia eller inledning til nödig kunskap at igenkienna . . . allahanda bergarter* (Stockholm, 1730), trans. into German as *Mineralogia et litographia Svecana,* (Stockholm–Leipzig, 1740).

II. SECONDARY LITERATURE. Works on Bromell are O. Hult, "Några anmärkningar om Olof och Magnus Bromelius," in *Svenska Linnésällskapets Årsskrift* (1926); and G. Regnéll, "On the Position of Palaeontology and Historical Geology in Sweden Before 1800," in *Arkiv för mineralogi och geologi,* **1,** no. 1 (1950), 1–64.

STEN LINDROTH

BROMWICH, THOMAS JOHN I'ANSON (*b.* Wolverhampton, England, 8 February 1875; *d.* Northhampton, England, 26 August 1929), *mathematics.*

Bromwich, whose father was a woolen draper, received his early education in Wolverhampton and in Durban, South Africa, where the family immigrated. He entered Cambridge in October 1892 as a pensioner of Saint John's College and graduated three years later as senior wrangler in a class that included E. T. Whittaker and J. H. Grace. He obtained a fellowship in 1897 but left Cambridge in 1902 to become professor of mathematics at Queen's College, Galway. Bromwich returned in 1907 as permanent lecturer in mathematics at Saint John's College and received the Sc.D. in 1909. He was elected to the Royal Society in 1906 and was active in the London Mathematical Society, serving as its secretary (1911–1919) and vice-president (1919, 1920). The first two decades of Bromwich's career were distinguished by numerous publications and vigorous teaching, but mental affliction led to diminished productivity in his later years and eventually to suicide.

Described by G. H. Hardy as the "best pure mathematician among the applied mathematicians at Cambridge, and the best applied mathematician among the pure mathematicians," Bromwich was well known for his precision, mastery of technique, and skill in algebraic manipulation. But Hardy also described Bromwich as lacking the power of "thinking vaguely" and Bromwich's work as "a little wanting in imagination."

The author of two books, two pamphlets, and some eighty papers, Bromwich is best known for his encyclopedic *Introduction to the Theory of Infinite Series* (1908). Although this book has been praised for its richness of detail and its abundance of examples, it has also been criticized for defects in its general structure—for example, its frequent failure to set off and to emphasize fundamental ideas. The book, based on Bromwich's lectures at Galway, incorporates many of his own researches separately published between 1903 and 1908.

Another series of researches culminated in Bromwich's Cambridge Tract, *Quadratic Forms and Their Classification by Means of Invariant Factors* (1906). In these publications Bromwich's creative powers are most fully evident, for in them he both introduced English readers to Kronecker's ideas and methods in the theory of quadratic and bilinear forms and advanced the knowledge of these forms.

Bromwich's first publication, as well as many later papers, was in applied mathematics. Especially under the influence of George Stokes, Bromwich did significant work in the mathematics of electromagnetism and of other subjects as well (including lawn tennis). Most memorable is a series of papers that began in 1916 with "Normal Coordinates in Dynamical Systems." In this paper Bromwich indicated how Oliver Heaviside's much criticized calculus of symbolic operators could be developed in a manner acceptable to pure mathematicians by treating his operators as contour integrals.

BIBLIOGRAPHY

I. ORIGINAL WORKS. Bromwich's two books are *Quadratic Forms and Their Classification by Means of Invariant Factors* (Cambridge, 1906); and *An Introduction to the Theory of Infinite Series* (London, 1908, 1926). For a bibliography of his papers, see below.

II. SECONDARY LITERATURE. Articles on Bromwich are G. H. Hardy, "Thomas John I'Anson Bromwich," in *Journal of the London Mathematical Society,* **5** (1930), 209–220; and Harold Jeffreys, "Bromwich's Work on Operational Methods," *ibid.,* 220–223. See also G. H. Hardy, *Proceedings of the Royal Society of London* (Section A), **129** (1930), i–x. All three of the above articles include bibliographies; the last includes a portrait. See also "Bromwich," in *Alumni Cantabrigienses,* Part II, Vol. I (Cambridge, 1940), 392.

MICHAEL J. CROWE

BRONGNIART, ADOLPHE-THÉODORE (*b.* Paris, France, 14 January 1801; *d.* Paris, 18 February 1876), *paleobotany, plant anatomy, plant taxonomy.*

The son of Alexandre Brongniart, the eminent geologist, Brongniart was trained by his father and at an early age collaborated with him. He rapidly showed signs of being a superior student, and his gifts were so carefully developed that he became a precocious scientist capable of an immediately high level of work.

Nothing in Brongniart's life indicates the slightest hesitation in his pursuit of science. Between 1817 and 1828 he was able to attend to his studies and his

initiation in science while carrying on original research. In 1818 he was registered for courses in medicine, but they constituted only a fraction of his occupations; two years later he published his first report, on a new genus of crustacean. After this youthful attempt Brongniart hoped to reach the level of the great biological movements of his time: research on the primary divisions of the vegetable kingdom, anatomy and taxonomic anatomy (following the work of Mirbel and Candolle), and the theory of generalized plant sexuality. The progress already made in these fields, as well as that in geology and botanical geography (he had early acquired a knowledge of tropical flora), heralded a new science of which Brongniart was to be the architect: the comparative morphology of living and fossil plants.

In 1822 Brongniart published his first important memoir, on the classification and distribution of fossil plants. In it he conceived of paleobotany as a part of botany and gave it a theoretical value of prime importance for biology as well as for geology. Coming as he did after such scholars as Ernst Schlotheim and Kaspar von Sternberg, Brongniart was not entirely an innovator, but his study did show an assurance previously unknown.

The masterworks of 1828, the *Prodrome* and the *Histoire des végétaux fossiles,* mainly confirmed and extended his early ideas, giving them foundation and breadth of perspective. The *Histoire,* which he had hoped to continue in a second volume (only the first parts appeared in 1837), was a long, methodical, detailed, and precise study that clearly showed Brongniart's two concerns: nomenclature and illustration. Its general principles and theoretical views were expressed in condensed form in the *Prodrome,* to striking effect. In it Brongniart recognized the existence of four successive periods of vegetation, each characterized geologically. Three were particularly well characterized: the first, extending to the end of the Carboniferous, by the vascular cryptogams; the third, covering the Jurassic and the Cretaceous, by ferns and the gymnosperms; the fourth, which was the Tertiary, by the dicotyledons.

Brongniart then divided the vegetable kingdom into six classes: Agamae (thallophytes), cellular cryptogams (liverworts and mosses, i.e., Hepaticae and Muscae), vascular cryptogams, and three classes of phanerogams: gymnosperms, monocotyledonous angiosperms, and dicotyledonous angiosperms. This excellent classification clearly indicated modern views, but unfortunately, for unknown reasons, Brongniart did not follow it in his later publications. For the first time gymnosperms were taken as a class and correctly placed among the phanerogams. After more than a century, the cotyledons were no longer the major criterion for classification.

Although Brongniart agreed with Cuvier's theories of fixity of species and cycles in the history of the earth, he, like Candolle before him, accepted the law of organic improvement of plants, adding to it a fundamental geological dimension. The sequence went from the structural simplicity of the Carboniferous plant life, to the intermediary structure of the Jurassic gymnosperms, to the dicotyledons of the Tertiary and the modern flora. This work led to the biological chain formulated by Hofmeister in 1851. Brongniart noted both the phenomena of extinction, which affected the genera and even the classes of the Carboniferous flora, and the correspondence between changes in fauna and flora and changes in climate.

At twenty-seven, Brongniart seemed to have reached the zenith of his creative power. The year before, he had passed his *agrégation* in medicine and had published a valuable memoir on the fertilization of phanerogams that followed up Amici's early research. The improvements in the microscope (notably by Amici) finally made possible the direct study of fertilization, so Brongniart decided to repeat Vaucher's investigation (which had been attempted by Brongniart's great-uncle, Romain Coquebert, as early as 1794): to follow the process of fertilization all the way to the fusion of the male and female germ cells. Brongniart's text confirmed and generalized the existence of the pollen tube; he also named the embryo sac and adopted the theory of epigenesis. But, most importantly, he confusedly provided a description of two fundamental discoveries: the existence of the tetrads, which appear during male sporogenesis, and the distinction between the fertilized egg and the seed. This work led to a new understanding of classification and of the alternation of generations.

In 1824 Brongniart and a few colleagues founded the *Annales des sciences naturelles.* He succeeded Desfontaines as professor of botany at the Muséum d'Histoire Naturelle in 1833, and the following year he was elected a member of the Académie des Sciences.

Until 1849 Brongniart extended his researches to the whole plant world, past and present, including taxonomy, anatomy, or biology. He was one of the first, after H. T. M. Witham's work of 1833, to use thin sections in paleobotany (inaugurated by W. Nicol). His most notable use of thin sections was in his famous anatomical observations on the *Sigillaria* (1839), a genus in the class of plants proper to the Primary era and related to the lycopods.

In 1849 Brongniart's article "Végétaux fossiles" appeared in d'Orbigny's *Dictionnaire universel d'histoire naturelle* and was also printed separately under the title *Tableau des genres de végétaux fossiles . . . .* This was the first attempt at a synthesis of paleobotany: the inventory of fossil genera as a whole and the place of these genera in natural classification.

After 1849 Brongniart's activity turned more and more to the systematic study of living plants, particularly the Neo-Caledonian flora: Proteaceae, Eleocarpaceae, Saxifragaceae, Cunoniaceae, Myrtaceae, Pittosporaceae, Dilleniaceae, Umbelliferae, Epacridaceae, palms, conifers, and so on. His articles appeared in such journals as *Annales des sciences naturelles, Annales du Muséum, Archives du Muséum, Comptes rendus de l'Académie des sciences,* and *Bulletin de la Société botanique de France.* Yet he had not abandoned his interest in paleobotany. A quarter of a century after the *Tableau des genres . . . fossiles,* his pupil Grand' Eury sent him some silicified seeds from Grand' Croix, near St. Étienne. Brongniart went to work with enthusiasm and made a last great discovery: the pollen chamber in fossil cycads, a structure that he and Bernard Renault also found in a living cycad species from Mexico—*Ceratozamia brongniart*—in 1846.

Brongniart was one of the greatest French botanists of the nineteenth century, and his work exerted a major influence on the progress of botany. It is possible, however, that he was too much influenced by Cuvier and too little by Lamarck, for the theoretical aspect of his work may not quite equal its descriptive excellence.

BIBLIOGRAPHY

I. ORIGINAL WORKS. Brongniart's writings include "Mémoire sur le *Limnadia,* nouveau genre de crustacés," in *Mémoires du Muséum d'histoire naturelle,* **6** (1820), 83–92; "Description d'un nouveau genre de fougère nommée *Ceratopteris,*" in *Bulletin de la Société philomatique de Paris,* **7** (1821), 184–187; "Sur la classification et la distribution des végétaux fossiles en général, et sur ceux des terrains de sédiment supérieur en particulier," in *Mémoires du Muséum d'histoire naturelle,* **8** (1822), 203–240, 297–348, also published separately; *Essai d'une classification naturelle des champignons, ou Tableau méthodique des genres rapportés jusqu'à cette famille* (Paris, 1825); "Recherches sur la génération et le développement de l'embryon dans les végétaux phanérogames," in *Bulletin de la Société philomatique de Paris,* **12** (1826), 170–175, and in *Annales des sciences naturelles,* **12** (1827), 14–53, 145–172, 225–296; "Mémoire sur la famille des Rhamnés," *ibid.,* **10** (1827), 320–386, his thesis for the M.D.; *Prodrome d'une histoire des végétaux fossiles* (Paris, 1828); *Histoire des végétaux fossiles, ou Recherches botaniques et géologiques sur les végétaux renfermés dans les diverses couches du globe,*

2 vols. (Paris, 1837); *Botanique du voyage de la Coquille pendant 4 années 1822–1825* . . . (Paris, 1829), with atlas; "Recherches sur la structure et les fonctions des feuilles," in *Annales des sciences naturelles,* **21** (1830), 420–458; "Observations sur la structure intérieure du *Sigillaria elegans,* comparée à celle des *Lepidodendron* et des *Stigmaria,* et à celle des végétaux vivants," in *Archives du Muséum d'histoire naturelle,* **1** (1839), 405–460; "Note sur un nouveau genre de Cycadées du Mexique," in *Annales des sciences naturelles,* 3rd ser., **5** (1846), 1–9; "Végétaux fossiles," in d'Orbigny's *Dictionnaire universel d'histoire naturelle,* XIII (Paris, 1849), 52–173, published separately as *Tableau des genres de végétaux fossiles considérés sous le point de vue de leur classification botanique et de leur distribution géologique* (Paris, 1849); *Rapport sur les progrès de la botanique phytographique* (Paris, 1868); "Études sur les graines fossiles trouvées à l'état silicifié dans le terrain houiller de Saint-Étienne," in *Annales des sciences naturelles,* section botanique, **20** (1874), 234, and *Comptes rendus de l'Académie des sciences,* **79** (1874), 343, 427, 497; "Sur la structure de l'ovule et da la graine des Cycadées, comparée à celle de diverses graines fossiles du terrain houiller," *ibid.,* **81** (1875), 305–307; and *Recherches sur les graines fossiles silicifiées* (Paris, 1881), with a preface on Brongniart's work by J.-B. Dumas.

II. SECONDARY LITERATURE. For biographical information on Brongniart, see Maxime Cornu, "Éloge de M. Ad. Brongniart," in *Revue scientifique,* **10** (1876), 564–574; Pierre Duchartre et al., *Discours prononcé le 21 fevrier 1876 sur la tombe de M. Adolphe Brongniart* (Paris, 1876), with a good list of works by Brongniart; J.-B. Dumas, "Les Brongniart, généalogies et compléments biographiques" (1923–1924), MS in Bibliothèque du Muséum d'histoire naturelle, and "La famille d'un échevin de Paris: Les Hazon. Généalogies et compléments historiques" (1939), MS in Bibliothèque du Muséum d'histoire naturelle; L. de Launay, *Une grande famille de savants: Les Brongniart* (Paris, 1940); and G. de Saporta, "Étude sur la vie et les travaux paléontologiques d'Adolphe Brongniart," in *Bulletin de la Société botanique de France,* 7th ser., **4** (1876), 373, meeting of 20 April.

Brongniart's work is discussed in Cornu and in Saporta (above). See also P. Bertrand, "La chaire d'anatomie comparée des végétaux vivants et fossiles du Muséum," in *Bulletin du Muséum d'histoire naturelle,* 2nd ser., **13,** no. 5 (1941), 369–391; K. Chester, "Fossil Plant Taxonomy," in W. B. Turrill, ed., *Vistas in Botany,* IV (Oxford, 1964), 238–297; F. H. Knowlton, *Fossil Wood and Lignite of the Potomac Formation,* U.S. Geological Survey Bulletin no. 56 (Washington, D. C., 1889), pp. 1–72; and L. F. Ward, "Historical Review of Paleobotanical Discovery," in U.S. Geological Survey, *Fifth Annual Report (1883–1885)* (Washington, D.C., 1885), pp. 368–425.

JEAN-FRANÇOIS LEROY

BRONGNIART, ALEXANDRE (*b.* Paris, France, 5 February 1770; *d.* Paris, 7 October 1847), *geology.*

Brongniart was the son of the distinguished Parisian architect Alexandre-Théodore Brongniart (1739–1813) and Anne-Louise Degremont. He studied at the École des Mines and later at the École de Médecine, and for a time acted as assistant to his uncle Antoine-Louis Brongniart (1742–1804), who was then professor of chemistry at the Jardin des Plantes. After serving as *aide-pharmacien* in the French forces in the Pyrenees, Brongniart returned to Paris; in 1794 he was appointed *ingénieur des mines,* and in 1797 became professor of natural history at the École Centrale des Quatre-Nations. In 1818 he was appointed *ingénieur en chef des mines,* and in 1822 he succeeded R. J. Haüy as professor of mineralogy at the Muséum d'Histoire Naturelle. Brongniart was elected a member of the Académie des Sciences in 1815. Most of his life was spent in Paris, in teaching, research, and administration. He is said to have been exceptionally helpful and generous to his students, for whom he opened his collections every Sunday; and he attracted distinguished gatherings of scientists at his evening *salons.*

Brongniart traveled widely in western Europe and published geological papers on areas ranging from Sweden to Italy. As a young man, immediately after the Revolution, he visited England to learn the techniques of the ceramics industry, and in 1800 he was appointed director of the Sèvres porcelain factory, a post he held until his death. The problems of ceramic technology occupied his attention increasingly toward the end of his life, and his last major work was the two-volume *Traité des arts céramiques* (1844). He married Cécile, daughter of the statesman-scientist Charles-Étienne Coquebert de Montbret; their only son was the botanist and paleobotanist Adolphe-Théodore Brongniart.

Brongniart's earliest scientific papers (the first was published in 1791) were on various zoological and mineralogical subjects. In the former he was strongly influenced by Georges Cuvier, who was almost exactly his contemporary. For example, his "Essai d'une classification naturelle des reptiles" (1800) emphasized the prime importance of careful comparative anatomy, and on that basis he divided the class Reptilia into four groups. He recognized, however, that one group, the batrachians, was significantly different from all the others, especially in the reproductive organs, and that this distinction was far more important than the more striking difference between the limbless snakes and the rest. In 1804 Pierre Latreille elevated the batrachians into a separate class, the amphibians; Brongniart's grouping of the true reptiles—into chelonians, saurians, and ophidians—has been retained, in essence, in modern systematics.

In 1807 Brongniart published *Traité élémentaire de minéralogie,* a work commissioned as a textbook for his and Haüy's courses at the Faculté des Sciences and the Muséum d'Histoire Naturelle. He adopted a simple scheme of classification based mainly on physical properties, but he also made extensive use of Haüy's crystallographic work. Like other mineralogists at this time, he could not easily distinguish some fine-grained rocks from true simple minerals; but he classed clay and basalt, for example, as *fausses espèces,* recognizing that they were *mélangées* although they were too fine-grained to be analyzed. He emphasized the importance of studying the modes of occurrence of minerals as well as their properties, but firmly avoided any discussion of their origins as being too speculative. The sole exception to this was a review of divergent opinions on the aqueous or igneous origin of basalt, but even in this he avoided expressing his own opinion.

Brongniart's early studies in zoology and mineralogy coalesced in the geological work that made him famous throughout the scientific world. Cuvier had already begun his series of spectacular reconstructions of extinct mammals from the Paris region; these fossils clearly belonged to several distinct periods, but he needed a reliable clue to their relative ages. He and Brongniart therefore collaborated in surveying the region and determining the order of the strata in which the fossils had been found. About 1804 they began a series of traverses of the region, and on 11 April 1808 they read their "Essai sur la géographie minéralogique des environs de Paris" before the Institute. The paper was first published in June 1808; a greatly enlarged version, accompanied by a large colored geological map and several horizontal sections, appeared in 1811. With characteristic modesty Brongniart allowed his name to appear after Cuvier's on this memoir, although the geological work seems to have been largely Brongniart's.

Nine "formations" (distinctive rock units) were recognized in the initial version of the work (the details were amended and amplified later, but the main conclusions were unchanged). The oldest was the Chalk, which underlay a series of later strata that had been deposited in succession, in a kind of gulf or embayment. There was no transition between the lowest, an unfossiliferous clay (*Argile plastique*), and the underlying Chalk; and at one locality a conglomerate showed that the Chalk must have been lithified before the clay was deposited, thus implying a long interval of time. The next formation, the *Calcaire grossier,* a series of limestones, was remarkable in that several subordinate beds could be distinguished over a very wide area, invariably in the same

order, by their distinctive assemblages of fossils: "This is a mark of recognition which up to the present time has not deceived us." Marine mollusks were the most abundant fossils (they were described and classified by Lamarck), but they were totally distinct from those of the Chalk. Slow deposition in a calm sea was inferred from the regular stratification and the excellent preservation of the fossils. These limestones passed laterally into an unfossiliferous *Calcaire silicieux.* Both these formations were succeeded by the *Formation gypseuse,* a series of marls and beds of gypsum; among the latter were those quarried for plaster at Montmartre, from which Cuvier was obtaining many of his most remarkable fossil vertebrates—mammals, birds, and reptiles that were unknown not merely in species but even in genus. Rare shells of freshwater genera, and a total absence of marine shells, confirmed the probable freshwater origin of the series; but the following *Sables et Grès marins,* with abundant marine fossils, indicated a return to marine conditions. Yet after an unfossiliferous sandstone (*Grès sans coquilliers*), a *Terrain d'eau douce* with freshwater shells demonstrated that the conditions had changed yet again. This was the highest, and therefore the youngest, of the regularly stratified deposits. But after all of these, and after the excavation of valleys, a superficial *Limon d'aterrissement* had been deposited; and in the valleys these deposits had yielded a fauna of extinct species of elephants, antelopes, and so forth. Although very modern in comparison with all the other deposits, this last formation clearly originated before historic times.

The significance of Brongniart's stratigraphy of the Paris "basin" was quickly recognized. The general nature of stratified sedimentary rocks and the importance of observing their order of superposition were commonplaces in geology before his time. The highest, and therefore most recent, stratified deposit that could be recognized over a wide area was the Chalk, however; only "superficial" deposits, assumed to be relatively recent in origin, were thought to overlie it. Brongniart's work proved that above the Chalk was a complex series of stratified rocks, many of them evidently formed by very slow deposition. By implication, therefore, the time that must have elapsed since the end of the Chalk period was greatly extended. This extension of geological time was the first important effect of the stratigraphy.

Second, the strata showed an alternation between marine and freshwater conditions, countering the earlier assumption that all stratified rocks had been deposited in a gradually shrinking ocean. So important was this conclusion that Brongniart devoted a separate memoir, "Sur les terrains qui paraissent avoir été formés sous l'eau douce" (1810), to arguing it in detail, demonstrating the close analogies between living freshwater mollusks and the corresponding fossils. In this memoir he also described similar freshwater deposits from far outside the Paris region, even into central France (Cantal), arguing that such extensive deposits were not improbable when compared with the Great Lakes of the present day.

This alternation of marine and freshwater conditions implied a broadly cyclic, or at least a repetitive, character for this part of geological time. With his usual caution, Brongniart refrained from speculating on the causes of these changes; but his stratigraphical conclusions were certainly influential in molding Cuvier's geological theory, as first set out in the *Discours préliminaire* to the *Recherches sur les ossemens fossiles* (1812). Here Cuvier used the rather sharp breaks between the successive marine and freshwater formations in support of his hypothesis of *sudden* changes of sea level as a cause of the extinction of terrestrial faunas; but the recurrence of broadly similar marine and freshwater shells in the successive formations proved that these sudden "revolutions" must have been local in their effects.

The third important feature of Brongniart's stratigraphy was his use of fossils for the detailed correlation of strata. Previously it had been normal practice to use the lithology, physical position, and fossil content of a formation, with varying relative emphases, as criteria for recognizing it in widely separated areas. But Brongniart's work demonstrated the value of precisely collected and identified fossils as criteria for tracing a detailed series of strata, which might differ little in either lithology or physical position, across an extensive area. It was the precision with which the method was applied that was original.

A similar detailed use of fossils had been made some years previously by William Smith, who worked on the Jurassic strata around Bath and subsequently over a wide area of England. Smith's work was known to English geologists, but its validity could not be assessed by the scientific community as a whole until, some years later than Brongniart, he eventually published his geological map (1815) and the illustrations of the characteristic fossils on which it was based (1816–1819). Although Smith's work had strict priority, Brongniart's independent discovery of the value of fossils as a tool for stratigraphy was the first to be published, and therefore had the greater influence on the direction of geological research. Brongniart's method was rapidly and successfully applied in other areas, not only to the recognition of similar strata younger than the Chalk but also to the analogous problems of the older strata.

Brongniart himself played an important part in this development. By 1822 he had traveled widely enough to be able to describe strata, equivalent to those of the Paris region, from many different parts of Europe: these descriptions were inserted in the *Description géologique des environs de Paris* (a new edition of the *Géographie minéralogique*). But this extension of Tertiary stratigraphy over a wider geographical area posed the fundamental problem of geological facies. Rocks of the same age could not be expected to have the same lithological characters if they were deposited under different conditions in different areas. Even within the Paris region Brongniart had recognized lateral changes in lithology; on a wider scale the changes became more general. It was this that led him to stress the primacy of fossil evidence over that of lithology as a criterion for age, wherever the two sources of evidence were found to conflict. Thus he recognized that the London Clay of southern England must be the approximate equivalent in age of the *Calcaire grossier* of Paris, although they were totally different in appearance: they occurred in equivalent positions in the succession and, more important, they had similar fossils.

Brongniart defended this methodology in a special memoir, "Sur les caractères zoologiques des formations" (1821), in which its validity was argued with reference to the strata equivalent to the Chalk. His most striking example was his discovery of fossils identical to those of the Chalk (more precisely, of the Greensand) in a hard black limestone outcropping more than 2,000 meters above sea level on a mountain in the Savoy Alps. This countered the earlier belief that strata formed at a single period should be relatively constant in both lithology and physical position; but Brongniart described a series of other occurrences of rocks with similar fossils, which bridged the vast difference between this black Alpine rock and the more usual appearance and position of the Chalk.

The *Mémoire sur les terrains de sédiment supérieurs* (1823) described a similar variety of occurrence, in rocks containing fossils identical to those of the Tertiary strata around Paris. Like the "Chalk" rocks, these varied greatly in lithology, some being associated with volcanic rocks; they might be flat-lying or highly folded; and they might outcrop at any altitude from sea level to the summits of the Alps. In spite of this variety, Brongniart maintained, it was far more satisfactory to accept them all as being of the same age than to assign the Alpine occurrences to a much earlier epoch simply on the grounds of their position. Although such differences of altitude seemed vast by human standards, he argued, they amounted to no more than a millimeter on a two-meter model globe, and should be kept in proportion. Nevertheless, although Brongniart himself drew no such conclusion, his demonstration of such spectacular elevation of relatively recent strata later acted as powerful evidence for a greatly expanded time scale for the earth's history in the hands of those who, like Charles Lyell, believed that the elevation had occurred slowly and gradually.

Brongniart's empirical demonstration of the primacy of fossils as criteria for correlation was justified by a theoretical argument that owed much to Cuvier's catastrophism. Brongniart stressed the relative uniformity of faunas in different areas at the present time, and argued that whereas a whole fauna might be suddenly and drastically extinguished, leaving few survivors, it would take a long time for a new fauna to replace it; each major period should therefore be characterized by a distinctive set of fossils, although a few might be common to more than one period. Brongniart recognized the possible effects of climatic differences on the faunas of a single period and the need to discount "derived" fossils, but he concluded that fossil evidence must be given greater weight than lithology or physical position in determining the relative age of a deposit: only *superposition évidente* could have priority over fossils.

In the oldest "Transition" (broadly, Lower Paleozoic) strata then known, great interest was aroused by the fossil trilobites, a class totally unknown in more recent strata, which nevertheless seemed remarkably "highly organized" for such an ancient period of earth history. In the *Histoire naturelle des crustacés fossiles* (1822) Brongniart published the first full-length study of the trilobites (in the same volume, A.-G. Desmarest made a similar study of the fossil remains of true crustaceans). He classified a wide variety of species from many parts of Europe and even from America, and attempted to group them according to their relative age. For the latter objective he had insufficient evidence from superposition and was misled, for example, by the undisturbed and "young-looking" strata in Scandinavia; but his systematic work on trilobites was an important contribution to the later unraveling of Paleozoic stratigraphy.

Among the distinctive rocks that were commonly thought to antedate even these earliest fossils were the coarse-grained crystalline rocks granite and gabbro (the evidence for an intrusive origin for granite was well-known but generally regarded as atypical; most lists of strata still showed granite as the earliest rock of all). It was therefore an important conclusion when Brongniart showed, in the "Gisement des ophiolites" (1821), that in the Apennines some gabbros and similar rocks actually overlay normal limestones and detrital rocks, and were not

the oldest rocks in the area. Brongniart had no fossil evidence of the age of the sediments but thought the limestones resembled those of the Jura (i.e., of Mesozoic age). This implied that at least one crystalline rock analogous to granite could have been formed much later than the earliest fossils. This conclusion served to emphasize still further the fallibility of distinctive rock types as criteria of particular periods of earth history.

Throughout his life Brongniart remained reluctant to speculate on the causes of the phenomena he described. This is best illustrated by his contribution to one of the most difficult geological puzzles of the period, the phenomena of erratic blocks and striated pavements. These features, which in the 1840s were recognized as the effects of slowly moving ice sheets, were in the 1820s generally attributed to some sudden "diluvial" action in the geologically recent past. In his paper "Blocs des roches des terrains de transport" (1828), Brongniart gave careful descriptions of erratic blocks and striated pavements, and also the first detailed account (with a map) of the sinuous ridges or eskers that cross the low-lying glaciated areas of Sweden. He pointed out that all these features indicated some extremely powerful transporting process acting from the north and able to move large blocks of rock even across the Baltic; but he offered this as a simple conclusion from his observations and refused to speculate further on the nature of the remarkable force involved.

Brongniart's last major geological work, the *Tableau des terrains qui composent l'écorce du globe* (1829), was the culmination of his life's work on the ordered classification and interpretation of rocks. It had a disappointing reception, however, and exerted little influence on the further development of geology. Yet in some ways it was an attempt to tackle problems that are still important in modern geology. Having recognized that the rocks formed at one period might be widely different in appearance, he was concerned to establish a system of nomenclature for the periods of earth history, which would not involve misleading references to particular rock types: in other words, he was trying to distinguish time units from rock units. But this led him to propose a cumbersome and largely novel nomenclature that was difficult to remember and therefore failed to win general acceptance. Moreover, although he expressed the intention of avoiding theorizing about causes, he implicitly accepted the theories of others. Thus, his first and main division of time was between a *période jovienne* (Recent) and a *période saturnienne* (all earlier time); the sedimentary rocks of the latter were divided into *Terrains clysmiens* ("diluvial" or glacial deposits) and *Terrains izemiens* (all other sediments). This implied a distinction between past and present and a unique role for the most recent "revolution" (the glacial period), which were far more questionable than he seemed to realize. On the other hand, he made a clear distinction between the *Terrains stratifiés ou Neptuniens*, which invariably occurred in the same order, and the *Terrains massifs ou Typhoniens* (broadly, igneous rocks), which might be intercalated at any point in the series. He also emphasized that the stratigraphical succession would have to be pieced together from many sections in different areas, correlated as well as possible with each other; and he urged the desirability of fixing type sections for the definition of stratal terms ("une suite de terrains admis comme type ou module"). In such ways he recognized the problems of stratigraphical geology more perceptively than most of his contemporaries. Although his classification had little effect on their thinking, he provided valuable lists of characteristic fossils for each *terrain* from the most recent back to the *Terrains hemilysiens* (pre-Carboniferous); and these were widely used in the rapidly developing stratigraphical research of the following decade.

In retrospect, Brongniart's influence on nineteenth-century geology might have been greater if he had been less cautious about theorizing. In spite of that limitation, however, the influence of his early work on the Paris region, and its later extension to the whole of western Europe, is difficult to overestimate. For this careful stratigraphical work provided the principal model on which much of the exceptionally productive geological research of the period 1810–1840 was based; and thus it lay at the root of the greatest achievement of early nineteenth-century geology, the elucidation of the main outlines of the history of the earth and of life on earth.

BIBLIOGRAPHY

Brongniart's principal writings are "Essai d'une classification naturelle des reptiles," in *Bulletin de la Société Philomathique*, **2** (1800), 81–82, 89–91, and *Mémoires de l'Institut de France*, **1** (1806), 587–637; *Traité élémentaire de minéralogie*, 2 vols. (Paris, 1807); "Essai sur la géographie minéralogique des environs de Paris," written with Georges Cuvier, in *Journal des mines*, **23**, no. 138 (June 1808), 421–458; *Annales du Muséum d'Histoire Naturelle*, **11** (1808), 293–326; *Mémoires de l'Institut Impérial de France*, année 1810 (1811), 1–274, also issued separately (Paris, 1811); and in Cuvier's *Recherches sur les ossemens fossiles*, I (Paris, 1812); "Sur les terrains qui paraissent avoir été formés sous l'eau douce," in *Annales du Muséum d'Histoire Naturelle*, **15** (1810), 357–405; "Eau (minéralogie et géognosie)," in *Dictionnaire des sciences naturelles*, **14** (1819), 1–62; "Sur le gisement des ophiolites (roches à base de serpentine), des euphotides, etc., dans quelques parties des Apennins," in *Annales des mines*, **6** (1821), 177–238; "Sur les caractères zoologiques des formations, avec application de ces caractères à la détermination de quelques terrains de craie," *ibid.*, 537–572; *Description géologique des environs de Paris*, written with Georges Cuvier, new ed. with additions by Brongniart (Paris, 1822); *Histoire naturelle des crustacés fossiles, sous les rapports zoologiques et géologiques*, written with A.-G. Desmarest (Paris, 1822); *Mémoire sur les terrains de sédiment supérieurs calcaro-trappéens du Vicentin, et sur quelques terrains d'Italie, de France, d'Allemagne, etc., qui peuvent se rapporter à la même époque* (Paris, 1823); *Classification et caractères minéralogiques des roches homogènes et hétérogènes* (Paris, 1827); "Notice sur les blocs des roches des terrains de transport en Suède," in *Annales des sciences naturelles*, **14** (1828), 5–22; *Tableau des terrains qui composent l'écorce du globe, ou Essai sur la structure de la partie connue de la terre* (Paris, 1829), also published as "Théorie de la structure de l'écorce du globe," in *Dictionnaire des sciences naturelles*, **54** (1829), 1–256; and *Des volcans et des terrains volcaniques* (Paris, 1829), also published as "Volcans," in *Dictionnaire des sciences naturelles*, **54** (1829), 334–446.

The most important biography is Louis de Launay, *Une grande famille de savants. Les Brongniart* (Paris, 1940). This is chiefly devoted to Alexandre Brongniart, and makes use of MS sources. It includes an extensive, though incomplete, list of Brongniart's published works.

M. J. S. RUDWICK

BRONN, HEINRICH GEORG (*b.* Ziegelhausen bei Heidelberg, Germany, 3 March 1800; *d.* Heidelberg, Germany, 5 July 1862), *paleontology, zoology*.

Fundamental systematic works in paleontology are Bronn's most enduring contribution to science. He was educated in public administration and natural science in Heidelberg, after which he traveled through northern Italy and southern France, making paleontological investigations. In 1833 he became professor of natural science at Heidelberg. For a short time Louis Agassiz studied with Bronn, and decades later returned to purchase Bronn's collection of fossils for the newly established Museum of Comparative Zoology at Harvard.

In 1831 Bronn's *Italiens Tertiär-Gebilde* distinguished different series of Tertiary strata on the principle that in successively more recent strata the number of extinct species diminishes while the number of modern species increases. His divisions correspond closely to those established as Eocene, Miocene, Older Pliocene, and Newer Pliocene in Lyell's *Principles of Geology* (1833). Bronn's extensive *Lethaea geognostica*, which sought to establish a chronological sequence of fossil organisms, summarized all that was then known in stratigraphy and paleontology. His later *Index palaeontologicus* and the *Lethaea geognostica* were for decades the chief reference works in paleontology. At his death Bronn left unfinished the enormous undertaking of systematizing the whole animal kingdom, recent as well as fossil forms, in *Die Klassen und Ordnungen des Thier-reichs*. From 1830 he edited the *Jahrbuch für Mineralogie, Geognosie, Geologie, und Petrefackten-kunde* with Karl von Leonhard, and later with Georg von Leonhard. Soon after Darwin's *Origin of Species* appeared in 1859, Bronn, at Darwin's suggestion, was responsible for having it translated into German.

Near the end of his life Bronn synthesized developmental laws of nature from his extensive and detailed paleontological studies. He rejected theories of development like those of Lamarck and Geoffroy St. Hilaire and the modification of one species into another. Instead, he explained progressive development, "the successive appearance of forms with more and more complicated organization," by a law of creation operating according to a definite plan. Species became extinct and were replaced by improved ones within the limits imposed by the external "conditions of existence." Bronn used this phrase, borrowed from Cuvier, to indicate adaptation to environment rather than functional harmony, as Cuvier had. The conditions of existence, which exerted a negative, restricting effect on organic development, varied as the earth's crust evolved. During the formation of the crust the primitive ocean was first modified by the appearance of islands and mountain chains, which then grew into continents, thereby dividing the earth's surface into separate oceans, inland seas, lakes, coastal plains, and mountain ranges. The organic kingdoms adhered to a law of *terripetal evolution* analogous to the development of the crust. At first entirely pelagic, they evolved littoral, then coastal, and finally continental forms.

Bronn emphasized that these changes, both organic and inorganic, had been gradual and continuous. Like many of his contemporaries, he criticized the new glacial theory of Louis Agassiz because it appeared to introduce a catastrophe into the history of the world. Bronn argued that the gaps then acknowledged in the paleontological and stratigraphic succession were illusory and would be bridged by the future discovery of transitional species and intermediate formations. (Compare Darwin's similar essay, "On the Imperfection of the Geological Record," *Origin of Species,* ch. 9.)

Bronn's contributions, both theoretical and systematic, were recognized by his contemporaries. In 1857 his "Laws of Evolution of the Organic World" won the prize of the Academy of Sciences of Paris. For the *Handbuch einer Geschichte der Natur* he was awarded a prize medal by the Scientific Society of Haarlem, and in 1861 he received the Wollaston Prize of the Geological Society of London.

BIBLIOGRAPHY

Bronn's main theoretical contributions are found in his *Untersuchungen über die Entwicklungsgeschichte der organischen Welt während der Bildungszeit unserer Erdoberfläche* (Stuttgart, 1858), of which the last chapter, summarizing the whole work, is available in English in *The Annals and Magazine of Natural History*, 3rd ser., **4** (1859), 81–90, 175–184.

His more important classificatory and descriptive works are *Gaea Heidelbergensis, oder Mineralogische Beschreibung der Gegend von Heidelberg* (Heidelberg, 1830); *Italiens Tertiär-Gebilde und deren organischen Einschlüsse* (Heidelberg, 1831); *Lethaea geognostica, oder Abbildungen und Beschreibungen der für die Gebirgs-Formationen bezeichnendsten Versteinerungen*, 2 vols. (Stuttgart, 1835–1838 and several later editions); *Handbuch einer Geschichte der Natur,* 2 vols. (Stuttgart, 1841–1843), which includes as its third part *Index palaeontologicus,* a systematic reduction of all published lists of fossils; and *Die Klassen und Ordnungen des Thier-reichs, wissenschaftlich dargestellt in Wort und Bild* (begun in 1859 and continued after Bronn's death), paleontology and zoology combined in one system.

For a list of his memoirs, see the *Royal Society Catalogue of Scientific Papers*, I, VII.

For biographical information, see the obituary notice in the *Quarterly Journal of the Geological Society of London*, **19** (1863), xxxii–xxxiii.

BERT HANSEN

BRØNSTED, JOHANNES NICOLAUS (*b.* Varde, Denmark, 22 February 1879; *d.* Copenhagen, Denmark, 17 December 1947), *chemistry.*

Brønsted entered the Faculty of Chemical Engineering at the Technical University of Denmark in 1897. Two years later he received his degree, then left the Technical University and entered the Faculty of Natural Sciences at the University of Copenhagen, from which he obtained the M.S. in chemistry in 1902. After a period of nonchemical research he was appointed assistant at the university's chemical laboratory in 1905, and from then on he was attached to the university, serving as professor of physical chemistry from 1908.

Since the conclusion of Julius Thomsen's studies on thermochemistry in 1886, physical chemistry had been somewhat neglected in Denmark, although the work of Ostwald, Arrhenius, and Nernst was followed up in most other countries. Brønsted took over Thomsen's idea of determining chemical affinity by measuring the maximum work of a chemical process, but instead of using calorimetric determinations, he used electromotive force measurements for galvanic cells, which give correct values at room temperature, whereas the calorimetric method gives values that are in error by an amount proportional to the entropy changes taking place for the process in the chemical reaction. He published the results in a series of thirteen monographs on chemical affinity (1906–1921). He defended the third paper of this series, on the affinity of mixing in binary systems, for the Ph.D. at the University of Copenhagen in 1908.

Other aspects of physical chemistry aroused Brønsted's interest after 1913: not only the determination of specific heats but also the determination of affinity constants, published in a series of studies on solubility (1921–1923) and on the specific interaction of ions (1921–1927). These studies evoked considerable interest among physical chemists, especially in the United States and in England, and from 1921 to about 1935 Brønsted's laboratory was crowded with foreign guests desiring to study under his guidance. The poor laboratory conditions were considerably improved when the International Education Board offered to defray the expenses connected with the building of a new Institute of Physical Chemistry, provided the Danish government would take over the operation of the institute, which began operation in 1930. Famous among these studies is a paper, written with V. K. la Mer, on the relation between activity coefficients and the ionic strength of the solution, a relation derived theoretically at the same time by P. Debye and E. Hückel.

Other achievements, too, deserve to be mentioned: Brønsted's definition of acids and bases (1923), simultaneously suggested in almost identical form by T. M. Lowry and in an extended version by G. N. Lewis; his studies on catalysis (1924–1933); and his work on the separation of isotopes of mercury and chlorine (1920–1922, 1929), done with G. von Hevesy.

In 1912 Brønsted published a short manual of physical chemistry, based on the thermodynamic cycle of Carnot. Before 1936, when a new edition had to be written, Brønsted had become convinced of the superiority of J. W. Gibbs's approach to thermodynamics, and the new, substantially enlarged edition was based on Gibbs's ideas.

Brønsted was unhappy with the classical formulation of the laws of thermodynamics, according to which heat is not directly comparable to other forms of energy. To him, heat, like other forms of energy,

can be considered as composed of a quantity factor (the entropy) and an intensity factor (the temperature). In this way it was possible to formulate the first law of thermodynamics as a work principle, whereas the second law was broadened to a heat-and-equivalence principle, including also irreversible reactions. A characteristic of this approach is that it relates thermodynamics to physical concepts rather than to mathematical complexities.

Brønsted's formulations, especially his use of the principles "work" and "heat," were not approved by the physicists, and angry discussions took place. He tried to concrete his principles in later works (1940, 1941, 1946), but no agreement had been reached by the time of his death.

BIBLIOGRAPHY

A list of 103 of Brønsted's 120 papers (i.e., those written up to 1935) is in Stig Veibel, *Kemien i Danmark,* II (Copenhagen, 1943), 80–88. Among his works are *Blandingsaffiniteten: binaere Systemer* (Copenhagen, 1908); *Grundrids af den fysiske kemi* (Copenhagen, 1912), new ed. entitled *Laerebog i fysisk kemi* (Copenhagen, 1936, 1943), also trans. into English by R. P. Bell (London, 1937); "Einige Bemerkungen über den Begriff der Säuren und Basen," in *Recueil des travaux chimiques des Pays-Bas et de la Belgique,* **42** (1923), 718–728; "The Activity Coefficients of Ions in Very Dilute Solutions," in *Journal of the American Chemical Society,* **46** (1924), 555–573, written with V. K. la Mer; "Die katalytische Zersetzung des Nitramids und ihre physikalisch-chemische Bedeutung," in *Zeitschrift für physikalische Chemie,* **108** (1924), 185–235, written with K. Pedersen; *Om syre- og basekatalyse* (Copenhagen, 1926); "The Fundamental Principles of Energetics," in *Philosophical Magazine,* 7th ser., **29** (1940), 449–470; "On the Concept of Heat," in *Kongelige Danske Videnskabernes Selskabs Skrifter,* **19,** no. 8 (1941), 79 ff.; and *Principer og problemer i energetiken* (Copenhagen, 1946), trans. by R. P. Bell as *Principles and Problems in Energetics* (New York, 1955), with an enthusiastic foreword by V. K. la Mer. There is an obituary with a complete bibliography by J. A. Christiansen in *Oversigt Danske Videnskabernes Selskabs 1948–1949,* pp. 57–79.

STIG VEIBEL

BROOKS, ALFRED HULSE (*b.* Ann Arbor, Michigan, 18 July 1871; *d.* Washington, D.C., 22 November 1924), *geology.*

Brooks was the dominant figure in the early geological exploration of Alaska and in the formulation of general concepts of the geological framework and natural resources of that then remote region; later he brought about the first applications of geology to military problems and thus became one of the founders of engineering geology.

Brooks was the only son and second of the four children of a self-made and distinguished mining engineer and geologist, Thomas Benton Brooks, who was well known for his studies of the iron and copper deposits of the Upper Peninsula of Michigan. Brooks received his elementary and secondary education in the Newburgh, New York, schools and from private tutors. He studied engineering in the Polytechnik Institut of Stuttgart (1889) and of Munich (1890), then entered Harvard in 1891. At Harvard he studied under Nathaniel Southgate Shaler and William Morris Davis, graduating with the B.S. in 1894.

His father's wide acquaintance among geologists had provided opportunities for Brooks's employment as a junior member of topographical mapping parties of the U. S. Geological Survey in Vermont (1888) and northern Michigan (1889), and in a geological party investigating potential iron ore lands in northern Michigan (1891). While recuperating from an illness in 1893, he undertook some independent geological studies of the Georgia coastal plain and in the region around Newburgh. He joined the Geological Survey as a geologist and petrographer in 1894, and spent the next several years studying various parts of the Appalachian Mountains. In August 1897, Brooks attended the VIIth International Geological Congress in St. Petersburg and then was in Paris until the following spring to study at the École des Mines of the Sorbonne, under Alfred Lacroix, F. A. Fouqué, Charles Bertrand, and Louis de Launay. His studies were terminated by a cable calling him to Washington, to participate in the geological exploration of Alaska.

This exploration had barely begun when Brooks first joined the Geological Survey. Although Alaska had been purchased in 1867, the federal government virtually ignored the new territory for several decades. Interest quickened, however, with the discovery of gold in Alaska and northwestern Canada in the 1880's; and beginning in 1890, several Survey geologists were attached to exploration parties under military, Coast and Geodetic Survey, or National Geographic Society sponsorship. Charles W. Hayes, one of these early geological explorers, was Brooks's first chief after his permanent appointment to the Survey. Working under him, Brooks became strongly attracted to the idea that he might assist in the sound scientific development of a new region.

The years 1898–1902 saw a series of long and difficult, but scientifically rewarding, treks through remote and largely unexplored parts of Alaska. During this period, Brooks undertook the exploration of hundreds of thousands of square miles. The geological exploration was conducted under the severest of difficulties; the geologist was required to divide his time between chopping trail for his pack train, assisting in the construction of rafts or boats when unfordable streams were encountered, and assisting in the preparation of a sketchy topographical map of the country through which he was passing—all the while attempting to gain some understanding of the significance of the rocks and topography.

Nevertheless, Brooks, during these years, discovered and named Rainy Pass, now an avenue of air transportation from Anchorage through the Alaska Range to northwestern Alaska; predicted and guided the discovery of the gold bonanzas of the ancient beaches buried beneath the coastal plain at Nome, discovered the tin placers of western Alaska, defined and described a scheme for the physiographical division of Alaska that has only recently been elaborated upon, and laid a general conceptual framework for future studies of the geological history and topographical development of Alaska that was beautifully expressed in his monograph "The Geography and Geology of Alaska" (1913).

In 1903 Brooks was placed in charge of the newly formed Alaska Branch of the United States Geological Survey. Annual trips to Alaska between 1903 and 1917 acquainted him with nearly every corner of the territory, and in the meantime his corps of dedicated but highly individualistic geologists completed much of the reconnaissance phase of the mapping of Alaska. His blending of scientific and practical interests resulted, during this period, in a series of major works on the coal and metal resources of Alaska and their possible development and use, and on possible railroad routes in Alaska. He was appointed vice-chairman of the Alaska Railroad Commission when it was formed by Congress in 1912, and he played a major role in bringing into existence Alaska's major artery of ground transportation, the Alaska Railroad, completed in 1923.

Shortly after World War I broke out, Brooks became impressed with the contributions that geologists might make to the planning of fortifications, to the evaluation of terrain on which fighting might occur, and to the location of adequate water and fuel for military bases and transport systems. His interest led to the creation of the Geologic Section of the American Expeditionary Force, of which he assumed charge in France in 1918. After the Armistice, he was assigned to the American Commission to Negotiate Peace, for which he prepared an analysis of the mineral industries of Lorraine, the Saar, Luxembourg, and Belgium.

Brooks resumed his post as chief Alaskan geologist of the U.S. Geological Survey in 1919, and retained that position until he died at his desk five years later. During those last years he was at work on a history of Alaska and a description of its resources and geological development, finally published as *Blazing Alaska's Trails* (1953).

Brooks was a small man, but vigorous and active throughout most of his life. A dark, closely trimmed full beard lent distinction to his rather serious features. In love with nature and the outdoors, he was a bit of a romantic, yet a man of unflinching intellectual honesty and almost excessive humility. He wrote with style and clarity, and devoted a good deal of his time to attempts to improve the prose produced by his Alaskan colleagues and subordinates. He led a quietly happy family life with his wife, the former Mabel Baker, whom he married in Washington, D.C., in 1903, and his two children, Mary and Benton.

Brooks served as president of the Geological Society of Washington in 1910–1911 and of the Washington Academy of Science in 1921. In 1913 he was awarded the Charles P. Daly Medal of the American Geographical Society and the Conrad Malte-Brun Medal of the Société de Géographie (Paris) for the excellence and importance of his work in the exploration and mapping of Alaska. In 1920 Colgate University conferred an honorary D. Sc. upon him. His name will always be associated with Alaska; after his death, the chain of rugged mountains that marks the continuation of the Rocky Mountains across northern Alaska was named the Brooks Range. In addition, the largest peak in the tin district of the western Seward Peninsula bears his name, as does a large river in southwestern Alaska.

BIBLIOGRAPHY

A complete list of Brooks's ninety-odd books, scientific papers, administrative reports, and popular articles is given in the lengthy memorial by Phillip S. Smith (see below). His most enduring work consists of the long series of monographic reports of his explorations in Alaska that appeared as parts of the Annual Reports, as Professional Papers, or as Bulletins of the U.S. Geological Survey; his monograph, *The Geography and Geology of Alaska: A Summary of Existing Knowledge,* U.S. Geological Survey Professional Paper 45 (Washington, D.C., 1906); and his book, *Blazing Alaska's Trails,* B. L. Fryxell, ed. (1953).

Other writings include short papers, written early in his career, on local geological problems in the Appalachians; notes calling attention to the occurrence of stream tin near the Bering Strait; notes on glacial phenomena; climber's notes on Mount McKinley and other peaks in the Alaska Range; summaries of gold, silver, copper, lead, zinc, tin, coal, and petroleum resources of Alaska; reports on transportation problems in Alaska; a lengthy series of reports on water supply, mining, and excavation problems in the areas of interest to the American Expeditionary Force during World War I; and several papers, written near the end of his life, on the future of Alaska and on the role there and elsewhere of applied geology.

Brooks's Alaskan field notes are in the Alaskan Geology Branch of the U.S. Geological Survey, Menlo Park, Calif.

A detailed account of Brooks's life is Phillip S. Smith, "Memorial to Alfred Hulse Brooks," in *Bulletin of the Geological Society of America,* **37** (1926), 15–48. Smith was Brooks's colleague and successor.

DAVID HOPKINS

BROOKS, WILLIAM KEITH (*b.* Cleveland, Ohio, 25 March 1848; *d.* Baltimore, Maryland, 12 November 1908), *zoology, embryology.*

William was the son of Oliver Allen Brooks, a Cleveland merchant, and Ellenora Bradbury Kingsley. Shy, retiring, and gentle, and afflicted by a congenital heart defect that became progressively more limiting in later life, Brooks inherited from his mother artistic skill, a studious, idealistic nature, and a dislike for the obvious and the trivial.

A graduate of Williams College in 1870, Brooks enrolled in the first Anderson School of Natural History on Penikese Island, Massachusetts, in the summer of 1873. There he met Louis Agassiz and at once developed the interest in marine organisms that was to determine the course of his career. He completed a thesis under Alexander Agassiz and, in June 1875, received the third Ph.D. conferred at Harvard. He was then appointed associate in biology at the new Johns Hopkins University to serve under H. Newell Martin, who was himself fresh from graduate study in physiology at Cambridge with T. H. Huxley and Michael Foster. Martin and Brooks developed a major new venture in graduate education (modeled on the German university) that led the way in the vigorous growth of American biology during the last quarter of the century. Much of Brooks's contribution to this venture and the bulk of his research were accomplished at the Chesapeake Zoological Laboratory, a movable marine station established each summer between 1878 and 1906 at various points along the Atlantic coast and in the West Indies. He spent his entire academic career at Johns Hopkins, rising in 1894 to the biology department chairmanship, a position he retained until his death.

Brooks was a descriptive evolutionary morphologist with a strong bias toward studies of whole organisms in their natural environment. A keen observer and an indefatigable amateur philosopher, he was among the late nineteenth-century morphologists who, accepting the transforming power of function in the tradition of Cuvier, added the new insights permitted by the Darwinian concept of the organism as a historical being. Organic form viewed both as a living record of its own ancestry and as dynamically adaptable to new circumstances of life lay at the center of Brooks's thought. For him, life was adjustment, or it was nothing; fitness, the adaptive response, was paramount: "The thing to be explained is not the structure of organisms, but the fitness of this structure for the needs of living things in the world in which they pass their lives." For him, nature was a language that a rational being may read. His reading led him to believe with Aristotle that the "essence of a living thing is not what it is made of or what it does, but why it does it"—in a word, its purpose. In thus withholding judgment on analytical, reductionist approaches, Brooks became unable to look beyond the confines of his own generation, and he did not participate in the transformation of morphology from a comparative to a causal science. Yet his more noteworthy students were somehow stimulated to share fully in that transformation; four of them—E. B. Wilson, T. H. Morgan, E. G. Conklin, and R. G. Harrison—laid the groundwork of much of modern cytology, embryology, and genetics.

In both their substance and their manner of presentation, Brooks's descriptions of the embryology, morphology, and life habits of marine invertebrates were memorable for their scope, their meticulousness, their wealth of illustration, their evolutionary insight, and their charming literary style. His studies of the pelagic tunicate *Salpa* are classic. He described the complex development of *Salpa* buds with unexcelled clarity and demonstrated their relation to the buds of the sessile tunicates. He discovered the remarkable fact that the *Salpa* embryo is first fashioned from follicle cells that are later replaced by regular blastomeres. Brooks's investigations of crustacea were equally fundamental. In several species he identified and collated the larval stages, a major morphological feat. He was the first to follow an entire crustacean life history from a single egg; this he did for *Lucifer,* remarkable among the arthropods in having an egg that cleaves totally. Brooks's descriptions of the life histories of several hydroid coelenterates still stand out for the perceptiveness with which their phylogenetic relationships were assessed. Yet he could also be wrong: his theory of heredity based on pangenesis had only the merit of stimulating others to explore more deeply. And he could be ineffective: an extensive analysis of the practical aspects of conserving the

Chesapeake Bay oyster won him only temporary notice despite the accuracy of his warnings.

In his own mind at least, Brooks's forte was his capacity to identify and reflect on the great issues of biology. His many papers and especially his major book, *The Foundations of Zoology,* are laden with rhetorical speculation which, as Brooks cautioned his readers, might at first seem obscure but "may, on review, be found consistent and intelligible."

BIBLIOGRAPHY

I. ORIGINAL WORKS. A complete list of Brooks's works is given in the biographical memoir by Conklin (see below). Collections of his scientific and popular articles are in the Eisenhower Library of the Johns Hopkins University and in the library of the Marine Biological Laboratory, Woods Hole, Massachusetts. His major publications were "The Genus *Salpa,*" in *Memoirs of the Biological Laboratory of the Johns Hopkins University,* **2** (1893), 1–303; and *The Foundations of Zoology* (New York, 1899).

Only fragments of Brooks's correspondence are known to exist; these are in the Brooks Papers and the D. C. Gilman Papers at Johns Hopkins, and in the Alexander Agassiz Papers at the Museum of Comparative Zoology, Harvard University. No systematic search through other possible locations has been made.

II. SECONDARY LITERATURE. There is no full biography of Brooks. Brief contemporary accounts of his life were prepared by two former students, E. A. Andrews and E. G. Conklin, the latter's essay being the more valuable. These and other helpful sources are E. A. Andrews, "William Keith Brooks, Zoologist," in D. S. Jordan, ed., *Leading American Men of Science* (New York, 1910), pp. 427–455; E. G. Conklin, "Biographical Memoir of William Keith Brooks, 1848–1908," in *Biographical Memoirs of the National Academy of Sciences,* **7** (1913), 23–88; D. M. McCullough, "William Keith Brooks and American Biology in Transition: A Re-evaluation of His Influence" (thesis, Harvard Univ., 1967); C. P. Swanson, "A History of Biology at the Johns Hopkins University," in *Bios,* **22** (1951), 223–262; and "William Keith Brooks. A Sketch of His Life by Some of His Former Pupils and Associates," in *Journal of Experimental Zoology,* **9** (1910), 1–52.

M. V. EDDS, JR.

BROOKS, WILLIAM ROBERT (*b.* Maidstone, England, 11 June 1844; *d.* Geneva, New York, 3 May 1921), *astronomy.*

Brooks was an enthusiastic and successful observer, whose efforts led to the discovery of twenty-seven comets. His family emigrated to Darien, New York, in 1857, and he spent the remainder of his life in western New York state. While still a child, Brooks developed an interest in observational astronomy and a talent for mechanical construction. In 1858 he built his first telescope, and with it observed Donati's comet. In his father's church, three years later, Brooks delivered the first of his many popular astronomical lectures.

In 1870 Brooks, now married to Mary E. Smith, settled in Phelps, New York, where he worked briefly as a commercial photographer. He increasingly devoted attention to construction and use of telescopes, making a two-inch refractor and reflectors of five and nine inches aperture. His garden, with this portable apparatus, became the Red House Observatory. Here, on 4 October 1881, Brooks discovered his first comet (comet 1881 F, Brooks-Denning), and during the subsequent seven years he found ten more. In 1888 he moved to Geneva, New York, to take charge of the newly established Smith Observatory. Even though this observatory, according to the wishes of its founder, was open for the entertainment and instruction of visitors every clear weekday evening, Brooks was able to discover sixteen more comets—most of them in the morning sky. In addition to his work at the observatory, Brooks was professor of astronomy at Hobart College from 1900, and at William Smith College from 1908 as well.

Brooks belonged to the Royal Astronomical Society, the Liverpool Astronomical Society, the American Association for the Advancement of Science, and the British Astronomical Association. For his cometary discoveries he was widely acclaimed by his contemporaries. He many times won the Warner Prize, and later the Donohoe Medal of the Astronomical Society of the Pacific, for discoveries of unexpected comets. He also won the Prix Lalande of the Académie des Sciences (1900); a gold medal at the Louisiana Purchase Exposition in St. Louis (1904); and a gold medal from the Astronomical Society of Mexico.

BIBLIOGRAPHY

I. ORIGINAL WORKS. Brooks's announcements of his discoveries and observations were published in astronomical journals (e.g., *Monthly Notices of the Royal Astronomical Society*), general scientific journals (e.g., *Scientific American*), and in local New York newspapers.

II. SECONDARY LITERATURE. See Brooks's obituary in *Monthly Notices of the Royal Astronomical Society,* **82** (1922), 246–247. Articles on him are in *The National Cyclopaedia of American Biography,* V (1894), 197–198; and in *Dictionary of American Biography,* III (1929), 91–92.

DEBORAH JEAN WARNER

BROOM, ROBERT (*b.* Paisley, Scotland, 30 November 1866; *d.* Pretoria, South Africa, 6 April 1951), *paleontology.*

Broom was the second son of John Broom, a designer of calicoes and Paisley shawls who, during Robert's youth, was engaged in business in Glasgow, and of Agnes Shearer Broom. As a child he was afflicted with asthma and other respiratory troubles that obliged him to spend a year at the seaside, where he was introduced to marine biology by a retired army officer, John Leavach. His father, an enthusiastic amateur botanist, encouraged the boy's interest in natural history, as did contact with well-known Glasgow naturalists who frequently visited at the Broom summer home near Linlithgow. Also from his father Robert acquired his facility at drawing and a liberal religious viewpoint. His mother belonged to the strict sect of the Plymouth Brethren; he retained strong religious beliefs throughout his life and sought to explain organic evolution as the result of some cosmic intelligence or plan.

Broom attended Hutcheson's Grammar School in Glasgow and in 1883 entered the University of Glasgow, where he assisted in the chemistry laboratory. He attended lectures of Sir William Thomson (later Lord Kelvin), but was most strongly influenced by the botanist F. O. Bower and the anatomist John Cleland, who introduced him to the work of Sir Richard Owen and the embryological researches of W. K. Parker. In 1889 he received his medical degree, and in 1892 he went to Australia. The following year he married Mary Baillie in Sydney, whence she had followed him from Scotland. After a brief visit with his father in Scotland in 1896, he went to South Africa early in 1897, and thereafter made it his home.

Broom practiced medicine most of his life, frequently in remote rural communities. From 1903 until 1910 he held the professorship of zoology and geology at Victoria College (now Stellenbosch University), and from 1934 until his death he served as curator of paleontology at the Transvaal Museum in Pretoria. Throughout his life, his research was interspersed with the duties of his profession. Fossil collecting was his hobby; he also collected paintings and stamps, and played chess.

His major contributions were to the study of the origin of mammals and the structure of their skulls, to the evolutionary history and classification of Permian and Triassic reptiles, and to the discovery and interpretation of the earliest human fossils. Broom also wrote extensively on the cause and mechanism of evolution and on a variety of other topics in zoology, anthropology, medicine, chemistry, and philately.

Broom was invited to deliver the Croonian lecture of the Royal Society of London in 1913; in 1920 he was elected to fellowship in the society. Numerous honorary doctorates, honorary fellowships in distinguished academies, and medals were awarded to him in his later years; these have been listed by Watson and by Cooke.

Between his medical calls in the back country of Australia, Broom began to investigate the anatomy of the native marsupials and primitive egg-laying monotremes. Scientific opinion at the time was divided over the question of the origin of mammals. Cope, Owen, and H. G. Seeley had pointed out many similarities between the structure of mammals and the fossil anomodont and theridont reptiles of South Africa.[1] Most zoologists preferred to derive mammals directly from the amphibians, as advocated by T. H. Huxley.

One of Broom's earliest investigations was of the development of Jacobson's organ, a sensory structure in the nose. In monotremes this organ is supported by a pair of small bones that Broom identified with the paired prevomers near the front of the palate of reptiles. In nine papers published between 1895 and 1935 he sought to demonstrate by both embryonic relationships and features of the palate of mammal-like reptiles that the reptilian and mammalian vomers were not homologous. He relied largely upon the similarity between the anomodont reptile *Dicynodon* and the platypus, despite his recognition that both of these were side branches from the main line of mammalian evolution.[2] Aside from the vomer question, Broom's interest in Jacobson's organ was renewed whenever young specimens of uncommon animals reached his hands, and he reported his findings in fifteen papers published between 1895 and 1939.

In the course of studying the embryonic development of the skull in the Australian phalanger *Trichosurus,*[3] Broom discovered that the mammalian alisphenoid bone does not form in the wall of the braincase but arises from the palate, like the slender epipterygoid bone of lizards and other reptiles (1907). Subsequently he was able to show this transition from reptilian to mammalian condition in the skulls of various mammal-like reptiles. In some ways this is the most important of Broom's many contributions to vertebrate morphology.

One of the major problems of mammalian development was the origin of the three auditory ossicles;[4] some students regarded them as the result of fragmentation of the single sound-transmitting bone in the ear of reptiles or amphibians; others followed Reichert (1838) and Huxley in the view that the outer two bones of the mammalian chain represent the articular and quadrate bones that form the jaw articulation of reptiles. Broom accepted the former view in 1890 and 1904, but in 1911 he reversed his opinion[5] and in 1912 showed how the bones of anomodont reptiles conformed to Reichert's theory. He presented a series of reconstructions suggesting the mode of transition from the reptilian to the mammalian ear condition.[6] In 1936 Broom turned again to this question, and noted that evidence of an extracolumellar portion of the stapes in therocephalians confirmed his earlier opinion that the tympanic membrane of mammal-like reptiles lay close behind the quadrate bone, rather than embedded in the notch of the angular.

Other morphological questions that engaged Broom's attention included the homologies of the variable number of bones at the base of the brain in mammals; the homologies of the coracoid bones of the shoulder region; the peculiarities of the epiphyses at the ends of the metacarpal and metatarsal bones; the arrangement of the reptilian tarsal bones; and the homologies of skull arches in lizards—a problem in which his conclusions based upon embryological and morphological studies were spectacularly confirmed in 1934 when Parrington described a Triassic ancestral lizard, *Prolacerta,* that shows an extremely early stage in the disappearance of the lower temporal arch.

But it is for the study of the fossil reptiles of the Karroo that Broom is most famous. In 1896, when he visited his father in Britain, he had an opportunity to examine Seeley's collection of African fossils at the British Museum. Grasping their significance for the problem of the origin of mammals, he sailed for South Africa.

The nineteenth-century work on the mammal-like reptiles by Owen and Seeley was largely descriptive. It had revealed considerable variety in the fauna and had shown that some of these fossils approached the structure of mammals more closely than did other known reptiles. Broom revealed the details of the skull structure of these animals by splitting specimens with a chisel or by sawing cross sections through them. He thus placed their classification on a firm morphological basis; showed that they had been derived from the pelycosaurs of North America, which his contemporaries had classified with the lizard-like *Sphenodon* of New Zealand; and demonstrated how the distinctive mammalian structures had arisen within the therapsid suborders. As early as 1902 he recognized that certain carnivorous therapsids had a far more primitive palate than the extremely mammal-like cynodonts that Seeley had discovered, and he proposed the suborder *Therocephalia* for the earlier forms. By 1905 he had arrived at the basic groupings of the African forms, which, modified in the light of later discoveries, are still used.

Beginning in 1905, Broom attempted to record the stratigraphic occurrence of various fossils in the thick sequence of Karroo deposits. Building on the earlier work of Seeley, he established the standard sequence of faunal zones. This attention to stratigraphy as well as to morphological detail prepared him for the brilliant synthesis of the African and North American Permian faunas at which he arrived after seeing the American fossils on a brief visit to the American Museum of Natural History in 1910.

Broom described an unbelievably large number of fossils. His brief descriptions are generally accompanied by rather unfinished sketches, which are praised by some of his colleagues for their remarkable fidelity and intuition, and condemned by others for showing structures still concealed by matrix and for carrying restoration beyond available evidence.[7]

These studies of Karroo fossils, as well as the embryological investigations of mammalian development, formed the basis for numerous essays on the origin of mammals, the earliest in 1908; the Croonian lecture to the Royal Society of London in 1913; and *The Origin of the Human Skeleton* and *The Mammal-like Reptiles of South Africa.*

Following World War I, Broom practiced medicine at Douglas, remote from fossil beds and contact with other scientists. It was during this period that his attention first turned to the problems of prehistoric man in Africa and the physical characteristics of African races.[8] His 1923 survey of the Hottentots, Bushmen, and extinct Korana race defined many of the problems of South African anthropology and laid the basis for subsequent work, which has not confirmed his views of racial relationships.[9]

When Raymond Dart announced the discovery of the *Australopithecus* skull at Taungs in 1925, Broom, on the basis of a personal examination of the specimen, supported Dart's conclusions as to its human relationships and phylogenetic importance. After he had been appointed curator of paleontology in the Transvaal Museum, he turned his attention to the Pleistocene cave deposits, hoping to find additional evidence of early man. This quest was rewarded by the discovery of *Plesianthropus* within a week of Broom's first visit to Sterkfontein. Other important specimens were found at Kromdraai in 1938, at Sterkfontein again in 1946–1947, and at Swartkrans in 1949. Broom has given a vivid account of the excitement of these discoveries in *Finding the Missing Link* (1950). He not only collected, but also prepared, illustrated, and described, this material when he was well over eighty years of age.[10]

Between the time Broom retired from medical practice in 1928 and his appointment at the Transvaal Museum in 1934, he wrote three books. *The Origin of the Human Skeleton* (1930) provides a rapid survey of vertebrate evolution, followed by discussion of the transition from reptiles to mammals, as shown by the mammal-like reptiles, and of the various problems that had held his attention for so many years. A final chapter deals with the inadequacies of the views of Lamarck and Darwin as explanations of evolution. *The Mammal-like Reptiles of South Africa and the Origin of Mammals* (1932) is illustrated with several hundred of Broom's rough restorations, which he defends as more useful than exact portrayal of fragmentary specimens. The problem of evolution and its causation is explored more boldly.

In *The Coming of Man. Was It Accident or Design?* (1933) Broom criticizes various theories of evolution in detail. He was fully conversant with the current ideas of geneticists on the roles of mutation and natural selection in producing evolution, but like most paleontologists of the early 1930's he found this view inadequate. Opposing Darwinism, Lamarckism, and evolution by mutation, Broom suggested there must have been intelligent spiritual agencies behind evolution. Arguing that all major evolutionary advances have come from small, generalized animals, and that all living animals are now too specialized to give rise to a completely new type of life, he concluded that further evolutionary advance is impossible. Evolution was over with the appearance of man, its latest and highest product, which must have been the goal of a directing Intelligence.

Educated at the height of the wave of evolutionary biology that followed Darwin's work, Broom devoted his career to unraveling the phylogenetic problems that the nineteenth-century morphologists and paleontologists had raised. His unrelenting drive to investigate these problems, his complete willingness to travel to regions where critical material might be found, and especially his unusual talent for combining paleontological and embryological research enabled him to contribute more to the story of mammalian origins than all his contemporaries together. When one considers his good fortune in obtaining fossil hominids at Sterkfontein within a week of his first inquiry there, as well as at other localities, is it any wonder that he strongly believed in his own Special Providence?

NOTES

1. E. D. Cope (1870v); R. Owen (1876, 1880); H. G. Seeley (1889–1895). These and other paleontological works cited below are listed in the bibliographies of vertebrate paleontology by Camp and by Romer, or in O. P. Hay, *Bibliography*

and Catalogue of the Fossil Vertebrates of North America, U.S. Geological Survey Bulletin 179 (Washington, D.C., 1902).

2. Broom's illustrations of the palate of Thrinaxodon ("The Vomer-Parasphenoid Question," Annals of the Transvaal Museum, 18 [1935], 23–31) clearly show the closer similarity of cynodont prevomers to the mammalian vomer, which F. R. Parrington emphasized in support of the opposite interpretation in the same year. In 1940 Parrington and Westoll virtually laid Broom's contention to rest.

3. This study was commenced in 1898 and published in 1909 ("Observations on the Development of the Marsupial Skull," Proceedings of the Linnean Society of New South Wales, 34, 192–219). It remains a principal source of knowledge of the development of diprotodont marsupials, according to G. R. DeBeer: The Development of the Vertebrate Skull (Oxford, 1939), p. 305.

4. The bones in question in mammals and their homologues are the malleus = articular bone of reptilian lower jaw; the incus = quadrate bone, which forms the articulation for the jaw at the back of the skull; and the stapes = part of the single auditory ossicle of reptiles, etc.

5. "On the Structure of the Skull in Cynodont Reptiles," Proceedings of the Zoological Society of London (1911), p. 917; full article on pp. 893–925.

6. Broom's study was published a year before the exhaustive analysis of embryological and morphological relationships of the auditory ossicles by Ernst Gaupp, "Die Reichertsche Theorie (Hammer-, Amboss- und Kieferfrage)," Archiv für Anatomie und Entwickelungsgeschichte; anatomische Abteilung des Archives für Anatomie und Physiologie . . ., Supplement-Band 1912.

7. Besides these studies of primitive reptiles, Broom wrote numerous articles on fossil fishes, amphibians, and dinosaurs of South Africa. While in Australia he had collected and described fossil marsupials from Pleistocene caves. In 1909 he first discussed African Pleistocene mammals, and after 1935 devoted much attention to these fossils (at least twenty-three papers). He demonstrated that the faunas associated with early fossil hominids were largely of extinct species and differed considerably from site to site.

8. This interest stemmed from the discovery of the Boskop skull by Fitzsimons in 1913.

9. L. H. Wells (1952) terms this "one of the most important landmarks in Anthropological research in South Africa."

10. Broom and Schepers (1946); Broom and Robinson (1952); and numerous short papers in various journals.

BIBLIOGRAPHY

I. Original Works. Lists of Broom's publications are given in R. Broom, "Bibliography of R. Broom, M.D., D.Sc., F.R.S.," in A. L. DuToit, ed., Robert Broom Commemorative Volume (Capetown, 1948), pp. 243–256; C. L. Camp et al., Bibliography of Fossil Vertebrates, Geological Society of America, Special Papers, no. 27 (1940), covering 1928–1933; no. 42 (1942), covering 1934–1938; Memoirs, no. 37 (1949), covering 1939–1943; no. 57 (1953), covering 1944–1948; and no. 84 (1961), covering 1949–1953; A. S. Romer et al., Bibliography of Fossil Vertebrates Exclusive of North America 1507–1927, Geological Society of America, Memoirs, no. 87 (1962), I; and D. M. S. Watson (see below).

Broom's major papers and books are "On the Origin of Mammals," in Philosophical Transactions of the Royal Society of London, 206B (1914), 1–48, the Croonian lecture of 1913; The Origin of the Human Skeleton; an Introduc-

tion to Human Osteology (London, 1930); The Mammal-like Reptiles of South Africa and the Origin of Mammals (London, 1932); The Coming of Man. Was It Accident or Design? (London, 1933); The South African Fossil Ape-Men. The Australopithecinae, Transvaal Museum Memoir no. 2 (Pretoria, 1946), written with G. W. H. Schepers; Finding the Missing Link (London, 1950); and Swartkrans Ape-Man, Paranthropus crassidens, Transvaal Museum Memoir no. 6 (Pretoria, 1952), written with J. T. Robinson.

II. Secondary Literature. Biographical sketches are Raymond A. Dart, "Robert Broom—His Life and Work," in South African Journal of Science, 48 (1951), 3–19; Austin Roberts, "Historical Account of Dr. Robert Broom and His Labours in the Interest of Science," in A. L. DuToit, ed., Robert Broom Commemorative Volume (Capetown, 1948), pp. 5–15, an account basic to most published obituaries— see also notes on Broom by Field Marshall J. C. Smuts, W. K. Gregory, and L. H. Wells in the same volume; and D. M. S. Watson, "Robert Broom," in Obituary Notices of Fellows of the Royal Society, VIII (1952), 37–70.

Twelve other obituaries are listed in Camp et al. (1961). Of these, Sonia Cole, in South African Archeological Bulletin, 6 (1951), 51, portrays his personality; H. B. S. Cooke, in South African Journal of Science, 47 (1951), 277–278, and R. F. Ewer, in Natal University Journal of Science, 8 (1952), 27–29, give additional insight into his methods, attitudes toward scientific research, and religious beliefs; W. E. Le Gros Clark, in Nature, 167 (1951), 752, provides an excellent, concise evaluation and tribute; and L. H. Wells, in Royal Society of Edinburgh Yearbook, 1950–1951 (1952), pp. 9–12, evaluates his contributions to anthropology.

Joseph T. Gregory

BROSCIUS, JOANNES. See Brożek, Jan.

BROUNCKER, WILLIAM (b. 1620; d. Westminster, London, England, 5 April 1684), mathematics.

Brouncker's father was Sir William Brouncker, who was created viscount of Castle Lyons, Ireland, in September 1645; the father died the same November, and was succeeded by the son. The title passed to William's brother Henry in 1684, and since both were unmarried, became extinct when Henry died in 1687. William's mother was Winefrid, daughter of William Leigh of Newenham, Warwickshire.

Brouncker entered Oxford University at the age of sixteen and showed proficiency in mathematics, languages, and medicine. He received the degree of Doctor of Physick in 1647, and for the next few years devoted himself mainly to mathematics.

He held several offices of prominence: Member of Parliament for Westbury in 1660, president of Gresham College from 1664 to 1667, commissioner for the navy from 1664 to 1668, comptroller of the treasurer's accounts from 1668 to 1679, and master of St. Catherine's Hospital near the Tower from 1681 to 1684.

Brouncker was the king's nominee for president of the Royal Society, and he was appointed without opposition—at a time when there were many talented scientists. He was reappointed annually, and he guarded his position zealously, possibly holding on to it for too long. He resigned in 1677, in effect at the suggestion of an election, and was succeeded by Sir Joseph Williamson. He was an enthusiastic supporter of the society's bias toward experimentation and was very energetic in suggesting and assessing experimental work until Hooke took over that job. Sprat's history records two experiments performed by Brouncker, one on the increase of weight in metals due to burning and the other on the recoil of guns.

His major scientific work was undoubtedly in mathematics. Much of his work was done in correspondence with John Wallis and was published in the latter's books.

One of Wallis' major achievements was an expression for π in the form of an infinite product, recorded in his *Arithmetica infinitorum*. This book states that Brouncker was asked to give an alternative expression, which he did in terms of continued fractions, first used by Cataldi in 1613, as

$$\frac{4}{\pi} = 1 + \frac{1^2}{2+} \frac{3^2}{2+} \frac{5^2}{2+} \cdots,$$

from which he calculated π correct to ten decimal places.

In an exchange of letters between Fermat and Wallis, the French mathematician had proposed for general solution the Diophantine equation $ax^2 + 1 = y^2$. Brouncker was able to supply an answer equivalent to $x = 2r/r^2 - a, y = r^2 + a/r^2 - a$, where r is any integer, as well as another answer in terms of continued fractions.

A paper in the *Philosophical Transactions* (**3** [1668], 753–764) gives a solution by Brouncker of the quadrature of a rectangular hyperbola. He arrived at a result equivalent to

$$\int_0^1 \frac{dx}{1 + x} = \frac{1}{1 \cdot 2} + \frac{1}{3 \cdot 4} + \frac{1}{5 \cdot 6} + \cdots$$

or

$$1 - \frac{1}{2} + \frac{1}{3} - \frac{1}{4} + \cdots,$$

and found similar infinite series related to this problem. In order to calculate the sum, he discussed the convergence of the series and was able to compute it as 0.69314709, recognizing this number as proportional to log 2. By varying the problem slightly, he was able to show that 2.302585 was proportional to log 10.

Brouncker also improved Neile's method for rectifying the semicubical parabola $ay^2 = x^3$ and made at least three attempts to prove Huygen's assertion that the cycloidal pendulum was isochronous. A letter from Collins to James Gregory indicates that Brouncker knew how to "turn the square root into an infinite series," possibly an allusion to the binomial series.

Brouncker was a close associate of Samuel Pepys, socially and professionally, and is mentioned many times in the *Diary*. Pepys valued his friendship highly, but sometimes doubted his professional ability. Brouncker shared with Pepys an interest in music, and his only published book is a translation (1653) of Descartes's *Musicae compendium* with notes as long as the work itself, including a mathematical attempt to divide the diapason into seventeen equal semitones.

His fame as a mathematician rests largely on an ability to solve problems set by others. If he had devoted himself more fully to his own studies, he would undoubtedly have been one of the best mathematicians during a period in which talent abounded.

A portrait by Sir Peter Lely is in the possession of the Royal Society.

BIBLIOGRAPHY

Works concerning Brouncker or his work are E. S. de Beer, ed., *The Diary of John Evelyn,* III (Oxford, 1955), 285–286, 332, 353; T. Birch, *History of the Royal Society,* Vol. I (London, 1756–1757); Lord Braybrooke, ed., *Diary and Correspondence of Samuel Pepys* (London, 1865); Sir B. Burke, *Extinct Peerages* (London, 1883), p. 78; M. H. Nicolson, *Pepys' Diary and the New Science* (Charlottesville, Va., 1965), pp. 11, 28–29, 109, 135; H. W. Robinson and W. Adams, *The Diary of Robert Hooke* (London, 1935); J. F. Scott and Sir Harold Hartley, "William Viscount Brouncker," in *Notes and Records of the Royal Society,* **15** (1960–1961), 147–156; T. Sprat, *History of the Royal Society* (London, 1667), pp. 57, 136, 228–229; J. Wallis, *Arithmetica infinitorum* (Oxford, 1656), p. 181; *Tractatus duo* (Oxford, 1659), p. 92; *A Treatise of Algebra* (Oxford, 1685), p. 363; D. T. Whiteside, "Brouncker's Mathematical Papers," in *Notes and Records of the Royal Society,* **15** (1960–1961), 157; A. à Wood, *Athenae oxonienses,* P. Bliss, ed. (London, 1820), p. 98.

JOHN DUBBEY

BROUSSAIS, FRANÇOIS JOSEPH VICTOR (*b.* near St. Malo, France, 17 December 1772; *d.* Paris, France, 18 November 1838), *medicine.*

Broussais began his medical studies at the Hôtel Dieu of St.-Malo and later attended the École de

Chirurgie Navale at Brest. After twice shipping out as a naval surgeon, he had earned the amount of money needed to finish his medical studies in Paris, where he received his doctor's degree in 1802. He then entered the Service de Santé Militaire, where he showed himself to be a conscientious doctor, continuously observing, writing, and teaching. His *Traité des phlegmasies* was written in Spain, from which he returned in 1814 to become a professor at the Val de Grâce. Broussais gave a course in practical medicine that attracted large, enthusiastic classes. His success lasted until his physiological doctrine—based in large part on therapeutic bleeding—was rejected by his students. It was also proved wrong by the 1832 outbreak of cholera, which Broussais treated, with catastrophic results, as acute gastroenteritis.

In 1834 the last number of the *Annales de la médecine physiologique* (which he had founded in 1822) was published, and in a last effort to regain his popularity, Broussais exploited the phrenology that Gall had made fashionable some twenty years earlier. In 1836, however, he began a type of teaching that questioned the immortality of the soul and the existence of God; it led to such violent scenes that the police were called in to restore order, and Broussais decided to leave the Val de Grâce. He became ill soon thereafter and died two years later of cancer.

The 1830 revolution had been a great boon to Broussais. Through government influence he had been exempted from the usual requirements and had won a chair at the Faculty of Medicine, a seat in the Académie des Sciences Morales et Politiques, the rank of inspector general in the Service de Santé Militaire, and had been made a commander of the Legion of Honor.

Broussais lived at a time when a monistic system of pathology was still possible. His was a kind of "Brownism" in reverse, in which the phenomena of illness are different from those of health only in intensity. Laennec and Bretonneau opposed a doctrine inspired by old theories of deep pathological states that did not admit individual illnesses, and desperately fought the idea of specificity, localization, or contagion. Everything came under the heading of gastroenteritis, and consequently was treated by repeated bleedings and debilitating diets. These had disastrous effects on patients who were hemorrhaging or who suffered from cancer, malaria, or syphilis. Some have wished to see Broussais's ideas on the nonspecific states of inflammation as making him a precursor in this field.

Nevertheless, by rejecting Pinel's concept of essential fevers and by affirming that fevers are only reactions to certain given inflammations, Broussais eliminated the ontological notion of illness, which considered pathological and physiological phenomena to be entirely different and saw diseases as real entities, independent of the organism. But even if there had been an idea in his system, one would look in vain for a method.

BIBLIOGRAPHY

I. ORIGINAL WORKS. Broussais's writings include "Recherches sur la fièvre hectique considérée comme dépendante d'une lésion d'action des différents systèmes, sans vice organique" (Paris, 1804), his thesis; *Histoire des phlegmasies ou inflammations chroniques* (Paris, 1808, 1816, 1822, 1826, 1828, 1838), also translated into Spanish by Suárez Pantigo (Madrid, 1828) and English by Isaac Hays and R. Eglesfeld Griffith (Philadelphia, 1831); *Examen de la doctrine médicale généralement adoptée et des systèmes modernes de nosologie,* 4 vols. (Paris, 1816–1834), also translated into Spanish by G. Lanuza (Madrid, 1822) and German by Reulin (Bern, 1820); articles in *Annales de la médecine physiologique* (1822–1834); *Traité de physiologie appliqué à la pathologie* (Paris, 1822); *Catéchisme de la médecine physiologique* (Paris, 1824), also translated into Spanish and into English by I. Hays and R. E. Griffith (Philadelphia, 1832); *Commentaire des propositions de pathologie consignées dans l'examen des doctrines médicales* (Paris, 1824); *De l'irritation et de la folie* (Paris, 1828); *Du cholera-morbus epidémique observé et traité* (Paris, 1832); *Mémoire sur la physiologie de la médecine* (Paris, 1832); *Mémoire sur l'influence que les travaux des médecins physiologistes ont exercé sur l'état de la médecine en France* (Paris, 1832); *Cours de pathologie et de thérapeutiques générales,* 4 vols. (Paris, 1833–1835); *Mémoire sur l'association du physique et du moral* (Paris, 1834); and *Cours de phrénologie fait à la Faculté de médecine de Paris* (Paris, 1836). Forty-five pages of Broussais's autograph letters are at the Faculty of Medicine, Paris, MS 402.

II. SECONDARY LITERATURE. Writings on Broussais are E. Ackerknecht, "La médecine à Paris entre 1800 et 1850," in *Conférences du Palais de la Découverte* (Paris, 1958), pp. 9–13, 17–18, 20, and *Medicine at the Paris Hospitals, 1794–1848* (Baltimore, 1967), pp. 10, 26, 28, 58, 61–79, 96, 212; J.-Z. Amussat, "Relation de la dernière maladie de Broussais," in *Gazette médicale de Paris,* **4,** no. 49 (7 Dec. 1838), 769–774; L. Babonneix, "Le centenaire de la mort de Broussais," in *Gazette des hôpitaux,* **111** (24 Sept. 1938), 1221–1228; E. Beaugrand, "Broussais," in *Dictionnaire Dechambre,* XI (1878), 160–163; L. J. Begin, *Application de la doctrine physiologique à la chirurgie* (Paris, 1823), pp. viii, 17–18, 61, 87, 93, 96; Michel Bert, "Essai sur Broussais" (Paris, 1957), thesis; P. Busquet, "Broussais," in *Les biographies médicales,* I (Paris, 1927–1928), 53–65, 69–80, with an important bibliography; Georges Canguilhem, "Essai sur quelques problèmes concernant le normal et le pathologique" (Strasbourg, 1943), thesis; J. des Cilleuls, "À propos du centenaire de la mort de Broussais," in *Revue du Service de santé militaire,* **110,** no. 4 (1939), 645–655;

Cornilleau, "À propos de Broussais," in *Progrès médical* (26 Nov. 1938), 1604–1609, 1610; F. Dubois, "Éloge de Broussais," in *Mémoires de l'Académie de médecine de Paris,* **14** (1849), 1–28; L. Duplais, *Histoire complète de Broussais* (Paris, 1891); H. Folet, "Broussais et le broussaisisme," in *France médicale,* **54** (1907), 137–157, 217–237, also in *Bulletin de la Société française d'histoire de la médecine de Paris,* **52** (1806), 239–314; M. Foucault, *Naissance de la clinique* (Paris, 1966), 175, 179, 186–187, 189–191, 194–196; Pierre Huard, "Broussais et nous," in *Ouest médical,* no. 15 (1959), 463–466; Jeanne Huet, "Broussais et son oeuvre" (thesis, Paris, 1938); René Laennec, *Traité de l'auscultation médiate . . .* (Paris, 1826), pp. xx–xxxii; P.-C. Louis, *Recherches sur les effets de la saignée dans quelques maladies inflammatoires . . .* (Paris, 1835); J. L. H. P. Peisse, *Les médecins contemporains* (Paris, 1827), pp. 1–56; J. Rochard, *Histoire de la chirurgie française au XIXème siècle* (Paris, 1875), pp. 114–123, 251–252; and R. Villey, *Réflexions sur la médecine d'hier et de demain* (Paris, 1966), pp. 53, 55, 56.

PIERRE HUARD

BROUSSONET (or **Broussonnet** or **Broussounet**), **PIERRE - AUGUSTE - MARIE** (*b.* Montpellier, France, 19 January 1761; *d.* Montpellier, 27 July 1807), *zoology, botany.*

Broussonet's family belonged to the bourgeoisie. His father, François Broussounet (des Terrasses), was a physician who taught at Montpellier's school of medicine. Broussonet's brother Victor studied there and later became its dean. Henri Fouquet, a professor at the medical school, was a relative, as was Jean Chaptal, who subsequently became minister of the interior.

As a child, Broussonet was a passionate collector of natural history specimens, cluttering his father's house with his finds. He also excelled in classical studies in Montpellier, Montélimar, and Toulouse. He thus was headed toward medical studies, which were both a family tradition and, at that time, the only avenue leading to the study of the natural sciences. Antoine Gouan, a convinced Linnaean, taught at the medical school, and apparently it was from him that Broussonet learned of Linnaeus' work. From then on, he worked to have it accepted. His thesis on respiration, which he defended in 1778, marked the end of Broussonet's formal studies. He received the doctorate on 27 May 1779, at the age of eighteen.

Broussonet's thesis was unanimously praised and seemed to the professors of the University of Montpellier to justify exceptional treatment. They asked that he, despite his youth, be made his father's successor when the latter retired. The request was not granted, although Broussonet himself went to Paris to plead his cause. His failure was compensated for, however, by the friendships he established with the

Paris scholars who made it possible for him to continue and extend the studies on fish that he had begun at Montpellier as early as 1779. Although the Paris ichthyological collections surpassed those that Broussonet had worked with until then, they were not complete enough for the work on which he planned to spend the greater part of his time. Consequently, he went to England to seek the specimens needed for the morphological and systematic work he had in mind.

London, which he reached in 1780, offered Broussonet all he could wish for: an active scientific community; naturalists already won over to Linnaeus' ideas; collections rich in new species; and a friend, Sir Joseph Banks, whose devotion never lagged. In addition, he was elected to the Royal Society.

Banks had brought back from Cook's first expedition a considerable number of exotic fish, which he turned over to Broussonet for study, thereby making it possible for Broussonet to start his *Ichthyologia,* which was to contain descriptions of 1,200 species. The first ten sections, in which he noted the important discovery of the *pseudobranchia,* were published in 1782. They were the only ones.

When he returned to France, Broussonet finished his "Notes ichthyologiques," and in 1785 he presented six of them before the Académie des Sciences. Their merit and the support of Daubenton, who, although anti-Linnaean, was kindly disposed toward Broussonet, resulted in his election to the Academy. The following year he presented a memoir on the *voilier,* his last work in ichthyology.

The growing unrest among the common people led to Broussonet's decision to abandon ichthyology. Many thought that the improvement of agricultural production, both in quality and in quantity, might appease those seeking reforms. Berthier de Sauvigny, the administrator of Paris, for whose food supply he was responsible, was one who held that view. He had met Broussonet while in England to study methods of cultivation and animal husbandry and had renewed the acquaintance in France. Berthier, who had revived the Société d'Agriculture, persuaded Broussonet to become its secretary. In addition, Daubenton, who in 1783 had accepted the chair of rural economy at the Alfort Veterinary School, passed on this heavy responsibility to his young friend.

Broussonet, having become an agronomist, tried to fulfill the duties of his new offices. Between 1785 and 1788 he regularly published short notices, both signed and anonymous, for the use of farmers. Many of them have not been identified to this day. Unfortunately, this work came too late, and the Revolution put an end to Broussonet's agricultural efforts.

In 1789 Broussonet, then twenty-eight, enthusiastically welcomed revolutionary ideas, as was characteristic of his generation. He turned to politics, but soon realized its dangers. His friend Berthier, held responsible for the current famine, was killed before his eyes. Broussonet, knowing he was in danger, fled Paris. In 1792 he took refuge in Montpellier but was accused of federalism and thrown in jail. He remained there only a few days, but his liberty was still precarious after his release. He therefore left Montpellier for Bagnères-de-Bigorre to join his brother, then a doctor in the army of Pyrénées-Orientales. On 19 July 1794 he crossed the Spanish border.

Although Broussonet was penniless, he was warmly received by the botanists Ortega and Cavanilles in Madrid, Gordon in Jerez, and José Correa de Serra in Lisbon. Sir Joseph Banks continued to be interested in him and helped him financially. But he was not accepted by the French who had emigrated earlier and looked upon him as a revolutionary. Having become friends with Simpson, American consul in Gibraltar, Broussonet accompanied him as physician on a diplomatic mission to Morocco, where he studied the flora.

In 1795, when he voluntarily returned to France, Broussonet's name was removed from the list of political refugees, and he regained possession of his property. Elected to the Institut in 1796, he requested appointment as a *voyageur de l'Institut,* stating that he wished to return to Morocco to continue his research. In 1797, therefore, he was named vice-consul at Mogador, a post created for him. There he carried on his work of collecting and describing plants and animals, as well as attending to his consular duties.

In 1799 Mogador was threatened by the plague. On 8 July, Broussonet sailed with his family to the Canary Islands, where he was made commissioner of commercial relations. He continued his collecting and observations, writing of them to Cavanilles, Charles l'Heritier, and Humboldt. The local authorities forbade him to travel, however, and Broussonet decided to leave his post. He asked to be sent to the Cape of Good Hope, where he hoped to create a botanical garden.

Chaptal, then minister of the interior, supported his young relative's request, and Broussonet was therefore named commissioner of commercial relations to the Cape on 15 October 1802. He returned to France in 1803 to prepare for this new assignment, only to learn that Chaptal had changed his mind and had had him made professor at the medical school of Montpellier, to succeed Gouan. He had to accept.

Broussonet took up his new position at once. His title, besides its teaching duties, gave him charge of the botanical garden of Montpellier. He restored its former layout and, helped financially by Chaptal, built a greenhouse, dug ponds, and enlarged the collections, of which he published a list in 1805. This was the *Elenchus plantarum horti botanici Monspeliensis,* the first in a projected series of works that promised to be considerable. But it was also the last. Broussonet was preparing to describe the 1,500 species collected at Tenerife when he suffered a stroke that caused a gradually worsening aphasia. On 17 August 1806 he notified the director of the medical school that he must resign his post, and a year later, he suffered a final stroke that caused his death.

BIBLIOGRAPHY

I. Original Works. Among Broussonet's works are *Variae positiones circa respirationem* (Montpellier, 1778), his doctoral thesis; "Mémoire sur les différentes espèces de chiens de mer," in *Mémoires de l'Académie royale des sciences* (1780), 641–680; *Ichthyologia sistens piscium descriptiones et icones* (London–Paris–Vienna–Leipzig–Leiden, 1782); "Essai de comparaison entre les mouvements des animaux et ceux des plantes et description d'une espèce de sainfoin dont les feuilles sont dans un mouvement perpétuel," in *Mémoires de l'Académie royale des sciences* (1784), 609–621; "Mémoire sur le voilier, espèce de poisson peu connue qui se trouve dans les mers des Indes," *ibid.* (1786), 450–455; "Observations sur la régénération de quelques parties des corps des poissons," *ibid.* (1786), 684–688; and *Elenchus plantarum horti botanici Monspeliensis* (Montpellier, 1805).

II. Secondary Literature. Works on Broussonet are F. Aubouy, "Auguste Broussonet et la flore de Montpellier," in *Annales de la Société d'horticulture et d'histoire naturelle de l'Hérault,* 2nd ser., **29** (1897–1898), 139–161; J. Caillé, "Un vice-consul de France au Maroc: Auguste Broussonet," in *Revue de l'Institut Napoléon,* no. 89 (1963), 157–166, which cites his writings during his period of travel; A. P. de Candolle, *Éloge de Mr. Auguste Broussonet prononcé dans la séance publique de l'École de médecine le 4 janvier 1809* (Montpellier, 1809), which cites his agricultural and botanical works; J. Castelnau, *Mémoire historique et biographique sur l'ancienne Société royale des sciences et lettres de Montpellier* (Montpellier, 1838), which cites his botanical works; G. Cuvier, "Éloge historique de Pierre-Auguste-Marie Broussonet," in *Éloges historiques des membres de l'Académie royale des sciences,* I (Strasbourg–Paris, 1819), 311–342; H. Dehérain, *Dans l'Atlantique* (Paris, 1912), which cites works from his period of travel; Durand, "Vie de M. Broussonet," Bibliothèque du Muséum National d'Histoire Naturelle de Paris, MS 1991-pièce 242–8 ff., a sketch, several times reworked, of a biography that seems never to have been completed (extracts in Roumeguère, below); E. Fournier, "Broussonet (Pierre Marie Auguste)," in M. H. Baillon, *Dictionnaire de botanique,* I (Paris, 1876), 499–500; F. Granel, "Un grand naturaliste montpelliérain P. M. Auguste Broussonet (1761–1807)," in *Pages médico-historiques montpelliéraines* (Montpellier, 1964), pp. 119–130; and "Les étapes scientifiques d'Auguste Broussonet," in *Monspeliensis Hippocrates,* no. 37 (1967), 25–34; H. Harant and G. Vidal, "Á propos du nom de Broussonet," *ibid.,* no. 8 (1960), 23–26; C. Martins, *Le jardin des plantes de Montpellier. Essai historique et descriptif* (Montpellier, 1854), pp. 1–91; L. Passy, *Histoire de la Société nationale d'agriculture de France,* I (Paris, 1912); G. Roumeguère, "Correspondance de Broussonet avec Alex. de Humboldt au sujet de l'histoire naturelle des îles Canaries," in *Mémoires de la Société nationale des sciences naturelles de Cherbourg,* **18** (1874), 304–317, which cites works written during his period of travel; and A. Thiébaut de Berneaud, *Éloge de Broussonet, premier fondateur de la Société Linnéenne de Paris* (Paris, 1824).

JEAN MOTTE

BROUWER, DIRK (*b.* Rotterdam, Netherlands, 1 September 1902; *d.* New Haven, Connecticut, 3 January 1966), *astronomy.*

Brouwer worked mainly in celestial mechanics, making elegant theoretical contributions but also pioneering in the use of high-speed digital computers to solve its problems with previously unattainable accuracy.

The fourth of six children born to Martinus Brouwer, a government employee, and his wife Louisa van Wamelen, Brouwer studied under Willem de Sitter at the University of Leiden, where he received the Ph.D. in 1927. He then came to the United States on a year's fellowship and joined the faculty of Yale University in 1928 as an instructor. In 1941 he became both professor of astronomy and successor to Frank Schlesinger as director of the Yale Observatory, posts he held, together with the editorship of the *Astronomical Journal,* for the rest of his life. He was married in 1928 to Johanna de Graaf and became an American citizen in 1937.

At Yale, Brouwer first assisted Ernest William Brown in his search for differences between predicted and observed positions of the moon that would reveal changes in the earth's rotation. In 1930 he found that some of the differences were due to incorrectly located reference stars. To get better positions for these stars, Brouwer turned to asteroids (1935), later investigating the origins of these small bodies in a paper extending the membership in Hirayama's families (1951) and one on Kirkwood's gaps (1963).

After Brown's death in 1938, Brouwer took up more general orbital problems. Papers he published in 1938 and 1946 formed the basis for a direct determination of planetary positions by stepwise numerical integration, which was realized in *Coordinates of the Five*

Outer Planets, 1653–2060 (1951), written jointly with Wallace John Eckert and Gerald Maurice Clemence. This was the first astronomical problem to be solved through use of a high-speed computer. In an address delivered in 1955, when he was awarded the Gold Medal of the Royal Astronomical Society for his outstanding contributions to celestial mechanics, Brouwer outlined the way in which computer techniques were changing his field.

The advent of artificial earth satellites in 1957 provided an application for two theoretical papers Brouwer had written in 1946 and 1947, and led to two more (1959, 1961) of significant merit.

Brouwer was an active member of the International Astronomical Union and influential in its adoption of a new set of fundamental astronomical constants in 1964. It was he who suggested the name for Ephemeris Time (1950) and provided data on the way it diverged from Universal Time between 1820 and 1950 (1952). He was elected to the National Academy of Sciences in 1951, given an honorary D.Sc. by the University of La Plata in 1961, and awarded the Bruce Medal of the Astronomical Society of the Pacific in 1966.

BIBLIOGRAPHY

I. ORIGINAL WORKS. Brouwer's dissertation, "Diskussie van de Waarnemingen van Satellieten I, II en III van Jupiter," was presented to the University of Leiden in April 1927 and incorporated into the paper "Discussion of Observations of Jupiter's Satellites Made at Johannesburg in the Years 1908–1926," in *Annalen van de Sterrewacht te Leiden,* **16** (1928), 7–99, with erratum on 99. Other works, referred to in text, are "Discussion of the Annual Term in the Residuals in the Moon's Longitude," in *Astronomical Journal,* **40** (1930), 161–168; "On the Determination of Systematic Corrections to Star Positions from Observations of Minor Planets," *ibid.,* **44** (1935), 57–63; "The Use of Rectangular Coordinates in the Differential Correction of Orbits," *ibid.,* **46** (1938), 125–132, written with W. J. Eckert; "On the Accumulation of Errors in Numerical Integration," *ibid.,* 149–153; "Integration of the Equations of General Planetary Theory in Rectangular Coordinates," *ibid.,* **51** (1946), 37–43; "The Motion of a Particle of Negligible Mass Under the Gravitational Attraction of a Spheroid," *ibid.,* 223–231; "A Survey of the Dynamics of Close Binary Systems," *ibid.,* **52** (1947), 57–63; *Coordinates of the Five Outer Planets, 1653–2060,* Vol. XII of *Astronomical Papers Prepared for Use of the American Ephemeris and Nautical Almanac* (Washington, D.C., 1951), written with W. J. Eckert and G. M. Clemence; "Families of Minor Planets and Related Distributional Problems," in *Astronomical Journal,* **55** (1951), 162–163; "A Study of the Changes in the Rate of Rotation of the Earth," *ibid.,* **57** (1952), 125–146; "The Motions of the Outer Planets," in *Monthly*

Notices of the Royal Astronomical Society (London), **115** (1956), 221–235, the George Darwin lecture delivered by Brouwer on 6 April 1955, when he received the Gold Medal of the Royal Astronomical Society; "Solution of the Problem of the Artificial Satellite Without Drag," in *Astronomical Journal,* **64** (1959), 378–397, errata in **65** (1960), 108; "Theoretical Evaluation of Atmospheric Drag Effects in the Motion of an Artificial Satellite," *ibid.,* **66** (1961), 193–225, appendix on 264–265, both written with Gen-ichiro Hori; and "The Problem of the Kirkwood Gaps in the Asteroid Belt," *ibid.,* **68** (1963), 152–159.

Brouwer also wrote two textbooks: *Spherographical Navigation* (New York, 1944), written with Frederic W. Keator and Drury A. McMillen; and *Methods of Celestial Mechanics* (New York, 1961), written with Gerald M. Clemence.

A complete list of Brouwer's works, with 156 items, follows Clemence's biographical memoir (see below).

II. Secondary Literature. The adoption of Brouwer's suggestion that time based on the year rather than the day be called Ephemeris Time is recorded in "Colloque Internationale sur les Constantes Fondamentales de l'Astronomie, Procès-verbaux des séances," in *Bulletin astronomique,* 2nd ser., **15** (1949 for 1950), 283; the citation made by John Jackson in announcing the award of the Gold Medal of the Royal Astronomical Society to Brouwer was printed in *Monthly Notices of the Royal Astronomical Society,* **115** (1955), 199–202; Louis George Henyey's "Posthumous Award of the Bruce Gold Medal to Professor Dirk Brouwer" appeared in *Publications of the Astronomical Society of the Pacific,* **78** (1966), 194–197; John Michael Anthony Danby wrote an obituary notice in *Quarterly Journal of the Royal Astronomical Society* (London), **8** (1967), 84–88; and Gerald Maurice Clemence's memoir can be found in *Biographical Memoirs. National Academy of Sciences,* Washington, **40** (1969), with portrait and list of publications.

Sally H. Dieke

BROUWER, LUITZEN EGBERTUS JAN (*b.* Overschie, Netherlands, 27 February 1881; *d.* Blaricum, Netherlands, 2 December 1966), *mathematics.*

Brouwer first showed his unusual intellectual abilities by finishing high school in the North Holland town of Hoorn at the age of fourteen. In the next two years he mastered the Greek and Latin required for admission to the university, and passed the entrance examination at the municipal Gymnasium in Haarlem, where the family had moved in the meantime. In the same year, 1897, he entered the University of Amsterdam, where he studied mathematics until 1904. He quickly mastered the current mathematics, and, to the admiration of his professor, D. J. Korteweg, he obtained some results on continuous motions in four-dimensional space that were published in the reports of the Royal Academy of Science

in Amsterdam in 1904. Through his own reading, as well as through the stimulating lectures of Gerrit Mannoury, he became acquainted with topology and the foundations of mathematics. His great interest in philosophy, especially in mysticism, led him to develop a personal view of human activity and society that he expounded in *Leven, Kunst, en Mystiek* ("Life, Art, and Mysticism"; 1905), where he considers as one of the important moving principles in human activity the transition from goal to means, which after some repetitions may result in activities opposed to the original goal.

Brouwer reacted vigorously to the debate between Russell and Poincaré on the logical foundations of mathematics. These reactions were expressed in his doctoral thesis, *Over de Grondslagen der Wiskunde* ("On the Foundations of Mathematics"; 1907). In general he sided with Poincaré in his opposition to Russell's and Hilbert's ideas about the foundations of mathematics. He strongly disagreed with Poincaré, however, in his opinion on mathematical existence. To Brouwer, mathematical existence did not mean freedom from contradiction, as Poincaré maintained, but intuitive constructibility.

Brouwer conceived of mathematics as a free activity of the mind constructing mathematical objects, starting from self-evident primitive notions (primordial intuition). Formal logic had its *raison d'être* as a means of describing regularities in the systems thus constructed. It had no value whatsoever for the foundation of mathematics, and the postulation of absolute validity of logical principles was questionable. This held in particular for the principle of the excluded third, briefly expressed by $A \lor \neg A$—that is, A or not A—which he identified with Hilbert's statement of the solvability of every mathematical problem. The axiomatic foundation of mathematics, whether or not supplemented by a consistency proof as envisaged by Hilbert, was mercilessly rejected; and he argued that Hilbert would not be able to prove the consistency of arithmetic while keeping to his finitary program. But even if Hilbert succeeded, Brouwer continued, this would not ensure the existence (in Brouwer's sense) of a mathematical system described by the axioms.

In 1908 Brouwer returned to the question in *Over de Onbetrouwbaarheid der logische Principes* ("On the Untrustworthiness of the Logical Principles") and—probably under the influence of Mannoury's review of his thesis—rejected the principle of the excluded third, even for his constructive conception of mathematics (afterward called intuitionistic mathematics).

Brouwer's mathematical activity was influenced by Hilbert's address on mathematical problems at the

Second International Congress of Mathematicians in Paris (1900) and by Schoenflies' report on the development of set theory. From 1907 to 1912 Brouwer engaged in a great deal of research, much of it yielding fundamental results. In 1907 he attacked Hilbert's formidable fifth problem, to treat the theory of continuous groups independently of assumptions on differentiability, but with fragmentary results. Definitive results for compact groups were obtained much later by John von Neumann in 1934 and for locally compact groups in 1952 by A. M. Gleason and D. Montgomery and L. Zippin.

In connection with this problem—a natural consequence of Klein's Erlanger program—Brouwer discovered the plane translation theorem, which gives a homotopic characterization of the topological mappings of the Cartesian plane, and his first fixed point theorem, which states that any orientation preserving one-to-one continuous (topological) mapping of the two-dimensional sphere into itself leaves invariant at least one point (fixed point). He generalized this theorem to spheres of higher dimension. In particular, the theorem that any continuous mapping of the n-dimensional ball into itself has a fixed point, generalized by J. Schauder in 1930 to continuous operators on Banach spaces, has proved to be of great importance in numerical mathematics.

The existence of one-to-one correspondences between numerical spaces R_n for different n, shown by Cantor, together with Peano's subsequent example (1890) of a continuous mapping of the unit segment onto the square, had induced mathematicians to conjecture that topological mappings of numerical spaces R_n would preserve the number n (dimension). In 1910 Brouwer proved this conjecture for arbitrary n.

His method of simplicial approximation of continuous mappings (that is, approximation by piecewise linear mappings) and the notion of degree of a mapping, a number depending on the equivalence class of continuous deformations of a topological mapping (homotopy class), proved to be powerful enough to solve the most important invariance problems, such as that of the notion of n-dimensional domain (solved by Brouwer) and that of the invariance of Betti numbers (solved by J. W. Alexander).

Finally, mention may be made of his discovery of indecomposable continua in the plane (1910) as common boundary of denumerably many, simply connected domains; of his proof of the generalization to n-dimensional space of the Jordan curve theorem (1912); and of his definition of dimension of topological spaces (1913).

In 1912 Brouwer was appointed a professor of mathematics at the University of Amsterdam, and in

the same year he was elected a member of the Royal Netherlands Academy of Science. His inaugural address was not on topology, as one might have expected, but on intuitionism and formalism.

He again took up the question of the foundations of mathematics. There was no progress, however, in the reconstruction of mathematics according to intuitionistic principles, the stumbling block apparently being a satisfactory notion of the constructive continuum. The first appearance of such a notion was in his review (1914) of the Schoenflies-Hahn report on the development of set theory. In the following years he scrutinized the problem of a constructive foundation of set theory and came fully to realize the role of the principle of the excluded third. In 1918 he published a set theory independent of this logical principle; it was followed in 1919 by a constructive theory of measure and in 1923 by a theory of functions. The difficulty involved in a constructive theory of sets is that in contrast with axiomatic set theory, the notion of set cannot be taken as primitive, but must be explained. In Brouwer's theory this is accomplished by the introduction of the notion of free-choice sequence, that is, an infinitely proceeding sequence of choices from a set of objects (e.g., natural numbers) for which the set of all possible choices is specified by a law. Moreover, after every choice, restrictions may be added for future possible choices. The specifying law is called a spread, and the ever-unfinished free-choice sequences it allows are called its elements. The spread is called finitary if it allows only choices from a finite number of possibilities. In particular, the intuitionistic continuum can be looked upon as given by a finitary spread. By interpreting the statement "All elements of a spread have property p" to mean "I have a construction that enables me to decide, after a finite number of choices of the choice sequence α, that it has property p," and by reflection on the nature of such a construction, Brouwer derived his so-called fundamental theorem on finitary spreads (the fan theorem). This theorem asserts that if an integer-valued function, f, has been defined on a finitary spread, S, then a natural number, n, can be computed such that, for any two free-choice sequences, α and β, of S that coincide in their first n choices, we have $f(\alpha) = f(\beta)$.

This theorem, whose proof is still not quite accepted, enabled Brouwer to derive results that diverge strongly from what is known from ordinary mathematics, e.g., the indecomposability of the intuitionistic continuum and the uniform continuity of real functions defined on it.

From 1923 on, Brouwer repeatedly elucidated the role of the principle of the excluded third in mathematics and tried to convince mathematicians that it must be rejected as a valid means of proof. In this connection, that the principle is noncontradictory, that is, that $\neg\neg(A \vee \neg A)$ holds, is a serious disadvantage. Using the fan theorem, however, he succeeded in showing that what he called the general principle of the excluded third is contradictory, that is, there are properties for which it is contradictory that for all elements of a finitary spread, the property either holds or does not hold—briefly, $\neg(\forall\alpha)$ $(P\,(\alpha) \vee \neg P\,(\alpha))$ holds.

In the late 1920's the attention of logicians was drawn to Brouwer's logic, and its relation to classical logic was investigated. The breakdown of Hilbert's foundational program through the decisive work of Kurt Gödel and the rise of the theory of recursive functions has ultimately led to a revival of the study of intuitionistic foundations of mathematics, mainly through the pioneering work of S. C. Kleene after World War II. It centers on a formal description of intuitionistic analysis, a major problem in today's foundational research.

Although Brouwer did not succeed in converting mathematicians, his work received international recognition. He held honorary degrees from various universities, including Oslo (1929) and Cambridge (1955). He was elected to membership in many scientific societies, such as the German Academy of Science, Berlin (1919); the American Philosophical Society, Philadelphia (1943); and the Royal Society of London (1948).

BIBLIOGRAPHY

I. Original Works. "Over een splitsing van de continue beweging om een vast punt 0 van R_4 in twee continue bewegingen om 0 van R_3's," in *Verslagen. Koninklijke akademie van wetenschappen te Amsterdam,* **12** (1904), 819–839; *Leven, Kunst en Mystiek* (Delft, 1905); *Over de Grondslagen der Wiskunde* (Amsterdam, 1907); "Over de onbetrouwbaarheid der logische principes," in *Tijdschrift voor wijsbegeerte,* **2** (1908), 152–158; "Die Theorie der endlichen Kontinuierlichen Gruppen, unabhängig von den Axiomen von Lie (erste Mitteilung)," in *Mathematische Annalen,* **67** (1909), 246–267, and ". . . (zweite Mitteilung)," *ibid.,* **69** (1910), 181–203; "Zur Analysis Situs," *ibid.,* **68** (1910), 422–434; "Beweis des Jordanschen Kurvensatzes," *ibid.,* **69** (1910), 169–175; "Beweis des Jordanschen Satzes für den n-dimensionalen Raum," *ibid.,* **71** (1912), 314–319; "Über eineindeutige, stetige Transformationen von Flächen in sich," *ibid.,* **69** (1910), 176–180; "Beweis der Invarianz der Dimensionenzahl," *ibid.,* **70** (1911), 161–165; "Über Abbildung von Mannigfaltigkeiten," *ibid.,* **71** (1912), 97–115, 598; "Beweis der Invarianz des n-dimensionalen Gebietes," *ibid.,* **71** (1912), 305–313; "Zur Invarianz des n-dimensionalen Gebiets," *ibid.,* **72** (1912), 55–56; "Beweis des ebenen Translationssatzes," *ibid.,* **72** (1912), 37–54;

"Beweis der Invarianz der geschlossene Kurve," *ibid.,* **72** (1912), 422–425; "Über den natürlichen Dimensionsbegriff," in *Journal für die reine und angewandte Mathematik,* **142** (1913), 146–152; "Intuitionism and Formalism," in *Bulletin of the American Mathematical Society,* **20** (1913), 81–96; review of A. Schoenflies and H. Hahn, *Die Entwicklung der Mengenlehre und ihrer Anwendungen. Erste Hälfte. Allgemeine Theorie der unendlichen Mengen und Theorie der Punktmengen* (Leipzig–Berlin, 1913), in *Jahresbericht der Deutschen Mathematikervereinigung,* **23** (1914), 78–83; "Begründung der Mengenlehre unabhängig vom logischen Satz vom ausgeschlossenen Dritten. Erster Teil: Allgemeine Mengenlehre," in *Verhandelingen Koninklijke akademie van wetenschappen te Amsterdam,* **12,** no. 5 (1918), 1–43, and ". . . II. Theorie der Punktmengen," *ibid.,* **12,** no. 7 (1919), 1–33; "Begründung der Funktionenlehre unabhängig vom logischen Satz vom ausgeschlossenen Dritten. Erster Teil: Stetigkeit, Messbarkeit, Derivierbarkeit," *ibid.,* **13,** no. 2 (1923), 1–24; "Intuitionistische Einführung des Dimensionsbegriffes," in *Proceedings. Koninklijke akademie van wetenschappen te Amsterdam,* **29** (1926), 855–863; "Über Definitionsbereiche von Funktionen," in *Mathematische Annalen,* **97** (1927), 60–75; "Essentially Negative Properties," in *Proceedings. Koninklijke akademie van wetenschappen te Amsterdam,* **51** (1948), 963–964; "Consciousness, Philosophy and Mathematics," in *Proceedings of the Tenth International Congress of Philosophy,* I (Amsterdam, 1949), 1235–1249. For Brouwer's topological work, consult the book by Alexandroff and Hopf listed below. Extensive bibliographies of his foundational work may be found in the books by Heyting and Van Heijenoort (see below). A complete edition of Brouwer's work is planned by the Dutch Mathematical Society.

II. Secondary Literature. Brouwer or his work is discussed in P. Alexandroff and H. Hopf, *Topologie* (Berlin, 1935), *passim;* P. Benacerraf and H. Putnam, *Philosophy of Mathematics* (Englewood Cliffs, N.J., 1964), pp. 66–84; J. van Heijenoort, *From Frege to Gödel, a Source Book in Mathematical Logic, 1879–1931* (Cambridge, Mass., 1967), pp. 334–345, 446–463, 490–492; A. Heyting, *Intuitionism, An Introduction* (Amsterdam, 1965), *passim;* S. Lefschetz, *Introduction to Topology* (Princeton, N.J., 1949), pp. 1–26, 117–131; S. C. Kleene and R. E. Vesley, *The Foundations of Intuitionistic Mathematics* (Amsterdam, 1965); G. Kreisel, "Functions, Ordinals, Species," in *Logic, Methodology and Philosophy of Science,* III, ed. B. van Rootselaar and J. F. Staal (Amsterdam, 1968), pp. 145–159; J. Myhill, "Formal Systems of Intuitionistic Analysis I," *ibid.,* pp. 161–178; A. S. Troelstra, "The Theory of Choice Sequences," *ibid.,* pp. 201–223.

B. van Rootselaar

BROWN, ALEXANDER CRUM (*b.* Edinburgh, Scotland, 26 March 1838; *d.* Edinburgh, 28 October 1922), *chemistry, physiology.*

Crum Brown was the son of Rev. John Brown, a Secessionist minister, and Margaret Crum. His uncle, Walter Crum, was a chemist and fellow of the Royal

Society. He went to Mill Hill School, London, and then Edinburgh University, where he studied medicine. He graduated in 1858, and in 1861 he received the M.D. for a thesis on the theory of chemical combination. In 1862 Crum Brown was awarded a D.Sc. by London University. In the same year, he went to Germany, where he worked under Kolbe and carried out what was probably the first synthesis of adipic acid. Returning to Edinburgh in 1863, he was appointed lecturer in chemistry, and professor in 1869, a position he held until 1908. He became a fellow of the Royal Society in 1879, and from 1891 to 1893 was president of the Chemical Society.

In his thesis Crum Brown discussed chemical structure and the application of mathematics to chemistry, the subjects that interested him most. The first attempts had just been made to represent the structure of compounds by various types of graphical formulas. Crum Brown was dissatisfied with the unwieldy diagrams invented by Kekulé and proposed a more convenient scheme. He represented constituent atoms by circles drawn around the usual letter symbols, with a number of lines proceeding from them according to their valences. He indicated atomic linkage by lines, first dotted and later solid. In 1865 he invented the symbol, which is still in use, of two parallel lines for a double bond. Unknown to him, Archibald Couper, also in Edinburgh, had already employed a similar system of letters and lines. However, the graphical formulas used today most resemble those suggested by Crum Brown. The latter were popularized by Frankland, who adopted them throughout his lectures.

Also in structural chemistry, in 1892 Crum Brown put forward the rule determining the positions of groups entering the benzene ring in the substitution of monoderivatives.

He was convinced that chemistry would one day achieve the perfection of a mathematical science. This was a common feeling, earlier expressed by Davy and Herschel. Crum Brown was inspired by a belief in the unified plan of the Creation. This would be revealed in the ultimate reduction of all physical sciences to dynamics. Just as optics and heat, in their maturity, had become branches of applied mathematics, so he expected chemistry, undeveloped and fragmentary, eventually to be mathematically deducible from mechanics. In 1867 he showed how some steps might be taken in this direction. Regarding chemical substances as operands and the processes performed on them as operators, he derived mathematical expressions corresponding to successive chemical substitutions. Although it was similar in appearance to Brodie's more elaborate operational calculus, his work was distinct from this. He thought Brodie

had been "too severe" on chemists who had used atomic language, and insisted that it could be adopted without believing in atoms. He stated that while physics showed matter to be molecular, chemists could use atomic symbols without concern for their physical significance. Even if matter were proved to be continuous, his graphical formulas would still be useful. This common pragmatic attitude to the atomic theory was soon attacked by Williamson. Crum Brown's address to the British Association in 1874 was a more realistic approach. Neither he nor Brodie made any lasting contribution to mathematical chemistry.

In physiology Crum Brown was fascinated by the effects produced through rotation. He investigated the various sensations of vertigo in a subject rotating blindfolded on a table. He correctly related these to the motion of liquid in the semicircular canals of the inner ear. His work appeared soon after Mach and Breuer had given the same explanation, but his theory was an advance in that it detailed the coordinated action of the canals on both sides of the head, which Mach had rejected. Crum Brown stated for the first time that the two horizontal canals differed from one another in that they received their stimuli from motions in opposite directions, thus allowing a blindfolded subject to distinguish between rotations to the left and to the right. To illustrate his theory, he constructed a mechanical model. This consisted of two heavy wheels fixed horizontally and side by side so that they could rotate about a vertical axis in opposite directions. Each wheel had a stop that prevented its rotation beyond a certain point in one direction; its rotation in the opposite direction was restricted by the stretching of a spring. The axle of each wheel contained an adjustable stopcock, which widened as the springs stretched and through which gas was passed from pipes and ignited.

Crum Brown said that the wheels represented the horizontal canals of the ear and that the inertia of the former corresponded with the inertia of the fluid contained in the latter. The stretching of the springs represented the stretching of the ampullae. The variation in the flames that occurred as the springs stretched and relaxed during the rotation of the wheels illustrated the different brain messages transmitted by the nerves as their endings were stimulated by the stretching of the ampullae during the rotation of the body.

BIBLIOGRAPHY

Crum Brown's papers are listed in the *Royal Society Catalogue of Scientific Papers,* I (1867); V (1877); IX (1891); XIII (1914). His other publications are in the *British Mu-*

seum *General Catalogue of Printed Books,* XXVII (1965). Ernst Mach discussed Crum Brown's work on rotation in his *Grundlinien der Lehre von den Bewegungsempfindungen* (Leipzig, 1875), pp. 104–110. Some useful information can be found in the obituary notice "Alexander Crum Brown," in *Journal of the Chemical Society,* **123** (1923), 3422–3431. See also David F. Larder, "Alexander Crum Brown and his Doctoral Thesis of 1861," in *Ambix,* **14** (1967), 112–132.

D. C. GOODMAN

BROWN, ERNEST WILLIAM (*b.* Hull, England, 29 November 1866; *d.* New Haven, Connecticut, 22 July 1938), *celestial mechanics.*

Brown, who early excelled in mathematics, won a scholarship to Christ's College, Cambridge, in 1884, and maintained close ties with that school throughout his life: he received a B.A. as sixth wrangler (1887), M.A. (1891), and D.Sc. (1897); and was a fellow (1889–1895) and honorary fellow (1911–1938). In 1891 he moved to the United States to become instructor in, and later (1893) professor of, mathematics at Haverford College. Brown went to Yale University in 1907—largely because Yale agreed to support the computing and publishing of his lunar tables—and he remained there as professor, Sterling professor of mathematics (1921–1931), the first Josiah Willard Gibbs professor of mathematics (1931–1932), and professor emeritus. Among his many honors were those from the Royal Society of London (fellowship, 1897; Royal Medal, 1914) and from the National Academy of Sciences (membership, 1923; Watson Medal, 1937).

While still a student, Brown was encouraged by his professor, George Howard Darwin, to study George Hill's papers on lunar theory, and from that time on, he devoted himself to reconciling lunar theory and observations by finding "in the most accurate way and by the shortest path the complete effect of the law of gravitation applied to the moon" ("Cosmical Physics," p. 185). By 1908 Brown had worked out, and published in five papers, his theory of the motion of the moon. Following Hill's example, he attacked the moon's motion as an idealized problem of three bodies, assuming the sun, earth, and moon to be spherical and the center of the earth-moon system to move in an elliptical orbit about the sun; he then considered inequalities resulting from the actual figures of the earth and moon, and the direct and indirect gravitational attractions of the other planets.

Brown's main objective was a new, accurate calculation of each coefficient in longitude, latitude, and parallax as great as one-hundredth of a second of arc, and the result was not to be in error by more than that amount; in fact, he included many terms with coefficients one order of magnitude smaller. Among the few lunar motions he could not account for by gravitation was the relatively large fluctuation in mean longitude; after rejecting numerous other possibilities, he explained this apparent deviation by irregular variations in the earth's rate of rotation.

After developing his lunar theory Brown proceeded, with the assistance of Henry B. Hedrick, to use it to construct new tables of the moon's motion. The numerical values of the constants were obtained by comparing the theory with 150 years of Greenwich observations, as analyzed by Philip H. Cowell. The tables were designed for actual computation of the moon's position, and in 1923 they were adopted by most national ephemerides. Although Brown included nearly 1,500 terms—nearly five times as many as had Peter Andreas Hansen, the author of the previously used table—the format of his tables made them as convenient to use as were Hansen's. The remainder of his work concerned the interaction of other members of the solar system, such as the Trojan group of asteroids, and the negligible gravitational attraction of Pluto for Uranus and Neptune.

BIBLIOGRAPHY

A bibliography of Brown's writings is in Schlesinger and Brouwer (see below). Among his works are "Theory of the Motion of the Moon," in *Memoirs of the Royal Astronomical Society,* **53** (1896–1899), 39–116, 163–202; **54** (1899–1901), 1–63; **57** (1908), 51–145; and **59** (1910), 1–103; *Tables of the Motion of the Moon,* 3 vols. (New Haven, 1919); and "Cosmical Physics," in *Nature,* **94** (1914), 184–190.

A biographical source is Frank Schlesinger and Dirk Brouwer, "Biographical Memoir of Ernest William Brown," in *Biographical Memoirs of the National Academy of Sciences,* XXI (Washington, D.C., 1939), 243–273.

DEBORAH JEAN WARNER

BROWN, ROBERT (*b.* Montrose, Scotland, 21 December 1773; *d.* London, England, 10 June 1858), *botany.*

In the eighteenth century the honorific designation of *princeps botanicorum* was bestowed by contemporary scholars first, it would seem, upon William Sherard (1659–1728) and later upon Linnaeus. Early in the nineteenth century Alexander von Humboldt referred to Robert Brown as *botanicorum facile princeps,* a designation both apt and just, for he rose intellectually above both these predecessors; although his works, like theirs, deal primarily with taxonomy and hence nomenclature, they embody many profound observations on morphology, embryology, and

516

plant geography. Brown was the first to investigate the continuous erratic motion (now known as the "Brownian movement") of minute particles suspended in a fluid. He noted the streaming of protoplasm and recognized the nucleus as an essential part of the living cell. He demonstrated the lack of an ovary around the ovule in Coniferae and similar plants, thus detecting the fundamental distinction between gymnosperms and angiosperms. His extraordinarily minute and critical study of floral and seed structure in a great diversity of plants, during their development as well as in their mature state, greatly improved the classification of plants into families and genera. Through his emphasis on deep-seated characters, as Martius stated in 1859, he "detected similarity when concealed and he separated that which had merely the appearance of likeness; he sympathetically demonstrated the hidden relations between the most diversified forms." Brown's influence upon his contemporaries was far-reaching. Moreover, largely through his farsightedness, the department of botany at the British Museum, London, came into existence to provide a national botanical collection available to the public and to grow into an internationally important center of phytotaxonomic research. Thus the reputation that Brown acquired during his lifetime as one of the greatest of botanists has proved well founded.

Brown's father, the Rev. James Brown, was a Scottish Episcopalian clergyman of strong independent views; the son inherited and retained his intellectual honesty and sturdiness of character, but lost his uncompromising religious faith. After education at Marischal College, Aberdeen, and the University of Edinburgh, where he completed his medical studies, young Brown joined the Fifeshire Regiment of Fencibles in 1795 as an ensign, with the duties of surgeon's mate, and accompanied the regiment to Ireland. He was then twenty-one. How he spent his time there during the next five years is evident from such entries as the following in his diary for 13 January 1800:

> At breakfast read part of the rules concerning the genders of German nouns in Wendelborn's grammar. After breakfast transcribed into my botanical common place book part of my notes on Sloane's Herbarium of Jamaican Ferns. Attended the Hospital from one till three o'clock, saw about 30 outpatients. Dined with Mr. Thor of the Aberdeen Fencibles and remained with him till half past eleven o'clock. Drank about a pint of port in negus. Conversation various. . . . About twelve o'clock finished the transcription of my notes on Sir Hans Sloane's Ferns. This transcription has not afforded me one new idea on the subject of Filices.

And so these day-to-day records go on: "At breakfast read the rules on the nouns of the first declension in Wendelborn's German grammar"; "At breakfast endeavoured to commit to memory rules concerning the German numerals"; "After breakfast, the auxiliary German verb *Können* To be able."

German nouns, German adjectives, German verbs, the structure of mosses and ferns, the examination of blood under the microscope, medical textbooks— such were the matters to which young Brown industriously gave his time, for his official duties seem to have been light. In these diary entries Brown's later scientific development is implicit; here is expressed that wandering curiosity and that determination to master a subject detail by detail which led to his eminence. Science later gained a rich reward through his knowledge of German acquired during this period of rigorous self-education; in 1841, for example, he brought C. K. Sprengel's then little-appreciated *Das entdeckte Geheimniss der Natur im Bau und in der Befruchtung der Blumen* (1793) to the attention of Charles Darwin.

In October 1798, apparently while in London on a recruiting mission, Brown was introduced by José Correa da Serra, then in exile from Portugal, to Sir Joseph Banks, whose house at Soho Square, with its rich library and herbarium, was the botanical center not simply of London but of Britain. Significantly, Correa referred to Brown as "a Scotchman, fit to pursue an object with constance and cold mind." Thus Brown came to the notice of Banks, who had ever an eye for talent, and of Banks's erudite botanist-librarian Jonas Dryander; he obviously impressed them both by his zeal and ability.

Accordingly, when in December 1800 plans had matured at the Admiralty for a voyage, commanded by Matthew Flinders, to survey the southern and northern coasts of Australia—or New Holland, as the continent was then called—Banks, whose opinion carried much weight at the Admiralty, offered Brown a recommendation for the post of naturalist aboard Flinders' ship, the *Investigator,* at a salary of £420, then a very substantial sum. Brown immediately accepted this attractive offer. He came to London and, until the sailing of the *Investigator* on 18 July 1801, spent his time studying the specimens, illustrations, and literature about New Holland plants available at Banks's house. He and Flinders were both twenty-seven years old; the botanical draughtsman, Ferdinand Bauer, was forty-one.

The *Investigator* stopped at the Cape of Good Hope, a region rich in Proteaceae, to which Brown later gave much attention, then sailed for the southwestern corner of Western Australia. Landing there on 8 December 1801, at King George Sound, both Brown and Bauer were challenged by the astonishing floral richness of this region, its plants in their diversity and strangeness far exceeding anything previously seen. Three weeks there yielded some 500 species, almost all of them new to science. No adequate guides for their classification then existed. Brown's task was to study their structure intimately, to group them into genera and species, and to make detailed descriptions. From Lucky Bay, which yielded 100 more species, the *Investigator* sailed eastward along the southern coast of Australia, passed through the Bass Strait, and turned northward to Port Jackson, which it reached on 8 May 1802. Here they stayed for twelve weeks. The *Investigator* now sailed northward along the east coast to Cape York and into the Gulf of Carpentaria. Unfortunately the *Investigator* had been damp, leaky, and unsound from the start, and Flinders dared not continue his survey. He sailed to Timor for provisions, then returned to Port Jackson, arriving there on 8 June 1803. Fortunately, Brown and Bauer stayed behind when Flinders set out in another ship on his unlucky return voyage to England, which he did not reach until 1810. Brown spent ten months in Tasmania; Bauer went to Norfolk Island. They reached England aboard the repaired *Investigator* in October 1805, bringing with them specimens of nearly 4,000 species of plants as well as numerous drawings and zoological specimens. Thereupon Banks recommended to the Admiralty that Brown prepare for publication "a succinct account" of his plants and that he receive a government salary while so doing, at the same time selecting representative specimens for the public collection (i.e., the British Museum). This task kept Brown busy during the next five years. By 6 January 1810 he had described nearly 2,200 species, over 1,700 of which were new (including 140 new genera), and had selected about 2,800 specimens.

Concurrently with this botanical activity Brown served the Linnean Society of London as "Clerk, Librarian and Housekeeper" from 1806 to 1822. In 1810 Jonas Dryander died, and Banks appointed Brown to succeed him as librarian and curator at Soho Square. He held these posts until Banks's death on 19 June 1820, when he became his own master, for Banks had bequeathed to "my infatigable and intelligent librarian Robert Brown" an annuity of £200 and the life tenancy of his Soho Square house, with the use and enjoyment of its library and collections; on Brown's death these were to pass to the trustees of the British Museum. Brown did not wait that long for their transfer into national keeping. In 1827 he bargained with the trustees for their im-

mediate transfer, stating that if the trustees agreed to form an independent botanical department in the British Museum, he would be willing to take charge of it, his own status to be that of an underlibrarian (the title then of the head or keeper of each separate museum department). The trustees accepted this reasonable stipulation, and Brown spent the winter of 1827/1828 moving the Banksian collections from Soho Square to Montague House, the old British Museum, Bloomsbury. Thereby Brown secured, for the first time in Britain, a nationally owned botanical collection available to the public; he remained in charge from 1827 to 1858. As his assistant he had John Joseph Bennett (1801–1876), who had trained as an apothecary and surgeon. Upon this pair fell the whole business of the department; as W. Carruthers said in 1876, "It is hard to realize that this time [1827/1828] and for eight more years all the work of the department, even the merest manual drudgery, had to be performed by Mr. Bennett or Mr. Brown."

The period from 1806 to 1820 (i.e., from the return of the *Investigator* to the death of Banks) was that of Brown's greatest creative endeavor; it was the period during which he worked under Banks's fatherly eye. After 1828 he published comparatively little. His earlier work relates to the flora of Australia but leads to other matters, linked more by Brown's methods of investigation—which took him from one problem to another, each receiving detailed methodical treatment—than by any general plan.

On Flinders' voyage Brown had many opportunities to study, in the living state, members of the family Proteaceae, which is well represented in Australia and South Africa; back in England, Banks, James Edward Smith, and others made their herbaria available to him. George Hibbert's collection of living plants, skillfully grown by his gardener Joseph Knight, and his herbarium, formed at the Cape of Good Hope by his collector David Niven, were particularly rich in Proteaceae; the same collections also attracted the attention of Richard Anthony Salisbury. On this material Brown based his classic paper "On the Proteaceae of Jussieu," which was read to the Linnean Society of London on 17 January 1809, Salisbury being present, but not published in the Society's *Transactions* (**10**, 15–226) until February 1810. It is notable not only for its clear exposition of the morphology of these plants, for its proposal of a new classification into genera based largely on floral details hitherto uninvestigated, for the definition of these genera and of the species, but also for its observations on geographical distribution and, surprisingly introduced, the androecium of Asclepiadaceae. Sharp practice by Salisbury deprived Brown of priority of publication.

In August 1809 there appeared Joseph Knight's book *On the Cultivation of the Plants Belonging to the Natural Order of Proteēae* [*sic*], described by Bishop Goodenough in December 1809 as "Salisbury's surreptitious anticipation of Brown's paper on the New Holland plants, under the name and disguise of Mr. Hibbert's gardener!" In it, described under other names, were genera and species known to have been recorded in Brown's manuscript; the preface acknowledged Salisbury's participation.

April 1810 saw the publication of Brown's paper "On the Asclepiadeae," subsequently issued in *Memoirs of the Wernerian Natural History Society* (**1** [1811], 12–78), in which he separated the family Asclepiadaceae from the Apocynaceae by the character of its pollen, and the first and only volume of his *Prodromus florae Novae Hollandiae*. His intent was "to include the generic and specific characters of all the plants known to be natives of New Holland." He himself paid the cost of printing. He gave twenty-four copies to leading botanists and learned societies and hoped, no doubt, to sell the rest of the 250 copies printed; in fact he sold twenty-four. The volume started with a survey of the ferns (Filices) and their allies, then dealt with Gramineae and other monocotyledons, followed by families of dicotyledons— among them Proteaceae, Scrophulariaceae, Apocynaceae, and Asclepiadaceae—covering 464 genera and some 2,000 species. It remains a work of fundamental importance for Australian botany. The two dominant systems of plant classification then were Linnaeus', based on the number of floral parts and frankly artificial but often convenient, and A. L. de Jussieu's, based on a wider range of characters and thereby bringing together plants that agreed more closely in the sum of their characters. Brown found neither system satisfactory when dealing with the bewildering variety of Australian plants. In the *Prodromus* he adopted, contrary to prevailing usage, a modified form of Jussieu's more natural system, amending the definition of families and genera, adding many new to science, and inserting a multitude of firsthand observations based not simply on Australian plants but also on plants from elsewhere. It immediately won the esteem of eminent contemporary botanists—as one said, "Everything here is new . . . and every part abounds with observations equally original and useful"—but it did not appeal to the book-buying public. Sadly disappointed by the sale of the first volume, Brown seems to have discontinued work on the second after 1817 and this volume, which would have covered Leguminosae, Myrtaceae, Compositae, and other families, was never published. The loss to science would have been greater had not

Brown incorporated some of this material in memoirs, appended to books of travel, that often were based upon fragmentary specimens which, as Martius remarked, could have been made so important and fruitful only by a genius like Brown.

The most important of these memoirs is probably the "General Remarks, Geographical and Systematical, on the Botany of Terra Australis," published in Flinders' *A Voyage to Terra Australis* (1814). Here Brown estimated the Australian species known to him at about 4,200 species, with the number of dicotyledons more than three times the number of monocotyledons, and established the families Pittosporaceae, Cunoniaceae, Rhizophoraceae, Celastraceae, Haloragaceae, and Stackhousiaceae. Brown's observations also found expression in further papers published by the Linnean Society, notably "Observations on the natural family of plants called Compositae" (*Transactions of the Linnean Society of London,* **12** [1818], 76–142), and in contributions to the second edition of Aiton's *Hortus Kewensis* (1812), notably on Cruciferae, Leguminosae, Myrtaceae, and Orchidaceae. Of great importance for the development of classification was not so much the precision of Brown's descriptions as his perception of relationships and his statements of the evidence for them, which led to the concept that certain characters had not so much absolute as relative worth, being constant, and hence valuable, in some groups but varying in others. Prophetically, he noted in 1810, from a consideration of the shape of pollen in Proteaceae and other families, that "it may be consulted with advantage in fixing our notions of the limits of genera." He introduced other characters, such as aestivation of the flower, into generic descriptions, deriving largely, it would seem, from his interest in ascertaining the early state and the development of organs. The cumulative effect of so many minute observations perspicuously correlated gave Brown's publications their high authority. Necessarily he left it to others to exploit by further investigation the lines of inquiry he indicated. After the disappointment of the *Prodromus* he turned from major works of synthesis and made important information available almost in a casual manner, as digressions or appendages to memoirs only remotely connected with it.

Thus, in 1831 Brown published as a pamphlet for private distribution his "Observations on the Organs and Mode of Fecundation in Orchideae and Asclepiadeae" (reprinted in *Transactions of the Linnean Society of London,* **16** [1833], 685–742), which contains his observations that the pollen of orchids, when placed upon the stigma, emits pollen tubes traceable into the ovary. Embedded in this paper is a discovery highly relevant to the cell theory, and thus to the development of cytology. Regarding the leaves of orchids, Brown stated:

> In each cell of the epidermis of a great part of this family, especially of those with membranous leaves, a single circular areola, generally somewhat more opake than the membrane of the cell, is observable. . . . only one areola belongs to each cell. . . . This areola, or nucleus of the cell as perhaps it might be termed, is not confined to the epidermis, being also found not only in the pubescence of the surface particularly when jointed, as in Cypripedium, but in many cases in the parenchyma or internal cells of the tissue. . . . The nucleus of the cell is not confined to the Orchideae but is equally manifest in many other Monocotyledonous families; and I have even found it, hitherto however in very few cases, in the epidermis of Dicotyledonous plants ["Observations" (1831), 19–21; *Transactions* (1833), 710–712].

A few earlier botanists evidently had observed the presence of this nucleus in some cells, as Brown himself points out, but he was the first specially to demonstrate its general occurrence in living cells and to give it the name "nucleus."

Brown's curiously incidental method of making known an important discovery resulting from long research is exemplified in a paper entitled "Character and Description of Kingia," appended to P. P. King's *Narrative of a Survey of the Intertropical and Western Coasts of Australia* (II [London, 1827], 536–563). Here occurs the remark

> It would entirely remove the doubts that may exist respecting the point of impregnation, if cases could be produced where the ovarium was either altogether wanting, or so imperfectly formed, that the ovulum itself became directly exposed to the action of the pollen. . . . such, I believe, is the real explanation of the structure of Cycadeae, of Coniferae, of Ephedra, and even of Gnetum [p. 555].

Brown then got rid of objections to this view that the ovule in these plants was not contained within an ovary, but he left it for others to emphasize that it established a fundamental difference between the gymnosperms (as they were later named) and the other flowering plants (i.e., the angiosperms). It remained for Hofmeister's later investigations to indicate the relevance of gymnospermy and angiospermy to the theory of the alternation of generations.

In the course of these microscopical explorations Brown passed from the study of the ovule to that of pollen grains, and thus came to investigate the phenomenon known as the Brownian movement, i.e., the continuous motion of minute particles suspended in

a fluid, which results from their being bombarded by molecules in like continuous motion.

In June 1827, when examining pollen grains of *Clarkia pulchella*, Brown observed particles suspended in a fluid within the grain which were evidently moving, and he concluded that their motions "arose neither from currents in the fluid nor from its gradual evaporation but belonged to the particle itself." He thereupon extended his observations, as was his wont, to numerous species belonging to many families of plants, and found such motion in the particles of all fresh pollen. This led him to inquire whether the property continued after the death of the pollen; he then found it even in herbarium specimens preserved for not less than a century. Ultimately, after examining powdered pit coal and glass, numerous rocks, and metals in a finely divided state, Brown stated that such active particles occurred in every mineral he could reduce to a powder sufficiently fine to be suspended in water. He published these results in 1828, in a privately printed pamphlet entitled *A Brief Account of Microscopical Observations Made in the Months of June, July and August, 1827, on the Particles Contained in the Pollen of Plants; and on the General Existence of Active Molecules in Organic and Inorganic Bodies*. He took care to point out that the motion of the particles within had earlier been "obscurely seen by Needham, and distinctly by Gleichen," but to Brown belongs the credit for establishing such motion as a property not simply of living pollen but of all minute particles, inorganic as well as organic, suspended in a fluid. Here again it remained for others to carry Brown's work much further and to demonstrate its relevance to the kinetic theory of gases.

The last of Brown's work was contained in Brown and Bennett's *Plante rariores Javanicae,* published in four parts (London, 1838, 1840, 1844, 1852). This scholarly book had an unfortunate history. Among the collections that came into Brown's hands was one made in Java by Thomas Horsfield between 1802 and 1818, comprising 2,196 species, according to Brown's statement, and thus representing a large part of the flora of a little-known area of great phytogeographical interest. Horsfield evidently hoped for a complete enumeration of his material classified and named by Brown, who, however, merely selected for publication "those subjects which appeared to possess the greatest interest, either on account of their novelty, or of their peculiarity of structure." Brown's other activities and his annual eleven-week holidays severely handicapped his participation in this work, and in any event the routine publication of new species had no more interest for him. He liked to let an inquiry lead him from fact to fact until he had obtained a general view and was in a position to write a monograph, for which he then substituted a synopsis or which he condensed into a footnote. The *Plantae rariores Javanicae* ultimately had only 258 pages and fifty plates, and Brown himself wrote on only thirty of Horsfield's 2,196 species. It must have been a severe disappointment to Horsfield. This led John Lindley to write that

> . . . it was the misfortune of Dr. Horsfield to place the very important collections of plants which he formed in Java in the early part of this century, in the hands of a gentleman who to an extensive acquaintance with the details of systematical botany adds habits of procrastination, concerning which we shall only say that they are fortunately unparalleled in the annals of natural history. . . . The fatigue of describing these 50 in the course of 30 years was moreover found to be so excessive that a second editor had to be added to the first, in order that the Herculean labour might be accomplished [*Gardener's Chronicle*, 1852 (26 June), 406–407].

Despite this, Brown's contributions are important for the supplementary observations that he added. Thus, to the description of *Loxonia acuminata* he appended a long essay on the classification of Gesneriaceae and a synopsis of the genera and species of the Cyrtandreae; under the description of *Pterocymbium javanicum* he inserted a synopsis of Sterculiaceae.

Brown's mind became so richly endowed over the years with the details of so much painstaking and critical investigation into the characters of plants, most of it done with the aid of the microscope, that to make them available in a major work of synthesis would have been a task beyond his industry, even had it been congenial to his temperament; instead, he adopted his peculiar, almost haphazard, presentation of isolated parts of his special information, which makes almost all his publications pregnant with unexpected indications of fruitful inquiry. Charles Darwin, who knew Brown well and for many years spent Sunday mornings in discussion with him, stated:

> He seemed to me to be chiefly remarkable for the minuteness of his observations and their perfect accuracy. He never propounded to me any large scientific views in biology. His knowledge was extraordinarily great, and much died with him, owing to his excessive fear of never making a mistake. He poured out his knowledge to me in the most unreserved manner, yet was strangely jealous on some points [*Autobiography of Charles Darwin*, N. Barlow, ed., (London, 1958), p. 103].

Brown never married and had no near relatives. He lived in the house left him by Banks from 1821 until his death; he died in the room that had been Banks's library. His many excursions abroad made him personally well known, particularly in Germany, where he was much esteemed. According to Martius, "he sat whole nights in his arm-chair, reading and thinking." Despite his quiet manner and unobtrusive way of life, Brown was by no means a recluse and was, according to Asa Gray, "very fond of gossip at his own fireside," and, according to W. J. Hooker, "really fond of society and calculated to shine in it; and to my certain knowledge, never so happy as when he is in it." His somewhat feminine but far from effeminate disposition had none of Lindley's aggressiveness; contemporaries who knew him well testify to his tenderness and kindness, but the company he liked was essentially that of his peers. He kept remote from controversy and public affairs, had no contact with university students, and went his tranquil way in continuous search of truth, untroubled by economic difficulties and a multiplicity of duties such as beset Lindley. He refused three professorships. Brown never lost interest in the plants of his Scottish homeland and often returned to Montrose; at the age of eighty, in 1853, he ascended Lochnagar, a mountain on which he had botanized just sixty years earlier.

Brown became a fellow of the Linnean Society in 1822, and was its president from 1849 to 1853; he was elected a fellow of the Royal Society in 1810. Numerous academies honored him with election to foreign membership. It was to the Munich Academy of Sciences that his friend of many years, Carl von Martius, delivered in 1859 a eulogy that both in the original German and in Henfrey's translation still provides an excellent general appreciation of Brown's character and his scientific achievements.

BIBLIOGRAPHY

I. ORIGINAL WORKS. Robert Brown's contributions to learned periodicals, travel books (in which they form botanical appendices), and so on are brought together in *The Miscellaneous Botanical Works of Robert Brown*, J. J. Bennett, ed., 2 vols. (London, 1866–1867); a less complete collection is the earlier *Robert Brown's vermischte botanische Schriften*, C. G. Nees von Esenbeck, ed., 5 vols. (Nuremberg, 1825–1834), which includes a reprint, with different pagination, of his *Prodromus florae Novae Hollandiae* (London, 1810), originally issued in an edition of 250 copies and republished in facsimile, with an introduction by W. T. Stearn, as no. 5 in the series Historiae Naturalis Classica (1960).

His unpublished MSS, notes, diary, and correspondence are at the British Museum (Natural History), South Kensington, London.

II. SECONDARY LITERATURE. Works on Brown are N. T. Burbidge, "Robert Brown's Australian Collecting Localities," in *Proceedings of the Linnean Society of New South Wales*, **80** (1956), 229–233; W. Carruthers, "John Joseph Bennett," in *Journal of Botany, British and Foreign*, **14** (1876), 97–105; J. B. Farmer, "Robert Brown, 1773–1858," in F. W. Oliver, *Makers of British Botany* (London, 1912), pp. 108–125; J. D. Hooker, "Eulogium on Robert Brown," in *Proceedings of the Linnean Society of London*, sess. 1887–1888 (1890), 5–67; C. F. P. von Martius, "Robert Brown, eine akademische Denkrede," in *Flora* (Regensburg), **42** (1859), 10–15, 25–31, repr. in Martius, *Akademische Denkreden* (Leipzig, 1866), pp. 365–381, and in *Annals and Magazine of Natural History*, 3rd ser., **3** (1859), 321–331, A. Henfrey, trans.; J. Ramsbottom, "Robert Brown, botanicorum facile princeps," in *Proceedings of the Linnean Society of London*, **144** (1932), 17–36; and W. T. Stearn, *Three Prefaces on Linnaeus and Robert Brown* (Weinheim, 1962).

WILLIAM T. STEARN

BROWNE, THOMAS (*b.* London, England, 19 October 1605; *d.* Norwich, England, 19 October 1682), *general science, natural history.*

Browne's father, Thomas, had come in early manhood from Chester to London, where he was a mercer, or silk merchant. There he married Anne Garroway of Acton, Middlesex. They lived in comfortable circumstances with their son and four daughters. The senior Browne died when his son was eight years old, but left ample means for his education. Accordingly, the boy was sent to Winchester College in 1615. William of Wykeham's famous school was Anglican and Royalist, and provided a sound classical education that was a good foundation for the erudition acquired by Browne in later years. He remained at Winchester for eight years, until, in 1623, he proceeded to Oxford. He matriculated at Broadgates Hall, which soon afterward was upgraded to become Pembroke College. Browne, although only a freshman, was called upon to deliver a Latin oration at the inauguration ceremony.

Winchester would have afforded the boy little or no opportunity for study of the natural sciences, so it was probably during the school holidays that he began to acquire his knowledge of natural history. At Oxford a chair of anatomy had just been established in addition to several other chairs of physical sciences. Browne's teachers included Dr. Clayton, an anatomist and Regius professor of medicine, and Dr. Thomas Lushington, a mathematician and clergyman. Clayton's influence directed Browne's attention to the study of medicine and human anatomy, but this could not begin seriously until he had taken his M.A. in philosophy in 1629. He then left Oxford and spent some weeks in Ireland with his stepfather, Sir Thomas Dutton, before proceeding to Montpellier for full training in medicine.

It is not known how long Browne remained in France, but his travels in several European countries cannot have occupied less than four years. He probably spent some time in Padua, but his final goal was Leiden, where he defended his thesis and received his M.D. in December 1633. During these travels he studied many subjects besides medicine, absorbing information of all kinds and acquiring knowledge of several modern languages.

English regulations required a medical man with a foreign degree to practice for four years with an established doctor before being allowed to have his M.D. by incorporation at Oxford or Cambridge. It is probable that Browne spent these years of apprenticeship somewhere in Oxfordshire, but no details are known. He took his M.D. at Oxford on 10 July 1637 and was then, at the age of thirty-two, free to practice anywhere that he chose. It was during these four years that Browne wrote his most famous book, *Religio medici*, which was not published until 1642. Influenced, it is believed, by his Oxford friend Dr. Lushington, Browne moved in 1637 to the East Anglia city of Norwich and established himself there as a physician. In 1641 he married Dorothy Mileham, from a neighboring village. They had twelve children, only four of whom survived their parents. Edward, the eldest son, became a well-known physician in London and was president of the College of Physicians in 1704. Browne was knighted in 1671 by King Charles II, who was visiting Norwich and wished to honor its most distinguished citizen.

Browne's *Religio medici* describes the religion and philosophy of a tolerant, humorous, and latitudinarian mind. He did not, however, expose in it much of his attitude toward the rapidly expanding world of science. Yet throughout his apprenticeship and first years in Norwich he must have been reading widely in travel, philosophy, medicine, and science, and compiling the notebooks from which he quarried his next, very long book, *Pseudodoxia epidemica: or, Enquiries Into Very Many Received Tenents, And Commonly Presumed Truths* (1646). In this he sought to dispel popular ignorance about many matters in history, folklore, philology, science, medicine, natural history, and embryology. He was, thus, to be designated an "enquirer after truth" rather than a "scientist" (a term not yet invented), his field of inquiry being as wide as all human knowledge. He accepted the authority of William Harvey, one of the first great experimental scientists, and told a young correspondent: "Be sure you make yourself master of Dr. Harvey's piece, *De circulatione sanguinis,* which discovery I prefer to that of Columbus." Browne conducted many experiments in physics, electricity (a word of his own coining), biology, and comparative anatomy, dissecting animals, birds, fishes, reptiles, worms, and insects. He became an acknowledged authority on the plants, animals, birds, and fishes of East Anglia. Many of his experiments are mentioned in his *Pseudodoxia epidemica* and his letters. Others, such as investigations of bubbles, and of coagulation, freezing, and other properties of matter remained in the privacy of his notebooks.

Throughout his active life Browne lived on the fringe of the scientific world. His profession was medicine; his hobbies were science and natural history. He was an earnest amateur and never, as far as is known, left Norfolk for London. He was elected a fellow of the College of Physicians, but was never a fellow of the Royal Society of London, nor did he betray any desire for this kind of recognition. His elaborate and highly latinized prose style was very different from the much more austere style deliberately adopted by the fellows of the Royal Society. He was content to correspond with various fellows, such as Henry Oldenburg (secretary of the Society), John Ray, Christopher Merrett, and the diarist John Evelyn, and occasionally to send communications through his son Edward.

He was deeply interested in archaeology; one of his most famous books was *Hydriotaphia, or, Urne-buriall* (1658), occasioned by the discovery of some supposed Roman (really Saxon) burial urns near Norwich. He corresponded with other eminent antiquaries, such as Sir William Dugdale, Elias Ashmole, and John Aubrey. With these manifold interests and occupations, it is not surprising that Browne is remembered as a learned man and a literary artist rather than for any important contributions to contemporary science. His qualities served to foster a general interest in science and, above all, to illuminate thought by truth concerning the material world.

BIBLIOGRAPHY

I. Original Works. Browne's works are *Religio medici* (pirated ed., London, 1642; 1st authorized ed., London, 1643), which also appeared in *Religio medici and Other (Shorter) Works*, L. C. Martin, ed. (Oxford, 1964); *Pseudodoxia epidemica* (London, 1646); *Hydriotaphia, or, Urne-buriall* (London, 1658); *The Garden of Cyrus* (London, 1658); *Miscellany Tracts* (London, 1684); *A Letter to a Friend* (London, 1690); *Posthumous Works* (London, 1712), with a biography by John Whitefoot; and *Christian Morals* (London, 1716), later edited, with a biography, by Samuel Johnson (London, 1756).

The following are collections of Browne's works: *The Works of Sir Thomas Browne,* Thomas Tenison, ed. (London, 1686); *Sir Thomas Browne's Works,* Simon Wilkin, ed., 4 vols. (London, 1836), which contains much biographical and scholarly material; *The Works of Sir Thomas Browne,* Sir Geoffrey Keynes, ed., 6 vols. (London, 1928–1932; rev. and enl. ed., 4 vols., London, 1964), which is the standard and only complete edition and includes miscellaneous material from manuscripts and letters.

II. Secondary Literature. Works on Browne are Joan Bennett, *Sir Thomas Browne* (Cambridge, 1962); Jeremiah Finch, *Sir Thomas Browne* (New York, 1950); Sir Edmund Gosse, *Sir Thomas Browne* (London, 1905); F. L. Huntley, *Sir Thomas Browne* (Ann Arbor, Mich., 1962); Sir Geoffrey Keynes, *A Bibliography of Sir Thomas Browne* (Cambridge, 1924; 2nd rev. ed., Oxford, 1968); and Oliver Leroy, *Le chevalier Thomas Browne* (Paris, 1931).

Geoffrey Keynes

BROWNRIGG, WILLIAM (*b*. High Close Hall, Cumberland, England, 24 March 1711; *d*. Ormathwaite, Cumberland, England, 6 January 1800), *chemistry*.

Except that he came of a family long settled in western Cumberland and apparently was apprenticed to a physician in Whitehaven some time before 1733, little is known of Brownrigg's background and early life. He studied in London and later at Leiden, where he obtained his doctorate in medicine in 1737. He took up practice in Whitehaven and in 1741 married Mary Spedding, daughter of the steward of the Lowther estates.

Sir James Lowther owned the Whitehaven collieries and encouraged Brownrigg in his investigations into the damps arising in the mines, arranging for firedamp to be piped from the mines to Brownrigg's laboratory as a source of heat. Brownrigg believed that a greater knowledge of these exhalations would help to decrease the mortality among miners; he also thought that there might be a connection between them and epidemic diseases, and that some would prove to be the same as the "elastic spirits" with which mineral waters were impregnated and to which the latter owed their properties. Four papers under the general heading "Of Damps" were communicated through Lowther to the Royal Society in 1741 and 1742, and led to Brownrigg's being elected a fellow in May 1742.

An extract from these was published in the *Philosophical Transactions* for 1765, as an addendum to a paper (for which Brownrigg received the Copley Medal) in which he virtually showed that the gas which could be expelled from water from Pouhon and other mineral springs on heating, and the expulsion of which led to the precipitation of dissolved solids, was identical with the chokedamp (i.e., carbon dioxide) of the mines.

Further experiments and observations made, he says, at about the same time, but not presented until 1774, dealt in detail with the dependence of the solubility of calcareous earths and iron salts on the dissolved gas. In the meantime (as he acknowledged), papers on the solubility of these earths and salts had been given respectively by Cavendish (1767) and Timothy Lane (1769). He expressed the view "that the mephitic air and martial earth, contained in the Pouhon water, strongly attract each other, and uniting together, form a concrete soluble in water" (*Philosophical Transactions,* 1774, p. 363), that is, calcium and ferrous carbonates combine with water and carbon dioxide to form bicarbonates, which are soluble.

Brownrigg's views on gases and his technique in handling them were an advance on those of Hales, and it seems not unjustifiable to claim a place for him in the direct line of British pneumatic chemists that includes Black, Cavendish, and Priestley. Particularly noteworthy is his opinion, contrary to that generally held in his day, that "two elastic fluids, altho' they both possess a repulsive quality, may yet in their other qualities, differ as much as inelastic fluids are found to differ; as water, for example, differs from oil of vitriol" (*Philosophical Transactions,* 1765, p. 238).

Much of the other work of Brownrigg, a man of wide interests, merits attention; here we mention only his investigation, the first by a trained European scientist, of platinum, specimens of which had been brought to England in 1741 by his brother-in-law, Charles Wood. A more thorough and accurate examination of the metal was made during the next decade by Scheffer in Sweden and Lewis in England.

BIBLIOGRAPHY

I. ORIGINAL WORKS. Brownrigg wrote two treatises of contemporary importance, both showing evidence of a painstaking accumulation of facts and a profound grasp of the problems involved. *The Art of Making Common Salt* (London, 1748) advocated the extensive manufacture of salt by the evaporation of seawater at selected sites on the east coast of England, with a view to drastically decreasing its price (almost all of it was imported and heavily taxed). An abstract by William Watson appeared in *Philosophical Transactions,* **45** (1748), 351–372. *Considerations on the Means of Preventing the Communication of Pestilential Contagion, and of Eradicating It in Infected Places* (London, 1771) dealt with measures that Brownrigg thought should be adopted if the plague, which had appeared in Europe that year, should spread to Britain.

The papers to which reference has been made in the text are "Of Damps," a series of four papers read 16 April 1741, 11 March 1742, 8 April 1742, 13 May 1742; the first was entitled "Some Observations Upon the Several Damps in the Coal Mines Near Whitehaven" and the others dealt, respectively, with the possible relations of these damps to epidemics, mineral waters, and the nature of common air. They were never published as a whole, but the MSS are preserved in the archives of the Royal Society. The other papers are "Several Papers Concerning a New Semi-metal Called Platina," in *Philosophical Transactions,* **46** (1749/1750), 584–596; "An Experimental Inquiry Into the Mineral Elastic Spirit, or Air, Contained in Spa Water; as Well as Into the Mephitic Qualities of That Spirit," *ibid.,* **55** (1765), 218–235, the extract from "Of Damps" following on 236–243; and "Continuation of an Experimental Inquiry, Concerning the Nature of the Mineral Elastic Spirit or Air Contained in the Pouhon Water, and Other Acidulae," *ibid.,* **64** (1774), 357–371.

II. SECONDARY LITERATURE. The contemporary biography by Joshua Dixon, his pupil, is eulogistic but invaluable: *The Literary Life of William Brownrigg, M.D., F.R.S., to Which is Added an Account of the Coal Mines Near Whitehaven* (London, 1801). J. Russel-Wood, in *Annals of Science,* **6** (1950), 186–196, 436–447; **7** (1951), 77–94, 199–206, gives a biographical sketch and discusses Brownrigg's published and unpublished work. J. McDonald, *A History of Platinum From the Earliest Times to the Eighteen-eighties* (London, 1960), appraises the work of Brownrigg, Scheffer, and Lewis, *inter alia,* on platinum.

E. L. SCOTT

BROWN-SÉQUARD, CHARLES-ÉDOUARD (*b.* Port Louis, Mauritius, 8 April 1817; *d.* Paris, France, 1 April 1894), *physiology.*

Brown-Séquard's father, Charles Edward Brown, was an American naval officer; his mother, Charlotte Séquard, was French. He was a British subject by birth, but just before becoming professor at the Collège de France in 1878 he became a French citizen. Brown-Séquard's early life was difficult. Born after his father's death, he was raised by his mother in modest circumstances. After receiving the M.D. in Paris on 3 January 1846, he became the protégé of Pierre Rayer and began his work at the hospital of La Charité. Although he always remained interested in the life of Paris and its scientific movements, Brown-Séquard had a restless nature and was unable to have a real home. Before receiving his degree he had lived in Mauritius, and after completing his studies he went to the United States. He practiced medicine and gave private courses in Philadelphia, New York, and Boston in 1852. After his marriage to Ellen Fletcher of Boston, Brown-Séquard returned to Paris and later settled again in Port Louis, where he distinguished himself in fighting a cholera epidemic. In 1854 he accepted a professorship at Virginia Medical College in Richmond, but returned to Paris in 1855. In 1856 he again gave courses in Boston but suddenly decided to live in England, where he taught at the Royal College of Surgeons in 1858. As a physician at the National Hospital for the Paralysed and Epileptics, Brown-Séquard lived in London from 1860 to 1863. He was elected to the Royal Society in 1861. Becoming in England more and more the slave of professional practice, he fled to Paris and then to Boston. The Harvard Medical School offered him the chair of physiology and pathology, which he held from 1864 to 1867. After the death of his wife in 1867, Brown-Séquard again left the United States for Paris, where he gave the course in comparative and experimental pathology at the Faculté de Médecine in 1869. The following year he settled once more in the United States, and married Maria Carlisle, of Cincinnati, Ohio, in 1872. His activity then knew no respite: he founded a new journal and organized a physiology laboratory in New York; lectured in Boston, London, Dublin, and Paris; and wrote several dozen scientific articles. His travel increased after his second wife's early death, and in 1877, in Geneva, he married an Englishwoman named Emma Dakin.

The high point of Brown-Séquard's scientific career came following the death of Claude Bernard, when he became professor of medicine at the Collège de France (3 August 1878). He retained this post until his death but divided his time between Paris and Nice, leaving his assistant, Arsène d'Arsonval, to give the winter courses. In 1886 Brown-Séquard was elected to the Académie des Sciences.

While a student, Brown-Séquard had become particularly interested in problems of physiology and conducted original experiments on gastric digestion and the function of the spinal cord. In his thesis he suggested that in the spinal cord sensations are transmitted through the gray matter rather than through the dorsal columns. He also described the phenomenon that was later known as traumatic spinal shock: marked diminution in reflex activity immediately after sectioning of the cord and its subsequent recovery and even hyperesthesia. His thesis contained the germ of his main discovery: crossing of the nervous pathways for conduction of sensation in the spinal cord. In 1849 he showed that transverse hemisection of the cord produces motor paralysis and hyperesthesia on the corresponding side and anesthesia on the opposite side of the body below the lesion (the Brown-Séquard syndrome). This discovery was confirmed by clinical observations and proved to be very useful in the diagnosis of neurological lesions.

In August 1852, while in the United States, Brown-Séquard demonstrated the existence of vasoconstrictive nerves. When the severed cervical sympathetic trunk was stimulated by a galvanic current, the phenomena described by Claude Bernard as following the section (increasing of the skin temperature, dilation of the blood vessels, sensitization) disappeared and were replaced by inverse phenomena. It must be said that Bernard carried out the same experiment independently of Brown-Séquard and obtained the same results. It should be noted that the publication of Brown-Séquard's experiment preceded that of Bernard's; but, on the other hand, Brown-Séquard's research in this field was directly inspired by Bernard's work and was the logical sequel to the experiments made public just before Brown-Séquard left Paris.

Other of Brown-Séquard's investigations concerned the artificial production of epileptic states through lesions of the nervous system (1856), and the irrigation of dead muscles with warm blood. He was successful in reviving the head of a dog eight minutes after decapitation by injecting oxygenated blood into the arterial trunks. In 1862 he demonstrated that section of the vagus nerve brought on dilation of the coronary arteries. Brown-Séquard was mistaken in opposing the theory of cerebral localizations, but it should be emphasized that we are greatly indebted to him for elaboration of the concept of nervous inhibition.

Brown-Séquard was a pioneer of endocrinology. In 1856 he proved that removal of the adrenal glands always caused death in animals. He also prolonged the survival of animals after adrenalectomy by injecting normal blood. These researches are open to criticism, and this is even more true of his celebrated experiments on "rejuvenation." On 1 June 1889 Brown-Séquard presented a sensational report to the Société de Biologie: he believed that he had "rejuvenated" himself with subcutaneous injections of a liquid extracted from the testicles of freshly killed guinea pigs and dogs. His extravagant claim stimulated the development of modern organotherapy and exerted a strong influence on later research on sex hormones.

Brown-Séquard's investigations show more intuition than critical sense. His great achievement was understanding that through "internal secretion" the cells become dependent on one another by means of a mechanism other than the action of the nervous system (1891).

BIBLIOGRAPHY

I. ORIGINAL WORKS. A good bibliography is in his autobiographic *Notice sur les travaux scientifiques de M. C. É. Brown-Séquard* (Paris, 1883). His principal books are *Recherches et expériences sur la physiologie de la moelle épinière* (Paris, 1846), his thesis; *Recherches expérimentales sur la transmission croisée des impressions dans la moelle épinière* (Paris, 1855); *Researches in Epilepsy* (Boston, 1857); and *Course of Lectures on the Physiology and Pathology of the Central Nervous System* (Philadelphia, 1860). The most important results of Brown-Séquard's research were first printed in the reports of the Société de Biologie (Paris) and of the Académie des Sciences. For instance, the *Comptes rendus de la Société de biologie* contains the description of the experimental hemisection of the spinal cord, **1** (1850), 70–73; and the first mention of the effects produced in man by injections of testicular extract, **41** (1889), 415–422. His fundamental experiments on the adrenal glands were published in the *Comptes rendus de l'Académie des sciences,* **43** (1856), 422–425, 542–546. He also published a great many articles in the three journals of which he was founder and editor: *Journal de la physiologie de l'homme et des animaux, Archives de physiologie normale et pathologique,* and *Archives of Scientific and Practical Medicine.*

II. SECONDARY LITERATURE. Works on Brown-Séquard are M. Berthelot, *Notice sur la vie et les travaux de M. Brown-Séquard* (Paris, 1904); E. Dupuy, "Notice sur M. le Pr. Brown Séquard, ancien président de la Société de biologie," in *Mémoires de la Société de biologie,* **46** (1894), 759–770; E. Gley, "C.-E. Brown-Séquard," in *Archives de physiologie normale et pathologique,* 5th ser., **6** (1894), 501–516; J. M. D. Olmsted, *Charles-Edouard Brown-Séquard. A Nineteenth Century Neurologist and Endocrinologist* (Baltimore, 1946); and F. A. Rouget, *Brown-Séquard et son oeuvre* (Port Louis, Mauritius, 1930). An interesting set of letters between Brown-Séquard and his assistant d'Arsonval is in L. Delhoume, *De Claude Bernard à d'Arsonval* (Paris, 1939).

M. D. GRMEK

BROŻEK (or **Broscius**), **JAN** (*b.* Kurzelow, near Sieradz, Poland, November 1585; *d.* Krakow, Poland, 21 November 1652), *mathematics.*

Brożek's father, Jakub, was an educated landowner who taught his son the art of writing and the principles of geometry. Jan went to primary school in Kurzelow and then to the University of Krakow, where he passed his baccalaureate in March 1605. Among his professors were Stanislaw Jacobeius and Walenty Fontanus. In March 1610 Brożek won the rank of *magister,* and in 1611 he was ordained a priest. His contacts with Adriaan Van Roomen (Romanus), an eminent Belgian mathematician then in Krakow, greatly influenced his studies.

Early in 1614 Brożek became a professor at the Collegium Minus of the University of Krakow, where he was assigned the chair of astrology, and in 1619 at the Collegium Maius. In 1618 he traveled to Torun, Danzig, and Frombork to gather material on Copernicus. In 1620, at Innsbruck, he met the astronomer Christoph Scheiner. From June 1620 to

June 1624 Brożek studied medicine in Padua, receiving his doctorate in medicine in 1624, and was physician to the bishop of Krakow until the autumn of 1625. In 1625 the University of Krakow elected him professor of rhetoric, and in 1629 he gave up his chair in astrology because he had received higher ecclesiastical orders and had become canon of St. Anne's church. He then passed his baccalaureate in theology and became professor of that discipline.

In 1630 Brożek gave up his chair of rhetoric, and from April 1631 to December 1638 he was director of the library of the Collegium Maius. He became active in organizing the teaching of "practical geometry," which was entrusted to his favorite pupil, Pawel Herka, with some supervision on his part during 1635 and 1636. In 1639 Brozek presented his library to the University of Krakow, along with a substantial sum for the purchase of additional books and instruments. He gave up his professorship and the apartment at the Collegium Maius, as well as the canonry of the church of St. Florent, and moved to Międzyrzecze. In 1648, however, he returned to Krakow, where he received the master of theology. In February 1650 he became doctor of theology, and rector of his university in 1652.

Brożek's loyalty to the University of Krakow, one of his strongest characteristics, even surpassed his attachment to the Catholic Church. On the side of the university he took part in the fight against the Jesuit domination of schools, sending reports to Rome and making ten trips to Warsaw (1627–1635) in order to defend the university's rights. In the course of his struggle he answered a letter from a priest, Nicolas Lęczycki, by publishing (1626) a satirical dialogue, *Gratis,* which was soon burned in the public square of Krakow. It provoked a long answer from a priest, Frédéric Szembek, entitled *Gratis plebański gratis wyćwiczony* ("The Priests' *Gratis* Gratuitously Beaten," Poznan, 1627).

It was Brożek's hope to write the history of the University of Krakow, showing its role in the general development of science and education in Poland, but fragments of manuscripts are all that remain. The most important are "De antiquitate litterarum in Polonia" and an excellent biography of Stanislaw Grzepski, Polish geometer and philologist of the sixteenth century. In spite of his being enlightened and erudite, a partisan of progress who was active in reforming the teaching of mathematics, Brożek was not free from astrological prejudices or belief in the magical properties of numbers and their relation to medicine.

Brożek was the author of more than thirty publications. The ones concerning Copernicus, and particularly those dealing with mathematics, which won him the reputation of being the greatest Polish mathematician of his time, are of considerable interest. Among the first are the poem *Septem sidera* (of doubtful authenticity) and many Copernican documents but, unfortunately, not the letters by and about Copernicus that Brożek collected but did not publish that are now lost. In the second group are his purely mathematical works and opuscules, the most important being *Arithmetica integrorum* (1620), a new didactic manual, in which logarithms, then recently discovered, were introduced in schools; *Aristoteles et Euclides defensus contra Petrum Ramum* (1638), reissued in 1652 and 1699 under the title *Apologia pro Aristotele . . .*; a dissertation containing original research on the star-shaped polygons; and two treatises entitled *De numeris perfectis* (1637, 1638), which brought new results, at the time, on perfect numbers and amicable numbers. There one finds the basic theorem of the elementary theory of numbers, better known as Fermat's theorem, which was published in 1670 (also without its proof).

Jan Brożek should not be confused with Nicolas Brożek, nephew or grandson of his sister (*b.* Kurzelow, *ca.* 1635; *d.* Krakow, 1676). His scientific and ecclesiastic career was very similar to Jan Brożek's, but with only slight results, even for his epoch.

BIBLIOGRAPHY

I. ORIGINAL WORKS. Among Brożek's more than thirty writings are *Arithmetica integrorum* (Krakow, 1620); *Gratis* (Krakow, 1626); *De numeris perfectis* (Krakow, 1637, 1638); and *Aristoteles et Euclides defensus contra Petrum Ramum* (Krakow, 1638), reissued as *Apologia pro Aristotele . . .* (Krakow, 1652, 1699). Available in manuscript are parts of "De antiquitate litterarum in Polonia" and the "Biography of Stanislaw Grzepski," and Brożek's diary for 1636–1643, with gaps, in the form of notes written in the margins of the "Ephemerides" edited by L. Eichstadt, MS Bibl. Jagellone, Krakow, sign. Mathesis 513 R.X.VI.12.

II. SECONDARY LITERATURE. Works dealing with Brożek are M. A. Baraniecki, *Arytmetyka*, 2nd ed. (Warsaw, 1894), pp. 43–49; H. Barycz, *Wstęp i przypisy do nowego wydania Gratisa* ("Introduction and Commentaries on the New Edition of *Gratis*"), Vol. LXXXII of Biblioteka Pisarzy Polskich (Krakow, 1929); and "Pierwszy historyk nauki i kultury w Polsce" ("First Historian of Science and Culture in Poland"), in *Księga pamiątkowa ku czci W. Sobieskiego* ("Commemorative Volume in Honor of W. Sobieski"; Krakow, 1932); A. Birkenmajer, "Brożek (Broscius), Jan," in *Polski słownik biograficzny* ("Dictionary of Polish Biography"), II (Krakow, 1937), 1–3; L. A. Birkenmajer, *Nikołaj Kopernik,* I (Krakow, 1900); A. Favaro, *Tito-Livio Burattini* (Venice, 1896), p. 74; W. Konczyńska, *Zarys historii Biblioteki Jagiellońskiej* ("Sketch of the History of the Jagellone Library"); Krakow, 1923); J. Krókowski, *De septem sideribus, quae Nicolao Copernico vulgo tribuuntur* (Krakow, 1926); a monograph on Brożek, with portrait; Z. Mysłakowski, *Walerian Magni,* Vol. LI A of *Rozprawy Wydziału matematyczno-przyrodniczego PAU* (Krakow, 1911); K. Piekarski, *Ex libris Jana Brożka,* Vol. III of *Silva rerum* (Krakow, 1927); E. Stamm, "Z historii matematyki XVII wieku w Polsce" ("History of Mathematics in the Seventeenth Century in Poland"), in *Wiadomości matematyczne,* **40** (1935); and S. Temberski, *Roczniki* (Krakow, 1897). A long monograph on Brożek, containing a reproduction of his portrait at the University of Krakow, was published by J. N. Franke (Krakow, 1884).

B. KNASTER

BRUCE, DAVID (*b.* Melbourne, Australia, 29 May 1855; *d.* London, England, 27 November 1931), *microbiology.*

Sir David Bruce won renown for discovering the bacterial cause of Malta fever and for extensive and fruitful researches on trypanosomiasis. His professional life was spent in the Army Medical Service and the Royal Army Medical Corps, in which he attained the special rank of surgeon general.

Bruce was the only son of Scottish parents who emigrated to Australia during the gold rush of the early 1850's. His father, David Bruce, accompanied by his wife, Jane Hamilton, left Edinburgh to install a crushing plant in a Victoria goldfield. When he was five years old, David's parents returned with him to Scotland and settled in Stirling. He attended high school until the age of fourteen, and then worked for a warehouse firm in Manchester. His ambition to become a professional athlete, for which his great physique fitted him, was frustrated by an attack of pneumonia at age seventeen. He resumed his studies, and in 1876 gained admission to the University of Edinburgh.

As a schoolboy, Bruce became an enthusiastic ornithologist and planned a university course in zoology. After he had completed his first year at Edinburgh as medalist in natural history, a physician friend persuaded him to study medicine. After graduating M.B., C.M. in 1881, he assisted a doctor in Reigate, where he met Mary Elizabeth Steele, six years his senior, daughter of the previous owner of the practice. They were married in 1883. Although childless, their marriage was singularly fortunate, for Mary Bruce proved an indispensable helpmate—domestically, socially, and scientifically.

Bruce found general practice uncongenial, and in August 1883 was commissioned surgeon captain in the Army Medical Service. The following year, he was posted to Malta, where he and his wife were quartered in the Valetta Hospital, which had no facilities for research. Impressed by Koch's recent discovery of the tubercle bacillus, Bruce decided to investigate Malta fever, which annually hospitalized around a hundred soldiers of the British garrison, for an average of three months. He purchased a microscope, and late in 1886 he found "enormous numbers of single micrococci" in the spleen of a fatally ill patient. Splenic pulp from four later patients, inoculated into Koch's nutrient agar, yielded cultures of a slowly growing "micrococcus." Bruce reported these findings in September 1887. Subsequent publications described further properties of the organism, for which he proposed the name *Micrococcus melitensis*. Its bacillary morphology was unrecognized until Bang isolated *Bacillus abortus* in 1897. In 1920, on the suggestion of Feusier and Meyer, the generic term *Brucella* was adopted for these closely related microorganisms. The epidemiology of the disease remained a mystery until 1905, when T. Zammit, a Maltese member of the Commission for the Investigation of Mediterranean Fever, the twelve-man team of experts headed by Bruce, implicated goat's milk as the disseminating vehicle. The disease was conquered when goat's milk was eliminated from the diet of the Malta garrison. The eponymous term "brucellosis" has now replaced such names as Malta, Mediterranean, and undulant fever.

Between these two phases of his work in Malta, Bruce had become famous for trypanosomiasis researches in Zululand and Uganda. After departing from Malta in 1889, he spent his leave discoursing in Koch's laboratory while his wife acquired the latest techniques in microscopy, staining, and media making. He then taught pathology at the Army Medical School at Netley, introducing the experimental attitudes and bacteriological methods of Pasteur, Lister, and Koch. In 1894 Bruce was posted to Natal, whose governor (a former lieutenant governor of Malta) asked him to investigate an epizootic, nagana, that was affecting cattle in northern Zululand.

After trekking for five weeks by ox wagon, the Bruces arrived at Ubombo, where they lived for two months in a wattle-and-daub hut, using the veranda as a laboratory. Bacteriological examinations of affected oxen proved negative; but intensive microscopic study of blood specimens revealed a motile, vibrating hematozoon, which Bruce later concluded was a trypanosome. The relationship of this parasite to nagana was demonstrated by inoculating blood from infected cattle into healthy horses and dogs: they became acutely ill, and their blood swarmed with hematozoa. The natural mode of transmission of the disease was revealed, as Bruce explained in his Croonian lectures (1915), when two oxen and several dogs, sent into a low-lying "fly belt" for a fortnight, acquired this same parasite in their blood. He was now convinced that nagana was identical with the "tsetse fly disease" described by Livingstone in 1858, and that this fly transmitted the causal trypanosome.

Recalled temporarily to Natal, the Bruces returned in September 1895 to their isolated hut in the Zululand bush and stayed almost two years. Bruce's *Preliminary Report* was published in December 1895 and was followed early in 1897 by his *Further Report*. These classic documents described the hematozoa of nagana, established the tsetse fly *Glossina morsitans* as the vector, and implicated regional wild game, such as antelope and buffalo (themselves immune and unaffected), as the trypanosomal reservoir. Living trypanosome samples were forwarded to the Royal Society, which in 1899 elected Bruce a fellow and published a paper by Plimmer and Bradford characterizing the parasite and naming it *Trypanosoma brucei*.

During the Boer War, Bruce distinguished himself at the siege of Ladysmith, where he directed a hospital and performed successful surgery. Mary Bruce received the Royal Red Cross for devoted work with the wounded, particularly as nursing sister in her husband's operating theater. They returned home in October 1901.

In 1903 Bruce was chosen to head the Royal Society's Sleeping Sickness Commission to Uganda. On behalf of the Foreign Office and at Patrick Manson's urging, the Society had organized a similar commission to investigate an epidemic in Uganda in 1902, but its activities were uncoordinated and two members had returned home. The Bruces reached Entebbe in March 1903, with Dr. David Nabarro and a sergeant technician, and met the remaining representative of the first commission, a young bacteriologist, Dr. Aldo Castellani.

Manson's tentative suggestion of *Filaria perstans* as the causal agent had proved untenable; but Castellani had recently noted trypanosomes in cerebrospinal fluid taken from five victims. Previously, he had grown streptococci from the cerebrospinal fluid and heart blood of more than thirty. Well aware of the potential significance of the trypanosomes, although perturbed at the conflicting evidence, Castellani did not wish to be ridiculed by Bruce, still less by Nabarro, who was little older than he and whose appointment to supersede him he resented. He therefore imparted his observations to Bruce, on condition that he (Castellani) should temporarily continue searching for trypanosomes, that he should then publish his findings as sole author, and that

Nabarro should not be informed. When Castellani left Entebbe three weeks later, he had demonstrated trypanosomes in twenty additional cases. He had also taught Bruce the techniques of lumbar puncture and of examining the cerebrospinal fluid for trypanosomes.

In 1902 Dutton had reported *Trypanosoma gambiense* in the blood of a febrile Englishman in Gambia and in 1903 Baker had diagnosed similar cases of trypanosome fever in Uganda, but no connection between these conditions and Uganda sleeping sickness was then suspected. At first Bruce appeared skeptical about trypanosomes as causal agents of human sleeping sickness, but soon after Castellani's departure Bruce and Nabarro amassed convincing evidence that this disease was caused by *T. gambiense* inoculated by the tsetse fly *Glossina palpalis.* Bruce returned to England in August 1903. The "Progress Report" by himself and Nabarro, sent from Entebbe, acknowledged Castellani's discovery; but the "Further Report," written by Bruce, Nabarro, and E. D. W. Greig, betrays a changed attitude that encouraged his supporters, particularly the zoologist Ray Lankester, to minimize Castellani's contribution. The resulting dispute broke into print intermittently for several years. Despite Nabarro's magnanimous support of Castellani, most subsequent accounts displayed bias, which J. N. P. Davies' carefully documented articles (1962, 1968) should help to correct.

From 1908 to 1910, Bruce rejoined the Royal Society's continuing commission in Uganda, where he directed researches into conditions governing the transmissibility of *T. gambiense* by *Glossina palpalis,* and studied cattle and game as potential reservoirs of the parasite. In 1911, he was appointed director of another Sleeping Sickness Commission, to investigate trypanosomiasis in Nyasaland. During the next two years, *T. rhodesiense* was identified as the main regional pathogen and *Glossina morsitans* as its vector; and certain other trypanosomal species pathogenic to domestic animals were characterized. The commission concluded that *T. rhodesiense* and *T. brucei* were identical, but this view was disputed by contemporary German authorities and now has no adherents.

From 1914 until he retired in 1919, Bruce was commandant of the Royal Army Medical College. During the war, his administrative abilities were fully utilized, especially as director of scientific research and as chairman of committees for the study of tetanus and trench fever. In his last years, Bruce suffered recurrent lung infections and wintered in Madeira. He died of cancer in his seventy-seventh year. His wife, who accompanied her husband on all his arduous trips,

working self-effacingly beside him as technician, microscopist, and draftswoman, predeceased him by four days. On his deathbed, Bruce requested that her outstanding assistance should always be emphasized in any biographical account of him.

Bruce's many distinctions included fellowship in the Royal Society and the Royal College of Physicians of London; honorary doctorates from the universities of Glasgow, Liverpool, Dublin, and Toronto; honorary memberships in several foreign academies and societies; and numerous medals of honor. He was appointed C.B. in 1905, knighted in 1908, and made K.C.B. in 1918. His abrupt manner, blunt speech, and egotistical personality endeared him to few; but his great energies and talents were dedicated to mankind's health and welfare, and he died poor. Moreover, he had vision and compassion, as shown in this closing passage from his presidential address, "Prevention of Disease," to the British Association, meeting at Toronto in 1924:

> We are all children of one Father. The advance of knowledge in the causation and prevention of disease is not for the benefit of any one country, but for all—for the lonely African native, deserted by his tribe, dying in the jungle of sleeping sickness, or the Indian or Chinese coolie dying miserably of beri-beri, just as much as for the citizens of our own towns.

BIBLIOGRAPHY

I. ORIGINAL WORKS. Bruce's major works are "Note on the Discovery of a Microorganism in Malta Fever," in *Practitioner,* **39** (1887), 161–170; "The Micrococcus of Malta Fever," *ibid.,* **40** (1888), 241–249; *Preliminary Report on the Tsetse Fly Disease or Nagana in Zululand* (Durban, 1895); *Further Report on the Tsetse Fly Disease or Nagana in Zululand* (London, 1897); "Progress Report on Sleeping Sickness in Uganda," in *Reports of the Sleeping Sickness Commission of the Royal Society,* **1** (1903), 11–88, written with David Nabarro; "Further Report on Sleeping Sickness in Uganda," *ibid.,* **4** (1903), 1–87, written with D. Nabarro and E. D. W. Greig; "The Development of *Trypanosoma gambiense* in *Glossina palpalis,*" in *Proceedings of the Royal Society,* **81B** (1909), 405–414, written with A. E. Hamerton, H. R. Bateman, and F. P. Mackie; "The Morphology of the Trypanosome Causing Disease in Man in Nyasaland," *ibid.,* **85** (1912), 423–433, written with D. Harvey, A. E. Hamerton, J. B. Davey, and Lady Bruce; "Trypanosomes Causing Disease in Man and Domestic Animals in Central Africa" (the Croonian lectures), in *Lancet* (1915), **1,** 1323–1330; (1915), **2,** 1–6, 55–63, 109–115; and "Prevention of Disease," in *Science,* **60** (1924), 109–124.

II. SECONDARY LITERATURE. Unsigned obituaries of Bruce are "Sir David Bruce, K.C.B., M. D. Edin., F.R.S.," in *Lancet* (1931), **2,** 1270–1271; and "Major-General Sir

David Bruce, K.C.B., LL.D., D.Sc., F.R.C.P., F.R.S.," in *Journal of the Royal Army Medical Corps,* **58** (1932), 1–4. Signed ones are J. R. Bradford, "Sir David Bruce—1855–1931," in *Obituary Notices of Fellows of the Royal Society,* **1** (1932), 79–85; S. R. Christophers, "Bruce, Sir David (1855–1931)," in *Dictionary of National Biography 1931–1940,* pp. 108–110; A. E. Hamerton, "Major-General Sir David Bruce, K.C.B., D.Sc., LL.D., F.R.C.P., F.R.S., Late A.M.S.," in *Transactions of the Royal Society of Tropical Medicine and Hygiene,* **25** (1931–1932), 305–312; D.W.T. and W.J.T., "Major-General Sir David Bruce, K.C.B., F.R.S.," in *Nature,* **129** (1932), 84–86; and C. M. Wenyon, "Major-General Sir David Bruce, K.C.B., F.R.S.," *ibid.,* 86–88.

Further information on Bruce's work can be found in M. T. Ashcroft, "A Critical Review of the Epidemiology of Human Trypanosomiasis in Africa," in *Tropical Disease Bulletin,* **56** (1959), 1073–1093; Aldo Castellani, "On the Discovery of a Species of Trypanosoma in the Cerebrospinal Fluid of Cases of Sleeping Sickness," in *Proceedings of the Royal Society,* **71** (1902–1903), 501–508; J. N. P. Davies, "The Cause of Sleeping Sickness? Part II," in *East African Medical Journal,* **39** (1962), 145–160, and "Informed Speculation on the Cause of Sleeping Sickness 1898–1903," in *Medical History,* **12** (1968), 200–204; E. R. Lankester, "Nature's Revenges: The Sleeping Sickness," in *The Kingdom of Man* (London, 1907), pp. 159–191; *Reports of the Commission Appointed by the Admiralty, the War Office, and the Civil Government of Malta for the Investigation of Mediterranean Fever, Under the Supervision of an Advisory Committee of the Royal Society,* 7 pts. in 1 vol. (London, 1905–1907); *Reports of the Sleeping Sickness Commission, Royal Society, Nos. 1–11* (London, 1903–1911); and C. Wilcocks, "Trypanosomiasis," in *Aspects of Medical Investigation in Africa* (London, 1962), pp. 59–90.

There is also enlightening correspondence. Two collections of letters are those of Bruce, in the library of the Royal Society of Tropical Medicine and Hygiene, London, and those of R. U. Moffat, former principal medical officer for Uganda, in Makerere College Library, Kampala. Individual letters are Aldo Castellani, ". . . The Exact History of how Colonel Bruce was Acquainted With My Observations . . .," in *The Times,* 8 July 1908, p. 18; E. Ray Lankester, in *The Times,* 19 Nov. 1903, p. 2, and 14 Aug. 1913, p. 4; and in *British Medical Journal,* 11 Aug. 1917, p. 198, and 17 Sept. 1917, pp. 402–403; and David Nabarro, in *Journal of Tropical Medicine and Hygiene,* 15 July 1908, pp. 224–225; *The Times,* 22 Sept. 1913, p. 21; and *British Medical Journal,* 15 Sept. 1917, pp. 374–375, and 6 Oct. 1917, pp. 467–468.

CLAUDE E. DOLMAN

BRUCE, JAMES (*b.* Stirlingshire, Scotland, 14 December 1730; *d.* Stirlingshire, 27 April 1794), *exploration.*

Bruce was the second son of David Bruce of Kinnaird and Marion Graham of Airth. Born into a wealthy landowning family, he entertained the idea of becoming a Church of England clergyman. He then decided instead to read for the Scottish bar, but later gave up legal studies also. Bruce served as consul-general at Algiers from March 1763 until the summer of 1765. He remained in Africa until March 1773, and then spent over a year in France, where he met the naturalist Buffon, and Italy before returning to London in June 1774.

Bruce's most notable journey began in Alexandria in June 1768. He traveled extensively in Ethiopia and claimed to have been the first European to find the source of the Nile (on 4 November 1770); he did know that the Portuguese Jesuit missionary Pedro Páez had been there more than a century earlier. Bruce actually had found the source of the Blue Nile, the main tributary of the White Nile, which it joins below Khartoum. He knew of the White Nile, although he denied that it was the major branch.

James Bruce is justly considered an explorer rather than an adventurer because of his scientific approach. Before setting out, he learned as much as was known about the geography, customs, and languages of the area. Bruce brought back drawings of buildings, fauna, and flora; collected seeds; and kept precise meteorological and astronomical records. His writings are generally accurate, and their embellishment in personal details is easily recognized. His *Travels,* which were not composed for more than twelve years after he left Africa, were written for a general rather than an academic audience; yet the grotesque and exotic material combined with his difficult and vain personality to arouse an adverse public reaction verging on disbelief. He retired to his estate during his last years and died at Kinnaird House.

BIBLIOGRAPHY

Bruce's *Travels to Discover the Source of the Nile in the Years 1768, 1769, 1770, 1771, 1772, and 1773,* 5 vols. (Edinburgh–London, 1790), was promptly translated into French and German. The second and third editions (8 vols., Edinburgh, 1804–1805; 1813) contain material from Bruce's notes that was added by Alexander Murray. There is a modern abridgment, *Travels to Discover the Source of the Nile by James Bruce,* C. F. Beckingham, ed. (Edinburgh, 1964), which offers a scholarly biographical introduction.

BERT HANSEN

BRÜCKE, ERNST WILHELM VON (*b.* Berlin, Germany, 6 September 1819; *d.* Vienna, Austria, 7 January 1892), *physiology.*

Brücke was the son of a painter and thought of

following his father's profession. Even though he became a doctor instead, he dealt throughout his life so intensively with questions concerning the theory of art that they form an integral part of his work.

In 1838 Brücke began studying at Berlin. His final teacher, whose assistant Brücke became in 1843, was the physiologist Johannes Müller, whose circle of friends and colleagues at that time included Hermann von Helmholtz, Emil Du Bois-Reymond, and, indirectly, Carl Ludwig. Brücke formed lifelong friendships with all these men. In 1842, on the basis of his dissertation *De diffusione humorum per septa mortua et viva,* he was graduated as a doctor of medicine and surgery. In this dissertation he tried to prove that the phenomena of osmosis are not to be related to any sort of uncertain vital force, but to weighable and measurable, repelling and attracting physiochemical forces; what he sought to prove was a part of the program of the new physical physiology. Du Bois-Reymond formulated it in the following way: "Brücke and I, we have sworn to each other to validate the basic truth that in an organism no other forces have any effect than the common physiochemical ones. . . . "

For this program the eye was an especially suitable subject for investigation. Brücke examined optical media, afterimages, stereoscopic vision, and the reflection of light from the backgrounds of the eyes of vertebrates; he also discovered the ciliary muscle named after him. His *Anatomical Description of the Human Eye* (1847) has become the standard anatomical-histological work for contemporary oculists.

His research on luminescence in animal eyes and his method of causing luminescence at will in the human eye created the foundation on which Helmholtz continued his work and which led to the invention of the ophthalmoscope in 1851 by the latter. How close Brücke himself had come to this discovery was later attested by Helmholtz: "He had merely neglected to ask himself to which optical image the rays reflected from the luminescent eye belonged."

In 1848 Brücke became professor of physiology at the University of Königsberg. The following year, he went in the same capacity to Vienna, where he founded a school for physiologists that eventually extended far beyond the borders of Austria and there worked until his death. Brücke's laboratory trained the Austrian physiologists S. Exner, A. Rollett, E. von Fleischl-Marxow, M. von Vintschgau, and A. Kreidl; the German W. Kühne; the Swede F. Holmgren; the Englishman T. Lauder-Brunton; and the Russians Elie Cyon, N. von Kowalewsky, and I. M. Setchenoff. Freud, who worked there from 1876

to 1882, considered Brücke the most highly respected teacher and the greatest authority in the field he had ever met.

Here, in the major city of a polyglot country, Brücke had an unusual opportunity to study linguistic and vocal physiology. To determine each sound of an arbitrary language in his own (alphabetical) characters and thereby to give a phonetic transcription was the aim of his *Characteristics of the Physiology and Taxonomy of Linguistic Sounds* (1856). With the aid of a labiograph he made the first attempt to measure exactly the length of strongly and weakly accented syllables in verse. He recorded the results of these measurements in a monograph, *The Physiological Bases of New High German Poetic Art* (1871). There is unmistakably evident here a typical endeavor of the times (primarily to analyze the effect of a work of art rationally, i.e., by means of scientific methods), as is also the case in Brücke's writings concerning the theory of art, which deal with the determination of the classical ideal of beauty. Such analysis was alien to Billroth's intuitively synthetic comprehension of art: "It is as if one wanted to describe how a good apple tastes; one has to eat it himself; if he does not then recognize it, he should stay with potatoes."

It is said that Brücke was one of the most versatile physiologists of his day. His *Lectures On Physiology* (1873–1874) confirms this; in it he added something of his own to almost every chapter. The diversity of his interests made limited specialization alien to Brücke. His investigations included the physiology of digestion; from 1850, Brücke studied the digestive tract microscopically and recognized the structures designated as Peyer's "glands" as the places where the lymphocytes develop. He explained the mechanism of the transfer of chyle by means of the contraction of intestinal villi. In his work on chyle, which was published for the most part in the *Proceedings of the Imperial Academy of Sciences in Vienna,* he encountered an abundance of questions concerning the reabsorption of fats, carbohydrates, and proteins. As a result, he developed many biochemical concepts. Brücke introduced the terms "achroödextrin" and "erythrodextrin" into physiological chemistry; he discovered that blood did not coagulate in uninjured vessels, and he became a pioneer in enzyme research through his experiments on peptic digestion. With these experiments he endeavored to produce the purest possible pepsin solutions. He tried to combine pepsin mechanically with small solid bodies such as calcium phosphate, sulfur, and cholesterol, and subsequently to extract it again from its adsorbates. He succeeded herein along two possible avenues of approach (through precipitation of calcium phosphate with water, or by treating the cholesterol precipitation with ether). But in order to reach his goal he needed control reactions for further purification, which he did not have.

Brücke is generally honored as a microscopist without it being pointed out that his microscopic investigations invariably grew out of his physiological inquiries and were determined by them. The investigation of function was his chief aim when he observed the flow of protoplasm in the stinging hairs of nettles or molecular motion in the salivary particles or—a classic example of the synthesis of histological, physical, and experimental methods—when he explained the changing of a chameleon's colors by the momentary shifting movements of the skin's pigment cells. Such diverse studies on the function of the most varied cells led Brücke to criticize the mechanistic ideas of structure in the cell theory of Matthias Schleiden and Theodor Schwann—of the cell as a shell formed by the cell membrane. While he and Max Schultze, a histologist from Bonn, were beginning to distinguish protoplasm as an essential cellular component, he was at the same time paving the way for a biological theory of cells in his investigation entitled *The Elementary Organisms.* In 1867–1868, with his experiments on the possibility of electric stimulation of muscles, Brücke moved into the specialty of his friend Du Bois-Reymond, i.e., general nerve and muscle physiology. Du Bois held that the stimulating effect of an electric current depended solely on how fast such a current was increased in the stimulated organ and not on how long the stimulus lasted. Brücke, on the other hand, observed that in curare-treated frog muscles a current that was increased too slowly remained ineffective. Accordingly, in electric stimulation the time factor had to be considered no less than the amount of current. In regarding the stimulus as a function of the "distance from the normal state," Brücke arrived at a new concept of the law on stimulation, which approximates modern concepts more closely than the first formulation by Du Bois-Reymond.

When Brücke resigned his teaching position in 1890, he had 143 publications to his credit. The range of this output is made evident by the number of different areas of work: physics, plant physiology, microscopic anatomy, physiological chemistry, physiological optics, and purely experimental physiology. He received many honors from numerous academies, including the highest Prussian order, the Order of Merit, and Austrian ennoblement. Such acclaim left untouched the genuine inner modesty of this great researcher, who was interested only in examining the events of nature with a view to their objective regularities.

BIBLIOGRAPHY

I. ORIGINAL WORKS. Note references in text. A complete list of works is in E. Th. Brücke, *Ernst Brücke* (Vienna, 1928). The most important works and the most important secondary literature are in E. Lesky, "Die Wiener medizinische Schule im 19. Jahrhundert," in *Studien zur Geschichte der Universität Wien,* VI (Graz–Cologne, 1965), 258 ff.

II. SECONDARY LITERATURE. See S. Exner, "Ernst von Brücke und die moderne Physiologie," in *Wiener klinische Wochenschrift,* 3 (1890), 807–812; obituary by A. Kreidl, *ibid.,* 5 (1892), 21 f. See also E. Suess, in *Almanach der Akademie der Wissenschaften in Wien,* 42 (1892), 184–189; and E. Brücke, "Ernst Wilhelm Brücke," in *Neue Österreichische Biographie,* V (1928), 66–73.

ERNA LESKY

BRUHNS, KARL CHRISTIAN (*b.* Plön, Germany, 22 November 1830; *d.* Leipzig, Germany, 25 July 1881), *astronomy.*

Trained as a locksmith, Bruhns came to Berlin in 1851 and worked as a mechanic. Even then his aim was to become an astronomer, and Encke, the director of the Berlin Observatory, to whom Bruhns had been recommended for his mathematical skill by a professor in Altona, recognized his great mathematical talents. After a year of carrying out complicated calculations for Encke in addition to his regular work, Bruhns was made an assistant at the observatory. In 1856 he graduated from the university with the thesis *De planetis minoribus inter Jovem et Martem circa solem versantibus* (Berlin, 1856), and in 1859 became lecturer in astronomy at the University of Berlin. Two years later he was appointed assistant professor of astronomy in Leipzig, becoming professor in 1868; he remained director of the observatory from 1860 until his death. In 1877–1878 he was rector of the university.

Under the influence of Encke, Bruhns's activities in his younger years centered on theoretical astronomy. Having made observations with the equatorial and meridian circle in Berlin, he took a greater interest in observational astronomy in Leipzig. His first act in Leipzig was to replace the antiquated observatory in the tower of the old castle in the middle of the town with a new one at the outskirts of the town. It was well equipped—for its time even excellently equipped. From 1900 on, however, it shared the lot of many German university observatories: unfavorable location and obsolete instruments; a place for teaching and training, but not a center of practical research.

Bruhns paid little attention to astrophysics, which flourished in the last years of his life. He was more interested in the fields related to astronomy—geodesy and meteorology—which he advanced considerably. He served on the Kommission für Mitteleuropäische Gradmessung and held the chair in the astronomical section of the Preussisches Geodätisches Institut in addition to his regular duties. Much of his work concerned the determinations of longitude between his observatory and Berlin, Vienna, Paris, and Munich, and other, less important, places.

More important was Bruhns's contribution to meteorology. In cooperation with Buys-Ballot and Jellinek, among others, he organized uniform worldwide weather observations and undertook to supervise those in his vicinity. He further tried to arouse the interest of agricultural circles, in particular, in a regular weather forecast in *Über das meteorologische Bureau für Witterungsprognosen im Königreich Sachsen* (1879).

Bruhns published such popular works as *Atlas der Astronomie* (1872) and also discussed natural science in general. It is therefore no surprise that he was responsible for the first comprehensive biography of Alexander von Humboldt (1871), which was supported by Loewenberg and Carus, among others. In this publication he wrote on Humboldt's work in astronomy, geodesy, and mathematics. Bruhns knew Humboldt personally and thought it urgent to memorialize this genius who was important to natural science in general. He also wrote a biography of Encke that gives an excellent insight into the work of the observatories in the first half of the nineteenth century. His historical concerns are displayed in other works, especially *Die astronomische Strahlenbrechung in ihrer historischen Entwicklung* (1861), written six years earlier.

In view of his wide-ranging interests, it is no wonder that Bruhns was influential. His superior lectures attracted many students; he was also active in the Astronomische Gesellschaft and initiated and equipped the first German astronomical expeditions. Unfortunately, these manifold tasks prevented him from promoting theoretical astronomy to the extent his outstanding ability would have allowed. His energy and enthusiasm, however, had a strong effect on his colleagues, which should not be ignored.

BIBLIOGRAPHY

Bruhns's books include *Geschichte und Beschreibung der Leipziger Sternwarte* (Leipzig, 1861); *Die astronomische Strahlenbrechung in ihrer historischen Entwicklung* (Leipzig, 1861); *Längendifferenz-Bestimmung Berlin-Leipzig* (Leipzig, 1865), written with W. Förster; *Längen-differenz-Bestimmung Leipzig-Gotha* (Leipzig, 1866), written with A. Auwers; *John Franz Encke, sein Leben und Wirken* (Leipzig, 1869); *Neues log.-trig. Handbuch auf 7 Dezimalen* (Leipzig, 1870); *Alexander von Humboldt, eine wissenschaftliche Biographie . . .,* 3 vols. (Leipzig, 1871); *Astronomisch-geodätische Arbeiten in den Jahren 1867–1875,* 4 vols. (Leipzig, 1871–1876; 1882); *Atlas der Astronomie* (Leipzig, 1872); and *Über das meteorologische Bureau für Witterungsprognosen im Königreich Sachsen* (Leipzig, 1879).

Numerous short papers appeared in *Astronomische Nachrichten,* **35–67** (1852–1866); in *Leipzig Gesellschaft der Wissenschaften. Berichte* (1872, 1878); and in *Leipzig Gesellschaft der Wissenschaften. Abhandlungen* (1873). Bruhns was also editor of 3 vols. in Publicationen des Preussischen Geodätischen Institutes (1871–1874); of 12 vols. of *Resultate aus den meteorologischen Beobachtungen, angestellt an meheren Orten im Königreich Sachsen* (Leipzig, 1866–1880); and of *Kalendar und statistisches Jahrbuch für Sachsen* (Leipzig, 1872–1882).

H. C. FREIESLEBEN

BRUMPT, ÉMILE (*b.* Paris, France, 7 March 1877; *d.* Paris, 7 July 1951), *parasitology.*

Brumpt began his career as *préparateur* at the Paris Faculté des Sciences in 1895 and became an assistant professor at the Faculté de Médecine in 1906. In that year he received his doctorate and in 1907 passed the *agrégation.* In 1919 he followed Raphael Blanchard as full professor in the chair of parasitology and was elected a member of the Académie de Médecine.

His rapid rise and brilliant career are explained by his works and his scientific authority. Brumpt, both a zoologist and a physician, was the originator of medical parasitology in France. He was led to this by experimental research and his numerous trips and sojourns in tropical lands. In 1901, as a second-year student, he made a two-year journey across Africa, from Abyssinia to the Congo, with the Bourg de Bozas mission. He later returned to Africa and also visited South America (especially Brazil) and the Far East.

Brumpt was a remarkable teacher and a most talented experimenter. He was the first to demonstrate, in 1904, the existence of a developmental phase in leeches of the trypanosomes of batrachians and fish. This cycle was noted again in 1911 in the tsetse carriers of *T. gambiense,* the agent causing sleeping sickness. In 1912, in Brazil, Brumpt described the life history of *Trypanosoma cruzi*—the agent of Chagas' disease—in *Triatoma,* a blood-sucking hemipteran. Chagas thought that trypanosoma developed in the general cavity and in the salivary glands of the bug and that infection was conveyed through biting. Brumpt in 1912 described the entire cycle and showed that the disease was transmitted through the feces, which infected the bite wound.

Brumpt studied all groups of parasites with his habitual thoroughness: the trypanosomes in Africa and South America, the *Piroplasma canis* and *bigemina,* the filariae, the *Bilharzia,* as well as the biology of the active and passive vectors of those parasites. His publications on mycology are important. He also studied recurrent fevers and exanthematic typhus. It was at this time, in 1933, that he contracted Rocky Mountain spotted fever and nearly died. In 1935 he brought back from Ceylon a strain of *Plasmodium gallinaceum,* the use of which has been of invaluable help in the chemotherapy of human malaria.

In 1923 Brumpt proved that the cysts of amoebas found in numerous individuals really belong to a nonpathogenic species that differs genetically from the dysenteric amoeba. In the same year, he founded the *Annales de parasitologie humaine et comparée.* He died just after completing the sixth edition of his *Précis de parasitologie.* He trained many students who continue the parasitological tradition that he began.

BIBLIOGRAPHY

Among Brumpt's 376 publications, the principal ones are his doctoral thesis in science, "Réproduction des hirudinées," in *Mémoires de la Société zoologique de France,* **33** (1901); *Mission de Bourg de Bozas. De la Mer Rouge à l'Atlantique à travers l'Afrique tropicale* (Paris, 1903); "Maladie du sommeil expérimentale chez les singes d'Asie et d'Afrique," in *Comptes rendus de la Société de biologie,* **56** (1904), 569; "Expériences relatives au mode de transmission des trypanosomes par les hirudinées," *ibid.,* **61** (1906), 77; *Les mycétomes,* his M.D. thesis (Paris, 1906); "Évolution de *Trypanosoma cruzi* chez *Conorhinus megistus, Cimex lectularius* et *Ornithodorus moubata,"* in *Bulletin de la Société de pathologie exotique,* **6** (1913), 752–758; "Le xénodiagnostic," *ibid.,* **7** (1914), 706–710; "Les piroplasmes des bovidés et leurs hôtes vecteurs," *ibid.,* **13** (1920), 416–460; "Recherches sur la bilharziose au Maroc," *ibid.,* **15** (1922), 632–641; "Les anophèles de Corse," in *Bulletin de l'Académie de médecine,* **93** (1925); "Réalisation expérimentale du cycle complet de *Schistosoma haematobium,"* in *Annales de parasitologie humaine et comparée,* **6** (1928), 440–446; "La ponte des schistosomes," *ibid.,* **8** (1930), 263–292; "Transmission de la fièvre exanthématique de Marseille par *Rhipicephalus sanguineus,"* in *Comptes rendus de l'Académie des sciences* (1930), 1028; "Épreuve de l'immunité croisée dans les fièvres exanthématiques," in *Comptes rendus de la Société de biologie,* **90** (1932), 1197; "Sensibilité du spermophile au Kala Azar chinois," *ibid.* (1935), 21–23; "La tularémie et ses hôtes vecteurs," in *Meditsinskaya parazitologia i parazitarnye bolezni* (1935), 23–28; "Une nouvelle fièvre récurrente humaine découverte à Babylone (Iraq)," in *Comptes rendus de l'Académie des sciences* (1939), 2029; "Étude épidémiologique de la fièvre récurrente des hauts plateaux mexicains," in *Annales de parasitologie humaine et comparée,* **17** (1939), 275–286; "Filarioses et éléphantiasis," in *Annales de la Société belge de médecine tropicale* (1947), 103; and *Précis de parasitologie,* 6th ed. (Paris, 1949).

HENRI GALLIARD

BRUNELLESCHI, FILIPPO (*b.* Florence, Italy, 1377; *d.* Florence, 16 April 1446), *architecture, engineering, geometry.*

While Brunelleschi was undoubtedly the first great Renaissance architect, it remains difficult to assess his importance to the history of science, and in particular to the development of a systematic mathematical perspective. Most of what is known of his life and work is derived from Vasari's *Lives of the Artists,* a book perhaps more notable for its charm than for its accuracy.

Brunelleschi was born into comfortable circumstances; his father, Ser Brunellesco di Lippo Lapi, was a notary and his mother, Giuliana, was a member of the noble Spini family. He had to abandon his formal education at an early age, but showed so much artistic talent that his father apprenticed him to a goldsmith.

Here, according to Vasari, "having become skilled in setting stones, and in niello work, and in the science of the motion of weights and wheels, not content with this, there awoke within him a great desire for the study of sculpture." It may well be that the mechanical knowledge gained in his apprenticeship aided Brunelleschi in the design and construction of engineering devices; certainly, he made some remarkable clocks.

The relationship between the craft of the goldsmith and the art of the sculptor in the fifteenth century is defined by the competition, open to both sculptors and goldsmiths, held in Florence in 1401 for the design of a pair of doors for the baptistery of the church of S. Giovanni. The sculptor Lorenzo Ghiberti won the commission and Brunelleschi, who had also submitted a design, went to Rome with the sculptor Donatello to study architecture. From 1402 to 1418, Brunelleschi lived alternately in Rome and Florence. It was perhaps during this period that, during one of his residences in Florence, he met Paolo dal Pozzo Toscanelli and learned geometry from him. He may also have learned some of the principles of perspective from Toscanelli; at any rate, Vasari states that he not only studied perspective, but also taught it to his friend Masaccio.

Vasari also tells of a meeting of architects and engineers in Florence in 1407 for the purpose of determining how to complete the cathedral of Sta. Maria del Fiore. The medieval architects of the building had intended a dome to be built over the crossing of the cathedral, but the problem of how to erect such a dome had never been solved. Brunelleschi entered the open competition for the design of the dome in 1418—Vasari says that he had already built a model for it—and won. He undertook the work in partnership with his rival Ghiberti, but the latter withdrew from the project. Brunelleschi worked on the cathedral dome from 1420 until his death, just after the lantern had been begun. He did not, as some sources suggest, rediscover the dome, but rather he invented a technique for building it without scaffolding.

Besides his work on the cathedral, Brunelleschi designed notable secular buildings—of which the Ospedale degli Innocenti is perhaps the outstanding example—and carried out military commissions. He may have drawn the plans for the fortress of Milan, constructed by the Sforzas; in 1415 he fortified the Ponte a Mare, and in 1435 he worked on the fortress of Vicopisano. Brunelleschi also worked on the fortification of the old citadel of Pisa and furnished the plans and built the model for the fortifications of the port of Pesaro. It seems likely that he always started such work with the construction of small-scale models; certainly he used such a model for the double dome of Sta. Maria del Fiore.

While many authors have considered Brunelleschi's chief scientific contribution to be his pioneering work in perspective (Vasari even credits him with the invention of monocular perspective), recent research has assigned him a more modest part. As an architect, Brunelleschi was certainly concerned with mathematical proportion, and from this an interest in the theory of perspective may well have been born. And in the Florence of the time, marked as it was by a self-consciously Academic exchange of ideas among artists and scientists, perspective would almost undoubtedly have been a subject for discussion; we know, for example, that Paolo Ucello was simultaneously at work on the problem, and eventually published a treatise on perspective projection that almost certainly incorporated many of Brunelleschi's ideas.

Brunelleschi's initial experiment in perspective may have been his ingenious painting of the baptistery as viewed from the porch of the cathedral. This painting, carefully rendered in perspective, was mounted on a thick wooden panel. A hole was then drilled through the panel at precisely the point that represented the eye of the artist. The aperture was, at the back of the panel, approximately the size of a lentil and widened to an opening about the size of a ducat at the front. The painting was placed to face a perpendicular arrangement of mirrors; when the viewer placed his eye to the hole at the back of the painting, he saw, through an optical illusion, the scene in three dimensions. (Brunelleschi made a second such picture showing the palace of the Seigniory, while Alberti made one of St. Mark's Square in Venice.)

Brunelleschi thus demonstrated his knowledge of conical projection and vanishing points, although it is possible that the concept of the optic box was Toscanelli's, and that Brunelleschi simply made it a reality. In any event, the idea of such a device, known to the ancients, may well have been drawn from the common scientific fund of the fifteenth century.

BIBLIOGRAPHY

The bibliography on Brunelleschi is not very extensive. His life as reported by Vasari has been followed by nearly all of his biographers. The most complete work so far is Venturi, *Brunelleschi* (Rome, 1923). Studies dealing with perspective are G. C. Argan, "The Architecture of Brunelleschi and the Origins of the Perspective Theory in the Fifteenth Century," in *Journal of Warburg and Courtauld Institutes* (1946); and J. B. Lemoine, "Brunelleschi et Ptolémée. Les origines géographiques de la 'boîte d'optique,'" in *Gazette des beaux arts* (1958). One might also consult Francastel, "Naissance d'un espace. Mythes et géométrie du quattrocento," in *Revue d'esthétique*.

BERTRAND GILLE

BRUNFELS, OTTO (*b.* Mainz, Germany, *ca.* 1489; *d.* Bern, Switzerland, 23 [?] November 1534), *botany.*

The earliest of the three "German fathers of botany" (the others being Jerome Bock and Leonhard Fuchs), Brunfels pioneered the dramatically sudden emancipation of botany from medieval herbalism.

Otto was the son of Johann Brunfels, a cooper; his mother's name is unknown. He received his early education locally and the master of arts degree at the University of Mainz in 1508/1509. Subsequently, he entered the Carthusian monastery in Strasbourg. He remained there until 1521, when, aided by Ulrich von Hutten, one of Luther's principal defenders, he fled the monastery and the Catholic faith as well. For the next three years he served as a pastor in Steinau and engaged in theological controversy. He returned to Strasbourg in 1524 and opened his own school. That same year he married Dorothea Heilgenhensin, who later helped to prepare his manuscripts for posthumous publication. There is no record of children from the marriage. He soon demonstrated his interest in medicine by editing and translating various older medical texts and by writing one of the earliest medical bibliographies, the *Catalogus* (1530). In that same year, Volume I of the *Herbarum vivae eicones* appeared, a book destined to change the direction of botany. Between 1530 and 1532, Brunfels supervised the publication of Volume II of the *Herbarum* and Volume I of the *Contrafayt Kreüterbuoch* while writing several other books. About this time, he moved to Basel, where he received the doctor of medicine degree from the university in late 1532. On 3 October 1533 he was appointed town physician in Bern for a period of six years. Approximately a year later, he fell seriously ill and died, possibly from diphtheria. He is commemorated by the genus *Brunfelsia* (*Solanaceae*), named in his honor by Charles Plumier in 1703.

Through his early theological and pedagogical writings and his wide correspondence (still unedited), Brunfels became associated with the local Strasbourg humanists, one of whom, Johann Schott, printed many of his books. Presumably it was through Schott that he became acquainted with the artist Hans Weiditz, whose name is inseparably linked with the *Herbarum*.

Judged by modern standards, the *Herbarum* is a curious combination of the old and the new. The text is a typical late-medieval collection of extracts uncritically compiled from earlier writings and possessing little independent value. The illustrations, on the other hand, are detailed, accurate renderings of plants executed with a realism that revolutionized botanical iconography. Most subsequent sixteenth-century herbals are the direct descendants of a method first enunciated under Brunfels' guidance. The impact of his contribution and the scientific value of the *Herbarum* would have been incalculably greater if the descriptions, like the illustrations, had been taken from nature.

The *Herbarum* is divided into *rhapsodiae* (chapters), each of which is devoted to one plant. The text, essentially a series of verbatim quotations from older authorities, is thematically connected by a concern to identify therapeutically useful plants. For this purpose, classical Greek and Latin names are correlated with the German vernacular names. The plants are not arranged in any systematic order, for it was not Brunfels' intention to propose a classification. Nevertheless, the arrangement is not alphabetical, and related species often appear on successive folios. Most of the plants described (approximately 230 species) were indigenous to Strasbourg and its environs. Over forty species were first described by Brunfels. Exotica, frequently encountered in the incunabula herbals, are ignored.

The bulk of each *rhapsodia* is devoted to the medicinal properties of the plant. Pertinent information includes preparation, administration, and dosage of some specified portion of the plant, time of collection, and the ailments for which the prepared drug was reputedly beneficial. Pharmacological uses are expressed in terms of the Galenic doctrine of "grades" and "temperaments." This information is derived almost exclusively from Brunfels' sources, forty-seven of whom are listed (sig. A iii^v). His main authorities were classical, principally Dioscorides, Pliny, and Galen, although medieval, Arabic, and especially contemporary Italian writers are also cited. Following the extracts from his authorities, there is often a section entitled "Iudicium nostrum" ("My Opinion"), in which Brunfels presents his own evidence.

At the end of Volume II of the *Herbarum* are twelve tracts, collectively entitled "De vera herbarum cognitione appendix," edited by Brunfels. The tracts are devoted primarily to the nomenclature of plants known to the ancients. Both Bock and Fuchs first appear as authors in this collection.

The *Contrafayt Kreüterbuoch*, a German adaptation, not a translation, of the *Herbarum,* was undertaken by Brunfels before the *Herbarum* was completed and prior to his departure for Basel. All but sixteen of the illustrations of the *Herbarum* are repeated, with about fifty additional figures. Not all of the plants discussed are illustrated, however. Altogether about 260 species were depicted in the *Herbarum* and the *Kreüterbuoch*. The text of the latter is better organized, the text being arranged under sectional headings dealing with nomenclature, appearance and form, habitat, time of collecting, and medical uses and properties. The long verbatim extracts were abandoned, although their content was closely paraphrased. Like the *Herbarum,* the *Kreüterbuoch* remained incomplete at Brunfels' death.

One other botanical work was published under Brunfels' name, the posthumous *In Dioscoridis historiam*. It is a series of illustrations taken from the same wood blocks as those used for the *Herbarum,* presented without preface or text save the plants' names, which appear alongside the illustrations.

The three volumes of the *Herbarum* contain 238 woodcut illustrations, ranging in size from full folio to small text figures and normally illustrating the text of the facing or adjacent folio. The illustrations, a happy combination of scientific accuracy and aesthetic charm, were designed by Weiditz, who also cut the majority of the blocks. Despite the width of even the finest lines (less than 200μ) and the fact that Weiditz had had no previous botanical training, details of floral structure and vegetative organography are readily apparent. Moreover, careful attention was given to the general appearance of the plant and its typical habitat. Usually the entire plant is depicted, all portions (root, stem, leaves, blossom, and fruit) receiving equal attention, even though, for example, the function of the stamens or the taxonomic importance of foliaceous bracts was then unappreciated. Leaves damaged by insects, broken petioles and bent stems, and blossoms in different stages of development leave no doubt that the illustrations were based on living plants. The drooping appearance of some stems and leaves suggests that the plant was dug up entire and had begun to wilt when illustrated. Owing largely to the fidelity of the woodcuts, the great majority of the plants discussed by Brunfels have been identified with reasonable certainty.

While Brunfels must be given credit for planning an illustrated herbal and overseeing its preparation, credit is also due Weiditz for executing the realistic illustrations. The *Herbarum* is the first printed botanical book in which scientific value can be assigned to the illustrations. Weiditz' contributions were noted by Brunfels, and through his appreciative comments in the preface of the *Kreüterbuoch* the artist assumes, for the first time, a recognized place in botanical literature. Some of Weiditz' watercolor drawings that served as the originals for the wood blocks of the *Herbarum* were discovered by Rytz in Bern. Their publication demonstrated that the success of the *Herbarum* was, in large measure, the result of Weiditz' participation.

Although Brunfels' other writings were of less scientific importance, they deserve a brief note because they were typical of the times and, contributing to his reputation, they facilitated the acceptance of his botanical work. Leaving aside his theological and pedagogical writings (about twenty-eight separate publications), his nonbotanical work was principally in medicine and pharamacology. In the former, Brunfels was active as a translator (Lanfranchi, Paul of Aegina, Galen) and as an editor (Dioscorides, Fries, Tanstetter, Serapion, and others). He was no less industrious in compiling practical texts designed for the use of physicians and apothecaries, which contained prescriptions and related pharmacological matter and were usually well indexed for ready reference. His most important pharmacological work was the *Reformation der Apotecken.* Originally written in Strasbourg, it was enlarged to serve as a city ordinance for apothecaries in Bern. It contains one of the earliest Swiss dispensatories. Brunfels' passion for compiling and organizing reference material, already evident in the "Appendix de usu et administratione simplicium" (*Herbarum,* I, fols. 273–329) was fully exhibited in his 'Ονομαστικόν, a comprehensive dictionary containing a wealth of material related to medicine, botany, alchemy, and metrology. One other writing, the *De diffinitionibus,* is of interest because of its criticism of astrology.

BIBLIOGRAPHY

I. ORIGINAL WORKS. Brunfels was active as editor, translator, and author.

His own works are *Von allerhandt apoteckischen Confectionen, Lattwergen, Oel, Pillulen, Trencken, Trociscen, Zuckerscheiblin, Salben und Pflastern . . .* (Strasbourg, ca. 1530; repr. Frankfurt, 1552); *Catalogus illustrium medicorum, sive de primis medicinae scriptoribus. . .* (Strasbourg, 1530); *Herbarum vivae eicones ad naturae imitationem, summa cum diligentia et artificio effigiatae, una cum effectibus earundem . . .,* 3 vols.: I (Strasbourg, 1530; repr. 1532, 1536, 1537; with II and III, 1539); II (Strasbourg, 1531 [colophon, 1532], 1536, 1537, 1539); III, Michael Heer, ed. (Strasbourg, 1536, 1537, 1539, 1540); *Contrafayt Kreüterbuoch,* 2 vols.: I (Strasbourg, 1532; repr., with different title, Strasbourg, 1534, 1539; with II, Frankfurt, 1546, 1551); II (Strasbourg, 1537, 1540); facsimile repr. of I (1532) and II (1537) (Munich, 1964); *Theses seu communes loci totius rei medicae. Item. De usu pharmacorum, deque artificio suppressam alvum ciendi, liber* (Strasbourg, 1532); *De diffinitionibus et terminis astrologiae libellus isagogicus,* in Julius Firmicus Maternus, *Ad Mavortium Lollianum astronomicon libri VIII* (Basel, 1533; repr. Basel, 1551); *Jatrion medicamentorum simplicium continens remedia omnium morborum quae tam hominibus quam pecudibus accidere possunt . . .,* 4 vols. (Strasbourg, 1533); 'Ονομαστικόν *medicinae . . .* (Strasbourg, 1534; repr., with different title, Strasbourg, 1543 [colophon, 1544]); *Weiber und Kinder Apoteck,* 2 vols. (Strasbourg, ca. 1534; *Annotationes in quatuor evangelia et acta apostolorum* (Strasbourg, 1535), which, besides autobiographical material, has the only known authentic portrait of Brunfels on the reverse of the title page; *Reformation der Apotecken . . .* (Strasbourg, 1536); *Epitome medices summam totius medicinae complectens . . .* (Paris, 1540); and *In Dioscoridis historiam herbarum certissima adaptatio . . .* (Strasbourg, 1543).

Among the works he edited are Alessandro Benedetti, *Anatomice; sive, De hystoria corporis humani libri quinque* (Strasbourg, 1528); Dioscorides, *Pharmacorum simplicium, reique medicae libri VIII, Jo. Ruellio interprete . . .* (Strasbourg, 1529); Lorenz Fries, *Spiegel der Artzney . . .* (Strasbourg, 1529; repr., with slightly changed title, Strasbourg, 1532, 1546); Georg Tanstetter von Thannau, *Artificium de applicatione astrologie ad medicinam, deque convenientia earundem . . .* (Strasbourg, 1531); and *Neotericorum aliquot medicorum introductiones* (Strasbourg, 1533).

He translated Guido Lanfranchi, *Kleyne Wundartznei . . . auss fürbit des Gregorii Flüguss . . .* (Strasbourg, 1528; repr. with slightly changed title, Strasbourg, 1529; Erfurt, 1529; Zwickau, 1529; Cöllen, n.d. [after 1529]; Frankfurt, 1552, 1569; Magdeburg, n.d. [not before 1578]); Paul of

Aegina, *Pharmaca simplicia, Othone Brunfelsio interprete. Idem, De ratione victus Gulielmo Copo Basiliensi interprete* . . . (Strasbourg, 1531); *In hoc volumine continentur . . . Joan. Serapionis Arabis de simplicibus medicini . . . Averrois Arabis de eisdem liber eximius. Rasis filii Zachariae de eisdem opusculum. . . . Incerti item autoris de centaureo libellus hactenus Galeno inscriptus. Dictionum Arabicarum juxta atque Latinarum index valde necessarius . . .* (Strasbourg, 1531); and Galen, *De ossibus ad tyrones* (Padua, 1551).

II. SECONDARY LITERATURE. Biographical data on Brunfels' life are meager and ultimately derive from the preface of the *Annotationes in quatuor evangelia.* Supplementing them are many references to him and his religious activities in contemporary theological and humanistic writings.

The following concern his scientific work: H. Christ, "Otto Brunfels und seine *Herbarum vivae eicones.* Ein botanischer Reformator des XVI. Jahrhunderts," in *Verhandlungen der Naturforschenden Gesellschaft in Basel,* **38** (1927), 1–11; A. H. Church, "Brunfels and Fuchs," in *Journal of Botany, British and Foreign,* **57** (1919), 233–244; F. A. Flückiger, "Otto Brunfels, Fragment zur Geschichte der Botanik und Pharmacie," in *Archiv der Pharmacie,* **212** (1878), 493–514; Friedrich Kirschleger, *Flore d'Alsace et des contrées limitrophes,* II (Strasbourg–Paris, 1857), xiii–xvii, which contains the identifications of 106 species figured in the *Herbarum;* E. H. F. Meyer, *Geschichte der Botanik,* IV (Königsberg, 1857), 295–303; Claus Nissen, *Die botanische Buchillustration,* 2 vols. (Stuttgart, 1951), I, 40–44; II, nos. 257–261; F. W. E. Roth, "Otto Brunfels. Nach seinem Leben und litterarischen Wirken geschildert." in *Zeitschrift für die Geschichte des Oberrheins,* n.s. **9** (1894), 284–320; "Die Schriften des Otto Brunfels. 1519–1536," in *Jahrbuch für Geschichte, Sprache und Literatur Elsass-Lothringens,* **16** (1900), 257–288, the best bibliography of Brunfels' writings, 49 publications plus 3 dubious ones, but still incomplete; and "Otto Brunfels 1489–1534. Ein deutscher Botaniker," in *Botanische Zeitung,* **58** (1900), 191–232, a well-documented biographical study; Alfred Schmid, "Zwei seltene Kräuterbücher aus dem vierten Dezennium des sechzehnten Jahrhunderts," in *Schweizerischen Gutenbergmuseum,* no. 3 (1936), 160–180, the only study of the quarto eds. of the *Kreüterbuoch* (1534, 1539, 1540, 1551) and the best bibliographical analysis of the complex dating of the various eds. and vols. of the *Herbarum;* Thomas Archibald Sprague, "The Herbal of Otto Brunfels," in *Journal of the Linnean Society* (London), **48** (1928), 79–124, a fundamental study with modern identifications of the plants figured by Brunfels; and Kurt Sprengel, *Geschichte der Botanik,* I (Altenburg–Leipzig, 1817), 258–262, containing the identifications, some dubious, of 131 species figured by Brunfels.

Also of interest are Karl Hartfelder, "Otto Brunfels als Verteidiger Huttens," in *Zeitschrift für die Geschichte des Oberrheins,* n.s. **8** (1893), 565–578; Heinrich Röttinger, "Hans Weiditz, der strassburger Holzschnittzeichner," in *Elsass-Lothringisches Jahrbuch,* **16** (1937), 75–125; Walther Rytz, *Pflanzenaquarelle des Hans Weiditz aus dem Jahre*

1529. *Die Originale zu den Holzschnitten im Brunfels'schen Kräuterbuch* (Bern, 1936); and Erich Sanwald, *Otto Brunfels 1488–1534. Ein Beitrag zur Geschichte des Humanismus und der Reformation. I. Hälfte 1488–1524* (Bottrop, Germany, 1932).

JERRY STANNARD

BRUNHES, JEAN (*b.* Toulouse, France, 25 October 1869; *d.* Boulogne-sur-Seine, France, 25 April 1930), *geography.*

Brunhes came from a family of university professors: both his father, Julien, and his older brother, Bernard, were professors of physics. Jean entered the École Normale Supérieure in 1889, and in 1892 he graduated and passed the *agrégation* in history and geography. His faculty adviser was Vidal de la Blache. On a scholarship from the Thiers Foundation from 1892 to 1896, he completed his education by taking courses in law, mining, and agriculture. He found his true vocation in geography when he wrote the thesis "L'irrigation, ses conditions géographiques . . . dans la péninsule ibérique et l'Afrique du Nord," which he defended in 1902.

Brunhes was named professor of general geography at the University of Fribourg in 1896, and in 1908 he was appointed to give a course in human geography at the University of Lausanne. He continued to work in human geography, a science that did not then exist in France.

In his *Anthropogéographie* the German geographer Friedrich Ratzel attempted to explain man in terms of nature and to make history and culture dependent on geography. In contrast, Brunhes saw in nature "not a tyrannical fatalism, but an infinite wealth of possibilities among which man has the power to choose" (S. Charléty, *Notes sur la vie et les travaux de M. J. Brunhes* [Paris, 1932], p. 13). He also believed that there is no social determinism whose laws can be ascertained. In his great work, *Géographie humaine* (1910), Brunhes presented the first attempt to coordinate the geographical phenomena resulting from the activities of man. It was illustrated with numerous photographs. In 1912 the Collège de France created a chair of human geography for him.

A member of the Académie des Sciences Morales et Politiques since 1927, Brunhes died suddenly of a stroke just after he and his daughter, Mme. Raymond Delamarre, had published *Les races,* a small, richly illustrated book.

Certain geographers have reproached Brunhes for having extended geography to cover all forms of human activity; others have criticized him for having limited the study of geography to what is "photographable." Nevertheless, he gave a decisive impetus to human geography.

BIBLIOGRAPHY

I. Original Works. Brunhes's writings include *La géographie humaine. Essai de classification positive. Principes et exemples* (Paris, 1910, 1912, 1925), trans. into English (Chicago–New York, 1920); 2 vols. in G. Hanotaux's *Histoire de la nation française:* I. *Géographie humaine de la France* (Paris, 1926), and II, *Géographie politique et géographie du travail* (Paris, 1926), written with P. Deffontaines; and *Les races* (Paris, 1930), written with his daughter, Mme. Raymond Delamarre. He also translated Isaiah Bowman's *The New World* as *Le monde nouveau. Tableau général de géographie politique universelle* (Paris, 1928).

II. Secondary Literature. Biographies of Brunhes are A. Allix, in *Les études rhodaniennes,* **6** (1930), 340–342; M. Boule, in *L'anthropologie,* **40** (1930), 514–515; V. Châtelain, in *Dictionnaire de biographie française,* fasc. 39 (1955), cols. 554–555; D. Faucher, in *Revue de géographie des Pyrénées et du Sud-ouest,* **1** (1930), 514–515; E. de Martonne, in *Annales de géographie,* **39** (1930), 549–553; and G. Vallaux, in *La géographie,* **34** (1930), 237–239.

Juliette Taton

BRUNO, GIORDANO (*b*. Nola, Italy, 1548; *d*. Rome, Italy, 17 February 1600), *philosophy.*

Bruno's baptismal name was Filippo; he took the name Giordano, by which he is always known, on entering the Dominican order. His father, Giovanni, was a soldier, and probably a man of fairly good position; his mother, Fraulissa Savolino, has been conjectured to have been of German descent, although there is no real evidence. Hardly anything is known of Bruno's early years in Nola, a small town near Naples.

At the age of fifteen, Bruno entered the Dominican order and became an inmate of the great Dominican convent in Naples. Here he acquired a grounding in Scholastic philosophy and the reverence for Thomas Aquinas (who had lived and taught in the Naples convent) that he professed throughout his life. Here, too, he became proficient in the art of memory, for which the Dominicans were noted, and was taken to Rome to display his mnemonic skill to Pope Pius V. Another influence which he may have come under in these early years was that of the famous natural magician and scientist Giambattista della Porta, who in 1560 had established in Naples his academy for investigating the secrets of nature. Bruno was formed during these years in Naples: his mind and character

never lost the imprint of his training as a friar; and it was as a passionate ex-friar that he wandered over Europe, combining philosophical speculation with a religious mission evolved through deep immersion in Renaissance magic and its Hermetic sources.

Bruno's religion was the moving force behind both his wandering career and his philosophical and cosmic speculations. He believed that he was reviving the magical religion of the ancient Egyptians, a religion older than Judaism or Christianity, which these inferior religions had suppressed but of which he prophesied the imminent return. It included a belief in the magical animation of all nature, which the magus could learn how to tap and to use, and a belief in metempsychosis. The historical origins of Bruno's "Egyptianism" and the printed sources whence he derived it are now clear, owing to the work done by scholars in fairly recent years on the Hermetic core of Renaissance Neoplatonism.

As propagated by Marsilio Ficino, Renaissance Neoplatonism included a firm belief that both Plato and his followers had been inspired by a tradition of *prisca theologia,* or pristine and pure theology, which had come down to them from the teachings of Hermes Trismegistus, a mythical Egyptian sage, and other figures supposedly of extreme antiquity. This belief rested on the misdating of certain late antique texts, of which the most important were the *Asclepius* and the *Corpus Hermeticum,* which were supposed to have been written by Hermes Trismegistus himself.

Ficino believed that these texts contained authentic revelations about ancient Egyptian religion and that in them their supposed author prophesied the coming of Christianity—and, hence, could take on sanctity as a Gentile prophet. The scraps of Platonic notions incorporated by the late antique Gnostic writers of the Hermetic texts were, for Ficino, evidence that these ancient "Egyptian" teachings were the pristine source at which Plato and the Neoplatonists had drunk. These beliefs could be supported from works of some Church Fathers, notably Lactantius. Nor were they peculiar to Ficino; on the contrary, the whole Renaissance Neoplatonic movement contained this Hermetic core, and the religious magic, or theurgy, taught by Hermes Trismegistus, particularly in the *Asclepius,* seemed corroborated by the intensive Renaissance study of the later Neoplatonists, such as Porphyry and Iamblichus. As a pious Christian, Ficino was encouraged by the sanctity of Hermes Trismegistus as a Gentile prophet to embark on the astral magic described in the *Asclepius,* which lies behind his own work on astral magic, the *De vita coelitus comparanda,* although he did this hesitantly and timidly, in fear of the Church's embargo on magic.

The extreme boldness and fearlessness that characterized Giordano Bruno are nowhere more apparent than in his choice of a religion. Discarding the belief in Hermes as a Gentile prophet, which sanctified the Hermetic writings for pious Christian Neoplatonists, Bruno accepted the pseudo-Egyptian religion described in the Hermetic texts as the true religion; he interpreted the lament in the *Asclepius* over the decay of Egypt and her magical worship as a lament for the true Egyptian religion, which had been suppressed by Christianity, although various signs and portents were announcing its return.

Among these signs was the heliocentricity announced by Copernicus—and it must be confessed that Copernicus himself did something to encourage such an interpretation of his discovery when, at a crucial point in his work, just after the diagram showing the new sun-centered system, he referred to Hermes Trismegistus on the sun as a visible god (a quotation from the *Asclepius*). In his defense of Copernicanism against the Aristotelians of Oxford, Bruno presented Copernicus as "only a mathematician" who had not understood the true inwardness of his discovery as he, Bruno, understood it—as portending a return to magical insight into living nature. In support of the movement of the earth, Bruno quoted a passage from one of the treatises of the *Corpus Hermeticum,* which states that the earth moves because it is alive.

The magical animism that permeates Bruno's philosophy of nature, his vision of the living earth moving round the sun, of an infinite universe of innumerable worlds moving like great animals in space, is inseparably connected with his pseudo-Egyptian religion. It is universal animism which makes possible the activities of the magus and justifies the techniques by which he attempts to operate on nature. Bruno aspired to become such a magus, using the techniques described in the *De occulta philosophia* of Henry Cornelius Agrippa von Nettesheim, a work that was itself the product of the Hermetic core within Renaissance Neoplatonism.

It is one of the most extraordinary features of Bruno's outlook that he seems to have believed that his religion could somehow be incorporated within a Catholic framework in the coming new dispensation. He never lost his respect for Thomas Aquinas, and his preaching of his new religion retained traces of Dominican preacher's training. Although Christ was for him a benevolent magus, as were Thomas Aquinas, Paracelsus, Ramón Lull, and Giordano Bruno himself, he proclaimed in the *Spaccio della bestia trionfante* that Christ was to remain in heaven as an example of a good life.

While still in the convent in Naples, he fell under suspicion of heresy and proceedings were instituted against him. The suspicion against him seems to have been of Arian tendencies; possibly his full "Egyptian" program was not yet developed. To avoid the process against him he left Naples in 1576. He went first to Rome, where he fell into new difficulties, from which he escaped by abandoning the Dominican habit and fleeing from Italy. Now began his long odyssey through France, England, Germany. He went first to Geneva, where he soon got into trouble and acquired a strong dislike of Calvinism.

From about 1579 to 1581 he was in Toulouse, where he lectured in the university on, among other things, the *Sphere* of Sacrobosco. From Toulouse he went to Paris; here his public lectures attracted the attention of King Henry III. His first published work, the *De umbris idearum* (Paris, 1582), is dedicated to Henry. It is an example of his transformation of the art of memory into a deeply magical art, and its title is taken from that of a magical book mentioned in the necromantic commentary on the *Sphere* of Sacrobosco by Cecco d'Ascoli, an author whom Bruno greatly admired. Bruno thus came before the world in his first Parisian period as a magician teaching some extremely abstruse art of memory that apparently gained the interest and approval of the king of France, who gave him letters of recommendation to the French ambassador in England. This is the first indication of some mysterious political, or politico-religious, undercurrent in Bruno's activities and movements.

Bruno crossed the Channel to England early in 1583; the royal letters of recommendation had the desired effect, for the French ambassador, Michel de Mauvissière, received him into the French embassy, where during the two years of his stay in England he lived as a "gentleman" attached to the embassy. He states that he often accompanied the ambassador to court and saw Queen Elizabeth, whom he addresses as "divine" in his works, an epithet that he had to try to explain away to the Inquisitors. The ambassadorial protection enabled Bruno to publish his extremely provocative works, in which he criticized Reformation Oxford as inferior in philosophical learning to the Oxford of the Middle Ages and attacked the whole social order of Elizabethan England for having destroyed, without adequately replacing, the institutions of Catholic times. His books were published clandestinely, with false imprints, by John Charlewood. As was to be expected, they aroused tumults against the bold ex-friar that were sometimes so violent that he dared not go outside the embassy.

Bruno opened his campaign in England with one of his obscure works on the magic art of memory, the *Triginta sigilli*; hidden away at the end of it there is a passionate advocacy of a new religion based on love, art, magic, and mathesis; it begins with an abusive dedication to the vice-chancellor and doctors of Oxford. This would seem to have been a strange preparation for his visit to Oxford in the train of the Polish prince, Albert Laski. A newly discovered source, first published in 1960, has thrown much light on Bruno's famous advocacy of the Copernican theory to the recalcitrant Aristotelians of Oxford. It appears that after Laski's party had left, Bruno returned to Oxford and delivered lectures that consisted mainly of quotation from Ficino's book on astral magic, *De vita coelitus comparanda,* with which he associated the opinion of Copernicus "that the earth did go round and the heavens did stand still." Bruno's unacknowledged quotations from Ficino were detected by some of his auditors, as is recounted in the newly discovered report of his speech. This new information about Bruno's Oxford lectures is external confirmation of what can also be clearly deduced from his works; that for Bruno, Copernican heliocentricity was associated with his magical and animist view of nature.

The brilliant dialogues in Italian that Bruno published while in England have been the most widely read of his works and were the main foundation for his reputation as a bold philosopher breaking out of the closed medieval universe into a new vision of the cosmos. This reputation is by no means undeserved, although it now has to be formulated in more accurate historical terms than those used by his nineteenth-century admirers, who were unaware that their hero was a magician and knew nothing of the complex political and religious situation in Elizabethan England, the scene of these exploits. In the *Cena de le ceneri* (1584) he defends Copernican heliocentricity against two Oxford "pedants." The angry protests that this attack aroused are described in *De la causa, principio e uno* (1584); Bruno here offers a slight apology for his attack on Oxford—but in the form of professing admiration for the friars of pre-Reformation Oxford, with whom he unfavorably compares their Protestant successors. This can have done little to improve the situation, and the censor can have been prevented from taking action against the book only because it was dedicated to the French ambassador. In the *De l'infinito, universo e mondi* (1584), Bruno sets forth his remarkable vision of an infinite universe and innumerable worlds infused with divine life.

In the *Spaccio della bestia trionfante* (1584), he turns to the moral, as apart from the physical or philosophical, side of his message, and outlines a universal moral and religious reform. The curious form of this work, which is based on the constellations from which vices are said to be expelled, to be replaced by virtues, is related to Bruno's adaptations of the art of memory. The *Cabala del cavallo Pegaseo* (1585) is an obscure discussion of the Jewish cabala. In the *De gli eroici furori* (1585), Bruno expresses himself in a sequence of beautiful poems followed by commentaries explaining their philosophic and mystical meanings. This book is dedicated to Philip Sidney, as is the *Spaccio della bestia trionfante.* All the other Italian dialogues, with the exception of the *Cabala del cavallo Pegaseo,* are dedicated to the French ambassador. One is left wondering how far the extraordinary philosophical, magical, and religious views that Bruno propagated from the safety of the French embassy were acceptable to the distinguished persons to whom he dedicated these books. They are all full of Hermetic influences and are bound up with the complex religious, or politico-religious, mission for which he seems to have believed that he had the support of the king of France and to which the French ambassador seems to have lent his protection.

Meanwhile, in France the Catholic League was rising in power; Henry III's position grew precarious; Mauvissière, the liberal ambassador, was recalled, and late in 1585 Bruno returned to Paris in his train. Immediately he began to talk and to publish, expounding his philosophy in an address delivered by a disciple in the Collège de Cambrai, which was tumultuously received. The king's support was indirectly withdrawn; and Bruno made himself notorious in a quarrel about a compass with Fabrizio Mordente, which may have had a political background. Paris became too dangerous for him, and in 1586 he fled, this time toward Germany.

At Wittenberg he felt happy for a time: the university allowed him to lecture, and he found that he greatly preferred German Lutherans to English Calvinists. Here he wrote a number of works, particularly on Lullism, which he believed that he understood better than Lull himself. But eventually here also trouble started, and after delivering a moving farewell oration to the doctors of Wittenberg, he went on to Prague, where he dedicated to Emperor Rudolph II his *Articuli adversus mathematicos* (1588), in which he professed to be strongly against mathematics. This book is illustrated with magical diagrams. In the Preface he urges the emperor to lead a movement of religious toleration and philanthropy. Yet even Rudolph, who collected strange people at his court, did not extend a warm welcome to Bruno; he gave him a little money, but no position, and Bruno wandered on to Helmstedt. Here he found support from Henry Julius of Brunswick-Wolfenbüttel, who may have been in sympathy with his ideas; at any rate, he allowed Bruno to deliver an oration on his recently deceased father which echoed the moral and religious program of the *Spaccio della bestia trionfante.* While at Helmstedt, Bruno was busily writing; the *De magia* and other works on magic preserved in the Noroff manuscript may have been written during this period. Henry Julius possibly gave him money toward the publication of the Latin poems that he had been writing during his travels; and Bruno went on to Frankfurt to supervise their printing.

The *De immenso et innumerabilibus,* the *De triplici minimo et mensura,* and the *De monade numero et figura* were published in 1591. In these poems, written in a style imitating that of Lucretius, Bruno expounded for the last time his philosophical and cosmological meditations, mingled, as in the works published in England, with powerful Hermetic influences. His last published work, also published in 1591 by Wechel at Frankfurt, was a book on the magic art of memory dedicated to the alchemist and magician Johannes Hainzell.

While at Frankfurt, Bruno received, through an Italian bookseller who came to the Frankfurt fair, an invitation from Zuan Mocenigo, a Venetian nobleman, to come to Venice and teach him the secrets of his art of memory. He accepted, and in August 1591, he returned to Italy, going first to Padua and then to Venice. There can be little doubt that Bruno believed, like many others at the time, that the conversion of Henry IV of France was a sign of vast impending religious changes in Rome, and that he and his mysterious mission would be well received in the approaching new dispensation. That he had no idea that he was running into danger is shown by the curious fact that he took with him the manuscript of a book that he intended to dedicate to Pope Clement VIII.

Bruno's reception in Italy was tragically other than he had expected. Mocenigo informed against him, and he was arrested and incarcerated in the prisons of the Inquisition in Venice. There followed a long trial, at the end of which Bruno recanted his heresies and threw himself on the mercy of the inquisitors. He had to be sent on to Rome for another trial, however, and there his case dragged on for eight years of imprisonment and interrogation. After some wavering, he finally refused to recant any of his views, with the result that he was burned alive as a dangerous heretic on the Campo de' Fiori in Rome.

The grounds on which Bruno was sentenced are unknown, for the *processo,* or official document containing the sentence, is irretrievably lost. It formed part of a mass of archives that were transported, by order of Napoleon, from Rome to Paris, where they were pulped. From the reports of the interrogations, it is, however, possible to form an idea of the drift of the case against him. To his major theological heresy, the denial of the divinity of the Second Person of the Trinity, was added suspicion of diabolical magical practices. It was probably mainly as a magician that Bruno was burned, and as the propagator throughout Europe of some mysterious magico-religious movement. This movement may have been in the nature of a secret Hermetic sect, and may be connected with the origins of Rosicrucianism or of Freemasonry. If any philosophical or cosmological points were included in his condemnation, these would have been inextricably bound up with his "Egyptianism."

The legend that the nineteenth century built around Bruno as the hero who, unlike Galileo, refused to retract his belief that the earth moves is entirely without foundation. Bruno's case may, however, have affected the attitude of the Church toward the Copernican hypothesis and may have encouraged the Inquisition's suspicion of Galileo. Although Galileo accepted the Copernican world view on entirely different grounds from Bruno, there are curious formal resemblances between his *Dialogo dei due massime sistemi del mondo,* in which the pedantic Simplicius takes the Aristotelian side, and Bruno's *Cena de le ceneri,* in which the Oxford pedants oppose the "new philosophy."

The history of Bruno's reputation is instructive. Abhorred by Marin Mersenne as an impious deist, he was more favorably mentioned by Kepler. Rumors of his diabolism seem to have been circulated, and were mentioned even by Pierre Bayle in one of the footnotes to his contemptuous article on Bruno. The eighteenth-century deist John Toland revived interest in some of his works. It was not until about the mid-nineteenth century that a revival on a large scale began to gather strength and the legend of the martyr for modern science was invented—of the man who died, not for any religious belief, but solely for his acceptance of the Copernican theory and his bold vision of an infinite universe and innumerable worlds. Statues in his honor proliferated in Italy; the literature on him became immense.

In the late nineteenth and early twentieth centuries, Giordano Bruno was one of the most widely known, and most frequently written about, philosophers of the Italian Renaissance. His ideas, isolated from their historical context, were interpreted in terms of the then dominant type of history of philosophy, for example, by Giovanni Gentile, and the large areas in his writings that are not intelligible in terms of straight philosophical thinking were neglected or ignored. Leo Olschki was probably one of the first to notice that no coherent philosophical system could be drawn from Bruno's works through this approach; and Antonio Corsano emphasized the magical ingredients in Bruno's thought and the politico-religious aspects of his activities. It is, however, the work that has been done in recent years on the Renaissance Hermetic tradition that has at last made it possible to place Bruno within a context in which his philosophy, his magic, and his religion can all be seen as belonging to an outlook that, however strange, makes historical sense.

Now that Giordano Bruno has been, as it were, found out as a Hermetic magician of a most extreme type, is he therefore to be rejected as of no serious importance in the history of thought? This is not the right way to pose the question. Rather, it should be recognized that Renaissance magic, and that turning toward the world as a revelation of the divine that is the motive force in the "religion of the world" that inspired Bruno, was itself a preparation or a stage in the great movement that, running out of the Renaissance into the seventeenth century, gradually shed its irrational characteristics for the genuinely scientific approach to the world. Bruno's leap upward through the spheres into an infinite universe, although it is to be interpreted as the experience of a Gnostic magician, was at the same time an exercise of speculative imagination presaging the advent of new world views. Although Bruno infused the innumerable worlds of which he had learned from Lucretius with magical animism, this was in itself a remarkable vision of a vastly extended universe through which ran one law. We can accept Bruno's Renaissance vision as prophetic of coming world views, although formulated within a very strange frame of reference.

Again, Bruno's atomism, derived from his study of Lucretius through magical interpretation of Lucretius in such a writer as Palingenius, whose *Zodiacus vitae* was one of Bruno's inspirations, may have stimulated the attention of other thinkers. The Renaissance interpretation of Lucretius, which was begun by Ficino, is a stage in the history of atomism which has not yet been adequately examined. When that history comes to be written, Bruno's magically animated atoms may be found to hold some transitional place in it.

Another example of Bruno's thought as a presage of scientific discovery is his remarkable intuition about the circular movement of the blood, which he based on parallelism between man and the universe; he believed that "spirit" is the driving force that moves the blood, the same spirit that is diffused through the universe and that Plato defined as "num-

ber which moves in a circle." Hence, the movement of the blood within the body, said Bruno, is circular, diffused from the heart in a circular movement.

One of the closest connections between Bruno and a seventeenth-century scientific philosopher is that which can be discerned in the influence of Bruno's *Cena de le ceneri* on William Gilbert's *De magnete*. The magnet is always mentioned in textbooks on magic as an example of the occult sympathies in action; and Bruno, when defending his animistic version of heliocentricity, brought in the magnet. Gilbert's language when defending heliocentricity in the *De magnete* is extremely close to that of Bruno; like Bruno, he cites Hermes and others who stated that there is a universal life in nature when he is arguing in favor of earth movement. The magnetic philosophy that Gilbert extended to the whole universe seems most closely allied to that of Bruno, and it is not surprising that Francis Bacon should have listed Gilbert with Bruno as proud and fantastic magi of whom he strongly disapproved.

Even the strangest and most formidably obscure of Bruno's works, those on his magic arts of memory, can be seen to presage, on the Hermetic plane, seventeenth-century strivings after method. Bruno aimed at arranging magically activated images of the stars in memory in such a way as to draw magical powers into the psyche. These systems were of an incredible complexity, involving combinations of memory images with the revolving wheels of Lull to form ways of grasping everything in the universe at once and in all possible combinations. Bruno's Hermetic computers, if one may be permitted to call them such, were almost certainly known to Leibniz, who was also familiar with the art of memory and with Lullism. When introducing his universal calculus, Leibniz uses language that is remarkably similar to that in which Bruno introduced his art of memory to the doctors of Oxford. The many curious connections between Bruno and Leibniz may, when fully explored, form one of the best means of watching the transitions from Renaissance occultism to seventeenth-century science.

Within that view of the history of thought in which the Renaissance magus is seen as the immediate precursor of the seventeenth-century scientist, Giordano Bruno holds a significant place, and his tragic death early in the first year of the new century must still arrest our attention as symbolic of a great turning point in human history.

BIBLIOGRAPHY

I. ORIGINAL WORKS. Bruno's Latin works are in *Opera latine,* Francisco Fiorentino, Vittorio Imbriani, C. M.

Tallarigo, Felice Tocco, and Girolamo Vitelli, eds., 3 vols. (Naples–Florence, 1879–1891), also in a facsimile reprint (Stuttgart–Bad Cannstatt, 1962). Latin works discovered and published since this edition are *Due dialoghi sconosciuti e due dialoghi noti,* Giovanni Aquilecchia, ed. (Rome, 1957); and *Praelectiones geometricae e ars deformationum,* Giovanni Aquilecchia, ed. (Rome, 1964). The Italian works are collected in *Dialoghi italiani,* Giovanni Gentile, ed., revised by Giovanni Aquilecchia (Florence, 1957), which contains all the Italian dialogues in one volume; one of the works, *La cena de le ceneri,* has been published separately with intro. and notes by Giovanni Aquilecchia (Turin, 1955).

Translations of Bruno's works include "Concerning the Cause, Principle, and One," Dorothea W. Singer, trans., in Sidney Greenberg, *The Infinite in Giordano Bruno* (New York, 1950), pp. 77 ff.; "On the Infinite Universe and Worlds," Dorothea W. Singer, trans., in her *Giordano Bruno, His Life and Thought* (New York, 1950), pp. 227 ff.; *Des fureurs héroïques,* Paul-Henri Michel, trans. (Paris, 1954); *The Expulsion of the Triumphant Beast,* Arthur D. Imerti, trans. (New Brunswick, New Jersey, 1964); *Giordano Bruno's "The Heroic Frenzies,"* Paul Eugene Memo, trans. (Chapel Hill, N.C., 1964).

II. SECONDARY LITERATURE. A bibliography of Bruno's works and of books and articles on him up to and including 1950 is Virgilio Salvestrini and Luigi Firpo, *Bibliografia di Giordano Bruno (1582–1950)* (Florence, 1958). Documentary sources on his life are Vincenzo Spampanato, ed., *Documenti della vita di Giordano Bruno* (Florence, 1933); and Angelo Mercati, ed., *Il sommario del processo di Giordano Bruno* (Vatican City, 1942). The standard biography is Vincenzo Spampanato, *Vita di Giordano Bruno* (Messina, 1921); on the trial, see Luigi Firpo, *Il processo di Giordano Bruno* (Naples, 1949).

The following brief selection from a vast literature includes books illustrative of the history of Bruno's reputation: Domenico Berti, *La vita di Giordano Bruno da Nola* (Florence, 1867); Felice Tocco, *Le opere latine di G. Bruno* (Florence, 1889), and *Le fonti più recenti del Bruno* (Rome, 1892); J. Lewis McIntyre, *Giordano Bruno* (London, 1903); Giovanni Gentile, *Giordano Bruno e il pensiero del Rinascimento* (Florence, 1920); Leo Olschki, *Giordano Bruno* (Halle, 1924), also translated into Italian (Bari, 1927); Ernst Cassirer, *Individuum und Kosmos in der Philosophie der Renaissance* (Berlin–Leipzig, 1927), also translated into English by Mario Domandi (New York, 1963); Antonio Corsano, *Il pensiero di Giordano Bruno* (Florence, 1940); Eugenio Garin, *La filosofia* (Milan, 1947); Walter Pagel, "Giordano Bruno: The Philosophy of Circles and the Circular Movement of the Blood," in *Journal of the History of Medicine and Allied Sciences,* **6** (1951), 116–125; Alexandre Koyré, *From the Closed World to the Infinite Universe* (Baltimore, 1957); Paolo Rossi, *Clavis universalis* (Milan, 1960), pp. 109–134; Paul-Henri Michel, *La cosmologie de Giordano Bruno* (Paris, 1962); Paul Oskar Kristeller, *Eight Philosophers of the Italian Renaissance* (Palo Alto, Calif., 1964), pp. 127–144.

This article is based on my books, *Giordano Bruno and*

the Hermetic Tradition (Chicago, 1964), and *The Art of Memory* (Chicago, 1966). On Bruno, Gilbert, and Bacon, see my essay "The Hermetic Tradition in Renaissance Science," in *Art, Science, and History in the Renaissance,* Charles S. Singleton, ed. (Baltimore, 1968), pp. 255–274.

FRANCES A. YATES

BRUNSCHVICG, LÉON (*b.* Paris, France, 10 November 1869; *d.* Aix-les-Bains, France, 18 January 1944), *philosophy.*

Brunschvicg, of Alsatian origin, achieved a brilliant record at the Lycée Condorcet. There his fellow students included Marcel Proust; Célestin Bouglé, a future sociologist; Xavier Léon; and Élie Halévy, in whose home, around 1885, he met Victor Hugo, Leconte de Lisle, and Bizet. His professor of philosophy, A. Darlu, taught him technical precision and severe self-criticism, and gave him a living example of a sage. In 1888 Brunschvicg entered the École Normale Supérieure with Halévy and Bouglé. At the Sorbonne he took the courses taught by Victor Brochard and Émile Boutroux; it was with the latter's son Pierre that he became more deeply interested in mathematics. He soon obtained the *licence ès lettres,* and received the *licence ès sciences* in 1891.

With F. Gazier, Brunschvicg and Boutroux prepared a fourteen-volume edition of Pascal (1904–1914). Brunschvicg also founded, with Xavier Léon and Élie Halévy, the *Revue de métaphysique et de morale* (1893). On 30 August 1891 he passed his *agrégation* in philosophy and became a professor at the *lycée* of Lorient until 1893; he then taught at the *lycée* of Tours until 1895 and at that of Rouen until 1900. On 29 March 1897 he presented his doctoral theses: *Qua ratione Aristoteles metaphysicam vim syllogismo inesse demonstraverit* and *La modalité du jugement.* In the same year he published the *Pensées* and *Opuscules* of Pascal.

In 1899 Brunschvicg married Cécile Kahn, who was active in social work and served as undersecretary for education in 1936–1937. They had four children, the first of whom died young. Brunschvicg was made professor at the Lycée Condorcet in 1900, and in 1903 succeeded Bergson at the Première Supérieure of the Lycée Henri IV. Promoted to the Sorbonne in 1909, he taught there and at the École Normale Supérieure for thirty years. After World War I he was elected to the Académie des Sciences Morales et Politiques (1919), of which he became president in 1932. Also in 1919 he founded the Societas Spinozana and received an honorary doctorate from the University of Durham. During World War II, Nazi persecution forced Brunschvicg to leave Paris. He took refuge first at Aix-en-Provence, then in the departments of Gers and Gard, and finally at Aix-les-Bains, where he died.

When Brunschvicg's own doctrine was taking shape, between 1886 and 1896, a reaction was becoming apparent against the dominant influence of Taine and Renan, the eclecticism of Victor Cousin, and psychology like that of Théodule Ribot. Drawing interest were Félix Ravaisson, Charles Renouvier, Jules Lachelier, Émile Boutroux, and, among the classical philosophers, Plato—whom Brunschvicg always opposed to Aristotle and, consequently, to Scholasticism—and Descartes, whose *Géométrie* he preferred to his *Cogito*. Spinoza was his favorite; he also commented on Pascal, with whom, by his own admission, he shared not a single idea except in science; Kant, who was then little known; and even Fichte. On the other hand, Brunschvicg always refused to follow Schelling and Hegel in their *Naturphilosophie*. Thus his critical idealism was already heralded, with the support of the reflective method.

This idealism had already taken form in *La modalité du jugement*. Judgment is an action that defines the mind. Far from finding the concept already present, as an image or a quasi thing—in any event, as a datum—as is supposed by conceptualists, especially Aristotle, the mind creates the concept through syntheses that form the basis of analysis. At times judgment asserts an intrinsic relationship between ideas, and it must then be classified at the level of *necessity*, in the modality of *interiority*. At times it repeatedly asserts a being as an externality, and then it must be classified at the level of the *real*, in the modality of *exteriority*. Finally, at times, knowing that it does not produce sensation, judgment discovers that it alone can produce at least all intelligible reality, and it must then be classified at the level of the *possible* in a *mixed* modality. This means that in the immanence of the mind, the only valuable knowledge is that which unites the interiority of thought with the exteriority of experience. Going from theory to practice, judgment again turns to *necessity* when the activity of the mind includes the conditions of its satisfaction, to *reality* when it does not include them, and to *possibility* when it feels in harmony with the external world.

If judgment is an action, it can be known only by its work, and this implies a method of *historical verification*. In this and this only, Brunschvicg is linked to the Port-Royal *Logic,* to Bernard Fontenelle, and to positivism. Verification is necessary in order not to lose oneself in the verbalism of the a priori. History tests doctrines. It chooses, disengaging from confusion the primitive—the infantile, the adolescent,

in short, the irrational—which it eliminates, and the innovator, the progress of conscience, of which it draws the curve. As from the complexity of facts scientists determine a law, both real and ideal, so Brunschvicg's historico-reflective method endeavors to unsnarl from the tangle of factual history a normative history in which intelligence never ceases to prove the legitimacy of its victory over all empiricism.

Of all the mind's works, is not science, especially mathematics, the best expression of its rationality? Consequently, Brunschvicg began by following the developments of mathematical philosophy in *Les étapes de la philosophie mathématique*. This was not the history of mathematics, but the underlining of its essential innovations: (1) Pythagorean dogmatism, which was shattered by the discovery of irrationals; (2) with Plato, the consciousness of operative dynamism; (3) with Aristotle, the appearance of formal logic; (4) the sinking of mathematics in the Middle Ages into syllogistic deduction; (5) the renaissance of Platonism with Descartes and the invention of analytical geometry; (6) the crisis brought about by infinitesimal calculus; (7) the revolution brought on by non-Euclidean geometries, symbolic logic, renewed intuitionism, and relativity. With what result? According to a contemporary mathematician, André Lichnérowicz, in *Les étapes*, which is probably the last book to treat of "mathematical philosophy," Brunschvicg foresaw the resolutely nonontological orientation and the unification—through the study of algebraic-topological structures—of today's mathematics.

L'expérience humaine et la causalité physique rediscovers, throughout the history of the accepted concepts of nature, the stages corresponding to those of mathematical philosophy, from the most primitive to the most recent, proceeding through Platonism, Aristotelianism, Scholasticism, Cartesian mechanism, and Hegelianism. "There is only one Universe" should be the only correct statement concerning causality for anyone who would defend the value of rational experience against the scorn of empiricism; the constantly unforeseen progress, always free and yet always linked, of physics. Once more the thesis of critical idealism is confirmed.

The lesson drawn from the history of science in *Les étapes* and *L'expérience humaine*, and from the studies on Pascal, Spinoza, and Descartes, was completed by the history of philosophy in Brunschvicg's third masterwork, *Le progrès de la conscience dans la philosophie occidentale*. Raymond Aron has shown how Brunschvicg, by depending on science without falling into positivism, by turning to historical development without losing timelessness, reached an ethics of creative man, free and rational—man at his highest, "equal to his own idea of himself."

Brunschvicg's influence is easily recognized in all types of thinkers: such moralists as René Le Senne and Georges Bastide, such aestheticians as Joseph Segond and Valentin Feldmann, and particularly such epistemologists as Gaston Bachelard, Robert Blanché, Jean Cavaillès, Alexandre Koyré, and Albert Lautmann.

BIBLIOGRAPHY

I. ORIGINAL WORKS. Brunschvicg's books are *La modalité du jugement* (Paris, 1897), 3rd ed., enl., entitled *La vertu métaphysique du syllogisme selon Aristote* (Paris, 1964); *Introduction à la vie de l'esprit* (Paris, 1900); *L'idéalisme contemporain* (Paris, 1905); *Les étapes de la philosophie mathématique* (Paris, 1912); *Nature et liberté* (Paris, 1921); *L'expérience humaine et la causalité physique* (Paris, 1922); *La génie de Pascal* (Paris, 1924); *Spinoza et ses contemporains* (Paris, 1924); *Le progrès de la conscience dans la philosophie occidentale* (Paris, 1927); *De la connaissance de soi* (Paris, 1931); *Pascal* (Paris, 1932); *Les âges de l'intelligence* (Paris, 1934); *La raison et la religion* (Paris, 1939); *Descartes et Pascal, lecteurs de Montaigne* (Neuchâtel, 1942); *Héritage des mots, héritage des idées* (Paris, 1945); *L'esprit européen* (Neuchâtel, 1947); *Agenda retrouvé, 1892–1942* (Paris, 1948); and *La philosophie de l'esprit* (Paris, 1950). His articles were collected as *Écrits philosophiques*, 3 vols. (Paris, 1949–1958).

II. SECONDARY LITERATURE. Works on Brunschvicg include Marcel Deschoux, *La philosophie de Léon Brunschvicg* (Paris, 1949); Bernard Elevitch, in *Encyclopedia of Philosophy* (New York, 1967), I, 408–409; Martial Gueroult, "Brunschvicg et l'histoire de la philosophie," in *Bulletin de la Société française de philosophie*, **48**, no. 1 (1954); and D. Parodi, *La philosophie contemporaine en France* (Paris, 1925), pp. 420–424, 427–431. Also of value are a special number of *Revue de métaphysique et de morale*, **55**, no. 1–2 (1945); and a commemoration of the fiftieth anniversary of the publication of *Les étapes* by A. Lichnérowicz, A. Koyré, R. P. Dubarle, and J. Wahl, *Bulletin de la Société française de philosophie*, **57**, no. 2 (1963).

YVON BELAVAL

BRUNSCHWIG (also **Brunswyck** or **Braunschweig**), **HIERONYMUS** (*b.* Strasbourg, France, *ca.* 1450; *d.* Strasbourg, *ca.* 1512), *surgery*.

After receiving an education in surgery, Brunschwig traveled extensively through Alsace, Swabia, Bavaria, Franconia, and the Rhineland as far as Cologne, practicing surgery and acquiring experience in the preparation of medicines, specifically in the technique of distillation. It is frequently stated that he studied medicine in Bologna, Padua, and Paris, but this assertion cannot be verified. Brunschwig himself never mentions this training, which at that time was unusual for a surgeon, and he clearly differentiates his sphere of activity from that of the physicians.

Brunschwig probably did not become a military surgeon like his contemporary Hans von Gersdorff; and his often-mentioned participation in the campaign against Charles the Bold and in the battle of Morat in 1476 is doubtful. His reports on these engagements, as well as on battle wounds, are largely secondhand. His employment as a surgeon in Strasbourg apparently left him enough time to become a writer and to continue his travels.

Brunschwig's works concern anatomy, treatment of wounds, and, in pharmacy, the preparation of medicines and simples. Written in German, they are directed primarily to barber-surgeons, barbers, and surgeons; his surgical texts, however, are also directed to laymen. They reveal an intense preoccupation with the medical tradition of Lanfranchi, Guglielmo Saliceti, Guy de Chauliac, Henri de Mondeville, and, through them, the tradition of Galen, Avicenna, Rhazes, Mesue, and Abul Kasim, all of whom Brunschwig cites as sources of his own knowledge. On the basis of his own experience, however, Brunschwig was also able to criticize their work. With its traditional knowledge, critical spirit, and careful citations, his *Cirurgia* (1497) is different from the books of his German-speaking forerunners, such as the *Buch der Bündth-Ertznei* (*ca.* 1460) by the empiricist Heinrich von Pfalzpaint (or Pfolspeunt) and the *Chirurgie* (1481) of Johann Schenk of Würzburg. In the treatment of wounds, fractures, and luxations, and in trepanation and amputation, he made extensive use of traditional methods.

Brunschwig's *Cirurgia*, which has become an important cultural-historical source for medicine and pharmacy because of its excellent illustrations, represents a substantial step forward in the German surgery of that time, which lagged behind that of Italy and France. On the other hand, his *Anathomia* (1497), which shows some familiarity with dissection, had little lasting effect; and his discussion of pestilence (1500), which contains an early description of syphilis, had no lasting effect at all. The *Liber de arte distillandi, de simplicibus* (1500) reveals greater originality; primarily because of the description, complemented by abundant illustrations, of chemical and distillation apparatus, this book became a pharmaceutical–technical handbook that was the authority far into the sixteenth century. Appended to it was a compilation of illnesses "a capite ad calcem," along with a list of vegetable distillates indicated for each case of illness. The *Liber de arte distillandi, de compositis* (1507) contains, among other things, a "Thesaurus pauperum" that—especially as it appeared in the 1512 edition—was often reprinted and became a model for later pharmacopeias for poor people.

Because of their completeness Brunschwig's compilations of the technical terms adaptable to pharmacy in the early sixteenth century and his records of his experience in the treatment of gunshot wounds and in surgery are noteworthy accomplishments. Even if they are not the first of their kind, they still represent an important link between the Middle Ages and modern times.

BIBLIOGRAPHY

I. ORIGINAL WORKS. Brunschwig's works are *Anathomia ossium corporis humani* (Strasbourg, 1497); *Buch der Cirurgia, Hantwirckung der Wundartzney* (Strasbourg, 1497), also trans. into English (London, 1525); *Liber de arte distillandi, de simplicibus. Das Buch der rechten Kunst zu distillieren die eintzigen Ding* (Strasbourg, 1500), also issued as *Medicinarius,* with a section entitled "De compositis" (Strasbourg, 1505); and *Liber pestilentialis de venenis epidemie. Das Buch der Vergift der Pestilentz* (Strasbourg, 1500). The *Medicinarius* was reissued as *Liber de arte distillandi, de compositis. Das Buch der waren Kunst zu distillieren die Composita* (Strasbourg, 1507) had a section entitled "Thesaurus pauperum," also published separately as *Apoteck für den gemainen Man* (Strasbourg, 1507). The works on distillation were reissued under the title *Grosses Buch der Destillation* (Strasbourg, 1512).

II. SECONDARY LITERATURE. Works on Brunschwig are A. Brunschwig, "Hieronymus Brunschwig," in *Annals of Medical History,* n.s. **1** (1929), 640–644; Gerhard Eis, "H. Brunschwig," in *Neue deutsche Biographie,* II (1965), 688; H. W. Grabert, "Nomina anatomica bei den deutschen Wundärzten Hieronymus Brunschwig und Hans von Gersdorff," dissertation (Leipzig, 1943); F. Hommel, "H. Brunschwig," in *Archiv für Geschichte der Mathematik, der Naturwissenschaften und der Technik,* **10** (1927), 155–157; G. Klein, Facsimile of the *Cirurgia* with introduction (Munich, 1911); H. E. Sigerist, Facsimile of the *Cirurgia,* with study on Hieronymus Brunschwig (Milan, 1923); J. Steudel, "Brunschwigs Anatomie," in *Grenzgebiete der Medizin,* **1** (1948), 249 f.; K. Sudhoff, "Brunschwigs Anatomie," in *Archiv für Geschichte der Medizin,* **1** (1907), 41–66, with a facsimile of the *Anathomia, ibid.,* 141–156; and *Deutsche medizinische Inkunabeln,* Vols. II and III in the series Studien zur Geschichte der Medizin (Leipzig, 1908); and F. Wieger, *Geschichte der Medizin und ihrer Lehranstalten in Strassburg vom Jahre 1497 bis zum Jahre 1872* (Strasbourg, 1885), pp. 4–15.

R. SCHMITZ

BRUNTON, THOMAS LAUDER (*b.* Roxburgh, Scotland, 14 March 1844; *d.* London, England, 16 September 1916), *physiology, pharmacology.*

Brunton received his formal scientific education at the University of Edinburgh (B.Sc., 1867; M.D., 1868; D.Sc., 1870) and spent two years in Continental laboratories, including Ludwig's in Leipzig and Kühne's in Amsterdam. In 1870 he settled in London, and the next year he was appointed lecturer in materia medica and casualty physician to St. Bartholomew's Hospital. He became assistant physician there in 1875, physician in 1897, and consulting physician in 1904. Brunton was made a fellow of the Royal Society in 1874 and of the Royal College of Physicians in 1876, was knighted in 1900, and was awarded a baronetcy in 1909.

Brunton's lifelong research interests centered on the physiology and therapy of the cardiovascular and digestive systems. In his prize-winning thesis of 1866 he investigated the pharmacological properties of digitalis, a subject to which he frequently returned. He also studied the cardiotonic actions of casca bark (*Erythrophloeum guineense,* 1880). In 1905 Brunton delivered a series of lectures at the University of London, later published as *Therapeutics of the Circulation* (1908), in which he took the many facets of his own work in the field and placed them in the context of contemporary knowledge.

While working as a resident physician in 1867, Brunton discovered that amyl nitrite, a drug already studied experimentally by Frederick Guthrie, Benjamin Richardson, and Arthur Gamgee, was useful in the relief of angina pectoris. Brunton's physiological approach to therapeutics is nowhere better illustrated than in this episode. His measurements of blood pressure led him to believe that angina is caused by transient bouts of hypertension and that amyl nitrite, the first known vasodilator, should therefore be efficacious. That angina was subsequently found to be caused by ischemia rather than hypertension did not invalidate Brunton's reasoning; the drug is still used in the treatment of this condition.

Brunton's early research on digestive physiology may be found in Burdon-Sanderson's *Handbook for the Physiological Laboratory* (1873). The section on digestion, written by Brunton, contains literally hundreds of experiments, each performed or verified by Brunton himself. His scattered papers on the digestive tract were collected in two later volumes (1886, 1901).

His work in digestive physiology led Brunton to consider diabetes, a condition that he tried to treat by the oral administration of raw muscle, in the hope that the glycolytic properties of the muscle would correct the faulty carbohydrate metabolism (1874). His concept of "organotherapy" was vindicated within fifteen years by the successful treatment of myxedema with thyroid extract.

In addition to his original contributions, Brunton played an important role in the development of pharmacology into an independent and rigorous science. In his Goulstonian lectures of 1877 (*Pharmacology and Therapeutics*) he surveyed the history and contemporary state of pharmacological research. His Croonian lectures of 1889 (*An Introduction to Modern Therapeutics*) dealt with molecular pharmacology in discussing the relation of chemical structure to physiological action. *A Textbook of Pharmacology, Therapeutics and Materia Medica* (1885), the first comprehensive treatise on pharmacology, remains his most important work. In it Brunton abandoned the traditional discussions of classic materia medica and emphasized the physiological actions of pure drugs. Immediately accepted as authoritative, the book was translated into French, German, Italian, and Spanish. Brunton's *Lectures on the Actions of Medicines* (1897), using the same basic structure, went through three editions in as many years.

Brunton was known to his contemporaries as a therapeutic activist. He envisioned an almost unlimited ability of scientific pharmacology to eradicate and prevent disease, stressing at the same time other modes of prophylaxis and therapy, such as massage, baths, exercise, and improved public health services.

BIBLIOGRAPHY

I. ORIGINAL WORKS. Brunton's writings include "On the Use of Nitrite of Amyl in Angina Pectoris," in *Lancet* (1867), **2**, 97–98; *On Digitalis* (London, 1868); the section on digestion in Burdon-Sanderson, *Handbook for the Physiological Laboratory,* I (London, 1873); "The Pathology and Treatment of Diabetes Mellitus," in *British Medical Journal* (1874), **1**, 1–3; *Pharmacology and Therapeutics* (London, 1880); *The Bible and Science* (London, 1881); *A Textbook of Pharmacology, Therapeutics and Materia Medica* (London, 1885); *On Disorders of Digestion* (London, 1886); *An Introduction to Modern Therapeutics* (London, 1892); *Modern Developments of Harvey's Work* (London, 1894), the Harveian oration for 1894; *Lectures on the Actions of Medicines* (1897); and *On Disorders of Assimilation, Digestion, etc.* (London, 1901). Brunton also edited the 3rd ed. of Murchison's *Clinical Lectures on Diseases of the Liver* (London, 1885).

II. SECONDARY LITERATURE. Additional biographical material may be found in the following obituary notices: *British Medical Journal* (1916), **2**, 440–442; *Lancet* (1916), **2**, 572–575; and *Proceedings of the Royal Society,* **89B** (1917), 44–48. For consideration of two relatively minor aspects of Brunton's work, see Fielding H. Garrison, "Sir Thomas Lauder Brunton, M.D. (1844–1916). An Apostle of Preparedness," in *The Military Surgeon,* **40** (1917), 369–377; H. Meade, *A History of Thoracic Surgery* (Springfield, Ill., 1961), pp. 430–458.

WILLIAM F. BYNUM

BRYAN, KIRK (*b.* Albuquerque, New Mexico, 22 July 1888; *d.* Cody, Wyoming, 21 August 1950), *geology, geomorphology.*

Bryan's parents taught in the Presbyterian Indian School in Albuquerque, and his father later practiced law in the same town. He was educated in the Albuquerque public schools and received the B.A. from the University of New Mexico in 1909. Then, with the encouragement of H. E. Gregory, professor of geology at Yale, Bryan entered that college as an undergraduate, receiving his second B.A. in 1910 and the Ph.D. in 1920.

From 1912 to 1926 Bryan was associated with the U.S. Geological Survey. During part of this time, 1914–1917, he also served as instructor in geology at Yale, and in 1918–1919 he was a private in the Army Corps of Engineers. Later he received a commission and served as a second lieutenant in the geological section of the army general headquarters. From 1926 until his death, Bryan taught at Harvard. He belonged to the American Association for the Advancement of Science, the Geological Society of America, the Geological Society of Washington, the Geological Society of Boston, the American Academy of Arts and Sciences, and the Society of Military Geologists, holding office in most of these societies. He was married in 1923 to Mary MacArthur.

The Kirk Bryan Fund, established by the Geological Society of America in 1951, supports the Kirk Bryan Award, which is presented, usually annually, for a significant published contribution to geomorphology or a related field.

Bryan's professional career began in the Geological Survey, where he was assigned to work on the general problem of water resources, particularly of groundwater in arid and semiarid regions. This work was directly predicated on the assumption that it had an immediate human use, and this "human" orientation played a significant role in his professional studies for the rest of his life. Bryan's work for the Geological Survey produced a series of publications reflecting his concern with irrigation, dam sites, and groundwater resources. His subsequent writings deal more with man's history, an interest reflected in his collaboration with archaeologists. Throughout, however, he was equally concerned with the processes of earth change and with geological history.

Bryan's first major contribution was the description of arid-climate landforms and discussion of the processes that led to them (1922); the fieldwork and basic observation had been carried out in the fall and early winter of 1917. The study "Erosion and Sedimentation in the Papago Country, Arizona" was a by-product of a survey of watering places in that desert area. In this work the use of the term "pediment" to describe a plain formed at the foot of mountains through the processes of erosion normal to the desert was firmly established in the literature of landscape evolution, although Bryan adapted the term from a 1912 report on desert surfaces by Sidney Paige. Bryan envisaged the pediment as a slope of transportation veneered with a few inches or a few feet of debris in transit. He indicated that the slope of the pediment surface changed with the size of particle in transport. He planned and, with the help of several graduate students, partially completed a field program to study the geology and geomorphology of the Rio Grande depression in New Mexico and southern Colorado. Among other things, this program focused on the history and origin of pediments.

Bryan's recognition of the pediment as an important topographic element in an arid landscape reflected his own geographic heritage. He was raised in the semiarid New Mexico Territory and spent the first fifteen years of his professional career in arid and semiarid lands, so it is not surprising that he was sensitive to the effects and changes of climate. In his initial study of pediments (1922) Bryan postulates the possibility that an increase in rainfall accounted for the dissection of many of the pediments in the Papago country. In that same study he outlined what came to be known as the "alluvial chronology" of late Pleistocene and Recent time in the southwest. The alternate periods of alluviation and erosion that he described were attributed to fluctuations of climate marked particularly by changes in effectiveness of precipitation. The assumption that climatic changes have taken place within the immediate geological past demanded the evidence for those changes. This Bryan sought in the soils, recent sediments, and landscape. In 1943 he and C. C. Albritton, Jr., published "Soil Phenomena as Evidence of Climatic Change," a paper that summarizes his interest in soils as climatic indicators and marks the beginning of a general interest in paleosoils on the part of geologists.

In 1932 Bryan wrote on the use of pollen in the reconstruction of North American Pleistocene climate. The technique had been used for many years in Europe but was little known in America; his continued interest was instrumental in establishing palynology in the United States. Likewise, Bryan

early recognized that the rigorous climate existing beyond the margins of the Pleistocene glaciers must have expressed itself by extensive frost action in the upper few feet of soil and rock. The effect of modern periglacial climate, as well as that of the past, was being reported by European workers in the 1920's. It was Bryan who drew the attention of American workers to the possibility of using frost forms as stratigraphic and environmental indicators. In 1946 he published a summary statement of the nature of the frost action on soils and coined the term "cryopedology" for its study.

In 1924 and 1925, Bryan participated in an archaeological expedition of the Smithsonian Institution to the Chaco Canyon in New Mexico. His goal was to determine, if possible, the conditions that led to the rise and fall of prehistoric Pueblo Bonito. The field study was the beginning of a long association between Bryan and archaeologists, although the report was not published until 1954. In 1940 the "Geologic Antiquity of the Lindenmeier Site" in Colorado was published in collaboration with L. L. Ray. It and the report on Sandia Cave, New Mexico (1941), stand as models of the application of geological studies to archaeological sites and problems.

BIBLIOGRAPHY

I. ORIGINAL WORKS. See "Erosion and Sedimentation in the Papago Country, Arizona with a Sketch of the Geology," in *Bulletin of the United States Geological Survey,* no. 730 (1922), pp. 19–90. A list of publications is in Esper S. Larsen, Jr., "Memorial to Kirk Bryan," in *Proceedings of the Geological Society of America, Annual Report for 1950* (1951), pp. 91–96. Posthumous publications and some minor earlier papers are not listed.

II. SECONDARY LITERATURE. Brief accounts of Bryan's life are given by Larsen (see above) and Frederick Johnson, "Kirk Bryan—1888-1950," in *American Antiquity,* **16** (1951), 253.

SHELDON JUDSON

BRYSON OF HERACLEA, *mathematics.*

The name Bryson occurs several times in Aristotle's writings. A "sophist" Bryson is mentioned as the son of Herodorus of Heraclea (*Historia animalium* VI, 5, 563a7; IX, 11, 615a10); is blamed for his "sophistic" (in fact, probably proto-Stoic) assertion that there is no such thing as "indecent" language (*Rhetoric* III, 2, 1405b9); and is blamed for his "eristic" and "sophistic" method of squaring the circle (*Posterior Analytics* I, 9, 75b40; *De sophisticis elenchis* 11, 171b16–172a4). A Bryson is named in Plato's *Epistles* XIII, where Polyxenus, teacher of Helicon, is designated as his ἐταῖρος. Theopompus, in Athen XI, 508d (*Fragmenta graecorum historicorum,* F. Jacoby, ed., 115F259), accuses Plato of having plagiarized Bryson's *Diatribes.* It seems preferable (in agreement with Natorp rather than Zeller) to assume that all the above passages refer to one and the same person, although it must be admitted that other biographical information preserved in Diogenes Laertius and Suda, particularly concerning his relations with Socrates, Euclid of Megara, Cleinomachus, Plato, Pyrrho, and Theodorus the Atheist, contain some chronological contradictions.

With the help of ancient commentators Bryson's method of squaring the circle, criticized by Aristotle, can tentatively be reconstructed as follows. We start with two squares, one inscribed in a circle, the other circumscribed. Then we construct successively regular circumscribed and inscribed polygons the perimeters of which approach as closely as we like to the circumference of the circle. Thus, exhausting the area by which one square is larger and the other is smaller than the circle, we eventually make the areas of the larger and the smaller polygon coincide, which means that their areas at that time equal the area of the circle, since the polygon and the circle are both smaller than the circumscribed polygons and greater than all the inscribed figures. Since we can always construct a square equal in area to a polygon, the problem of how to square the circle is solved.

Aristotle criticizes this method because it is based on a principle that is too general and not peculiar to the matter at hand. By this he probably means a principle like this: If two quantities, one larger and one smaller than a third, become equal, they also become equal to that third quantity. It seems that Bryson's method can, however, be defended against Aristotle and can be considered another anticipation of the principles underlying the method of exhaustion.

No other opinions of Bryson have survived. But since his name is linked with that of Polyxenus, who has been credited with having been the first to put forward the so-called third-man argument, and since Plato was accused of plagiarizing Bryson, it could be that there were similarities between Bryson's *Diatribes* and Plato's *Parmenides,* in which the third-man argument is indeed discussed.

BIBLIOGRAPHY

In addition to the sources listed in the text, see John Philoponus, *In Analytica posteriora,* XIII, pt. 3 of *Commentaria in Aristotelem Graeca* (1909), 111–115, 149; Pseudo-Alexander of Aphrodisias, *In Sophisticos elenchos,* III, pt. 3 of *Commentaria . . .* (1898), 76, 90, 92; and Themistius, *Analytica posteriora paraphrasis,* V, pt. 1 of *Commentaria . . .* (1900), 19–20.

Literature that deals with Bryson includes T. L. Heath, *A History of Greek Mathematics,* I (Oxford, 1921), 223–225; Paul Natorp, "Bryson 2," in Pauly-Wissowa, *Real-Encyclopädie,* III, pt. 1 (1897); W. D. Ross, *Aristotle's Prior and Posterior Analytics* (Oxford, 1949), 536 f.; and E. Zeller, *Die Philosophie der Griechen,* 5th ed., II, pt. 1 (1922), esp. 250, n. 4.

A different interpretation of Bryson's attempt to square the circle, according to which he proposed establishing some kind of proportion between the circumscribed and the inscribed circles as extremes, the middle term being the square in question, is in A. Wasserstein, "Some Early Greek Attempts to Square the Circle," in *Phronesis,* **4** (1959), 92–100, esp. 95–100.

PHILIP MERLAN

BRYTTE (also **Britte, Brit,** or **Brute**), **WALTER** (*fl.* Oxford, England, second half of fourteenth century), *astronomy.*

According to Brodrick,[1] Brytte was elected to a fellowship at Merton College in 1377, and in MS Digby 15 (fol. 96v) he is mentioned as *quondam socius collegii de Merton.* This is almost all we know about his life, except for an old tradition related by Wood[2] that he was a follower of John Wycliffe (Bachelor of Merton 1356) and author of the book *De auferendis clero possessionibus.* For this reason R. L. Poole[3] and later A. B. Emden[4] tentatively identified him with a layman who in 1391 was tried for heresy before the bishop of Hereford. Nothing has come to light to substantiate this, however, so we are left with the only work that can safely be ascribed to him: the treatise *Theorica planetarum secundum dominum Walterum Brytte,* with the incipit *Circulus eccentricus, et egresse cuspidis, et ingredientis centri idem sunt,* which is extant in at least eight manuscripts, four of which were identified by Bjørnbo.[5]

Many elementary manuals of planetary theory are known under the title *Theorica planetarum,* and Brytte's treatise has often been confused not only with a similar text by an earlier Mertonian scholar, Simon Bredon (fellow 1330, *d.* 1372), but also with the extremely popular and much used "Old *Theorica planetarum,*" which has been ascribed to Gerard of Cremona and to many other authors but is actually an anonymous textbook written in the second half of the thirteenth century. Recent research has cleared up much of the confusion, with the result[6] that although the "Old *Theorica*" certainly served as a prototype for Brytte, his work is neither a simple copy among several hundred others nor a commentary of the usual kind. It must be regarded as a revised version with strongly individual features. Of course, Brytte retained many of the notions current at his time, such as the "physical" doctrine of ethereal spheres as guidance mechanisms for the planets. On the other hand, he rearranged the traditional matter in a more logical way, dealing more fully with the theory of Venus and discarding the very confused chapter on latitudes in the "Old *Theorica.*"

The most interesting characteristic of the *Theorica* is Brytte's obvious efforts to remedy some of the worst errors of the older text by means of his insight into kinematics, which clearly stemmed from the great Merton school of mechanics that flourished before and at the middle of the century. Where the "Old *Theorica*" spoke simply of "motion," Brytte carefully distinguishes between "physical" (i.e., linear) velocity and "astronomical" (i.e., angular) velocity, just as he is familiar with both uniform and nonuniform motion and with the composition of angular velocities. These kinematic concepts are applied to planetary theory, with the consequence that Brytte, unlike the author of the old text, is able to state the correct condition for a planet's being stationary: that the apparent angular velocity of the planet on the epicycle is equal but opposite to the angular velocity of the epicycle center on the deferent. Yet he is unable to deduce a correct geometrical construction from this principle, so that like most medieval astronomers, he determines the stationary points by means of tangents from the center of the earth to the epicycle. Thus his efforts to make the new kinematics useful to astronomy did not result in a correction of this persistent error in the elementary teaching of astronomy in the Middle Ages.[7]

NOTES

1. P. 219.
2. I, 475.
3. II, 1266.
4. Pp. 270–271.
5. Pp. 112 ff.
6. Pedersen, "The *Theorica planetarum* Literature," pp. 225 ff.
7. An ed. of Brytte's treatise by Pedersen is in press.

BIBLIOGRAPHY

The MSS of the *Theorica planetarum* are British Museum Egerton 847, 104v–122v, and Egerton 889, 7r–17r; and Bodleian Library Bodl. 300, 45r–53v; Digby 15, 58v–96v; Digby 48, 96r–112v; Digby 93, 37r–51v; Digby 98, 132r–145r; and Wood D.8, 93–112r. An edition of the *Theorica* is Pedersen, *Theorica Planetarum. Texts and Studies in Mediaeval Astronomy* (in press).

Works dealing with Brytte or the *Theorica* are A. A.

Bjørnbo, "Walter Brytte's *Theorica planetarum,*" in *Biblioteca mathematica,* **6** (1905), 112 ff.; G. H. Brodrick, *Memorials of Merton College* (Oxford, 1885), p. 219; A. B. Emden, *A Biographical Register of the University of Oxford to A. D. 1500* (Oxford, 1957), I, 270 f.; Olaf Pedersen, "The *Theorica planetarum* Literature of the Middle Ages," in *Classica et mediaevalia,* **23** (1962), 225 ff.; R. L. Poole, in *Dictionary of National Biography,* II, 1266; and Anthony à Wood, *Antiquities of Oxford* (Oxford, 1786), I, 475.

OLAF PEDERSEN

BUACHE, PHILIPPE (*b.* Paris, France, 7 February 1700; *d.* Paris, 24 January 1773), *cartography.*

Buache studied with and continued the work of Guillaume Delisle. Initially charged with classifying the maps, plans, and journals in the Naval Archives, he was appointed chief royal geographer in 1729. The next year the Royal Academy of Sciences elected him assistant geographer, a post created for him and held by him until his death. In 1755 Buache was appointed geography tutor to the children of the duke of Burgundy. For their use he had a globe built and atlases compiled; these items are preserved in the Bibliothèque Nationale.

Buache's *Essai de géographie physique . . .,* presented to the Academy in 1752 and published soon afterward, contains most of his ideas as well as new methods, some of which later exerted great influence. He abandoned descriptive work and began theoretical study of the structure of the globe, of which, he believed, the mountain chains are the "bones." At the same time Buache brought out the *Carte physique et profil du canal de la Manche,* in which he showed the underwater configurations by means of contour lines designating ten-fathom intervals.

Buache's theory of submarine basins and "backbones," which was based on the *Carte,* became well known. However, Dainville has pointed out the prior use of such hydrographic contour lines by the Dutch engineer Nicolas Cruquius, who in 1729 made quite an accurate map of the underwater contours of the mouth of the Meuse. Buache must have known of this map through his work in the Naval Archives. Whatever the case may be, after Buache hydrographers perfected the presentation of underwater contours; the technique was later applied to land contours.

In *Considérations . . . sur les nouvelles découvertes au nord de la Grande Mer* (1753) Buache went so far as to posit the existence of Alaska and a connection between America and Asia—"because of the direction of the capes, the mountains, the rivers, and the glaciers."

Although his theories on river basins, basins on the ocean floor, and such were at times overgeneralized, and thus hindered the progress of geography, Buache's work as a whole constituted a definite contribution to cartography.

BIBLIOGRAPHY

I. ORIGINAL WORKS. Buache's works are *Parallèle des fleuves des quatre parties du monde* (Paris, 1751); *Essai de géographie physique . . .* (Paris, 1752); *Carte physique et profil du canal de la Manche* (Paris, 1752); *Considérations géographiques et physiques sur les nouvelles découvertes au nord de la Grande Mer,* 3 vols. (Paris, 1753); *Mémoire sur les différentes idées qu'on a eues de la traversée de la Mer glaciale arctique et sur les communications ou jonctions qu'on a supposées entre diverses rivières* (Paris, 1754); *Cartes et tables de la géographie physique ou naturelle* (Paris, 1754); and *Mémoire sur le comète qui a été observé en 1531, 1607, 1682 . . .* (Paris, 1757). Available in MS is "Mémoires et notes sur les tremblements de terre," Bibliothèque Nationale, Paris, Dept. des Manuscrits, f. fr. n. acq. 20236–20237.

II. SECONDARY LITERATURE. Works on Buache are H. Balmer, *Beiträge zur Geschichte der Kenntnis des Erdmagnetismus* (Aarau, Switzerland, 1956); F. de Dainville, "De la profondeur à l'altitude. Des origines marines de l'expression cartographique du relief terrestre par cotes et courbes de niveau," in Michel Mollat, ed., *Le navire et l'économie maritime du moyen-âge au XVIIIe siècle principalement en Méditerranée* (Paris, 1958), pp. 195–213; L. Drapeyron, *Les origines de la reforme de l'enseignement géographique en France. Les deux Buache* (Paris, 1888); Grandjean de Fouchy, *Histoire de l'Académie des sciences,* II (Paris, 1772), 135; F. Hoeffer, in *Nouvelle biographie générale,* VII (Paris, 1855), cols. 676–678; F. Marouis, in *Dictionnaire de biographie française,* VII (1956), cols. 591–592; and Poggendorff, I, 323–324.

JULIETTE TATON

BUCH, [CHRISTIAN] LEOPOLD VON (*b.* Stolpe, Germany, 25 April 1774; *d.* Berlin, Germany, 4 March 1853), *geology.*

Buch, one of thirteen children, was born on his family's estate, about ninety kilometers from Berlin. His father, a *Geheimer Legationsrath* in the Prussian civil service, spent his leisure time in composing a history of Brandenburg, where the Buchs had been known since the twelfth century. His mother was a member of the famous Arnim family. The family fortune must have been considerable, since Buch's scientific zeal and passion for travel were never seriously hampered by a need to work for a living. Indeed, throughout his life he wandered extensively and almost at will, much in the manner of the medieval traveling scholar.

When he was fifteen years old, Buch was sent to Berlin to study mineralogy and chemistry for a semester; these studies were a requirement for admission to the Bergakademie, the school of mining at Freiburg. Buch spent three years at the Bergakademie under the guidance of A. G. Werner, who taught lithology and geognosy, and was the chief exponent of the Neptunist theory of the origin of rocks. Alexander von Humboldt was a fellow student, and he and Buch became lifelong friends. After another year's training in law and government (and incidentally mineralogy) at the universities of Halle and Göttingen, in 1796 Buch entered the Prussian civil service as an inspector of mines, and was commissioned to make a geognostic survey of Silesia.

Although Buch performed some early chemical experiments, like most of Werner's followers he disliked chemistry, whose "despotic aid was in no way requisite for the independence of mineralogy." Chemistry could at most be of practical value, and the furnace only provided information on the commercial value of ores. The real scientific interest of minerals lay in their intrinsic substance or essence, with which true mineralogy ought to concern itself. Buch stated that, in accordance with what he had learned from Werner, the specific gravity, hardness, cleavage, color, and luster of a mineral belong to the mineral itself, whereas chemical reaction was no more than an external activity (although he did use muriatic acid to distinguish between calcite and dolomite).

A good exposition of Werner's natural system was given by D. L. G. Karsten, another of Werner's students, who arranged a well-known private mineral collection and provided a two-volume *catalogue raisonné* for it. Both collection and catalog were bought by the Irish Academy of Science, whose president, Richard Kirwan, exclaimed, according to Buch, that only by studying both had he come to understand true, and hence Wernerian, mineralogy, whereupon he abandoned his chemical pursuits.

Chronology was of little importance for the Wernerians. Their willful neglect of this fundamental aspect of geology is partly explained by the tenets of *Naturphilosophie*—although few geologists actually studied Schelling and Hegel, whose philosophy may be considered an attempt to state explicitly what was implied in the thought of many during the Enlightenment. What Hegel has to say about geology is particularly revealing. He derides the simple conclusion that of two superimposed layers, the higher must be of later formation. It is, he says, as if someone looking at a house concludes with profound wisdom that the ground floor was built first, then the next floor above it, and so on. Hegel goes on to say:

> But this sequence contains something more profound. The meaning and the spirit of the process is the intrinsic connection, the necessary relation of these formations whereunto the "after-each-other" adds nothing at all. The general law of this sequence of formations has to be understood, without need for any form of history; this is the essential. . . . It is Werner's great merit, to have drawn attention to this sequence and to have looked at it throughout with correct eyes. The internal connection exists in the present as a "side-by-side" and this connection must depend upon the quality, upon the content of these things themselves; the history of the earth is thus on the one side empirical, on the other side concluded from empirical data. To determine how things were millions of years ago (and there we may be free with years) is not interesting, the real interest being confined to that which is now in existence—to this system of different formations [*Encyklopädie*, pt. 2, sec. 339, *Zusatz*].

Naturphilosophie here warns against finding out how the things that we see came into being, but encourages us to study the relationships of such things to see whether and how they are mutually consistent (whatever consistency may mean in the case of geological formations). These mysterious relationships had some part in Buch's unflagging interest in superposition; they led him to his conclusion, on seeing a formation of micaceous schist that was covered in one exposure by slate and in another by sandstone, that the schist could not in these two occurrences be the same, although he could find no perceptible difference.

Naturphilosophie was not wholly harmful in its influence on geology, however. The idea of plumbing essential relationships stimulated geologists in their task of classifying minerals. It must likewise have acted as a stimulus to field geology, holding out as it did a promise of revealing the portentous thoughts of the World-Spirit. Werner's students were so zealous, d'Aubuisson tells us, that they ran out into the mountains as soon as classes were over. Moreover, for practical purposes the skill to recognize and name rocks and ascertain their distribution in the terrain, coupled with the empirical knowledge of their association with ores, coal, and salt, led to excellent results.

The Neptunist system was in principle very rigid. The primitive rocks—granite, gneiss, and micaceous schist—were deposited in that order, followed by the Floetz formations, graywacke shale, and limestone. These were followed by alluvial deposits and the products of volcanoes. In practice, this theory was a bit more flexible; Werner modified it by adding a

transition formation that fell between the primitive rocks and the Floetz formations and that could consist of slate, marble, and so forth. He also allowed for intercalation of all kinds of rocks as accidental formations. Only the independent (*selbständige*) formations had to conform to the rule that, according to Werner, must hold everywhere on earth. He believed that this rule about the right order of succession was necessarily true and did not have to be verified outside Saxony. This is in line with the claim of *Naturphilosophie* that all significant features in nature could be deduced by logic alone.

The height at which a given formation occurred was of great importance, and on many of his trips Buch measured relevant heights. "With due precautions," he said, "I have hardly any trouble in carrying a mercury barometer with me."

In principle, only granite could form the highest mountains, being the first rock deposited before the universal ocean withdrew from its highest level. As the water level descended, other formations would be deposited in their proper order. What is most baffling today is the notion that mountains and valleys were at once formed in their present shapes and positions. Steep precipices of a granite mountain were ascribed to chaotic conditions in the primitive ocean. Gneiss could be deposited—like crystals in a beaker—on such a vertical wall, its streaky pattern thus standing on end.

This was the original and most rigid version of Werner's theory: many incongruous elements had to be brought in to account for what is actually observed. Buch showed great versatility and some originality in applying a startling number of odd and drastic devices. He was grievously unlucky in these guesses and rightly complained of frequent disappointments.

An awkwardness existed in the trees that were found in some coal mines, standing upright in the position in which they had grown. Since this could not have happened under water, the Neptunists were forced to postulate a previous withdrawal of the ocean from all altitudes above those of the mines, and then to hypothesize a return of the water to explain younger formations covering high mountains. They supposed that large caverns in the earth could in turn drain and fill the oceans. Buch found this idea attractive, since the currents in the ocean could then be used to explain the positions of some rock formations.

One of Buch's earliest geognostic publications (1797) dealt with Landeck, a corner of Silesia on the Bohemian frontier. The paper aroused a great deal of interest, and was translated into French and English. In it, Buch provides a Neptunist interpretation of the region and states that the area, which is enclosed on all sides by mountains, had once been a lake. The lake had overflowed at a point on the east side of the area, and a valley, through which the Landeck area is now drained, had been carved out there by erosion. (In later years Buch stubbornly denied that erosion could modify a landscape to any extent.) The mountains that surround Landeck are composed of primitive gneiss and micaceous schist, except for a gap in the northern corner of the area. In this corner, the mountains are composed of the same Floetz sandstone that covers the Landeck plain. In the northern corner the sandstone reaches 500 meters above its general level. Buch's conjecture was that the sandstone came down from the north and in rushing through the gap in the primitive mountains dammed itself up to such a height.

Leaving Silesia in September 1798, Buch set out on a walking trip to see Italy, especially Vesuvius, with his own eyes. While the Napoleonic Wars halted him for six months on the northern side of the Alps, he explored the Tyrol, often accompanied by his friend Humboldt. They found a good agreement with Werner's teaching: peaks of granite in the highest central part, flanked by gneiss, schist, and limestone in due order. When, in the spring, Buch was able to cross the Brenner Pass, he expected to find a symmetrical arrangement on the south side; to his distress, he found quite different formations with enormous masses of porphyry and dolomite. The whole of Werner's beautiful system collapsed in confusion. The device that Buch had used to impose order on Landeck came to his aid once again. Clearly, what had happened was that on the northern side of the pass the formation flood that had brought the gneiss, schist, and limestone had come, naturally enough, from the north and had been stopped by the granite mountains, which, according to Werner's theory, were already there at their full height. The floods from the south had arrived independently, at other stages in the workings of nature, and hence had brought other rocks. (This idea of damming up the formation floods recurs several times in Buch's work—for example, the Trauf, an escarpment that forms the northwest edge of the Jurassic system in southern Germany and consists of coral limestone, was considered to have been an effective barrier reef against floods coming from the south.)

As Buch continued his journey through Italy, the French campaign kept him near Rome for eight months. The imposing remains of extinct volcanoes proved so refractory to Werner's theory that Buch complained, "Only two days at Vesuvius and all this confusion could be set right." But when he had wandered around Naples for eight weeks, he wrote to the editor of *Gilberts Annalen der Physik:* "My friends who believed that after seeing a real volcano, I now could say something definite on the diverging opinions about our basalts, will be badly disappointed." This refers to the battle over basalt, in which almost everyone with a claim to general knowledge took sides—although, regarding the whole of Werner's and Hutton's conflicting theories, basalts generally were not the most important issue.

From 1801 to 1803 Buch worked near Neuchâtel, and in the spring of 1802 he went to the Auvergne for six weeks. This excursion has often been referred to as momentous in bringing about Buch's alleged conversion to Volcanism and even to Plutonism.

In Auvergne, Buch found hemispherical elevations that lacked craters and correctly interpreted them as tholoids. He was struck by the frequent eruptions of lava near the bases of volcanoes, and theorized that the flanks of the volcanoes were formed by thin strata of the country rock that had been heaved up to form the tentlike roof of a large conical cavern filled with lava. Buch's theory of elevation craters was given considerable attention in the nineteenth century, although today it is not easy to see exactly what he meant by the term. He sometimes asserted that the elevation crater is not a volcano, and that it lacks a crater proper; a volcano may be spoken of properly only when a crater, and thus a direct channel to the interior of the earth, is present.

In Italy, Buch had looked in vain for the combustible matter—coal or pyrite—that, according to Werner, was necessary for volcanic action. In Auvergne he found volcanoes standing immediately upon granite, which precluded the presence of other, deeper rocks. He was then led to suppose that the granite was transformed into Domite, a type of trachyte found in the Puy de Dome, and then in a continuous action changed into basaltic lava.

Buch's observational work was much better than his speculations. Both in Auvergne and elsewhere he recorded hundreds of observations with touching fidelity, irrespective of the hypothesis that each might support or gainsay. His writings, however, flatly contradict the facile assertion that he arrived in Auvergne a Neptunist and returned a Volcanist. While it is true that he had to concede that the basalt in Auvergne had been a lava, he could not believe that the basalt in Saxony was of the same origin. (Today these basalts are interpreted as sills, according to Hutton's ideas on subterranean or Plutonic lava intrusions. Buch could not have held this view because of the important amount of erosion necessary for these sills to be visible.) In Saxony, such mighty masses of lava would have had to have been the product of correspondingly large volcanoes, the absence of which compelled him to seek other origins because Buch, like other Neptunists, excluded the action of erosion. (Werner himself was more tolerant in this respect and did not object to the concept of an original continuous deposit of basalt that later came to be separated by erosional valleys.)

Buch further objected to the idea of a lava flow stopping at the edge of a flat hill top. Why, he asked, did it not flow on down the slope? He judged the steep precipices, formed by columns of basalt tens of meters long, to be as alien to the idea of the end of a lava flow as to the (in his opinion) exclusively gentle slopes made by erosion. The Neptunist concept of precipitation—which could often be sharply delimited by a slight change in the substratum—explained this phenomenon to Buch's satisfaction. This provides a striking example of Buch's persistent denial of the effectiveness of erosion, a denial that would seem to have become more stubborn with the years if we compare this with his 1797 explication of the valley that drains Landeck.

Buch published the results of his explorations in *Geognostische Beobachtungen auf Reisen durch Deutschland und Italien,* which appeared in two volumes (1802, 1809). This work was primarily of geological interest, although much of Buch's later work may be considered a part of the *belles lettres* of the century. (An earlier short work on kreuzstein, or harmotone, is the only one that has crystallography as its main subject.)

In 1806, when he was thirty-two, Buch was elected a member of the Royal Academy of Berlin. (In due time he was elected a member of academies in Paris, London, and Vienna, while scores of minor scientific societies competed to offer him honorary memberships.) In his speech to the Berlin Academy, Buch spoke of fundamental principles. He presented the interplay of natural forces as one great onward movement that unified all things, from the crystallization of granite to the highest strivings of human intelligence. No deity of any description played any part in this scheme of things; religion was apparently the least of Buch's concerns.

Buch continued his travels, making a lengthy visit to Scandinavia in 1806 and 1807. In 1815 and 1816 he visited the Canary Islands. In two books of travels, *Reise durch Norwegen und Lappland* (1810) and *Physikalische Beschreibung der Canarischen Inseln* (1825), geological data occupy a modest space among Buch's observations of the landscape, climate, flora and fauna, customs of the inhabitants, and vicissitudes of the road.

His explorations in the southern Alps had suggested to Buch that the towering height of the Dolomites might be the result of upheaval, for which he sought the active agent in porphyry, including monozite. He concluded that the magnesia in which this rock is rich would also have been active in transforming the original limestone into dolomite. Buch thus came to visualize great subterranean activities; in 1815, in the Canary Islands, he ingeniously demonstrated the interdependence of the volcanoes of the archipelago. Since two volcanoes never happened to erupt at the same time, he argued that eruption of one volcano relieved the pressure upon the others. Hence, the masses of material underneath all the volcanoes may be seen as filling one cavern, by which the volcanoes are interconnected.

Buch's view of effective subterranean masses soon grew to encompass the whole world. A treatise of 1842, "Ueber Granit und Gneiss," illustrates the later development of Buch's Wernerism and demonstrates the remarkable consequences to which his refusal to consider erosion led him. Granite and gneiss cover southern Finland and Sweden, while, stretching west from Leningrad, Silurian strata cover the Baltic provinces and the isle of Gotland, and further recur in six small patches in Sweden. These latter, we would now say, represent erosional remnants, hills a few hundred meters high in which the Silurian strata are horizontal, as they are in Gotland and Russia. Buch was compelled to admit that the Silurian strata in the six hills are a remnant of a continuous sedimentary layer that had once extended through a large part of Sweden, but was hard pressed to account for the disappearance of the greater part of it. Since he could not explain it by erosion, he had recourse to the novel, non-Wernerian principle of metamorphism. In Buch's conjecture, the Silurian rocks had been metamorphosed by the action, probably vaporous, of the underlying granite. This theory further served to explain the scarcity of granite in Scandinavia, about which Buch had worried a great deal; the granite is largely hidden from view by the large Silurian deposits that now appear as gneiss.

The basalt-topped hills were pushed up by a subterranean mass of basalt; the sheets on top thus represent possibly fiery extrusions. Buch thought that the lower mass of basalt, situated between the granite and Silurian layers, served as a shield against the metamorphic action of the granite and thus preserved the Silurian layers in their original state. He concluded that the large parts of Russia covered with nonmetamorphosed Silurian strata must be underlain by basalt.

Buch dismissed as nonsense the notions that the

stairlike outline of these hills could be due to weathering and erosion and that the relative height of the hills was due to protection by the more resistant basalt. On one of the six hills, Kinnekulle, no more than a mere dot of basalt is visible at the center of the uppermost Silurian layer; how, Buch asked, could this have afforded protection? Buch conceded that the Silurian layers in all the hills had once been continuous, but it is hard to understand what, in his view, had become of the missing segments. He believed that these rocks must have been reworked by metamorphism, but how they were brought down from the steps of the staircase is not explained. His account of the area is marked by his keen eye for geological observation, trained by Werner, but as soon as past events are brought into consideration, all is dim and misty. It might have been better if Buch had followed Hegel's advice and refrained from peering into the past.

Buch's somewhat more actualistic view of sedimentation displayed in this instance may have been the result of his extensive work in stratigraphy and paleontology. This had been Buch's chief concern since his fiftieth year. His first major achievement in this field consisted in distinguishing between ammonites and nautilidae (1829, 1839) and observing the intricate suture lines in the former. The Wernerians, trained as they were in thoughtful observation and accurate description, soon felt at home with paleontology. We may imagine Buch's delight as he contemplated the orderly succession of faunas, the characteristics of each being in part determined by its predecessors, and all bearing witness to that great onward movement he had enlarged upon in the speech to the Berlin Academy. He was aware of the value of guide fossils, and sought to enhance their usefulness with careful drawings and descriptions.

Buch's fundamental error, perhaps, sprang from the prejudice, older than *Naturphilosophie,* that the earth was specially created as a place for man to dwell in. Hegel's comparison with a house is suggestive of how time could be considered unimportant and of motives that might lead to the rejection of all except the barest minimum of erosion. It is not very interesting to know how long it took to build the house; we are interested in its present state and whether it is appropriate to our purpose. If we have to think about the building operations, they surely were carried out according to a plan. It would serve no purpose to build some walls with the intention of demolishing them in order to use the stones for other walls. The idea of a purposeful construction bars access to the principle of uniformity.

For more than forty years Buch brooded over one specific problem, that of the erratic blocks distributed over Germany. In southern Silesia, Buch had determined that these blocks came from the Sudets; he had identified the kinds of rocks and observed that they became smaller as they occurred in more northern locations. Farther north, there appeared blocks of a kind alien to the mountains of the south; Buch could but conclude that these, strewn copiously over half of Holland and large parts of Germany and Poland, had been brought from Scandinavia. He was, however, unable to decide what agent had brought them, and felt inclined to attribute their presence to the then rather commonly invoked mighty floods. In Switzerland, erratic blocks from the Alps were found in the Juras, at an appreciable height above the intervening Swiss plain; J. A. de Luc held that these had been hurled through the air by great explosions. Buch objected to this unlikely device, and judged it impossible that blocks from Scandinavia should have been so hurled across the Baltic Sea far into Germany. He further opposed the notion (propounded by Hutton and Agassiz and Charpentier) that the blocks had been transported by glaciers, and explained the polished surfaces of the rocks by ascribing them to differential movements along the curved, onion-like partings generally seen in fresh granite. He even contended that he had seen the same polish on a surface just laid bare by quarrying. Swedish scientists had measured the striae on the polished rocks to determine the direction of transport; Buch halfheartedly agreed with them, since they cited currents as a moving agent. But when Berzelius, among others, concluded that the masses carried southward must represent an appreciable erosion of the land in Sweden, Buch would have no part of it. However intimately he might have come to know the enormous volumes of Mesozoic and Tertiary formations, he apparently refused to give a moment's thought to where these masses might have come from.

Buch, who never married, referred to himself as a wandering hermit. In later years, however, he got over his shyness in joining larger parties, and when, around 1830, scientists began to meet on field trips, Buch regularly attended. For example, in his last summer he met with naturalists in Koblenz, with Swiss geologists in Sion, with French scientists in Metz, and with German naturalists in Wiesbaden. He then traveled through Basel to Le Puy, where he had an appointment with Daubrée to study the basalt of the Vivarais. In the late autumn he was in Paris with Mitscherlich and Rose; Rose accompanied him back to Berlin by train.

Buch was free of all anxiety that others should unfairly profit from his accomplishments; in the accounts of his journeys, each new phenomenon is recorded either as a matter of fact or as something first observed by a companion. An extreme example was his anonymous publication, in 1826, of a geological map of Germany, which embodies the solid core of a long life's work. This map, which covered forty-two sheets, was reissued in 1842.

Buch's many published works are written in a highly attractive style that easily conveys his thoughts. His proficiency as an author enables us to learn of the theory and practice of Neptunism, about which the scarce and constrained writings of Werner tell us little.

A week before his death Buch was with friends in the Humanist Club until late at night. He complained of nothing more severe than chilblained toes, but the next day his first serious illness set in. He was buried in the Buch family vault at Stolpe.

BIBLIOGRAPHY

I. ORIGINAL WORKS. Buch's works were brought together as *L. von Buch's gesammelte Schriften,* J. Ewald, J. Roth, H. Eck, and W. Dames, eds., 4 vols. (Berlin, 1867–1885); Vol. I contains J. Ewald, "Leopold von Buch's Leben und Wirken bis zum Jahre 1806," pp. v–xlviii. For the individual works listed below, the Roman and Arabic numerals in parentheses refer to the *Gesammelte Schriften.* Among Buch's works are "Mineralogische Beschreibung der Karlsbader Gegend," in *Kohler und Hoffmann Bergmannisches Journal,* **5,** pt. 2 (1792), 383–424 (I, 3–23); *Beobachtungen über den Kreuzstein* (Leipzig, 1794) (I, 24–35); *Versuch einer mineralogischen Beschreibung von Landeck* (Breslau, 1797) (I, 38–72); "Considérations sur le granite," in *Journal de physique,* **49** (1799), 206–213 (I, 101–108); "Mémoire sur la formation de la leucite," *ibid.,* 262–270 (I, 109–117); "Sur les volcans," in *Bibliographia Britannica,* **16** (1801), 227–249 (I, 132–142); *Geognostische Beobachtungen auf Reisen durch Deutschland und Italien,* 2 vols. (Berlin, 1802–1809) (I, 143–523); "Ueber das Fortschreiten der Bildungen in der Natur," his inaugural address to the Königliche Akademie der Wissenschaften (17 April 1806) (II, 4–12); *Reise nach Norwegen und Lappland* (Berlin, 1810) (II, 109–563); *Physikalische Beschreibung der Canarischen Inseln* (Berlin, 1825) (III, 225–646); and "Ueber Granit und Gneiss," in *Abhandlungen der Königlichen Akademie der Wissenschaften, Berlin* (1844) (IV, pt. 2, 717–738).

His unpublished diary is in the possession of the geology department of the University of Berlin. Buch was responsible for the first geological map of Germany (1826), although it does not bear his name. Consisting of forty-two sheets, it was the first map of this sort to cover a fairly large area of Europe. It was reissued in 1842.

II. SECONDARY LITERATURE. Works on Buch are H. von Dechen, *Leopold von Buch; sein Einfluss auf die Entwick-*

lung der Geognosie (Bonn, 1853); S. Günther, *A. v. Humboldt, L. v. Buch* (*P*), Vol. XXXIX in the series Geisteshelden (Führende Geister) (Berlin, 1900), 185–271; W. Haidinger, "Zur Erinnerung an Leopold von Buch," in *Jahrbuch der Kaiserlich-Königlichen Geologischen Reichsanstalt,* IV (1853), 207–220; G. F. Hegel, *Encyklopädie der philosophischen Wissenschaften,* 3rd ed. (Heidelberg, 1830), pt. 2, "Die Philosophie der Natur," sec. 339, *Zusatz;* H. Hölder, *Geologie und Paläontologie in Texten und Geschichte,* II, pt. 11 of Orbis Academicus; Problemgeschichten der Wissenschaft (Freiburg im Breisgau, 1960), see Index; and R. Hooykaas, *The Principle of Uniformity in Geology, Biology and Theology,* 2nd ed. (Leiden, 1963).

W. NIEUWENKAMP

BUCHANAN, JOHN YOUNG (*b.* Glasgow, Scotland, 20 February 1844; *d.* London, England, 16 October 1925), *oceanography, chemistry.*

After graduating from the University of Glasgow in 1863, Buchanan studied chemistry at Marburg, Bonn, Leipzig, and Paris. He was appointed chemist, physicist, and geologist of the pioneering oceanographic expedition of the *Challenger* (1872–1876), under the leadership of Charles Wyville Thomson. He continued his oceanographic studies in his private laboratory in Edinburgh and on ocean cruises. Among his few long-time scientific associates was Prince Albert of Monaco.

Buchanan's participation in the *Challenger* expedition shaped his scientific career. His work dealt mainly with the design and improvement of oceanographic instruments and observational methods, and with data collection—essential aspects of a young science. His research, always original and based on observations, was carried out with the utmost thoroughness and precision.

Certain of Buchanan's publications contain important generalizations. He prepared the first reliable surface salinity map of the oceans. His analysis of spatial and seasonal distributions of salinity and temperature contradicted the widely adopted thermal circulation theory originated by Humboldt. Buchanan's observations and speculations (1877, 1886) on thermohaline circulations in vertical planes were utilized and confirmed—at least for the subtropics—by J. W. Sandström in 1908 and A. Merz in 1925. Buchanan demonstrated that vertical currents from submarine sources supplied the cold surface water that is generally observed along the western shores of continents. He produced many valuable and meticulous studies on the physical and chemical properties of seawater and sea ice, and on the constitution, formation, and distribution of concretionary deposits of iron and manganese oxides discovered by the *Challenger*. He received much attention for his demonstration of the inorganic nature of the gelatinous deep-sea deposit that leading naturalists had thought to be a protoplasmic slime. Buchanan's studies in limnology helped to establish the generality of the temperature stratification of temperate lakes and the concept of the thermocline (1886), and he pioneered in quantitative studies of seasonal variations in heat content of lakes. Buchanan seems to have worked purely for his own satisfaction, accomplishing more than his publications would indicate.

BIBLIOGRAPHY

I. Original Works. Buchanan collected most of his publications in four volumes: *Experimental Researches on the Specific Gravity and the Displacement of Some Saline Solutions* (Edinburgh, 1912); *Scientific Papers, Vol. 1* (Cambridge, 1913); *Comptes rendus of Observation and Reasoning* (Cambridge, 1917); and *Accounts Rendered of Work Done and Things Seen* (Cambridge, 1919). Most of his papers published in scientific journals (more than 100) are listed in the Royal Society of London's *Catalogue of Scientific Papers* (London, 1867–1925), VII, 291; IX, 386–387; XIII, 885. Some of Buchanan's more important papers are "On the Distribution of Salt in the Ocean, as Indicated by the Specific Gravity of Its Waters," in *Journal of the Geographical Society* (London), **47** (1877), 72–86; "On the Distribution of Temperature in Loch Lomond During the Autumn of 1885," in *Proceedings of the Royal Society of Edinburgh,* **13** (1886), 403–428; and "On Similarities in the Physical Geography of the Great Oceans," in *Proceedings of the Geographical Society* (London), **8** (1886), 753–768.

II. Secondary Literature. Information on Buchanan's life may be found in two obituaries: in *Proceedings of the Royal Society of London,* **110A** (1926), xii–xiii; and *Proceedings of the Royal Society of Edinburgh,* **45** (1925), 364–367.

Gisela Kutzbach

BUCHER, WALTER HERMAN (*b.* Akron, Ohio, 12 March 1889; *d.* Houston, Texas, 17 February 1965), *geology.*

During his youth Bucher and his parents, Maria Gebhardt and August Bucher, moved to Germany. He received his higher education at the University of Heidelberg, graduating in 1911 with a Ph.D. in geology. He returned to America shortly thereafter and joined the faculty of the University of Cincinnati, remaining there for twenty-seven years. In 1940 Bucher moved to Columbia University as professor of structural geology and became chairman of the geology department in 1950. Six years later, having gained emeritus status, he became a consultant to Humble Oil and Refining Company in Houston, Texas, where he was employed until his death.

While at the University of Cincinnati, Bucher produced his major work, *The Deformation of the Earth's Crust* (1933), an explanation of the origin of orogenic belts. It was an attempt to compile "all essential geological facts of a general nature that bear on the problem of crustal deformation and to derive from them inductively a hypothetical picture of the mechanics of diastrophism. . . ." Tectonic observations were presented as carefully worded generalizations that Bucher called laws; interpretations of the laws were designated opinions. From these building blocks he constructed a theory. Bucher's thesis combines the contraction of the earth by cooling with gravitational forces. Such contraction leads to global fractures of the crust. These lesions, which rise from several hundred kilometers under the earth's mantle and penetrate the crust, allow the escape of heat, volatile substances, and water vapor to the surface. This weakens the crust along the fractures, causing it to form welts and furrows.

Bucher believed that the earth's crust was divided by associated linear swells and basins, or welts and furrows (crustal folds). Since the thickened sediments of furrows, uplifted in the formation of welts, are subjected to the force of gravity, their own weight and the resulting stress cause them to buckle into folds or to collapse and spread, producing the sort of rock deformation associated with mountainous regions. Support for his theory was provided by numerous experiments with Plasticine, glass (Christmas tree ornaments), and wax models of the earth, which he described in his book.

Extensions of this theory are presented in "The Role of Gravity in Orogenesis" (1956) and in the symposium *The Crust of the Earth* (1955). In addition to these broad theoretical endeavors, Bucher published many articles on geophysics and structural geology. His essential reliance on radical forces for the orogenic mechanism is now less popular than theories of primarily tangential movement, such as a continental drift.

Bucher received an honorary D.Sc. from Princeton University in 1947, the William Bowie Medal of the American Geophysical Union in 1955, and the Penrose Medal of the Geological Society of America in 1960. He served as president of the Geological Society of America in 1954 and was a member of the National Academy of Sciences, the American Association for the Advancement of Science, and the Ohio Academy of Sciences.

Bucher married Hannah E. Schmid in 1914. They had two sons and two daughters.

BIBLIOGRAPHY

I. ORIGINAL WORKS. Among Bucher's works are *The Deformation of the Earth's Crust* (Princeton, 1933; repr. New York, 1957); "The Role of Gravity in Orogenesis," in *Bulletin of the Geological Society of America,* **67** (1956), 1295–1318; "Deformation in Orogenic Belts," in *The Crust of the Earth,* Arie Poldervaart, ed. (New York, 1955), pp. 343–368; "Continental Drift Versus Land Bridges," in *Bulletin of the American Museum of Natural History,* **99**, no. 8 (1952), 72–258; "Volcanic Explosions and Overthrusts," in *Transactions of the American Geophysical Union, 14th Annual Meeting* (1933), pp. 238–242; and "Geologic Structure and Orogenic History of Venezuela," in *Memoirs. Geological Society of America,* no. 49.

II. SECONDARY LITERATURE. Details of Bucher's life are in *Current Biography,* XVIII (1957), 84–86; and in *Modern Men of Science,* J. Green, ed. (New York, 1966), pp. 74–75.

MARTHA B. KENDALL

BUCHERER, ALFRED HEINRICH (*b.* Cologne, Germany, 9 July 1863; *d.* Bonn, Germany, 16 April 1927), *physics.*

Alfred Bucherer's father, Heinrich Bucherer, was the owner of a chemical factory in Cologne. His mother was English. Besides his interests in chemistry and technology, the father was an art lover; his wife was a devotee of music and languages, and it was in such surroundings that Alfred Bucherer was raised. He exhibited unusual talents, not only in mathematics and the physical sciences but in philology as well. He was a man who was equally at home in the worlds of physics, chemistry, technology, and philology.

After spending the year 1884 studying at the Technische Hochschule at Hannover, Bucherer went to the United States, to Johns Hopkins, where he continued his technical studies and at the same time studied philology. At Hopkins he came under the influence of the chemist Ira Remsen. While studying under Remsen he became engrossed in thermodynamics, and as a direct consequence of this work, he obtained a patent for the separation of aluminum from its sulfide. He returned to the United States in 1893 to spend a year studying at Cornell. His intimate knowledge of vector analysis stemmed from his work during this period.

Bucherer completed his formal education in 1895 under Braun at Strasbourg. His topic, the effects of magnetic fields on the electromotive force, was another direct outcome of his work with Remsen. Bucherer continued traveling and studying for the next three years, spending part of that time with Ostwald at Leipzig.

He became *Privatdozent* at Bonn in 1899 and was to remain connected with Bonn in one way or another until his death. In 1912 he became professor of physics and in 1923 honorary professor of physics. He maintained an active laboratory in the university until his death.

With his arrival at Bonn, Bucherer's academic interests became modified. He discontinued his work in physical chemistry and became more and more involved in problems in physics. Besides his patent for the separation of aluminum from its sulfide, a second patent, which Bucherer had obtained in 1892, was for the transmission of pictures by wireless. It seems that it was in the interest of making this patent more fruitful that Bucherer turned to the questions of the nature of the electron and the effects of the motion of bodies on electromagnetic phenomena.

In 1904 in a monograph on the theory of electrons (*Mathematische Einführung in die Elektronentheorie*) Bucherer produced his own theory of the moving electron, which rivaled the theories of Max Abraham and H. A. Lorentz. Whereas Abraham's theory was predicated on a rigid electron and Lorentz's theory was predicated on an electron that contracted in the direction of motion, Bucherer's theory assumed an electron that contracted, but in such a way as to maintain a constant volume. According to Bucherer, the contraction was such that the moving electron became an ellipse with axes given by $as^{1/3}$, $as^{-1/6}$, $as^{-1/6}$ where a is the radius of the spherical resting electron and s is given by $(1 - v^2/c^2)$, v being the velocity of the electron and c being the velocity of light. This led to a prediction for the transverse mass of the moving electron which was midway between the predictions of Abraham and Lorentz and Einstein, Einstein's special theory of relativity making predictions for the transverse mass identical with those of Lorentz.

This result was within the range of experimental values for the mass of the moving electron obtained by Wilhelm Kaufmann in 1906. Kaufmann's data, however, which he held to be in favor of the Abraham theory, were suspect. In order to settle the question, Bucherer decided to undertake his own measurements of the specific mass of the electron. This he did in 1908. In a remarkable and abrupt turnabout, he concluded that the data he obtained supported not his own theory but the theory of Einstein.

Bucherer's lively and polemical style was responsible for his often getting into arguments in the literature. This was especially true of his work on the mass of the moving electron. While he ended up supporting Einstein in this case, he was never completely happy with the relativistic formulation of physics.

BIBLIOGRAPHY

I. ORIGINAL WORKS. *Die Wirkung des Magnetismus auf die elektromotorische Kraft*, diss. (Leipzig, 1896); *Mathematische Einführung in die Elektronentheorie* (Leipzig, 1904); "Das deformiert Elecktron und die Theorie des Elektromagnetismus," in *Physikalische Zeitschrift*, **6** (1905), 833–834; "On a New Principle of Relativity in Electromagnetism," in *Philosophical Magazine*, **13** (1907), 413–429; "Messungen an Becquerelstrahlen. Die experimentelle Bestätigung der Lorentz-Einsteinschen Theorie," in *Deutsche physikalische Gesellschaft, Verhandlungen*, **10** (1908), 688–699; "On the Principle of Relativity and the Electromagnetic Mass of the Electron, A Reply to Mr. Cunningham," in *Philosophical Magazine*, **15** (1908), 316–318; "On the Principle of Relativity. A Reply to Mr. Cunningham," *ibid.*, **16** (1908), 939–940; "Antwort auf die Kritik von Besterlmeyer bezüglich meiner experimentelle Bestätigung des Relativitätsprinzips," in *Annalen der Physik*, **30** (1909), 974–986; "Gravitation und Quantentheorie I," *ibid.*, **68** (1922), 1–10; "Gravitation und Quantentheorie II," *ibid.*, 546–551.

II. SECONDARY LITERATURE. Max Abraham, *Theorie der Elektrizität*, 2 vols. (Leipzig, 1904–1905); Stanley Goldberg, "Early Response to Einstein's Special Theory of Relativity," unpublished doctoral thesis (Harvard University, 1968), chs. 1, 2; E.T. Whittaker, *A History of the Theories of Aether and Electricity*, 2 vols. (New York, 1960).

STANLEY GOLDBERG

BUCHNER, EDUARD (*b.* Munich, Germany, 20 May 1860; *d.* Focsani, Rumania, 13 August 1917), *chemistry.*

Buchner came from an old Bavarian family of scholars. His father, Ernst, was professor of forensic medicine and obstetrics as well as editor of the *Ärztliches Intelligenzblatt* (later *Münchener medizinische Wochenschrift*).

Upon graduating from the Realgymnasium in Munich, he served in the field artillery and then studied chemistry at the Technische Hochschule in Munich. After a short while, however, Buchner had to abandon his studies because of financial problems; for four years he worked in canneries in Munich and in Mombach. In 1884, with the assistance of his brother Hans, he was able to resume his chemical studies, this time at the organic section of the chemical laboratory of the Bavarian Academy of Sciences in Munich, under Adolf von Baeyer. Buchner's first work in organic preparative chemistry resulted from the suggestions of Theodor Curtius, an assistant in the organic section, and were done under his direction; his work with Curtius on the chemistry of diazoacetic ester led to a warm friendship.

While studying chemistry, Buchner also worked at the Institute for Plant Physiology, under Karl von Nägeli. Here he became interested in the problems of alcoholic fermentation, the subject of his first publication (1886). In this paper he arrived at the significant conclusion that, contrary to Pasteur's contention, the absence of oxygen is not a necessary prerequisite for fermentation.

Buchner obtained his doctorate in 1888 under Baeyer and in 1890 was appointed his teaching assistant. He became *Privatdozent* the following year. His *Habilitationsschrift* dealt with research on pyrazole, the five-membered heterocyclic derivative of antipyrine. Baeyer procured the funds for him to set up his own laboratory for fermentation chemistry, but up to 1893 Buchner published only one other paper on the physiology of fermentation, a comparative study of the behavior of fumaric and maleic acids.

In 1893 Buchner succeeded Curtius as head of the Section for Analytical Chemistry at the University of Kiel, and in 1895 he was appointed associate professor there. The following year he became professor of analytical pharmaceutical chemistry in Tübingen and, while there, published his pioneering work, *Alkoholische Gärung ohne Hefezellen* (1897).

In 1898 Buchner accepted an appointment as full professor of general chemistry at the College of Agriculture in Berlin and simultaneously he became director of the Institute for the Fermentation Industry.

In 1900 he married Lotte Stahl, daughter of a Tübingen mathematician. Two sons and one daughter resulted from this marriage.

Scientifically, Buchner's Berlin years were his most productive period, especially in the field of the biochemistry of the fermentation process. Nevertheless, he felt that professionally he was not able to develop his knowledge: he missed teaching in a chemical institute of a university. He had to wait a long time before he was invited to teach at a university, however, perhaps because of having insulted the Ministry of Education official in charge of the Prussian academic institutions. After being kept waiting by the official, Buchner rebuked him by pointing to his pocket watch.

After receiving the Nobel Prize in chemistry in 1907 for his work on cell-free fermentation, Buchner was appointed to the chair of physiological chemistry at the University of Breslau in 1909. Two years later he was invited to Würzburg, an invitation that he accepted with alacrity. In Würzburg he was also able to pursue his hobbies of hunting and mountain climbing.

Politically, Buchner was an admirer of Bismarck and a follower of the National Liberal party. He volunteered for active duty at the outbreak of World War I and in August 1914 was sent to the front as a captain of an ammunition supply unit. He was promoted to major in 1916, but in that same year he was called back to Würzburg to resume teaching. In 1917 he again volunteered for front-line duty and was sent to Rumania, where on 11 August he was wounded by shrapnel and died two days later.

Central to Buchner's experimental work are three papers published in 1897, which dealt with his sensational discovery of cell-free fermentation, the turning point for the study of enzymes. In the history of enzymology, it is quite proper to differentiate between the pre-Buchner and post-Buchner periods.

The basis of fermentation chemistry or enzyme chemistry is Berzelius' thesis[1] that all reactions in living organisms are initiated and regulated by catalysts. This of course applies to the processes of fermentation and putrefaction. Originally, the terms "ferment" and "enzyme" designated primarily fermentation, but also putrefaction or a gas-producing agent. Hence, it is understandable that "the history of the conversion of fermentable sugar through yeast overlaps with the history of fermentation processes in general. It was this outstandingly important process in the production of alcoholic beverages that was the prototype of fermentation processes."[2]

Between 1830 and 1860, prior to Buchner's discovery, two theories of fermentation had divided the scientific world into vitalists and mechanists. Liebig was the exponent of the mechanists. According to his theory,[3] formulated in 1839, yeast causes fermentation because, as a body in a state of continuous decomposition, it stimulates the sugar molecules to decompose into alcohol and carbon dioxide. Although this appeared to be analogous to the then known fermentative reactions (the decomposition of amygdalin into hydrocyanic acid and sugar by emulsion, the proteolysis of egg albumin by pepsin, the decomposition of starch by diastase), Liebig refused to ascribe the character of a "catalytic force," as formulated by Berzelius, to the action of yeast.

The mechanical theory of fermentation, regardless of whether it interpreted yeast as an expression of a "catalytic force" or of a body in the process of decomposing, clashed with Pasteur's vitalistic interpretation of the fermentation process. In 1836 Cagniard de la Tour had reported to the Paris Academy that yeast consisted of living organisms, and the next year Theodor Schwann and Friedrich Kützing were to reach the same conclusion. On the basis of these discoveries and as a result of his own observations and experiments, Pasteur (between 1857 and 1860) formulated the thesis that alcoholic fermentation was an expression of the vital action of the yeast fungi and inseparably bound to this physiological action.[4] Fermentation was therefore not a catalytic but a vital process. Then Pasteur differentiated between soluble enzymes, which can be separated from the vital processes and therefore are also effective outside the organism, and ferments, which are inseparably bound to a living organism and its vitality. Although such researchers as Berthelot, Traube, and Hoppe-Seyler subsequently defended the view that there were active enzymes in living cells, comparable to those acting outside the cell, Pasteur's view of the unalterable connection between vitality and fermentation nevertheless found acceptance among the majority of scientists.

Efforts to isolate the fermentation-producing agent from yeast cells remained unsuccessful. This was the problem Buchner attacked anew in 1893 at the suggestion of his brother Hans, who was engaged in the extraction of powerful pathogenic substances from bacteria. The problem was how to obtain cell fluid, in as pure a state as possible, for therapeutic research. Buchner's approach was an attempt to destroy yeast cells in order to extract their fluid. At the suggestion of Martin Hahn, an assistant of his brother's, Buchner pulverized yeast in a mortar with one part quartz sand and one-fifth part diatomaceous earth; this became a thick paste within a few minutes. This paste was then wrapped in canvas and subjected to a pressure of ninety kilograms per square centimeter, yielding 500 milliliters of fluid from 1,000 grams yeast.

At first, hardly any thought was given to the idea of producing fermentation with the fluid expressed from yeast. Rather, Buchner and Hahn concentrated on preserving the easily decomposed fluid by adding concentrated sucrose solution. In 1896 Buchner discovered that this mixture soon exhibited lively gas formation. In 1897 he published three papers on the results of these first experiments with cell-free alcoholic fermentation, and by the end of 1902 he had published fifteen more papers on the same subject. In 1903 the first comprehensive presentation of his achievements was published by the two Buchners and Martin Hahn as *Die Zymase-Gärung*.

Buchner called the active, fermentation-producing agent of the expressed fluid "zymase." This eliminated the previously valid distinction between the soluble enzymes, effective outside the cell, and the ferments, whose effectiveness is linked to cell structure and cell activity. Accordingly, life and fermentation are not unalterably bound to each other. Instead, fermentation is a chemical, enzymatically catalyzed process.

Through painstaking experimentation, Buchner defended this basic fact against various objections, particularly those of the physiologist Max Rubner, the biochemist Hans von Euler-Chelpin, and the botanist Wilhelm Ruhland. He was able to prove that neither the few intact yeast cells present in the expressed fluid nor any "living plasma particles" cause the sugar conversion that occurs in the fermentation process. Addition of a mixture of alcohol and ether to the fluid yielded a precipitate that could be preserved as a powder without the zymase losing its effectiveness. He also obtained a fully fermentative dry substance by killing the yeast cells through addition of alcohol or acetone to a yeast suspension. He gave the name "zymin" to the substance after it had been washed and dried with ether. It cannot grow but is fully effective in fermentation experiments.

Further test series concerned the chemical properties of the expressed fluid, a yellow-brown opalescent liquid which becomes ineffective after prolonged storage because a proteolytic enzyme, endotryptase, destroys the active principle. The fluid also loses its effectiveness through heating, which causes precipitation of its proteins. In addition to zymase, the fluid contains a series of other enzymes: catalase (diluted fluid decomposes hydrogen peroxide into water and oxygen) as well as enzymes resulting from the splitting of disaccharides and polysaccharides. From the latter, Buchner deduced that not only the simple sugars, glucose and fructose, but also complex sugars, maltose and saccharose (disaccharides), as well as the polysaccharide glycogen, are fermentable. Attempts to separate these enzymes from the zymase were almost always unsuccessful.

In the chemistry of alcoholic fermentation, Buchner and his assistants were confronted by three questions between 1904 and 1917: (1) Is zymase a homogeneous enzyme? (2) In order to be active, does it require the presence of additional substances, especially the presence of a coenzyme? (3) What is the chemical nature of the intermediate products in the decomposition of sugar into alcohol and carbon dioxide? In the experimental treatment of these questions, however, Buchner and his assistants were no longer alone. The scientific world had realized that the fluid expressed from yeast could be profitably studied in order to explain the chemistry of fermentation. The English scientists A. Harden and W. J. Young had been working on these problems since 1904, the St. Petersburg botanist L. Ivanov since 1906, and A. von Lebedev since 1910; and if the reaction chain of alcoholic fermentation can be considered fully explained, it is because of their successful initial experiments. In this phase Buchner and his circle of co-workers take second place. True, they kept up with these developments, but they were not the pacesetters.

Buchner suggested that lactic acid, methylglyoxal, glyceraldehyde, and dihydroxyacetone were the intermediate products of the fermentation of alcohol. It has only recently been established that glyceralde-

hyde and dihydroxyacetone, in the form of the respective phosphates, are indeed intermediate products of the decomposition of sugar by yeast as well as by animal cells.

Buchner was also interested in the fermentation phenomena of other microorganisms. In 1902 he published a paper on the enzymes of *Monilia candida* and other milk-sugar yeasts. In subsequent years he worked on acetous fermentation (1906), butyrous fermentation (1908), and citrous fermentation (1909). These investigations also served to confirm that characteristic life phenomena can be attributed to the regularities of enzyme-catalyzed chemical reactions.

Buchner's revolutionary discoveries in biochemistry overshadow his work in preparative organic chemistry. The starting point of these studies was the synthesis of diazoacetic ester, by means of which Curtius discovered a new group of compounds in 1883. This aliphatic diazo compound is highly reactive. Buchner experimented systematically with it, first under the direction of Curtius and later independently. Between 1885 and 1905 he published forty-eight papers treating preparation of nitrogenous compounds, especially pyrazole, as products of the action of diazoacetic ester on unsaturated acid esters, and the synthesis of trimethylene carboxylic acids by adding diazoacetic ester to fumaric acid ester and heating the mixture. With the aid of brucine salts, Buchner separated the resulting racemic mixture into its two enantiomorphic substances. The papers also concerned the products of reaction of diazoacetic ester with aromatic hydrocarbons (benzene, toluene, *m*-xylene, and *p*-xylene). The result of this work was the synthesis of cycloheptatriene and cycloheptanecarboxylic acid. Thus a new direction was furnished for a synthesis of compounds in the cycloheptane series.

After 1905 Buchner published only six additional studies in preparative organic chemistry, an indication that biochemical problems fully occupied his time.

NOTES

1. *Jahresberichte von Berzelius,* **15** (1835), 245.
2. Carl Oppenheimer, *Die Fermente und ihre Wirkungen,* 2nd ed. (Leipzig, 1903), p. 302.
3. *Annalen der Chemie,* **30** (1839), 362.
4. *Annales de chimie et de physique,* **58** (1860), 323.

BIBLIOGRAPHY

I. ORIGINAL WORKS. All of Buchner's writings are listed in Poggendorff, IV, 200, and V, 182; references to his obituaries are in VI, 362. A complete bibliography can also be found in the appendix to C. Harries, in *Berichte der Deutschen chemischen Gesellschaft*, **50** (1917), 1843–1876. For a comprehensive presentation of his work on fermentation, see *Die Zymase-Gärung* (Munich, 1903), written with Hans Buchner and Martin Hahn; "Alkoholische Gärung des Zuckers," in *Bulletin de la Société chimique de France*, **7** (1910), 1–22; "Neuere Ansichten über die Zymase," in *Sitzungsberichte der Physikalisch-medizinischen Gesellschaft zu Würzburg* (1917), written with S. Skraup; and "Cell-free Fermentation," in *Nobel Lectures Chemistry 1901–1921* (Amsterdam–London–New York, 1966).

II. SECONDARY LITERATURE. The history of the fermentation problem is discussed in M. Delbrück and A. Schrohe, *Hefe, Gärung und Fäulnis* (Berlin, 1904); C. Graebe, *Geschichte der organischen Chemie* (Berlin, 1920); F. F. Nord, in F. F. Nord and R. Weidenhagen, *Handbuch der Enzymologie* (Leipzig, 1940); and C. Oppenheimer, *Die Fermente und ihre Wirkungen,* 4th ed. (Leipzig, 1913). For further literature see the works cited in the notes.

On Buchner's work in organic synthesis, see P. Walden, *Geschichte der organischen Chemie seit 1880* (Berlin, 1941). The history of the discovery of cell-free fermentation is discussed in M. von Gruber, in *Münchener medizinische Wochenschrift* (1907).

HERBERT SCHRIEFERS

BÜCHNER, FRIEDRICH KARL CHRISTIAN LUDWIG (*b.* Darmstadt, Germany, 29 March 1824; *d.* Darmstadt, 1 May 1899), *medicine, philosophy, history of science.*

Büchner was the most influential nineteenth-century German representative of a consistent materialism. His major accomplishments were the dissemination of the methods and results of the natural sciences and his work against a dogmatic, metaphysically determined formation of the consciousness. That this could not always take place without biased presentations and controversies, sometimes at the expense of scientific exactness and thoroughness, does not greatly lessen the value of Büchner's works.

The third son of Ernst Büchner, a physician who later became archducal medical adviser, and of Karoline Reuss, Ludwig Büchner entered the University of Giessen in 1842 and studied physics, chemistry, botany, mineralogy, and philosophy. Later, following his father's wishes, he studied medicine and passed the examinations of this faculty in 1848. In the same year, he graduated after submitting "Beiträge zur Hall'schen Lehre von einem excito-motorischen Nervensystem" as his dissertation. One of its theses was that the personal soul is unthinkable without its material substrate.

As a student Büchner took an active part in the republican attempts at reform by working for democratic journals. He also published the *Nachgelassene*

Schriften (1850) and a biography of his brother Georg, the famous playwright.

After further studies in Würzburg, with Rudolf Virchow, and in Vienna, Büchner became academic lecturer in Tübingen in 1854. In the following years he lectured on physical diagnosis, medical encyclopedia, and forensic medicine. He also served as assistant physician at the university clinic and as a medicolegal expert.

In 1854 the convention of German natural scientists and physicians was held in Tübingen, and Büchner wrote a series of reports on the talks given at the convention. These reports and Jacob Moleschott's *Kreislauf des Lebens* (1852) stimulated him to write his first and most famous work, *Kraft und Stoff* (1855). Büchner ascribed the favorable reception of this book (the first edition was sold out within a few weeks) to the public's weariness of discussions of politics and literature. In the wake of the 1848 revolution his ideas were considered dangerous by the clergy and the conservative elements, who therefore forced Büchner to resign his university lectureship. The kind and extent of the polemic conducted becomes evident on reading the Preface and Notes in subsequent editions of *Kraft und Stoff,* as well as the collection of essays *Aus Natur und Wissenschaft* (1862).

In the following years Büchner practiced medicine in Darmstadt and published numerous works meant to disseminate knowledge of the natural sciences. These, like *Kraft und Stoff,* were translated into many languages. In 1860 he married Sophie Thomas. He made lecture tours of Germany and the United States (1874), and in 1881 he founded the Deutschen Freidenkerbund.

As guidelines for his works Büchner took Lamettrie's statement that experience and observation must be our sole guides and Bernhard Cotta's opinion that the empirical investigation of nature has no purpose but to find the truth, regardless of whether it seems reassuring or hopeless, beautiful or ugly, logical or inconsistent, wise or foolish.

Starting with the old materialism and the writings of Ludwig Feuerbach, Büchner tried to base the theses of the materialistic concept of the world on empirical foundations and thus to prepare fruitful philosophical discussions. He defined force as "expression for the cause of a possible or an actual movement." Physics, as the science of forces (mechanical force, gravity, heat), revealed that forces are inseparable from matter. Force and matter could not be destroyed; they were one and the same thing, seen from different aspects. There could be no force without matter, and no matter without force.

To consider matter as of minimal value when

compared with the spiritual is meaningless, according to Büchner, for without an exact knowledge of matter and its laws, no insight is conceivable. Elements unchangeable in quantity and quality combine to form the various inorganic and organic substances, and their transformations take place according to laws; the laws of nature are unchangeable and generally valid. The attempt to "elucidate" phenomena by arbitrarily naming them is to be avoided (for instance, the "vital force" assumed by Justus Liebig). Büchner justifiably conceived the works of Darwin (for the dissemination of which he is especially to be lauded), Lyell, Kirchhoff, and Haeckel, and also the development of chemistry (which forced elimination of the abrupt barrier between inorganic and organic combinations), to be confirmations of his point of view.

BIBLIOGRAPHY

I. ORIGINAL WORKS. Büchner's writings include *Kraft und Stoff. Empirisch-naturphilosophische Studien* (Frankfurt am Main, 1855), later entitled *Kraft und Stoff oder Grundzüge der natürlichen Weltordnung* (20th ed., Leipzig, 1902), also trans. as *Force and Matter, or Principles of the Natural Order of the Universe* (London, 1884; repr. New York, 1950); *Natur und Geist* (Frankfurt am Main, 1857; 3rd ed., Leipzig, 1876); *Physiologische Bilder,* I (Leipzig, 1861; 3rd ed., 1886), II (Leipzig, 1875; new ed., 1886); *Aus Natur und Wissenschaft, Studien, Kritiken und Abhandlungen,* I (Leipzig, 1862; 3rd ed., 1874), II (Leipzig, 1884); *Sechs Vorlesungen über die Darwin'sche Theorie von der Verwandlung der Arten und die erste Entstehung der Organismenwelt* (Leipzig, 1868), later entitled *Die Darwin'sche Theorie von der Entstehung und Umwandlung der Lebewelt* (5th ed., Leipzig, 1890); *Der Mensch und seine Stellung in der Natur in Vergangenheit, Gegenwart und Zukunft* (Leipzig, 1869; 3rd ed., 1889), trans. as *Man in the Past, Present and Future* (London, 1872); *Der Gottesbegriff und dessen Bedeutung in der Gegenwart* (Leipzig, 1874), 3rd ed. entitled *Gott und die Wissenschaft* (Leipzig, 1897); *Aus dem Geistesleben der Thiere, oder Staaten und Thaten der Kleinen* (Berlin, 1876; 4th ed., Leipzig, 1897), trans. as *Mind in Animals* (London, 1903); *Liebe und Liebes-Leben in der Thierwelt* (Leipzig, 1879, 1885); *Licht und Leben* (Leipzig, 1882, 1897); *Die Macht der Vererbung und ihr Einfluss auf den moralischen und geistigen Fortschritt der Menschheit* (Leipzig, 1882, 1909); *Der Fortschritt in Natur und Geschichte im Lichte der Darwinschen Theorie* (Stuttgart, 1884); *Der neue Hamlet* (Zurich, 1885; new ed., Giessen, 1901), written under the pseudonym Karl Ludwig; *Über religiöse und wissenschaftliche Weltanschauung* (Leipzig, 1887); *Thatsachen und Theorien aus dem naturwissenschaftlichen Leben der Gegenwart* (Berlin, 1887); *Das künftige Leben und die moderne Wissenschaft* (Leipzig, 1889); *Fremdes und Eigenes aus dem geistigen Leben der Gegenwart* (Leipzig, 1890); *Das goldene Zeitalter, oder das Leben vor*

der Geschichte (Berlin, 1891); *Das Buch vom langen Leben, oder, die Lehre von der Dauer und Erhaltung des Lebens (Makrobiotik)* (Leipzig, 1892), *Darwinismus und Sozialismus, oder der Kampf um das Dasein und die moderne Gesellschaft* (Leipzig, 1894; 2nd ed., Stuttgart, 1906); *Am Sterbelager des Jahrhunderts* (Giessen, 1898, 1900); *Im Dienste der Wahrheit* (Giessen, 1900), with a biography of the author by Alex Büchner; and *Last Words on Materialism and Kindred Subjects* (London, 1901).

II. SECONDARY LITERATURE. Writings dealing with Büchner or his work are Arthur Drews, *Die deutsche Spekulation seit Kant,* II (Leipzig, 1895), 267–281; Julius Frauenstädt, *Der Materialismus. Seine Wahrheit und sein Irrthum. Eine Erwiderung auf Louis Büchner's "Kraft und Stoff"* (Leipzig, 1856); and Friedrich Albert Lange, *Geschichte des Materialismus und Kritik seiner Bedeutung in der Gegenwart,* II (5th ed., Leipzig, 1896), 89–97, also available in English as *The History of Materialism* (London, 1877–1879).

JOACHIM THIELE

BUCHOLZ, CHRISTIAN FRIEDRICH (*b.* Eisleben, Germany, 19 September 1770; *d.* Erfurt, Germany, 9 June 1818), *chemistry, pharmacy.*

Bucholz's father, an obscure apothecary, died in 1775, leaving his five-year-old son the heir to a pharmacy. Two years later the boy's mother married an eminent Erfurt pharmacist named Voigt. At a very early age, Bucholz showed a talent and liking for chemical research, and under the tutelage of his stepfather and his uncle, the pharmaceutical chemist W. H. S. Bucholz, he rapidly acquired the background and training necessary to his chosen profession. In 1784 he was sent to Kassel as apprentice to the pharmacist Karl Wilhelm Fiedler. There he not only learned his professional duties but also taught himself languages and natural science. Bucholz left Kassel in 1789 and went to Ochsenfurt, Franconia, where for two years he worked as an apothecary's assistant; he then moved to Mulhouse, where for three years he was an associate in an apothecary. Here he completed his first publication, a paper on the crystallization of barium acetate, in 1794. Toward the end of 1794 he returned to Erfurt and took over the pharmacy he had inherited from his father. The following year, he married and began raising a family.

Bucholz's researches in chemistry were primarily of an analytical nature. Altogether, he published over a hundred articles in German chemical and pharmaceutical journals, including Scherer's *Neues allgemeines Journal der Chemie,* Trommsdorff's *Journal der Pharmacie,* Gehlen's *Journal für die Chemie und Physik* (of which he was, after 1804, one of the editors), and Schweigger's *Journal für Chemie.* Some of his more important papers were translated into French (primarily for the *Annales de chimie* and the *Journal des mines*) and English (especially for *Nicholson's Journal*). In addition, he published several books on chemistry and pharmacy.

Bucholz made a few important, but no primary, contributions to chemistry. He investigated in detail some of the more obscure compounds of sulfur. He made extensive analyses of the salts of molybdenum, tungsten, and tin, and he extracted uranium compounds from pitchblende. Bucholz distinguished strontium and barium oxides from the hydroxides of those metals by showing that the former were infusable whereas the latter were not. He investigated methods for the separation of copper and silver, iron and manganese, nickel and cobalt, and magnesium and calcium. He also carried out numerous mineral analyses and investigated several organic compounds, including camphoric acid, which he identified.

In 1808 Bucholz received the doctorate in pharmacy from the University of Rinteln, and in 1809 the University of Erfurt awarded him a Ph.D. and a position as *Assessor* (assistant) at its College of Medicine. In the following year, he was made a professor at the University of Erfurt and was given a place on the Faculty of Philosophy. He became privy councillor in the tiny principality of Schwarzburg-Sonderhausen in 1815. Bucholz was also active in the attempt to improve the lot of his fellow pharmacists. He cooperated with F. A. C. Gren in the establishment of an institution for retired pharmacists, and with J. B. Trommsdorff he founded an apothecaries' syndicate.

Bucholz's health began to fail about 1813. During the occupation of Erfurt by the French in 1813, he was cruelly imprisoned with about thirty of his fellow citizens and held for ransom. As a result, he suffered further illnesses and, finally, total blindness. In his final years he was able to publish only with the aid of his student Rudolph Brandes. Since Bucholz made no signal contribution to his field, his reputation, which had been founded on a large number of exacting analytical researches, did not survive long after him.

BIBLIOGRAPHY

I. ORIGINAL WORKS. Two of Bucholz's books are *Beiträge zur Erweiterung und Berichtigung der Chemie,* 3 vols. (Erfurt, 1799–1802); and *Grundriss der Pharmacie mit vorzüglicher Hinsicht auf die pharmaceutische Chemie* (Erfurt, 1802). See list in Schreger article (below).

II. SECONDARY LITERATURE. A detailed and heavily footnoted life of Bucholz, containing references to works not cited in the usual sources, is T. Schreger, in J. G. Ersch

and J. G. Gruber, eds., *Allgemeine Encyclopädie der Wissenschaften und Künste,* XIII (Leipzig, 1824), 303–305. See also Poggendorff, I, 330; and J. R. Partington, *A History of Chemistry,* III (London, 1962), 581–582.

J. B. GOUGH

BUCKINGHAM, EDGAR (*b.* Philadelphia, Pennsylvania, 8 July 1867; *d.* Washington, D.C., 29 April 1940), *physics.*

Edgar Buckingham is best known for his early work on thermodynamics and for his later study of dimensional theory. Especially attracted to problems that could not be solved by pure calculation but required experimentation as well, he showed more clearly than anyone before him how the planning and interpretation of experiments can be facilitated by the method of dimensions, later called dimensional analysis.

Buckingham graduated from Harvard in 1887 and received his Ph.D. at Leipzig in 1893. His book on thermodynamics (1900) carried the reader from the simplest facts of temperature measurement through the equilibrium of heterogeneous systems. It was a powerful contribution toward clarifying the subject.

Between 1891 and 1901, Buckingham taught physics at Harvard, Bryn Mawr College, and the University of Wisconsin. He entered government service as an assistant physicist in the Bureau of Soils in 1902, and was employed by the Bureau of Standards from 1905 until his retirement in 1937. His natural ability as a teacher and lecturer was evident in his lectures on technical thermodynamics in the Naval Postgraduate School at Annapolis (1911–1912) and in the graduate program of the National Bureau of Standards (1912–1913). Buckingham served as a technical expert on the Council of National Defense during World War I and as an associate scientific attaché with the United States Embassy in Rome from 1918 to 1919. He was frequently called upon during his years with the Bureau of Standards to advise the Navy Department on steam turbine and propeller research.

Buckingham's treatise on thermodynamics was followed by fifty or more scientific papers. The subjects included soil physics, properties of gases, blackbody radiation, acoustics, fluid mechanics, and dimensions. Several of his noteworthy papers on dimensional theory, listed in the bibliography, awakened a lively interest in dimensional methods and their practical application.

He pointed out the advantages of dimensionless variables and how to generalize empirical equations. His frequently cited "pi-theorem" serves to reduce the number of independent variables and shows how to experiment on geometrically similar models so as to satisfy the most general requirements of physical as well as dynamic similarity.

BIBLIOGRAPHY

Buckingham's works include *An Outline of the Theory of Thermodynamics* (New York, 1900); "Physically Similar Systems . . .," in *Physical Review,* 2nd ser., **4** (1914), 345–376; "Windage Resistance of Steam Turbine Wheels," in *Bulletin of the Bureau of Standards,* **10** (1914), 191–234; "Model Experiments and the Forms of Empirical Equations," in *Transactions of the American Society of Mechanical Engineers,* **37** (1915), 263–296; "Notes on the Methods of Dimensions," in *Philosophical Magazine,* 7th ser., **42** (1921), 696–719; see also **48** (1924), 141–145; and "Dimensional Analysis of Model Propeller Tests," in *Journal of the American Society of Naval Engineers,* **48** (1936), 147–198.

MAYO DYER HERSEY

BUCKLAND, WILLIAM (*b.* Axminster, England, 12 March 1784; *d.* Islip, England, 14 August 1856), *geology, paleontology.*

Buckland's father, Charles, was rector of Templeton and Trusham; his mother, Elizabeth, was the daughter of a landed proprietor established in Devon since the seventeenth century. Buckland became interested in rocks and fossil shells by playing among them in the valley of the River Axe, in local quarries, and at the seashore around Lyme Regis. He went on collecting rambles with his father, who had a taste for ammonites and related shells. He also collected birds' eggs and observed the habits of fishes. At Winchester School, Buckland was a good Latin student and became familiar with chalk formations through the common practice of digging for field mice in nearby chalk pits. Environment, family, church, and school experiences had fixed his interest on natural history by the time he entered Oxford.

Buckland won a competitive examination for a scholarship at Corpus Christi College in 1801. He graduated in 1804 with a very good examination and continued in residence, supporting himself on his scholarship and by taking pupils. He was elected fellow of his college and admitted to holy orders in 1809.

Around this period some people at Oxford, partly stimulated by John Kidd's lectures, were showing an interest in geology. Among the members of this group, besides Buckland, were J. J. and W. D. Conybeare, Charles Daubeny, John and Philip Duncan, and W. J. Broderip. The latter introduced Buckland to fieldwork, and Buckland considered the younger man

to be his tutor in geology. Broderip was knowledgeable in conchology; he had been instructed by Joseph Townsend, a friend of William Smith. Buckland was thus initiated into the new fossil geology at the beginning of his career. Broderip remained a close friend and scientific adviser; and Buckland sought out Townsend and Benjamin Richardson, another friend of Smith's, on his trips from Oxford to Axminster. Other early geological friends were Henry De la Beche, who grew up at Lyme Regis, and George Greenough.

In 1813 Buckland was elected reader in mineralogy to succeed Kidd, and became a fellow of the Geological Society of London; his first publication, of sorts, was in 1814. His lectures included geology, and were well received. He was appointed to a new readership (not professorship) in geology in 1818; the motives and politics of this endowment have not been satisfactorily explained. Thereafter Buckland usually styled himself "professor" on matter published in London and "reader" on matter published in Oxford. He gave two sets of lectures yearly until 1849, and usually prepared new lecture notes each year. Apparently he emphasized causal explanations of the visible phenomena. Buckland was an active participant in town affairs; among other matters, he was instrumental in introducing gas lighting in 1818, and became chairman of the Oxford gas company.

From 1808 to 1815 Buckland made geological tours of England and other parts of the British Isles. In 1816, with Greenough and W. D. Conybeare, he began his European tours, which eventually took him to Germany, Poland, Austria, Italy, Switzerland, and France. Cuvier visited him at Oxford in 1818, and he visited Cuvier at Paris several times.

Buckland was awarded the Copley Medal of the Royal Society for his cavern researches published in 1822. He was president of the Geological Society of London in 1824–1825 and again in 1840–1841, and was a member of the Council of the Royal Society from 1827 to 1849. In 1825 he accepted a country parsonage in the gift of his college, presumably so that he could marry, but was then appointed a canon of Christ Church, Oxford. These canonries were among the richest governmental rewards for academic distinction without serious administrative responsibilities. Buckland married Mary Morland, of Sheepstead House, near Abingdon, Berkshire, the same year; they had five children who survived. Mary Buckland assisted her husband with his writing, and by drawing illustrations and reconstructing fossils according to his instructions.

Buckland's Continental trips, especially those of 1826 and 1827, made him aware of German attempts to found an annual meeting of scientific men. His public prominence and international contacts made him an obvious choice for president and host of the second meeting of the British Association for the Advancement of Science in 1832 (the first full scientific meeting, since the one in 1831 was largely devoted to organizing the association). He was thereafter active at its meetings. He played a major role in the establishment of the Museum of Practical Geology and affiliated activities of his friend De la Beche.

Buckland was made dean of Westminster in 1845 by the Tory prime minister, Robert Peel, an admirer of his work. He left Oxford for London rather willingly, feeling that he had tried for forty-four years to spread a taste for science at the university, and had failed. We can see that he had raised geology to rank alongside the more prominent sciences, such as anatomy, and had helped foster the growing interest in science that led to its inclusion in the examination curriculum and to the building of the Oxford Museum, in the next decade. His own scientific work, while perhaps ultimately not so significant as that being done in physics at Cambridge, and not leading to an "Oxford school of geology," did give Oxford an international name in science that it did not have in humanistic or biblical scholarship.

As dean of Westminster, Buckland was a vigorous administrator, repairing the physical deterioration of the abbey and the school, and restoring the school scholastically to the status of an effective modern educational institution. He took an interest in local sanitary reform. Basically a liberal in Anglican Church politics, he took particular pleasure in acting as host for the consecration of four missionary bishops, a move opposed by some factions.

Buckland held the rectory of Islip, seven miles from Oxford, as a country home. He was a useful rector, and retired there when, at the end of 1849, he contracted a mysterious illness characterized by apathy and depression. He died seven years later. The autopsy showed that damage to the base of the skull caused by a carriage accident in Germany thirty years before had developed into an advanced state of decay. His wife died a year later, apparently as a result of the same accident. Both were buried in Islip churchyard.

Personally, Buckland was characterized by great energy. His whole life and his household were organized around geology. His unfailing sense of humor puzzled and annoyed some of his more Victorian-minded colleagues, such as Charles Lyell and Adam Sedgwick, and led John Henry Newman to distrust geology altogether. On the other hand, John Ruskin found him stimulating, as did most of his other auditors. Buckland took religion and geology seriously, but took himself, other geologists, and most geological theories much less so.

Buckland was not given to synthesis or system building, and there is a danger of attributing too much importance to his general theoretical positions, which were often derivative. His importance lay, rather, in helping to redefine the nature and method of a geological explanation. British stratigraphers before about 1815 had often been satisfied with a tracing of the strata (largely the secondary formations) or had gone all the way to a total system of geological dynamics. Following the suggestion of Cuvier in the first edition of his *Discours préliminaire,* Buckland and other geologists wished to produce detailed explanations that would in effect constitute a geological history, period by period, of the events in a given locality. To help in doing so, Buckland transferred Cuvier's method of reconstructing fossil animals to geology proper: that is, he tried to reason from the analogies of the existing world (Cuvier's *création actuelle*) to the events of a past world, even though Cuvier himself had cast some doubt on the validity of this process in geology.

Nothing is more characteristic of Buckland's papers than the use of some immediately observable contemporary analogy—the habits of modern hyenas, the cavities formed by air bubbles in clay, the geographical locus of modern animals. His method also differed from that of Cuvier's *Discours* in not depending primarily on paleontological evidence. Although Buckland was one of Cuvier's great admirers and seemingly enjoyed correcting him on all kinds of specific points, his own method was to bring together stratigraphical, petrological, dynamic, and paleontological reasoning and observations on modern forms and habits of life to explain the phenomena of a given locality. This is well exemplified by his paper of 1830, written with De la Beche, on the geology of the neighborhood of Weymouth, which utilizes the techniques he had developed over the previous fifteen years.[1]

In paleontology Buckland's most interesting work was on still-existing forms, such as hyenas and bears, and on marine shells. Cuvier was not much interested in conchology, the study of variations among shells per se; Buckland's emphasis, while including the organisms that produced the shells, was perhaps a bit more in the conchological tradition of William Smith and James Sowerby.

Buckland was thus one of the men, perhaps the ablest and probably the most acute, who built a typically "British" geology, based on careful local stratigraphy and local dynamic explanations but revivified by the addition of fossil evidence. This British geology was recognizable as such for the next half-century, regardless of the ideological conceptions (uniformitarian or catastrophist, for example) of the geologist involved. Cuvier was delighted by the results and, in later editions of the *Discours,* cited Buckland as one of the men who had brought into being the new geology whose possibility was only indicated in the *Discours* itself.

On more particular points of theory, the actual sources of Buckland's positions cannot be documented without a study of private papers, although his relation to some positions of his predecessors can be indicated. The processes postulated by James Hutton for cyclic continent building were dismissed by many geologists as being unobservable and therefore of little scientific importance. Buckland ignored such hypothetical views in classifying theorists. He used "Huttonian" to designate those who explained the earth's surface features by the slow action of atmospheric agents. He opposed such geologists; he believed many surface features had originated in local elevations and dislocations. Like many British geologists, he agreed with Saussure, who had used the idea of a massive "debacle" of water to explain much valley excavation, distribution of alluvial gravel, and erratic transport. Unlike Kidd, but like Townsend, Buckland felt that geology could present positive evidence of this debacle. Like Townsend, he was inclined toward volcanism, although it played no essential role in his own work, and he was effective in spreading a taste for the study of volcanic action among British scientists in the 1820's. Basically anti-Wernerian, he nevertheless looked for a worldwide identification of equivalent strata. In opposition to Cuvier's suggestion, Buckland believed that the current continents are more or less permanent, and were dry land before the most recent catastrophe or debacle; their period of submersion under the ocean had been long before that. Like other geologists who had studied the false alarms of the eighteenth century, he was skeptical of evidence of fossil human bones in strata earlier than the debacle; he examined new cases carefully but concluded each time that the point was not proved.

If no other indication is given, the dates in the text of this essay indicate when the paper in question was read, not when it was published. Buckland's first important paper was read in 1816, when he was thirty-two years old. He modified his own theorizing concerning the cause of the deluge to take into account Louis Agassiz's glacial hypothesis in 1840, when he was fifty-six. A slow starter, he was alert throughout his career to adopt or react to new proposals.

The paper of 1816, on specimens from the plastic clay, shows a number of Buckland's continuing themes.[2] He was studying the British equivalent of the *argile plastique* of Cuvier and Alexandre Brongniart, located above the chalk and below the London clay. They had suggested, on the basis of the differences in organic remains, that each deposition was of immense scale and that a long time had intervened between the formations. Buckland confirmed the identity of the French and English formations on the basis of petrographical considerations, and the long periods involved on the basis of the processes that could have produced the rocks and fossils of the strata. The chalk must first have been consolidated; its breaking up produced chalk pebbles whose smoothness and roundness argued the long-continued action of water. These pebbles were mixed in with the clay before or during its solidification, and there were periods of repose long enough for myriad oysters whose shells were attached to the pebbles to live and die undisturbed. Thus Buckland added comparative geology, local dynamics, and stratigraphical and petrological considerations to the French fossil approach, in order to show the long periods involved and the great time gaps in this part of the geological record.

In 1819 Buckland delivered his inaugural lecture as reader in geology; it was published as *Vindiciae geologicae* in 1820. Ostensibly it was an orthodox presentation of geology as useful to religion, in response to an evangelical Presbyterian, the famous Scots preacher Thomas Chalmers, who objected not to geology but to any kind of natural theology. Geology extends the reign of final causes, said Buckland; it shows the existence of a recent universal deluge and the recent origin of man; geological epochs came (as Chalmers suggested) before the creation story, so there is no need to reconcile them with the biblical days of creation. Actually, the lecture was a careful definition of an independent position. Buckland corrected Cuvier as to the permanence of modern continents. He surrounded quotations from Deluc with a text that contradicted Deluc on the essential point: Buckland insisted that the world was made for all its inhabitants, not for man alone. He contradicted Kidd, now his faculty colleague, who believed that the Mosaic flood had taken place miraculously but had left no geological traces; Buckland maintained the reverse. His real antagonist, however, was an evangelical within the Anglican Church, John Bird Sumner, who was later archbishop of Canterbury. By careful selection Buckland made it appear that Sumner's position supported his own; but Buckland carefully avoided asserting a physical miracle, his "creative interference" being always a final, not an efficient, cause. Buckland's insistence on the actual evidence of a deluge was partly an answer to Sumner's insistence that the Mosaic records were much more reliable than geological evidence. The notion that with Buckland "Cuvier and orthodoxy were triumphant"[3] is an old one, but incorrect. For years one of Buckland's roles was to keep room clear for an independent evaluation of scientific evidence within the Anglican community, in spite of increasing pressures from Evangelicalism and, later, from Tractarianism.

Buckland's major work on the geological evidence for a recent deluge was his paper on the quartz pebbles of Lickey Hill in Worcestershire, read later in 1819.[4] By tracing the distribution of these pebbles as far east as London, he thought to trace the path of the deluge and to show that some valleys were scooped out by its waters. This paper, with its conclusion that such superficial gravel appears in similar circumstances all over the world, represents the high point of Buckland's belief in universal formations and universal events; and it is presented in unusually dogmatic form as compared to Buckland's more usual qualified assertions. In the next year came his first published dealings with non-European rocks, in a brief paper on resemblances between specimens from Madagascar and New South Wales, and English rocks; here he was more moderate.[5] In his major paper on the structure of the Alps in 1821, Buckland showed that formations on the flanks of the mountains were the equivalent of certain secondary formations in England, and that there is a regular order of succession in Alpine districts identical with that of England.[6] The table of equivalents annexed to the paper is quite useful. This paper was perhaps the most important work on the Alps between J. G. Ebel's treatise of 1808 and the work of Sedgwick and Murchison around 1830.

Buckland continued his dynamic and stratigraphic researches, and his important summary was "On the Formation of the Valley of Kingsclere," read in 1825.[7] As opposed to simple Huttonian erosion, he believed in the multicausal origin of valleys, in which elevation, fracture, diluvial currents, and erosion had all played their parts. And he noted that the Savoy Alps had been elevated from the ocean floor since the deposition of the Tertiary strata.

In 1822 Buckland published his study of the fossil bones found in Kirkdale Cave in Yorkshire, and in 1823 expanded it into a full-scale treatise, *Reliquiae diluvianae*.[8] The dedication to Bishop Shute Barrington, Sumner's patron in the church, pointedly hoped it would no longer be asserted that there is no geo-

logical evidence for a universal deluge but reminded the bishop that the deluge's physical cause was still unknown.

The deluge, however, was not the important novelty of the *Reliquiae*. Buckland considered the work his "hyena story,"[9] for he proposed that the cave had been the den of hyenas; he not only found fossil feces ("coprolites") and tooth-marked bones, but also made observations on the habits of modern hyenas. His important conclusion was that species of animals that now exist together only in the tropics had coexisted in northern Europe with species still in existence, and that this demonstrated a tropical climate in antediluvial times, before the deluge buried the bones in a layer of mud. Further, the bones and caves showed that Europe had then been dry land much as it is now. In another cave Buckland found a human skeleton which, since the cave showed signs of human disturbance in historic time, he took to be postdiluvial.

The *Reliquiae* was well received for its scientific content, although some critics felt that Buckland had pushed the use of analogies from "modern causes" too far. Cuvier was very pleased with it, although he did not fully concede the general validity of Buckland's reasoning concerning climate. Buckland's assertion of the reality of the Mosaic flood as shown by paleontological evidence, although praised by his friend Edward Copleston in the *Quarterly Review,* was widely attacked by other critics and even by James Smithson, who, somewhat confused, was under the impression that he was defending Buckland from an attack by Granville Penn.[10] Buckland's Oxford students found the idea more amusing than convincing. Apparently it needed only to be stated clearly and fully in order to seem unconvincing; in the popular *Conversations on Geology* of 1828 the instructress says that Penn's theory was "no less fanciful than Mr. Buckland's."[11] Buckland's geological evidence for a large-scale force or agent acting in geologically recent times remained intact, but he quietly abandoned its identification with the Mosaic flood. For several years he intended a second volume of the *Reliquiae* but never published it because he could propose no convincing physical cause of the debacle.

Buckland took part in the giant saurian hunt of the 1820's, perhaps more as a follower than as a leader, although he deserves much of the credit for the Megalosaurus. He sometimes acted as geological intermediary between the discoverer in the field (who was often a layman) and such expert anatomists as Clift and Broderip. His own striking contribution was his paper (1829) on the coprolites of Ichthyosauri.[12] These coprolites permitted the reconstruction of a soft internal organ of an extinct species and indicated the species' eating habits; they proved that carnivorous "warfare" had always been a law of nature "to maintain the balance of creation." Further, their preservation in vast amounts furnished a "geological chronometer" of a period of undisturbed accumulation at the bottom of a sea. Coprolites should therefore be looked for in all periods when vertebrates had existed.

Toward the end of 1828 Charles Lyell and Roderick Murchison mounted an attack on Buckland's valley-formation ideas. W. D. Conybeare labeled the debate one between "fluvialists" (Lyell and Murchison) and "diluvialists" (Conybeare and Buckland). Since the fluvialists could only show that the particular valleys they discussed were caused by erosion, and since Buckland himself had shown that some valleys were so caused, the debate was inconclusive; and Lyell agreed to Buckland's general position in his *Principles of Geology*.[13] The debate seems, however, to have stimulated Adam Sedgwick and William Hopkins to extend Buckland's notions of elevation and dislocation as agents of surface formation in the 1830's and 1840's.

In 1830 Buckland was nominated to write the geological work in a series of books on natural theology that stemmed from the will of the eccentric eighth earl of Bridgewater; the final contracts were signed in 1832. We may assume that most of his energies until 1836 were directed to this project. Thus his celebrated explanations of the habits of the fossil *Megatherium* and the present-day sloth were devoted to showing how perfect their organization is for their mode of life,[14] and the same examples reappear in the Bridgewater treatise.

Buckland was in the middle of a general conservative revolt at Oxford, led by the Tractarians, and his treatise was completed during the spring of 1836, when their fierce opposition to the appointment of the mildly liberal R. D. Hampden as professor of divinity drove a wedge of bitterness into the Anglican Church. Buckland's natural theology conceded nothing to the new religious challenge. His position was essentially the same as in 1819, but its theological liberalism was by now more obvious, and was presented at length and without subterfuge. Buckland particularly emphasized William Paley's position that the world was not made for man alone but for the pleasure of all species of life; in relation to the object to be attained, all organic mechanisms are equally good, are evidence of beneficent adaptation. He reasserted that it is futile to try to reconcile geological epochs with the days of creation in Genesis, and now openly renounced the identification of his geological

deluge with the Mosaic flood. He went no further toward admitting miracles as physical causes than he had done in 1819. The final cause of successive organic systems, he said, is the purpose of maintaining the greatest possible amount of life on earth at all times. He was insistent that the past was regulated by the same laws and processes as the present, and showed the same kind of ecological balance. This demonstrated the unity of the Deity (whereas the Tractarians were fond of saying that natural theology tended to polytheism).

As a geological system Buckland chose, possibly borrowing from De la Beche and Conybeare, progressive development from an initially hot earth, with discontinuous assemblages of organic life being created and dying out. To express a secular development while simultaneously rejecting continuous progress and transmutation, he deliberately kept the rhetoric of the Great Chain of Being, but with missing links or gaps in the present creation being filled up by fossil organisms from past time periods. This was a noteworthy change from Cuvier, and a major step in the conversion of a balanced Malthusian ecology into a system maintaining its balance while it changed over time. Although not agreeing with Charles Lyell's uniformitarianism, Buckland cited the *Principles of Geology* with respect. The treatise was the major general view of paleontology produced in Britain in the period; Buckland's own new contributions were on mollusks, especially the mechanical contrivances (for example, syphons) used in chambered shells.

His Bridgewater treatise was Buckland's last sustained independent scientific work. He became increasingly interested in Roman archaeology and in the practical applications of geology, particularly the drainage of farms and the use of manures. He spread knowledge of Liebig's work but also advocated the widespread use of the natural phosphates contained in the large beds of coprolites he had identified.

In the period from 1838 to 1840 Buckland at last found a physical cause for a geologically recent catastrophe. Louis Agassiz convinced him that much of his evidence constituted signs of widespread glaciation. He and Agassiz delivered papers to the Geological Society of London in November 1840 on glaciation in Britain, and Buckland gave two more in 1840 and 1841.[15] He did not agree completely with Agassiz, however. He thus had the opportunity, of which he took full advantage in his presidential address to the Geological Society in 1841,[16] to accuse both the "glacialists" (Agassiz) and the "diluvialists" (by whom he meant especially Roderick Murchison) of "extreme opinions." He himself compromised by asserting the influence both of glaciers and of the torrents of water released as the glaciers melted, and of the icebergs drifted along in waters. An explanation for Saussure's debacle had been found at last.

NOTES

1. "On the geology of the neighbourhood of Weymouth and the adjacent parts of the coast of Devon," in *Transactions of the Geological Society of London,* 2nd ser., **4** (1836), 1–46.
2. "Description of a series of specimens from the plastic clay near Reading, Berks," *ibid.,* **4** (1817), 277–304.
3. Robert Knox, *The Races of Men* (London, 1850), p. 170.
4. "Description of the quartz rock of the Lickey Hill in Worcestershire, and of the strata immediately surrounding it; with considerations on the evidence of a recent deluge, afforded by the gravel beds of Warwickshire and Oxfordshire, and the valley of the Thames from Oxford downwards to London; and an Appendix, containing analogous proofs of diluvian action. Collected from various authorities," in *Transactions of the Geological Society of London,* **5** (1821), 506–544.
5. "Notice on the geological structure of a part of the island of Madagascar, founded on a collection transmitted to the Right Honourable the Earl Bathurst, by Governor Farquhar, in the year 1819; with observations on some specimens from the interior of New South Wales," *ibid.,* 476–481.
6. "Notice of a paper laid before the Geological Society on the structure of the Alps and adjoining parts of the continent, and their relation to the secondary and transition rocks of England," in *Annals of Philosophy,* n.s. **1** (Jan.–June 1821), 450–468.
7. "On the formation of the valley of Kingsclere and other valleys by the elevation of the strata that enclose them; and on the evidence of the original continuity of the basins of London and Hampshire," in *Transactions of the Geological Society of London,* 2nd ser., **2** (1829), 119–130.
8. "Account of an assemblage of fossil teeth and bones of elephant, rhinoceros, hippopotamus, bear, tiger, and hyaena, and sixteen other animals discovered in a cave at Kirkdale, Yorkshire, in the year 1821: with a comparative view of five similar caverns in various parts of England, and others on the continent," in *Philosophical Transactions,* **112** (1822), 171–235; *Reliquiae diluvianae* (London, 1823). The article constitutes the first section of the book. The first edition of the book sold out and there was a second edition in 1824.
9. North, "Paviland Cave," p. 103.
10. [Edward Copleston], "Buckland-*Reliquiae Diluvianae,*" in *Quarterly Review,* **23** (1823), 138–165; James Smithson, "Some observations on Mr. Penn's theory concerning the formation of the Kirkdale cave," in *Annals of Philosophy,* n.s. **8** (July–Dec. 1824), 50–60.
11. (London, 1828), p. 341.
12. "On the discovery of coprolites, or fossil faeces, in the lias at Lyme Regis, and in other formations," in *Transactions of the Geological Society of London,* 2nd ser., **3** (1835), 223–236.
13. (London, 1830), I, 171–172.
14. "On the adaptation of the structure of the sloths to their peculiar mode of life," in *Transactions of the Linnean Society,* **17** (1837), 17–28.
15. "Memoir on the evidences of glaciers in Scotland and the north of England," in *Proceedings of the Geological Society of London,* **3** (1838–1842), 332–337; "Second part of memoir on the evidence of glaciers in Scotland and the north of England," *ibid.,* 345–348; "On the glacio-diluvial phenomena in Snowdonia and the adjacent part of north Wales," *ibid.,* 579–584.
16. "Presidential Address for 1841," *ibid.,* 509–516.

BIBLIOGRAPHY

I. ORIGINAL WORKS. The list of articles in the Royal Society's *Catalogue of Scientific Papers* (I, 702–705) is handy but incomplete, and the serious student will want to use the list of publications given by Francis Buckland in his "Memoir of the Author," printed in the 1858 ed. of Buckland's Bridgewater treatise, *Geology and Mineralogy Considered With Reference to Natural Theology.* This is in infuriating disarray but is tolerably complete; it lists most but not all abstracts in the British Association's *Reports,* three separately printed sermons, and the forty-odd brief abstracts in the *Proceedings* of the Ashmolean Society of Oxford (most of which are of little importance). The following corrections may be noted (numbers are those of Francis Buckland's list): No. 3: 1823; 2nd ed., 1824. No. 14: n.s. **10** (1825); same as no. 55. No. 19: unlocated, but probably same as no. 68. No. 24: published at the end of William Phillips, *A Selection of Facts From the Best Authors, Arranged so as to Form an Outline of the Geology of England and Wales* (London, 1818). No. 56: same as no. 70. No. 58: same as no. 1. No. 69: II (1814)—this is not listed by any author's name but is "compiled by the Secretaries." No. 29 in the Ashmolean Society list is not in its *Proceedings* but is no. 45 in the main list. To this list may be added "Notice of a Series of Specimens From Mr. Johnson's Granite Quarries," in *Reports of the British Association,* **11** (1841), trans. sect., 64; "Notice of Perforations in Limestone," *ibid.,* **12** (1842), trans. sect., 57; and "On the Cause of the General Presence of Phosphorus in Strata," *ibid.,* **19** (1849), trans. sect., 67.

Francis Buckland refers to a paper entitled "On the Coasts of the North of Ireland." This appears to be W. D. Conybeare, "Descriptive Notes Referring to the Outline of Sections Presented by a Part of the Coasts of Antrim and Derry. . . . From the Joint Observations of the Rev. W. Buckland," in *Transactions* of the *Geological Society of London,* **3** (1816), 196–216. It is not Buckland's "first important paper."

There seem to be no major collections of Buckland's papers. The most interesting group may be that at the National Museum of Wales, Cardiff. There are some papers, especially letters to Buckland, in the Devon County Record Office, Exeter. Christ Church has 21 letters and some material on Buckland's career as canon. The University Museum, Oxford, has MS material relating to his lecture notes and publication drafts. The Bodleian Library has 46 scattered letters, and there are about 35 in the Whewell papers, Trinity College, Cambridge. There are probably others elsewhere.

II. SECONDARY LITERATURE. The biographical material presented by his children—Francis Buckland's "Memoir," cited above, and Anna B. Gordon, *The Life and Correspondence of William Buckland* (New York, 1894)—is indispensable but incomplete and sometimes vague. Two articles by F. J. North are based on unpublished materials: "Paviland Cave, the 'Red Lady', the Deluge, and William Buckland," in *Annals of Science,* **5** (1942), 91–128; and "Centenary of the Glacial Theory," in *Proceedings of the*

Geologists' Association, **54** (1943), 1–28. Otherwise there has been no serious treatment of Buckland's work, nor does any general work place it adequately in the history of geology. Attempts, both inadequate, to place Buckland's theological position in its contemporary intellectual setting are Reijier Hooykaas, *Natural Law and Divine Miracle* (London, 1959), pp. 147, 190–201; and W. F. Cannon, "Problem of Miracles in the 1830's," in *Victorian Studies,* **4** (1960), 5–32. The latter incorrectly attributes to Buckland a statement of belief in physical miracles.

WALTER F. CANNON

BUCQUET, JEAN-BAPTISTE MICHEL (*b.* Paris, France, 18 February 1746; *d.* Paris, 24 January 1780), *chemistry.*

Bucquet, the son of a lawyer, was destined for the bar by his father, but he soon abandoned jurisprudence to take up the study of medicine. He became *docteur-régent* at the Faculty of Medicine in Paris in 1770, by which time chemistry had become his main interest. His enthusiasm for it was prompted by the conviction that chemistry held the key to natural history and medicine, and, toward the end of 1770, he began to give courses in which he linked natural history and chemistry.

From 1775 to 1777, Bucquet was professor of pharmacy at the Faculty of Medicine and, at the death of Augustin Roux in 1776, he was elected to succeed him in the chair of chemistry. Bucquet gave his first public course in chemistry in 1777. He continued the chemistry courses he had been giving in private laboratories, in addition to those at the Faculty, until ill health forced him to abandon these private courses in the autumn of 1779. At different times during his career Bucquet also gave courses in botany, physiology, anatomy, hygiene, and medicine.

In February 1777 Bucquet was elected associate of the Société Royale de Médecine, and he took the place of Sage as *adjoint-chimiste* at the Academy of Sciences in Paris on 14 January 1778.

Bucquet's aim was to integrate chemistry with all the subjects related to it, but he found the published work in chemistry too unreliable to act as a basis for his project. Accordingly, he decided to repeat much of the experimental work that had already been done. Because of this decision and his early death, he made little original contribution to chemistry.

Among Bucquet's published works are memoirs on the analysis of minerals and the chemistry of gases. He modified David Macbride's apparatus to produce and investigate "fixed air" (carbon dioxide) and showed that quicklime would react with it only in aqueous solution. Later, after collecting and measuring the carbon dioxide produced by heating marble,

and confirming that carbon dioxide was acid, he suggested the name *acide crayeux* for it. Bucquet's work on gases was probably of great use to Lavoisier.

The memoirs on ethers and the analysis of blood, which Bucquet read, were never published. Of these, the one on ethers, read in March 1777, is the more interesting. In addition to the memoirs, Bucquet published books on mineral and plant chemistry. His work on plant chemistry seems to be the first detailed account of that branch of chemistry to be published.

From 1777 on Bucquet worked with Lavoisier on a number of topics, and the project they conceived of repeating most of the fundamental experiments done in chemistry up to that time, in preparation for an early draft of Lavoisier's *Traité de chimie,* was so perfectly in keeping with Bucquet's avowed aims that there is little doubt that he was the originator. Bucquet seems to have been the first to teach Lavoisier's theory, which he began to include in his courses as early as 1778.

BIBLIOGRAPHY

I. ORIGINAL WORKS. Bucquet's doctoral theses, which are to be found in the Arsénal Library, Paris, are "An digestio alimentorum, vera digestio chymica?" (Jan. 1769); "An recèns nato, lac recèns enixae matris?" (Mar. 1769); "An in febre malignâ balneum?" (Jan. 1770); and "An in partu difficili, sola manus instrumentum?" (Mar. 1770).

His books are *Introduction à l'étude des corps naturels tirés du règne minéral,* 2 vols. (Paris, 1771); and *Introduction à l'étude des corps naturels tirés du règne végétal,* 2 vols. (Paris, 1773).

Published memoirs are "Premier mémoire sur plusieurs combinaisons salines de l'arsenic," in *Mémoires mathématiques et physiques . . . par divers savans,* **9** (1780), 643–658; "Seconde mémoire sur les combinaisons salines de l'arsenic," *ibid.,* 659–672; "Expériences physico-chimiques sur l'air qui se dégage des corps dans le temps de leur décomposition, et qu'on connoît sous le nom vulgaire d'air fixé," *ibid.,* **7** (1776), 1–17; "Sur quelques circonstances qui accompagnent la dissolution du sel ammoniac par la chaux vive, par les matières métalliques et par leurs chaux, relativement aux propriétés attribuées à l'air fixé," *ibid.,* **9** (1780), 563–575; "Analyse de la zéolite," *ibid.,* 576–592; "Sur l'analyse de l'opium," in *Mémoires de la Société royale de médecine* (1779), 399–404; *Sur la manière dont les animaux sont affectés par différens fluides aériformes méphitiques, et sur les moyens de remédier aux effets de ces fluides; précédé d'une histoire abrégée de ces différens fluides aériformes ou gaz* (Paris, 1778); and *Rapport sur l'analyse du rob antisyphillitique du Sr. Laffecteur* (Paris, 1779).

Manuscript works are a letter to an unknown person, concerning the preparation of different kinds of ether, dated Paris, 22 Aug. 1773, Bibliothèque de Besançon, MS

1441, fols. 135–136; "Sur les moyens d'obtenir facilement les éthers nitreux et marin," Académie des Sciences, MS in dossier for 19 Mar. 1777; "Analyse chimique du sang," Académie des Sciences, MS in Bucquet dossier; "Notice abrégée de différents mémoires de chymie dont quelquesuns sont les fruits de mes recherches particulières, les autres ont été faits et rédigés conjointement avec Mr. Lavoisier," Académie des Sciences, MS in Bucquet dossier. Manuscript records of courses given by Bucquet are "Précis des leçons de chimie de feu M. Bucquet," Bibliothèque de St. Brieuc, MS 106; "Analyse du cours de phisiologie de M. Bucquet, commencé le 17 août 1773, fini le 21 octobre 1773," Bibliothèque de Rheims, MS 1021 (N fonds); and Lavoisier's laboratory notebooks, Vol. V, Académie des Sciences, MS.

II. Secondary Literature. Works on Bucquet are E. McDonald, *Jean-Baptiste Michel Bucquet (1746–1780)—His Life and Work*, M.Sc. dissertation (Univ. of London, 1965); and "The Collaboration of Bucquet and Lavoisier," in *Ambix*, **13**, no. 2 (1966), 74–83.

E. McDonald

BUDAN DE BOISLAURENT, FERDINAND FRANÇOIS DÉSIRÉ (worked Paris, France, *ca.* 1800–at least 1853), *mathematics.*

Almost nothing is known of Budan's life except for the information he provided on the title pages of his published works. He was a doctor of medicine and an amateur mathematician. He was educated in the classics and occasionally quoted Virgil and Horace in his works. A royalist, he published a Latin ode on the birth of the posthumous son of the duke of Burgundy. Budan was named *chevalier* of the Legion of Honor in 1814. He held the post of inspector general of studies at the University of Paris for over twenty years; this post may have been responsible for his interest in finding mathematical methods that would be easy for beginning students to use.

Budan is known in the theory of equations as one of the independent discoverers of the rule of Budan and Fourier, which gives necessary conditions for a polynomial equation to have *n* real roots between two given real numbers. He announced his discovery of the rule and described its use in a paper read to the Institut de France in 1803 and published the paper, with explanatory notes, as *Nouvelle méthode pour la résolution des équations numériques d'un degré quelconque,* in 1807.

Budan's definitive formulation of his rule was the following: "If an equation in *x* has *n* roots between zero and some positive number *p*, the transformed equation in $(x - p)$ must have at least *n* fewer variations [in sign] than the original" ("Appendice," p. 89). The "transformed equation in $(x - p)$" is the original polynomial equation developed in powers of $(x - p)$.

In modern notation: let $P(x) = 0$ be the given polynomial equation, and let $G(x - p) = P(x)$. Then $G(x - p) = 0$ is what Budan called the "transformed equation in $(x - p)$." The term "variation in sign" is borrowed from Descartes's rule of signs: No polynomial can have more positive roots than there are variations in sign in the successive terms of that polynomial. Indeed, Budan appears to have been led to his rule by Descartes's rule of signs.

Budan's first formulation of his rule assumed that all the roots of the original equation were real. In this case, Budan's rule tells exactly how many roots there are between zero and *p*, just as Descartes's rule gives the exact number of positive roots in the same case. Budan stated that, for the case of all real roots, his rule could be derived from Descartes's rule. It is not difficult to reconstruct such a derivation, even though Budan did not give it, once one has observed that when *x* is between zero and *p*, $(x - p)$ is negative.

The need for a rule such as his was suggested to Budan by Lagrange's *Traité de la résolution des équations numériques* (1767). This seems to have been almost the only nonelementary work Budan had read, and it influenced him greatly. He quoted Lagrange to show that it would be useful to give the rules for solving numerical equations entirely by means of arithmetic, referring to algebra only if absolutely necessary. Budan's goal was to solve Lagrange's problem—between which real numbers do real roots lie?—purely by methods of elementary arithmetic. Accordingly, the chief concern of Budan's *Nouvelle méthode* was to give the reader a mechanical process for calculating the coefficients of the transformed equation in $(x - p)$. He did not appeal to the theory of finite differences or to the calculus for these coefficients, preferring to give them "by means of simple additions and subtractions."[1] His *Nouvelle méthode* includes many specific numerical examples in which the coefficients are calculated and the number of sign changes in the polynomials *P* and *G* are compared; he intended this to be a simple and practical procedure.

In 1811 Budan presented a proof for his rule to the Institute; he published the proof, along with a reprint of his original article, as *Appendice à la nouvelle méthode,* in 1822. A. M. Legendre, reporting to the Institute in 1811 on Budan's rule and its proof, recognized the utility of being able to know that there could be no real roots between two given real numbers. Apparently unaware of the prior work of Joseph Fourier, he stated that the result was new.[2] Legendre added that the proof given by Budan was valid only after certain gaps were filled, notably the assumption without proof of Segner's theorem (1756): If $P(x)$ is multiplied by $(x - a)$, the number of variations in sign in the product polynomial is at least one greater than that in $P(x)$. Budan himself did not appreciate the force of this objection; he protested that there was nothing wrong with using a known result, although in fact he assumed it without stating it and, until Legendre's remark, did not seem to realize that the proof needed it.

Budan's success in discovering a correct rule and giving a reasonably satisfactory proof of it shows that, at the beginning of the nineteenth century, it was still possible for one without systematic training in mathematics to contribute to its progress; but mathematics was giving increasing attention to rigor and precision of statement, qualities slighted in Budan's work. The professionals were about to take over. Fourier's simultaneous and independent discovery, using derivatives, exemplifies the powerful methods available to one thoroughly schooled in mathematics. J. C. F. Sturm (1836) gave a necessary *and sufficient* condition for a root to lie between two bounds, thus completely solving the theoretical problem of how many roots lie between given limits. Yet Budan's rule remains the most convenient for computation, although finding bounds on roots is no longer the major business of the algebraist.

NOTES

1. This method is fairly efficient. It is equivalent to the use of successive synthetic divisions, a method often discussed in works on the theory of equations. See, e.g., W. S. Burnside and A. W. Panton, *The Theory of Equations* (Dublin–London, 1928), I, 10 ff., 64 ff.

2. Fourier taught his version of the rule before 1797, although it was not published until after his death, in 1831. Fourier's version is: If $f(x)$ is a polynomial of degree n, the number of real roots of $f(x) = 0$ lying between a and b cannot exceed the difference in the number of changes in sign in the sequence $f(b), f'(b), f''(b), \cdots, f^n(b)$ and that of the sequence $f(a), f'(a), f''(a), \cdots, f^n(a)$. See J. Fourier, *Analyse des équations déterminées,* pp. 98–100; on his priority, see the "Avertissement" to that work by C. L. M. H. Navier, p. xxi. Although the formulations of Budan and Fourier are equivalent, the great difference in conception argues for independence of discovery.

BIBLIOGRAPHY

I. ORIGINAL WORKS. Budan's writings are *Nouvelle méthode pour la résolution des équations numériques d'un degré quelconque* (Paris, 1807), and "Appendice à la nouvelle méthode," in *Nouvelle méthode pour la résolution des équations numériques d'un degré quelconque, revue, augmentée d'un appendice, et suivie d'un apperçu concernant les suites syntagmatiques* (Paris, 1822).

II. SECONDARY LITERATURE. Additional information may be found in J. Fourier, *Analyse des équations déterminées* (Paris, 1830 [*sic*]), which includes C. L. M. H. Navier, "Avertissement de l'éditeur," pp. i-xxiv, dated 1 July 1831; and F. N. W. Moigno, "Note sur la détermination du nombre des racines réelles ou imaginaires d'une équation numérique, comprises entre des limites données. Theorèmes de Rolle, de Budan ou de Fourier, de Descartes, de Sturm et de Cauchy," in *Journal de mathématiques pures et appliquées,* **5** (1840), 75–94.

JUDITH V. GRABINER

BUDD, WILLIAM (*b.* North Tawton, Devon, England, 14 September 1811; *d.* Clevedon, Somerset, England, 9 January 1880), *medicine, epidemiology.*

Budd, a pioneer epidemiologist and a precursor of the Pasteurian germ theory of disease, was born in a small town near the northern edge of Dartmoor. His father, Samuel Budd, practiced surgery there; his mother was the former Catherine Wreford, who came of an old Devon family. Of their ten children, William was the fifth of nine sons. The children received their primary education at home, but their father had inherited landed property from his grandfather, an Anglican clergyman, and could afford to send all his sons to good universities. Six of them graduated as doctors of medicine, three from Edinburgh and three from Cambridge. Two of Budd's older brothers, George and Richard, became fellows of the Royal College of Physicians of London, and George and William were elected fellows of the Royal Society.

Budd's professional training was unusually prolonged, partly because of two severe illnesses. An attack of typhoid fever interrupted his medical studies at the École de Médecine in Paris, where he intermittently spent three and a half years between October 1828 and September 1837, under such well-known teachers as Broussais, Cruveilhier, Lisfranc, Louis, Orfila, and Ricord. During the intervals Budd assisted his father, except for the winter of 1835–1836, when he attended the Middlesex Hospital, London. In the autumn of 1837, he went to Edinburgh University to complete the courses required for the M.D. degree. He graduated in August 1838, returned to general practice at North Tawton for about eighteen months, and was then appointed assistant physician to the Dreadnought, the Seaman's Hospital at Greenwich. An illness, which Budd apparently considered a second attack of typhoid, forced his early resignation. In 1841 he moved to Bristol and spent the rest of his working life in that city.

Budd was appointed physician to St. Peter's Hospital in 1842, lecturer in medicine at Bristol Medical College in 1845, and physician to the Bristol Royal Infirmary in 1847. He founded the Bristol Microscopical and Pathological societies, and served ten years as councillor of the Bath and Bristol branch of the Provincial Medical and Surgical Association, becoming its president in 1855–1856. Thereafter he played an active part on the Council of the British Medical Association until 1866. Budd gave valuable evidence before the Health of Towns Commission in 1841, and before the Royal Sanitary Commission in 1869. For the originality and importance of his views on infection and epidemiology, he was elected a fellow of the Royal Society in 1871.

In 1847, Budd married Caroline Mary Hilton, daughter of a landowner in Kent; they had three sons and six daughters. Although he had a healthy appearance and a fine physique, Budd was subject to attacks of intense headache, and in later life to bouts of nervous exhaustion, attributed to overwork. In 1873 he suffered a stroke, which left him an invalid. He died at the little seaside town of Clevedon, and was buried in Arnos Vale Cemetery, Bristol.

Budd's distinction as a physician was fostered by his family environment, thorough training, and warm humanity. His medicopolitical involvements, like his epidemiological and sanitary investigations, were governed by a sense of obligation to extend medical knowledge and to improve the public health. His forthrightly expressed convictions on the communicability and prevention of certain diseases, involving a scientific approach and inductive logic, set him apart from his medical contemporaries. John Tyndall praised him as "a man of the highest genius," whose "doctrines are now everywhere victorious, each succeeding discovery furnishing an illustration of his marvellous prescience."

Budd's essential doctrine, that specific infective agents determine the epidemic phenomena of communicable diseases, stemmed from his investigations of over eighty cases of typhoid at North Tawton in 1839–1840. Long before he described this epidemic in 1859, he had concluded that the "poisons" of typhoid and cholera multiply in the victim's intestines and are "cast off." His pamphlet *Malignant Cholera* (1849), which declared this disease to be waterborne, appeared about a month after the comparable *Mode of Communication of Cholera* by John Snow, whose priority he fully acknowledged. Budd's report erred in claiming that a fungus was the causal agent. Among preventive measures he stressed disinfection of the patient's excreta as well as purification of the water supply. His regimen successfully curbed the spread of cholera in Bristol during the 1866 outbreak.

In his classic monograph *Typhoid Fever* (1873), Budd integrated and expanded several previously published papers. This scholarly, fearless, and occa-

sionally scornful document impressively marshaled the evidence that indicates the disease is contagious. Many of his medical contemporaries were "noncontagionists" or "miasmatists," who buttressed their beliefs by the outmoded but die-hard dogma of spontaneous generation, or by such fashionable fallacies as Murchison's pythogenic theory (that the intestinal fevers arise *de novo* from filth and neglect), and Pettenkofer's theory that the specific agents of typhoid and cholera are not infective until they have undergone metamorphosis in suitable soil. Budd's task was especially difficult because these heresies were popular within the ranks of the "sanitary reformers," whose main objectives he ardently supported.

In the 1860's Budd applied his principles *mutatis mutandis* to other communicable diseases of man, such as diphtheria, scarlet fever, and tuberculosis. His masterly report of a sheep-pox epizootic and reviews of rinderpest and hog cholera reinforced his basic contentions: that each specific agent of contagion multiplies at certain sites within the sick host, is eliminated and transported by definite routes, and can be destroyed or interrupted in its passage to other susceptible hosts.

Budd invested his contagious agents with fairly precise properties—e.g., reproducibility and relative lack of resistance to heat and to disinfectants—but he was almost as noncommittal about their exact nature as Fracastoro (unknown to him) had been about *contagium vivum* three centuries before. There were formidable impediments to accurate visualization of these microbic agents, including the high heat resistance of some species of sporulating contaminants, the inadequate resolving power of available microscopes, and the lack of solid nutrient media on which pathogenic bacteria could be grown and differentiated. Within a few years of Budd's death, these deficiencies had been remedied by Pasteur, Abbe, and Koch.

BIBLIOGRAPHY

I. ORIGINAL WORKS. Budd's works include "Remarks on the Pathology and Causes of Cancer," in *Lancet,* **2** (1841–1842), 266–270, 295–298; *Malignant Cholera: Its Mode of Propagation and Its Prevention* (London, 1849); "On Intestinal Fever: Its Mode of Propagation," in *Lancet,* **2** (1856), 694–695; "Intestinal Fever Essentially Contagious," *ibid.,* **2** (1859), 4–5, 28–30, 55–56, 80–82; "On Intestinal Fever," *ibid.,* 131–133, 207–210, 432–433, 458–459, and **1** (1860), 187–190, 239–240; "Diphtheria," in *British Medical Journal,* **1** (1861), 575–579; "Observations on Typhoid or Intestinal Fever: The Pythogenic Theory," *ibid.,* **2** (1861), 457–459, 485–487, 523–525, 549–551, 575–577, 604–605, 625–627; "On the Occurrence (Hitherto Unnoticed) of Malignant Pustule in England," in *Lancet,*

2 (1862), 164–165; "Variola Ovina, Sheep's Small-Pox; or the Laws of Contagious Epidemics Illustrated by an Experimental Type," in *British Medical Journal,* **2** (1863), 141–150; "Investigation of Epidemic and Epizootic Diseases," *ibid.,* **2** (1864), 354–357; "The Siberian Cattle Plague; or, the Typhoid Fever of the Ox," *ibid.,* **2** (1865), 169–179; "Typhoid (Intestinal) Fever in the Pig," *ibid.,* 81–87; "Asiatic Cholera in Bristol in 1866," *ibid.,* **1** (1867), 413–420; "Memorandum on the Nature and the Mode of Propagation of Phthisis," in *Lancet,* **2** (1867), 451–452; "Scarlet Fever, and Its Prevention," in *British Medical Journal,* **1** (1869), 23–24; and *Typhoid Fever; Its Nature, Mode of Spreading, and Prevention* (London, 1873; New York, 1931).

II. SECONDARY LITERATURE. Works on Budd include G. T. Bettany, "Budd, William," in *Dictionary of National Biography,* VII (1886), 220–221; W. Michell Clarke, "William Budd, M.D., F.R.S., 'In Memoriam,'" in *British Medical Journal,* **1** (1880), 163–166; E. W. Goodall, *William Budd, M.D. Edin., F.R.S.* (Bristol, 1936); and W. C. Rucker, "William Budd, F.R.S., Pioneer Epidemiologist," in *Bulletin of the Johns Hopkins Hospital,* **28** (1916), 208–215.

CLAUDE E. DOLMAN

BUERG, JOHANN TOBIAS. See **Bürg, Johann Tobias.**

BUFFON, GEORGES-LOUIS LECLERC, COMTE DE (*b.* Montbard, France, 7 September 1707; *d.* Paris, France, 16 April 1788); *natural history.*

Buffon was the son of Benjamin-François Leclerc and Anne-Cristine Marlin, both of whom came from the bourgeoisie. Anne Marlin was related to a rich financier whose money enabled Benjamin to become, in 1717, lord of Buffon and of Montbard, and *conseiller* to the Burgundian parliament. Georges-Louis, the naturalist, was the eldest of five children, of whom three others entered the church, where two of them rose to high position. In 1717 the Leclerc family moved to a fine house in Dijon, where they occupied an important place in society. The intellectual life of that provincial capital was active but not oriented toward science at that particular time.

Georges-Louis was a pupil at the Collège des Jésuites in Dijon from 1717 to 1723. He was only an average student, although he distinguished himself by his bent for mathematics. His father undoubtedly wanted him to have a legal career, and he did study law in Dijon between 1723 and 1726. As early as 1727, however, he became friendly with the young Swiss mathematician Gabriel Cramer, a professor at the University of Geneva. In 1728 he went to Angers, where he may have studied medicine and botany, as well as mathematics, with Père de Landreville, pro-

fessor at the Collège de l'Oratoire. A duel forced him to leave Angers in October 1730, and he embarked on a long journey through Southern France and Italy with a young English nobleman, the duke of Kingston, and his tutor, Nathaniel Hickman, an obscure member of the Royal Society.

Buffon returned to France in 1732 and, despite his father's opposition, obtained his mother's fortune (she had died during his absence). At the same time, he began to make himself known in Parisian political and scientific circles. His first works on the tensile strength of timber were written at the request of the minister of the navy, Maurepas, who was seeking to improve the construction of war vessels. Buffon's *Mémoire sur le jeu du franc-carreau,* a study of probability theory, contributed to his admission to the Académie Royale des Sciences as *adjoint-méchanicien* on 9 January 1734. For six years he divided his time among finance (his fortune soon became considerable); research in botany and forestry (he wrote several dissertations and translated Stephen Hales's *Vegetable Statiks* into French in 1734); and mathematics (he wrote dissertations and in 1740 translated Newton's *The Method of Fluxions and Infinite Series* into French from the English translation of the original Latin manuscript, published in 1736 by John Colson). At the end of this time he also became interested in chemistry and biology and conducted some microscopic research on animal reproduction. In June 1739 he became an *académicien-associé* and transferred from the mechanical to the botanical section. That July, through the influence of Maurepas, he succeeded Dufay as *intendant* of the Jardin du Roi.

Each spring, from 1740 on, Buffon left Paris for Montbard, to administer his estates, continue his research, and edit his writings. His robust constitution allowed him to adhere to a well-organized schedule: he arose at dawn and spent the morning at his work, and the afternoon at his business affairs. For fifty years, Buffon spent the summer on his estate, returning to Paris in the fall. At the end of this time, he had doubled the area of the Jardin du Roi, enriched its collections, and enlarged its buildings considerably; moreover, he himself had become rich, having been showered with pensions and having increased his landholdings. He had published the thirty-six volumes of *Histoire naturelle* and was famous throughout Europe and even in America; he was a member of the Académie Royale des Sciences, the Académie Française, the Royal Society of London, and the academies of Berlin and St. Petersburg, among others. Catherine II bestowed gifts upon him, and Louis XV made him Comte de Buffon and commissioned the sculptor Augustin Pajou to do a bust of him.

In 1752 Buffon, scarcely inclined to be governed by his feelings, nevertheless married for love. His wife, Françoise de Saint-Belin-Malain, a pretty girl of twenty, was of gentle birth although poor. Mme. de Buffon led a retiring life and died young, in 1769, leaving a five-year-old son. Toward the end of his life, Buffon developed a Platonic affection for the wife of the famous Swiss financier Jacques Necker. His most serious personal worries were caused by his son, an unstable spendthrift, who was to die on the guillotine during the Terror.

In addition to his scientific works, Buffon published several speeches delivered before the Académie Française, of which only one—*Discours sur le style,* delivered on 25 August 1753, the day of his acceptance—is significant. This speech is of interest not only for the literary ideas that it contains, but also for its embodiment of Buffon's conception of the value of the original work of the scholar, which, according to him, lies less in the discovery of facts than in their organization and presentation.

Buffon's works may be grouped into two main categories, the *Mémoires* presented to the Académie des Sciences and the *Histoire naturelle.* The *Mémoires,* which appeared between 1737 and 1752, deal with mathematics (theory of probability), astronomy (the law of attraction), physics (optics), plant physics (tensile strength of wood), forestry, physiology, and pyrotechnics (aerial rockets). Buffon considered most of these subjects again in the *Supplément à l'Histoire Naturelle* (I, II, IV, 1774–1777; for a complete description, see Hanks, pp. 275–281).

Buffon's works appeared in many editions throughout the eighteenth and nineteenth centuries; the list, with an analysis of each original edition, may be found in the bibliography by E. Genet-Varcin and J. Roger (1954). One must emphasize the importance of the chronology of the various texts, since Buffon's ideas evolved considerably as he assembled his great work.

It was probably his interest in mathematics that first drew Buffon toward science. He was reputed to have already discovered Newton's binomial theorem by himself when he was twenty years old; at this time he became associated with Gabriel Cramer. Their correspondence deals with all types of problems—mechanics, geometry, probability, theory of numbers, differential and integral calculus.

Buffon's first original work was the memoir *Sur le jeu de franc-carreau,* which introduced differential and integral calculus into the theory of probability by extending the latter to the field of surfaces. The study

of the Petersburg paradox led Buffon to certain moral considerations that he clarified in the *Essai d'arithmétique morale* (published in the *Supplément,* IV, 1777). In that work, as well as in his memoirs on the tensile strength of wood and his research in the cooling of planets, Buffon obviously considered mathematics more as a means of clarifying the idea of reality than as an autonomous and abstract discipline. His reasoning is that of an engineer, a moralist, or a philosopher, rather than that of a pure mathematician. This is why he refused to accept the notion of infinity, which he considered to be no more than *une idée de privation,* and why, in his discussion with Clairaut on the law of attraction (1745), he insisted that a simple force ought to be represented by a simple algebraic formula. It was this "realism" that prevented him from becoming a pure mathematician. In fairness, however, it must be pointed out that, with Clairaut and Maupertuis, he was one of the first French disciples of Newton.

A philosopher as well as a naturalist, Buffon throughout his works made observations on the nature and value of science. His most important writing on this subject is the *Discours sur la manière d'étudier et de traiter l'histoire naturelle* (1749), but the *Théorie de la terre* and the *Histoire des animaux* of the same date are also significant.

Breaking with the spirit of his time, Buffon attempted to separate science from metaphysical and religious ideas. As a disciple of Locke he denied idealistic metaphysics, stating that mental abstractions can never become principles of either existence or real knowledge; these can come only as the results of sensation. He thereby also brushed aside Plato, Leibniz, and Malebranche. He also rejected teleological reasoning and the idea of God's direct intervention in nature (herewith abandoning Newton): "In physics one must, to the best of one's ability, refrain from turning to causes outside of Nature" (*Théorie de la terre, preuves,* art. V).

Buffon was particularly sensitive to the disorder that appeared to rule nature: "It would appear that everything that can be, is" (*Sur la manière . . .*). He found fault with classifiers, especially Linnaeus, for trying to imprison nature within an artificial system, since man cannot even hope to understand nature completely. Only in mathematics is there evident truth because that particular science is man-made. Physics deals only with the probable. Buffon did not fall into the pit of skepticism, however. He thought that man should construct a science not based on certitudes but derived from nature.

As time went on, Buffon's ideas changed. In the two *Vues de la nature* (*Histoire naturelle,* XII, XIII,

1764 and 1765), he seems to admit that man is actually capable of ascertaining fundamental laws of nature, and in the *Époques de la nature* (1779) he shows how the history of the earth obeys these laws.

Buffon viewed the study of the earth as a necessary prerequisite to zoology and botany and in 1749 wrote the *Histoire et théorie de la terre,* followed by nineteen chapters of *preuves.* He returned to this subject in the *Supplément* (II, V) and devoted his last work to mineralogy.

In the *Théorie de la terre,* Buffon, like most of his contemporaries, states neptunian views. He has no hesitations about animal or plant fossils or the stratigraphic principles set forth by Sténon. The presence of sea fossils and sedimentation of rock beds indicate former submersion of present continents, of which the topography, shaped under the water by ocean currents, is diminished by erosion and the action of the waters that carry earth to the sea. No explanation of the reemergence of formerly submerged continents is offered. Buffon resolutely refused to accept the notion of catastrophes, including the biblical flood, which many of his contemporaries upheld. He offered several hypotheses (such as subsidence of the ground or earthquakes) to account for the displacement of the sea, but he insisted that such changes "came about naturally." Buffon was an advocate of "real causes": "In order to judge what has happened, or even what will happen, one need only examine what is happening. . . . Events which occur every day, movements which succeed each other and repeat themselves without interruption, constant and constantly reiterated operations, those are our causes and our reasons" (*Oeuvres philosophiques,* p. 56A).

On the other hand, in his cosmogony Buffon also rejected slow causes. According to Newton, planets and their movement had been created directly by God: this was the only possible explanation of the circumstance that the six planets then known revolved in the same direction, in concentric orbits, and almost on the same plane. Buffon's cosmogony was designed to replace the intervention of God by means of a natural phenomenon, a "cause whose effect is in accord with the laws of mechanics." He then hypothesized that a comet, hitting the sun tangentially, had projected into a space a mass of liquids and gases equal to 1/650 of the sun's mass. These materials were then diffused according to their densities and reassembled as spheres which necessarily revolved in the same direction and on almost the same plane. These spheres turn on their own axis by virtue of the obliquity of the impact of the comet on the sun; as they coalesced, they assumed the form of spheroids flattened on both poles. Centrifugal force, due to their rapid rotation, tore from these spheres the material that then became the satellites of the new planets.

This cosmogony, one of the first based on Newtonian celestial mechanics, is remarkable for its coherence. It is founded on the then generally accepted idea that comets are very dense stars, at least at their nucleus. But it also raises some serious difficulties, which were brought to light by Euler: according to the laws of mechanics, the material torn from the sun should have fallen back into it after the first revolution; the densest planets should be farthest away from the sun; and the planetary orbits should always coincide at the point of initial impact. Finally, as early as 1770, it became apparent that comets had a very low density, which destroyed the impact hypothesis.

Not only did Buffon retain this hypothesis, but he also made it the basis for a new theory of the earth, published in 1779 as *Époques de la nature.* In 1749, in the *Théorie de la terre,* Buffon juxtaposed a plutonian cosmogony and a neptunian theory of the earth. In 1767, however, Buffon became convinced (probably by Jean-Jacques d'Ortous de Mairan's *Dissertation sur la glace* of 1749 and *Nouvelles recherches sur la cause générale du chaud en été et du froid en hiver* of 1767) of the existence of a heat peculiar to the terrestrial globe. He saw it as the residue of primitive solar heat and immediately undertook large-scale experiments on the cooling period of globes of varying materials and diameters. He extrapolated the results of his experiments, published in Volumes I and II of the *Supplément,* in order to calculate the time required for the cooling of the earth and other planets.

The *Époques de la nature* presents a plutonian history of the earth—a piece was torn from the sun, the mass took form, the moon was torn from it by centrifugal force, and then the globe solidified during the first epoch. In the course of this solidification, primitive mountains, composed of "vitreous" matter, and mineral deposits were formed (marking the second epoch). The earth cooled, and water vapors and volatile materials condensed and covered the surface of the globe to a great depth. The waters were soon populated with marine life and displaced the "primitive vitreous material," which was pulverized and subjected to intense chemical activity. Sedimentary soil was thus formed, derived from rocks composed of primitive vitreous matter, from calcareous shells, or from organic debris, especially vegetable debris such as coal. In the meantime, the water burst through the vaults of vast subterranean caverns formed during the cooling period; as it rushed in, its level gradually dropped (third epoch). The burning of the accumulated combustible materials then produced volcanos and earthquakes, the land that emerged was shaped in relief by the eroding force of the waters (fourth epoch). The appearance of animal life (fifth epoch) preceded the final separation of the continents from one another and gave its present configuration to the surface of the earth (sixth epoch) over which man now rules (seventh epoch).

This work is of considerable interest because it offers a history of nature, combining geology with biology, and particularly because of Buffon's attempt to establish a universal chronology. From his experiments on cooling, he estimated the age of the earth to be 75,000 years. This figure is considerable in comparison to contemporary views which set the creation of the world at 4000–6000 B.C. In studying sedimentation phenomena, however, Buffon discovered the need for much more time and estimated a period of as long as 3,000,000 years. That he abandoned that figure (which appears only in the manuscript) to return to the originally published figure of 75,000 years, was due to his fear of being misunderstood by his readers. He himself thought that "the more we extend time, the closer we shall be to the truth" (*Époques de la nature,* p. 40).

The *Époques de la nature* contains a great deal of mineralogical material that was restated and elaborated in the *Histoire naturelle des minéraux.* Buffon's work on mineralogy was handicapped by its date of appearance, immediately before the work of Lavoisier, Haüy, and J. B. L. Romé de l'Isle. Although it was soon out of date, Buffon's book does contain some interesting notions, particularly that of the "genesis of minerals," that is, the concept that present rocks are the result of profound transformations brought about by physical and chemical agents. Buffon did not have a clear concept of metamorphic rocks, however. It is also noteworthy that Buffon was one of the first to consider coal, "the pyritous and bituminous matter," and all of the mineral oils as products of the decomposition of organic matter.

In the second volume of the *Histoire naturelle* (1749), Buffon offers a short treatise on general biology entitled *Histoire des animaux.* He takes up this subject again in the *Discours sur la nature des animaux* (*Histoire naturelle,* IV [1753]) and in a great many later texts. Although he deals with nutrition and development in these, he is most interested in reproduction. This, of course, was a question much discussed at that time, but for Buffon reproduction represented the essential property of living matter.

Buffon rejected the then widely accepted theory of the preexistence and preformation of embryos. He spurned its dependence on the direct intervention of God and held it to be incapable of explaining hered-

ity. He further refuted the connected theories of ovism and animalculism because no one had actually seen the egg of a viviparous animal and because spermatozoa were not "animalcules," but rather aggregates of living matter that were also to be found in female sexual organs. On the latter point Buffon was the victim of erroneous observations made during the course of a series of experiments conducted, with Needham's help, in the spring of 1748.

The essentials of Buffon's theory of reproduction may be found long before this date, however. He set forth the principle of epigenesis because it exists in nature and allows heredity to be understood. Buffon revived the ideas of certain physicians of the late seventeenth century who were faithful to an old tradition, and assumed that nutritive matter was first used to nourish the living being and then was utilized in the reproduction process when growth was completed. After being ingested, the nutritive matter received a particular imprint from each organ, which acted as a matrix in the reconstitution of that organ in the embryo. But Buffon departs from his predecessors on two points: (1) he sees the action of these molds as capable of modifying the nutritive substance internally, due to "penetrating forces" (conceived of on the basis of Newtonian attraction), and (2) he considers nutritive material to be already living. Buffon also conceived of living universal matter composed of "organic molecules," which are a sort of living atom. His thinking was therefore formed by a mechanistic tradition, complicated by Newton's influence, and balanced by a tendency toward vitalist concepts.

This tendency diminished as time passed. In 1779, in the *Époques de la nature,* Buffon dealt with the appearance of life on the earth—that is, the appearance of living matter, or organic molecules. He explained that organic molecules were born through the action of heat on "aqueous, oily, and ductile" substances suitable to the formation of living matter. The physicochemical conditions that made such formation possible were peculiar to that period of the earth's history; consequently spontaneous generation of living matter and organized living creatures can no longer occur. Buffon thus resolved the contradiction in his text of 1749, in which he maintained that while living matter was totally different from the original matter, nevertheless "life and animation, instead of being a metaphysical point in being, is a physical property of matter" (*Oeuvres philosophiques,* 238A–B).

In 1749 Buffon saw nothing short of disorder in nature. The only notion that corresponded to reality was the idea of species, to which he gave a purely biological definition: "One should consider as being of the same species that which by means of copulation perpetuates itself and preserves the similarity of that species" (*ibid., Histoire des animaux,* p. 236A). If the product of such mating is sterile, as is the mule, the parents are of different species. Any other criterion, particularly resemblance, is insufficient "because the mule resembles the horse more than the water spaniel resembles the greyhound" (*ibid., Histoire naturelle de l'âne,* p. 356A).

If the species exists in nature, the family does not: ". . . one must not forget that these *families* are our creation, we have devised them only to comfort our own minds" (*ibid.,* p. 355B). All classification is therefore arbitrary and has no merit other than convenience. Buffon violently attacked Linneaus and praised Tournefort. He himself followed an order that he believed to be "easier, pleasanter, and more useful" than any other, without being any more arbitrary— "taking the objects that are the most interesting to us because of their relation to us, and gradually moving toward those that are more distant" (*ibid., Sur la manière . . . ,* p. 17B). In the order Buffon followed, the dog follows the horse because, in reality, the dog "is accustomed, in fact, to [so] follow" (*ibid.,* p. 18A). Buffon's order is formed by a philosophical bias rather than by science.

For Buffon to admit the concept of family, it would have to correspond to a reality. Thus:

> If these families really existed, they could have been formed only through the crossing, successive variation, and degeneration of original species; and if one once concedes that there are families of both plants and animals, that the donkey is of the horse family and only differs because it has degenerated, one could also say that the monkey is a member of the family of man and is merely a degenerated man, that man and monkey have a common origin just like the horse and mule, that each family . . . has only one founder and even that all animals came from one single animal which, with the passage of time, by simultaneously perfecting itself and degenerating, produced all of the races of the other animals [*ibid., Histoire naturelle de l'âne,* p. 355B–356A].

Because he rejected the concept of family and denied the value of making classifications, Buffon also rejected, at the beginning of his work, the hypothesis of generalized transformism offered by Maupertuis in 1751 in the *Système de la nature.* Buffon's theory of reproduction and the role he attributes to the "internal mold," as the guardian of the form of the species, prevented him from being a transformist.

This same theory of reproduction did not prevent Buffon from believing in the appearance of varieties within a species, however. Buffon believed in the heredity of acquired characteristics; climate, food, and domestication modify the animal type. From his exhaustive research for the *Histoire naturelle des quadrupèdes,* Buffon came to the conclusion that it was necessary to reintroduce the notion of family. But he attributes to this word—or to the word *genus,* which he also uses—a special meaning: a family consists of animals which although separated by "nature," instinct, life style, or geographical habitat are nevertheless able to produce viable young (that is, animals which belong biologically to the same species, e.g., the wolf and the dog). What the naturalist terms species and family, then, will thus become, for the biologist, variety and species. Buffon was thus able to write, in 1766, the essay *De la dégénération des animaux*—in which he showed himself to be a forerunner of Lamarck—while he continued to affirm the permanence of species in the two *Vues de la nature* (1764–1765) and *Époques de la nature* (1779).

Buffon's final point of view concerning the history of living beings can be summarized as follows: No sooner were organic molecules formed than they spontaneously grouped themselves to form living organisms. Many of these organisms have since disappeared, either because they were unable to subsist or because they were unable to reproduce. The others, which responded successfully to the essential demands of life, retained a basically similar constitution— Buffon affirms unity in the plan of animals' composition and, in variations on that plan, the principle of the subordination of organs. Since the earth was very hot and "nature was in its first stage of activity," the first creatures able to survive were extremely large. The earth's cooling drove them from the North Pole toward the equator and then finally caused their extinction. Buffon offered this in explanation of the giant fossils discovered in Europe and North America, which he studied at length (to the point of becoming one of the founders of paleontology). The organic molecules which were left free in the northern regions formed smaller creatures which in turn moved toward the equator, and then a third and fourth generation, which also moved south. Originating in Siberia, these animal species spread out to southern Europe and Africa, and toward southern Asia and North America. Only South America had an original fauna, different from that of other continents.

In the process of migration, the species varied in response to environment. There are few varieties of the large mammals because they reproduce slowly. The smaller mammals (rodents, for example) offer a large number of varieties because they are very prolific. The same is true of birds. Going back to the basic types, quadrupeds may be divided into thirteen separate species and twenty-five genera. But Buffon was not a transformist, because he believed that these thirty-eight primitive types arose spontaneously and simultaneously from an assembly of organic molecules.

As a naturalist and as a paleontologist Buffon was forced to uphold the variability of animal form; as a biologist he had to admit the permanence of hereditary types. He was never able to resolve this difficulty, although he stated the problem quite clearly.

"Love of the study of nature," Buffon wrote, "implies, in the human mind, two attributes which appear to be opposed, the broad outlook of an ardent spirit that grasps everything in one glance and the minute attention of a hard-working instinct that concentrates on only one point" (ibid., Sur la manière..., p. 7A). Buffon liked to deal with great biological and zoological problems, but his work is above all a detailed description of quadrupeds, birds, and minerals. To him, the "true method" is "the complete description and exact history of each thing in particular" (ibid., p. 14B). This "history" goes beyond simple morphological description:

> The history of one animal should be ... that of the entire species of that particular animal; it ought to include their procreation, gestation period, the time of birth, number of offspring, the care given by the mother and father, their education, their instincts, their habitats, their diet, the manner in which they procure food, their habits, their wiles, their hunting methods [ibid., 16A–B].

Physiological characteristics allow species separated by habitat or mores to be grouped together biologically; conversely, the habitats or habits of each animal permit distinctions between species or varieties. The description should also include a study of animal psychology, in particular that of social species (as monkeys and beavers). Buffon's method became more and more comparative, and in some works, he drew up genealogical tables of the varieties of each species. Buffon tried always to observe personally the animals he discussed. Nevertheless, pure description became boring to him, and he entrusted it to his associates.

In the Histoire naturelle de l'homme, published in 1749 (Histoire naturelle, II, III), and in many of his other works as well, Buffon studied the human species by the same methods that he applied to animal species, including the psychological, moral, and intellectual life of man. At the same time that he proclaimed the absolute superiority that the ability to reason gives man over animals, he demonstrated how the physiological organization and development of the sensory organs make reasoning possible. Through-

out his work Buffon specifies that reason developed only through language, that language grew out of life in society, and that social life was necessitated by man's slow physiological growth (since man is dependent on his mother long after birth). For the same reason, the elephant is the most intelligent of animals, while social life makes beavers capable of astonishing work.

It was, therefore, as a physiologist and as a naturalist that Buffon studied man and his reason; and it was as a biologist that he affirmed the unity of the human species. Aside from a few safe formulas, theology never comes into the picture. According to the Époques de la nature—and, in particular according to its manuscript—it is clear that the human species has had the same history as the animals. Buffon even explains that the first men, born on an earth that was still hot, were black, capable of withstanding tropical temperatures. Through the use of the resources of his intelligence and because of the invention of fire, clothes, and tools, man was able to adapt himself to all climates, as animals could not. Man is therefore the master of nature; and he can become so to an even greater degree if he begins to understand "that science is his true glory, and peace his true happiness" (Époques de la nature, p. 220).

Buffon's work is of exceptional importance because of its diversity, richness, originality, and influence. Buffon was among the first to create an autonomous science, free of any theological influence. He emphasized the importance of natural history and the great length of geological time. He envisioned the nature of science and understood the roles of paleontology, zoological geography, and animal psychology. He realized both the necessity of transformism and its difficulties. Although his cosmogony was inadequate and his theory of animal reproduction was weak, and although he did not understand the problem of classification, he did establish the intellectual framework within which most naturalists up to Darwin worked.

BIBLIOGRAPHY

I. ORIGINAL WORKS. See Oeuvres complètes de Buffon, J. L. Lanessan, ed., followed by Buffon's correspondence, 14 vols. (Paris, 1884–1885), still considered to be the best edition; Oeuvres philosophiques de Buffon, J. Piveteau, ed. (Paris, 1954), which contains a bibliography by Mme. E. Genet-Varcin and J. Roger that lists most works on Buffon published before 1954; and Les Époques de la nature, critical ed. by J. Roger (Paris, 1962), with an introduction, reproduction of the MS, notes, scientific vocabulary, and bibliography.

II. SECONDARY LITERATURE. Works on Buffon, both with more recent bibliographies, are L. Hanks, Buffon avant *l'histoire naturelle* (Paris, 1966); and J. Roger, *Les sciences de la vie dans la pensée française du 18e siècle* (Paris, 1964), pp. 527–584.

JACQUES ROGER

BULLER, ARTHUR HENRY REGINALD (*b.* Birmingham, England, 19 August 1874; *d.* Winnipeg, Canada, 3 July 1944), *mycology.*

Buller was the son of A. G. Buller, magistrate and county councillor for Birmingham. He received the B.Sc. from the University of London in 1896 and the Ph.D. from the University of Leipzig in 1899. He began his professional career at the International Marine Biological Station, Naples, in 1900–1901, then served as lecturer and demonstrator in botany at the University of Birmingham from 1901 to 1904. From 1904 to 1936 he was professor of botany at the University of Manitoba. Buller belonged to many societies, among them the British Association, British Mycological Society (president, 1913), Botanical Society of America (president, 1928), Canadian Phytopathological Society (president, 1920), Royal Society of Canada (president, 1927–1928), and Royal Society of London. He was the recipient of the Flavelle Medal (Royal Society of Canada, 1929), the Natural History Society of Manitoba Medal (1936), and the Royal Medal (Royal Society of London, 1937), as well as honorary degrees from the University of Manitoba (1924), University of Saskatchewan (1928), University of Pennsylvania (1933), and University of Calcutta (1938).

When Buller arrived at the University of Manitoba in 1904, he threw himself energetically into the founding and development of its department of botany, which soon became one of the most outstanding in Canada. He was also one of a small group of its original staff who were largely responsible for guiding the young institution during the early years of its rapid development. Later, when his worldwide reputation would have underwritten a large graduate section, he steadfastly refused to accept more than the few graduates whose work he could personally supervise; but that select group justified him and themselves by their subsequent contributions. One aspect of his position at Winnipeg which appealed greatly to Buller was that his commitments there permitted him to spend three or four months each year at Birmingham, where he worked in the laboratories or the library, or studied nature in the woods and fields. In later years his summers were spent at the herbarium of the Royal Botanical Gardens, Kew, to whose library he bequeathed his miscellaneous manuscripts. Buller retired to England in 1936, but in 1939,

while he was attending the International Congress of Microbiology in New York, World War II broke out and left him stranded there. He returned to Winnipeg, where once again he became deeply immersed in his researches. Indeed, when in 1944 he developed a brain tumor, his chief worry during the weeks of hopeless struggle was that all of his planned researches had not been completed.

Early in his career Buller had published several articles in scientific journals, and by 1909 he had accumulated enough material for a book to be entitled *Researches on Fungi.* He submitted his manuscript to a society, but was informed it would have to be reduced by about half before it could be published. To him this meant sheer mutilation of his manuscript, and accordingly he arranged for its publication at his own expense. Between 1909 and 1934, five additional volumes of *Researches on Fungi* were published in like manner, although the later ones were subsidized in part by the National Research Council of Canada. The Royal Society of Canada sponsored the posthumous publication in 1950 of Volume VII. These volumes were characterized, as were all his writings and all his lectures, by a unique style. The ease, clarity, precision, and grace with which Buller expressed his thoughts reveal a fine feeling for the choice and meaning of words, and reflect his familiarity with and love of English classics—the works of Milton and Shakespeare being especially beloved and extensively memorized.

The *Researches on Fungi* is both Buller's *magnum opus* and a magnificent memorial to his genius and his zeal. It will long remain a primary reference source for mycologists and biologists concerned with the problems of spore production and liberation in the fungi, of social organization within that group, and of epidemiology in general. While the independent manner of its publication ensured an eminently readable, profusely and beautifully illustrated series of volumes, it greatly limited the number that could be printed. Consequently, even before the last volume was published, the early ones were already collector's items, and complete sets were available in relatively few libraries. This unfortunate condition was remedied in part by the reissue in 1959 of Volumes I to VI. Unfortunately, this reprint is also out of print, and only Volume VII (1950) is presently available. Buller bequeathed his magnificent personal scientific library of over 2,000 volumes to the Canada Department of Agriculture Laboratory of Plant Pathology at Winnipeg.

The casual reader of the *Researches* might underestimate the substance of Buller's contributions. His meticulous, detailed, and thoroughgoing investigation of fungus after fungus might suggest that he was lost in details, whereas he was making very sure of his foundation before he compared individuals and combined them in groups on the basis of both form and function. At times, too, his reasoning sounds teleological until one remembers he was an ardent Darwinian and realizes that he was really looking for adaptations in form and function that made certain species successful and certain groups dominant. This approach and his insistence on dealing only with living materials paid handsome dividends in new discoveries in mycology and interpretations of older ones, and exerted a profound influence in many other areas of biological research. While each of his volumes makes a significant and original contribution in and beyond the area of its chief concern, Volume VII, which deals with sexuality in rust fungi, is monumental. In it is the distillation of all he had learned about that group of fungi, which constitutes the greatest threat to mankind's food supply: it also contains basic contributions in many fields of research, including epidemiology, genetics, and plant breeding, as well as mycology and plant pathology.

In 1941 Buller published in the *Botanical Review* a classic article entitled "The Diploid Cell and the Diploidisation Process in Plants and Animals With Special Reference to Higher Fungi." In it he reviewed the phenomenal advances during the previous decade in the knowledge of social organization and sexuality in the higher fungi, and integrated the new discoveries into the framework of previous knowledge so as to highlight areas still to be explored. This, too, is Buller at his best; and fortunately the article is generally available.

To students of the fungi, regardless of which of their many aspects may be their concern, Buller's works will always be a basic point of reference. Fungal taxonomy has been all but revolutionized by his insistence that only living material be utilized. His studies on the bionomics of production, liberation, and dispersal of fungus spores has made a science of epidemiology. His studies on sexuality of fungi and others which these have spawned have at long last resolved many problems in fungal phylogeny and given to it a rational foundation on which unity and perhaps even continuity may some day rest.

Of Buller's many and varied contributions, few had the impact and significance of his discovery that, in the Hymenomycetes, a haploid mycelium could be diploidized by a dikaryotic diploid mycelium. In homage to him, Quintanilha (1939) designated this as the Buller phenomenon. Within four years this had stimulated investigation in so many areas that Buller, in his diploid cell article, redefines the Buller phe-

nomenon as "in Basidiomycetes and Ascomycetes, the diploidisation of a unisexual mycelium or the unisexual rudiment of a fructification by a bisexual mycelium." Convincing supporting evidence in the Uredinales was supplied by Craigie's demonstration (1927) of the function of the pycnia of the rust fungi and by a number of subsequent contributions by Newton, Johnson, and Brown (1930–1940) in their studies with *Puccinia graminis*. These established the scientific foundation for the origin and variation of rust races and hence also of the problem of rust control.

BIBLIOGRAPHY

I. ORIGINAL WORKS. A complete list of Buller's publications accompanies the biographical sketch by W. F. Hanna, C. W. Lowe, and E. C. Stakman in *Phytopathology*, **35** (1945), 577–584. Fairly complete lists are in *Who's Who in Canada* (1938–1939) and *Who's Who* (1944). *Researches on Fungi*, I–VI, was published in London (1909–1934); VII, G. R. Bisby, ed., was published in Toronto (1950); it was reissued (I–VI only) in New York (1959). His major article is "The Diploid Cell and the Diploidisation Process in Plants and Animals With Special Reference to Higher Fungi," in *Botanical Review,* **7** (1941), 334–345.

II. SECONDARY LITERATURE. A. M. Brown, "The Sexual Behaviour of Several Plant Rusts," in *Canadian Journal of Research,* **18** (1940), 18–26; J. H. Craigie, "Discovery of the Function of the Pycnia of the Rust Fungi," in *Nature,* **120** (1927), 765–767; T. Johnson and Margaret Newton, "Crossing and Selfing Studies with Physiological Races of Oat Stem Rust," in *Canadian Journal of Research,* C, **18** (1940), 54–67; Margaret Newton, T. Johnson, and A. M. Brown, "A Study of the Inheritance of Spore Colour and Pathogenecity in Crosses Between Physiological Forms of *Puccinia graminis tritici,*" in *Scientific Agriculture,* **10** (1930), 775–798; and A. Quintanilha, "Contribution à l'étude génétique du phénomène de Buller," in *Comptes rendus de l'Académie des sciences,* **205** (1937), 745.

D. L. BAILEY

BULLIALDUS, ISMAËL. See **Boulliau, Ismaël.**

BULLOCH, WILLIAM (*b.* Aberdeen, Scotland, 19 August 1868; *d.* London, England, 11 February 1941), *bacteriology.*

Bulloch participated in the early development of medical bacteriology in Britain and won lasting recognition as a historian of that science. He came from a plain-living, scholarly Aberdonian family. His father, John Bulloch, an accountant, and his mother, Mary Malcolm, had two sons and two daughters. William was the younger son, and with his brother,

John Malcolm, a distinguished London journalist, shared the literary talent, with predilections for history and genealogy, that their father and grandfather had displayed. He attended Aberdeen Grammar School until 1884, and King's College, Aberdeen, for two years before enrolling in medicine at Marischal College. After graduating in 1890 with highest honors, he studied pathology at Aberdeen, Leipzig, and various other European medical centers before returning briefly to Aberdeen in 1894 to present a prize-winning M.D. thesis. Courses in bacteriology at the Pasteur Institute from Émile Roux, Elie Metchnikoff, and Émile Duclaux were followed by a short assistantship to Victor Horsley, professor of pathology at University College, London.

In July 1895 Bulloch took charge of the serum laboratories at the British (later, Lister) Institute of Preventive Medicine. In 1897 he was appointed bacteriologist to the London Hospital and lecturer on bacteriology and pathological chemistry to its medical school, and in 1919 became Goldsmith's professor of bacteriology at the University of London. After officially retiring in 1934, Bulloch served these institutions as consulting bacteriologist and emeritus professor. He was elected a fellow of the Royal Society in 1913, received an honorary LL.D. from Aberdeen in 1920, and held the following lectureships: Horace Dobell (Royal College of Physicians, 1910), Tyndall (Royal Institution, 1922), and Heath Clark (University of London, 1937). Bulloch's brief marriage in 1901 to Anna Molbo, a Danish pianist, was dissolved. In 1923 he married Irene Adelaide Baker, widow of an Australian cricketer, who survived him. In his last years, Bulloch suffered from paralysis agitans. He died in the London Hospital following a minor operation.

Although a lackadaisical administrator, Bulloch was an unforgettable lecturer. A clever mimic and raconteur, he enjoyed dramatizing the foibles and accomplishments of famous bacteriologists at home and abroad, many of whom were personal friends. His knowledgeableness and scrupulosity brought him membership on various technical advisory committees and the chairmanship, in 1932, of the Lister Institute's board of governors. His bibliography totals more than a hundred titles, and he was generally sole author. The earliest reports, dating from 1892, were histoneurological; but the scope soon broadened to include, for instance, descriptions of a new anaerobic jar or bacterial filter, and investigations of such contemporary problems as Ehrlich's diphtheria toxin "spectra" and antitoxin assay, Almroth Wright's opsonins and vaccine therapy (especially as related to tuberculosis), and the Wassermann test for syphilis. This work, always carefully performed and meticu-

lously recorded, seldom revealed new knowledge of signal importance, but facilitated critical appraisal of others' claims. After 1910 Bulloch deserted the laboratory for the library, and his publications were mainly painstaking reviews of hereditary diseases, notably hemophilia, whose genetics fascinated him, and tributes to distinguished bacteriologists. His innate compilatory and historical talents were best expressed in his contributions to monographs on diphtheria (1923) and surgical catgut (1929), and to *A System of Bacteriology* (1929–1931), culminating in his scholarly masterpiece, *The History of Bacteriology* (1938).

BIBLIOGRAPHY

I. ORIGINAL WORKS. The fullest bibliography of Bulloch's works (106 items) is that provided by his stepson-in-law, Clifford Dobell, as an appendix (pp. 842–853) to the detailed obituary by a former pupil, J. C. G. Ledingham (see below). Among the more original and characteristic publications are "Hyaline Degeneration of the Spinal Cord," in *Brain,* **15** (1892), 411–413; "A Contribution to the Study of Diphtheria Toxin," in *Transactions of the Jenner Institute of Preventive Medicine,* 2nd ser. (1899), 46–55; "A Simple Apparatus for Obtaining Plate Cultures or Surface Growths of Obligate Anaerobes," in *Zentralblatt für Bakteriologie, Parasitenkunde, Infektionskrankheiten und Hygiene,* Abt. I, **27** (1900), 140–142; "The Chemical Constitution of the Tubercle Bacillus," in *Journal of Hygiene,* **4** (1904), 1–10, written with J. J. R. MacLeod; "On the Relation of the Suprarenal Capsules to the Sexual Organs," in *Transactions of the Pathological Society of London,* **56** (1905), 189–208, written with J. H. Sequeira; "The Principles Underlying the Treatment of Bacterial Diseases by the Inoculation of Corresponding Vaccines," in *Practitioner,* **75** (1905), 589–610; "On the Transmission of Air and Micro-organisms Through Berkefeld Filters," in *Journal of Hygiene,* **9** (1909), 35–45, written with A. J. Craw; *The Problem of Pulmonary Tuberculosis Considered From the Standpoint of Infection* (London, 1910); "L'Abbate Spallanzani. 1729–1799," in *Parasitology,* **14** (1922), 409–412; *Diphtheria: Its Bacteriology, Pathology and Immunology* (London, 1923), written with Frederick W. Andrewes, S. R. Douglas, Georges Dreyer, *et. al.; The Preparation of Catgut for Surgical Use,* Medical Research Council Special Report Series, no. 138 (London, 1929), written with L. H. Lampitt and J. H. Burhill; "History of Bacteriology," in *A System of Bacteriology in Relation to Medicine,* I (London, 1930), 15–103 (Bulloch was chairman of the committee that prepared this nine-volume work, and contributed numerous articles besides the opening chapter); and *The History of Bacteriology* (London, 1938; repr. 1960).

Bulloch's authoritative contributions on rheumatic fever, plague, tuberculosis, and relapsing fever, in Clifford Allbutt and Humphry Davy Rolleston, *A System of Medicine*

(London, 1899), survived several editions. He also wrote articles for Karl Pearson's *Treasury of Human Inheritance* (London, 1912), including those on diabetes insipidus, angioneurotic edema, and (with P. Fildes) hemophilia.

Bulloch's purely historical writings include tributes to Spallanzani, Pasteur, Koch, and Lister. Among his more notable obituaries are those on Emanuel Klein, Charles Creighton, Sir Alexander Ogston, Waldemar Haffkine, Shibasaburo Kitasato, Sir William Watson Cheyne, Émile Roux, and Theobald Smith.

II. SECONDARY LITERATURE. Obituaries include P. Fildes, "William Bulloch. 1868–1941," in *Journal of Pathology and Bacteriology,* **53** (1941), 297–308; J. C. G. Ledingham, "William Bulloch. 1868–1941," in *Obituary Notices of Fellows of the Royal Society,* **3** (1941), 819–843; J. McIntosh, "Prof. William Bulloch, F. R. S.," in *Nature,* **147** (1941), 504–505; and H. M. Turnbull, "Professor William Bulloch M.D., LL.D., F.R.S.," in *British Medical Journal* (1941), **1**, 341–342. Other references to Bulloch's life and work are C. E. Dolman, "Tidbits of Bacteriological History," in *Canadian Journal of Public Health,* **53** (1962), 269–278; and "Paul Ehrlich and William Bulloch: A Correspondence and Friendship (1896–1914)," in *Clio medica,* **3** (1968), 65–84.

CLAUDE E. DOLMAN

BUNGE, GUSTAV VON (*b.* Dorpat [now Tartu], Estonia, 19 January 1844; *d.* Basel, Switzerland, 5 November 1920), *physiology.*

Gustav von Bunge was the son of the botanist Alexander von Bunge. The father was famous for his botanical studies in Siberia and China. The elder Bunge's teaching and research work in Dorpat (1836–1867) made the university a center for the study of botany.

At Dorpat the biochemist Carl Schmidt became both teacher and promoter of Gustav von Bunge as a student of chemistry, and employed him as an assistant in his laboratory from 1872 onward. Schmidt inspired him, above all else, to tackle the problem of mineral (inorganic) metabolism, and as early as 1874, the year in which he received his doctorate and became an associate professor of physiology, the first significant results of his experiments in that area appeared.

In 1882 Bunge received the degree of doctor of medicine at the University of Leipzig; in 1884 the University of Kiev made him an honorary doctor. In 1885 he answered an invitation from the University of Basel, became extraordinary professor of medicine there, and then in 1886, an ordinary professor of physiological chemistry. His most famous student was the physiologist Emil Abderhalden.

Gustav von Bunge showed himself to be a first-rate nutritional scientist, especially in recognizing the sig-nificance of mineral salts in the diet of men and other mammals, together with all of its consequences. One of his very first studies on this subject created quite a stir. It dealt with the role of salt (sodium chloride) in nourishment and concluded that herbivores absorb large excesses of potassium in their diet. This led to an increased salt elimination, and thereby to considerable salt losses to the organism and to a correspondingly increased salt requirement. It was typical of Bunge not to remain content after discovering certain physiological facts, and he immediately set about to figure out their ethnological, social, and sociological significance. He found that hunting and nomadic peoples who lived exclusively on meat did not require salt, and actually detested it, whereas vegetarians could not exist without adding salt to their diet. Therefore, the discovery and utilization of salt must have played a very important role in man's transition from a nomad into a settled agricultural worker.

An important point that Bunge brought up in his studies on the role of salt in man's diet was of a phylogenetic nature: The high salt content of vertebrates attests to their descent from inhabitants of the sea. Since ontogenesis repeats phylogenesis, then the salt content of a vertebrate should be greater the younger the vertebrate is; this was precisely what Bunge was able to demonstrate when he determined the salt content in the cartilage of cattle embryos in the various stages of their development and in that of calves of various ages.

Another area in which Bunge did research was the quantitative analysis of mineral substances in nutrients and the related question of the necessity of a constant supply of salt for the full-grown organism. In connection with the question of the quantitative and qualitative mineral requirement of growing and fully grown organisms there are the analyses of ash constituents in the milk of humans and various other animal species, undertaken first by Bunge in Dorpat and then in Basel by his student Abderhalden. Great differences were found above all in lime content. This phenomenon was explained by the fact that the lime content of the milk and the growth rate of the animal in question were in each case positively correlated.

Proceeding from the importance of lime supply in the development of the organism, two works appeared between 1901 and 1904 concerning "increased sugar consumption and its dangers." Limitation of the supply of calcareous nutrients (calcareous fruits) in favor of consumption of chemically pure sugar was viewed as the reason for arrested skeletal development and for the frequent appearance of tooth decay.

One of the main problems posed in Bunge's studies had to do with iron metabolism. The crux of his study on this subject was his search for the ferriferous precursors of red blood pigment in food. According to the theory of the inability of animal cells to synthesize complicated organic compounds, prevalent at that time, it was unthinkable that inorganic iron found in food and resorbed from it might be utilized to synthesize hemoglobin in the organism. Accordingly, Bunge attempted to isolate an organic iron complex out of egg yolk. In Basel, Bunge's students Häusermann and Abderhalden conducted feeding experiments on anemic animals by adding a hemoglobin, hematin, or iron salt supplement to an iron-poor diet. The results of these experiments seemed to confirm Bunge's thesis: only organically bound iron can be resorbed and utilized for the building up of hemoglobin. Iron-rich vegetables similarly have a favorable influence on laboratory-produced anemia, which meant to Bunge that even in these nutrients, iron is found organically bound.

A prerequisite for conducting such studies on iron metabolism was the control of a perfectly functioning method of quantitative iron determination. With the help of this method, Jaquet and Bunge, in 1889, succeeded in determining the iron content of blood pigment exactly and thereby establishing a firm basis for the elucidation of the constitution of the hemoglobin molecule.

Although nutritional physiology formed the center of Bunge's research activities, there is another area of his work that should not be overlooked. This is the study he pursued with Schmiedeberg on the synthesis of hippuric acid from benzoic acid and glycine in the animal organism (1876). This is important not only because it recognized the kidneys as the site of synthesis, but also because the methods he applied to investigation of metabolic problems are still used universally.

To most of the public, composed of physicians and laymen, Gustav von Bunge is known primarily for such monographs as *Vegetarianismus* and *Die Alcoholfrage*. He saw in alcohol consumption the roots of many types of illnesses and social evils. It is therefore not astonishing that he became a champion of the abstinence movement and a great enthusiast of the prohibition laws in the United States.

BIBLIOGRAPHY

I. ORIGINAL WORKS. Bunge's works are *Der Vegetarianismus* (Berlin, 1885; 2nd ed., 1900); *Die Alcoholfrage* (Leipzig, 1887), trans. into 12 languages; *Die zunehmende Unfähigkeit der Frauen, ihre Kinder zu stillen, die Ursache dieser Unfähigkeit, die Mittel zur Verhütung* (Munich, 1900; 4th ed., 1905), trans. into French; *Lehrbuch der physiologischen und pathologischen Chemie* (Leipzig, 1887; 4th ed., 1898), trans. into five languages; *Lehrbuch der Physiologie des Menschen*, 2 vols. (Leipzig, 1901; 2nd ed., 1905); *Lehrbuch der organischen Chemie für Mediziner* (1906); all other works are registered in Poggendorff, III, 214; IV, 204–205; and VI, 369, which also contains the eulogies on Bunge.

II. SECONDARY LITERATURE. A biography of Bunge, together with an assessment of his work, is that by C. M. McCay, in *Journal of Nutrition*, **49** (1953), 3–19. See also F. Lieben, *Geschichte der physiologischen Chemie* (Leipzig-Vienna, 1935); K. E. Rothschuh, *Geschichte der Physiologie* (Berlin–Göttingen–Heidelberg, 1953).

HERBERT SCHRIEFERS

BUNSEN, ROBERT WILHELM EBERHARD (*b.* Göttingen, Germany, 31 March 1811; *d.* Heidelberg, Germany, 16 August 1899), *chemistry.*

Bunsen was the youngest of four sons born to Christian Bunsen, chief librarian and professor of modern languages at the University of Göttingen. His ancestors on his father's side had lived in Arolsen, where many of them held public office, frequently as master of the mint; his mother was the daughter of a British-Hanoverian officer named Quensel.

Bunsen began school in Göttingen but transferred to the Gymnasium at Holzminden, from which he graduated in 1828. Returning to Göttingen, Bunsen entered the university, where he studied chemistry, physics, mineralogy, and mathematics. His chemistry teacher was Friedrich Stromeyer, who had discovered cadmium in 1817. Bunsen received his doctorate in 1830, presenting a thesis in physics: "Enumeratio ac descriptio hygrometrorum."

Aided by a grant from the Hanoverian government, Bunsen toured Europe from 1830 to 1833, visiting factories, laboratories, and places of geologic interest. In May 1832, he saw a new steam engine in K. A. Henschel's machinery factory in Kassel. Later that year, in Berlin, he studied Christian Weiss's geognostic and mineralogic collections; met Friedlieb Runge, the discoverer of aniline, and Gustav Rose; and worked in Heinrich Rose's laboratory. He visited Justus Liebig in Giessen and met Eilhard Mitscherlich in Bonn for a geological trip through the Eifel Plateau. In September 1832, Bunsen arrived in Paris. There he worked in Gay-Lussac's laboratory and met such prominent scientists as Jules Reiset, Henri-Victor Regnault, Théophile Pelouze, and César Despretz. While in France, Bunsen visited the porcelain works at Sèvres. From May to July 1833, he traveled to Vienna, where he toured several industrial plants.

In the fall of 1833 Bunsen became *Privatdozent* at

the University of Göttingen. He succeeded Friedrich Wöhler at the Polytechnic School in Kassel in January 1836. In October 1838 he was appointed professor extraordinarius of chemistry at the University of Marburg and became professor ordinarius four years later. Bunsen spent part of 1851 at Breslau, where he became acquainted with Gustav Kirchhoff, with whom he later did important research in spectroscopy. In 1852 he succeeded Leopold Gmelin at the University of Heidelberg. Although offered a position as Mitscherlich's successor at the University of Berlin in 1863, Bunsen remained at Heidelberg until he retired in 1889, at the age of seventy-eight. A laboratory, constructed for him by the government of Baden, was completed in the summer of 1855; there Bunsen did his research and guided the work of numerous young men who became well-known scientists during the second half of the nineteenth century. Bunsen never married; his teaching and research consumed most of his time, and he traveled widely, either alone or with friends.

Bunsen was a most devoted teacher. He presented 100 hours of lectures during each of seventy-four semesters in a course entitled "Allgemeine Experimentalchemie." The lectures, which changed little through the years, were concerned with inorganic chemistry; organic chemistry was excluded. Theoretical aspects were at a minimum: neither Avogadro's hypothesis nor the periodic law of the elements— developed by his own students, Dmitri Mendeleev and Lothar Meyer—was mentioned. In his research, as in his teaching, Bunsen emphasized the experimental side of science. He enjoyed designing apparatus and, being a skilled glassblower, he frequently made his own glassware. He was also an expert crystallographer. Bunsen developed and improved several pieces of laboratory equipment, including the Bunsen burner, the Bunsen battery, an ice calorimeter, a vapor calorimeter, a filter pump, and a thermopile.

A man of wide scientific interests, Bunsen did some early research in organic chemistry but later abandoned this field and concentrated on inorganic chemistry. His most important work was the development of a variety of analytical techniques for the identification, separation, and measurement of inorganic substances. Throughout his life Bunsen gave much attention to geology. He was also interested in the application of experimental science to industrial problems.

His first research was on the insolubility of metal salts of arsenious acid, carried out in 1834. While involved in this work, Bunsen discovered that hydrated ferric oxide could be used as an antidote for arsenic poisoning. The ferric oxide is effective, he explained, because it combines with arsenic to form ferrous arsenite, a compound insoluble in both water and body fluids. This finding, still used today, was Bunsen's only venture into physiological chemistry. In other early research, he analyzed a sample of allophane, an aluminum silicate, taken from a lignite bed near Bonn. In 1835 and 1836 Bunsen set forth the compositions and crystal measurements of a new series of double cyanides, showing, for example, that ammonium ferrocyanide and potassium ferrocyanide are isomorphous. He also discovered the double salt of ammonium ferrocyanide and ammonium chloride.

Bunsen's only work in organic chemistry was an investigation of compounds of cacodyl, an arsenic-containing organic compound, the results of which appeared in five papers published between 1837 and 1842. In 1843, Bunsen lost the use of his right eye in an explosion of cacodyl cyanide. The first known cacodyl compound, alkarsine, had been prepared in 1760 by L. C. Cadet de Gassicourt, by distilling a mixture of dry arsenious oxide and potassium acetate. Alkarsine is a highly reactive, poisonous, spontaneously inflammable substance having heavy brown fumes and a nauseating odor. Its chemical composition was shown by Bunsen to be $C_4H_{12}As_2O$, as Berzelius had suggested. Berzelius called the compound *kakodyl oxide* (from the Greek κακόδης, "stinking"). Bunsen conducted a detailed study of cacodyl derivatives, obtaining the chloride, iodide, cyanide, and fluoride by reacting concentrated acids with the oxide. Using vapor density techniques, he determined the molecular formulas of the derivatives and realized that the cacodyl radical, $C_4H_{12}As_2$, was preserved as an "unchangeable member" through the numerous reactions. This conclusion supported the radical theory of organic compounds advocated by Liebig and Berzelius. Bunsen put forth further evidence for the radical theory when he isolated the free radical by heating the chloride with zinc in an atmosphere of carbon dioxide. After presenting his papers, Bunsen withdrew from the controversy over the merits of the radical theory and turned to inorganic chemistry. It remained for his students, Adolph Kolbe and Edward Frankland, to show in 1853 that cacodyl compounds contain dimethylarsenic, $As(CH_3)_2$, and for Auguste Cahours and Jean Riche to demonstrate that free cacodyl is $As_2(CH_3)_4$. Finally, in 1858 Adolph von Baeyer, another of Bunsen's students, clarified the relationships among the members of the cacodyl series.

Between 1838 and 1846, Bunsen developed methods for the study of gases while he was investigating the industrial production of cast iron in Germany and, in collaboration with Lyon Playfair, in England. He demonstrated the inefficiency of the process: in the charcoal-burning German furnaces, over 50 percent of the heat of the fuel used was lost in the escaping gases; worse, in the coal-burning English furnaces, over 80 percent was lost. Valuable by-products, such as ammonia, went unrealized and were among the gases lost to the atmosphere. Further, it was accidentally discovered that potassium cyanide was formed from potassium carbonate and atmospheric nitrogen at high temperatures. In an 1845 paper, "On the Gases Evolved From Iron Furnaces With Reference to the Smelting of Iron," Bunsen and Playfair suggested techniques that could recycle gases through the furnace, thereby utilizing heat otherwise lost. They also discussed ways by which valuable escaping materials could be retrieved.

Bunsen compiled his research on the phenomena of gases into his only book, *Gasometrische Methoden* (1857). This work brought gas analysis to a level of accuracy and simplicity reached earlier by gravimetric and titrimetric techniques. Dividing the book into six parts, Bunsen presented methods of collecting, preserving, and measuring gases; techniques of eudiometric analysis; new processes for determining the specific gravities of gases; results of investigations on the absorption of gases in water and alcohol using an absorptiometer he himself had devised; and results of experiments on gaseous diffusion and combustion. On the problem of gaseous absorption, Bunsen, assisted by several students, showed the experimental limits within which Henry's law of pressures and Dalton's law of partial pressures are valid.

Greatly interested in geology, Bunsen accompanied a scientific expedition to Iceland in 1846, the year after the eruption of the volcano Hekla. The expedition, sponsored by the Danish government, lasted three and one-half months and included Sartorius von Waltershausen and Bergman, both from Marburg, and Alfred DesCloizeaux, a French mineralogist. Bunsen collected gases emitted from the volcanic openings and studied the action of these gases on volcanic rocks. He performed extensive chemical analyses of eruptive rocks, insisting that instead of determining what minerals were in a rock, the chemical composition of the rock as a whole should be ascertained. Bunsen concluded that volcanic rocks are mixtures, in varying proportions, of two extreme kinds of rock: one kind acidic and rich in silica (trachytic), the other kind basic and less rich in silica (pyroxenic). He thought that the formation of different kinds of rock could be traced to their differences in melting-point behavior under pressure. Although this explanation is no longer accepted, his observations contrib-

uted a great deal to the development of modern petrology. Bunsen also explored geysers, and at the Great Geyser made daring temperature measurements at several depths shortly before it erupted. He found that the temperature of water in the geyser tube, although high, did not reach the boiling point for a particular depth and corresponding pressure. He concluded that the driving force for eruption is supplied by steam that enters the tube under great pressure from volcanic vents at the bottom. As the steam lifts the column of water, the effective pressure above the water is reduced. This change in the water's depth results in a lowering of the boiling point and enables the already hot water to boil.

Through the 1840's and 1850's Bunsen made a number of improvements in the galvanic battery. In 1841 he made a battery, known since as the Bunsen battery, with carbon, instead of the more expensive platinum or copper, as the negative pole. To prevent disintegration of the carbon pole by the nitric acid electrolyte, Bunsen treated the carbon, a mixture of coal and coke, with high heat. Forming a battery from forty-four subunits, Bunsen was able to generate a light of great intensity. Later, he made a battery with chromic acid instead of nitric acid, as well as one with zinc and carbon plates in chromic acid. In 1852 Bunsen began to use electrochemical techniques to isolate pure metals in quantities sufficient for determining their physical and chemical properties. He prepared chromium from a solution of the chloride and magnesium from the fused chloride. He pressed magnesium into wire and used it as a light source in his subsequent photochemical experiments. Commercial manufacture of magnesium was also undertaken and the element came into general use as a brilliant illuminating agent.

In the mid-1850's Bunsen prepared sodium and aluminum from their molten chlorides. With the assistance of Augustus Matthiessen, Bunsen isolated lithium and several alkaline earth metals—barium, calcium, and strontium—from their fused chlorides. Bunsen, with William Hillebrand and T. H. Norton, prepared the rare earth metals of the cerium group—cerium, lanthanum, and didymium. To obtain the specific heats of these rare elements, Bunsen devised a sensitive ice calorimeter that measured the volume rather than the mass of the ice melted and required only a small sample of the metal. From the specific heats, the atomic weights of these elements and the formulas of their compounds were calculated. Finally, the Bunsen battery made possible the electrolysis of a variety of organic compounds and the isolation of organic radicals by Kolbe and Frankland, who began their work under Bunsen's direction in Marburg.

Between 1852 and 1862 Bunsen collaborated with Sir Henry Roscoe on photochemical research involving the chemical combination of equal volumes of hydrogen and chlorine when they were illuminated. For this experiment they altered a reaction vessel devised by John Draper in 1843. Bunsen and Roscoe found that for some time after the experiment started—a time they called the induction period—no reaction took place; then the reaction rate slowly increased until a constant rate, proportional to the intensity of the light source used, was reached. The effect of the incident light was related to the wavelength and followed a law of inverse squares. Further, the illumination of chlorine alone before it entered the reaction chamber did not alter the length of the induction period. While variations of temperature within the range 18°–26° had little effect on the reaction, the presence of oxygen appeared to have a catalytic effect. Bunsen and Roscoe determined that the energy of the light radiated by the sun in one minute is equivalent to the energy needed for the conversion of 25×10^{12} cubic miles of a hydrogen-chlorine mixture into hydrogen chloride.

Bunsen developed his well-known burner during the 1850's, building upon the inventions of Aimé Argand and Michael Faraday. The Bunsen burner, with its nonluminous flame, quickly supplanted the blowpipe flame in the dry tests of analytical chemistry. Bunsen used his burner to identify metals and their salts by their characteristic colored flames. Other experiments with the burner yielded data for melting points and rate of volatility of salts.

In the 1860's Bunsen and Kirchhoff worked together to develop the field of spectroscopy. Kirchhoff realized in 1859 that when colored flames of heated materials, which usually give bright, sharp emission spectra, are placed in the path of an intense light source, they absorb light of the same wavelength that they otherwise emit, and produce characteristic absorption spectra. Bunsen saw that analyses of absorption spectra could be made in order to determine the composition of celestial and terrestrial matter. He further predicted that spectral analysis could aid in the discovery of new elements that might exist in too small quantities or be too similar to known elements to be identifiable by traditional chemical techniques. Spectral analysis led to Bunsen and Kirchhoff's announcement in 1860 of a new alkali metal, cesium, detected in a few drops of the alkaline residue from an analysis of mineral water obtained from Durkheim. The element was named cesium (from the Latin *caesius*, "sky blue") because of its brilliant blue spectral lines. Cesium salts had previously been mistaken for compounds of potassium. The following year the element rubidium (from the Latin *rubidus*, "dark red") was detected from the spectrum of a few grains of the mineral lepidolite. By comparison, forty tons of mineral water were needed to yield 16.5 grams of cesium chloride and rubidium chloride that could be used in the chemical investigation of the compounds of these new elements. In 1862 Bunsen succeeded in isolating metallic rubidium by heating a mixture of the carbonate and charcoal. During the years that followed, several other elements were identified by spectroscopic methods: thallium (Crookes, 1861), indium (Reich and Richter, 1863), gallium (Lecoq de Boisbaudran, 1875), scandium (Nilson, 1879), and germanium (Winkler, 1886).

Bunsen was concerned with a variety of additional analytic work. In 1853 he developed a technique for the volumetric determination of free iodine using sulfurous acid. In 1868 he worked out methods for separating the several metals—palladium, ruthenium, iridium, and rhodium—that remain in ores after the extraction of platinum; as part of this project Bunsen constructed a filter pump for washing precipitates. With the assistance of Victor Meyer, he conducted a government-sponsored study of the mineral water of Baden; results were published in 1871. He described the spark spectra of the rare earths in 1875. Late in his life Bunsen used a steam calorimeter that he had built to measure the specific heats of platinum, glass, and water.

Bunsen was honored by several European scientific societies. In 1842 he was elected a foreign member of the Chemical Society of London. He became a corresponding member of the Académie des Sciences in 1853, and a foreign member in 1882. He was named a foreign fellow of the Royal Society of London in 1858 and received its Copley Medal in 1860; Bunsen and Kirchhoff received the first Davy Medal in 1877. Finally, Bunsen's scientific contributions to industry were recognized by the English Society of Arts, which awarded him the Albert Medal in 1898.

BIBLIOGRAPHY

I. ORIGINAL WORKS. Bunsen's writings include *Gasometrische Methoden* (Brunswick, 1857; enl. ed., 1877), trans. by Henry E. Roscoe as *Gasometry; Comprising the Leading Physical and Chemical Properties of Gases* (London, 1857); *Photochemical Researches,* 5 pts. (London, 1858–1863), written with Henry E. Roscoe and pub. in German as *Photochemische Untersuchungen* (Leipzig, 1892); *Chemische Analyse durch Spectralbeobachtungen* (Vienna, 1860), written with Kirchhoff; and *Gesammelte Abhandlungen,* Wilhelm Ostwald and Ernst Bodenstein, eds., 3 vols. (Leipzig, 1904). Also of interest, all in Klassiker der exacten Wissenschaften, are *Untersuchungen über die Kakodylreihe,* Adolf von Baeyer, ed., no. 27; and *Photochemische Untersuchungen,* W. Ostwald, ed., nos. 34, 38.

II. SECONDARY LITERATURE. Works on Bunsen are Theodore Curtin's article in Eduard Farber, *Great Chemists* (New York, 1961), pp. 575–581, a trans. from *Journal für praktische Chemie* (1900); O. Fuchs's article in F. D. G. Bugge, *Das Buch der grossen Chemiker,* II (Berlin, 1930), 78–91; Georg Lockemann, *Robert Wilhelm Bunsen. Lebensbild eines deutschen Forschers* (Stuttgart, 1949); Ralph E. Oesper, "Robert Wilhelm Bunsen," in *Journal of Chemical Education,* **4** (1927), 431–439; W. Ostwald's article in *Zeitschrift für Elektrochemie,* **7** (1900), 608–618; J. R. Partington, *A History of Chemistry,* IV (London, 1964), 281–293; H. Rheinboldt, "Bunsens Vorlesung über allgemeine Experimentalchemie," in *Chymia,* **3** (1950), 223–241; Henry E. Roscoe, "Bunsen Memorial Lecture" (delivered 29 Mar. 1900), in *Journal of the Chemical Society,* **77,** pt. 1 (1900), 513–554; and *Bunseniana. Eine Sammlung von humoristischen Geschichten aus den Leben von Robert Bunsen* (Heidelberg, 1904).

SUSAN G. SCHACHER

BUONAMICI, FRANCESCO (*b*. Florence, Italy, first half of the sixteenth century; *d*. 1603), *medicine, natural philosophy.*

Buonamici's importance for the history of science derives less from his career as a Florentine physician than from his having taught physics at Pisa while Galileo was a student there, giving credence to the theory that Galileo's *Juvenilia* (commonly held to be class notes written in 1584) were based on Buonamici's lectures. A copy of Buonamici's *De motu* was in Galileo's personal library; there are resemblances between portions of this and Galileo's early writings (including Galileo's *De motu,* composed *ca.* 1590), although Galileo later attacked Buonamici's teachings in a discourse printed in 1612.

The full title of Buonamici's principal work is *De motu libri X, quibus generalia naturalis philosophiae principia summo studio collecta continentur, necnon universae quaestiones ad libros De Physico audito, de Caelo, de Ortu et Interitu pertinentes explicantur; multa item Aristotelis loca explanantur, et Graecorum, Averrois, aliorumque doctorum sententiae ad theses peripateticas diriguntur* ("Ten books on motion, in which are contained general principles of natural philosophy, culled with great care, and in which are worked out all questions relating to [Aristotle's] books of the *Physics, On the Heavens,* and *On Generation and Corruption;* again, many texts of Aristotle are explained, and the opinions of the Greeks, of Averroës, and of other doctors are brought to bear on Peripatetic theses"). The work, as the title indicates, is more than a treatise on motion; it is a com-

plete course in natural philosophy, consisting of 1,031 closely packed pages in the folio edition of 1591. The principles around which Buonamici organizes his course are the four causes of motion, or change; the various types of motion (straight-line, alteration, growth, and so forth); and the relation of motion to the heavenly bodies.

In content the work is a masterpiece of Renaissance eclecticism: Buonamici takes cognizance of the humanist tradition (for example, interspersing Greek poetry throughout the text) as well as of such Greek commentators on Aristotle as Alexander of Aphrodisias and John Philoponus; he cites approvingly such mathematicians as Archimedes (at some length), Nicomachus, and Campanus; he gives attention to the Paduan Averroists and the various Platonic and Neoplatonic schools, ranging from the Arabs to the Florentine Academy; and he continually casts a respectful eye toward Thomas Aquinas, Duns Scotus, and other Scholastics. His citation of authorities is pretentious but generally inaccurate, leading one to believe that he relied heavily on secondary sources; teachings he ascribes to Aquinas, for example, may have been held by contemporary Thomists but certainly are not to be found in Aquinas. He occasionally mentions such fourteenth-century thinkers as Walter Burley, the Calculator (Richard Swineshead), and Albert of Saxony, but he reports their contributions to the development of mechanics only superficially. Among his immediate predecessors and contemporaries, those who attract his attention include Alessandro Achillini and Ludovico Buccaferrea, both of Bologna; Francesco Vicomercati of Milan; Scaliger; and Cardano. Throughout his work Buonamici reveals himself generally as an orthodox and traditional Aristotelian who cites the views of "moderns" (*iuniores*) mainly to refute them.

In mechanics, Buonamici held a theory of "self-expending" (as opposed to inertial) impetus, and accepted uncritically the pretended initial acceleration of projectiles. He rejected the theory of "accidental" gravity invoked by Parisian terminists to explain the acceleration of bodies in free fall, maintaining that Aristotle's explanation is sufficient. Similarly, he preferred Aristotle's rules for calculating the ratios of motions, velocities, and distances of travel to those of Albert of Saxony and other "Latins," which he seems to have drawn from Achillini's *In quaestione de motuum proportionibus,* a work of which he is generally critical.

BIBLIOGRAPHY

I. ORIGINAL WORKS. *De motu libri X* (Florence, 1591), in folio, is quite rare; a copy is in the library of Princeton

University; the work also exists in a 1592 edition, in quarto. Alexandre Koyré provides most of the Latin text, with French translation, of Bk. 4, chs. 37–38, dealing with the increase of speed in natural motion; of Bk. 5, chs. 35–36, dealing with projectile motion; and small portions of the Latin text of Bk. 1, chs. 10–11, dealing with the relation of mathematics to physical science, in his *Études galiléennes* (Paris, 1939), pp. 18–41, 267–268, 279. There is a copy of *Discorsi poetica nella Accademia fiorentina in difesa d'Aristotile . . . xix di settembre 1587* (Florence, 1597) in the Bibliothèque Nationale, Paris. Copies of *De alimento libri V* (Florence, 1603) are in the British Museum, London, and the Bibliothèque Nationale, Paris; *ibid.*, Venice, 1604.

II. SECONDARY LITERATURE. Some details concerning Buonamici may be found in J. H. Zedler, ed., *Grosses vollständiges Universal-Lexikon,* IV (Halle–Leipzig, 1733; repr. Graz, 1961), col. 569; Antonio Favaro, ed., *Le opere di Galileo Galilei,* Edizione Nazionale (Florence, 1890), esp. I, 9–13; and I. E. Drabkin and Stillman Drake, eds., *Galileo Galilei: On Motion and On Mechanics,* Univ. of Wisconsin Publications in Medieval Science, no. 5 (Madison, Wis., 1960), provides an English translation of Galileo's *De motu,* with introduction and notes by Drabkin, who calls attention to possible influences of Buonamici on Galileo, pp. 10, 49n, 55n, 78n, 79n; see also the bibliography on pp. 10–11.

WILLIAM A. WALLACE, O.P.

BUONANNI, FILIPPO (*b.* Rome, Italy, 7 January 1638; *d.* Rome, 30 March 1725), *natural sciences.*

Buonanni, one of the most learned Jesuits of his time, was a pupil of Athanasius Kircher, and in 1680 succeeded his master as teacher of mathematics at the Collegium Romanum; in 1698, he was appointed curator of the Kircherian Museum, which he described in his *Museum Collegii Romani Kircherianum* (1709).

Erudite in a number of fields, including numismatics and ecclesiastical history (writing on both subjects), Buonanni made extensive studies in the natural sciences; he constructed his own microscope with three lenses (according to Tortona's system), which proved to be an ingenious mechanism for continual observation. In his *Ricreazione dell'occhio e della mente nell'osservazione della chiocciole* (1681), a work valuable for its many illustrations of shells, he explicitly affirmed his belief in the spontaneous generation of mollusks and rekindled the controversy over generation that had flared in 1671 between Kircher and Francesco Redi. Buonanni's position was anachronistic, since the Aristotelian theory of spontaneous generation had been disproved by Redi in his *Esperienze intorno alla generazione degli insetti* (1668) and by Marcello Malpighi, who had demonstrated the pathogenesis of oak galls from the development of fertilized insect eggs in his *Anatome plantarum* (1679).

Buonanni made no personal observations on the phenomenon of generation in the lower animals; neither had he understood the validity of Nicolaus Steno's declaration that "the oysters and other shells originate from the eggs, not from putrescence," or the statement of the English naturalist Martin Lister that "snails are generated by coition, which we observed often in many of their kinds." He based his belief in the spontaneous generation of mollusks partly on the authority of Aristotle and Kircher and partly on a report by Camillo Picchi of Ancona that "the conches called 'Ballani' (mollusks of the kind *Balanus*) live only in some rocks and not in others," but principally upon an anatomical error of his own; he was convinced, as he stated in his *Ricreazione,* that the mollusks had no hearts. If this were so, they had no blood; Aristotle had written that no bloodless animal is oviparous, and that "all conches are generated spontaneously by the mud—oysters by dirty mud, the others by sandy mud." Convinced that the conches were heartless and bloodless, Buonanni believed that both observation and authority supported the idea of spontaneous generation.

Two years after the publication of the *Ricreazione,* Antonio Felice Marsili, archdeacon of Bologna, brought out his own *Relazione sul ritrovamento dell'uova di chiocciole,* in which he described and, indeed, provided drawings of the eggs of snails, some of which visibly contained minuscule snails. Redi, because of Buonanni's opposition to his conclusions on the oviparous generation of insects, harshly criticized Buonanni in his *Osservazioni* (1684), pointing out his rival's error regarding the absence of the heart in snails (the existence of which Redi demonstrated) and asserting, further, that all snails had hearts. He was ruthless in his exposure of Buonanni's mistakes in methodology and ridiculed Buonanni's attempts to demonstrate spontaneous generation of insects from putrefied hyacinth flowers and to establish that certain putrefied flowers or leaves generated only certain kinds of insects.

Buonanni replied (1691) to Redi's criticism, but his reply was judged by contemporaries as inadequate, and indeed inane. On the other hand, it should be recorded that he did deny the existence of the mythical *remora,* the reality of which had been accepted from Aristotle and Pliny right down to Girolamo Cardano in the mid-sixteenth century. His rational classification of shells was novel and useful. The quality of his illustrations of various insects was excellent—particularly those of the fly, louse, mite, flea, and mosquito. Indeed, his drawings of the *Culex pipiens* (common house mosquito) are the best of the seventeenth century.

BIBLIOGRAPHY

I. ORIGINAL WORKS. Buonanni's works include *Ricreazione dell'occhio e della mente nell'osservazione delle chiocciole* (Rome, 1681); *Recreatio mentis et oculi in observatione animalium testaceorum,* the 2nd ed. of the *Ricreazione* (Rome, 1684); *Observationes circa viventia quae in rebus non viventibus reperiuntur* (Rome, 1691), which has as an appendix the *Micrographia curiosa, sive rerum minutissimarum observationes, quae, ope microscopii recognitae, ad vivum exprimuntur a Patre Philippo Bonanni Societatis Jesu sacerdote,* containing some interesting observations on early microscopes and a precise description of his own microscope; and *Museum Collegii Romani Kircherianum descriptum* (Rome, 1709).

II. SECONDARY LITERATURE. Works on Buonanni are J. A. Battarra, *Rerum naturalium historia existentium in Museo Kircheriano edita iam a P. Phil. Bonanni, nunc vero novo methodo cum notis illustrata ac observationibus locupletata a Johanne Antonio Battarra,* 2 vols. (Rome, 1773–1782); Ugo Faucci, "Contributo alla storia della dottrina parassitaria delle infezioni," in *Rivista di storia delle scienze mediche e naturali,* 26 (1935), 136–193, which includes Kircher's biological views (see note 29, p. 147, and note 30, p. 183); A. Neviani, "Un episodio della lotta fra spontaneisti ed ovulisti. Il Padre Filippo Buonanni e l'Abate Anton Felice Marsili," in *Rivista di storia delle scienze mediche e naturali,* 26 (1935), 211–232; and F. Redi, *Osservazioni intorno agli animali viventi che si trovano negli animali viventi* (Florence, 1684), pp. 58–88. The Buonanni microscope is illustrated in Clay and Court, *History of the Microscope* (London, 1932), pp. 41–44, 84–86.

PIETRO FRANCESCHINI

BUONO, PAOLO DEL (*b.* Florence, Italy, 26 October 1625; *d.* Poland, 1659), *mechanics, physics.*

Del Buono was the son of Leonido and Bartolomea Andreini. He studied in Pisa under Famiano Michelini. A member of the Poor Regular Clerics of the Mother of God of the Pious Schools (Scolopi), Del Buono was learned but eccentric. He deserves much credit, however, for arousing a keen interest in the sciences in his pupil Leopoldo de' Medici, who in 1657–1667 was a patron of the Cimento Academy. Del Buono received his degree in Pisa in 1649. Six years later he went to Germany in the service of Emperor Ferdinand III, who appointed him president of the mint and offered him honors and rich prizes if he could devise a mechanism to draw water from mines. In order to make practical studies, in 1657 and 1658 he visited the imperial mines in the Carpathians, accompanied by Geminiano Montanari, a doctor of jurisprudence whom he had instructed in the sciences. The death of the emperor and the disturbances that broke out in Germany made it necessary for him to go to Poland, where he died about a year later.

Del Buono is included among the correspondents of the Cimento Academy, along with his older brother, Father Candido, and his younger brother, Anton Maria.

Several of Del Buono's letters to Prince Leopold are extant. In them he refers to the observations, made in several observatories, of a comet that was then visible. His contributions include an instrument to demonstrate the incompressibility of water and a communication from Vienna that states that water enclosed in glass vials with very thin necks generates air in amounts dependent on the temperature of the environment. The Cimento Academy confirmed this phenomenon, concerning which Giovanni Borelli and Viviani gave conflicting explanations.

BIBLIOGRAPHY

Lettere inedite di uomini illustri, Angelo Fabronio, ed., I (Florence, 1773), 94, 151, 200.

Angelo Fabronio, *Vitae italorum doctrina excellentium qui saeculis XVII et XVIII fioruerunt,* 12 vols. (Pisa, 1778–1785).

Notizie degli aggrandimenti delle scienze fisiche accaduti in Toscana nel corso degli anni LX del sec. XVII°, raccolte dal dottor Giovanni Targioni Tazzetti, G. Bouchard, ed., I (Florence, 1780), 182, 519; II, pt. 1 (Florence, 1780), 309.

Raffaele Caverni, *Storia del metodo sperimentale in Italia* 6 vols. (Florence, 1891–1892), II, 263.

Galileo Galilei: Le opere, Antonio Favaro *et al.,* eds., national ed., 20 vols. (Florence, 1890–1909; reprinted 1929–1939). There is a short biography of Del Buono in XX, pt. 6; see also XXV, pt. 3, 352, letter from Ward to Galileo of 7 September 1641.

A. NATUCCI

BUONVICINO, COSTANZO BENEDETTO. See **Bonvicino, Costanzo Benedetto.**

BUOT, JACQUES (*d. ca.* 1675), *astronomy, physics, geometry.*

Buot was a member of the Académie des Sciences of Paris from the time it was founded in 1666; as such he received an annual stipend of 1,200 livres.

Buot probably was present on 16 July 1667 when Huygens observed the exact hour at which the diameter of the ring of Saturn seemed to be parallel to the horizon. From this observation, Huygens calculated the inclination of the ring to the equator as 8°58' and to the ecliptic as 31°22'; Buot found a value of 31°38'35" for the latter. (As early as 1659, in his *Systema Saturnium,* Huygens had attempted to determine these values as precisely as possible.) On 15 August 1667 Huygens, Jean Picard, Jean Richer, and

Buot repeated the experiment and obtained values of 9°32′50″ and 32°0′.

Buot made a further contribution to astronomy by inventing the *équerre azimutale,* an instrument for finding the intersection of the meridian with a horizontal plane. He was also active as a physicist, once again drawing upon Huygens' work. In 1667 Huygens and members of the Accademia del Cimento in Florence had made experiments to determine the forces that cause water to expand on congelation. In 1670 Buot repeated these experiments for water and oils and observed that the congealing of water differs from that of oils. In 1669 Buot joined Huygens and others in the discussions on the causes of gravitation that were held by the Academy; in his *mémoire* of 21 August 1669, he showed himself opposed to the action-at-a-distance theory.

Condorcet wrote that Buot died in 1675. A letter from Olaus Römer to Huygens, dated 30 December 1677, states, however, *Dominus Buot post aliquot mensium morbum fato appropinquare creditur*—"After an illness of some months Mr. Buot seems to feel that his end is drawing near." The *Comptes des bâtiments* gives the date of his last stipend as 10 June 1676.

BIBLIOGRAPHY

I. ORIGINAL WORKS. Buot's writings include *Usage de la roüe de proportion, avec un traité d'arithmétique* (Paris, 1647); and "Équerre azimutale," in Gallon, ed., *Machines et inventions approuvées par l'Académie royale des sciences depuis 1666 jusqu'en 1701,* I (Paris, 1735), 67–70.

II. SECONDARY LITERATURE. Works dealing with Buot are Condorcet, *Éloges des Académiens de l'Académie royale des sciences, morts depuis 1666 jusqu'en 1699* (Paris, 1773), p. 157; J. Guiffrey, *Comptes des bâtiments du roi, sous le règne de Louis XIV,* I (Paris, 1881), 163, 227, 299, 378, 449, 565, 650, 782, 856; Panckoucke, ed., *Histoire de l'Académie royale des sciences 1666 à 1698,* I (Paris, 1777), 121; and *Oeuvres complètes de Christiaan Huygens,* VI (The Hague, 1895), 58–66, 139–142, 143–147; VIII (The Hague, 1899), 54; XV (The Hague, 1925), 43, 93, 94, 478; XIX (The Hague, 1937), 182, 183, 344, 630; E. Maindron, *L'Académie des sciences* (Paris, 1888), p. 98; and D. Shapeley, "Pre-Huygenian Observations of Saturn's Rings," in *Isis,* **40** (1949), 12–17.

H. L. L. BUSARD

BURALI-FORTI, CESARE (*b.* Arezzo, Italy, 13 August 1861; *d.* Turin, Italy, 21 January 1931), *mathematics.*

After obtaining his degree from the University of Pisa in December 1884, Burali-Forti taught at the Scuola Tecnica in Augusta, Sicily. In 1887 he moved to Turin after winning a competition for extraordinary professor at the Accademia Militare di Artiglieria e Genio. In Turin he also taught at the Scuola Tecnica Sommeiller until 1914. He remained at the Accademia Militare, teaching analytical projective geometry, until his death. He was named ordinary professor in 1906 and held a prominent position on the faculty; in 1927 he was the only ordinary among twenty-five civilian professors.

After an early attempt to obtain the *libera docenza* failed because of the antagonism to the new methods of vector analysis on the part of some members of the examining committee, he never again attempted to obtain it and thus never held a permanent university position. (The *libera docenza* gave official permission to teach at a university and was required before entering a competition for a university chair.) He was assistant to Giuseppe Peano at the University of Turin during the years 1894–1896, but he had come under Peano's influence earlier, however, and had given a series of informal lectures at the university on mathematical logic (1893–1894). These were published in 1894. Many of Burali-Forti's publications were highly polemical, but to his family and his friends he was kind and gentle. He loved music; Bach and Beethoven were his favorite composers. He was not a member of any academy. Always an independent thinker, he asked that he not be given a religious funeral.

The name Burali-Forti has remained famous for the antinomy he discovered in 1897 in his critique of Georg Cantor's theory of transfinite ordinal numbers. The critique begins: "The principal purpose of this note is to show that there exist *transfinite numbers* (or *ordinal types*) a, b, such that a is neither equal to, nor less than, nor greater than b." Essentially, the antinomy may be formulated as follows: To every class of ordinal numbers there corresponds an ordinal number which is greater than any element of the class. Consider the class of all ordinal numbers. It follows that it possesses an ordinal number that is greater than every ordinal number. This result went almost unnoticed until Bertrand Russell published a similar antinomy in 1903. It should be noted, however, that Cantor was already aware of the Burali-Forti antinomy in 1895 and had written of it to David Hilbert in 1896.

Burali-Forti was one of the earliest popularizers of Peano's discoveries in mathematical logic. In 1919 he published a greatly enlarged edition of the *Logica mathematica,* which contained many original contributions. He also contributed much to Peano's famous *Formulaire de mathématiques* project, especially with his study of the foundations of mathematics (1893).

Burali-Forti's most valuable mathematical contributions were his studies devoted to the foundations of vector analysis and to linear transformations and their various applications, especially in differential geometry. A long collaboration with Roberto Marcolongo was very productive. They published a series of articles in the *Rendiconti del Circolo matematico di Palermo* on the unification of vectorial notation that included a full analysis, along critical and historical lines, of all the notations that had been proposed for a minimal system. There followed a book treating the fundamentals of vector analysis (1909), which was almost immediately translated into French. Their proposals for a unified system of vectorial notation, published in *L'enseignement mathématique* in 1909, gave rise to a polemic with various followers of Josiah Gibbs and Sir William Hamilton that lasted into the following year and consisted of letters, responses, and opinions contributed by Burali-Forti and Marcolongo, Peano, G. Comberiac, H. C. F. Timerding, Felix Klein, E. B. Wilson, C. G. Knott, Alexander Macfarlane, E. Carvallo, and E. Jahnke. The differences in notation continued, however, and the Italian school, while quite productive, tended to remain somewhat isolated from developments elsewhere. Also in 1909 Burali-Forti and Marcolongo began their collaboration in the study of linear transformations of vectors.

Burali-Forti's introduction of the notion of the derivative of a vector with respect to a point allowed him to unify and greatly simplify the foundations of vector analysis. The use of one simple linear operator led to new applications of the theory of vector analysis, as well as to improved treatment of operators previously introduced, such as Lorentz transformations, gradients, and rotors, and resulted in the publication (1912–1913) of two volumes treating linear transformations and their applications. Burali-Forti was able to apply the theory to the mechanics of continuous bodies, optics, hydrodynamics, statics, and various problems of mechanics, always refining methods, simplifying proofs, and discovering new and useful properties. He did not live to see the completion of his dream, a small encyclopedia of vector analysis and its applications. The part dealing with differential projective geometry (1930) was Burali-Forti's last work.

The long collaboration with Marcolongo—their friends called them "the vectorial binomial"—was partly broken by their divergent views on the theory of relativity, the importance of which Burali-Forti never understood. With Tommaso Boggio he published a critique (1924) in which he meant "to consider Relativity under its mathematical aspect, wishing to point out how arbitrary and irrational are its founda-

tions." "We wish," he wrote in the preface, "to shake Relativity in all its apparent foundations, and we have reason for hoping that we have succeeded in doing it." At the end he stated: "Here then is our conclusion. Philosophy may be able to justify the space-time of Relativity, but mathematics, experimental science, and common sense can justify it NOT AT ALL."

Burali-Forti had a strong dislike for coordinates. In 1929, in the second edition of the *Analisi vettoriale generale,* written with Marcolongo, we find: "The criteria of this work . . . are not different from those with which we began our study in 1909, namely, an absolute treatment of all physical, mechanical, and geometrical problems, independent of any system of coordinates whatsoever."

BIBLIOGRAPHY

Besides his scientific publications, Burali-Forti wrote many school texts. In all, his publications total more than two hundred.

No complete list of the works of Burali-Forti has been published, but the following may be considered representative: *Teoria delle grandezze* (Turin, 1893); *Logica matematica* (Milan, 1894; 2nd ed., rev., Milan, 1919); "Una questione sui numeri transfiniti," in *Rendiconti del Circolo matematico di Palermo,* **11** (1897), 154–164; *Lezioni di geometria metrico-proiettiva* (Turin, 1904); *Elementi di calcolo vettoriale, con numerose applicazioni alla geometria, alla meccanica e alla fisica-matematica,* written with R. Marcolongo (Turin, 1909), translated into French by S. Lattès as *Éléments de calcul vectoriel, avec de nombreuses applications à la géométrie, à la mécanique et à la physique mathématique* (Paris, 1910); "Notations rationelles pour le système vectoriel minimum," in *L'enseignement mathématique,* **11** (1909), 41–45, written with Marcolongo; *Omografie vettoriali con applicazioni alle derivate rispetto ad un punto ed alla fisica-matematica* (Turin, 1909), written with Marcolongo; *Analyse vectorielle générale,* 2 vols. (Pavia, 1912–1913), written with Marcolongo; *Espaces courbes. Critique de la relativité* (Turin, 1924), written with Tommaso Boggio; and *Analisi vettoriale generale e applicazioni,* Vol. II, *Geometria differenziale* (Bologna, 1930), written with P. Burgatti and Tommaso Boggio.

A work dealing with Burali-Forti is Roberto Marcolongo, "Cesare Burali-Forti," in *Bollettino dell'Unione matematica italiana,* **10** (1931), 182–185.

HUBERT C. KENNEDY

BURDACH, KARL FRIEDRICH (*b.* Leipzig, Germany, 12 June 1776; *d.* Königsberg, Germany, 16 July 1847), *physiology.*

Karl Friedrich Burdach was a natural scientist typical of his peers and representative of a distinctive period in the intellectual life of Germany—the Romantic age of the early nineteenth century. Guided by the tenets of *Naturphilosophie,* he made significant contributions, particularly to neuroanatomy. His penchant for extreme systematization, however, led him to publish in his many treatises much that later workers ridiculed as "unscientific."

The son of a physician, Burdach was encouraged to undertake medical training. He began his studies at the University of Leipzig in 1793, and received the doctor of philosophy degree five years later, in August 1798. He was still unqualified to practice, however, since at the time Leipzig did not offer any clinical training. He therefore proceeded to Vienna and the great clinician Johann Peter Frank, not only because of Frank's fame and the attractions of Vienna, but also because of Frank's reported adherence to the Brunonian system of medicine, which had fascinated the young man during his training. At the end of his year at Vienna, Burdach began to search—unsuccessfully—for an academic position. He formally became doctor of medicine at Leipzig in June 1799, and settled down to private practice and private lecturing while awaiting a university appointment. During this period, which lasted until 1811, the young man turned to medical writing as a means of supplementing his income and making his name known.

In these early works, Burdach's sympathies for the Romantic philosophy of nature were obvious. Although he took issue with the *Naturphilosophen* followers of Lorenz Oken and Friedrich Schelling on points of method and doctrine, his works represent an attempt to understand particular aspects of the natural world as integral parts of a coherent whole. Burdach was guided by the credo "Those who have thoughts have always seen more than those who merely wanted to see with their own eyes"; he approached the study of natural phenomena with the conviction that nature is totality and unity, an "Idea" of which all individual things are partial representations and in which they participate. To know nature, then, one needs both to study and to reflect on individual phenomena.

In the summer of 1811 Burdach was finally successful in obtaining a position, as professor of anatomy, physiology, and forensic medicine at the University of Dorpat. The new-found financial freedom and increased spare time allowed him finally to begin firsthand research, and his choice of areas reflected his general interests. He began intensive studies of the anatomy of the human brain, and of embryonic and animal brains; he also studied in detail the classic works on embryology, in particular those from Harvey to the treatise by Johann von Autenrieth (1797). It is clear that both interests, which were to

remain with Burdach, stemmed from his conviction that a knowledge of the world could be obtained only through a rational intellectual analysis of all aspects of man's life.

Animated by the desire to return to Germany, in 1813–1814 Burdach applied for and received the recently vacated professorship of anatomy at Königsberg. In addition to an increase in salary and the title *Hofrath,* he obtained permission to create and head an anatomical institute. For the prosectorship of the institute he finally obtained the services of Karl Ernst von Baer, a former student of his at Dorpat, and the Konigliche Anatomische Anstalt in Königsberg was formally opened on 13 November 1817. Within it, Burdach taught courses in anatomy, physiology, propaedeutics, and the life of the fetus, and Baer—treated more as colleague than assistant— dealt with zootomy, human anatomy, and fetal physiology. The research carried out at the institute was reported in yearly *Berichte.*

The first results of Burdach's examination of the nervous system were reported in the first *Bericht* (1818), and a complete treatment of the subject appeared in *Vom Baue und Leben des Gehirns,* the first volume of which appeared in 1819. The work is one of the best examples of the approach taken by the Romantic physiologists. It seeks to be comprehensive and systematic; Burdach maintained that one must know formation and life in order to arrive at the real goal, knowledge of the nature of the total entity. He argued that every coherent, systematic work must proceed in accordance with a particular point of view, and he stated his explicitly: Nature is a unity, of which all phenomena, including those of the mind, partake, and an ideal *Sein* lies at the base of all appearances. It follows that since both reason and appearances are aspects of nature, examination of that unity may proceed by two paths: observation and reflection, or, as Burdach put it, "contemplating ideas in their necessity and demonstrating them in their reality."

Burdach sought to show that the nervous system was itself a unity and not just a conglomerate of various anatomical structures. He examined the parts of the brain with the intent of delineating the systems of which they were elements, and was particularly interested in such integrating structures as the intracerebral connecting paths and the fiber tracts. This entailed a thorough anatomical examination, and Burdach provided precise and detailed descriptions of many parts and their relationships. He is credited with the explanation of the relationship of the olive to its surrounding region and with the clarification of the nature of many of the fasciculi. In the anatomical nomenclature prior to the Basel reforms, the column of fibers in the spinal cord now called the fasciculus cuneatus and first described by Burdach was known as the "column of Burdach." He described several of the nuclei of the thalamus and pointed out the division of the lentiform nucleus of the corpus striatum into putamen and globus pallidus. Among the other structures he named were the claustrum, the brachium conjunctivum (superior cerebellar peduncle), and the cuneus. But such observational advances were only way stations on the path to knowledge of the "Idea" of the brain. Thus, a third volume, *Leben des Gehirns,* followed the first two anatomical volumes. This was an attempt at a physiology of the central nervous system, and contained discussions of meningitis, the function of the cerebral gyri, and the connection of the corpora quadrigemina with the hearing function.

In 1820 the question arose of the desirability of producing a second edition of Burdach's 1810 physiology text. Instead, he chose to embark on a more ambitious course—a large-scale treatment of all physiology as a whole:

> I gave myself the task of deriving the life of man primarily from the nature of life as known through consideration of the entire organic realm. This knowledge, however, was to come from a view of the whole of nature derived from the combining of the appearances and the laws of organic and inorganic life [*Rückblick auf mein Leben,* p. 336].

Burdach thus intended to produce a statement of the nature of life through a study of all the individual appearances that are a part of life—a science of experience, based on nondemonstrable premises. For the work he recruited collaborators and assistants in many ancillary fields: Baer, Heinrich Rathke, the botanist C. W. Eysenhardt, and, for later volumes, Johannes Müller, Theodor von Siebold, and Gabriel Valentin. The first volume of the text, *Die Physiologie als Erfahrungswissenschaft,* appeared in 1826.

The form of the work was determined for Burdach by his conception of physiology. The ultimate goal of physiology was knowledge of the human spirit (*Geist*); but the essence (*Wesen*) of anything, he pointed out, takes root only in the whole of reality, and only therein will it be completely known. Thus, in order to know man, physiology must view the whole of nature and consider all the phenomena of the world. For Burdach, as for many of his contemporaries, physiology was no longer a study of the functions or uses of organic parts, but of life and its appearances. "Physiology is therefore the apex of all

natural science, the point of unity of the knowledge of reality."

The ten volumes of the work were to be divided between a consideration of life in general as an ordered progression of processes and the particular functions and processes of living things. However, the death of Burdach's wife in 1838 forced the termination of the work after the sixth volume, with the complete plan unrealized. The first three volumes published dealt with the history of *Leben an sich*: generation (Vol. 1); embryonic life, beginning with the development of the egg (Vols. II and III); and independent life, leading to death (Vol. III). The incomplete second part treated some of the systems involved in the vegetative aspects of life: the blood, the blood circulation, and the associated functions of nutrition and secretion. Incomplete though it was, the text was for a time well known and widely read.

The discussion of development in Volume II, prepared largely by Baer and Rathke, indirectly had a profound influence on the development of modern embryology. Baer submitted an entire treatise on the formation of the embryo; Burdach, however—a man convinced of the correctness of his ideas—rearranged the discussion to conform to his larger system, breaking up Baer's treatise and distributing it throughout the work. Baer, angry at what he considered such cavalier treatment, proceeded to publish his treatise separately, as the first part of his *Ueber Entwicklungsgeschichte der Thiere* (1828), the first great work of modern embryology.

The last of Burdach's major works was the four-volume *Blicke ins Leben* (1842–1848). It was written as the culmination of one aspect of Burdach's scientific life, and it exhibited characteristic elements of the thought not only of Burdach but also of most Romantics. Burdach was always optimistic about the unlimited knowledge of the human spirit available to man; he strove always to be rational, since reason is an aspect of the Absolute; and he strove always for universality, seeking true knowledge, which is knowledge of the totality of nature. With the preparation that Burdach believed he had obtained from a lifetime's properly directed scientific work, he sought to show the reader how, from a scientific point of view, all existence can and must be seen as a harmonious whole. Thus, religion and morality must properly be based on science. The first two volumes (1842) continued Burdach's developmental studies by seeking to set forth a phylogeny of the human soul. The third (1844) contained general reflections on human existence, and the last volume, published posthumously in 1848, was Burdach's autobiography.

BIBLIOGRAPHY

I. ORIGINAL WORKS. A fairly complete bibliography of Burdach's works, compiled by T. H. Bast, is available in *Annals of Medical History,* **10** (1928), 45–46. Much of Burdach's observational work was published in the seven *Berichte von der Königlichen Anatomischen Anstalt zu Königsberg* (1818–1824). His treatise on the brain and spinal cord, *Vom Baue und Leben des Gehirns,* was published in three vols. (Leipzig, 1819–1826). *Die Physiologie als Erfahrungswissenschaft* appeared in six vols. (I, Leipzig, 1826; II–VI, Königsberg, 1828–1840). There was also a 2nd ed. of vols. I–III (Königsberg, 1835–1838). Some of the views that had not appeared in this work were included in *Anthropologie für das gebildete Publicum* (Stuttgart, 1837). Burdach's autobiography, *Rückblick auf mein Leben,* was completed and published posthumously as the fourth and last vol. of *Blicke ins Leben* (Leipzig, 1842–1848). A. W. Meyer has published translations of two of Burdach's embryological treatises, prefaced by a short biographical sketch, in his *Human Generation. Conclusions of Burdach, Döllinger and von Baer* (Stanford, 1956), pp. 3–25. These are *De primis momentis formationis foetus* (1814) and *De foetu humano adnotationes anatomicae* (1828). This choice is somewhat puzzling: the first treatise, as Meyer himself notes, was written to satisfy the requirements for joining the faculty at Königsberg; Burdach called it "a premature birth" and refused to send out copies of it. The second essay was a vehicle for congratulations to Sömmering from the Königsberg faculty on the occasion of his jubilee, and the few observations are drawn from the second vol. of Burdach's *Die Physiologie als Erfahrungswissenschaft.* The embryological content of that work, however, has not yet been examined.

II. SECONDARY LITERATURE. Theodor Bast published a biographical sketch of Burdach, drawn entirely from his autobiography, in *Annals of Medical History,* **10** (1928), 34–46. Sections of the autobiography were reprinted (without the original pagination) in Erich Ebstein, ed., *Ärzte-Memoiren aus vier Jahrhunderten* (Berlin, 1923), pp. 158–165. A portrait of Burdach faces p. 158. The interaction of Burdach's researches and reflections is briefly but interestingly discussed in H. B. Picard, "Philosophie und Forschung bei K. F. Burdach," in *Medizinische Monatsschrift* (Stuttgart), **5** (1951), 125–128. Meyer (see above) briefly discusses the controversy between Burdach and Baer that led to publication of the latter's *Ueber Entwicklungsgeschichte der Thiere.* Baer's point of view is given in his *Nachrichten über Leben und Schriften des Herrn Geheimrathes Doctor Karl Ernst von Baer mitgetheilt von ihm selbst* (St. Petersburg, 1865), pp. 417–419, 455–471.

ALAN S. KAY

BURDENKO, NICOLAI NILOVICH (*b.* Kamenka [near Penza], Russia, 3 June 1876; *d.* Moscow, U.S.S.R., 11 November 1964), *neurology.*

Burdenko was born into a village family of some education. From 1886 to 1890 he studied at the Penza parochial school and from 1891 to 1897 was a student in the seminary there. In 1897 he entered the Tomsk University Medical School, transferring in 1901 to the Yuriev University (Tartu) Medical School, from which he graduated in 1906. As a student he was greatly influenced by the ideas of Nikolai Ivanovich Pirogov and the works of Pavlov. In 1903 he joined V.G. Tsego Manteifel's surgical clinic. In 1909, after presenting his doctoral thesis "Materialy k voprosu o posledstviakh perevyazki venaeportae" ("Data on the Effects of Dressing the Venae Portae"), he was employed in laboratories, clinics, hospitals, and libraries in Germany and Switzerland. He learned the surgical methods of August Bier, O. Hildebrandt, F. Krause, and Hermann Oppenheim. Under Constantin von Monakow, in Zurich, he studied anatomy and the histology of the central nervous system and neurological surgery.

After 1910 he held the chair of assistant professor of surgery at Yuriev University and became adjunct professor of surgery and anatomy. After the death of Tsego Manteifel, in 1917, he was professor ordinarius at the school's surgical clinic. From 1918 to 1923 he headed the Voronezh Medical Institute's surgical clinic and in 1923 he was appointed to the chair of anatomy and surgery at the Moscow State University Institute. From 1924 to the end of his life he devoted himself to organizing the clinic's neurological department. After 1929 he was director of the neurological clinic of the Health Ministry's roentgenology institute; this was the precursor of the Central Neurosurgical Institute (founded in 1934), which is today the Burdenko Neurosurgical Institute of the U.S.S.R. Academy of Medical Sciences. Burdenko further made use of his experiences in three wars (the Russo-Japanese War, World War I, and World War II) to lay the basis for Soviet military field surgery.

Burdenko wrote more than 300 articles on clinical and theoretical medicine. His earliest clinicoexperimental research was concerned with the physiology of the liver, the duodenum, the stomach, and the pancreas; his later work deals with a wide variety of problems in anatomy, physiology, biochemistry, histology, and pathology. He was a pioneer of Soviet neurosurgery (and especially of an important school of surgery that is marked by its readiness to experiment) and the teacher of the first generation of Soviet neurosurgeons. He made contributions to the oncology of the central nervous system and the vegetative nervous system; to the pathology and circulation of the blood and the fluids, edema and swelling of the brain; and to the operative treatment of various serious conditions of the nervous system.

Burdenko held many honorary posts. After 1939 he was Chairman of the Board of Directors of the U.S.S.R. College of Surgeons and after 1937, Chairman of the Medical Sciences Council of the U.S.S.R. Ministry of Health. He was the first president of the U.S.S.R. Academy of Medical Sciences, editor of *Sovremennaya khirurgiya* from 1944 to 1946, editor of *Neirokhirurgia,* and a member of the editorial board of *Khirurgiya* and *Voenno-meditsinskii zhurnal.* He was an honorary member of the International Society of Surgeons, the British Royal Society of Surgeons, and the Paris Academy of Surgeons. He was a deputy to the Supreme Soviet of the U.S.S.R. and a Hero of Socialist Labor.

BIBLIOGRAPHY

Burdenko's collected works have been published in seven volumes (Moscow, 1950–1952). See also C. M. Bagdasarian, *Nikolai Nilovich Burdenko* (Moscow, 1954).

N. A. GRIGORIAN

BURDON-SANDERSON, JOHN SCOTT (*b.* Jesmond, near Newcastle-on-Tyne, England, 21 December 1828; *d.* Oxford, England, 23 November 1905), *pathology, physiology.*

Burdon-Sanderson was the son of Richard Burdon, a onetime Oxford don who later severed his connection with the Church of England and became active in evangelical work, and Elizabeth Sanderson, daughter of Sir James Sanderson, M.P., a London merchant who was twice lord mayor of London. Intended by his family for the law, he early developed an interest in natural science. After private instruction at home, he entered the University of Edinburgh in 1847 to study medicine. Among the teachers who influenced him there were John Balfour, John Goodsir, and John Hughes Bennett. Upon graduating M.D. in 1851, he was awarded a gold medal for his thesis on the metamorphosis of the colored blood corpuscles.

In the autumn of 1851, Burdon-Sanderson traveled to Paris, where he studied chemistry in the laboratories of Charles Gerhardt and Charles Wurtz, and attended Claude Bernard's lectures on physiology. Late in 1852, he settled in London to practice medicine, and in August 1853 married Ghetal Herschell, daughter of the Rev. Ridley Herschell. In the same year, he was appointed medical registrar at St. Mary's Hospital, where he later served as lecturer on botany (1854–1855) and on medical jurisprudence

(1855–1862). He was medical officer of health for the parish of Paddington from 1856 to 1867 and inspector for the medical department of the Privy Council from 1860 to 1865. The duties attached to these positions led him into his first work in pathology. He also served on the staffs of the Brompton Hospital for Consumption (1859–1863; 1865–1871) and Middlesex Hospital (1863–1870).

About 1870, Burdon-Sanderson resigned his hospital appointments in order to devote himself exclusively to scientific research. In the same year, he was appointed professor of practical physiology and histology at University College, London, succeeding Michael Foster. In 1874 he succeeded William Sharpey as Jodrell professor of human physiology at University College and remained there until 1882, when he became the first occupant of the Waynflete chair of physiology at Oxford University. His appointment met with violent opposition from antivivisectionists at Oxford (he was notorious for having co-authored a guide to vivisection), and funds for a laboratory of physiology were secured only with great effort. He resigned the Waynflete chair in 1895 to become Regius professor of medicine at Oxford. During his tenure in this chair, several essential reforms were achieved, including the creation of a complete course in pathology and bacteriology.

Burdon-Sanderson's reputation in pathology resulted primarily from his pioneer experimental investigations of contagious diseases and the infective processes. These began with his demonstration in 1865 of the particulate nature of the infective agent in cattle plague and with his confirmation in 1867 of Jean Villemin's experiments on the inoculability of tuberculosis in animals. Although he was generally considered one of the leading exponents in England of the germ theory of disease, there is an ambiguity in his views that makes it difficult to summarize his position simply. In 1869, in his widely discussed work, "On the Intimate Pathology of Contagion," he confirmed Auguste Chauveau's conclusion that the contagium in vaccine lymph was particulate, since the aqueous portion of the lymph was inactive while the solid portion was active. At the same time, he suggested that the infective particles were probably "organised beings" which owed their pathogenicity to their organic development. But when he later demonstrated that bacteria were invariably present in septicemia and pyemia, he avoided the conclusion that the bacteria were directly causative; and as late as 1877 he held that "there is but one case [splenic fever] in which the existence of a disease germ has been established" (*Nature,* **17** [1877], 86). His cautious attitude toward the germ theory resulted from the conflicting nature of the evidence then available, and from his own tendency toward theoretical skepticism. Although not unreasonable, this caution obscures his position as a prophet of the germ theory.

In physiology Burdon-Sanderson's earliest work dealt with the effects of respiratory movements on the circulation (Croonian lecture, 1867), but he later devoted himself almost exclusively to electrophysiological investigations, most notably those on the leaf of *Dionaea muscipula* (the Venus's-flytrap). While experimenting on insectivorous plants for Charles Darwin in 1873, he found that a pronounced electrical current accompanied the familiar closing of the flytrap leaf after stimulation of its excitable hairs. He suggested that this current was indicative of rapidly propagated molecular changes in the leaf cells, and compared this process with the corresponding process in active animal muscle.

Like Michael Foster at Cambridge, Burdon-Sanderson was an important force in establishing physiology as an independent discipline in England. He urged the adoption of the experimental approach to pathology as well as to physiology, and from 1871 to 1878 he was professor superintendent of the newly created Brown Institution, the first laboratory for pathology in England. Among his students at University College, London, were William Bayliss, Francis Gotch, Victor Horsley, William Osler, and G. J. Romanes. The group that later worked under him at Oxford—although it included Gotch—was, in general, less eminent.

Burdon-Sanderson's versatile achievements brought him numerous honors. He was elected a fellow of the Royal Society in 1867, delivered its Croonian lecture on three occasions (1867, 1877, and 1899), and was awarded its Royal Medal in 1883. The Royal College of Physicians elected him a fellow in 1871, appointed him Harveian orator in 1878, and awarded him the Baly Medal in 1880. He was president of the British Association for the Advancement of Science in 1893, and was created a baronet in 1899.

BIBLIOGRAPHY

I. ORIGINAL WORKS. Burdon-Sanderson's early position on the germ theory of disease is best revealed in the following papers: "Introductory Report on the Intimate Pathology of Contagion," in *Twelfth Report of the Medical Officer of the Privy Council* [1869], Parliamentary Papers (London, 1870), pp. 229–256; "Preparations Showing the Results of Certain Experimental Inquiries Relating to the Nature of the Infective Agent in Pyaemia," in *Transactions of the Pathological Society*, **23** (1872), 303–308; remarks

in the discussion on the germ theory of disease, *ibid.*, **26** (1875), 284–289; and "The Occurrence of Organic Forms in Connection With Contagious and Infective Diseases," in *British Medical Journal* (1875), **1**, 69–71, 199–201, 403–405, 435–437. For his later position, see his "Croonian Lectures on the Progress of Discovery Relating to the Origin and Nature of the Infective Diseases," in *Lancet* (1891), **2**, 1027–1032, 1083–1088, 1149–1154, 1207–1211. The first announcement of his discovery of the electric current in *Dionaea* appeared in the *Report of the British Association*, **43** (1873), 133. The most elaborate accounts of his electrophysiological investigations of *Dionaea* and of muscle are "On the Electromotive Properties of the Leaf of Dionaea in the Excited and Unexcited States [1881]," in *Philosophical Transactions of the Royal Society*, **173** (1882), 1–55; and "Croonian Lecture on the Relation of Motion in Animals and Plants to the Electrical Phenomena Which Are Associated With It [1899]," in *Proceedings of the Royal Society*, **65** (1900), 37–64. Burdon-Sanderson edited *Handbook for the Physiological Laboratory* (London, 1873), which he wrote with E. Klein, Michael Foster, and T. Lauder Brunton; this was the first work of its kind in English. His letters and private papers are deposited in the library of University College, London.

II. SECONDARY LITERATURE. The basic source for Burdon-Sanderson's life and work is Lady [Ghetal] Burdon-Sanderson's *Sir John Burdon Sanderson: A Memoir, With Selections From His Papers and Addresses*, completed and edited by his nephew, J. S. Haldane, and his niece, E. S. Haldane (Oxford, 1911). This valuable book is an unusually good example of its genre. For other accounts, see Arthur MacNalty, in *Proceedings of the Royal Society of Medicine* (London), **47** (1954), 754–758; *British Medical Journal* (1905), **2**, 1481–1492; *Lancet* (1905), **2**, 1652–1655; and Francis Gotch, in *Dictionary of National Biography*, supp. 2, I (1912), 267–269; *Proceedings of the Royal Society* (London), **79B** (1907), iii–xviii; and *Nature*, **73** (1905–1906), 127–129. When seeking references to Burdon-Sanderson in indexes and catalogs, check under both surnames.

GERALD L. GEISON

BÜRG, JOHANN TOBIAS (*b.* Vienna, Austria, 24 December 1766; *d.* Wiesenau, Austria, 25 November 1834), *astronomy.*

His parents were poor, and Bürg was destined to become a craftsman, until he received a fellowship from the Imperial Commission for Education. At Vienna University he studied mathematics and astronomy under Triesnecker and Hell. He became a physics teacher at the lyceum of Klagenfurt, Carinthia, in 1791, and the following year he returned to Vienna as assistant at the university observatory. After 1802 Bürg traveled. For two years he was calculator at the observatory of Seebergen, near Gotha, under Zach. After his return to Vienna he worked again at the university observatory and became professor of mathematics and astronomy at the university in 1806. In the same year, in a competition of the Paris Academy, he received an award for his new lunar ephemerides (see below). He became a knight of the Order of Leopold in 1808. From that year on, Bürg suffered from progressive deafness. In 1813 he took a leave of absence from his teaching duties. He hoped to succeed Triesnecker at the observatory, but Littrow was chosen. Bürg retired in 1819. He lived in Vienna until 1825, when he moved to Wiesenau, Carinthia. He never married.

Bürg began his practical astronomical observations while still a university student. After his appointment as professor he cooperated in, and was adviser to, the survey of Austria, but his main interest was calculation. He worked on the Viennese ephemerides for many years and was coeditor with Triesnecker.

Bürg was one of the leading calculating astronomers of his time, and his most important work was the recalculation of lunar ephemerides. He improved Laplace's perturbation theory of the complicated motion of the moon by adding more terms of the perturbation function: for the influence of the sun—considered not as the central body but as a disturbing one—and for the oblateness of the earth. Thus he found in the secular motion of the moon a term with a period of about 180 years and an amount of 13.8″. Taking this into consideration and making use of more recent observations, Bürg's lunar ephemerides proved to be much more accurate than those of his predecessors. From 1813 to 1820 they formed the basis of the lunar ephemerides in the *Nautical Almanach* of the British Admiralty.

BIBLIOGRAPHY

I. ORIGINAL WORKS. Bürg's writings include *Ephemerides astronomicae anni 1794 [-1806] a Francesco de Paula Triesnecker . . . et Joanne Burg . . . supputatae* (Vienna, 1793–1805); and "Tables de la lune," in *Tables astronomiques publiées par le Bureau des Longitudes* (Paris, 1806). Shorter articles are in *Berliner astronomisches Jahrbuch; Monatliche Korrespondenz zur Beförderung der Erd- und Himmelskunde;* and *Zeitschrift für Astronomie und verwandte Wissenschaften.*

II. SECONDARY LITERATURE. Further information on Bürg may be found in Johann Volkamer von Ehrenberg, "Johann Tobias von Bürg," in *Carinthia,* **25** (1836), 66 ff.; Johann Steinmayr, S. J., "Die Geschichte der Universitäts-Sternwarte," pt. 3 (Vienna, ca. 1935), MS at observatory of University of Vienna; Constant von Wurzbach, in *Biographisches Lexikon des Kaiserthums Oesterreich,* pt. 2 (1857), 196–198; and Martin Wutte, "Zum Gedächtnis des Astronomen J. T. Bürg," in *Carinthia,* **124** (1934), 143 ff.

JOSEF MAYERHÖFER
THOMAS WIDORN

BURGER, HERMAN CAREL (*b.* Utrecht, Netherlands, 1 June 1893; *d.* Utrecht, 27 December 1965), *physics, medical physics.*

Burger was named for his father, a first engineer with the Dutch navy; his mother was Jeanne Marie Cecile Docen. He received his primary education at the school of the Moravian Brothers, Zeist, the Netherlands, and attended the State High School in Utrecht, from which he graduated in 1911. In 1912 Burger matriculated at the University of Utrecht, where he studied physics and mathematics. He received his Ph.D., *cum laude,* 31 May 1918. From 1918 until 1920 he was an assistant in theoretical physics in Utrecht, and for the following two years he worked at the physical laboratory of Philips Industries. In 1922 he returned to the University of Utrecht as chief assistant in the physics department, and from 1927 to 1950 he had the title of lecturer. From 1950 until 1963 Burger was professor of medical physics in Utrecht. (In 1926 Burger had been offered a professorship at the University of Delft; he preferred, however, to remain in Utrecht.) Burger was awarded an honorary doctorate by the University of Nijmegen in 1963, and in 1964 he received the Einthoven Medal from the University of Leiden. He was the first Dutch citizen to deliver the Einthoven lecture.

Burger had great faith in men, and was extremely loyal and helpful to friends and students; he was mild in his judgments when he could see good intentions but very hard when there were none. He had vacillated between physics and mathematics or medicine as a course of study; he chose the former but was delighted when he was able to combine all of them. His precise mind was receptive to all types of information, but he was strongly opposed to every form of superstition and unscientific reporting (see his reports on the divining rod, 1930 and 1960).

Burger's work, aside from his teaching, can be divided into two parts: that before and that after World War II. Before the war the emphasis in Burger's work was on intensity measurements and spectral analysis. In connection with the atomic theory of Bohr and Rutherford, the determination of the intensity of spectral lines was an important factor in further theoretical development. In Utrecht in the 1920's this kind of experimentation flourished as the result of the development of measuring apparatus: Moll and Burger refined apparatus for detecting radiation—vacuum thermoelements, the bolometer, and the galvanometer; Burger and Van Cittert experimented with high-resolution apparatus and studied the influence of the apparatus on the shape of the spectral line; and Ornstein and Burger worked with intensity measurements themselves. During this period Burger also worked on liquid crystals.

Burger's younger brother, Eduard, had been a physician for a number of years, and the scientific contact between them was very close. In 1938 Burger's brother made a study on vectorcardiography that led Burger to the second period of his lifework, medical physics. His interest was primarily in electrocardiography, especially vectorcardiography. He also studied heart sounds, ballistocardiography, pumping rate of the heart per minute, stenosis, and pulse-wave reproduction. Besides conducting these studies, for many years Burger taught elementary physics to medical, veterinary, and dental students, covering the application of physics to medicine. In later years his teaching was extended to medical students who were more advanced in their studies.

Under Burger's leadership the Foundation for Biophysics flourished in the postwar years because he established various working groups. He was also successful in bringing together professors and staff members interested in medical physics by organizing colloquia.

BIBLIOGRAPHY

Burger's works include *Oplossen en Groeien van Kristallen,* his Ph.D. dissertation (Utrecht, 1918); *Het Onderwijs in de Natuurkunde aan Studenten in de Geneeskunde* (Utrecht, 1923); *Leerboek der Natuurkunde,* 3 vols. (Groningen, 1920–1936), written with W. J. H. Moll; *Voorlopige Beschrijvingen van een vijftigtal natuurkundige Leerlingenproeven* (Groningen, 1929), written with W. Reindersma *et al.; Natuurkundige proeven voor Leerlingen* (Groningen, 1934–1937), written with W. Reindersma *et al.; Objektive Spektralphotometrie* (Brunswick, 1932), written with W. H. J. Moll and L. S. Ornstein; and *Heart and Vector* (1969), ed. by H. W. Julius, Jr. A survey of Burger's work from 1908 to 1933 appears in a work dedicated to Ornstein by his colleagues and pupils (Utrecht, 1933). This work contains approximately 50 titles of articles written by Burger, alone or with others, such as "Beziehung zwischen inneren Quantenzahlen und Intensitäten von Mehrfachlinien," in *Zeitschrift für Physik,* **23** (1924), 258–266, written with H. B. Dorgelo, also in the Ornstein survey, p. 98; *Leerboek der Natuurkunde,* R. Kronig, ed. (1947; 6th ed., 1962), ch. 12, trans. as *Textbook of Physics* (1954; 2nd ed., 1959), ch. 12; *Medische Physica* (Paris, 1949), written with G. C. E. Burger; *Grensgebied* (Amsterdam, 1952); "Het begrip Arbeid in Natuurkunde, Fysiologie, en Geneeskunde," Einthoven lecture, 1964, in *Leidse Voordrachten,* **42.** Burger also published a great many articles in scientific journals.

J. G. VAN CITTERT-EYMERS

BURGERSDIJK (or **Burgersdicius**), **FRANK** (*b*. Lier, near Delft, Netherlands, 3 May 1590; *d*. Leiden, Netherlands, 19 February 1635), *natural philosophy.*

Burgersdijk was a farmer's son. His elementary and secondary studies were at the Latin school of Amersfoort and the Delft Gymnasium (1606–1610). He matriculated at Leiden University as a philosophy student on 6 May 1610. Burgersdijk was a distinguished student, obtaining his doctorate in 1614. His first appointment was at the Protestant academy of Saumur, where he was professor of philosophy from 1616 to 1619; here he composed his *Idea philosophiae naturalis.* He returned to Leiden as professor of logic and ethics, and delivered his inaugural lecture, "De fructu et utilitate logices," in 1620. Burgersdijk was promoted to the chair of philosophy in 1628 and became a leading figure at the university, serving as rector (1629, 1630, 1634) and writing influential textbooks on natural philosophy, metaphysics, logic, ethics, and politics.

The reason for Burgersdijk's popularity is apparent from his first book, *Idea philosophiae naturalis,* which became the model for his later writings. His treatment of his subjects is clear, logical, concise, and well organized. The method of ordered studies that he adopted was designed to impart "solid erudition." Proceeding by his method of definition and division, he explored the whole of natural philosophy in twenty-six disputations, each of which was a series of *theses* that could be further studied by consulting the *pro* and *contra* authorities listed. A further collection of disputations was given in the *Collegium physicum.* On the problems of natural philosophy Burgersdijk was strikingly insensitive to the new science, being content to draw upon the neo-Scholastic commentators of the late sixteenth century. Although a Protestant himself, Burgersdijk drew predominantly from Catholic sources, showing particular liking for the Iberian authors Suárez, Periera, and Toletus, and the Coimbra commentaries. His conservatism in astronomy is illustrated by his simplified edition of Sacrobosco's *Sphaera.* He showed greater originality in the *Institutionum logicarum,* his most popular work, in which he sought a compromise between Aristotelian and Ramist logic, regarding as particularly important the roles of division and definition, which he considered equal to syllogism and method.

Burgersdijk's highly successful textbooks made him the dominant figure in the final stage of Dutch Scholasticism, and his authority extended to England and Germany. His textbooks held their place in the universities long after his ideas had been eclipsed by Cartesianism.

BIBLIOGRAPHY

I. ORIGINAL WORKS. Burgersdijk's works relating to natural philosophy are *Idea philosophiae naturalis sive methodus definitionum et controversarum physicarum* (Leiden, 1622; at least eight later eds.); *Institutionum logicarum libri duo* (Leiden, 1626; at least twenty-seven eds., nine pub. in England); *Institutionum logicarum synopsis* (Leiden, 1626), almost as popular as the preceding work; *Sphaera J. de Sacro-Bosco decreto in usum scholarum ejusdem provinciae recensita ut et latinitus et methodus emendata sit* (Leiden, 1626; two later eds.); *Collegium physicum in quo tota philosophia naturalis aliquot disputationibus perspicue et compendiose explicatur* (Leiden, 1632; four later eds.); and *Institutionum metaphysicarum libri II* (Leiden, 1640).

II. SECONDARY LITERATURE. Of the works given below, Dibon, Risse, and Wundt give assistance toward the compilation of a bibliography of Burgersdijk's words. See Paul Dibon, *La philosophie néerlandaise au siècle d'or*, I (Amsterdam, 1954), 96–120, 150–153; *Nieuw Nederlandisch biographisch Woordenboek, 1911–1937*, VII, 229; Wilhelm Risse, *Die Logik der Neuzeit*, I (Stuttgart–Bad Cannstatt, 1964), 515–520; and Max Wundt, *Die deutsch Schulmetaphysik des 17 Jahrhunderts* (Tübingen, 1939), pp. 87–89.

CHARLES WEBSTER

BÜRGI, JOOST (*b*. Liechtenstein, 28 February 1552; *d*. Kassel, Germany, 31 January 1632), *mathematics, astronomy*.

There is no precise account of Bürgi's youth. Most likely he received no systematic education, for he did not even know Latin, the scientific language of his time. From 1579 he was the court watchmaker to Duke Wilhelm IV, and he probably completed his education while working in the duke's observatory at Kassel. There he worked on the construction of several instruments, especially astronomical ones, and made astronomical observations, developing his skill, inventiveness, and accuracy. Bürgi also improved instruments for use in practical geometry. His proportional compasses competed with those of Galileo for priority, although both were probably no more than an improvement of devices already in use.

The fame of Bürgi's instruments, which made possible more accurate astronomical observations in the observatory at Kassel, drew the attention of scientists assembled at the court of Emperor Rudolf II, who tried to establish a science center in Prague and to enlist prominent European scientists. After the death of Wilhelm IV, Bürgi entered the service of Rudolf and became his court watchmaker, also holding this position under Rudolf's successors Matthias and Ferdinand II. He lived in Prague from about 1603 and became assistant to and computer for Kepler, who was working on the results of astronomical observations made by Tycho Brahe. Even after the imperial court moved to Vienna and the leading foreign scientists left Prague, and the Bohemian anti-Hapsburg

revolt was defeated (1620), Bürgi remained in Prague. Here he became scientifically isolated, which lessened the favorable response to his results. Shortly before his death (probably as late as 1631) Bürgi returned to Kassel.

In mathematics Bürgi was by no means a theoretician, but an indefatigable and inventive computer whose help Kepler appreciated. Bürgi's manuscript "Arithmetics" was taken to Pulkovo with Kepler's unpublished papers. In this manuscript Bürgi uses (probably independently of Stevin) the decimal point and sometimes substitutes a small arc for it. Starting from the method known as *regula falsi*, Bürgi also elaborated the method of approximate calculation of the roots of algebraic equations of higher degree. The need to make the tables of sines more precise led him to undertake this problem. His tables of sines, which have the difference $2''$, were never published, and not even the manuscript exists.

The computation of the tables of sines and the elaboration of astronomical data led Bürgi to an easier method of multiplying large numbers. From about 1584 he was engaged, like several other astronomers and computers in the sixteenth century, in the improvement of "prosthaphairesis," the method of converting multiplication into addition by means of trigonometrical formulas—for example, $\sin \alpha \cdot \sin \beta = 1/2[\cos(\alpha - \beta) - \cos(\alpha + \beta)]$. Later, possibly at the end of the 1580's, the idea of logarithms occurred to him. Although he did not know Stifel's *Arithmetica integra*, in which the idea of comparing arithmetic and geometric progression is outlined, Bürgi learned of it from other sources. He had computed the tables of logarithms before his arrival in Prague, but he did not publish them until 1620, under the title *Arithmetische und geometrische Progress-Tabulen, sambt gründlichem Unterricht, wie solche nützlich in allerley Rechnungen zu gebrauchen, und verstanden werden sol;* however, the instruction promised in the title remained in manuscript.

The geometrical progression begins with the value 100,000,000 and has the quotient 1.0001. A term of the arithmetical progression 0, 10, 20, 30, 40, $\cdots$ corresponds to each term of the geometrical series. The tables extend to the value 1,000,000,000 in the geometrical progression, with the corresponding value 230,270,022 in the arithmetic progression. Consequently, Bürgi's logarithms correspond to our so-called natural logarithms with the base e. By their arrangement they are in fact antilogarithmic, for the basic progressions are logarithms. This circumstance could have made the use and spread of the tables more difficult, but the fate of Bürgi's work was influenced much more by the disintegration of the scientific and cultural center in Prague after 1620. The Prague edition of the tables remained almost unnoticed, and only a few copies were saved; probably the only complete copy is kept, together with the handwritten "instruction," in the library at Danzig. Thus, Bürgi's greatest discovery had no apparent influence on the development of science.

BIBLIOGRAPHY

Bürgi's only published work is *Arithmetische und geometrische Progress-Tabulen, sambt gründlichem Unterricht, wie solche nützlich in allerley Rechnungen zu gebrauchen, und verstanden werden sol* (Prague, 1620), repr. in H. R. Gieswald, *Justus Byrg als Mathematiker und dessen Einleitung zu seinen Logarithmen* (Danzig, 1856).

There is neither a detailed biography nor an analysis of Bürgi's scientific work. Basic bibliographic data in the following works can be of use: G. Vetter, "Dějiny matematických věd v českých zemích od založení university v r. 1348 až do r. 1620" ("History of Mathematics in the Bohemian Lands From the Foundation of the University in 1348 until 1620"), in *Sborník pro dějiny přírodních věd a techniky* (Prague), **4** (1958), 87–88; and "Kratkii obzor razvitija matematiki v cheshtskikh zemliakh do Belogorskoi bitvy," in *Istoriko-matematicheskie issledovaniya*, **11** (Moscow, 1958), 49, 512; E. Voellmy, "Jost Bürgi und die Logarithmen," in *Beihefte zur Zeitschrift für Elemente der Mathematik*, no. 5 (1948); and E. Zinner, *Deutsche und niederländische astronomische Instrumente des 11.–18. Jahrhunderts* (Munich, 1956), pp. 268–276.

LUBOŠ NOVÝ

BURIDAN, JEAN (*b.* Béthune, France, *ca.* 1295; *d.* Paris, France, *ca.* 1358), *philosophy, logic, physics.*

Although Jean Buridan was the most distinguished and influential teacher of natural philosophy at the University of Paris in the fourteenth century, little is known of his personal life. He was born in the diocese of Arras, and went as a young cleric to study at the University of Paris, where he was first enrolled as a student in the College of Cardinal Lemoine and later became a member of the College of Navarre. It is probable that he obtained his master of arts degree soon after 1320, since a document dated 2 February 1328 mentions him as rector of the university in that year. Other documents, relating to benefices whose revenues provided his financial support and bearing the dates 1329, 1330, 1342, and 1348, describe him as a "very distinguished man," as a "celebrated philosopher," and as "lecturing at Paris on the books of natural, metaphysical, and moral philosophy." Two passages in his own writings indicate that at some date prior to 1334 he made a visit to

the papal court at Avignon and, on the way, climbed Mt. Ventoux in order to make some meteorological observations.

In 1340 Buridan was rector of the university for a second time, and in that year he signed a statute of the faculty of arts which censured certain masters for the practice of construing texts in a literal sense rather than in accordance with the intentions of the authors, warning that this practice gave rise to "intolerable errors not only in philosophy but with respect to Sacred Scripture." One of the articles of censure bears on a statement known to have been made by Nicolaus of Autrecourt, whose skeptical views on causal inferences were attacked by Buridan in his own writings. The last documentary mention of Buridan occurs in a statute dated 12 July 1358, where his name appears as witness to an agreement between the Picard and English nations of the university. It is not unlikely that he fell victim to the Black Plague, which in 1358 took the lives of many of those who had managed to survive its first outbreak in 1349.

Buridan was a secular cleric rather than a member of a religious order, and he remained on the faculty of arts to the end of his life without, apparently, seeking to obtain a degree in theology. In his lifetime he was held in high esteem by his colleagues, students, and ecclesiastical superiors; and for nearly two centuries after his death his teachings in natural philosophy and logic were of paramount influence in the universities of northern and eastern Europe. A document in the archives of the University of Cologne, dated 24 December 1425, speaks of the preceding century as "the age of Buridan," and when George Lockert, in 1516, edited one of Buridan's works, he stated that Buridan still ruled the study of physics at Paris. In later centuries, the story of the ass who starved to death because he could not choose between two equally desirable bundles of hay was attributed to Buridan, and another story, presumably legendary but perpetuated by the poet François Villon, related that Buridan had been involved in scandalous relations with the wife of Philip V of France and had, by the king's order, been tied in a sack and thrown into the Seine.

The extant writings of Buridan consist of the lectures he gave on subjects in the curriculum of the faculty of arts at Paris. In the fourteenth century this curriculum was based largely on study of the treatises of Aristotle, along with the *Summulae logicales* of Peter of Spain and other medieval textbooks of grammar, mathematics, and astronomy. Buridan composed his own textbook of logic, *Summula de dialectica*, as a "modern" revision and amplification of the text of Peter of Spain; he also wrote two treatises on advanced topics of logic, entitled *Consequentiae* and *Sophismata,* which are among the most interesting contributions to late medieval logic. All of his other works are in the form of commentaries and of critical books of *Questions* on the principal treatises of the Aristotelian corpus. The literal commentaries are extant only in the unpublished manuscript versions, but the books of *Questions* on Aristotle's *Physics, Metaphysics, De anima, Parva naturalia, Nicomachean ethics,* and *Politics* were published, along with Buridan's writings in logic, after the invention of the printing press.

The only modern edition of a work by Buridan is that of his *Questions* on Aristotle's *De caelo et mundo,* previously unedited, which appeared in 1942. Most of the printed editions represent the lectures Buridan gave during the last part of his teaching career, although earlier versions are to be found among the unpublished manuscript materials. Until a critical study of the manuscripts is made, however, there is no sure way of determining any order of composition for Buridan's works, nor of tracing the development of his thought over the thirty-odd years of his academic career.

Buridan made significant and original contributions to logic and physics, but as a philosopher of science he was historically important in two respects. First, he vindicated natural philosophy as a respectable study in its own right. Second, he defined the objectives and methodology of scientific enterprise in a manner that warranted its autonomy with respect to dogmatic theology and metaphysics; this achievement was intimately connected with the fourteenth-century movement known as nominalism and with the controversies precipitated at the universities of Oxford and Paris by the doctrines associated with William of Ockham. Buridan's own philosophical position was thoroughly nominalistic, and indeed very similar to that of Jean de Mirecourt, a theologian of Paris whose teachings were condemned in 1347 by the chancellor of the university and the faculty of theology. Buridan himself was able to escape the charges of theological skepticism that were directed against his fellow nominalists of the theological faculty. He owed his good fortune in part, no doubt, to his prudence and diplomacy. Primarily, however, he could ward off criticism for the fundamental reason that he employed the logical and epistemological doctrines of nominalism in a methodological, rather than a metaphysical, way in formulating the character and the evidential foundations of natural philosophy.

The formal logic presented in Buridan's *Summula de dialectica* is closely related, in topical structure and terminology, to the so-called terminist logic of the thirteenth century, represented by the textbooks of William of Sherwood and Peter of Spain. Although it presupposes the nominalist thesis that general terms are signs of individuals, and not of common natures existing in individuals, it does not exhibit any strong evidence of direct influence by the logical writings of Ockham; it may well have been developed independently of such influence on the basis of the modern logic (*logica moderna*) already well established in the arts faculties of Oxford and Paris. The doctrine of the supposition of terms, basic to this logic, is used in defining the functions of logical operators or syncategorematic signs in determining the truth conditions of categorical propositions of various forms and in formulating the laws of syllogistic inference, both assertoric and modal. Treatises on topical arguments, fallacies, and the demonstrative syllogism conclude the work.

Buridan's *Sophismata,* designed to constitute a ninth part of the *Summula,* apparently was written much later in his life, for it contains criticisms of the theory of propositional meanings, or *complexe significabilia,* which Gregory of Rimini introduced in 1344. This work presents a fully developed analysis of meaning and truth which corresponds closely to that of Ockham's *Summa logicae.* It goes beyond the work of Ockham, however, in presenting original and highly advanced treatments of the problem of the nonsubstitutivity of terms occurring in intensional contexts and the problem of self-referential propositions represented by the Liar paradox. Buridan's treatment of these problems exhibits a level of logical insight and skill not equaled until very recent times. His treatise *Consequentiae,* which develops the whole theory of inference on the basis of propositional logic, marks another high point of medieval logic, the significance of which has been appreciated only in the twentieth century.

Buridan's philosophy of science is formulated in his *Questions* on the *Metaphysics,* and is applied to the concepts and problems of natural science in his *Questions* on the *Physics.* The Aristotelian definition of science as knowledge of universal and necessary conclusions by demonstration from necessary, evident, indemonstrable premises is accepted. A sharp distinction is made, however, between premises in which the necessity is determined by logical criteria or by stipulated meaning of the terms, and those in which evidence rests on empirical confirmation and which are called necessary in a conditional sense, or "on the supposition of the common course of nature." Only in the latter sense do the principles of the natural sciences have evidence and necessity.

These principles are not immediately evident; indeed we may be in doubt concerning them for a long time.

But they are called principles because they are indemonstrable, and cannot be deduced from other premises nor be proved by any formal procedure; but they are accepted because they have been observed to be true in many instances and to be false in none.[1]

The significance of this theory of scientific evidence lies in its rejection of the thesis, held by most of the scholastic commentators on Aristotle, that the principles of physics are established by metaphysics and that they are necessary in the sense that their contradictories are logically or metaphysically impossible. This metaphysical interpretation of Aristotelian physics led Bishop Étienne Tempier and the faculty of theology at Paris to condemn, in 1277, doctrines taught by members of the arts faculty as truths necessary to philosophy, although contradictory to dogmas of the Christian faith. By construing the principles of the sciences of nature as inductive generalizations whose evidence is conditional on the hypothesis of the common course of nature, Buridan was able to concede the absolute possibility of supernatural interference with the natural causal order, and yet to exclude such supernatural cases as irrelevant to the purposes and methodological procedures of the scientific enterprise. Nicolaus of Autrecourt, demanding that scientific principles have absolute necessity and certainty, had argued that a science of nature based on causal laws established by inductive generalization had no evidence whatsoever, since it could not be known in any given instance whether or not God was producing an effect without a natural cause. Buridan refers to Nicolaus' position in these words:

It has hereby been shown that very evil things are being said by certain ones who seek to undermine the natural and moral sciences because absolute evidence is not possessed by most of their principles and conclusions, it being supernaturally possible for them to be rendered false. For in these sciences absolutely unconditional evidence is not required, and it is enough if we have conditional or hypothetical evidence of the kind described above.[2]

The conception of scientific enterprise formulated by Buridan as a means of justifying its pursuit within the framework of the Christian doctrine of divine omnipotence is the conception within which science has operated since the late seventeenth century. To make science compatible with Christian dogma, Buridan had to break its traditional ties with metaphysics and define its principles methodologically, in terms of their value in "saving the phenomena." He still encountered some theological difficulties in applying this method within the domain of physics, as did Galileo three centuries later; but after the time of Buridan, natural philosophy had its own legitimacy

and ceased to be either only a handmaiden of theology or a mere exposition of the doctrines of Aristotle.

The *Questions* composed by Buridan on problems raised in Aristotle's *Physics* and *De caelo et mundo* exhibit his application of these criteria of scientific method and evidence to the critical evaluation of Aristotle's theories and arguments and to the diverse interpretations of them offered by Greek, Moslem, and Christian scholastic commentators. The general scheme and conceptual framework of analysis, within which Aristotle's physics and cosmology are formulated, is accepted by Buridan as the working hypothesis, so to speak, of natural philosophy. But the scheme is not sacrosanct, and Buridan not infrequently entertains alternative assumptions as being not only logically possible but also possibly preferable in accounting for the observed phenomena. While the authority of Aristotle had often been challenged on the ground that his positions contradicted Christian doctrine, it had come, in Buridan's time, to be challenged on grounds of inadequacy as a scientific account of observed facts. Buridan's major significance in the historical development of physics arises from just such a challenge with respect to Aristotle's dynamic theory of local motion and from his proposal of an alternative dynamics which came to be known as the impetus theory.

An obvious weakness of Aristotle's dynamics is its inability to account for projectile motions, such as the upward motion of a stone thrown into the air after it has left the hand of the thrower. According to the assumptions of Aristotelian physics, such a motion, being violent and contrary to the natural movement of the stone toward the earth, required an external moving cause continuously in contact with it. Since the only body in contact with it is the air, Aristotle supposed that in some way the air pushes or pulls such a body upward. This feeble explanation drew criticism in antiquity and from medieval Moslem commentators and gave rise to a theory that the violent action of the thrower impresses on the stone a temporary disposition, of a qualitative sort, which causes it to move for a short time in the direction contrary to its nature. This disposition was called an impressed virtue (*virtus impressa*), and it was held to be self-expending and quickly used up because of its separation from its source. Franciscus de Marchia, a Franciscan theologian who taught at Paris around 1322, gave a full presentation of this theory, and it is likely that Buridan was influenced by it.

In treating of the problem of projectile motion in his *Questions* on Aristotle's *Physics* (VIII, question 12), Buridan expounded Aristotle's theory of propulsion by the air and rejected it with arguments similar to those that Marchia had used. His own solution was in some respects like that of Marchia, but in one crucial point it was strikingly different. The tendency of the projectile to continue moving in the direction in which it is propelled, which Buridan calls *impetus* rather than *virtus impressa,* is described as a permanent power of motion, which would continue unchanged if it were not opposed by the gravity of the projectile and the resistance of the air. "This impetus," he says in another discussion given in his *Questions* on the *Metaphysics,* "would endure forever [ad infinitum] if it were not diminished and corrupted by an opposed resistance or by something tending to an opposed motion."[3]

The suggestion given here of the inertial principle fundamental to modern mechanics is striking, as are some further uses that Buridan makes of the impetus concept in explaining the accelerated velocity of free fall, the vibration of plucked strings, the bouncing of balls, and the everlasting rotational movements ascribed to the celestial spheres by Greek astronomy. Buridan defines impetus in a quantitative manner, as a function of the "quantity of matter" of the body and of the velocity of its motion; thus, he seems to conceive of impetus as equivalent to what in classical mechanics is called momentum, defined as the product of mass and velocity. In treating the action of gravity in the case of freely falling bodies, Buridan construes this action as one imparting successive increments of impetus to the body during its fall.

> It must be imagined that a heavy body acquires from its primary mover, namely from its gravity, not merely motion, but also, with that motion, a certain impetus such as is able to move that body along with the natural constant gravity. And because the impetus is acquired commensurately with motion, it follows that the faster the motion, the greater and stronger is the impetus. Thus the heavy body is moved initially only by its natural gravity, and hence slowly; but it is then moved by that same gravity as well as by the impetus already acquired, and thus it is . . . continuously accelerated to the end.[4]

The effect of a force, such as gravity, is thus conceived of as a production of successive increments of impetus, or of velocity in the mass acted upon, throughout the fall. It is a short step from this to the modern definition of force as that which changes the velocity of the body acted upon, implying the correlative principle that a body in uniform motion is under the action of no force. Buridan does not quite take this step, since he retains the Aristotelian assumption that a constant cause must produce a constant effect, and ascribes the increase in velocity to the addition of impetus as an added cause acting along with the gravity.

Yet his theory obviously requires a distinction between impetus as a "conserving cause" of motion and gravity as a "producing cause" of the motion conserved by the impetus; his failure to draw the consequence of this distinction was perhaps because he did not attempt a mathematical analysis involving the concept of instantaneous velocities added continuously with time. Whether Buridan construed the acceleration as uniform with respect to time elapsed, or with respect to distance traversed, is not clear. He probably regarded the two functions as equivalent, a view that, however impossible from a mathematical point of view, was retained into the seventeenth century, when Descartes and Galileo (in his letter to Sarpi of 1604) sought to prove that velocity increases in proportion to time elapsed from the premise that velocity increases in direct proportion to distance of fall.

Buridan's concept of impetus is further distinguished from the modern inertial concept by the fact that he construes rotational motion at uniform angular velocity as due to a rotational impetus analogous to the rectilinear impetus involved in projectile motion. Galileo did likewise, and was in this respect nearer to Buridan than to Newton. But Buridan makes a striking use of his impetus concept, in its rotational sense, by arguing that since the celestial spheres posited by the astronomers encounter no external resistance to the rotational movements and have no internal tendency toward a place of rest (such as heavy and light bodies have), their uniform rotational motions are purely inertial and require no causes acting on them to maintain their motions. There is, therefore, no need to posit immaterial intelligences as unmoved movers of the heavenly spheres, in the manner that Aristotle and his commentators supposed. "For it could be said that God, in creating the world, set each celestial orb in motion . . . and, in setting them in motion, he gave them an impetus capable of keeping them in motion without there being any need of his moving them any more."[5] It was in this way, Buridan adds, that God rested on the seventh day and committed the motions of the bodies he had created to those bodies themselves.

It is clear that Buridan's impetus theory marked a significant step toward the dynamics of Galileo and Newton, and an important stage in the gradual dissolution of Aristotelian physics and cosmology. Buridan did not, however, exploit the potentially revolutionary implications of his analysis of projectile motion and gravitational acceleration, or generalize his impetus theory into a theory of universal inertial mechanics. Thus, in discussing the argument of Aristotle against the possibility of motion in a void, Buridan accepted the principle that the velocity of a natural motion in a corporeal medium is determined by the ratio of the motive force to the resisting force of the medium, so that if there were no resisting medium, the motion would be instantaneous. This is scarcely consistent with the analysis of gravitational acceleration as finite increments of impetus given to the falling body by its gravity, and Buridan made no effort to harmonize these two different approaches within a common theory.

In a question bearing on the *De caelo et mundo,* Buridan asks whether it can be proved that the earth is at rest, with the celestial spheres rotating around it, as Aristotle supposed. He states that many people of his time held it to be probable that the earth rotates on its own axis once a day and that the stellar sphere is at rest. And he adds that it is "indisputably true that if the facts were as this theory supposes, everything in the heavens would appear to us just as it now appears."[6] In support of the hypothesis, he invokes the principle that it is better to account for the observed phenomena by fewer assumptions or by the simplest theory, and argues that since the earth is a small body and the outer sphere is a very large one, it is more reasonable to attribute the rotation to the earth than to suppose the enormously faster rotation of the much larger sphere. After giving this and other arguments in favor of the theory of diurnal rotation of the earth, Buridan makes it quite clear that they cannot be refuted by any of the traditional arguments purporting to prove that the earth is at rest. He says that for his part he chooses to hold that the earth is at rest and the heavens in motion; and he offers, as a "persuasion" for this view, the argument that a projectile thrown straight upward from the earth's surface will fall back to the same spot from which it was thrown.

This argument does not seem consistent with Buridan's own impetus theory, unless he had in mind a point made later by his pupil Albert of Saxony, who held that the lateral impetus shared by the projectile with that of the surface of the rotating earth would be insufficient to carry it over the greater arc which it would have to traverse, when projected outward from the earth's surface, in order to fall back at the same spot. Not only Albert of Saxony, but also another pupil of Buridan's, Nicole Oresme, took over this discussion of the earth's rotation; Oresme concluded that it is impossible to prove either side of the question, since the motion is purely relative. Oresme said that he accepted the view that the earth is at rest, but only because this seemed to be assumed by the Bible. It is of interest to note that when Copernicus was a student at Cracow, Buridan's works in

physics were required reading in the curriculum of that university.

While rejecting the theory of the diurnal rotation of the earth, Buridan says that the earth is not immobile at the center of the world, and proves it as follows: Because the dry land protruding from the ocean is mostly on one side of the earth, the center of volume of the earth does not coincide with its center of gravity. The earth, however, is the center of the world in the sense that its center of gravity is equidistant from the inner surface of the celestial spheres. But this center of gravity is continuously altered by the erosion of the dry land, which slowly gets washed into the sea; and consequently the whole mass of the earth slowly shifts from the wet side to the dry side in order to keep its center of gravity at the center of the universe.

Buridan's significance in the history of science lies more in the questions he raised than in the answers he gave to them, although in some cases his answers opened up new theoretical possibilities that were undoubtedly influential in the rise of modern mechanics in the seventeenth century. The impetus theory was taken over by Buridan's pupils and was made known throughout central Europe, although in a degenerate form that fused it with the older theory of a self-expending *virtus impressa* and introduced a number of confusions and errors that Buridan himself had avoided. It was in this degenerate form that it was conveyed to Galileo by his teacher Buonamici, so that Galileo had to take the step that Buridan had taken three centuries earlier when he discarded Marchia's theory of the self-expending impressed force in favor of impetus as an enduring condition only changed or diminished by opposed forces. Buridan's application of the impetus concept to the analysis of free fall, although retained and made known by Albert of Saxony, was forgotten by most of the later teachers of physics, even when they retained the concept in dealing with projectile motion.

Even when Buridan's specific contributions to physical problems were forgotten, however, the influence of his conception of scientific evidence and method remained operative; and it may be said that the idea of mechanics, in the modern sense, became established in early modern times through the work of Buridan and of his contemporaries. In particular, Buridan may be credited with eliminating explanations in terms of final causes from the domain of physics, which he does very explicitly in his *Questions* on the *Physics* (II, questions 7 and 13) and in his *Questions* on the *De caelo et mundo* (II, question 8). The mechanistic conception of nature, construed as a methodological assumption more than as a metaphysical thesis, emerged in the fourteenth century as a natural development from Buridan's philosophy of science. He was not an experimental scientist or a mathematical physicist; but as a philosopher of science he did much to clear the way for, and to point the way to, the development of modern science in these directions.

NOTES

1. *Qu. in Metaph.* II, Qu. 2 (1518), fol. 9*v*.
2. *Ibid.,* Qu. 1 (1518), fol. 9*r*.
3. *Ibid.* (1518), fol. 73*r*.
4. *Qu. De caelo et mundo* (1942), 180.
5. *Qu. in Phys.* VIII, Qu. 12, fol. 121*r*.
6. *Qu. De caelo et mundo* II, Qu. 22 (1942), 227.

BIBLIOGRAPHY

I. ORIGINAL WORKS. Early editions of Buridan's works include *Quaestiones super decem libros Ethicorum Aristotelis ad Nicomacheum* (Paris, 1489, 1513, 1518; Oxford, 1637); *Sophismata Buridani* (Paris, 1489, 1491, 1493; best ed., by Antonius Denidel and Nicolaus de Barra, Paris, *ca.* 1495), trans. by Theodore K. Scott as *John Buridan: Sophisms on Meaning and Truth* (New York, 1966); *Summula de dialectica,* with commentary by John Dorp of Leiden (Lyons, 1490, 1493, 1495, 1510; as *Perutile compendium totius logicae Joannis Buridani,* Venice, 1499; there are many later editions); *Consequentiae Buridani* (Paris, 1493, 1495, 1499); *Quaestiones super octo physicorum libros Aristotelis,* ed. Johannes Dullaert Gandavensis (Paris, 1509, 1516); *Quaestiones et decisiones physicales insignium virorum . . . ,* ed. Georgius Lockert (Paris, 1516), which contains *Quaestiones in libros De anima, De sensu et sensato, De memoria et reminiscentia, De somno et vigilia, De longitudine et brevitate vitae,* and *De iuventate et senectute; In Metaphysicen Aristotelis quaestiones argutissimae magistri Joannis Buridani* (Paris, 1518); and *Quaestiones in octo libros Politicorum* (Paris, 1530; Oxford, 1640).

More recent editions are *Quaestiones super libris quattuor De caelo et mundo,* ed. E. A. Moody (Cambridge, Mass., 1942); and "Giovanni Buridano, Tractatus de suppositionibus," ed. Maria Eleina Reina, in *Rivista critica di storia della filosofia,* 12 (1957), 175–208, 323–352.

A list of manuscripts of Buridan's works, both published and unpublished, can be found in Edmond Faral, "Jean Buridan, Notes sur les manuscrits, les éditions et le contenu de ses oeuvres," in *Archives d'histoire doctrinale et littéraire du moyen-âge,* 15 (1946), 1–53.

II. SECONDARY LITERATURE. Works on Buridan include J. Bulliot, "Jean Buridan et le mouvement de la terre," in *Revue de philosophie,* 25 (1914), 5–24; Marshall Clagett, *The Science of Mechanics in the Middle Ages* (Madison, Wis., 1959), 505–599; E. J. Dijksterhuis, *De Mechanisering van het Werelbild* (Amsterdam, 1915); Pierre Duhem, *Études sur Léonard de Vinci,* II (Paris, 1909), 379–384, 420–423, 431–438, and III (Paris, 1913), 1–259, 279–286, 350–360;

Pierre Duhem, *Le système du monde,* Vols. VI–VII (Paris, 1954–1958); and Edmond Faral, "Jean Buridan, maître-ès-arts de l'Université de Paris," in *Histoire littéraire de la France,* 38 (1949), 462–605.

The following works of Anneliese Maier should be consulted: *Die Vorläufer Galileis im 14. Jahrhundert* (Rome, 1949); *Zwei Grundprobleme der scholastischen Naturphilosophie,* 2nd ed. (Rome, 1951), 201–235; *Metaphysische Hintergründe der spätscholastischen Naturphilosophie* (Rome, 1955), 300–335, 348 ff., 384 ff.; "Die naturphilosophische Bedeutung der scholastischen Impetustheorie," in *Scholastik,* 30 (1955), 321–343; and *Zwischen Philosophie und Mechanik* (Rome, 1958), 332–339.

Also of value are works by E. A. Moody: "John Buridan on the Habitability of the Earth," in *Speculum,* 16 (1941), 415–425; "Ockham, Buridan, and Nicholas of Autrecourt," in *Franciscan Studies,* 7 (June, 1947), 113–146; "Galileo and Avempace; The Dynamics of the Leaning Tower Experiment," in *Journal of the History of Ideas,* 12 (1951), 163–193, 375–422; *Truth and Consequence in Medieval Logic* (Amsterdam, 1953); and "Buridan and a Dilemma of Nominalism," in *Harry Austryn Wolfson Jubilee Volume* (Jerusalem, 1965), 577–596.

Additional works concerning Buridan are Karl Prantl, *Geschichte der Logik im Abendlande,* IV (Leipzig, 1870), 14–38; A. N. Prior, "Some Problems of Self-reference in John Buridan," in *Proceedings of the British Academy,* 48 (1962), 281–296; Maria Eleina Reina, "Note sulla psicologia di Buridano," in *Arti grafiche grisetti* (Milan, 1959), p. 9 ff.; Maria Eleina Reina, "Il problema del linguaggio in Buridano," in *Rivista critica di storia della filosofia,* 15 (1959), 367–417, and 15 (1960), 141–165, 238–264; Theodore K. Scott, "John Buridan on the Objects of Demonstrative Science," in *Speculum,* 40 (1965), 654–673; G. Federici Vescovini, "La concezione della natura di Giovanni Buridano," in *La filosofia della natura nel medievo: Atti del III Congresso Internazionale di Filosofia Medievale* (Milan, 1964); G. Federici Vescovini, *Studi sulla prospettiva medievale* (Turin, 1965), 137–163; James J. Walsh, "Buridan and Seneca," in *Journal of the History of Ideas,* 27 (1966), 23–40; and James J. Walsh, "Nominalism and the Ethics: Some Remarks About Buridan's Commentary," in *Journal of the History of Philosophy,* 4 (1966), 1–13.

ERNEST A. MOODY

BURLEY, WALTER (*b.* England, *ca.* 1275; *d. ca.* 1345?), *logic, natural philosophy.*

A colophon to the final version of Burley's commentary on the *Logica vetus* that is dated 1337 stipulates that the work was composed in its author's sixty-second year, a factor which places Burley's birth about 1275, possibly in one of the two towns named Burley in Yorkshire. Although almost nothing is known of his youth, it seems most reasonable to presume that Burley began his studies at Oxford sometime during the last decade of the thirteenth century, for two works dated 1301 and 1302 already designate him as a master in arts. He may have at this time also been a fellow of Merton College, although the first definite connection we have with Merton derives from the bursorial roll of 1305. It seems very probable that, during his regency in arts at Oxford, Burley composed his earliest versions (later to be revised and expanded) of expositions on almost all of Aristotle's works in logic, natural philosophy, and moral philosophy.

In 1310 (at the latest) we find him in Paris, where he began his theological studies, a stage in his career first definitely documented by his citation as *doctor sacre theologie* in a colophon dated 1324. We lack further information concerning Burley's work as a theologian and have thus far not been able to discover his *Commentary on the Sentences,* but his first treatise dealing with the intension and remission of forms (the so-called *Tractatus primus* written between 1320-1327) indicates that Thomas Wilton, also a former fellow of Merton College, was at some point his *socius* and master of theology in Paris.

Burley most likely remained in Paris until 28 February 1327, at which time he was appointed as an envoy of Edward III to the papal court. Indeed, the official connections Burley then began with English public figures seems to have continued, intermittently, for the remainder of his years. Yet this is not to say that this new phase to his career marked the end, or even a substantial lessening, of his academic pursuits. For, just as during his years in Paris, he continued to set down numerous logical and philosophical works.

In Bologna in 1341 for a disputation and again at Avignon in November 1343, our last document mentioning Burley is a register revealing his acquisition of a rectory in Kent on 19 June 1344. It seems unlikely that he lived much beyond that date.

In terms of the literary activity, Burley remained, throughout his career, fundamentally an arts graduate. For, if one sets aside his lost work on the *Sentences,* all but one or two items among the formidable mass of his writings deal with logic and philosophy. He was, to begin with, an Aristotelian commentator with a vengeance, composing two—sometimes three—different versions of a commentary on a single work.

Thus, he wrote commentaries on all of the Aristotelian logical books, including Porphyry's *Isagoge* and the *Liber de sex principiis* ascribed to Gilbert de la Porrée, apparently formulating an initial version of his comments during his earlier Oxford period. Many of the commentaries were later revised, the final version of his complete *Expositio super artem veterem* being written only in 1337. To this already

very substantial body of logical literature one must add Burley's numerous opuscula and treatises on the so-called *parva logicalia* (which constituted, in large part, medieval additions to the logic of Aristotle) and, in particular, the two redactions of his magnum opus in logic, the *De puritate artis logicae.* The earlier, shorter version of this work appears to have been composed (in incomplete form) before the appearance (*ca.* 1324) of the *Summa logicae* of William of Ockham. Indeed, the second version (1325-1328) of Burley's treatise can in many respects be viewed as a reply to some of Ockham's contentions. Yet it is not merely as an anti-Ockhamist tract that Burley's revised *De puritate artis logicae* is of importance; for, at least in the view of its modern editor, Philotheus Boehner, its implicit subsumption of syllogistic under the more general theory of consequences involving unanalyzed propositions strongly suggests Burley to have been a logician of appreciable competence.

As concerns natural philosophy once again one must begin by noting the extensive roster of Burley's Aristotelian commentaries: *Expositiones* or *Questiones* (and again often in multiple versions) on the *Physica, De caelo, De generatione et corruptione, Meteorologica, De anima, Problemata, Parva naturalia, De motu animalium, Metaphysica* (possibly), plus Averroës' *De substantia orbis.* Of these commentaries, those on the *Physics* are undoubtedly the most important. The earliest version appears to have been written at some point before 1316. Apparently also of an early date are the separate *Questiones* on the *Physics,* extant in a single (incomplete) manuscript (MS Basel, Universitätsbibliothek F.V.12). We are more fully informed, however, concerning Burley's definitive version of his comments on the *Physics:* Book I was finished in Paris in 1324, Books II-VI, again in Paris, by 1327, while the final redaction of Books VII-VIII was written between 1334-1337. Although this last effort which Burley devoted to the exposition and analysis of Aristotle's *Physics* contains, it appears, the most significant of his contributions to natural philosophy, at least some of what he has to offer here also appears, in more elaborate form, within various independent treatises and opuscula, most notably the *Tractatus de formis* (which contains his criticisms of Ockham's identification of substance and quantity), the quodlibetal question *De primo et ultimo instanti,* and his two treatises on the intension and remission of forms (resp. the *Tractatus primus* and *Tractatus secundus*).

Burley turned to moral philosophy and varia rather late in his life, completing his exposition of Aristotle's *Ethics* in 1333-1334 and of the *Politics* in 1340-1343. His immensely popular history of philosophers, the

De vita et moribus philosophorum, also appears to derive from the early 1340's.

If one excludes Burley's importance within the history of formal logic, it is clear that the very small segment of his voluminous work within natural philosophy which has hitherto received careful study makes any estimate of his significance for the history of later medieval science radically incomplete and tentative. Yet in spite of this, there are two of Burley's contentions which, to judge merely from the attention they received within the works of other medieval natural philosophers, are surely to prove of more than ephemeral importance: his view of the proper limits to be assigned temporal processes through the ascription of first or last instants, and his view of the nature of motion.

De primo et ultimo instanti. This brief treatise was a quodlibetal question disputed by Burley at Toulouse sometime before 1327. Its subject derived directly from Aristotle's discussion in the *Physics* (Book VI, ch. 5, and Book VIII, ch. 8) of the problem of first and last moments within a given change which occurred over a given time interval. Without unraveling Aristotle's treatment and proposed resolution of the puzzle, suffice it to say that Burley (and a multitude of other Scholastics as well) correctly focused upon the relevant variables within the problem as stated by Aristotle when they formulated what was to become a standard distinction concerning the first and last instants of a given temporal process or change. Briefly, the change may be limited intrinsically at both ends (*incipit et desinit*) by an instant which belongs to the temporal interval covering the change in question (*primum vel ultimum instans esse*), or limited extrinsically by a first or last instant which does not belong to the appropriate interval (*primum vel ultimum instans non esse*), in which case, of course, an *ultimum instans non esse* immediately precedes the time denominated by the change, while a *primum instans non esse* immediately follows it. Given this, in four *regulae* Burley explicitly stipulates the mutual exclusiveness of intrinsic and extrinsic instants as limits for both the beginning and the completion of a given change. The problem is then, however, to decide just which kinds of things can be said to begin or end by possessing just which kind (intrinsic or extrinsic) of limit. Although the many cases that Burley considers in making this decision involve complexities that cannot be expounded here, some notion of his procedure should be indicated. Thus, a *res successiva,* a given temporal motion or change or a time interval itself, can, following Aristotle, only have extrinsic limits at both ends. The same is true of a *res permanens* which depends in its being on a *res successiva* (the truth of the proposition "Socrates is running" is Burley's example of such a *res permanens,* since it depends on the existence of a given run of Socrates, which is a *res successiva*). On the other hand, intrinsic limits are naturally appropriate when a given permanent thing itself has only instantaneous existence. And Burley goes on to ascribe what he feels to be proper limits to other cases of *res permanentes* undergoing change, specifically to changes explicable in terms of the intension and remission of forms as viewed under his own special theory concerning the nature of such intension and remission.

On the Nature of Motion. Indeed, to state Burley's view with respect to this much discussed problem of motion is, in effect, to set forth the basis of his theory of intension and remission of forms, a theory most elaborately developed and expressed in his *Tractatus primus.* Some theorists, of whom Ockham is a prominent but not the earliest example, had argued that motion consists of nothing else besides the mobile and the place, quality, or quantity that it successively acquires. The form successively acquired was called (1) the *forma fluens.* Burley admitted that motion could be viewed in this way, but said that it could also be considered as (2) a flux (*fluxus formae*), or (3) a successive quantity. As a flux, motion was the acquisition of the terminus of motion or the transmutation by means of which the terminus was acquired. As a successive quantity, motion was the measure of the motion taken in the second (*fluxus*) sense. Motion as a *forma fluens* belonged to the same category as its terminus (place, quality, or quantity); as a *fluxus formae* it either belonged to or constituted the whole of the Aristotelian category of passions or affectations; as a successive quantity, it belonged to the category of quantity.

Why was it necessary, according to Burley, that motion be not only a *forma fluens* but also a flux? For Burley, places, qualities, and quantities were individual and simple. A body at a given time had only one place, one quality of a given type, and one quantity of a given type. In the case of quality, for example, the not uncommon assumption that a compound simultaneously contained both hot and cold combining to produce a single sensible result was to Burley not only false, it was self-contradictory. Qualities like hot and cold were for him sensible by definition. They were not hypothetical underlying realities without separate effect. It followed further, on this view, that one quality could not be part of another. Similar conclusions could be applied to place and quantity.

Since this was Burley's view of the forms to be acquired, his conception of the *forma fluens* theory could not be the same as Ockham's. Ockham spoke of *the* form acquired or *the* terminus of motion, and assumed that this final form somehow contained the forms acquired along the way. A single form was acquired part by part, and this was the *forma fluens.* For Burley, every instant of motion corresponded to a different form, and these forms were neither part of, nor contained in, the terminus of motion. The *forma fluens* was any one of these instantaneous forms, but no one of these forms could represent the whole motion since the terminus (with successive acquisition assumed) represented the whole motion for Ockham. To represent more than an instant within a motion, Burley needed another existential referent. He might have chosen the entire collection of instantaneous *formae fluentes.* Durand of St. Pourcain did just this, saying that the continuity of these forms unified them (cf. Maier, *Studien,* II, 70–73). For Burley, the forms, analogous to points, could not be continuous, and hence could not be treated as a unity. As a unified referent he chose instead the means by which the forms were acquired, i.e., the transmutation or flux. The *forma fluens* conception, he admitted, was truer to the physical reality of motion (*entitas rei*), but the *fluxus formae* conception was truer to the significance of the term "motion" (*Physics,* Bk. III, Text 4).

If Burley's views of motion are typical of other parts of his physics as yet less well-known, the motivation for his conclusions was not simply a willingness to multiply entities beyond necessity, but also his view of forms as empirical, simple, and separate, and his refusal to assume hypothetical connections between them.

BIBLIOGRAPHY

I. LIFE AND WRITINGS. The three fundamental articles are A. B. Emden, *Biographical Register of the University of Oxford to A.D. 1500* (Oxford, 1957–1959), I, 312–314; Conor Martin, "Walter Burley," in *Oxford Studies Presented to Daniel Callus* (Oxford, 1964), pp. 194–230; J. A. Weisheipl, "Ockham and Some Mertonians," in *Mediaeval Studies,* **30** (1968), 174–188. Father Weisheipl will also shortly publish his "Repertorium Mertoniense" in a future volume of *Mediaeval Studies,* which will include a complete list, together with editions and extant manuscripts, of Burley's works. Cf. Zofia Wlodek, "Les traités de Walter Burleigh dans les manuscrits des bibliothèques en Pologne," in *Mediaevalia philosophica polonorum,* **11** (1963), 152–156.

II. TEXTS OF BURLEY'S WORKS. *Early Printed Editions and Manuscripts.* (Note: Only selected early editions and a few MSS of works important within the history of science are listed; see Weisheipl's forthcoming "Repertorium

Mertoniense" for a complete listing.) *Expositio super artem veterem* (final version completed 1337; Venice eds., 1481, 1497, 1519). *Expositio super libros duos posteriorum analyticorum* (Venice, 1497). *De sophismatibus,* in St. Bonaventure, *Opera omnia* (Bassani, 1767), cols. 467 ff. *Tractatus de universalibus realibus* (Venice, 1492–1493). *Expositio librorum physicorum,* the definitive version (Venice, 1482, 1491, 1501; Bologna, 1589). *Expositio librorum physicorum* (early, pre-1316 version), MS Cambridge, Gonville & Caius 448/409, pp. 172–543. *Questiones super libros physicorum* (also early; incomplete, Books I–IV only), MS Basel, Universitätbibliothek, F.V.12, ff. 108r–171v. *Expositiones super libros:* (1) *De anima;* (2) *Parva naturalis;* (3) *De generatione et corruptione;* (4) *De caelo;* (5) *De substantia orbis;* (6) *De motu animalium,* MS Vat. lat. 2151, 1r–108v, 149r–256r. *Tractatus de formis,* MSS Vat. lat. 2151, ff. 131r–148r; Vat. lat. 2146, ff. 235r–244v. *Tractatus de potentiis anime,* MS Vat. lat. 2146, ff. 252v–256v. *Tractatus primus (sive Tractatus de activitate, unitate et augmento formarum activarum habentium contraria suscipientium magis et minus),* MS Vat. lat. 817, ff. 203r–223r. *Tractatus secundus (sive Tractatus de intensione et remissione formarum)* (Venice, 1496). *Opuscula varia,* MSS Vat. lat. 2146, ff. 235r–256v; Lambeth Palace 70, ff. 8r–306r. *Expositio librorum ethicorum* (Venice, 1481, 1500).

Modern Editions. See *De puritate artis logicae, Tractatus longior, With a Revised Edition of the Tractatus Brevior,* Philotheus Boehner, ed. (New York, 1955). Part 1 of Tractatus II of the *Tractatus longior* was republished, together with a brief introduction and an English translation, by Ivan Boh, "Burleigh: On Conditional Hypothetical Propositions," in *Franciscan Studies,* **23** (1963), 4–67. "*De primo et ultimo instanti,*" Herman and Charlotte Shapiro, eds., in *Archiv für Geschichte der Philosophie,* **47** (1965), 157–173. Shapiro has also published—sometimes with the assistance of others—editions of the following brief opuscula of Burley: "*De relativis,*" in *Franciscan Studies,* **22** (1962), 155–171; "*De qualitatibus,*" in *Franziskanische Studien,* **45** (1963), 256–260; "*De ente,*" in *Manuscripta,* **7** (1963), 103–108; "*De deo, natura et arte,*" in *Medievalia et humanistica,* **15** (1963), 86–90; "*De diffinitione,*" in *Mediaeval Studies,* **27** (1965), 337–340; "*De potentia activa et passiva,*" in *Modern Schoolman,* **43** (1966), 179–182; "*De toto et parte,*" in *Archives d'histoire doctrinale et littéraire du moyen age,* **24** (1966), 299–303; and "*De sensibus,*" in *Mitteilungen des Grabmann-Institutes der Universität München,* Heft 13 (Munich, 1966). *De vita et moribus philosophorum* has been edited, together with an old Spanish translation, by H. Knüst (Tübingen, 1886); cf. J. O. Stigall, "The Manuscript Tradition of the *De vita et moribus philosophorum* of Walter Burley," in *Medievalia et humanistica,* **11** (1957), 44–57, and J. N. Hough, "Platus, Student of Cicero, and Walter Burley," *ibid.,* pp. 58–68.

III. SECONDARY LITERATURE. A. *Logic.* Philotheus Boehner's high opinion of Burley as a logician is succinctly stated in his *Medieval Logic. An Outline of Its Development from 1250 to c. 1400* (Chicago, 1952), pp. 44–51, 84–89. This opinion, seemingly shared by Boh (*vide supra et infra*), has been criticized by L. Minio-Paluello in *Oxford Maga-*

zine, **71** (1953), 200–201. A. N. Prior, "On Some *Consequentiae* in Walter Burleigh," in *New Scholasticism,* **27** (1953), 433–446. Ivan Boh, "A Study in Burleigh: *Tractatus de regulis generalibus consequentiarum*," in *Notre Dame Journal of Formal Logic,* **3** (1962), 83–101; "Walter Burleigh's Hypothetical Syllogistic," *ibid.,* **4** (1963), 241–269; "An Examination of Some Proofs in Burleigh's Propositional Logic," in *New Scholasticism,* **38** (1964), 44–60. Ernest A. Moody, *Truth and Consequence in Mediaeval Logic* (Amsterdam, 1953), *passim.*

B. *Natural Philosophy and General.* Absolutely fundamental are the five volumes of Anneliese Maier's *Studien zur Naturphilosophie der Spätscholastik,* which contain numerable expositions and analyses of aspects of Burley's work within the context of similar material as treated by other late medieval Scholastics: I. *Die Vorläufer Galileis im 14. Jahrhundert,* 2nd ed. (Rome, 1966); II. *Zwei Grundprobleme der scholastischen Naturphilosophie,* 3rd ed. (Rome, 1968); III. *An der Grenze von Scholastik und Naturwissenschaft,* 2nd ed. (Rome, 1952); IV. *Metaphysische Hintergrunde der spätscholastischen Naturphilosophie* (Rome, 1955); V. *Zwischen Philosphie und Mechanik* (Rome, 1958).

Other articles by Maier also directly concerned with Burley are "Zu Walter Burleys Politik-Kommentar," in *Recherches de théologie ancienne et médiévale,* **14** (1947), 332–336; "Zu einigen Problemen der Ockhamforschung," in *Archivum Franciscanum historicum,* **46** (1953), 181–194; "Handschriftliches zu Wilhelm Ockham und Walter Burley," *ibid.,* **48** (1955), 234–251; "Ein unbeachteter 'Averroist' des XIV Jahrhunderts: Walter Burley," in *Medioevo e rinascimento: Studi in onore di Bruno Nardi* (Florence, 1955), 477–499; "Zu Walter Burleys Traktat *De intensione et remissione formarum*," in *Franciscan Studies,* **25** (1965), 293–321. Maier has included these articles (save the last), together with addenda, in her *Ausgehendes Mittelalter: Gesammelte Aufsätze zur Geistesgeschichte des 14. Jahrhunderts,* 2 vols. (Rome, 1964–1967).

See also L. Baudry, "Les rapports des Guillaume d'Occam et de Walter Burleigh," in *Archives d'histoire doctrinale et littéraire du moyen âge,* **9** (1934), 155–173; A. Koyré, "Le vide et l'espace infini au XIVe siècle," *ibid.,* **17** (1949), 75–80; three articles of S. H. Thomson, "Walter Burley's Commentary on the *Politics* of Aristotle," in *Mélanges Auguste Pelzer* (Louvain, 1947), pp. 557–579; "An Unnoticed *Questio theologica* of Walter Burley," in *Medievalia et humanistica,* **6** (1950), 84–88; "Unnoticed *questiones* of Walter Burley on the *Physics,*" in *Mitteilungen des Instituts für österreichische Geschichtsforschung,* **62** (1954), 390–405; four articles by H. Shapiro, "Walter Burley and Text F1," (i.e. of Book IV of the *Physics*), in *Traditio,* **16** (1960), 395–404; "Walter Burley and the Intension and Remission of Forms," in *Speculum,* **34** (1959), 413–427 (use in conjunction with Anneliese Maier on the same topic); "A Note on Walter Burley's Exaggerated Realism," in *Franciscan Studies,* **20** (1960), 205–214; "More on the 'Exaggeration' of Burley's Realism," in *Manuscripta,* **6** (1962), 94–98.

A brief treatment of Burley's view on first and last

instants, together with other late Scholastic discussion of the same problem, may be found in Curtis Wilson, *William Heytesbury: Medieval Logic and the Rise of Mathematical Physics* (Madison, Wis., 1956), pp. 29–56.

John Murdoch
Edith Sylla

BURNET, THOMAS (*b.* Croft, Yorkshire, England, *ca.* 1635; *d.* London, England, 27 September 1715), *cosmogony, geology.*

Little is known of Burnet's family or early childhood other than that his father was John Burnet and that he attended the Freeschool of Northallerton, where he attracted the attention of his teacher, Thomas Smelt. In 1651 he was admitted as pensioner at Clare Hall, Cambridge. Although he was officially a student of William Owtram's and closely associated with John Tillotson, he was most influenced by Ralph Cudworth. Sometime after receiving his bachelor's degree in 1655, Burnet followed Cudworth to Christ's College, became a fellow of the college in 1657, and received his M.A. in 1658. He became proctor of the college in 1667 and remained listed as a fellow until 1678, even though he was not in residence all of that time. While at Cambridge, Burnet worked closely with the Cambridge Platonists, especially Cudworth and Henry More. In 1671 he went abroad as governor to the young earl of Wiltshire and later made a second tour of Europe with the grandson of the duke of Ormonde, the earl of Orrery. During his travels he started writing his theory of the earth, the first two parts of which he completed soon after his return to England.

Burnet published these two parts, the books concerning the Deluge and Paradise, under the title *Telluris theoria sacra* in Latin in 1681 and produced an English version in 1684. The immediate reaction to the book was favorable. Many praised the style and thought; a few questioned the theory. In 1685 Burnet, who had been ordained in the Anglican Church, was made Master of the Charterhouse at the recommendation of the duke of Ormonde. In 1686, when the king tried to have Andrew Popham, a Roman Catholic, admitted as a pensioner at the Charterhouse, Burnet effectively opposed the appointment. Shortly after William III ascended the throne, Burnet became chaplain in ordinary to the king and clerk of the closet.

During this time *The Sacred Theory of the Earth* had become a subject of controversy. Christianus Wagner, Herbert Crofts, bishop of Hereford, and Erasmus Warren attacked it. For a time Burnet ignored the criticisms, then answered by expanding his theory. In 1689 he published a new Latin edition containing two additional books, and in 1691 he completed a similar English edition that included his "Review of the Theory of the Earth" and a reply to Warren's objections.

The Sacred Theory of the Earth was Burnet's attempt to combine the idealism of the Cambridge Platonists, Scripture, and an explanation of the features of the earth's surface in order to account for the past and present states of the earth and to offer a prophecy about its future. He believed that there were four major events in the earth's history: its origin from chaos, the universal deluge, the universal conflagration, and the consummation of all things. The first two of these had already happened; the last two were yet to come. These four events divided the history of the earth into three periods. The first, from the Creation to the Deluge, Burnet described as the state of paradise and the antedeluvian world. This earth differed in form and constitution from the present earth. Its surface, which covered the waters and a great abyss, was smooth, regular, and uniform, without mountains or seas. The material of this surface was moist, oily earth suitable to sustain living things. When the surface caved into the abyss, an event due to the continued drying action of the sun, and was no longer smooth, the fluctuations of the waters over this irregular earth caused the universal deluge. This marked the end of the first period.

The second, or present, era was for Burnet the age between the Deluge and the Conflagration. During this time the surface and interior of the earth undergo slow but continual change and thus, when the time comes in the plan of Divine Providence, the earth will be ready and able to burn. The final period, that of the millennium, is the era following the universal conflagration, when there will be a new heaven and a new earth in which the blessed will enjoy a life of peace and tranquillity. At the end of the millennium the earth will be changed into a bright star, and the consummation of all things predicted in Scripture will be fulfilled.

The expanded theory occasioned more controversy and more replies from Burnet. In 1692 he attempted to reconcile the account of creation in Genesis with his theory in *Archaelogiae philosophicae*. This book aroused such opposition for its allegorical treatment of Scripture that Burnet, although he had dedicated the book to William III, was forced to resign his position at court. He retired to the Charterhouse and remained there until his death. He was buried in the vault of the Charterhouse chapel a week after he died.

Burnet spent the last years of his life writing in defense of his theory. Most of the attacks upon it were upon religious grounds. Warren, Crofts, John Beaumont, and others accused him of a too liberal or allegorical interpretation of Scripture or of eliminating the necessity of God's working in the universe. John Keill, however, attacked the Cartesian mechanical basis of the theory and refuted it in terms of Newtonian mechanics. In his replies to these, Burnet either reiterated his own interpretation of Scripture or, when unable to refute a logical or mathematical argument against him, pointed out a minor inconsistency in his opponent's work. In his later, minor writings, he applied his method of scriptural interpretation to theological questions.

Burnet's importance in the history of scientific thought is due less to his theory itself than to certain aspects of it that became standards in the then growing science of geology. For more than a hundred years after Burnet, writers discussing the origin of and changes in the surface of the earth felt impelled to reconcile their theories with the account of creation in Genesis. His emphasis on the importance of the Deluge and on the explanation of the formation of mountains continued in geologic writings. Finally, Burnet's style was such that *The Sacred Theory of the Earth* was considered readable long after his death and the ideas expressed in it were widely disseminated. Whether accepted or ridiculed, the theory helped popularize the idea that the features of the earth's surface were constantly changing.

BIBLIOGRAPHY

I. ORIGINAL WORKS. Burnet's writings are *Telluris theoria sacra* (London, 1681, 1689, 1702; Amsterdam, 1694, 1699), trans. into English as *The Sacred Theory of the Earth* (London, 1684, 1690–1691, 1697); and *Archaelogiae philosophicae* (London, 1692, 1728), trans. into English as *The Ancient Doctrine Concerning the Originals of Things* (London, 1692 [this contains only chs. 7–10 of Bk. 2], 1729, 1736).

Burnet's replies to works about *The Sacred Theory of the Earth* are *An Answer to the Exceptions Made by Mr. Erasmus Warren, Against the Sacred Theory of the Earth* (London, 1690); *A Review of the Theory of the Earth and of Its Proofs: Especially in Reference to Scripture* (London, 1690); *A Short Consideration of Mr. Erasmus Warren's Defense of His Exceptions Against the Theory of the Earth. In a Letter to a Friend* (London, 1691); *Some Reflections Upon the Short Considerations of the Defense of the Exceptions Against the Theory of the Earth* (London, 1692); and *Reflections Upon the Theory of the Earth, Occasioned by a Late Examination of It. In a Letter to a Friend* (London, 1699).

Other works by Burnet are *De statu mortuorum et resurgentium liber. Accessit epistola (ad virum clarissimum A.B.) circa libellum de archaelogiis philosophicis* (London,

1720), trans. into English as *Of the State of the Dead and of Those That Are to Rise* (partial ed., London, 1727; complete ed., 1728); *De fide et officiis Christianorum* (London, 1722), trans. into English as *The Faith and Duties of Christians* (London, 1728); *De future Judaeorum restauratione* (London, 1727), an appendix to the 1727 ed. of *De statu mortuorum*; and *A Re-survey of the Mosaic System of the Creation With Rules for the Right Judging and Interpreting of Scripture. In Two Letters to a Friend* (London, 1728).

Works published anonymously but credited to Burnet are *Remarks Upon an Essay Concerning Humane Understanding* [by J. Locke] *in a Letter Addressed to the Author* (London, 1697); *Second Remarks Upon an Essay Concerning Human Understanding. In a Letter Address'd to the Author: Being a Vindication of the First Remarks Against the Answer of Mr. Locke at the End of His Reply to the Bishop of Worcester* (London, 1697); *Third Remarks Upon an Essay Concerning Human Understanding. In a Letter Addressed to the Author* (London, 1699); and *An Appeal to Common Sense: or, a Sober Vindication of Dr. Woodward's State of Physick. By a Divine of the Church of England* (London, 1719).

II. Secondary Literature. Marjorie Hope Nicolson, *Mountain Gloom and Mountain Glory: The Development of the Aesthetics of the Infinite* (Ithaca, N.Y., 1959), pp. 184–270, concerns Burnet and his work.

There is no bibliography on Burnet, but the following works on *The Theory of the Earth* may be helpful: John Beaumont, "Considerations on a Book Entitled The Theory of the Earth Published Some Years Since by the Learned Dr. Burnet," in *Philosophical Transactions*, **17** (Sept. 1693), 888–892, and *A Postscript to a Book Entituled Considerations on Dr. Burnet's Theory of the Earth* (London, 1694); Herbert Crofts, *Some Animadversions Upon a Book Intituled the Theory of the Earth* (London, 1685); Robert Hooke, "Animadversions on Burnet's Theory, 1689," MS at the Royal Society, London; John Keill, *An Examination of Dr. Burnet's Theory of the Earth, Together With Some Remarks on Mr. Whiston's New Theory of the Earth* (Oxford, 1698), and *An Examination of the Reflections on the Theory of the Earth Together With a Defense of the Remarks on Mr. Whiston's New Theory* (Oxford, 1699); Melchoir Leydekker, *M. Leydeckeri de republica Hebraeorum . . . subjicitur archaelogia sacra, qua historia creationis et diluvii Mosica contra Burneti profanam telluris theoriam asseritur* (Amsterdam, 1704); Archibald Lovell, *A Summary of Material Heads Which May Be Enlarged and Improved into a Compleat Answer to Dr. Burnet's Theory of the Earth* (London, 1696); Matthew Mackaile, *Terrae prodromus theoricus. Containing a Short Account of the New System of Order and Gradation, in the World's Creation. By Way of Animadversions Upon Mr. T. Burnet's Theory of His Imaginary Earth, etc.* (Aberdeen, 1691); Robert St. Clair, *The Abyssinian Philosopher Confuted; or, Telluris theoria Neither Sacred nor Agreeable to Reason* (London, 1697); Christianus Wagner, *Animadversions in . . . T. Burnetii Telluris theoriam sacram, etc.* (Leipzig, n.d.); and Erasmus Warren, *Geologia; or, a Discourse Concerning the Earth Before the Deluge, Wherein the Form and Properties Ascribed to It, in a Book Intituled the Theory of the Earth, Are Excepted Against and It Is Made to Appear That the Dissolution of That Earth Was Not the Cause of the Universal Flood* (London, 1690); *A Defense of the Discourse Concerning the Earth Before the Flood: Being a Full Reply to a Late Answer to Exceptions Made Against the Theory of the Earth, etc.* (London, 1691); and *Some Reflections Upon the Short Consideration of the Defense of the Exceptions Against the Theory of the Earth* (London, 1692).

Suzanne Kelly

BURNHAM, SHERBURNE WESLEY (*b.* Thetford, Vermont, 12 December 1838; *d.* Chicago, Illinois, 11 March 1921), *astronomy.*

Burnham, an indefatigable observer, was a self-trained amateur astronomer. His formal education ended with his graduation from Thetford Academy. He then became an accomplished shorthand reporter and, except for six months spent at the Washburn Observatory and four years at the Lick Observatory, worked full time in law courts until his retirement at age sixty-four in 1902. From 1897 to 1914 Burnham was professor of practical astronomy at the Yerkes Observatory, living in Chicago and commuting to Williams Bay, Wisconsin, for two nights each week to use the forty-inch telescope. For his astronomical work Burnham was honored by the Royal Astronomical Society (member, 1874; associate, 1898; Gold Medal, 1894) and the Académie des Sciences (Prix Lalande, 1904), and by Yale (M.A., 1878) and Northwestern (Sc.D., 1915) universities.

Burnham's significant contributions to the study of double stars were the discovery of numerous visual binary systems, the measurement of their separation and position angles, and a critical compilation of information concerning all known northern pairs. When Burnham began observing in 1870, it was commonly assumed that the Struves and Herschels had found most of the binaries visible in the Northern Hemisphere. With the aid of excellent telescope lenses figured by Alvan Clark & Sons, as well as extraordinarily keen vision, Burnham proved otherwise. Indeed, many of his discoveries were new companions of stars or star systems that had already been carefully scrutinized. The culmination of these efforts came in 1900, with the publication of *A General Catalogue of 1290 Double Stars Discovered from 1871 to 1899 by S. W. Burnham.*

Burnham devoted most of his time at large telescopes to measuring difficult pairs—those with separations less than 1″ and those of unequal magnitudes. He also measured the positions of components of suspected binaries relative to background stars for evidence of common proper motion, and hence of physical relation. For these measurements Burnham designed and used a filar micrometer with greatly improved bright-wire illumination. To help identify his discoveries Burnham compiled, and finally published, *A General Catalogue of Double Stars Within 121° of the North Pole,* the first comprehensive and critical survey of all (13,665) known binaries in this region.

BIBLIOGRAPHY

I. ORIGINAL WORKS. Burnham's writings include "The Position Micrometer of the Washburn Observatory," in *English Mechanic,* **34** (1881), 39–40; *A General Catalogue of 1290 Double Stars Discovered from 1871 to 1899 by S. W. Burnham, Arranged in Order of Right Ascension with all the Micrometrical Measures of Each Pair,* Publications of the Yerkes Observatory, no. 1 (Chicago, 1900), the introduction to which includes an often-quoted autobiography and references to his nineteen original lists of double stars; *A General Catalogue of Double Stars Within 121° of the North Pole,* Carnegie Institution Publication no. 5 (Washington, D.C., 1906); and *Measures of Proper Motion Stars Made with the 40-Inch Refractor of the Yerkes Observatory in the Years 1907 to 1912,* Carnegie Institution Publication no. 168 (Washington, D.C., 1913).

II. SECONDARY LITERATURE. Works on Burnham consist primarily of obituaries written by his colleagues and published in various astronomical journals.

DEBORAH JEAN WARNER

BURNSIDE, WILLIAM (*b.* London, England, 2 July 1852; *d.* West Wickham, England, 21 August 1927), *mathematics.*

Burnside's research was in such diverse fields as mathematical physics, complex function theory, geometry, group theory, and the theory of probability. On the basis of his work in the first two fields, he was elected a fellow of the Royal Society in 1893. It was to the theory of groups, however, that he made his most significant contributions. The beginnings of an interest in groups can be detected in papers of 1891 and 1892, in which groups of linear fractional transformations of a complex variable are involved. By 1894 the theory of groups of finite order had become the central concern of much of his research, and for the next twenty years Burnside remained one of the most active contributors to its development. A number of his results have become an integral part of the modern theory of groups and their representations.

With the hope of stirring up interest in group theory in England, Burnside published his *Theory of Groups* in 1897. It was the first treatise on groups in English and also the first to develop the theory from the modern standpoint of abstract groups vis à vis permutation groups, although this approach had already been pioneered by H. Weber in his *Lehrbuch der Algebra* (1896). One topic Burnside excluded from his book was that of linear groups, because it did not seem that any result could be obtained most directly by considering linear transformations. This opinion soon became outdated, however, with G. Frobenius' development of the theory of group representations and characters (1896–1899), and Burnside was one of the first to recognize the importance of Frobenius' ideas and to contribute to their development, simplification, and application.

Using group characters, Burnside was able to prove, for example, that every transitive group of prime degree is either solvable or doubly transitive (1901) and that every group of order $p^a q^b$ (p and q prime) is solvable (1904). The latter result greatly extended results of Sylow ($b = 0$, 1872), Frobenius ($b = 1$, 1895), and Jordan ($b = 2$, 1898). It was also Burnside who discovered that groups of odd order admit no nontrivial real irreducible representations, and he was led by its consequences to suspect that every group of odd order is solvable. W. Feit and J. G. Thompson finally established this in 1962 with a proof that involves, among other things, frequent applications of Burnside's discovery.

Because he was convinced of the important role that representation theory was destined to play in the future advancement of group theory, Burnside devoted considerable space to its systematic presentation in the second edition of *Theory of Groups* (1911). This edition was widely read and is now considered a classic.

BIBLIOGRAPHY

I. ORIGINAL WORKS. Besides *Theory of Groups of Finite Order* (Cambridge, 1897, 1911), Burnside also composed a treatise on probability, *Theory of Probability* (Cambridge, 1928), which was published posthumously.

II. SECONDARY LITERATURE. The only article dealing with Burnside's life and work in any detail is A. R. Forsyth's obituary notice in *Proceedings of the Royal Society,* **117A** (1928), xi–xxv; the emphasis is upon Burnside's early work, and insufficient attention is paid to his role in the development of the theory of groups. Some idea of the latter can be obtained from the historical and survey articles scattered throughout *The Collected Works of George Abram Miller,* 5 vols. (Urbana, Illinois, 1935–1959), esp. II, 1–18 and III, 1–15. See also H. Burkhardt and H. Vogt, "Sur les groupes discontinus," in *Encyclopédie des sciences mathématiques,* I, 1, fasc. 4 (Paris–Leipzig, 1909), 532–616.

THOMAS HAWKINS

BURRAU, CARL JENSEN (*b.* Elsinore, Denmark, 29 July 1867; *d.* Gentofte, Denmark, 8 October 1944), *astronomy, actuarial mathematics.*

Burrau studied mathematics at Copenhagen University and was an assistant astronomer at the university observatory from 1893 to 1898. He subsequently worked as an actuary. From 1906 to 1912 he lectured at Copenhagen University on practical mathematics. In his researches as an astronomer and as an actuary he was a disciple of T. N. Thiele.

In 1892 the Royal Danish Academy, at Thiele's suggestion, presented an astronomical prize problem concerning librations in the *problème restreint* with two equal masses in circular movement round their common center of gravity. In his solution, Burrau was the first to point out that a series of periodic orbits, into which the third (massless) body moves, develops into a limiting orbit of ejection from (or collision with) one of the masses. It was a pioneer achievement, the first step taken in the systematic search for periodic orbits in the three-body problem that was later carried out by E. Strömgren and his pupils (in its early years, in collaboration with Burrau).

Burrau's dissertation (1895) deals with the derivation of the constants of a measuring machine for photographic determination of star positions. He suggested a development of Bessel's classic method and discussed previously proposed simplifications.

The "distance" from these studies to actuarial work is short. In an obituary, Kristensen, who audited Burrau's lectures on practical mathematics, mentions "his ability to combine scientific points of view with instructions for using them in practice." Burrau's little book on actuarial mathematics, *Forsikringsstatistikens Grundlag,* which was originally written as a series of lectures and appeared in Danish, German, and Italian, is a similar attempt to use his mathematical knowledge in the domain in which he worked for most of his life. Later, he and B. Strömgren published a paper on dividing a frequency curve into its components.

BIBLIOGRAPHY

I. ORIGINAL WORKS. Burrau's writings include "Recherches numériques concernant des solutions périodiques d'un cas spécial du problème des trois corps," in *Astronomische Nachrichten,* **135** (1894), 233–240; **136** (1894), 161–174; "Undersøgelser over Instrumentkonstanter

ved Kjøbenhavns Universitets Astronomiske Observatoriums Maaleapparat for fotografiske Plader," his dissertation, Univ. of Copenhagen (1895); a review of Darwin's *Periodic Orbits* (1897), in *Vierteljahrsschrift der Astronomischen Gesellschaft,* **33** (1898), 21–33, containing information on the early development of the three-body problem; "Über einige in Aussicht genommene Berechnungen betreffend einen Spezialfall des Dreikörper-Problems," *ibid.,* **41** (1906), 261–266; and *Forsikringsstatistikens Grundlag* (Copenhagen, 1925), originally published in German in *Wirtschaft und Recht der Versicherung,* **56** (1924). Papers are in *Publikationer og mindre Meddelelser fra Københavns Observatorium* (1913–1934).

II. SECONDARY LITERATURE. Articles on Burrau are *Dansk Biografisk Leksikon,* IV (1934), 365–366; and S. Kristensen, in *Skandinavisk Aktuarietidskrift,* **28** (1945), 128–130.

AXEL V. NIELSEN

BUSCH, AUGUST LUDWIG (*b.* Danzig, Prussia, 7 September 1804; *d.* Königsberg, Prussia, 30 September 1855), *astronomy.*

Busch was introduced to astronomy by Friedrich Bessel, whose assistant he became in 1831. When Bessel died in 1846, Busch succeeded him as director of the astronomical observatory in Königsberg. There he chiefly reduced the observations made by James Bradley in Kew and Wanstead, and from these he deduced improved values for the constants of aberration and nutation. Busch was also a pioneer in astronomical photography; in 1851 he succeeded in taking a daguerreotype of the eclipsed sun. Ill health prevented him from fully developing his work.

BIBLIOGRAPHY

Busch's published works include his *Reduction of the Observations Made by J. Bradley at Kew and Wansted* (Oxford, 1838); and *Verzeichnis sämtlicher Werke Bessels* (Königsberg, 1849). Poggendorff, I, gives a more complete list of his work.

BERNHARD STICKER

BUSK, GEORGE (*b.* St. Petersburg, Russia, 12 August 1807; *d.* London, England, 10 August 1886), *medicine, natural history, anthropology.*

George Busk was the second son of Robert Busk, an English merchant in St. Petersburg, and Jane Westley, daughter of John Westley, customshouse clerk at St. Petersburg. His grandfather, Sir Wadsworth Busk, was attorney general of the Isle of Man, and an uncle was Hans Busk, scholar and minor poet.

Busk received his medical education at St. Thomas'

and St. Bartholomew's hospitals, and became a member of the Royal College of Surgeons in 1832. He then became surgeon to the Seaman's Hospital Society, recently founded for the relief of merchant seamen, and served at Greenwich on the hospital ship *Dreadnought,* which had been given to the society by the Admiralty. Although not actually at sea, he made good use of his time and the available clinical material. Busk is credited with having worked out the pathology of cholera and having made important observations on scurvy. A few of his notes on scurvy are still extant at the Royal College of Surgeons, but no direct evidence of work on cholera has been found. It is probable that there has been confusion with Busk's work on fasciolopsiasis, which culminated in his description of the fluke now eponymically styled *Fasciolopsis buski,* the adult stage of which occurs in the small intestine among natives of India and eastern China. The disease causes toxic symptoms and acute diarrhea, and thus may have been termed cholera.

When Busk resigned from the *Dreadnought* in 1854, he apparently retired from active surgical practice and turned to biology and teaching. In 1843 he had been among the first elected to fellowship of the Royal College of Surgeons. From 1856 to 1859 he was Hunterian professor of comparative anatomy at the college, and his lecture notes survive in its archives. They make somewhat dull reading now, but his philosophical approach is shown by remarks on reproduction and sexual physiology in invertebrates. "Time was when the difficulty of the physiologist lay in understanding reproduction without the sexual process. At the present day it seems to me the process is reversed and that the question before us is why is sexual union necessary?" (R.C.S. 275.6.3).

In 1850 Busk was made a fellow of the Royal Society. He was four times its vice-president and received its Royal Medal in 1871. His industry and zeal were enormous. He was president of the Royal College of Surgeons in 1871 and belonged to the Linnean Society (vice-president and zoological secretary), the Geological Society (Lyell Medal, 1878; Wollaston Medal, 1885), the Microscopical Society (foundation member, 1839; president, 1848–1849), the Anthropological Society (president, 1873–1874), and the Zoological Society. He was editor of the *Microscopic Journal* (1842), the *Quarterly Journal of Microscopic Science* (1853–1868), the *Natural History Review* (1861–1865), and the *Journal of the Ethnological Society* (1869–1870). Busk was also a member of the Senate of London University, treasurer of the Royal Institution, and the first Home Office inspector under the Cruelty to Animals Act, a difficult position that he fulfilled with tact and humanity. From 1841, he

contributed some seventy papers to scientific journals.

Busk's two main interests in science were the Bryozoa (Polyzoa) and paleontology. In 1856 he formulated the first scientific arrangement of the Bryozoa, the notes and drawings for which are extant (R.C.S. 275.e.3). In the same year, the name *Buskia* was given to a genus of Bryozoa. His collection is at the Natural History Museum, which also has anthropological material collected by him, notably the Gibraltar cranium, a Neanderthal type he found (but did not recognize as such) in 1868. He was an authority on craniometry, and his opinions were much sought on fossil identification.

Busk is thus to be seen as a classifier and investigator whose work, although it may now appear insignificant, was ancillary to and provided corroborative evidence for, the ideas of Darwin, Lyell, and Richard Owen. He was therefore closely connected with the development of zoology and anthropology. A dull writer and lecturer, he was described as an excellent surgical operator and a man of "unaffected simplicity and gentleness of character."

Busk married his cousin Ellen, daughter of Jacob Hans Busk, on 12 August 1843. His portrait in oils was painted by his daughter in 1884 for the Linnean Society; a copy is in the Royal College of Surgeons. Busk died at his home in Harley Street, London.

BIBLIOGRAPHY

I. ORIGINAL WORKS. Early in his career Busk translated three works of other authors: J. J. S. Steenstrap, *On the Alternation of Generations* (London, 1845); A. Kölliker, *Human Histology,* 2 vols. (London, 1853–1854); and *Wedl's Rudiments of Pathological Histology* (London, 1855), which he also edited. Among his own works are *A Catalogue of the Marine Polyzoa in the British Museum,* 3 vols. (London, 1852–1875); sections on Polyzoa in J. MacGillivray, *Narrative of the Voyage of H. M. S. Rattlesnake* (London, 1852), and W. B. Carpenter, *Catalogue of Mazatlan Shells* (London, 1859); *A Monograph of the Fossil Polyzoa of the Crag* (London, 1859); "Parasites, Venomous Insects and Reptiles," in Holme's *Surgery,* 4 vols. (London, 1860–1864), app.; "On the Caves of Gibraltar in Which Human Remains and Works of Art Have Been Found," in *Transactions of the International Congress of Prehistoric Archaeology* (Norwich meeting, 1868); "On a Method of Graphically Representing the Dimensions and Proportions of the Teeth of Mammals," in *Proceedings of the Royal Society,* **17** (1869/70), 544; "Descriptions of the Animals Found in Brixham Cave," in J. Prestwich, *Report on the Exploration of Brixham Cave* (London, 1873); "Report on the Exploration of the Caves of Borneo, Note on the Bones Collected," in *Proceedings of the Royal Society,* **30**

(1879/80), 319; and *Report on the Polyzoa Collected by H. M. S. Challenger,* 2 vols. (London, 1884–1886).

The titles of 73 papers are listed in the Royal Society's *Catalogue of Scientific Papers,* I (1867), VII (1877), IX (1891), and XIII (1914). Busk's papers in MSS are in the library of the Royal College of Surgeons, 275.c.1–12; they are listed in *Annual Report of the Royal College of Surgeons* (1930), p. 18.

II. SECONDARY LITERATURE. Obituary notices are *British Medical Journal* (1886), **2**, 346; *Lancet* (1886), **2**, 313; *Nature,* **34** (1886), 387; *Proceedings of the Linnean Society,* **7** (1886), 36; *Quarterly Journal of the Geological Society* (1886); and *The Times* (11 Aug. 1886).

K. BRYN THOMAS

BUTEO, JOHANNES (*b.* Charpey, Dauphine, France, *ca.* 1492; *d.* Romans-sur-Isère, Dauphine, *ca.* 1564–1572), *mathematics.*

Buteo's father, François, seigneur d'Espenel, is said to have had twenty children. Because he did not wish to be a burden to his parents, Buteo entered the Abbaye de St.-Antoine about 1508. He had so much feeling for languages and mathematics, we are told, that he soon could comprehend Euclid in the original Greek. In 1522 he was sent to Paris, where he studied under Oronce Fine. By 1528 he longed for his monastic life and returned to St.-Antoine; he was abbot during two of his years there. In 1562, during the first of the Wars of Religion, he had to leave the monastery and take refuge with one of his brothers in Romans-sur-Isère. He died there of grief and boredom. His original French name was Jean Borrel (*bourreau* means "executioner," but is also a popular name for the buzzard, and in this last sense is translated as *Buteo*). There were such variants as Boteo, Butéon, and Bateon.

Buteo published his works only after he was sixty years old. The *Opera geometrica* contains fifteen articles on different subjects, the last six showing his interest in law through treatment of such mathematical aspects of jurisprudence as division of land and inheritances. The first nine articles treat mechanical, arithmetical, and geometrical problems. The most original is *Ad problema cubi duplicandi,* in which he refutes Michael Stifel's claim of an exact solution to this problem and gives an approximate one.

This is also the main theme of *De quadratura circuli,* in which Buteo refutes the pretensions of those who claimed to have found the solution of the quadrature, most notably those of his master, Oronce Fine. By contrast, he discusses appreciatively the approximations found by Bryson, Archimedes, and Ptolemy. He also mentions two approximate values for π: 3-17/120 (from Ptolemy) and $\sqrt{10}$ (Indian, although he believed it to be Arab).

In the second part of this work, Buteo criticizes errors of many of his contemporaries, particularly in terminological questions. An interesting point is his proof that the author of the proofs of Euclid's *Elements* was not Theon, as was the current opinion, but Euclid himself. Here, too, are the beginnings of the famous dispute involving Peletier, Clavius, and many others on the angle of contact. In the *Apologia* (1562) Buteo pursued his refutation of Peletier's theories.

Buteo's most important work, the *Logistica,* was divided into five books, of which the first two deal with arithmetic, the third deals with algebra, and the last two present many problems in both fields. Terms such as "million" and "zero," and symbols such as p and m for $+$ and $-$ show Italian influence. There is a good treatment of simultaneous linear equations, with notations borrowed from Stifel; and there are approximations to $\sqrt{a}$ and $\sqrt[3]{a}$ influenced by Chucquet through Estienne de la Roche. The work was not practical enough to be reprinted, however.

Buteo's fame rests only on his books. He has been a solitary figure in his love of mathematics and mechanics, and he wanted to be so. As far as we know, he had no pupils; and his criticism, often excessively sharp, must have estranged other mathematicians.

BIBLIOGRAPHY

I. ORIGINAL WORKS. Buteo's works are *Opera geometrica* (Lyons, 1554; reissued 1559. See *British Museum, General Catalogue of Printed Books* for information on reprinted articles.); *Logistica, quae et arithmetica vulgo dicitur in libros quinque digesta . . . eiusdem ad locum Vitruvij corruptum restitutio* (Lyons, 1559, 1560); *Ad locum Vitruvij corruptum restitutio* was reprinted in J. Polenus, *Exercitationes Vitruvianae primae* (Padua, 1739), and M. Vitruvius, *Architectura,* IV, part 2 (Utini, 1825–1830), 37–43; *De quadratura circuli libri duo . . . Eiusdem annotationum opuscula in errores Campani, Zamberti, Orontij, Peletarij, Io. Penae interpretum Euclidis* (Lyons, 1559); and *Apologia adversus epistolam Jacobi Peletarii depravatoris Elementorum Euclidis* (Lyons, 1562).

II. SECONDARY LITERATURE. There is no biography of Buteo. The best sources for information on his life are J. A. de Thou, *Histoire universelle . . . depuis 1543 jusqu'en 1610* (The Hague, 1740), III, 493; and L. Moréri, *Le grand dictionnaire historique* (Paris, 1759; this edition only). G. Wertheim wrote on *Logistica* in *Bibliotheca mathematica,* **2** (1901), 213–219. On *Opera geometrica* and *De quadratura,* see Moritz Cantor, *Vorlesungen über Geschichte der Mathematik,* II (Leipzig, 1913), 561–563, but with the emendations by G. Eneström, in *Bibliotheca mathematica,* **12** (1912), 253.

J. J. VERDONK

IBN BUṬLĀN, ABU'L-ḤASAN AL-MUKHTĀR IBN ʿABDŪN IBN SAʿDŪN (*b.* Baghdad, *ca.* beginning eleventh century; *d.* Antioch, 460/1068), *medicine.*

He was a Christian physician who first practiced in Baghdad. His master, Abu'l-Faraj ibn al-Ṭayyib, was also a Christian. He taught at a hospital founded in Baghdad by ʿAḍud al-Dawla, who held him in high esteem and who made him study a great many medical works. Ibn Buṭlān also knew well Abu'l-Ḥasan Thābit ibn Ibrāhīm al-Ḥarrāni and felt that the latter had taught him most of the practical medicine he knew.

In 440/1049 he left his native city, and came to Fusṭāṭ, Egypt, by way of al-Raḥba, al-Ruṣāfa, Aleppo, Antioch, and Lattaquié. There he met the physician ʿAlī ibn Riḍwān with whom he engaged in sharp controversy. Then he continued on to Constantinople, where the plague was rampant. From there he returned to Antioch. Finally, tired of his wanderings and disappointed by his associations with ignorant people, he retired to a monastery in that city where he remained as a monk until his death.

Ibn al-Qifṭī has preserved for us an account he made of his trip (which was later used by Yāqūt). In it he displays his curious, observing, open-minded character; in particular, his description of Antioch is both interesting and precise (sites, monuments, fortifications). He furnishes us with a specific recollection of the coexistence between Christians and Moslems in Lattaquié, and of the customs practiced in that city. He shows himself to be hungry for contacts with men of learning in all the lands he visited. But it appears that his somewhat difficult, overbearing personality did not make for prolonged relationships. Ibn al-Qifṭī recalls that in Aleppo he was an utter failure with the Christians, whose community he wanted to dominate and whose religious life he wanted to reform.

But it is his controversy with Ibn Riḍwān (excerpts of which have been preserved by Ibn al-Qifṭī) that proves how cunning and tough he was beneath a facade of gentleness. He reminded his adversary that on Judgment Day his patients would demand justice against their poor physicians and that he would have to face his accusers, who would be much more unmerciful than Ibn Buṭlān himself was. He prayed to God that Ibn Riḍwān should be enlightened.

Among the many questions he dealt with, mention can be made of (1) the difficulty of eradicating prejudices and doubts brought about by a purely book-oriented concept of science; (2) the obligation not to condemn the ancients merely by superficial reflection on seemingly contradictory statements: interesting observations on the logic of interpreting texts and the essence of languages and problems of Galen and Aristotle and obvious inconsistencies in works by Aristotle himself; (3) the discussion with a student of Ibn Riḍwān who, in treating everyday fever, practiced purges to treat blood thickness and bleedings to counteract bile; (4) anomalies in the relationship of food and disease to warm and cold climates (i.e., winter and summer), the internal temperature of the body, and why the need to urinate wakes one up when one dreams that this urge has been satisfied, whereas in an erotic dream there is a discharge of sperm during sleep itself.

In developing this theme, Ibn Buṭlān first grapples with questions of physics (the nature of the attraction of iron to magnets), geometry (Euclid's negative definition of the point), an examination of Aristotle's definition of place (if there is no place outside of this world, then the enveloping sphere moves in local motion but not in one single place). He also defended Ḥunayn ibn Isḥāq against the obtuseness of Ibn Riḍwān.

Thus it is clear that Ibn Buṭlān had scientific and philosophical knowledge that extended beyond his knowledge of medicine. Besides Aristotle and Galen he refers to Themistius, Porphyry, and Anebo. He was part of an era that came out of the era of translations, but which, by means of clinical experimentation and observation, sought to verify, extend, and correct the heritage of the Ancients by applying it according to the tradition introduced a century earlier by Rāzī.

BIBLIOGRAPHY

I. ORIGINAL WORKS. *Taqwīm al-ṣiḥḥa* ("Health Tables"), trans. into Latin as *Tacuini sanitatis Elluchasem Elimithar medici* (Strasbourg, 1531–1532), and into German by M. Herum as *Schachtafeln der Gesundheit* (Strasbourg, 1532); *Daʿwat al-aṭibbāʾ* ("Vocation of Physicians"), Bassara Zalzal, ed. (Alexandria, 1901); *Tadbīr al-amrāḍ al-ʿāriḍa ʿala'l-akthar bi'l-aghdhiya al-maʾlūfa wa'l-adwiya al-mawjūda yantafiʿu bihā ruhbān al-adyira wa-man baʿuda min al-madīna* ("Diet for Diseases Caused Mainly by Customary Food, and Current Remedies Practiced by Monks in Monasteries and Other Persons Living Far Away From Cities"), in manuscript form; *Risāla fī shirāʾ al-raqīq wa-tqlīb al-ʿabīd* ("Treatise on the Purchase and Examination of Slaves"), instructions for detecting bodily defects in slaves, in manuscript form; *Maqāla fī anna'l-farrūkh aḥarru min al-farkh* ("Dissertation: the Chick Is Warmer Than the Fledgling").

II. SECONDARY LITERATURE. Ibn Abī Uṣaybiʿa, Müller, ed., I, 241; Ibn al-Qifṭī, Lippert, ed., p. 294; Leclerc, *Histoire de la médecine arabe*, I, 489; H. Derenbourg, *Vie d'Usama b. Munqid* (anecdotes on Ibn Buṭlān's sense of observation, used by E. G. Browne, *Arabian Medicine,* French trans., *La médecine arabe* [Paris, 1933], pp. 81–82); Brockelmann, *Geschichte der arabischen Literatur* (Leiden, 1943) I, 636, Supp. I, p. 885; *Encylopédie de l'Islam,* article on Ibn Buṭlān; M. Meyerhof and J. Schacht, *The Medico-philosophical Controversy Between Ibn Butlan and Ibn Ridwan, a Contribution to the History of Greek Learning Among the Arabs* (Cairo, 1937); I. Krachkowski, *Izbrannie sochinenia,* IV (Moscow, 1957), 266–267.

R. ARNALDEZ

BUTLEROV, ALEKSANDR MIKHAILOVICH (*b.* Chistopol, Kazanskaya [now Tatarskaya, A.S.S.R.], Russia, 6 September 1828; *d.* Butlerovka, Kazanskaya, Russia, 17 August 1886), *chemistry.*

Butlerov's father, Mikhail Vasilievich Butlerov, a retired lieutenant colonel, and mother, Sofia Mikhailovna, owned part of Butlerovka village. Butlerov received his primary education in a private boarding school, later attended a Gymnasium in Kazan, and studied at Kazan University from 1844 to 1849.

Immediately after graduating from the university, Butlerov began teaching chemistry there, at first (1849–1850) part-time, then as Carl Claus's official assistant; from 1852, after Claus's transfer to Dorpat University, he taught all the chemistry courses in the university. Between 1860 and 1863 he was twice rector of the university. From 1868 to 1885 Butlerov was a professor of chemistry at St. Petersburg University. In 1885, after thirty-five years of service, he retired but continued to teach special lecture courses at the university.

In 1852 he married Nadezhda Mikhailovna Glumilina, niece of the writer S. T. Aksakov.

In 1870 Butlerov was selected a junior scientific assistant of the St. Petersburg Academy of Sciences; the following year he became an associate member, and in 1874 a full member. From 1857 he was a member of the Chemical Society of Paris, and from 1869 of the Russian Chemical Society. He was chairman from 1878 to 1882 of the chemistry section of the Russian Physics and Chemistry Society, formed in 1878 by the merging of the chemistry and physics societies. Butlerov was also an honorary or foreign member of the Chemical Society of London (from 1876), the American Chemical Society (1876), the Czech Chemical Society (1880), the German Chemical Society (1881), the Russian Physics and Chemistry Society (1882), the Russian Technical Society (1885), and of many others.

Butlerov became interested in chemistry while still at boarding school. He experimented independently and once, following an explosion in the boarding

school kitchen, was placed in a punishment cell, from which he was led to dinner with a board inscribed "Great Chemist" tied to his chest. This ironic inscription proved to be prophetic. At Kazan University, Butlerov studied chemistry under N. N. Zinin, as well as Claus, the discoveror of ruthenium. Under Zinin's influence Butlerov decided to devote himself to chemistry; at home he built a laboratory, where he prepared isatin, alloxazine, and other organic compounds. After Zinin left for St. Petersburg, however, Butlerov devoted his energies to another of his interests, entomology. His thesis, for which he received the degree of candidate of natural sciences, was published as *Dnevnie babochki Volgo-Uralskoy fauny* ("Diurnal Butterflies of the Volga-Ural Fauna"). He had collected the material for the thesis during his excursions around Kazan and during a trip to the steppes on the east bank of the Volga River and near the Caspian Sea in the spring and summer of 1846.

As early as 1851 Butlerov defended his master's dissertation, "Ob okisleny organicheskikh soedineny" ("On the Oxidation of Organic Compounds"). On the whole, this work was a historical survey. It includes few original thoughts, although his remarks that isomerism is based on molecular structure and that changes in chemical characteristics are associated with structural changes are worthy of mention. Butlerov included with his master's dissertation his first experimental work on the oxidizing action of osmic acid on organic compounds. His doctoral dissertation, "Ob efirnykh maslakh" ("On Essential Oils"), which he defended at Moscow University in 1854, was also mainly a historical survey. Both of these remained in manuscript form and were not published until 1953 in Volume I of his *Sochinenia* ("Works").

Butlerov's teaching ability immediately attracted the attention of both his students and his colleagues, but initially he taught by lecture only—work in the laboratory was not required of his students, and he himself worked there only sporadically. Until 1857, Butlerov devoted much more time to experiments set up in his greenhouses and in fields. He reported on this research in a great many articles and notices, most of which were published in the *Zapiski* ("Notes") of the Kazan Economic Society in which he was active. In this period he made unsuccessful attempts to build a soap factory and to improve the production of phosphorus matches.

In the early 1850's Butlerov adhered to obsolete theoretical views (he, as well as Claus, taught chemistry from a textbook by C. Löwig, the author of one version of the theory of radicals); but in 1854, on Zinin's advice, he familiarized himself with the work of Laurent and Gerhardt and became one of their passionate supporters. However, the greatest changes in his work and thought resulted from his trip abroad in 1857–1858. During his travels Butlerov met such eminent young chemists as Kekulé and Erlenmeyer and spent about half a year in Paris, participating in the meetings of the Paris Chemical Society, which had just been formed, and working for two months in Wurtz's laboratory.

Markovnikov, in his reminiscences of Butlerov, gives this evaluation of the significance of Butlerov's trip:

> He did not have to finish his education, as did most of those [Russians] sent abroad. He had to see, rather, how scientific experts worked, to observe the origin of ideas and to enter into intimate relations with these ideas, which the scientists readily exchanged in personal conversations . . . that were often held privately and not committed to print. . . . With a basic reserve of scientific knowledge, and possessing absolute fluency in French and German, he had no difficulty standing on an equal footing with the young European scientists, and owing to his outstanding abilities, choosing the correct direction [*Zhurnal Russkogo fiziko-khimicheskogo obshchestva*, **19** (1887), supp., 76].

In Wurtz's laboratory Butlerov began his first series of experimental investigations. Discovering a new way to obtain methylene iodide, he studied many derivatives of methylene and their reactions. As a result, he was the first to obtain hexamethylenetetramine (urotropine) and a polymer of formaldehyde which in the presence of limewater is transformed into a sacchariferous substance (containing, as was established by E. Fischer, α-acrose). This was the first complete synthesis of a sacchariferous substance.

On the other hand, Butlerov did not succeed in obtaining either dihydroxymethylene, $CH_2(OH)_2$, or the free methylene radical itself, instead of which he obtained its dimer—ethylene. However, both of these negative results served as material for future generalizations. These investigations showed the trait characteristic of Butlerov's work, the effort to study a reaction in full, not neglecting its by-products. They were usually completed with very small quantities of the substances involved and enabled him to perfect his skill in experimentation.

Work on the methylene series ended in 1861, when Butlerov stated the basic ideas of the theory of chemical structure and directed his experimental investigations toward the verification and support of his new theory. He arrived at the theory of chemical structure through continuous research and a recognition of the unsatisfactory state of theoretical chemistry. Although he developed a theory of types similar to Gerhardt's,

defended it in print, and on returning from abroad employed it as the basis of a lecture course in organic chemistry, he clearly recognized that he must go beyond Gerhardt.

Butlerov attempted to develop Dumas's theory of carbonaceous types, but all conventional viewpoints proved unsatisfactory for the explanation of addition reactions, which he had come across in describing the results of his work on the methylene series. Summing up his research, he arrived at the theory of chemical structure, which, according to Markovnikov, he began to expound in his lectures as early as 1860.

At the end of the 1850's and the beginning of the 1860's, the theoretical side of chemistry did not correspond to the sum of its empirical data and knowledge. Kekulé, Wurtz, and the majority of other chemists adhered to the theory of polyatomic radicals, which was a further development of Gerhardt's theory of types; Kolbe and his school developed a unique theory of carbonaceous types; and Berthelot used "formation equations." Several chemists—for example, Kekulé (in 1861)—began in despair to reject rational formulas, based on one or another theoretical representation, and turned to empirical formulas. At precisely this juncture Butlerov read his paper "O khimicheskom stroeny veshchestv" ("On the Chemical Structure of Substances") at the chemical section of the Congress of German Naturalists and Physicians in Speyer (September 1861).

In this paper (*Sochinenia*, I, 561), Butlerov defined the concept of chemical structure: "Assuming that each *chemical* atom is characterized by a specific and limited quantity of chemical force [affinity], with which it participates in the formation of a substance, I would call this chemical bond or [this] capacity for the mutual union of atoms into a complex substance *chemical structure*."

From this definition it follows that the concept of chemical structure (the term is found in the work of Russian chemists before Butlerov, but it is used in another sense) could be brought forward only after there had been a sufficiently clear definition of the concepts "atom" (the attribute "chemical" left open the question of the possibility of its further separation into "physical" atoms), "valency" (the quantity of an atom's affinity), and "interatomic bond." Thus, the following can be considered as the preconditions for the existence of a theory, within chemistry itself, of chemical structure: (1) sufficiently clear concepts of atomic theory and molecular theory—which was achieved at the Congress of Chemists in Karlsruhe (1860); (2) development of the study of valency in the form ascribed to valency by Kekulé (1857–1858); (3) the creation of the concept of interatomic bond, as it was formulated in the works of Kekulé and Couper (1858).

Butlerov advanced the basic proposition of the classical theory of chemical structure:

> I consider it possible, for the time being, to change the well-known rule—to wit, that the nature of a compound molecule is determined *by the nature, quantity, and arrangement* of elementary component parts—in the following manner: *the chemical nature of a compound molecule is determined by the nature of its component parts, by their quantity, and by their chemical structure* [*Sochinenia*, I, 70].

This proposition, as is evident from its wording, broke with the traditional view that the properties of molecules are determined principally by the nature of the space grouping of atoms in the molecules, by the relative position of the atoms, and by the distances separating the atoms; these problems could not be studied by methods then available. All the remaining propositions of the classical theory of chemical structure are directly or indirectly associated with this proposition.

Butlerov noted means for determining the chemical structure of molecules and formulated the rules that should be followed in this determination. He gave primary importance to those synthetic reactions in which the participating radicals retain their chemical structure. He foresaw the possibility of regrouping but believed that after a detailed study of matter from the point of view of chemical structure, the general laws for regrouping would be deduced.

Leaving open the question of the preferred structural formulas, Butlerov explicitly expressed his opinion about their sense: When the general laws of the relationship between the chemical properties of substances and their chemical structure became known, the corresponding formula would be an expression of all these properties.

The only incorrect proposition in Butlerov's paper was the supposition concerning the possibility of a primordial (i.e., inherent in free atoms) difference in units of affinity (valency). In connection with this hypothesis Butlerov was the first to produce a model of a carbon tetrahedron (it was irregular). Having subjected the hypothesis to experimental verification and having rejected it, he further developed the theory of chemical structure in a long article, "Über die verschiedenen Erklärungsweisen einiger Fälle von Isomerie." However, the propositions stated in the article were implied in his paper delivered at Speyer.

Guided by the propositions he had formulated, Butlerov explained the existence of isomerism, stating that isomers were compounds possessing the same elementary composition but different chemical structure. Discovery of the facts of isomerism, which did not correspond to this definition, led to the establishment by van't Hoff and Le Bel of stereochemistry, which Butlerov did not accept immediately and, when he did, only in part; specifically, he accepted only the explanation of the optical activity of organic compounds as the result of the presence of asymmetric carbon atoms.

Butlerov explained the relationship of the properties of isomers—and of organic compounds in general—to their chemical structure by the existence of "the mutual influence of atoms," which is transmitted along the bonds; as a result of this influence, atoms possess different "chemical values" depending on their structural environment. This general proposition was given concrete expression in the form of many "rules" by Butlerov himself and, especially, by his students Markovnikov and Popov. In this century these rules, as well as the whole concept of atoms' mutual influence, have received an electron interpretation.

Of great importance for the consolidation of the theory of chemical structure was its experimental corroboration in the work of Butlerov's school. Butlerov himself deserves credit for the prediction and proof of positional and skeletal isomerism. Having unexpectedly obtained tertiary butyl alcohol, he was able to decipher its structure and predicted (later proving, with the aid of his students) the existence of its homologues; he also predicted (1864) the existence of two butanes and three pentanes and, later, that of isobutylene. The formulas of his two butanes were represented as follows:

$$\begin{cases} CH_3 \\ CH_2 \\ CH_2 \\ CH_3 \end{cases} \quad \text{and} \quad CH \begin{cases} CH_3 \\ CH_3 \\ CH_3 \end{cases}$$

As early as 1866 Butlerov reported the synthesis of isobutane. Regarding this he wrote (*Sochinenia*, I, 199): "The principle of chemical structure . . . can now serve as the best guide in researching questions related to isomerism. Using this principle, one can predict phenomena that could be neither predicted nor explained by prior [theoretical] viewpoints."

In the second half of the 1860's the nature of unsaturated compounds was still unexplained. A series of investigations conducted by Butlerov, completed at the beginning of the 1870's, led to a conclusion supporting the hypothesis that they contain multiple bonds.

Butlerov's indication that sulfur had a valence of six and his experimental proof of the tetravalence of lead must be considered contributions to the theory of valency. Throughout the 1860's he gave much attention to organometallic compounds and developed methods, widely used by his school, for synthesizing organic zinc compounds.

In order to promulgate the theory of chemical structure throughout organic chemistry, Butlerov published *Vvedenie k polnomu izucheniyu organicheskoy khimy* ("An Introduction to the Complete Study of Organic Chemistry"), the second edition of which was published in German under the title *Lehrbuch der organischen Chemie*. E. von Meyer, a student of Kolbe's school (which rejected the theory of chemical structure), considered the work to be a magnificent textbook on organic chemistry that greatly influenced the development and popularization of the structural theory.

In 1867–1868 Butlerov went abroad to aid in the publication of the German edition of his book; he traveled to Algiers for a rest but nearly perished on the way; the ship encountered a violent storm and was off course for several days, out of control and half swamped. There was another goal of his trip, however. The official decree concerning his mission stated that a purpose of the voyage was to enable him to explain to foreign chemists his right to major participation in the development of contemporary chemistry.

Thus, Butlerov's trip was connected with the defense of his priority. Until then there had been a tendency to credit the creation of structural theory to Kekulé (Couper's name was not yet known), for in 1857–1858 he had stated the theoretical propositions that served as the preconditions for the emergence of the theory of chemical structure, and in 1865 he had quite successfully extended the theory to aromatic compounds. Formulas representing conclusions drawn on the basis of several of Kekulé's (and Couper's) valency rules coincided with structural theory (in 1868 L. Meyer stated this viewpoint very clearly in opposition to Butlerov's attempts to defend his priority), while within the framework of this theory, the deduction of formulas was based on the study of the properties of the relevant molecules, as well as on the valency of atoms. It was forgotten, however, that in his textbook and in many magazine articles, Kekulé used the "theory of polyatomic radicals" even after 1861 and that, having changed his views in 1864, after Butlerov's criticism, stated that in his textbook he "had always given preference to one form of rational formulas, specifically, to the one that reflects the views concerning atom bonds as the method of forming molecules" [*Lehrbuch der organischen Chemie* . . ., II, pt. 2 (1864), 244–245].

Markovnikov immediately spoke out against this historically incorrect contention, but the legend was nonetheless created. Kekulé gave the hint, L. Meyer developed it, and Schorlemmer reproduced it in *The Rise and Development of Organic Chemistry* (London, 1879). In his *Benzolfest* (1890) Kekulé told how the structural theory came to him as he rode on the top of a London bus in 1857 or 1858. Since then, this elegant tale has fluttered along the pages of histories of chemistry and of anniversary articles, although long ago Markovnikov indicated Butlerov's basic role in the creation and initial development of the classic theory of chemical structure.

Butlerov's second great service—this time to chemistry in Russia—was the creation of the first Russian school of chemists. After his return from abroad in 1858, he equipped his laboratory with gas and expanded it; his students had to complete required practical work; and his first "disciples" appeared. Of these, V. V. Markovnikov, A. M. Zaytsev, and A. P. Popov occupied professorial chairs in universities during Butlerov's lifetime. Nonetheless, in the 1860's Butlerov sought to leave Kazan. One reason for this was his unsuccessful term as rector. In March 1860 he had become the last "crown" (i.e., appointed by the imperial government) rector of Kazan University; however, striving not only to institute liberal changes but also to halt student abuse of individual teachers, Butlerov came into severe conflict with the student body. This forced him to request retirement, which was granted in August 1861. Nonetheless, in November 1862 Butlerov became—against his wishes—the first elected rector of the university. The outbreak of a struggle between groups of professors and Butlerov's clash with a trustee led to his retirement in July 1863. He was bitter about the experience and tried to find a position outside Kazan. Only the insistence of his friends (as well as the birth of a son in April 1864) stopped him from departing immediately.

In May 1868 Butlerov was made professor of chemistry at St. Petersburg University. He continued teaching there until 1885, when he retired on pension but continued to give special lecture courses. His followers at St. Petersburg form a prominent group of Russian organic chemists—the most famous being A. E. Favorski and I. L. Kondakov. At various times G. G. Wagner, D. P. Konovalov, and F. M. Flavitsky worked in his laboratory. Butlerov's outstanding characteristic as an instructor was that he taught by example; the students could always observe what he was doing and how he was doing it.

Butlerov was an advocate of higher education for women; he participated in the organization of university courses for women (1878) and lectured to them on inorganic chemistry. He also created laboratory courses in chemistry. In addition, Butlerov delivered in St. Petersburg, as he had earlier done in Kazan, a large number of public lectures, most of which had a chemical-technical basis.

Surprisingly, election to the Academy of Sciences hardly aided Butlerov's scientific activity, since the condition of its laboratory was so deplorable that not until 1882, after thorough repairs, could he transfer his experimental work there. A struggle for the right of Russian scholars to recognition of their service by the academy weakened Butlerov's position within the academy. For example, in 1874 Butlerov and Zinin failed in their advocacy of Mendeleev's candidacy for membership. In November 1880 Mendeleev was again nominated by Butlerov to the seat that became vacant after Zinin's death. The second blackballing of Mendeleev elicited a storm of indignation throughout the nation. At the same time, the faction within the academy that had prevented Mendeleev's election proposed their own candidates for membership and for academic prizes. Thus, in January 1882, after Mendeleev's failure to be elected Beilstein was nominated. Seeing Beilstein as a protégé of that same anti-Russian faction, Butlerov energetically opposed his candidacy and succeeded in depriving Beilstein of the requisite number of votes. In order to attain this end, however, Butlerov was forced to turn directly to public opinion, publishing in the Moscow newspaper *Rus* a long article with the provocative title "Russkaya ili tolko Imperatorskaya Akademia nauk v St.-Petersburge?" ("[Is There] a Russian or Merely an Imperial Academy of Sciences in St. Petersburg?").

The work of Butlerov and his students can be classified as follows:

(1) Research designed to confirm the theory of chemical structure and to synthesize theoretically possible isomers. Trimethyl acetic acid was obtained, its genetic connection with pinacolone alcohol was established, and the correct structure of pinacolone alcohol and pinacol were given. In addition, Butlerov gave a general schema of pinacolin rearrangement. Concluding this set of experiments, pentamethylethanol was synthesized.

(2) Investigation of polymerization reactions. The possibility of the polymerization of ethylene (unsuccessfully), propylene, butene-2, and isobutylene was studied. The mechanism of the polymerization of isobutylene was especially carefully studied, since the polymerization stops at the dimer and trimer stages; Butlerov sought to study "the simplest instance of pure and, perhaps, less complex polymerization of the ethylene series of hydrocarbons." His students simultaneously studied the polymerization of amylene.

Thus, Butlerov was the first to begin the systematic study of the mechanism of polymerization reactions based on the theory of chemical structure; this was continued in Russia by his successors and was crowned by S. V. Lebedev's discovery of the industrial means of producing synthetic rubber.

(3) Secondary results of the study of polymerization. During the attempts to polymerize ethylene, the conditions were found under which it could be hydrated to obtain ethanol. Studying the polymerization of isobutylene and amylene, and having found their isomers in the reaction mixture, in 1876 Butlerov generalized that a dynamic equilibrium can exist between two isomeric forms. These ideas concerning reversible equilibrium isomerizations are found in Butlerov's work as early as 1862–1866. Subsequently, C. Laar proposed the term "tautomerism" for these phenomena, but his representation of the mechanism of reversible isomerism proved to be less correct than Butlerov's.

(4) Random research in chemistry (organic, inorganic, and physical) and even in physics. Thus, not considering the a priori rejection of Prout's hypothesis to be possible, Butlerov arrived at the assumption of the possibility of changes in atomic weights—for example, under the influence of luminous rays. The experiments undertaken did not, of course, yield positive results.

To Butlerov's St. Petersburg period belong his statements defending and substantiating the theory of chemical structure, from an epistemological point of view, against attacks by his colleagues Menschutkin and, to a lesser degree, Mendeleev. His speech "Sovremennoe znachenie teory khimicheskogo stroenia" ("The Contemporary Significance of the Theory of Chemical Structure," 1879) and his article "Khimicheskoe stroenie i teoria zameshchenia" ("Chemical Structure and the Theory of Substitution," 1885) include such statements. Against Menschutkin's positivist orientation, which in this instance followed Berthelot, Butlerov advanced the thesis that chemists had not only the right, but also the responsibility, to speak of molecules and atoms as if speaking of things that in fact exist and, doing this, to preserve the conviction that this belief would not become a baseless abstraction.

A course of lectures ("A Historical Essay on the Development of Chemistry in the Last Forty Years"), given by Butlerov in 1879–1880 at St. Petersburg University, served as partial substantiation of the theory of chemical structure. In the end, Menschutkin, who was Butlerov's successor in the chair of organic chemistry at St. Petersburg, changed his position, supporting the theory of chemical structure.

Butlerov was the organizer and propagandist for scientific apiculture in Russia. He published many articles and notices in the Russian and foreign press, and in 1886 founded the *Russkii pchelovodnyi listok* ("Russian Apiculture Leaflet").

While in St. Petersburg, Butlerov had yet another unusual interest—spiritualism. He was convinced that "medium" phenomena could be studied by scientific methods and even spoke on this theme at the seventh conference of Russian naturalists (Odessa, August 1883). However, experiments with mediums, conducted in the presence of a scientific commission, ended in complete failure. Mendeleev, who participated in the commission, later wrote, "Our spiritists obviously do not see deception." P. D. Boborykin, a student of Butlerov's at Kazan University, defined his passion as an "atavism of religiosity."

BIBLIOGRAPHY

I. Original Works. Butlerov's writings include *Vvedenie k polnomu izucheniyu organicheskoy khimy* ("Introduction to the Complete Study of Organic Chemistry"), 3 pts. (Kazan, 1864–1866), trans. into German as *Lehrbuch der organischen Chemie zur Einführung in das specielle Studium derselben,* 4 pts. (Leipzig, 1867–1868); *Stati po mediumizmu* ("Articles on Mediumism"; St. Petersburg, 1889); *Stati po pchelovodstvu* ("Articles on Apiculture"; St. Petersburg, 1891); *Izbrannye raboty po organicheskoy khimy* ("Selected Works on Organic Chemistry"), in the series Klassiki Nauki (Moscow, 1951), with a bibliography of his chemical works; *Nauchnaya i pedagogicheskaya deyatelnost. Sbornik dokumentov* ("Scientific and Pedagogic Activity. A Collection of Documents"; Moscow, 1961), with a list of the archives where Butlerov's MSS are preserved; and *Centenary of the Theory of Chemical Structure. Collection of Papers of A. M. Butlerov, A. S. Couper, A. Kekulé, and V. V. Markovnikov* (Moscow, 1961). His writings are collected in *Sochinenia* ("Works"), 3 vols. (Moscow, 1953–1958); Volume III includes a complete bibliography of his works.

II. Secondary Literature. Works on Butlerov are *A. M. Butlerov, 1828–1928* (Leningrad, 1929), a collection of articles on Butlerov; G. V. Bykov, *Istoria klassicheskoy teory khimicheskogo stroenia* ("History of the Classical Theory of Chemical Structure"; Moscow, 1960); "La correspondance des chimistes étrangers avec A. M. Butlerov," in *Archives internationales d'histoire des sciences,* **14** (1961), 85–97; *Aleksandr Mikhailovich Butlerov* ("A Sketch of his Life and Activity"; Moscow, 1961); and "The Origin of the Theory of Chemical Structure," in *Journal of Chemical Education,* **39** (1962), 220–224; G. V. Bykov and J. Jacques, "Deux pionniers de la chimie moderne, Adolphe Wurtz et Alexandre M. Boutlerov, d'après une correspondance inédite," in *Revue d'histoire des sciences,* **13** (1960), 115–134; G. W. Bykow und L. M. Bekassowa, "Beiträge zur

Geschichte der Chemie der 60-er Jahre des XIX. Jahrhunderts. I. Briefwechsel zwischen E. Erlenmeyer und A. M. Butlerow (von 1862 bis 1876)," in *Physis,* **8** (1966), 179–198; "II. F. Beilsteins Briefe an A. M. Butlerow," *ibid.,* 267–285; "III. Die im Brieform verfasste Chronik der Herausgabe eines Lehrbuchs für Chemie," *ibid.,* **10** (1968), 5–24; G. V. Bykov and L. V. Kaminer, *Literatura ob A. M. Butlerove i po istory klassicheskoy teory khimicheskogo stroenia* ("Literature on A. M. Butlerov and the History of the Classical Theory of Chemical Structure"; Moscow, 1962); W. N. Dawydoff, *Über die Entstehung der chemischen Structurlehre unter besonderer Berücksichtigung der Arbeiten von A. M. Butlerov* (Berlin, 1959); J. Jacques, "Boutlerov, Couper et la Société Chimique de Paris (notes pour servir à l'histoire des théories de la structure chimique," in *Bulletin de la Société chimique de France* (1953), 528–530; H. M. Leicester, "Alexander Mikhailovich Butlerov," in *Journal of Chemical Education,* **17** (1940), 203–209; and "Contributions of Butlerov to the Development of Structural Theory," *ibid.,* **36** (1959), 328–329; "Pisma russkikh khimikov k A. M. Butlerovu" ("Letters of Russian Chemists to A. M. Butlerov"), in *Nauchnoe nasledstvo* ("Scientific Heritage"), Vol. IV (Moscow, 1961); and *Zhurnal Russkogo fizikokhimicheskogo obshchestva,* **19,** supp. (1887), devoted to speeches and articles by G. G. Gustavson, A. M. Zaytsev, V. V. Markovnikov, and N. A. Menschutkin in memory of Butlerov.

G. V. Bykov

BÜTSCHLI, OTTO (*b.* Frankfurt am Main, Germany, 3 May 1848; *d.* Heidelberg, Germany, 2 February 1920), *zoology, mineralogy.*

Bütschli was the son of a confectioner whose family had come from Switzerland several generations earlier. As a youth his scientific appetite was whetted by the lectures and the museum of the Senkenbergische Naturforschende Gesellschaft in Frankfurt, which also inspired his fellow townsmen August Weismann and Richard Goldschmidt. Bütschli studied mineralogy, chemistry, and paleontology at the Karlsruhe Polytechnic Institute and in 1865–1866, at the age of seventeen, was assistant to the paleontologist Karl von Zittel. Next he traveled to Heidelberg, where he finished his doctorate in mineralogy, with minors in zoology and chemistry, in 1868.

During his year of required military service, Bütschli had decided that his true interest was zoology, so he went to Leuckart's laboratory in Leipzig for a semester of advanced study after he left the army in 1869. In the fall of the same year Bütschli returned to Frankfurt and was recalled to military service when the Franco-Prussian War broke out in 1870. During this period his first cytological paper, on the structure of the germ strings of insects, appeared. After the war Bütschli went to Kiel, where he was assistant to the taxonomist Möbius for two years; among his works completed there is a monograph on free-living nematodes. These organisms permitted detailed study of the living cell, and Bütschli used them successfully for many years.

Dissatisfied with the situation in Kiel and desiring greater freedom for his promising cytological researches, Bütschli returned to Frankfurt in 1873 and spent the next three years working on the problems of cell division, fertilization, and the conjugation of the ciliates. In 1876 he presented the results of these studies in a thesis for admission as *Privatdozent* at the Karlsruhe Polytechnic Institute. At the age of thirty Bütschli was named professor of zoology and paleontology at Heidelberg. Here he remained for the rest of his life, declining attractive positions elsewhere; he retired in 1918, at the age of seventy, and spent the last two years of his life working on a textbook that he did not finish before his death from influenza.

Bütschli's monograph of 1876, "Studien über die ersten Entwickelungsvorgänge der Eizelle, die Zelltheilung und die Konjugation der Infusorien," was important as a pioneer work in the development of several areas of cytology and cell theory. In it he was the first to identify and order sequentially the stages of nuclear division in several types of animal cells, simultaneously with Strasburger's work on the division of plant cells and several years prior to Flemming's studies on mitosis. Bütschli demonstrated that the polar bodies of eggs arise through atypical cell division, and in studying fertilization he was the first to describe the fertilization cone and to prove that normally only one sperm enters the egg.

The monograph was in press when Oscar Hertwig's paper on fertilization in the sea urchin appeared, and Bütschli added an appendix in which he discussed the significance of Hertwig's discoveries in relation to his own. Hertwig had succeeded where Bütschli had failed, in following the sperm from penetration to karyogamy. However, Bütschli's description of many of the stages of fertilization and cleavage were more complete, at least partially because of differences in material. He clearly illustrated the fusion of male and female pronuclei in the eggs of snails, but did not recognize the true identity of the male pronucleus because of confusion created by the presence of the several micronuclei that make up the female pronucleus and gradually fuse before karyogamy.

The illustrations in this monograph are remarkable, especially when one considers that all of the observations were made on unstained material treated only with one percent acetic acid. (The use of carmine as a biological stain did not become common until a few years later.) Bütschli clearly illustrated dividing cells and noted what he called rodlets (chromosomes) that made up the "nuclear plate," which, in his view, divided into halves at the climax of nuclear division. The failure to illustrate nuclear-division stages earlier than metaphase was possibly due to the lack of staining techniques. Bütschli's illustrations of the zygotene "bouquet" stage and of diakinesis during the first meiotic division of spermatogonia in the roach were excellent.

The second half of this monograph was devoted to the conjugation of the ciliates. In these organisms, unlike most other animals, reproduction and the sexual processes are not closely associated. Bütschli was the first to recognize this and to demonstrate that conjugation was not a reproductive process per se, but a sexual reorganization of the cell similar to fertilization. In his view, both conjugation and fertilization brought about a rejuvenation of the cell, either through some effect of the conjugation process or through the acquisition of new nuclear material. This idea formed the basis of subsequent work on the ciliate life cycle by Maupas, R. Hertwig, Calkins, and others. Bütschli recognized that the micronuclei of ciliates were comparable with the nuclei of other cells and that they divided by similar processes. He was thus able to prove that these organisms were unicellular animals and to disprove the earlier views of their reproduction, which were based upon a false analogy between the ciliates and the Metazoa. Instead of comparing the ciliate with the whole metazoan organism, Bütschli compared it with the cell of the metazoan.

Bütschli drew many conclusions from these studies, some of which were well ahead of his time. Above all, he argued that cells were physicochemical systems and that cellular phenomena could best be understood in physical-chemical terms. As he said in the preface to his 1876 monograph:

Morphology composes only a part of the nature of organic forms. Each form must be capable of being explained in itself from given bases and influences. Only when it is shown that one organic form proceeds from another, and when the conditions of this appearance are known—as is hardly true in a single case today—is a material present in which it might be possible to seek a causal-mechanical explanation [of the phenomenon]. . . . If we conceive of the elementary organisms [cells] as the building blocks of morphology, our understanding of the elementary organisms is altered, for the type of morphological observation of [multi]cellular organisms [previously] used loses its justification and physiological methods come to the fore. The phenomena on and in the elementary organisms can be more precisely stated only through a knowledge of the physical-chemical conditions of their appearance and disappearance [pp. 1–2].

In keeping with this conviction, he proposed a model for cell division based upon changes in surface tension.

It is perhaps strange that Bütschli did no further work in nuclear cytology, especially since the field was making rapid advances at the time; however, his deepest interest was in the cytoplasm as a physical-chemical system. He thus devoted his first ten years at Heidelberg to a detailed study of the protozoa, for he felt that life processes and the nature of protoplasm could be studied in unicellular organisms better than in Metazoa. These studies culminated in a three-volume monograph (1880–1889), a critical review of the whole field that included much original work by Bütschli himself—he checked many dubious points—and a complete bibliography of all previously published work. These volumes, which remain a basic reference work, contain many important theoretical discussions, such as Bütschli's hypothesis of the sexuality of the ciliates, and are still of considerable taxonomic importance.

During the years spent on the protozoan studies, Bütschli approached the structural problems of protoplasm more closely through extensive observation of the protoplasm of rhizopods and ciliates. These studies eventually led to the "alveolar theory of protoplasm," which he first discussed in print in 1889 and summarized in *Untersuchungen über microskopische Schäume und die Struktur des Protoplasmas* (1892). In Bütschli's view, protoplasm had an alveolar structure, being composed of a two-phase system similar to an emulsion. In keeping with his fundamental mechanistic conviction, Bütschli felt that many of the properties of living protoplasm could be explained on a physical-chemical basis, and thus he spent much time experimenting with various emulsions of oil and soapy solutions of mineral salts that appear to duplicate the physical properties of living protoplasm to a remarkable degree. This work represented a great advance, for it was the first theory of protoplasmic structure to have a comprehensive observational and experimental basis, and at the same time it provided a physical-chemical model of the underlying phenomena of colloidal materials. This work was, of course, limited by the techniques and concepts of the time; however, more recent knowledge of protoplasm gained by electron microscopy and by colloid and protein chemistry does not detract from Bütschli's pioneer study, which in respect to observation, analysis, and synthesis remains a model of

scientific work in biology. With this work Bütschli felt that he had traced to the root the problems he had posed for himself as a young man.

Following his extensive work on protoplasm, Bütschli proceeded to examine a great number of organic and inorganic materials of a colloidal nature. These studies were published mainly in *Untersuchungen über Strukturen* (1898), which included 300 photomicrographs. This pioneer use of photomicrography was a reflection of Bütschli's effort to present his observations as realistically and precisely as possible. These studies, together with the work on protoplasm, provided one of the bases of the subsequent development of colloid chemistry. After finishing *Untersuchungen über Strukturen*, Bütschli turned to the analysis of many mineral materials of biological origin: shells of mollusks, crustaceans, and echinoderms; tests of Foraminifera; and the spicules of sponges. In 1900 he published a short book on the structure of coagulated sulfur and a monograph on the structure of natural and synthetic silica gels.

At the age of sixty Bütschli returned to purely zoological work and began to prepare a comprehensive textbook of comparative anatomy, which had long been one of his secret loves. This work was to include both vertebrates and invertebrates; although more than a thousand pages of the work were finally published, Bütschli did not live to finish this ambitious undertaking.

BIBLIOGRAPHY

I. ORIGINAL WORKS. Complete bibliographies of Bütschli's works are in *Die Naturwissenschaften,* **7** (1920), 567–570; and *Sitzungsbericht der Heidelberger Akademie der Wissenschaften,* Kl. B (1920), 13–19. His works include "Studien über die ersten Entwickelungsvorgänge der Eizelle, die Zelltheilung und die Konjugation der Infusorien," in *Abhandlungen der Senkenbergische naturforschende Gesellschaft,* **10** (1876), 1–250; *Protozoa,* I, pts. 1–3, in H. G. Bronn's *Klassen und Ordnen des Thier-Reichs* (Leipzig, 1880–1889); *Untersuchungen über microskopische Schäume und die Struktur des Protoplasmas* (Leipzig, 1892), trans. by E. A. Minchin, A. Black, and C. Black as *Investigations on Microscopic Foams and on Protoplasm* (London, 1894); *Untersuchungen über Strukturen, insbesondere über Strukturen nichtzelliger Erzeugnisse des Organismus und über ihre Beziehungen zu Strukturen welche ausserhalb des Organismus entstehen* (Leipzig, 1898); *Vorlesungen über vergleichende Anatomie,* 2 vols. (Leipzig, 1910–1925); and an untitled autobiography with the running head "Das Lebenswerk Otto Bütschli's," in *Sitzungsbericht der Heidelberger Akademie der Wissenschaften,* Kl. B (1920), 1–12.

II. SECONDARY LITERATURE. Works on Bütschli are H. Freundlich, "Otto Bütschli als Kolloidchemiker," in *Die Naturwissenschaften,* **7** (1920), 562–564; Richard B. Goldschmidt, "Otto Bütschli 1848–1920," *ibid.,* 543–549; "Otto Bütschli, Pioneer of Cytology (1848–1920)," in *Science, Medicine, and History* (Oxford, 1953), pp. 223–232; V. Goldschmidt, "Otto Bütschli's Verhältnis zur Kristallographie und Mineralogie," in *Die Naturwissenschaften,* **7** (1920), 564–567; Clara Hamburger, "Otto Bütschli als Protozoenforscher," *ibid.,* 559–561; Max Hartmann, "Otto Bütschli und das Befruchtungs- und Todproblem," *ibid.,* 555–558; L. Rhumbler, "Otto Bütschli's Wabentheorie," *ibid.,* 549–555; and Josef Speck, "Über Bütschli's Erklärung der karyokinetischen Figur," *ibid.,* 561–562.

JAMES D. BERGER

BUYS BALLOT, CHRISTOPH HENDRIK DIEDERIK (*b.* Kloetinge, Netherlands, 10 October 1817; *d.* Utrecht, Netherlands, 3 February 1890), *meteorology, physical chemistry.*

The son of Anthony Jacobus Buys Ballot, Dutch Reformed minister, and Geertruida Françoise Lix Raaven, Buys Ballot attended the Gymnasium at Zaltbommel and the *Hogeschool* (now University) of Utrecht, where he was active in student affairs before receiving his doctorate in 1844. He became lecturer in mineralogy and geology at Utrecht in 1845, and in 1846 he added theoretical chemistry. In 1847 he was appointed professor of mathematics, and from 1867 until his retirement in 1888 he was professor of physics. In 1854 he founded the Royal Netherlands Meteorological Institute (K.N.M.I.), a world center for atmospheric research, whose chief director he remained until his death. A deeply religious man, noted for his proverbial modesty, Buys Ballot became a prominent lay leader of the Walloon church. He was twice married; five of his eight children survived him. He was elected to the Royal Academy of Sciences of Amsterdam in 1855 and to the Royal Belgian Academy. He was decorated by the Dutch, Austrian, and Prussian governments. As a teacher he wrote textbooks in chemistry, mathematics, and physics.

Although he is best known for the law to which he gave his name, Buys Ballot's principal accomplishments were the shape he gave (with others) to the field of meteorology in its formative years. He started as a chemist and shifted to meteorology when his speculations on the relation between molecular structure and the properties of matter (put forward in 1843 but not published until 1849) were badly received by his teachers for lack of experimental foundations. In meteorology, which was growing in importance as the spread of the telegraph made synoptic observations possible, Buys Ballot labored unceasingly for the widest possible network of simultaneous observations, which he published in a series of yearbooks beginning in 1851. He was a leader of the international meteorological cooperation that began with the Brussels Conference in 1853, and he served as chairman of the International Meteorological Committee from its founding at the Vienna Congress in 1873 until 1879. He also was responsible for Dutch participation in the International Polar Year.

His contributions to meteorology were twofold. First, he suggested that only the deviations from the mean state were important for understanding. Second, in spite of his stated devotion to the motto *Sine hypothesi scientia nulla,* his research consisted chiefly of examining long time series for regularities that he was more concerned to establish than to interpret. This overwhelming preoccupation with data gave his papers a strongly Baconian flavor; he left to others the development of the theoretical side of meteorology, to which his training might have led.

In 1857, noting that on his synoptic charts of the Netherlands the wind blew at right angles to the pressure gradient, Buys Ballot published the fact, later stating it in the form now known as Buys Ballot's law: "When you place yourself in the direction of the wind, . . . you will have at your left the least atmospheric pressure" (British Association for the Advancement of Science, *Transactions,* **32** [1863], 20–21). In this he had been anticipated by James Henry Coffin and William Ferrel, and he failed to explain, as Ferrel had, that the law results from the deflecting force of the earth's rotation. Although his theoretical understanding did not go much beyond Dove's, Buys Ballot left his mark on the science of meteorology as one of its chief organizers.

BIBLIOGRAPHY

A complete list of Buys Ballot's works is an appendix to the biography cited below. On his meteorological work, see his *Beredeneerd register van het Koninklijk Nederlandsch Meteorologisch Instituut* (Utrecht, 1882). His law is first stated in "Note sur les rapports de l'intensité et de la direction du vent avec les écarts simultanées du baromètre," in *Comptes rendus de l'Académie des sciences,* **45** (1857), 765–768. His ideas in physical chemistry were expanded in "Über die Art und Bewegung welche wir Wärme und Electricität nennen," in *Annalen der Physik,* **103** (1858), 240–259.

A biography is Ewoud van Everdingen, *C. H. D. Buys Ballot 1817–1890* (The Hague, 1953), by one of Buys Ballot's successors at the K.N.M.I.

HAROLD L. BURSTYN

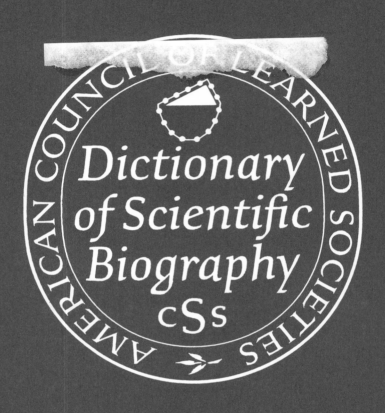

AMERICAN COUNCIL OF LEARNED SOCIETIES

Dictionary
of Scientific
Biography

cSs